19. $\displaystyle\int e^u \, du = e^u + C$

20. $\displaystyle\int a^u \, du = \frac{1}{\ln a} a^u + C, \; a \neq 1$

21. $\displaystyle\int u e^{au} \, du = \frac{e^{au}}{a^2}(au - 1) + C$

22. $\displaystyle\int \frac{du}{1 + e^u} = \ln\left(\frac{e^u}{1 + e^u}\right) + C$

23. $\displaystyle\int \frac{du}{a + be^{cu}} = \frac{u}{a} - \frac{1}{ac} \ln|a + be^{cu}| + C$

24. $\displaystyle\int \ln u \, du = u \ln u - u + C$

25. $\displaystyle\int u \ln u \, du = \frac{u^2}{2} \ln u - \frac{u^2}{4} + C$

26. $\displaystyle\int \frac{du}{u \ln u} = \ln|\ln u| + C$

27. $\displaystyle\int u^m \ln u \, du = u^{m+1}\left[\frac{\ln u}{m+1} - \frac{1}{(m+1)^2}\right] + C$

28. $\displaystyle\int \sin^2 u \, du = \frac{u}{2} - \frac{1}{4} \sin 2u + C$

29. $\displaystyle\int \sin^3 u \, du = -\frac{1}{3} \cos u (\sin^2 u + 2) + C$

30. $\displaystyle\int \cos^2 u \, du = \frac{1}{2} u + \frac{1}{4} \sin 2u + C$

31. $\displaystyle\int \cos^3 u \, du = \frac{1}{3} \sin u (\cos^2 u + 2) + C$

32. $\displaystyle\int \frac{du}{1 \pm \sin u} = \mp \tan\left(\frac{\pi}{4} \mp \frac{u}{2}\right) + C$

33. $\displaystyle\int \frac{du}{1 + \cos u} = \tan\left(\frac{u}{2}\right) + C$

34. $\displaystyle\int \frac{du}{1 - \cos u} = -\cot\left(\frac{u}{2}\right) + C$

APPLIED CALCULUS

THIRD EDITION

Dennis Berkey
Boston University

Saunders College Publishing
Harcourt Brace College Publishers

Fort Worth   Philadelphia   San Diego   New York   Orlando   Austin
San Antonio   Toronto   Montreal   London   Sydney   Tokyo

Text Typeface: Times Roman
Compositor: York Graphic Services
Publisher: John Vondeling
Executive Editor: Jay Ricci
Developmental Editor: Alexa Barnes
Managing Editor: Carol Field
Project Editor: Janet Nuciforo
Copy Editor: Charlotte Nelson
Manager of Art and Design: Carol Bleistine
Senior Art Director: Christine Schueler
Text Designer: Caroline McGowan
Cover Designer: Lawrence R. Didona
Text Artwork: York Graphic Services
Director of EDP: Tim Frelick
Production Manager: Carol Florence
Marketing Manager: Monica Wilson

About the Cover:
Modeling predator-prey relationships, manufacturing costs, and harvesting renewable resources requires fundamental concepts of calculus.

Cover Credits: Background photo: © Neal Lavey/Phototake, NYC; Top photo: Frank Oberle/Tony Stone Images; Middle photo: Matthew McVay/Tony Stone Images; Bottom photo: Luis Castaneda/ The Image Bank.

Printed in the United States of America

Applied Calculus, Third Edition

ISBN: 0-03-076173-5

Library of Congress Catalog Card Number: 93-086829

89   039   98765

This book was printed on paper made from waste paper, containing 10% post-consumer waste and 40% pre-consumer waste, measured as a percentage of total fiber weight content.

PREFACE

This text is intended for use in a full-year course in calculus for students majoring in business, economics, environmental science, biological science, or one of the social sciences. It assumes only a basic competence with college algebra.

Emphasis

The goal of this text is to enable the student to understand the fundamental principles of the differential and integral calculus, to master the basic techniques for applying these principles, and to appreciate the broad applicability of these principles and techniques to real, applied problems in a broad range of disciplines. Students who have mastered this text should be able to recognize and exploit the notions of function, graph, rate of change, optimization, mathematical model, average value, and area of a region bounded by a curve, as well as the ways in which these concepts can be used to describe and analyze phenomena occurring in nature and in business. These features help accomplish this goal:

- Relevant theorems are clearly stated and interpreted immediately by examples and illustrations. Proofs are given only when they are instructive and accessible to students with the stated background.
- The writing style strives for mathematical precision, while making effective use of intuitive and heuristic discussion where appropriate. Primary emphasis is on the applications of the mathematical ideas, rather than on their justifications.
- The principal applications are in business and economics and in the life sciences. Business and economics topics include revenue, cost, profit, marginal rates, inventory control, annuities, present value, revenue streams, and many others. Increasing student interest in ecology, environmental science, and other branches of the life sciences has led to greater coverage in this edition of applications in these fields, including models for population growth and decline, epidemics, drug dispersal, human growth, and others.
- The current, and important, trend toward the increased use of graphing calculators, personal computers, and student-centered learning environments is supported through the tutorial writing style, the large number of worked examples, and the

many applied examples and exercises contained in the text. Because the technology components of contemporary teaching are evolving so rapidly, specific use of graphic calculators and personal computers is accomplished through the ancillary materials provided with the basic text. This approach allows both the student and the instructor to decide for themselves the type and role of technology.

Distinguishing Features

Several features of this text are specifically intended to help students master the techniques of the calculus.

- Many of the nearly 500 worked examples are presented in the split strategy/solution format, in which an outline of the important steps in the solution appears in the "strategy" column. This helps students to see *why* as well as *how* the steps are performed and to understand what is required in developing modern problem-solving strategies of their own.

- Over 3000 exercises are presented, coordinated carefully with the worked examples; they gradually increase in difficulty within each set. Word problems, many of them open-ended, are included in nearly every set.

- Special care has been taken to introduce and illustrate key concepts with applied and illustrative examples. This edition makes increased use of examples from ecology and environmental science. Proofs, when given, are placed at the ends of discussions so that they may be omitted if the instructor so wishes.

- Each section ends with one to three "Practice Problems," a new feature specifically designed to test the student's basic mastery of the central methods of the section. Worked solutions to the Practice Problems appear at the end of each Exercise Set.

- Each chapter ends with a comprehensive Summary Outline of all of the important ideas and techniques in the chapter and with a set of Review Exercises. Although the Summary Outline is organized according to the order of appearance of topics in the chapter (with page references), the Review Exercises are not ordered. They provide a more realistic "test" than the end-of-section exercises, which are tightly embedded in a discussion of a particular topic.

- A clear, understandable writing style and conversational tone have been used throughout.

- Some reference is made to the use of programmable calculators and personal computers in the text and in the exercises. (Much more appears in the ancillary materials.) Four BASIC programs are included in the appendix as models. Although other formats and languages have become popular, these simple BASIC programs illustrate the way in which a computation can be organized to implement a method from the calculus.

Organization

This text follows a common organization of topics. An introductory chapter reviews the essentials of college algebra required for the course. Limits are then introduced in the context of finding the slope of a curve, leading to a discussion of rate of change of a function and the rudiments of differentiation (Chapter 2). This is followed immediately by applications of differentiation to finding relative extrema and to max–min and related rate problems (Chapter 3). The goal here is to provide students with an immediate payoff for the theory and techniques of differentiation and to get them working with applications and word problems as quickly as possible. Chapter 3 also includes two sections on curve sketching, to emphasize the relationship between the graph of a function and its derivatives.

The logarithmic and exponential functions are introduced in Chapter 4, where further applications of the derivative and heavy emphasis on its role in models for population growth are developed. Chapter 4 concludes with a new section on mathematical modeling that explains the ways in which applications of the derivative have been appearing in word problems and discusses, more generally, how mathematical models arise.

Chapter 5 begins with a discussion of the antiderivative, its applications, and the method of integration by substitution. Next, the definite integral is introduced as the limit of an approximation scheme for areas of regions in the plane, the relationship between definite integrals and antiderivatives is established, and a broad range of applications of the definite integral is presented. Chapter 7 concerns techniques of integration and improper integrals. Chapter 8 treats multivariable topics, including partial differentiation, Lagrange multipliers, multiple integrals, and a new section on linear approximations for functions of two variables. The theory of infinite sequences and series, including Taylor polynomials and series, is presented in Chapter 9. Chapter 10 is a brief discussion of differential equations. The final chapter (Chapter 11) presents the theory of probability for discrete and continuous random variables, with particular attention to the normal and exponential probability distributions.

Changes to the Third Edition

In addition to a careful working of the second edition, with critical reviewing by a number of users, several significant content changes have been made for this edition.

- Chapter 1 contains new material on business applications, including straight-line depreciation and average cost.
- The treatment of limits in Chapter 2 has been reorganized, with the material on limits at infinity now comprising a separate section at the end of the chapter. The introduction to slope as a rate of change has been rewritten to motivate better the introduction to the derivative. The material on applications of the derivative has been expanded, with the business applications now comprising a separate section. Many more applications to life science have been added in the examples and exercises.

- Chapter 3 contains new examples and expanded discussions of logistic growth curves, asymptotes in business models, inventory cost control, elasticity of demand, marginal analysis, and linear approximations.

- Chapter 4 contains an entirely new section on mathematical modelling, designed to introduce the student to the larger concept of mathematical models of a more general type than the simple equations for exponential and logistic growth; this includes statistical and computer-based models.

- Chapter 5 contains new material on antiderivatives, the method of substitution, the Fundamental Theorem of Calculus, and applications including revenue streams, present value, and business decision making.

- Chapter 6, on the trigonometric functions, contains a greater treatment of even and odd functions and a number of new examples and exercises on predator-prey systems.

- Chapter 7, on techniques of integration, contains an expanded discussion of substitution in definite integrals and additional material on calculating present value for revenue streams.

- Chapter 8, on multivariable calculus, contains a new discussion of competitive and complementary products and an entirely new section on linear approximations and the total differential.

- Chapter 9, on infinite series, contains additional applications, such as lot sampling for defectives, and an expanded treatment of the properties of power series.

- Chapters 10 and 11, on differential equations and probability distributions, contain new examples and significantly revised Exercise Sets.

- Many new examples and over 400 new exercises have been added. In addition, more than 25% of the exercises carried over from the second edition have been revised and rewritten.

Supplements

The following aids for students and instructors are available from the publisher:

Student Solutions Manual, written by Fred Wright of Iowa State University, is available for purchase. It contains chapter summaries, completely worked-out solutions to the odd-numbered exercises in the text, and 10–15 additional practice problems with solutions for each chapter. (The answers to most odd-numbered exercises also appear at the back of the book.) In effect, this ancillary increases the number of worked examples available for study and practice.

Visualization of Calculus Concepts: For the TI-85, TI-81, SHARP EL9300, and CASIO fx-7700G, written by Shirley Glover, Ron Marshall, and Nicholas Norgaard of Western Carolina University, contains sample programs, examples, and exercises for these graphing calculators and is also available for purchase. The manual is designed to emphasize the graphical and numerical meaning of several key calculus concepts, especially limits, derivatives, and integrals.

Instructors who adopt this text may receive, free of charge, the following items:

Instructor's Manual, also written by Fred Wright, contains completely worked-out solutions to all the end-of-section and review exercises to assist the instructor in the classroom and in grading assignments.

Computerized Test Bank, prepared by Jack Porter and Vrunda Prabhu of the University of Kansas, has almost 1200 multiple-choice and open-ended questions and is available for IBM^R and Macintosh^R computers. Instructors can edit these questions, add their own, and record student grades with the gradebook software. A **Printed Test Bank** of these items organized by chapter is also available.

Graph 2D/3D, written by George Bergeman of Northern Virginia Community College, is for IBM computers and is an interactive tutorial software package. It provides graphical support for solving exercises in the text. Students can also use its computational capabilities as a "super calculator" to perform otherwise cumbersome operations, thus permitting concentration on concepts and problem-solving skills.

Acknowledgments

Preparation of the third edition of this text has involved an extensive program of reviewing, for both pedagogical and mathematical content as well as for accuracy. Many colleagues were involved in this process. Their contributions are gratefully acknowledged, as are those of individuals who made similar contributions to the first and second editions.

Reviewers for the first edition were the following mathematicians:
Michael Bleicher, *University of Wisconsin, Madison*
Philip L. Bowers, *Florida State University, Tallahassee*
C. Kenneth Bradshaw, *San Jose State University*
Fred Brauer, *University of Wisconsin, Madison*
Edward A. Conners, *University of Massachusetts, Amherst*
Raymond Coughlin, *Temple University, Philadelphia*
Robert W. Deming, *SUNY, Oswego*
Garrett Etgen, *University of Houston*
Alec Ingraham, *New Hampshire College*
Edward M. Landesman, *University of California, Santa Cruz*
James W. Maxwell, *Oklahoma State University*
Eldon L. Miller, *University of Mississippi*
Mary Ellen O'Leary, *University of South Carolina*
William Perry, *Texas A&M University*
Donald R. Sherbert, *University of Illinois*
Henry A. Warchall, *University of Texas, Austin*
Fred Wright, *Iowa State University*

Reviewers for the second edition were the following mathematicians:
Alfred Bachman, *California Polytechnic State University*
Howard Beckwith, *California State University*

Fred Brauer, *University of Wisconsin, Madison*
John Busovicki, *Indiana University of Pennsylvania*
Jim Cribbs, *City College, San Francisco*
Ronald W. Dickey, *University of Wisconsin, Madison*
Paul Krajkiewcs, *University of Nebraska*
Jack Porter, *University of Kansas*
Steve Reyner, *SUNY, Oswego*

Reviewers of the third edition were the following mathematicians:
John Busovicki, *Indiana University of Pennsylvania*
Rod Capistran, *North Dakota State University*
Harvey Greenwald, *California Polytechnic State University, San Louis Obispo*
Vuryl Klassen, *California State University, Fullerton*
Cecil Mast, *University of Notre Dame*
Donna McCracken, *University of Florida*
Phil Montgomery, *University of Kansas*
J. Marshall Osborn, *University of Wisconsin, Madison*
Pat Pacitti, *SUNY, Oswego*
Deborah Pascal, *Sacramento City College*
Jack Porter, *University of Kansas*
Holly Puterbaugh, *University of Vermont*
Georgia Pyrros, *University of Delaware*
Daniel Shae, *University of Wisconsin, Madison*
Brad Shelton, *University of Oregon*
James Sieber, *Shippensburg University*
Matthew Swinsick, *Central Connecticut State University*
Russell Thompson, *Utah State University*
Melvin Woodward, *Indiana University of Pennsylvania*

Accuracy reviewers who read and checked the manuscript scrupulously in all stages, from original text through galley and page proofs, were Sudhir Goel, Valdosta State College; Richard Nadel, Florida International University; and Laurence Small, Los Angeles Pierce College. Duane Deal, of Ball State University, contributed a careful and most helpful critique of the second edition in preparation for final editing of this edition.

The Saunders College Publishing team has continued to provide me with excellent support, especially Developmental Editor Alexa Barnes, Executive Editor Jay Ricci, Project Editor Janet Nuciforo, and Publisher Liz Widdicombe. In Boston, my assistants Lisa Doherty and Karen Rodman played important roles in keeping the project on schedule.

Finally, I remain privileged to acknowledge the continuing warm and strong support from my students, my colleagues in the Department of Mathematics and the administration of Boston University, and most especially my family: Cathy, Cristin, Aaron, and Jessica Berkey.

Dennis D. Berkey
November 1993

PREFACE TO THE STUDENT: WHY LEARN CALCULUS?

More students than ever before are studying calculus, for a variety of reasons. This book is written for students majoring in business and in life and social sciences (including biology, environmental science, economics, and other social sciences). Before launching into the particular mathematical topics to be addressed, we wish to describe, in a completely pedestrian way, the principal reasons why we believe a student would want to *learn* calculus (as opposed simply to study it).

We suggest three principal reasons:

1. Calculus provides useful *mathematical models* for phenomena of interest to the non-mathematics major, including, as examples, the spread of pollution and disease, the growth and optimal harvesting of biological populations (such as fish or fir trees), and the behavior of financial instruments and markets.
2. Calculus can help determine the *rates of change* among variables of interest, such as the growth of an investment as a function of time or the change in population size due to changes in birth rate or in significant health factors.
3. Calculus can help measure the difference between functions, usually on finite intervals. This is useful, for example, in comparing the actual experience in the growth of a biological population with what was predicted by a mathematical model.

Knowing calculus will enable you to do many other useful things as well. Because this text begins with a review chapter on precalculus topics followed by a somewhat technical discussion of limits of functions, we want you to have these main, practical themes in mind from the beginning.

Calculus and Mathematical Models

Figure 1 gives an example of one of the mathematical models that we shall present in this text. It is the graph of the *logistic growth curve*. This is one kind of *growth model* for biological populations of plants or animals. Here the value $P(t)$ represents the size of the biological population after t units of time have elapsed. Such logistic models result from a biological *law of growth* stating that

the rate of growth is proportional to the product of the current population size and the remaining capacity of the biological niche   (1)

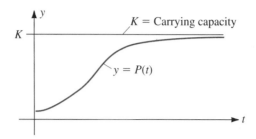

Figure 1 The logistic growth model.

In Chapter 4 of this text we shall show that statement (1) determines a population function $y = P(t)$ such as that graphed in Figure 1, even though we have not given an explicit equation determining the function $y = P(t)$. Later in the text we shall show how to solve certain types of *differential equations* that arise from models such as the law corresponding to logistic growth in equation (1).

These observations about logistic growth in biological populations demonstrate some of the great diversity of mathematical models. Some are in the form of explicit equations, such as the Antoine equation for the relationship between the vapor pressure P and temperature t of a pure liquid:

$$\log P = \frac{-A}{t + C} + B$$

where A, B, and C are empirically determined constants and t is in units of degrees centigrade. Other mathematical models can take the form of equations about *rates of change* among relevant variables (rather than equations involving the variables themselves), or even computer programs. What characterizes mathematical models are their functions of *specification, quantification,* and *prediction:* Relationships among the relevant variable are specified, relevant data (inputs) can be supplied to the model, and predictions (outputs) are then produced by the model, based on the given data.

As we develop the various mathematical topics in this text, we shall introduce a large number of applications, some of which are appropriately thought of as mathematical models. Section 3.11 contains a more complete discussion of mathematical models.

Rates of Change

One of the most useful applications of the calculus is determining the *rate of change* of one variable with respect to changes in another variable. This application commonly occurs if the variable of interest is a function of time, as in the population function $P(t)$ associated with the logistic growth model. In Chapter 2 we develop the concept of the *derivative* of a function, which is a second function measuring the rate of change of the first.

What would we mean by the rate of change for the population function $P(t)$ in the logistic growth model? If $P(t)$ were a linear function, with a straight line for its graph, the rate of increase of population with respect to time would be the slope of that line, or $m = \dfrac{\Delta P}{\Delta t}$. Because $P(t)$ is nonlinear, its rate of increase is the slope of the line that "best approximates" the graph of $P(t)$ at the time in question. (We shall give precise meaning to this phrase in Chapter 2.)

Figure 2 shows how we think about the rate of increase of population at the time $t = t_0$. It is the slope of the line "tangent" to the graph of $P(t)$ at the point corresponding to time t_0. In Chapter 2 we shall explain this use of the term "tangent" and find a number of techniques for calculating its slope.

Figure 3 illustrates one topic associated with models for the growth of biological populations from which harvesting occurs, such as forests or fisheries: *maximum sustainable yield*. This phrase represents the usual goal of such harvesting, which is to maximize the amounts that can be harvested without damaging the population that is being harvested.

In the example of a fishery, we would expect the maximum sustainable yield to occur at some population size that was neither large nor small relative to the "carrying capacity" of the pond or tank in which the fish are confined. Too small a population obviously makes poor use of the available environment. Too large a population leads to overcrowding and a general degradation of the environment, both of which typically result in high losses due to death. The same observations apply to tree lots. (For example, think of fir tree farms that produce Christmas trees.) Planting trees too far apart wastes valuable land. Planting them too close together results in tree loss due to competition for sunlight and soil nutrients.

Population ecologists believe that to maximize the harvesting yield the population should be maintained at the size for which the population is increasing most rapidly. Thus, in Figure 3 the value P on the y-axis is labeled MSY (for maximum sustainable yield) because it corresponds to the point where the slope of the "tangent," and therefore the rate of increase in population size, is the largest.

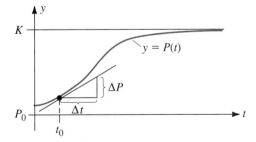

Figure 2 The slope of the "tangent" gives the rate of increase in population at time t_0.

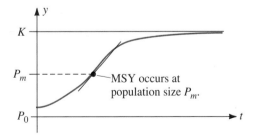

Figure 3 Maximum sustainable yield (MSY) occurs where population growth is a maximum.

This brief discussion of maximum sustainable yield illustrates how mathematical models can be used to analyze certain aspects of the process or phenomena they model.

Measuring the Difference Between Functions

In precalculus mathematics, students learn how to begin with a pair of functions and form the sum, difference, product, and quotient of these two functions. The values of such combinations can be computed from the individual values for any given number in the common domain. There is often a practical need, however, to measure the difference between two functions *over an entire interval,* which is something that precalculus mathematics is unable to accomplish.

Figure 4 illustrates an example of such a situation. The black curve is the graph of the (ideal) population function $P(t)$ associated with the model for logistic growth. The red curve shows the approximate growth in the rabbit population after these animals were introduced on the continent of Australia in 1859. Population ecologists would describe the red curve by saying that the actual rabbit population "overshot" the carrying capacity of the continent, then oscillated up and down over time as it more closely resembled the ideal logistic curve. The shaded regions in Figure 5 show what we mean by the "difference between two functions over an interval." For each time between a and b, the difference between the size of the rabbit population, $R(t)$, and the population size predicted by the logistic growth model, $P(t)$, is the distance between the corresponding points on the two graphs. The difference between the two functions *on the interval* $[a, b]$ is represented by the area of the shaded region, bounded by the graphs of the two functions.

In Chapter 5 we shall develop the concept of the *definite integral,* which will enable us to find the areas of regions bounded by the graphs of functions such as in this example. The definite integral has many other uses, although a great number of them can be described in geometric terms as the difference between two functions on an interval.

The theory, techniques, and applications associated with the *derivative* and the *definite integral,* which we have only briefly hinted at in this discussion, comprise

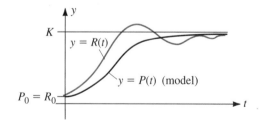

Figure 4 Growth of the rabbit population following its introduction in Australia.

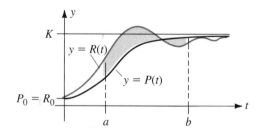

Figure 5 The difference between the functions $R(t)$ and $P(t)$ on $[a, b]$ is the area of the shaded region.

most of what is taught in a first course on calculus and all of what is presented in this text except for Chapters 9 and 11. Chapter 9 discusses the topics of infinite sequences and series, and the discussion ties back to the derivative and the definite integral in the latter sections. Chapter 11 discusses some elementary notions of probability theory, with applications also to mathematical modelling.

These are the major themes in what lies ahead. Although the actual calculus topics do not begin until Chapter 2, we urge you to review Chapter 1 carefully to brush up on important precalculus topics. Before concluding this introductory section, we wish to comment on two current developments in the teaching of calculus and other mathematics subjects in schools, colleges, and universities.

Technology

With the recent development of powerful hand-held graphing calculators and sophisticated mathematical software capable of performing symbolic calculations (i.e., doing algebra and even calculus for you), many teachers are incorporating such technology into their courses. Although such devices are not essential to learning calculus, they can be very helpful in illustrating concepts, reducing the drudgery of long calculations, and providing a rapid-response setting for asking "what if" types of questions. You may already be familiar with such technologies. Moreover, we have included a number of exercises designed for students with access to the more powerful hand-held calculators, without or without graphing capabilities. These problems are strictly optional, however, and the reader without access to such devices should not feel short-changed. Moreover, students *with* such technology should not become complacent about the need to *understand,* without the aid of a calculator, the principal aspects of the subject and the techniques by which it is put to use. More advanced courses in mathematics, as well as the skill of knowing where and how to apply these ideas, depend on an intimate, working familiarity of these "basics," for which a calculator cannot substitute.

Calculus Reform

The 1980s brought a welcome focus of attention on the way undergraduate mathematics, especially calculus, is taught in the United States. Several major themes have emerged in these discussions, including a strong interest in using graphing calculators and computer workstations to teach calculus, reduce the range of topics covered in the traditional calculus courses and textbooks, and provide more motivation, illustration, and applications of the topics that remain. The movement has even embraced slogans, such as making calculus "a pump, not a filter" for students who study it. All of these concerns result from a deep interest in helping students become more successful with, and attracted to, their study of mathematics.

Technology is important and very useful, but it is not capable of fully replacing the teacher or the textbook, except possibly in schools able to provide a "computing-intensive" environment for students. Most students cannot do this, although a great many are now providing computer laboratories or requiring students to purchase powerful hand-held calculators.

Issues of motivation, illustration, and application have received much attention in this and earlier editions. The split strategy/solution format used in many of the worked examples was developed in the first edition, and continues here, to provide insight into the "thought process" of writing out a clear and correct solution to a given problem. Much use is made of the elementary concepts from business, economics, and population ecology in introducing new topics and illustrating the resulting techniques. Although some reviewers have objected that such discussions "get in the way of the mathematics," we believe that the opportunity to see how an idea arises in an applied, if not "real-world," setting is helpful to you, to enliven the discussion and tie the notion to practical experience as well as the related mathematics.

Learning Calculus Successfully

Our principal concern is for your success in learning calculus. This will be measured not just by your course grade, but also by the extent to which you are able to apply your understanding in later courses and in applied situations throughout your career.

Success requires a commitment on your part to *active learning*—taking responsibility yourself for developing an excellent command of the theory and techniques discussed in this text and in your course. A recipe is hard to provide, and the requirements vary greatly among individuals.

Classroom experience provides some generally sound advice: attend class regularly; do not fall behind in your assignments—mathematics is a highly vertical subject and you need to understand today's discussion to understand tomorrow's; and work exercises regularly. Do not confine your efforts to a single set of exercises at any one setting—moving back and forth among a number of exercise sets as you study will prepare you for the necessary skill of reading an examination question and deciding first what is being asked before deciding how to respond. Finally, it is important to make full use of your professor and any assistants by consulting them frequently with questions and concerns. The formality of mathematics sometimes conveys to students the mistaken notion that mathematics faculty are not as accessible to students and interested in their development as are professors of psychology, history, or any other subject. Mathematics education is a human enterprise, as is mathematics itself, and it is important to make it the subject of conversation and debate, as well as reading, lecturing, and implementation on computers.

We wish you excellent success in learning calculus. If you have any concerns or suggestions about this text, or about related issues, I would very much enjoy hearing from you.

Dennis D. Berkey
November 1993

CONTENTS

Chapter 4   Exponential and Logarithmic Functions   293

Chapter 5   Antiderivatives and the Definite Integral   361

Chapter 6   Trigonometric Functions   447

Chapter 11   Applications to Probability Theory   793

Appendix I: BASIC Computer Programs   A.1

Appendix II: Mathematical Tables   A.7

Answers to Odd-Numbered Exercises   A.11

Index   I.1

INDEX OF APPLICATIONS

Biological Sciences

Ecology

Social Sciences

General Topics

CHAPTER

1

Analyzing how far maturing birds will be found from their birth nest involves a mathematical model called ''Kettle curves.'' The equations for Kettle curves, as well as other mathematical *functions* and their graphs, are discussed in this chapter.

(Ronald Austing/Photo Researchers, Inc.)

Numbers, Functions, and Graphs

1.1 Working with Real Numbers

One of the principal goals of this text is to help you use calculus to measure rates at which quantities change. For example, in studying a production model in economics, you might wish to know if a certain component of cost is increasing or decreasing, or a psychology student armed with data from an experiment might wish to know how response time varies with experience.

Before proceeding to develop techniques for measuring changes among quantities, we need to review briefly several properties of the number system used to measure these quantities and to agree on the meaning of certain mathematical notation. This should prevent confusion later on and allow us to take full advantage of the power of the language of mathematics.

Integers and Real Numbers

The real numbers may be identified with points on the **number line,** as illustrated in Figure 1.1. The **integers** are the special subset of the real numbers $\{\cdots -3, -2, -1, 0, 1, 2, 3, \cdots\}$ as illustrated in Figure 1.2.

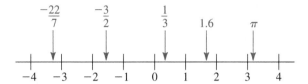

Figure 1.1 All locations on the number line correspond to real numbers.

Figure 1.2 The integers form a special subset of the real numbers.

We emphasize the distinction between integers and other real numbers because certain quantities are measured only as integers. For example, Figure 1.3 illustrates a typical relationship between the time following the injection of a certain drug in a person's bloodstream and the concentration of that drug in the person's blood. In this example both time, t, and concentration, c, are represented by all real numbers within certain ranges. Compare this example with Figure 1.4, which represents a typical relationship between the number, x, of personal computers produced per day by a manufacturer and the total daily cost, C, of manufacturing these computers. Here only integer values of x make sense.

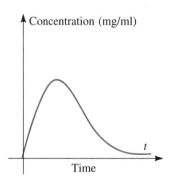

Figure 1.3 Both drug concentration and time are represented by real numbers.

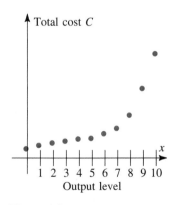

Figure 1.4 Production level x is measured only in integers.

In general, the theory of the calculus applies only to variables that can equal any real number (within certain ranges, sometimes). In order to deal with variables that can equal only integer values, such as production levels, we shall often *assume* that such variables can equal any real number. For example, Figure 1.5 illustrates how we might think about the relationship between output and cost in Figure 1.4 in this way. In such situations we shall be careful to note this assumption and the effect it might have on our calculations.

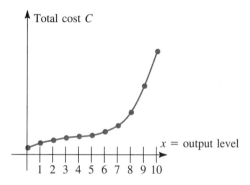

Figure 1.5 Effect of assuming that production level can equal any real number between 0 and 10. (Compare with Figure 1.4.)

Inequalities

The statement "$a < b$," read "a is less than b," means that a lies to the left of b on the number line (see Figure 1.6). This can also be written "$b > a$" and read "b is greater than a." The statement "$a \le b$" means that a is less than or equal to b.

Figure 1.6 The statement $a < b$ means a lies to the left of b.

☐ **EXAMPLE 1**

Each of the following inequalities is true. Note especially e and f.

(a) $2 < 6$ (e) $-10 < -5$
(b) $-3 < 5$ (f) $-2 > -4$
(c) $x^2 \ge 0$ (g) $-2 < \sqrt[3]{8} < 3$
(d) $\pi > 3$ (h) $-\pi < 0 \le x^2$ ■

Interval Notation

You are probably familiar with **set builder notation** used to specify certain sets of real numbers. For example, the set S_1 of all real numbers between 2 and 7 (but not including 2 or 7) can be written as

$$S_1 = \{x \mid 2 < x < 7\}$$

while the set S_2 consisting of the numbers 2, 7, and all real numbers between 2 and 7 is written as

$$S_2 = \{x \mid 2 \leq x \leq 7\}.$$

Such sets of real numbers, which include all real numbers between two given numbers, are called **intervals.** It is important to have a notation for intervals that indicates precisely whether or not each of the endpoints is included. We shall use the following notation for intervals:

$[a, b]$	means	$\{x \mid a \leq x \leq b\}$	(both endpoints included)
$[a, b)$	means	$\{x \mid a \leq x < b\}$	(only left endpoint included)
$(a, b]$	means	$\{x \mid a < x \leq b\}$	(only right endpoint included)
(a, b)	means	$\{x \mid a < x < b\}.$	(neither endpoint included)

The conventions for graphing intervals on the number line are illustrated in Figure 1.7.

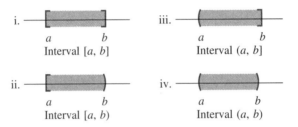

Figure 1.7 Various types of intervals.

Intervals of the form $[a, b]$, which include both endpoints, are called *closed* intervals. Those of the form (a, b), which include neither endpoint, are called *open.*

□ EXAMPLE 2

(a) A rain gauge has the shape of a cup 6 inches deep. If x represents the depth of water in the gauge after one month, the closed interval $[0, 6]$ represents the possible values of x.

(b) Let r be the radius of a piston that is to slide inside a cylinder of radius 10 cm. The possible values for r lie in the open interval $(0, 10)$. Why are 0 and 10 excluded? ∎

Infinite Intervals

Often we will need to specify sets consisting of all numbers larger or smaller than a given number. We do so by using the infinity symbol, ∞, as follows:

$[a, \infty)$	means	$\{x \mid x \geq a\}$
(a, ∞)	means	$\{x \mid x > a\}$
$(-\infty, a]$	means	$\{x \mid x \leq a\}$
$(-\infty, a)$	means	$\{x \mid x < a\}.$

It is important to note that the symbol ∞ is *not* a number. Rather, it is just a symbol used to denote all numbers to the right or left of a given number on the number line.

☐ **EXAMPLE 3**

The negative real numbers are those in the interval $(-\infty, 0)$, while the nonnegative real numbers constitute the interval $[0, \infty)$. Can any number be both nonnegative and nonpositive? Which, or why? ■

Properties of Inequalities

We will frequently need to "solve" inequalities in one or more variables. The following theorem summarizes the relevant properties of inequalities.

Theorem 1

Let a, b, and c be real numbers. Then

  (i) If $a < b$, then $a + c < b + c$ for any number c.
  (ii) If $a < b$ and $c > 0$, then $ac < bc$.
  (iii) If $a < b$ and $c < 0$, then $ac > bc$.
  (iv) If $a < b$ and $b < c$, then $a < c$.

Solving Inequalities

The following examples show how Theorem 1 can be used to "solve" inequalities involving a variable such as x, t, etc. In using Theorem 1, be especially careful when multiplying (or dividing) both sides of an inequality by a negative number. As part (iii) states, this reverses the sense of the inequality.

☐ **EXAMPLE 4**

Solve the inequality $3x - 4 < 8$. ■

Strategy · · · · · · · ·
Isolate x by

(i) adding 4 to both sides, and

(ii) multiplying both sides by $\frac{1}{3}$.

Solution
Using Theorem 1, we have

$$3x - 4 < 8$$
$$3x - 4 + 4 < 8 + 4$$
$$3x < 12$$

$$\frac{1}{3}(3x) < \frac{1}{3}(12)$$

$$x < 4.$$

The solution set is therefore

$$\{x \mid x < 4\} \quad \text{or} \quad (-\infty, 4).$$

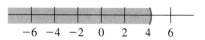

$$-6 \quad -4 \quad -2 \quad 0 \quad 2 \quad 4 \quad 6$$

Figure 1.8 Solution of Example 4.

(See Figure 1.8.) ■

☐ **EXAMPLE 5**

Solve the inequality $10 - 3x \leq 37$.

Strategy · · · · · · · ·

Solve inequality by

(i) adding -10 to both sides

(ii) multiplying both sides by $-\frac{1}{3}$ *and reversing the inequality.*

Solution

Proceeding as before, we have

$$10 - 3x \leq 37$$
$$10 - 3x + (-10) \leq 37 + (-10)$$
$$-3x \leq 27$$

$$\left(-\frac{1}{3}\right)(-3x) \geq \left(-\frac{1}{3}\right)(27) \qquad \text{(Note reverse of inequality)}$$

$$x \geq -9.$$

The solution set is $[-9, \infty)$. (See Figure 1.9.)

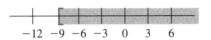

−12 −9 −6 −3 0 3 6

Figure 1.9 Solution of Example 5.

☐ **EXAMPLE 6**

Bob is the manager of conservation lands for his county. He wishes to purchase young oak trees for planting at various locations. The saplings cost $20 each, and there is a flat delivery charge of $200 from the supplier. If $5000 is available for this project, how many trees can Bob purchase?

Strategy · · · · · · · ·

Label the unknown quantity x.

Find an expression for the total cost.

Write the inequality total cost ≤ 5000.

Solve by subtracting 200 from both sides,

and then dividing both sides by 20.

Solution

Let x be the number of trees purchased

The total cost of the order is then $20x + 200$, including shipping. The condition that must be satisfied is therefore

$$20x + 200 \leq 5000.$$

Thus,

$$20x + 200 - 200 \leq 5000 - 200$$

or

$$20x \leq 4800$$

so

$$x \leq 4800/20 = 240.$$

Bob should therefore order 240 trees.

☑ PRACTICE PROBLEMS 1.1

1. Solve the following inequality

$$x + 5 \le -7 + 4x.$$

2. Students are planning a party, to be held at a lodge that charges $50 to rent the hall, plus $12 per person to attend the party. If $1000 is available, what is the maximum number of students who can attend the party?

Exercise Set 1.1

In each of Exercises 1–10 determine whether the quantity described is measured by integers alone or by any real number.

1. Rainfall on a particular day

2. Height of a building, in feet

3. Volume of water in a beaker

4. Age

5. Inventory in a bookstore

6. Drug concentration in the bloodstream

7. U.S. auto production

8. Altitude

9. Temperature

10. Time

In each of Exercises 11–20 match the interval illustrated with one of the intervals a–j below.

11. 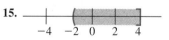   **a.** $[-4, 2]$

12. 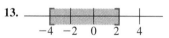   **b.** $(-2, 4]$

13. 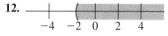   **c.** $[2, \infty)$

14. 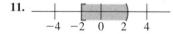   **d.** $[-2, 2)$

15. 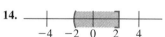   **e.** $(-\infty, 2]$

16.    **f.** $[-2, 4)$

17. 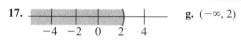   **g.** $(-\infty, 2)$

18.    **h.** $(-2, \infty)$

19.    **i.** $(-2, 2]$

20. 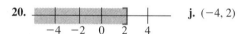   **j.** $(-4, 2)$

21. True or false? Every integer is also a real number.

22. True or false? There is no largest integer. Is there a largest real number?

23. For how many integers m is $\dfrac{1}{m}$ also an integer?

In Exercises 24–33 solve the inequality for x, expressing the solution set as an interval or a pair of intervals.

24. $2x > 10$ **25.** $6x - 2 \le 16$

26. $6 - 5x \ge 16$ **27.** $4 - 2x \le 12$

28. $4 - 3x > 5$ **29.** $6 + x \le 2x - 5$

30. $x - 7 \ge 3 - x$ **31.** $5 - 3x < 7 - 2x$

32. $(x - 4)^2 \ge x^2 - x + 12$ **33.** $x(6 + x) \ge 3 + x^2$

34. Restrictions in some U.S. Post Offices limit the dimensions of a parcel that can be mailed according to the rule "length plus girth not to exceed 108 inches." Write an inequality giving the possible girths g for a package 28 inches long.

35. A manufacturer of dishwashers produces a portable model and a built-in model. The portable costs $200 to produce, and the built-in model costs $250. Write an inequality involving the number of portables P and the number of built-in models B in a production run showing that the total cost of production cannot exceed $10,000.

36. Refer to Exercise 35. If the production run must include at least 15 portables, what is the maximum number of built-in models that can be produced?

37. Carol runs a catering business and charges $12 per person at a party, plus a $50 delivery charge per party. How many guests can a host afford, including the host, if $300 is available to pay Carol?

38. A cylindrical container is to be made of two different kinds of materials. The material for the top and bottom costs $10 per square foot and the material for the side wall costs $30 per square foot. If the container has radius r feet and height h feet, write an inequality stating that the total cost of the material from which the container is made does not exceed $1000. (Ignore waste material.)

39. A rectangular window 54 inches high is to have between 1296 and 1620 square inches of area. Write an inequality that must be satisfied by its width w.

40. Paul is an automobile salesman. He earns a base salary of $900 per month plus 2% commission on each car that he sells. How many $10,000 cars must he sell in order to earn at least $2000 per month?

41. Lisa, a computer saleswoman, is offered the choice of two compensation plans. Plan A pays a monthly salary of $1100 plus 2% commission on all sales. Plan B pays only a commission of 3% on all sales. She is to market only one model of computer, which sells for $20,000.
  a. Let x be the number of computers that she sells in a given month. Write an inequality that must be satisfied for Plan A to provide higher compensation than Plan B.
  b. For which sales levels x will Plan B provide greater compensation?

42. Refer to Exercise 41. If compensation Plan B is changed to a commission of 4% on all sales, for which sales levels x will Plan B provide greater compensation?

43. A bag of a dozen oranges weighs 3 pounds. Each orange weighs at least 3 ounces. What is the most any single orange can weigh?

☑ **SOLUTIONS TO PRACTICE PROBLEMS 1.1**

1. Subtracting $4x$ from both sides of the inequality

$$x + 5 \leq -7 + 4x$$

gives

$$(x - 4x) + 5 \leq -7 + (4x - 4x)$$

or

$$-3x + 5 \leq -7.$$

Subtracting 5 from both sides gives

$$-3x + (5 - 5) \leq -7 - 5$$

or

$$-3x \leq -12.$$

Then, dividing both sides by -3 (which requires us to reverse the inequality) gives

$$x \geq 4.$$

2. Let x be the number of students attending the party. Then the total cost for this lodge hall is $(50 + 12x)$ dollars. The requirement that this amount not exceed $1000 can be written

$$50 + 12x \leq 1000.$$

Subtracting 50 from both sides gives

$$12x \leq 950$$

and dividing both sides by 12 gives

$$x \le \frac{950}{12} = 79.16666.$$

Thus, at most 79 students can attend.

1.2 Graphs of Equations

In order to represent graphically a relationship between two variables, we make use of the **Cartesian coordinate plane.** For example, Figure 2.1 illustrates the number q of television sets that a manufacturer can sell per month at selling price p if the variables p and q are related by the equation $p + 2q = 1000$. The significance of the point $P = (500, 250)$ is that the manufacturer will be able to sell 250 sets per month if the price per set is \$500. Similarly, the interpretation of the point $(1000, 0)$ is that no one will buy the manufacturer's television sets if the price is increased to \$1000. The purpose of this section is to describe the coordinate plane and its use in constructing graphs of equations.

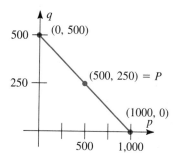

Figure 2.1 Graph of relationship $p + 2q = 1000$ between price p and monthly sales q.

The Coordinate Plane

Figure 2.2 shows that the coordinate plane is constructed by superimposing two number lines at right angles with the zero marks coincident at a point labeled $(0, 0)$ called the **origin.** We have labeled the horizontal number line the x-axis and the vertical number line the y-axis.

With these axes in place we assign to each point P in the plane a unique ordered pair of numbers (a, b), called the **coordinates** of P. (See Figure 2.3.) The first number, a, is called the x-coordinate of P. It is the location where a vertical line through P meets the x-axis. Similarly, the y-coordinate, b, is the location where a horizontal line through P meets the y-axis. Figure 2.4 shows the coordinates of several particular points in the plane.

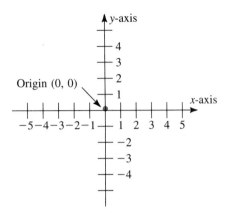

Figure 2.2 The coordinate plane.

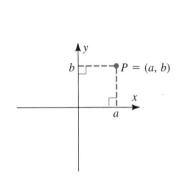

Figure 2.3 Method for assigning coordinates (a, b) to P.

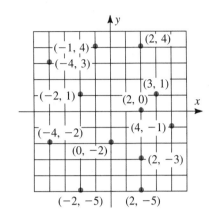

Figure 2.4 Coordinates of various points in the plane.

To find the point Q in the xy-plane corresponding to the given coordinates $Q = (c, d)$, we reverse the procedure described above, constructing a vertical line through $x = c$ on the x-axis and a horizontal line through $y = d$ on the y-axis. The two lines meet at the desired point $Q = (c, d)$.

It is not necessary for the coordinate axes to be labeled x and y. Any two variables may be used. For example, economists often use the price p and demand q for a particular good or service, as in Figure 2.1. However, it is essential that the first number, a, in the coordinate pair (a, b) refer to the horizontal axis and that the second number, b, refer to the vertical axis.

☐ **EXAMPLE 1**

Table 2.1 shows, for each of the past six census years, the approximate percentage of U.S. citizens in the 25–29 age group who had completed four years of high school. Plot these data on a coordinate plane.

Table 2.1

t = years	1940	1950	1960	1970	1980	1990
p = percentage	38	52	61	76	84	85

Solution: If we let n be the number of years after 1940, we can restate the data in Table 2.1 as in Table 2.2

Table 2.2

n = years after 1940	0	10	20	30	40	50
p = percentage	38	52	61	76	84	85

Then, using n to represent time on the horizontal axis and p to represent the percentage of citizens completing high school on the vertical axis, we plot the points

$$P_1 = (0, 38)$$
$$P_2 = (10, 52)$$
$$P_3 = (20, 61)$$
$$P_4 = (30, 76)$$
$$P_5 = (40, 84)$$
$$P_6 = (50, 85)$$

as illustrated in Figure 2.5.   ■

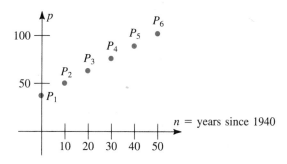

Figure 2.5 Percent of 25–29 year olds completing high school versus time.

Graphs of Equations

Example 1 shows how the coordinate plane can be used to illustrate relationships between two variables from a set of data. We shall be concerned primarily with using the coordinate plane to represent equations involving two variables. We do this by means of the *graph* of an equation.

Definition 1

The **graph** of an equation involving the variables x and y is the set of all points $P = (x, y)$ whose coordinates satisfy the given equation.

One method of attempting to sketch the graph of an equation is to find and plot several points on the graph by the following method. First, select a particular number for one variable. Then insert this number into the equation and attempt to solve for the other variable. If successful, you will have determined a point on the graph. After finding several such points, you can attempt to sketch a curve through these points.

☐ **EXAMPLE 2**

Sketch the graph of the equation $xy = 1$.   ■

Strategy · · · · · · · · ·

Solve the equation for y by multiplying both sides by $\dfrac{1}{x}$.

Solution

Beginning with the equation $xy = 1$, we find that

$$\left(\frac{1}{x}\right)xy = \left(\frac{1}{x}\right)1$$

so

$$y = \frac{1}{x}.$$

Select several numbers x. Find corresponding values of y.

Then if $x = 1$, $\quad y = \dfrac{1}{1} = 1$

if $x = 2$, $\quad y = \dfrac{1}{2}$

if $x = 3$, $\quad y = \dfrac{1}{3}$, etc.

Similarly if $x = -1$, $\quad y = \dfrac{1}{-1} = -1$

if $x = -2$, $\quad y = \dfrac{1}{-2} = -\dfrac{1}{2}$

if $x = -3$, $\quad y = \dfrac{1}{-3} = -\dfrac{1}{3}$, etc.

Plot the points (x, y) obtained, and sketch in the curve.

Thus for each number x the corresponding value of y is just the *reciprocal*, $\dfrac{1}{x}$.

Finally, note that no y corresponds to $x = 0$ since division by zero is not defined. Figure 2.6 shows these points and the graph of the equation $xy = 1$. ■

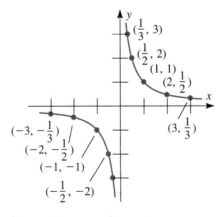

Figure 2.6 Graph of the equation $xy = 1$.

There are two difficulties with the method of plotting points to sketch graphs of equations. One is that it can be quite time consuming (although those with access to computers can write simple programs to plot large numbers of points quickly). The other difficulty is that the method is simply not very reliable. How do you know whether you have sketched the curve correctly between successive points?

One of the goals of the calculus is to develop more accurate techniques for analyzing graphs of equations. An important tool in doing this is an understanding of the equations associated with lines in the plane.

Equations for Lines

Suppose that ℓ is a nonvertical line in the plane. If $P_1 = (x_1, y_1)$ and $P_2 = (x_2, y_2)$ are distinct points on ℓ, the **slope** of ℓ is defined to be the ratio

$$m = \frac{y_2 - y_1}{x_2 - x_1}. \tag{1}$$

(See Figure 2.7.) That is, the slope of a line is the ratio of the vertical change to the horizontal change between any two distinct points on the line.

For a given line the value of m is independent of the particular choices for (x_1, y_1) and (x_2, y_2). Notice that expression (1) for slope is not defined if $x_1 = x_2$. For this reason we say that *a vertical line has undefined slope*. Figure 2.8 shows the slopes of several lines through the origin.

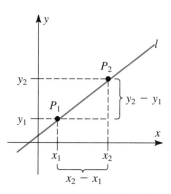

Figure 2.7 Slope $m = \dfrac{y_2 - y_1}{x_2 - x_1}$.

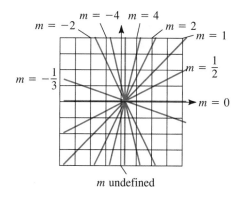

Figure 2.8 Various slopes.

☐ **EXAMPLE 3**

Find the slope of the line through the points

(a) $(-7, 2)$ and $(3, -3)$,   and

(b) $(-1, -4)$ and $(7, 16)$.

Solution: From equation (1) for slope we have

(a) $m = \dfrac{-3 - 2}{3 - (-7)} = \dfrac{-5}{10} = -\dfrac{1}{2}$,   and

(b) $m = \dfrac{16 - (-4)}{7 - (-1)} = \dfrac{20}{8} = \dfrac{5}{2}$. ∎

Now suppose ℓ is a line with slope m that contains the point (x_1, y_1). To find an equation for ℓ, we let (x, y) denote the coordinate of any other point on ℓ. Then, by equation (1)

$$m = \frac{y - y_1}{x - x_1}.$$

Multiplying both sides of this equation by $x - x_1$ gives

$$y - y_1 = m(x - x_1) \tag{2}$$

Equation (2) is called the **point-slope** form of the equation for ℓ since the slope m and the coordinates of one point on ℓ are required to write this equation.

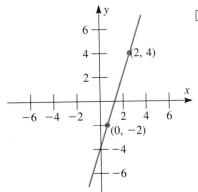

Figure 2.9 Line $y = 3x - 2$.

☐ **EXAMPLE 4**

Find an equation for the line with slope 3 containing the point $(2, 4)$.

Solution: Using equation (2) with $m = 3$, $x_1 = 2$, and $y_1 = 4$, we obtain

$$y - 4 = 3(x - 2)$$

so

$$y - 4 = 3x - 6$$

or

$$y = 3x - 2.$$ ∎

(See Figure 2.9.)

☐ **EXAMPLE 5**

Find an equation for the line through $(-3, 4)$ and $(1, -2)$.

Strategy · · · · · · ·
First, find the slope.

Solution
Since the slope is not given, we calculate it from the two given points using equation (1):

$$m = \frac{-2 - 4}{1 - (-3)} = \frac{-6}{4} = -\frac{3}{2}.$$

Then, use point-slope form of the line to find an equation.

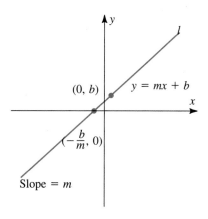

Figure 2.10 Line $y = -\dfrac{3}{2}x - \dfrac{1}{2}$.

Then, using the point $(x_1, y_1) = (-3, 4)$ and the point-slope equation (2), we have

$$y - 4 = \left(-\frac{3}{2}\right)(x - (-3))$$

or

$$y - 4 = -\frac{3}{2}(x + 3)$$

so

$$y - 4 = -\frac{3}{2}x - \frac{9}{2}.$$

Thus

$$y = -\frac{3}{2}x - \frac{1}{2}.$$

(See Figure 2.10.)

■

If we solve equation (2) for y, we obtain

$$y = m(x - x_1) + y_1$$
$$= mx - mx_1 + y_1$$

or

$$y = mx + b \qquad (3)$$

where $b = -mx_1 + y_1$. Equation (3) is called the **slope-intercept form** of the equation for ℓ. This is because the number b is the **y-intercept,** or the y-coordinate of the point on ℓ with x-coordinate zero. (See Figure 2.11.)

Figure 2.11 Line with equation $y = mx + b$ has y-intercept b.

Any equation of the form $Ax + By = C$ with $B \neq 0$ can be brought to the slope-intercept form (3), so it follows that its graph must be a line. Equations of this type are called **linear equations.**

□ EXAMPLE 6

Graph the linear equation $6x + 2y = 8$.

Strategy · · · · · · ·

Solve for y to obtain slope-intercept form.

Read off slope m and y-intercept b by comparing with equation (3).

Solution

Solving for y, we obtain

$$6x + 2y = 8$$
$$2y = -6x + 8$$
$$y = -3x + 4.$$

This is a line with slope -3 and y-intercept 4. (See Figure 2.12.)

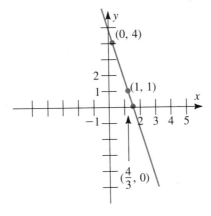

Figure 2.12 Graph of $y = -3x + 4$.

Linear Models

Equations are often used as mathematical models to predict future values of a variable that changes with time. If the variable y satisfies an equation of the form $y = mx + b$, we say that it is a **linear model** for the variable y. In such models the slope m and the y-intercept b often have special meanings associated with the model. The following example from economics shows how the y-intercept may be interpreted as a "fixed cost."

□ EXAMPLE 7

A manufacturer of garage door openers finds that the total cost C in dollars of producing x openers per week is given by the equation

$$C = 500 + 60x.$$

What is the significance of the constant 500? What is the significance of the slope $m = 60$?

Solution: This equation gives a typical linear model for cost in terms of production level. If *no* openers are made, that is, if $x = 0$, the result is $C = 500$. Thus $500 is the fixed cost per week of being in business (having a factory, electricity, equipment, etc.) as opposed to the cost of materials and labor that go into the manufacture of a particular opener. This fixed cost does not involve x, the number of units produced. The significance of the slope $m = 60$ is that the total cost of production increases by $60 for each increase of 1 unit in production. In Chapter 2 we will introduce the terminology *marginal cost* for this quantity. Note in Figure 2.13 that only nonnegative values of x make sense. ■

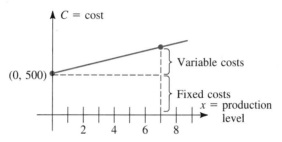

Figure 2.13 *y*-intercept is fixed cost.

□ **EXAMPLE 8**

The demand q for television sets produced by the manufacturer described at the beginning of this section is related to the selling price p by the equation $q = -\frac{1}{2}p + 500$. The graph of this equation is a straight line with slope $m = -\frac{1}{2}$ and with q-intercept $q = 500$, as illustrated in Figure 2.1. This is a *linear model for demand*. ■

Straight-Line Depreciation

A common linear model for the depreciation of capital assets (such as computers, vehicles, machinery, etc.) is called **straight-line depreciation.** It is a method for calculating the value of the asset after it has been in service for a period of time assuming that the loss in value, or depreciation, is constant from year to year.

More precisely, let us assume that an asset has an acquisition cost C, a useful lifetime of N years, and a salvage value S after N years. Then the *total* loss in value (depreciation) over the N years of its useful lifetime is $C - S$, and the depreciation in any one of these N years is $(C - S)/N$. Thus, after t years in service the asset has lost

$$D = t\left(\frac{C - S}{N}\right) \qquad \text{(total depreciation)} \qquad (3)$$

in value, and its depreciated value, after t years, is

$$V = C - D$$

$$= C - t\left(\frac{C - S}{N}\right) \qquad \text{(depreciated value)} \qquad (4)$$

Both the equation for total depreciation D, and for depreciated value V, are linear models.

□ EXAMPLE 9

An office manager purchases a computer costing $5000 that has a useful life of five years and a salvage value of $500 at the end of this period. Find linear equations for

(a) D, the total depreciation after t years, and
(b) V, the depreciated value after t years.

Strategy · · · · · · · ·
Identify the initial cost, salvage value, and depreciation period.

Solution
In this example we have

$$C = 5000 \quad \text{(acquisition cost)}$$
$$S = 500 \quad \text{(salvage value)}$$

and

$$N = 5 \quad \text{(depreciation period)}$$

Determine $\dfrac{C-S}{N}$, the rate of depreciation.

Thus, the annual rate of depreciation is

$$\frac{C-S}{N} = \frac{5000 - 500}{5} = 900.$$

Using equations (3) and (4) we find that, after t years, the total amount of depreciation is

Write the linear equations (3) and (4) using this value.

$$D = 900t, \quad 0 \le t \le 5$$

and the depreciated value of the computer is

$$V = 5000 - 900t, \quad 0 \le t \le 5.$$

Thus, for example, $V(1) = 5000 - 900(1) = 4100$ dollars, $V(2) = \$3200$, etc. (See Figure 2.14.) ■

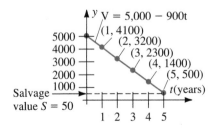

Figure 2.14 Straight-line depreciation model in Example 9.

Note that in Example 9 the slope of the depreciation model $V = 5000 - 900t$ is $m = -900$. It represents the amount by which the computer loses its value annually. This is called the *rate of depreciation*. We shall have much more to say about rates of change in later chapters.

☐ **EXAMPLE 10**

On San Nicolas Island it was found that of the 11 species of birds present in 1917, only 5 remained in 1968. (However, six new species had arrived.) Assuming a linear rate of decline in the number of original bird species,

(a) find a linear model for this decline,   and
(b) determine the year, predicted by this model, by which time all original species will have left the island.

Strategy · · · · · · · ·

Name the variables.

Solution

We begin by letting t represent the number of years since 1917, and letting y represent the number of original species remaining.

Organize data.

We may then summarize the given data as follows:

t	y	(t, y)
0	11	$(0, 11)$
51	5	$(51, 5)$

Find the slope.

$$m = \frac{y_2 - y_1}{t_2 - t_1}$$

The phrase "linear model" refers to a linear equation and a corresponding straight line for its graph. From the data $(t_1, y_1) = (0, 11)$ and $(t_2, y_2) = (51, 5)$, we find that

$$\text{slope} = m = \frac{5 - 11}{51 - 0} = -\frac{2}{17}$$

Find y-intercept.

and the y-intercept is $b = 11$ (corresponding to time $t = 0$).

Write linear equation in slope-intercept form.

Thus, the linear equation is

$$y = -\frac{2}{17}t + 11.$$

Find extinction time by setting $y = 0$ and solving for t. (This number must then be added to 1917.)

This equation predicts that the number of original species will reach zero when

$$0 = -\frac{2}{17}t + 11$$

or when $t = \dfrac{187}{2} = 93.5$, which corresponds to the year $t = 1917 + 94 = 2011$.

(Note that we rounded *up* to the next whole year, since the model does not predict extinction until after the year 2010 begins. (See Figure 2.15.) ■

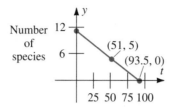

Figure 2.15 Linear model for bird-species extinction.

Of course, the method of Example 10 should be used only when the desired model is assumed to be linear, that is, when the data points lie on a straight line. In practice the actual model is often nonlinear (meaning a more general curve), or more than two data points are given, requiring the ''best fitting'' straight line to be determined somehow. We shall address both situations later in this text.

Vertical and Horizontal Lines

A vertical line has the property that all x-coordinates of points on the line are the same. It has an equation of the form $x = a$.

On a horizontal line, all points have the same y-coordinates. A horizontal line has equation $y = b$. (It's just $y = mx + b$ with $m = 0$.)

Figure 2.16 shows the graphs of the vertical line $x = 2$ and the horizontal line $y = 1$.

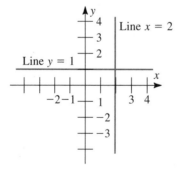

Figure 2.16 Horizontal and vertical lines.

Parallel and Perpendicular Lines

There are special relationships between the slopes of parallel or perpendicular lines.

Theorem 2

Let $\ell_1: y = m_1 x + b_1$ and $\ell_2: y = m_2 x + b_2$ be equations for lines where neither m_1 nor m_2 is zero. Then

(i) ℓ_1 and ℓ_2 are *parallel* if and only if $m_1 = m_2$ and

(ii) ℓ_1 and ℓ_2 are *perpendicular* if and only if $m_1 m_2 = -1$.

Theorem 2 says that parallel lines have the same slope, while perpendicular lines have slopes that are negative reciprocals of each other.

☐ **EXAMPLE 11**

For the line $\ell_1: 3y - 9x = 12$ find an equation for

(a) the line ℓ_2 that is parallel to ℓ_1 and contains the point $(2, 0)$ and

(b) the line ℓ_3 that is perpendicular to ℓ_1 and contains the point $(3, -2)$. ■

Strategy · · · · · · · ·

First, find the slope of ℓ_1 by putting equation in slope-intercept form.

Solution

(a) Solving the ℓ_1 equation for y gives

$$3y - 9x = 12$$
$$3y = 9x + 12$$
$$y = 3x + 4.$$

Take $m_2 = m_1$ by Theorem 1.

The slope of ℓ_1 is therefore $m_1 = 3$. The slope of ℓ_2 must also be $m_2 = 3$ because the lines are parallel. Since $(2, 0)$ is on ℓ_2, an equation for ℓ_2 is

Find equation for ℓ_2 using point-slope form.

$$y - 0 = 3(x - 2)$$

or

$$y = 3x - 6.$$

Find m_3 from equation $m_1 m_3 = -1$.

(b) Since ℓ_1 and ℓ_3 are perpendicular, we must have

$$m_3 = -\frac{1}{m_1} = -\frac{1}{3}.$$

Find equation for ℓ_3 using point-slope form.

Using this slope and the point $(3, -2)$, we find an equation for ℓ_3 to be

$$y - (-2) = -\frac{1}{3}(x - 3)$$

$$y + 2 = -\frac{1}{3}x + 1$$

$$y = -\frac{1}{3}x - 1.$$

Each of these lines is sketched in Figure 2.17. ■

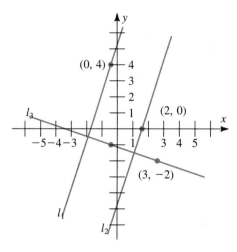

Figure 2.17 Parallel and perpendicular lines.

☑ PRACTICE PROBLEMS 1.2

1. Find an equation for the line containing the points $(-3, 5)$ and $(6, -13)$.
2. Find a linear equation giving the total cost of renting an entertainment hall for a party involving x students if the fixed price for use of the hall is $500 and the additional charge per student is $12. What is the literal meaning of the y-intercept in this problem?

Exercise Set 1.2

1. Plot the following points in the coordinate plane.
   a. $(4, 2)$ **b.** $(-6, 3)$ **c.** $(-2, 0)$
   d. $(1, -3)$ **e.** $(-3, -3)$ **f.** $(6, -2)$

2. Plot the following points in the coordinate plane.
   a. $(1, -3)$ **b.** $(4, -2)$ **c.** $(-3, 1)$
   d. $(-1, -3)$ **e.** $(5, 1)$ **f.** $(1, 5)$

In each of Exercises 3–12 draw a rough sketch of the graph of the given equation by first plotting several points.

3. $3x - y = 5$

4. $y = x^2 - 3$

5. $y = \sqrt{x} + 2$

6. $y - x^2 = 4$

7. $x - y = 1$

8. $x = y^2$

9. $y + \sqrt{x} = 4$

10. $x = \dfrac{4}{y}$

11. $y = \dfrac{1}{x - 2}$

12. $2x^2 + y = 3$

13. True or false? Every line has a slope.

14. True or false? Every real number can be the slope of a line.

15. Find a if the line through $(2, 4)$ and $(-2, a)$ has slope 3.

16. Find b if the line through $(b, 1)$ and $(1, -5)$ has slope 2.

In Exercises 17–31 find an equation for the line determined by the given information.

17. Slope 4 and y-intercept -2

18. Slope -2 and y-intercept -5

19. Slope zero and y-intercept -5

20. Through $(-1, 6)$ and $(3, 2)$

21. Through $(4, 1)$ and with slope -4

22. Through $(1, 3)$ and with slope -3

23. x-intercept -3 and y-intercept 6

24. Through $(-3, 5)$ and vertical

25. Through $(5, -3)$ and horizontal

26. Through $(-2, 4)$ and $(-6, 8)$

27. Through $(0, 2)$ and $(-1, -4)$

28. Through $(1, 4)$ and parallel to the line with equation $2x - 6y + 5 = 0$

29. Through $(5, -2)$ and parallel to the line with equation $3x - 5y = 15$

30. Through $(1, 3)$ and perpendicular to the line with equation $3x + y = 7$

31. Through $(4, -1)$ and perpendicular to the line through the points $(-2, 5)$ and $(-1, 9)$

In Exercises 32–41 find the slope and y-intercept of the line determined by the given equation. Graph the line.

32. $x = 7 - y$ **33.** $3x - 5y = 6$

34. $x + y + 3 = 0$ **35.** $2x = 10 - 3y$

36. $y = 5$ **37.** $y - 2x = 9$

38. $x = -3$ **39.** $y = x$

40. $3x - y = 9$ **41.** $9x - 5y = 45$

42. A state has an income tax of 5% on all income over $5000.
   a. Write an equation that determines a person's tax T in terms of income i for a person earning more than $5000.
   b. At what income level will an individual owe $800 in state income taxes?

43. The cost C per unit time of producing flashlights for a particular manufacturer is known to be linearly related to the production level. That is, $C = mx + b$, where x is the number of flashlights produced per week and m and b are constants. The cost of producing 20 flashlights per week is $200, while the cost of producing 100 flashlights per week is $600.
   a. Find m and b.
   b. Find the cost of producing 150 flashlights per week.
   c. What is the manufacturer's fixed weekly cost?

44. World production of crude steel increased from 700 billion metric tons in 1986 to 770 billion metric tons in 1990. Assuming a continuing linear increase in production, what production level do these data predict for
   a. 1994?   **b.** 1998?

45. The consumer price index rose from a level of $C_1 = \$100$ in 1967 to a level of $C_2 = \$293$ in 1982.
   a. Based on these data find a linear model for C in terms of time. (Let 1967 be $t = 0$.)
   b. What value of the consumer price index does this model predict for the year 1997?

46. In 1981 there were 12 billion shares of stock traded on the New York Stock Exchange. In 1991 the number was 45 billion. According to the linear equation determined by these data, what volume is predicted for the years
   a. 1996?   **b.** 2001?

47. The index of industrial production for Germany rose from 105 in 1988 to 120 in 1991. Assuming a continuing linear increase, what value of this index is predicted for the years
   a. 1994?   **b.** 1997?

48. An automobile assembly plant is planned at a total construction cost of $100 million and a useful life of 20 years. It is assumed to have no salvage value at the end of this period.
   a. Find a straight-line depreciation model for the depreciated value of the plant, V, after t years.
   b. What is the depreciated value after 12 years?
   c. What is the annual rate of depreciation?

49. A milk company purchases a delivery truck costing $20,000. If it is assigned a useful life of four years and a salvage value of $2000, find the following:
   a. A straight-line depreciation model for the depreciated value of the truck after t years.
   b. The value of the truck after 18 months.
   c. The time t at which the truck will have depreciated to half its original value. (Be careful not to ignore salvage value.)
   d. The annual rate of depreciation.

50. Carol's automobile is said to have a useful life of three years and a salvage value of $2500. If, under a straight-line depreciation model, it is depreciating at a rate of $4600 per year,
   a. What was its original value?
   b. When had it depreciated to a value $V = \$9400$?

51. Paul, an enterprising student, wishes to purchase an ice-cream truck. The truck is currently worth $12,000 and is depreciating at the constant rate of $200 per month. Paul currently has $6000 and, through earnings and interest, can increase this amount by $400 monthly.
   a. Find a straight-line depreciation model for the value V of the ice-cream truck in terms of $t = $ time, measured in months.

b. Find a linear model for the amount A available to Paul after t months.

c. When can Paul afford to buy the truck?

d. What will the selling price be?

52. Concerning Paul's ice-cream truck in Exercise 51, find a straight-line depreciation model for the value of the truck t years after the student's purchase, assuming a depreciation period of two years and a salvage value of $1000.

53. Demand for 10-day tours to Switzerland is found to be 200 reservations per month when tours are priced at $2000 and 40 reservations per month when priced at $3600.

a. Find a linear model for demand D in terms of price p.

b. What demand does this model predict for tours priced at $p = \$3000$?

c. What is the price for which demand equals zero?

d. What is the D (vertical) intercept for this linear model? Does it have any practical meaning?

☑ SOLUTIONS TO PRACTICE PROBLEMS 1.2

1. The slope of the line through the points $P = (-3, 5)$ and $Q = (6, -13)$ is

$$m = \frac{y_2 - y_1}{x_2 - x_1} = \frac{-13 - 5}{6 - (-3)} = \frac{-18}{9} = -2.$$

Using the point $P = (-3, 5)$ and the slope $m = -2$, we obtain the equation

$$y - 5 = -2(x - (-3))$$

or

$$y = -2x - 1.$$

2. If C represents total cost, then

$$C = 12x + 500.$$

The y-intercept $b = 500$ means that if the hall is rented, but *no* students attend the party (i.e., if $x = 0$), the total cost is $500.

1.3 Distance in the Plane; Equations for Circles

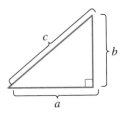

Figure 3.1 The Pythagorean theorem: $c^2 = a^2 + b^2$.

We will sometimes need to calculate the distance between two points P and Q in the coordinate plane. By this distance we mean the length of the line segment ℓ joining the points P and Q. Figure 3.2 illustrates the fact that if P has coordinates $P = (x_1, y_1)$ and Q has coordinates $Q = (x_2, y_2)$, then the line segment ℓ is the hypotenuse of the right triangle with vertices P, Q, and $R = (x_2, y_1)$. By the **Pythagorean theorem** (see Figure 3.1) the lengths of the sides of this triangle satisfy the equation

$$D^2 = (x_2 - x_1)^2 + (y_2 - y_1)^2.$$

Taking square roots of both sides of this equation gives the desired expression for D. (See Figure 3.2.)

Definition 2	The distance between the two points (x_1, y_1) and (x_2, y_2) in the coordinate plane is

$$D = \sqrt{(x_2 - x_1)^2 + (y_2 - y_1)^2}. \tag{1}$$

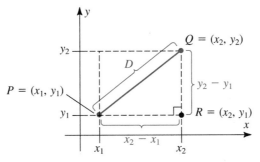

Figure 3.2 Distance D between (x_1, y_2) and (x_2, y_2) is $D = \sqrt{(x_2 - x_1)^2 + (y_2 - y_1)^2}$.

☐ **EXAMPLE 1**

Find the distance between the points $P = (-3, 2)$ and $Q = (5, -4)$.

Solution: Using equation (1) with $(x_1, y_1) = (-3, 2)$ and $(x_2, y_2) = (5, -4)$, we obtain

$$D = \sqrt{(5 - (-3))^2 + (-4 - 2)^2}$$
$$= \sqrt{8^2 + (-6)^2}$$
$$= \sqrt{100}$$
$$= 10.$$ ■

Note that the distance D between any two points will always be a nonnegative number.

Equations for Circles

The definition of distance in the plane gives a definition for circles that allows us to find their corresponding equations.

Definition 3

A **circle** is the set of all points in the plane lying at a fixed distance r (called the **radius**) from a fixed point P (called the **center**).

Using the distance formula in equation (1) we can find an equation for the circle with center (h, k) and radius r. If we let $P = (x, y)$ be any point on the circle, the condition of Definition 3 that the distance between the point $P = (x, y)$ and the center (h, k) equal r can be written, using equation (1), as

$$\sqrt{(x - h)^2 + (y - k)^2} = r.$$

Squaring both sides of this equation gives

$$(x - h)^2 + (y - k)^2 = r^2.$$

For easy reference we restate this result as a theorem.

Theorem 3

The circle with center (h, k) and radius r has equation

$$(x - h)^2 + (y - k)^2 = r^2. \tag{2}$$

Equation (2) is called the **standard form** for the equation of a circle, since the radius r and the coordinates (h, k) of the center are easy to identify from this equation. (See Figure 3.3.)

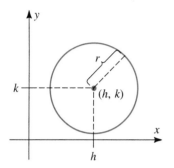

Figure 3.3 The circle with center (h, k) and radius r has equation

$$(x - h)^2 + (y - k)^2 = r^2.$$

☐ **EXAMPLE 2**

The circle with center $(h, k) = (0, 0)$ and radius $r = 1$ has equation

$$x^2 + y^2 = 1$$

since $h = 0$, $k = 0$, and $r = 1$ in equation (2) gives this result. This is called the **unit circle.** (See Figure 3.4.) ■

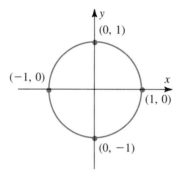

Figure 3.4 Unit circle

$$x^2 + y^2 = 1.$$

☐ **EXAMPLE 3**

An equation for the circle with center $(-4, 3)$ and radius 5 is found by setting $h = -4$, $k = 3$, and $r = 5$ in equation (2). We obtain

$$[x - (-4)]^2 + (y - 3)^2 = 5^2$$

or

$$(x + 4)^2 + (y - 3)^2 = 25$$

which we can write as

$$(x^2 + 8x + 16) + (y^2 - 6y + 9) = 25$$

or

$$x^2 + 8x + y^2 - 6y = 0.$$ ■

Completing the Square

In order to determine whether an equation involving quadratic (i.e., second degree) expressions in both x and y corresponds to a circle, we must attempt to bring the equation into the form of equation (2). Doing so requires the technique of **completing the square,** which goes as follows.

Recall that the result of squaring the binomial $(x + a)$ is the quadratic expression

$$(x + a)^2 = x^2 + 2ax + a^2. \tag{3}$$

The technique of completing the square answers just the opposite question: What constant, when added to the expression $x^2 + bx$, will produce a perfect square, as in equation (3)? By examining the right side of equation (3), you can see that *the constant term, a^2, in a perfect square is the square of half the coefficient of x.* We therefore "complete the square on $x^2 + bx$" as follows:

$$x^2 + bx = \left[x^2 + bx + \left(\frac{b}{2} \right)^2 \right] - \left(\frac{b}{2} \right)^2$$

$$= \left(x + \frac{b}{2} \right)^2 - \frac{b^2}{4}.$$

It is important to note that whatever constant is added to the expression $x^2 + bx$ must also be subtracted from the result, so that the values of the expression are not changed.

☐ **EXAMPLE 4**

Here are three examples of completing the square.

(a) $x^2 + 6x = (x^2 + 6x + 3^2) - 3^2$

$\qquad = (x + 3)^2 - 9$

(b) $x^2 - 8x = [x^2 - 8x + (-4)^2] - (-4)^2$

$\qquad = (x - 4)^2 - 16$

(c) $x^2 + \dfrac{3}{4}x = \left[x^2 + \dfrac{3}{4}x + \left(\dfrac{3}{8} \right)^2 \right] - \left(\dfrac{3}{8} \right)^2$

$\qquad = \left(x + \dfrac{3}{8} \right)^2 - \dfrac{9}{64}.$ ◼

The next example shows how the technique of completing the square is used to identify the equation for a circle.

☐ **EXAMPLE 5**

Describe the graph of the equation

$$x^2 + y^2 + 6x - 2y + 6 = 0.$$ ◼

Strategy · · · · · · · ·

Complete the square on x and y terms and try to bring equation into form of equation (2).

Solution

We write the given equation as

$$(x^2 + 6x) + (y^2 - 2y) + 6 = 0. \tag{4}$$

To complete the square on the first term, we add the square of half the coefficient of x, that is, we add $\left(\dfrac{6}{2}\right)^2 = 9$. This gives

Completing the square in x.

$$(x^2 + 6x) = (x^2 + 6x + 9) - 9 = (x + 3)^2 - 9. \tag{5}$$

Similarly, we complete the square on the second term as

Completing the square in y.

$$(y^2 - 2y) = (y^2 - 2y + 1) - 1 = (y - 1)^2 - 1. \tag{6}$$

Substituting the expressions in equations (5) and (6) into equation (4) gives the equation

Combining the results.

$$[(x + 3)^2 - 9] + [(y - 1)^2 - 1] + 6 = 0$$

or

$$(x + 3)^2 + (y - 1)^2 = 4.$$

Compare with equation (2).

The graph is therefore a circle with center $(-3, 1)$ and radius $r = \sqrt{4} = 2$. ■

☐ EXAMPLE 6

Ecologists refer to the Kettle curve as describing the dispersion of seeds or other biological organisms whose dispersal is passive (e.g., seeds that are windblown, acorns that bounce along the ground, offspring that may or may not remain close to the nest). A typical Kettle curve is shown in Figure 3.5. (We will study its associated equation in Chapter 4.)

In any particular application, the Kettle curve determines a family of concentric circles containing the circular regions corresponding to the various percentages of the organisms retained within the given distance in a unit of time. (See Figure 3.6.)

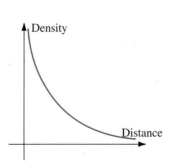

Figure 3.5 Typical Kettle curve.

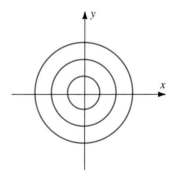

Figure 3.6 Regions of dispersal for Kettle curve.

Suppose it is known that the 20% of the birds hatched in a certain tree remain within the region enclosed by the graph of the equation

$$x^2 + 6x + y^2 - 4y + 9 = 0$$

where x and y are in units of miles.

(a) What is the location of the tree?

(b) What is the shape and size of the region?

Solution: We complete the square as in the preceding example:

$$x^2 + 6x = (x^2 + 6x + 9) - 9 = (x + 3)^2 - 9$$

and

$$y^2 - 4y = (y^2 - 4y + 4) - 4 = (y - 2)^2 - 4$$

or

$$\begin{aligned} x^2 + 6x + y^2 - 4y + 9 &= (x^2 + 6x) + (y^2 - 4) + 9 \\ &= [(x + 3)^2 - 9] + [(y - 2)^2 - 4] + 9 \\ &= (x + 3)^2 + (y - 2)^2 - 4. \end{aligned}$$

Thus

$$(x + 3)^2 + (y - 2)^2 = 2^2$$

and the region is seen to be a circle with center (tree) at $(-3, 2)$ and radius 2 miles.

☑ PRACTICE PROBLEMS 1.3

1. Describe the graph of the equation

$$x^2 + 14x + y^2 - 8y + 56 = 0.$$

2. A tree is located at point $(7, 12)$ on a landscape plot. An arborist reports that 45% of the seedlings due to this particular tree will sprout within 9 units of the tree. Find an equation describing this region on the plot.

Exercise Set 1.3

In each of Exercises 1–8 find the distance between the given points.

1. $(2, -1)$ and $(0, 2)$

2. $(3, 1)$ and $(1, 3)$

3. $(0, 2)$ and $(1, -9)$

4. $(1, -3)$ and $(6, 6)$

5. $(1, 1)$ and $(-1, -1)$

6. $(-2, -2)$ and $(1, 2)$

7. $(-4, 2)$ and $(-3, -5)$

8. $(0, -9)$ and $(-6, 0)$

9. Verify that the **midpoint** of the line segment joining the points (x_1, y_1) and (x_2, y_2) has coordinates $\left(\dfrac{x_1 + x_2}{2}, \dfrac{y_1 + y_2}{2}\right)$. (*Hint:* Use the distance formula.)

10. Use the result of Exercise 9 to find the midpoints of the line joining the following pairs of points.

a. $(0, 0)$ and $(0, 6)$

b. $(1, 3)$ and $(4, 7)$

c. $(-1, 2)$ and $(7, 4)$

In Exercises 11–15 find an equation for the circle with the stated properties.

11. Center $(0, 0)$ and radius 3

12. Center $(2, 4)$ and radius 6

13. Center $(4, 3)$ and radius 2

14. Center $(-2, 4)$ and radius 3

15. Center $(-6, -4)$ and radius 10

In Exercises 16–21 complete the square on the given expression.

16. $x^2 + 6x$

17. $x^2 - 10x$

18. $t - t^2$

19. $8x - x^2$

20. $x^2 - 6x + 5$

21. $3 - 2t - 2t^2$

In each of Exercises 22–27 find the center and radius of the circle whose equation is given.

22. $x^2 - 2x + y^2 - 8 = 0$

23. $x^2 - 2x + y^2 + 6y - 12 = 0$

24. $x^2 + y^2 + 4x + 2y - 11 = 0$

25. $x^2 + 14x + y^2 - 10y + 70 = 0$

26. $x^2 - 6x + y^2 - 4y + 8 = 0$

27. $x^2 + y^2 - 2x - 6y + 3 = 0$

28. Does the point $(1, 1)$ lie inside or outside the circle with equation $x^2 - 4x + y^2 + 6y = 3$? Why or why not?

29. Does the point $(2, 1)$ lie inside or outside the circle with equation $x^2 - 2x + y^2 - 4y + 1 = 0$?

30. Find an equation for the line tangent to the circle with equation $x^2 + y^2 - 6x - 8y = 0$ at the origin. (*Hint:* The tangent to a circle at point P is perpendicular to the radius of the circle at P.)

31. A tree is located at the point $(2, 4)$ on a landscape grid. Paul, the landscaper, wants to ensure that a sprinkler head is located within 5 units of the tree. Will locating the sprinkler head at location $(0, 0)$ satisfy this concern? Why or why not?

32. Sarah is interested in the dispersal rate of acorns from oak trees. She collects data from two trees from which she concludes that 50% of the acorns from tree A remain within the region with equation

$$x^2 - 4x + y^2 - 6y + 4 = 0$$

and 50% of the acorns from tree B remain within the region with equation

$$x^2 + 2x + y^2 + 2y - 7 = 0.$$

a. Describe these regions.

b. Where are the trees located?

c. Do the regions overlap? Why or why not?

☑ **SOLUTIONS TO PRACTICE PROBLEMS 1.3**

1. We complete the square as in Examples 5 and 6:

$$x^2 + 14x + y^2 - 8y + 56$$
$$= [(x^2 + 14x + 49) - 49] + [(y^2 - 8y + 16) - 16] + 56$$
$$= [(x + 7)^2 - 49] + [(y - 4)^2 - 16] + 56$$
$$= (x + 7)^2 + (y - 4)^2 - 9$$

so the equation can be written

$$(x + 7)^2 + (y - 4)^2 = 3^2$$

which has a graph that is a circle with center at $(-7, 4)$ and radius $r = 3$.

2. The region is a circle with center $(7, 12)$ and radius $r = 9$:

$$(x - 7)^2 + (y - 12)^2 = 9^2$$

or

$$x^2 - 14x + y^2 - 24y + 112 = 0.$$

1.4 Functions and Their Graphs

The linear equation $y = mx + b$ is one example of how two variables can be related. The concept of a *function* is helpful in studying more general relationships between quantities.

A function is any rule between two kinds of objects that assigns one (and *only* one) object of the second kind to each object of the first kind. Here are some examples of functions we have already seen.

☐ EXAMPLE 1

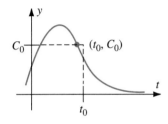

The relationship between the concentration of a drug in a patient's bloodstream and the length of time that has elapsed since its injection (Figure 4.1) is an example of a *function:* for each time $t_0 > 0$ there is a unique concentration C_0 of the drug in the blood supply.   ■

☐ EXAMPLE 2

Figure 4.1   Concentration of a drug in the bloodstream is a function of time.

Another such relationship occurs in a straight-line depreciation model, where the depreciated value of a capital asset V is a function of time (Figure 4.2). Selecting a time, t_0, completely determines the associated value V_0.   ■

☐ EXAMPLE 3

Still another example is the relationship between the demand for a product D and the price p for which it sells (Figure 4.3). Once a price p_0 is selected, the corresponding demand D_0 is determined.   ■

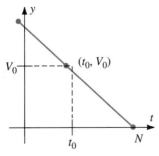

Figure 4.2   Depreciated value V of an asset is a function of time.

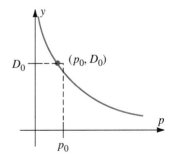

Figure 4.3   Demand D for an item as a function of its selling price p.

☐ **EXAMPLE 4**

We can see that the equation $xy = 1$ defines y as a function of x by solving the equation for y: $y = \dfrac{1}{x}$. In this form it is clear that any choice of a number x_0 determines a unique value $y_0 = \dfrac{1}{x_0}$ (see Figure 4.4). ■

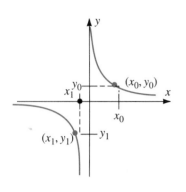

Figure 4.4   The equation $y = \dfrac{1}{x}$ determines y as a function of x.

However, not all equations involving two variables are functions. For example, in the equation

$$x^2 + y^2 = 4$$

we observe that

$$\text{if} \quad x = 0, \ y^2 = 4, \quad \text{so} \quad y = 2 \quad or \quad y = -2$$
$$\text{if} \quad x = 1, \ y^2 = 4 - 1, \quad \text{so} \quad y = \sqrt{3} \quad or \quad y = -\sqrt{3}.$$

Figure 4.5 illustrates what is going wrong here. The graph of the equation $x^2 + y^2 = 4$ is a circle. It has the property that any x in the interval $(-2, 2)$ is associated with *two* values of y.

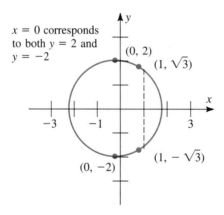

Figure 4.5   The equation $x^2 + y^2 = 4$ is *not* a function. Some x's correspond to *two* y's.

At this point a formal definition of function will help make our discussion of functions more precise.

Definition 4	A **function** from set A to set B is a rule that assigns to each element of set A one and only one element of set B. Set A is called the **domain** of the function.

In other words, a function is an input-output device. For each input from the domain, the function produces a unique output. The terminology "domain" helps to distinguish the input set from the outputs. Referring to our previous examples, we see that

(i) The domain of the drug concentration function in Example 1 is $[0, \infty)$. Negative values of time do not make sense.

(ii) The domain of the depreciated value function V in Example 2 is $[0, N]$ where N is the useful lifetime of the asset.

(iii) The domain of the demand function in Example 3 would need to be specified as a subinterval of $(0, \infty)$. Prices too small or too large would be unrealistic.

(iv) The domain of the function $y = \dfrac{1}{x}$ is all real numbers except $x = 0$ because division by zero is not defined.

Notation for Functions

We usually denote a function by a letter, such as f, and we write $f(x)$ to mean the *value* (output) that the function f assigns to the input x. Thus for the linear equation $y = 2x - 1$ we write

$$f(x) = 2x - 1$$

to emphasize that the numbers y are indeed values of a function, and we obtain particular values of this function as follows:

$$f(0) = 2(0) - 1 = -1$$
$$f(6) = 2(6) - 1 = 11$$
$$f(-3) = 2(-3) - 1 = -7$$

etc.

Equations for Functions

Most of the functions with which we shall be concerned will be specified by equations such as

$$f(x) = x^3 - 6x + 6 \qquad (f \text{ as a function of } x)$$

or

$$f(t) = 32 - 16t^2 \qquad (f \text{ as a function of } t)$$

or

$$f(s) = \frac{s^2 - 1}{s + 1}. \qquad (f \text{ as a function of } s)$$

In such cases the variable appearing on the right-hand side of the equation is referred to as the **independent** variable. The **values** of the function comprise what is sometimes called the **dependent** variable. The advantage of using the function notation

$f()$ is that it specifies clearly the independent variable. Figure 4.6 illustrates the function concept and terminology.

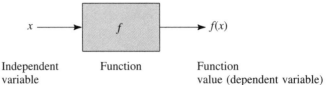

| Independent variable | Function | Function value (dependent variable) |

Figure 4.6 A function produces a unique output $f(x)$ from an input x. $f(x)$ is the *value* that the function assigns to the number x.

When a function is specified by an equation, the domain, unless otherwise specified, is assumed to be all numbers for which the expression defining the function makes sense.

☐ **EXAMPLE 5**

For the functions $f(x) = x^2 - 2x + 1$ and $g(x) = \sqrt{x + 3}$ we have

(a) $f(5) = 5^2 - 2 \cdot 5 + 1 = 25 - 10 + 1 = 16$

(b) $f(-1) = (-1)^2 - 2(-1) + 1 = 1 + 2 + 1 = 4$

(c) $g(6) = \sqrt{6 + 3} = \sqrt{9} = 3$

(d) $g(-1) = \sqrt{-1 + 3} = \sqrt{2}$.

However, $g(-5) = \sqrt{-5 + 3} = \sqrt{-2}$ is not defined. ∎

☐ **EXAMPLE 6**

The domain of the function $f(x) = 1 + 2x - x^2$ is all real numbers, $(-\infty, \infty)$, since the right-hand side is defined for all x. ∎

☐ **EXAMPLE 7**

Find the domain of the function $f(x) = \sqrt{x - 2}$.

Solution: Since square roots of negative numbers are not defined, we must have $x - 2 \geq 0$, or $x \geq 2$. The domain is $[2, \infty)$. ∎

☐ **EXAMPLE 8**

Find the domain of the function $f(t) = \dfrac{1}{t^2 - t - 2}$.

Solution: The denominator can be factored as

$$t^2 - t - 2 = (t - 2)(t + 1)$$

so we can write

$$f(t) = \frac{1}{(t-2)(t+1)}.$$

The right-hand side is not defined when $t = 2$ or $t = -1$, since these numbers produce a factor of zero in the denominator. The domain consists of all other numbers t, that is, the intervals $(-\infty, -1)$, $(-1, 2)$, and $(2, \infty)$. ■

Range of a Function

Generally speaking, the range of a function is the set of all its possible values. A more precise definition is the following:

Definition 5

If f is a function with domain A, the *range* of f is the set of values $\{f(x) \mid x \in A\}$.

Determining the range of a function is sometimes a matter of "inspection," taking into account what values can be produced by selecting various numbers in the domain.

☐ **EXAMPLE 9**

The range of the squaring function $f(x) = x^2$ is $[0, \infty)$, since all nonnegative numbers are squares (of their square roots). ■

☐ **EXAMPLE 10**

The range of the function $f(x) = \dfrac{1}{x}$ is the pair of intervals $(-\infty, 0)$ and $(0, \infty)$. We leave the explanation to you. ■

☐ **EXAMPLE 11**

The range of the function

$$V(t) = C - \left(\frac{C-S}{N}\right)t$$

giving the depreciated value of a capital asset as a function of t, is the interval $[S, C]$ where S is the salvage (final) value and C is the original cost. (See Section 1.2.) ■

Graphs of Functions

When functions are specified by equations, such as $f(x) = x^2 - 4$, we can graph the function on the coordinate plane by plotting the independent variable on the horizontal axis and values of the function on the vertical axis. That is, we plot the

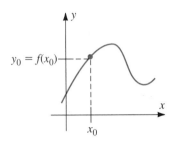

Figure 4.7 Graphing the function $y = f(x)$. Each point on the graph has coordinates $(x, f(x))$ for some number x.

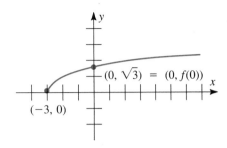

Figure 4.8 Graph of $f(x) = \sqrt{x + 3}$.

points $(x, f(x))$. (See Figure 4.7.) Figure 4.8 shows the graph of the function $f(x) = \sqrt{x + 3}$.

Since a function assigns only one value to each x in its domain, the graph of a function can have only one point corresponding to each x-coordinate. That is why a circle cannot be the graph of a function. (See Figure 4.9.) Since all points on a vertical line $x = a$ have the *same* x-coordinates, we have the following property (see Figure 4.10):

Vertical Line Property: The graph of a function must have the property that any vertical line can intersect the graph at most once.

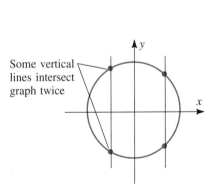

Some vertical lines intersect graph twice

Figure 4.9 A circle does not have the vertical line property.

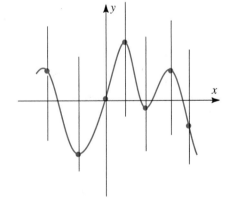

Figure 4.10 Graph of a function must have the vertical line property.

Applications to Business and Economics

Several types of functions are useful in modelling various aspects of economic activity. For example, suppose that the independent variable x represents the number of items of a particular kind that a manufacturing company produces per week. The variable x is then referred to as the *production level* for that item. Here are three important functions of production level:

(i) The cost function, $y = C(x)$, gives the total cost of producing and marketing x items per unit of time.
(ii) The revenue function, $y = R(x)$, gives the total amount of money received from the sale of x items.
(iii) The profit function, $y = P(x)$, gives the profit for the company in producing and selling x items per unit time.

We will assume that all items manufactured by the company in a given unit of time are sold during that same unit of time, so that

$$
\text{profit} = \text{revenue} - \text{cost}
$$

or $\qquad\qquad\qquad\qquad\qquad\qquad\qquad\qquad\qquad$ (1)

$$
P(x) = R(x) - C(x)
$$

The following examples involve these three functions.

□ **EXAMPLE 12**

The cost to a company of producing goods usually consists of two types of costs. The *fixed costs* are the ongoing costs of maintaining a manufacturing facility (cost of building, electricity, managers' salaries, advertising, etc.). The *variable costs* are the costs directly assignable to the production of a particular item (cost of materials, direct cost of labor, shipping costs, etc.). Thus

$$
\text{total costs} = \text{fixed costs} + \text{variable costs.} \qquad (2)
$$

If a bicycle manufacturer has fixed costs of $500 per week and variable costs of $30 per bicycle, find an equation for the total cost of producing x bicycles per week.

Solution: Since the variable costs are $30 per bicycle, the total variable costs in producing x bicycles are $30x. With fixed costs of $500 per week, equation (2) gives total costs as

$$
C(x) = 500 + 30x, \qquad x \geq 0 \qquad (3)
$$

dollars per week at production level x. This cost function is graphed in Figure 4.11. Note that the domain of C is $[0, \infty)$, since negative production levels are not defined. This is the meaning of the inequality $x \geq 0$ in line (3). The *range* of this function is $[500, \infty)$. ∎

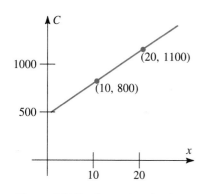

Figure 4.11 Total cost function in Example 12.

□ **EXAMPLE 13**

Suppose the bicycle manufacturer in Example 12 sells the bicycles for $80 each. Find the revenue function R associated with output level x.

Solution: Total revenue is simply price per bicycle ($80) multiplied by the number of bicycles, x. Thus

$$R(x) = 80x, \qquad x \geq 0$$

dollars. The graph of the revenue function appears in Figure 4.12. ■

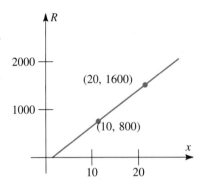

Figure 4.12 Revenue function in Example 13.

□ **EXAMPLE 14**

The bicycle manufacturer in Examples 12 and 13 wants to make a profit, of course.

(a) Find the profit function P.
(b) Find the output levels x at which $P(x)$ is positive.

Solution: Using equation (1) and the results of Examples 12 and 13, we find that

$$\begin{aligned}
P(x) &= R(x) - C(x) \\
&= 80x - (500 + 30x) \\
&= 50x - 500, \qquad x \geq 0.
\end{aligned}$$

Thus $P(x)$ will be positive when

$$50x - 500 > 0$$

or

$$50x > 500$$

or

$$x > \frac{500}{50} = 10 \text{ bicycles per week.}$$

That is, the bicycle manufacturer must produce and sell 11 or more bicycles per week in order to show a profit. All three functions C, R, and P are graphed on the same coordinate axes in Figure 4.13. ■

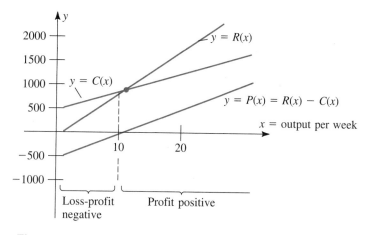

Figure 4.13 Profit, loss, and revenue functions.

An Application to Ecology: A Model for Animal Foraging

Some biologists believe that animals "optimize" their choice of which foods (vegetation and other animals) to eat according to the expenditure of time and energy that is required to find and consume the food item. For example, cats prey on mice, which are relatively easy to catch and consume, when compared, say, to birds.

Figure 4.14 suggests a model for how this optimization might be described. Let the x- and y-variables represent the size of the food item and the energy required to obtain it. For a particular food item one can imagine two functions relating y to x: the cost function, giving the amount of energy $y = C(x)$ required to find and eat the given item, and the benefit function $y = B(x)$ giving the amount of food energy obtained from a food item of size x.

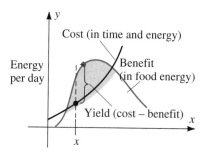

Figure 4.14 Model for optimization of food choice.

The proposed model reflects the assumptions that (a) the energy cost in consuming a given food item increases as the size of the item increases, and (b) the benefit obtained from a food item peaks at a certain size and then declines as the item increases in size (and complexity).

According to this model, the animal "optimizes" its food choice by selecting the food size for which the benefit most exceeds the cost, as illustrated in Figure 4.14. The term "yield" is sometimes used to refer to the difference between benefit and cost, just as the term "profit" represents the difference between revenue and cost in the business setting.

✅ **PRACTICE PROBLEMS 1.4**

1. For the function $f(x) = \dfrac{3 - \sqrt{x}}{x^2 + 1}$ find
   a. $f(0)$
   b. $f(4)$
   c. $f(x + h)$.
2. What is the domain of the function in Problem 1?
3. A state charges an income tax of 5% on all earnings in excess of $15,000 per year, with a surcharge of 0.5% on income in excess of $50,000. Find an expression for the function $T(x)$ giving the tax due on incomes x in excess of $50,000.

Exercise Set 1.4

In Exercises 1–8 identify the given rule as either a function or not necessarily a function, and explain your reasoning.

1. The assigning of postage charges to packages

2. The calculation of federal income tax

3. Listing the names of your professors' children

4. The matching of companies with the products they produce

5. The calculation of average daily temperature

6. Your daily weight

7. A listing of textbooks required for various college courses

8. A monthly electric bill for your home

9. For the function $f(x) = 7 - 3x$ find
   a. $f(0)$ **b.** $f(3)$
   c. $f(a)$ **d.** $f(x + h)$
   e. the domain of f **f.** the range of f

10. For the function $f(x) = \dfrac{1}{x - 7}$ find
    a. $f(8)$ **b.** $f(b)$
    c. $f(-1)$ **d.** $f(x + h)$
    e. the domain of f **f.** The range of f

11. For the function $f(x) = \dfrac{x + 3}{x^2 - x + 2}$ find
    a. $f(0)$ **b.** $f(-3)$
    c. $f(-1)$ **d.** $f(x + h)$

12. For the function $f(x) = \dfrac{\sqrt{6 - x}}{1 + x^2}$ find
    a. $f(2)$ **b.** $f(6)$
    c. $f(-3)$ **d.** $f(x + h)$

In Exercises 13–20 label the graph as either a function or not a function. (Use x as the independent variable.)

13.
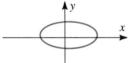

14.
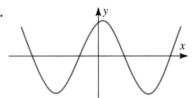

15.
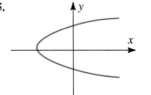

16.

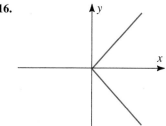

17.

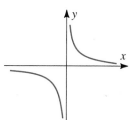

18.

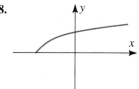

19.

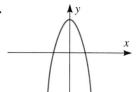

20.

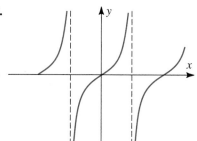

In Exercises 21–28 state the domain of the given function.

21. $f(x) = \dfrac{1}{x^2 - 7}$

22. $f(x) = \dfrac{x - \sqrt{x}}{x - 3}$

23. $f(s) = \dfrac{s^2 - 1}{s + 1}$

24. $f(t) = \dfrac{t}{1 + \sqrt{t}}$

25. $g(x) = \dfrac{1}{\sqrt{1 - x^2}}$

26. $f(x) = \dfrac{1}{x^2 - 3x - 4}$

27. $f(x) = \dfrac{\sqrt{x}}{x^3 - x}$

28. $f(x) = \sqrt{(x - 1)(x + 1)}$

29. What is the range of the function $f(x) = x^2 + 6x + 7$?

30. What is the range of the function $f(x) = x^3 - x^5$?

31. The cab fare from an airport to a nearby city is $2 per mile plus 50¢ for a bridge toll. Write the cost C as a function of the mileage x.

32. An automobile rents for $10 per day plus 20¢ per mile. Write a function $y = C(x)$ for the cost per day as a function of mileage.

33. Jill's company produces lawnmowers. It has fixed costs of $1000 per week and variable costs of $70 per lawnmower. Express the total weekly costs C as a function of the weekly production level x.

34. Refer to Exercise 33. If Jill can sell her mowers for $150 each,
 a. Find the revenue function R.
 b. Find the manufacturer's weekly profit function P.
 c. How many lawnmowers must the producer sell per week in order to show a profit?

35. Market research indicates that the demand D for a certain type of umbrella is related to its selling price by the function $D(p) = 800 - 40p$, $0 \le p \le 20$. Here p is the selling price in dollars and $D(p)$ is the number of umbrellas that will be sold per week at price p.
 a. How many umbrellas will be sold per week at the price of $5?
 b. At what price will demand be greatest?
 c. At what price will demand have become zero?

36. A tool rental agency can rent 500 jackhammers per year at a daily rental of $30. For each one dollar increase in the daily rental fee 20 fewer jackhammers are rented per year.
 a. Express the yearly revenues from jackhammer rentals, R, as a function of the daily rental price p.
 b. At what price will revenues reach zero?

37. A hotel has 400 identical rooms. At daily rates below $50 per room all rooms will be filled. For each dollar increase in daily rate above $50, ten rooms will remain vacant. Express the daily revenues R as a function of the daily room rent p.

38. A supermarket manager discovers that after x hours of experience, a new employee at the checkout register can handle $N(x)$ customers per hour where

$$N(x) = 32 - \frac{24}{\sqrt{x+1}}, \qquad x \geq 0.$$

a. How many customers can a new employee (no experience) handle per hour?

b. According to this model, does the employee's speed ever stop improving?

c. What is the "upper limit" of the speed? Can it ever be achieved?

39. A typing instructor observes that after n weeks of instruction a student can, on average, type $W(n)$ words per minute where

$$W(n) = \sqrt{400 + 80n}.$$

a. Graph this "learning curve" by plotting points.

b. How many words per minute can a new student type on the first day ($n = 0$) of class?

c. Is there a maximum speed associated with this model?

40. A bank pays 8% interest on savings accounts, compounded once per year. Tom places $1000 in a savings account and makes no further deposits. Express the amount in the account, P, as a function of the number of years that the funds have been on deposit.

41. Ajax Company, an underwriter of homeowners' insurance, charges an annual premium of $100 plus 0.5% of the face amount of the policy.

a. Express the annual premium P as a function of the face amount of the policy, x.

b. What is the premium for a $150,000 policy?

42. Refer to Exercise 41. Bjax Insurance Company, a competing underwriter, charges an annual premium of $200 plus 0.3% of the face amount of the policy.

a. Which company has a lower premium for a $150,000 policy?

b. For what policy face amount are the two companies' premiums equal?

43. Carbon dioxide levels at the South Pole are reported to have risen from 315 parts per million in 1958 to 322 parts per million in 1966 and to 329 parts per million in 1974.

a. Using $t = 0$ to correspond to the year 1958, find a linear function giving this carbon dioxide level as a function of time.

b. What level does this function predict for the year 1998?

44. Refer to the animal foraging model in Figure 4.14. If the cost function is $C(x) = \frac{x^2}{4}$ and the benefit function is $B(x) = 8x - x^2$, find

a. The yield, $Y(x) = B(x) - C(x)$ at $x = 4$.

b. The numbers x where the benefit is zero.

c. The numbers x where cost equals benefit.

✓ SOLUTIONS TO PRACTICE PROBLEMS 1.4

1. a. $f(0) = \dfrac{3 - \sqrt{0}}{0^2 + 1} = 3$

b. $f(4) = \dfrac{3 - \sqrt{4}}{4^2 + 1} = \dfrac{1}{17}$

c. $f(x + h) = \dfrac{3 - \sqrt{x + h}}{(x + h)^2 + 1}$

2. The domain is $[0, \infty)$ because the square root term f is defined only for nonnegative numbers.

3. $T(x) = 0.05(x - 15{,}000) + 0.005(x - 50{,}000)$
$= 0.055x - 1000$

1.5 Some Special Types of Functions

In Section 1.4 we presented several economic applications of linear functions— those of the form $f(x) = mx + b$. Many other types of functions are also important in applications. For example, a cost function $y = C(x)$ for a producer of a good or

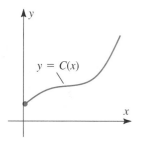

Figure 5.1 A nonlinear function $C(x)$ giving the cost of producing x items per unit time.

service is often nonlinear. Figure 5.1 shows one typical cost function. Note that following a short startup period, costs rise slowly as production increases, due primarily to efficiencies that can be achieved. But eventually costs rise rapidly as production capacity becomes strained (additional equipment is required, overtime wages are required, etc.).

Figure 5.2 shows the result of combining the cost function in Figure 5.1 with a linear revenue function $R(x) = px$ to form the profit function $y = P(x) = R(x) - C(x)$. Unlike the linear profit function of Example 14, Section 1.4, this profit function actually becomes negative (i.e., shows a loss) for higher production levels.

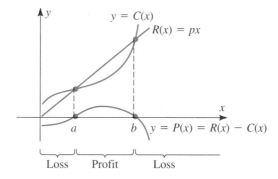

Figure 5.2 The profit function $P(x) = R(x) - C(x)$ is positive only in the interval (a, b). Losses result for production levels in $[0, a)$ or in (b, ∞).

☐ **EXAMPLE 1**

An automobile manufacturer has determined that the cost of producing x hundred automobiles per week is given by the function

$$C(x) = 2 + \sqrt{x + 2} + 0.1(x - 3)^3$$

where $C(x)$ is in millions of dollars. The automobile company sells this particular model for \$15,000 per automobile. The revenue function, also in millions of dollars, is therefore

$$
\begin{aligned}
R(x) &= (\$15{,}000) \times (\text{number of cars sold}) & \\
&= (\$15{,}000) \times (100x) & (x \text{ is in units of hundreds}) \\
&= \$1{,}500{,}000x & (\text{in dollars}) \\
&= \$1.5x & (\text{in millions of dollars})
\end{aligned}
$$

The profit function is therefore

$$
\begin{aligned}
P(x) &= R(x) - C(x) \\
&= 1.5x - 2 - \sqrt{x + 2} - 0.1(x - 3)^3.
\end{aligned}
$$

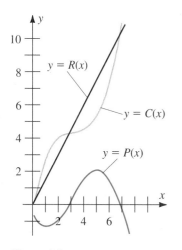

Figure 5.3 The revenue function $R(x) = \dfrac{3}{2}x$ and the resulting profit function $P(x) = R(x) - C(x)$.

Each of these functions is graphed in Figure 5.3. The range of production for which profits are positive is approximately (280,690), and the maximum profit appears to be approximately 2 million dollars per week at a production level of approximately 500 cars per week. ∎

The purpose of this section is to review several types of nonlinear functions that we will encounter in various applications later on.

Power Functions

Among the simplest types of functions are the power functions of the form

$$f(x) = x^n$$

where n is a positive integer. Figures 5.4 and 5.5 show how we can sketch the graphs of the power functions $f(x) = x^2$ and $g(x) = x^3$ by first plotting particular points.

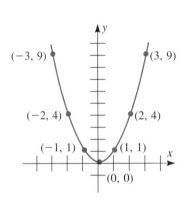

Figure 5.4 Graph of $f(x) = x^2$.

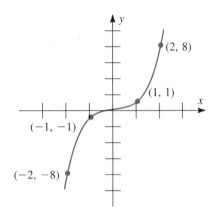

Figure 5.5 Graph of $g(x) = x^3$.

Figures 5.6 and 5.7 show the graphs of the power function $f(x) = x^4$ and $g(x) = x^5$. (What can you conjecture about the shape of the graph of the function $h(x) = x^n$ for n even versus n odd?)

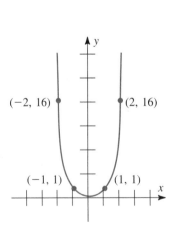

Figure 5.6 Graph of $f(x) = x^4$.

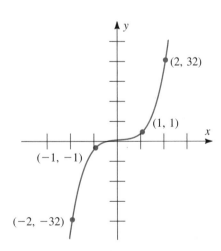

Figure 5.7 Graph of $f(x) = x^5$.

Figure 5.8 shows the graphs of several functions of the form $f(x) = ax^2$. Note that each of these resembles the graph of $f(x) = x^2$, except that the y-coordinates have each been multiplied by the constant a. Note that the graph of $f(x) = ax^2$ opens upward when $a > 0$ and downward when $a < 0$.

x	0	1	-1	2	-2	3	-3
$f(x) = x^2$	0	1	1	4	4	9	9

x	0	1	-1	2	-2
$g(x) = x^3$	0	1	-1	8	-8

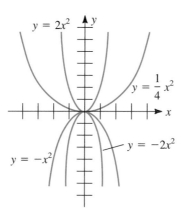

Figure 5.8 Functions of the form $f(x) = ax^2$.

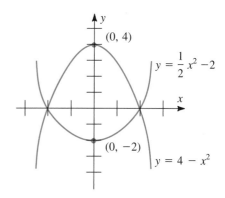

Figure 5.9 Functions of the form $g(x) = ax^2 + b$.

Quadratic Functions

Each of the graphs in Figure 5.9 is a **parabola.** In general, a parabola is a curve that, when properly positioned in the coordinate plane, is the graph of a function of the form $f(x) = ax^2$. We shall not make a detailed study of parabolas, but later on we shall be able to show that the graph of any function of the form $f(x) = Ax^2 + Bx + C$ is a parabola (Figure 5.9). Such functions are called **quadratic** functions.

Polynomials

Quadratic functions are just one type of more general functions called **polynomials.** These are functions of the form

$$f(x) = a_n x^n + a_{n-1} x^{n-1} + \cdots + a_1 x + a_0$$

where $a_0, a_1, \ldots, a_2$ are constants, $a_n \neq 0$, and n is a positive integer. Like quadratic functions, polynomials are defined for all numbers x. The integer n is called the **degree** of the polynomial. Here are some examples:

$$f(x) = x^3 - 6x^2 + 3x - 4 \qquad \text{(degree 3)}$$
$$f(x) = x^5 - 6x^2 + 14 \qquad \text{(degree 5)}$$
$$f(x) = 9 - 6x^2 + x^7. \qquad \text{(degree 7)}$$

Figure 5.10 shows the graph of the polynomial $f(x) = x^3 - 4x + 1$. In general, the higher the degree of the polynomial, the greater the number of "turns" in its graph. We will see later how calculus locates these turns rather easily.

Figure 5.10 Graph of polynomial $f(x) = x^3 - 4x + 1$.

Rational Functions

Rational functions are quotients of polynomials. That is, they are functions of the form

$$f(x) = \frac{p(x)}{q(x)}$$

where $p(x)$ and $q(x)$ are polynomials. It is important to note that the domain of a rational function excludes all numbers for which the denominator equals zero, since division by zero is not defined. Figure 5.11 shows the graph of the rational function $f(x) = \dfrac{x}{x-2}$. Note that $x = 2$ is excluded from the domain of this function.

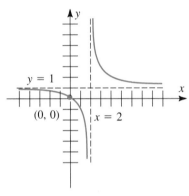

Figure 5.11 Graph of the rational function $f(x) = \dfrac{x}{x-2}$.

Other Power Functions;
Laws of Exponents

Finally, we note that the power function $f(x) = x^r$ can be defined for numbers r other than just positive integers. The following definition and theorem review the meaning and properties of $f(x) = x^r$ when r is a rational number. (A rational number is any quotient of integers: $r = n/m$, where n and m are integers and $m \neq 0$.)

Definition 6

Let x and y be real numbers and let n and m be positive integers. Then

(a) x^n means $x \cdot x \cdot x \cdot \ldots \cdot x$ (n factors)

(b) x^{-n} means $\dfrac{1}{x^n}$ whenever $x \neq 0$.

(c) $x^{1/n} = y$ means $y^n = x$. (Here $x \geq 0$ if n is even.)

(d) $x^{m/n}$ means $(x^{1/n})^m$.

(e) x^0 means 1 whenever $x \neq 0$.

☐ **EXAMPLE 2**

(a) $2^5 = 2 \cdot 2 \cdot 2 \cdot 2 \cdot 2 = 32$

(b) $6^{-2} = \dfrac{1}{6^2} = \dfrac{1}{36}$

(c) $16^{3/4} = (16^{1/4})^3 = 2^3 = 8$

(d) $(-27)^{2/3} = [(-27)^{1/3}]^2 = (-3)^2 = 9$

But note that $(-27)^{1/2}$ is not defined since $(-27)^{1/2} = y$ would mean $y^2 = -27$, which has no solution. ■

Example 2 points out the fact that power functions of the form $f(x) = x^{m/n} = (x^{1/n})^m$ are not defined for negative x when n is an even integer. For example, compare the graphs of $f(x) = \sqrt{x} = x^{1/2}$ and $g(x) = x^{-3/2}$ in Figure 5.12 with the graphs of $f(x) = x^{1/3}$ and $g(x) = x^{-2/3}$ in Figure 5.13.

The following theorem recalls the *laws of exponents,* which we must use in working with power functions.

Theorem 4
(Laws of Exponents)

Let x and y be real numbers, and let n and m be integers. Then

(a) $x^n \cdot x^m = x^{n+m}$.

(b) $\dfrac{x^n}{x^m} = x^{n-m}, \qquad x \neq 0.$

(c) $(x^n)^m = x^{nm}$.

(d) $x^{m/n} = (x^{1/n})^m = (x^m)^{1/n}, \qquad x \geq 0$ if n even.

(e) $(xy)^n = x^n y^n$.

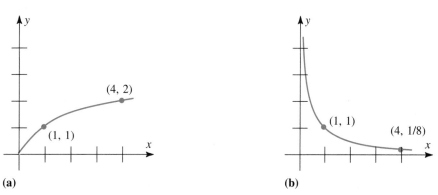

(a)   **(b)**

Figure 5.12 Functions of the form $f(x) = x^{m/n}$ are not defined for $x < 0$ if n is an even integer. (a) Domain of $f(x) = \sqrt{x} = x^{1/2}$ is $[0, \infty)$. (b) Domain of $g(x) = x^{-3/2} = \dfrac{1}{x^{3/2}}$ is $(0, \infty)$.

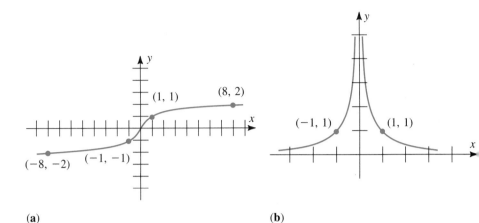

(a)   **(b)**

Figure 5.13 Functions of the form $f(x) = x^{m/n}$ are defined for all x except possibly $x = 0$, when n is an odd integer. (a) Domain of $f(x) = \sqrt[3]{x} = x^{1/3}$ is $(-\infty, \infty)$.

(b) Domain of $g(x) = x^{-2/3} = \dfrac{1}{x^{2/3}}$ consists of $(-\infty, 0)$ and $(0, \infty)$.

☐ **EXAMPLE 3**

Using the Laws of Exponents the expression

$$\frac{(4x^2y)^3}{8xy^{-2}} \text{ may be simplified as follows:}$$

$$\frac{(4x^2y)^3}{8xy^{-2}} = \frac{4^3 \cdot (x^2)^3 \cdot y^3}{8xy^{-2}} = \frac{4^3 \cdot x^6 \cdot y^3}{8 \cdot x \cdot y^{-2}}$$

$$= \left(\frac{64}{8}\right)\left(\frac{x^6}{x}\right)\left(\frac{y^3}{y^{-2}}\right) = 8x^5y^5. \qquad ■$$

☑ **PRACTICE PROBLEMS 1.5**

1. Graph the power function $f(x) = 2(x - 3)^{1/3}$.
2. Graph the "learning curve" $T(x) = 10[1 + 4(x + 3)^{-1/2}]$ giving the amount of time required for a press operator to set a printing press up for a new run, where x is the number of set-ups already performed.

Exercise Set 1.5

In Exercises 1–10 simplify the given expression as much as possible.

1. $27^{2/3}$

2. $81^{5/4}$

3. $4^{-3/2}$

4. $9^{-3/2}$

5. $\dfrac{2(3x)^4}{6x^2}$

6. $\dfrac{4x^3\sqrt{y}}{(x^2y)^{2/3}}$

7. $\dfrac{(3x^2y^{-1})^3}{\sqrt{xy}}$

8. $\dfrac{\sqrt{4x^4y^3}}{\sqrt{y}}$

9. $\dfrac{6(xy)^3}{x^{2/3}y^{-3/2}}$ **10.** $\dfrac{(27x^6y^2)^{-1/3}}{3x^{-2}y^{4/3}}$

11. True or false? Every linear function is a polynomial.

12. True or false? Some polynomial functions are quadratic functions.

In Exercises 13–20 graph the given power function.

13. $f(x) = \dfrac{1}{2}x^2 - 3$ **14.** $f(x) = -x^3$

15. $f(x) = 3x^{2/3}$ **16.** $f(x) = 2x^{3/2}$

17. $f(x) = -4x^{1/3}$ **18.** $y = (x - 4)^{-1/2}$

19. $y = -x^{-2/3}$ **20.** $f(x) = 2x^{-2}$

In Exercises 21–26 graph the given quadratic function by plotting points.

21. $f(x) = (x - 3)^2 - 4$ **22.** $f(x) = \dfrac{1}{2}(x + 1)^2 - 2$

23. $f(x) = x^2 - 2x + 3$ **24.** $f(x) = x^2 + 4x + 6$

25. $f(x) = -2x^2 - 4x + 1$ **26.** $f(x) = -\dfrac{3}{2}x^2 - 6x - 3$

In Exercises 27–32 graph the given polynomial function by plotting points.

27. $f(x) = x^3 + 4$ **28.** $f(x) = x^3 + x$

29. $f(x) = 4 - x^4$ **30.** $f(x) = x^3 - 4x + 2$

31. $f(x) = x^3 - x^2 - 2x + 2$ **32.** $f(x) = 1 - 3x + x^3$

In Exercises 33–38 graph the given rational function by plotting points and noting where the denominator equals zero.

33. $f(x) = \dfrac{1}{x - 3}$ **34.** $f(x) = \dfrac{3}{2 + x}$

35. $f(x) = \dfrac{1 - x}{1 + x}$ **36.** $f(x) = \dfrac{x}{1 + x^2}$

37. $f(x) = \dfrac{x^3}{1 + x}$ **38.** $f(x) = \dfrac{x + 1}{1 - x^2}$

39. A rectangle has area 80 cm. Write a function w that gives the width of the rectangle in terms of its length. What is the domain of this function?

40. The statement that "the function f is *proportional* to the function g" means that $f(x) = kg(x)$ for some constant k and for all x common to the domains of f and g. Examples of one quantity being proportional to the *square* of another arise

frequently in nature. For example, empirical evidence shows that the air resistance R for a moving automobile is proportional to the *square* of its speed, v. Write this statement in function form and discuss the nature of the associated graphs.

41. Your *utility function* associated with a certain commodity may be described as a measurement of your level of satisfaction associated with the possession of x units of the given commodity. For example, if $U(x)$ is your utility function for your consumption of x slices of pepperoni pizza, then $U(1)$ is the satisfaction you get from eating one slice, $U(2)$ the satisfaction from eating 2 slices, etc.
   a. Sketch the utility function $U_1(x) = \sqrt{x + 2}$.
   b. Sketch the utility function $U_2(x) = 6x - x^2$.
   c. In your opinion, which utility function seems more appropriate for the example of consuming x slices of pizza? Why?
   d. In your opinion, which utility function seems more appropriate for winning x thousands of dollars? Why?

42. The demand for a certain model of sports car is determined to be $D(p) = \sqrt{400 - p^2}$ cars per week where p is the selling price of the car in thousands of dollars.
   a. What is the domain of D?
   b. What is the demand per week at price $p = \$12{,}000$ per car?
   c. Sketch the graph of this demand function.

43. After x repetitions, an assembly worker can perform a certain task in $T(x) = 30\left(1 + \dfrac{2}{\sqrt{x + 1}}\right)$ seconds.
   a. How quickly will the employee perform the task on the fourth try?
   b. Graph this "learning curve."

44. In foreign language instruction it is observed that a person will have learned an average of $N(t) = 10t - 0.5t^2$ vocabulary terms in t continuous hours of study. Graph this quadratic "learning curve."

45. A manufacturer of garage doors finds that the total cost of manufacturing x garage doors per week is approximately $C(x) = 400 + 40x + 0.2x^2$.
   a. Sketch the graph of this cost function.
   b. What are the manufacturer's fixed costs?

46. The manufacturer in Exercise 45 can sell his garage doors for $100 each.
   a. Find the revenue function $y = R(x)$, which gives the amount received by the manufacturer from the sale of x items.

b. Find the manufacturer's weekly profit function $y = P(x) = R(x) - C(x)$.

c. Sketch the graphs for all three functions C, R, and P on the same set of axes. Estimate the production levels x between which profit is positive.

47. A manufacturer of rocking chairs finds that the total cost of producing x rocking chairs per day is $C(x) = 500 + 10\left(\dfrac{x-5}{5}\right)^3$ dollars. The chairs sell for $p = \$100$ each.

a. Find $C(5)$, $C(30)$, $C(40)$, and $C(50)$.

b. Find the revenue function $R(x) = px$.

c. Find the profit function $P(x) = R(x) - C(x)$.

d. Find $P(t)$, $P(30)$, $P(40)$, and $P(50)$.

e. Why are profits not largest at the largest production level?

48. The cost of producing x pairs of athletic shoes per day is found by a producer to be $C(x)a = 600 + 5(x - 10)^{1/3} + 15x$. If the shoes can be sold for \$30 per pair, find the following:

a. The cost of producing $x = 10$, $x = 37$, and $x = 135$ pairs of shoes.

b. The revenue function $R(x) = px$.

c. The profit function $P(x) = R(x) - C(x)$.

d. The profit resulting from production levels $x = 10$, $x = 37$, and $x = 135$ pairs per day.

✓ **SOLUTIONS TO PRACTICE PROBLEMS 1.5**

1. The graphs of f is just the graph of the functions $g(x) = x^{1/3}$, (a) shifted to the right 3 units, and (b) with each y-coordinate multiplied by 2. (See Figure 5.14.)

2. The graph of T is shown in Figure 5.15.

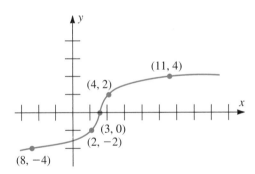

Figure 5.14 Graph of $f(x) = 2(x-3)^{1/3}$.

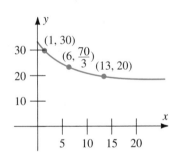

Figure 5.15 Graph of $T(x) = 10[1 + 4(x + 3)^{-1/2}]$.

1.6   Finding Zeros of Functions

If $P(x)$ represents a manufacturer's weekly profit from the sale of x items, the values of the function P may be either positive or negative, depending on the output level x. An output level x_0 for which $P(x_0) = 0$ is called a *break-even* level, for obvious reasons. (See Figure 6.1.) The problem of finding break-even levels is just one example of the more general problem of finding the **zeros** of a given function f, that is, of finding the numbers x_0 for which $f(x_0) = 0$. (See Figure 6.2.)

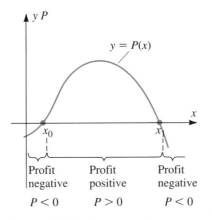

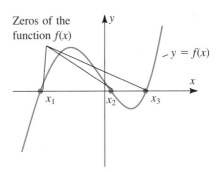

Figure 6.1 Break-even levels of production, x_0 and x_1, for the profit function $y = P(x)$.

Figure 6.2 Zeros of the function f are numbers x for which $f(x) = 0$.

Finding Zeros by Factoring

When the equation for a function can be factored, the zeros of the function are just the zeros of the individual factors. For example, the zeros of the function $f(x) = (x - 2)(x + 1)$ are $x_1 = 2$ and $x_2 = -1$, since $x - 2 = 0$ when $x = 2$, and $x + 1 = 0$ when $x = -1$. These are *all* the zeros of f since $f(x)$ cannot equal zero unless one of its factors does. (See Figure 6.3.)

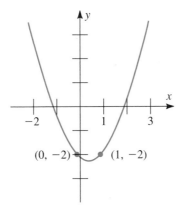

Figure 6.3 For $f(x) = x^2 - x - 2 = (x - 2)(x + 1)$ the zeros are $x_1 = -1$ and $x_2 = 2$.

The following are additional examples of finding zeros of functions by factoring.

□ **EXAMPLE 1**

Find the zeros of the function $f(x) = x^2 - 3x - 4$.

Strategy · · · · · · · ·

Factor the right-hand side of the equation for f.

Set each factor equal to zero and solve for x.

Check answers by substituting x in $f(x)$ and verifying that $f(x) = 0$.

Solution

Since $f(x) = x^2 - 3x - 4$

$$= (x + 1)(x - 4)$$

we will have $f(x) = (x + 1)(x - 4) = 0$ when $x + 1 = 0$ or when $x - 4 = 0$. Now

$$x + 1 = 0 \text{ gives } x = -1$$

and

$$x - 4 = 0 \text{ gives } x = 4.$$

The zeros of f are therefore $x_1 = -1$ and $x_2 = 4$.

To check this answer, we substitute these numbers into the expression $f(x)$:

$$f(-1) = (-1)^2 - 3(-1) - 4 = 1 + 3 - 4 = 0$$
$$f(4) = 4^2 - 3 \cdot 4 - 4 = 16 - 12 - 4 = 0$$

so both answers are correct. ■

□ **EXAMPLE 2**

A manufacturer of central air-conditioning units finds that the total cost of producing x units per week is $C(x) = 10,000 + 350x + 25x^2$ dollars. If the manufacturer can sell each unit for $1600, what are the break-even level(s) of production?

Strategy · · · · · · · ·

Find the weekly profit function $P = R - C$.

Solution

Since the revenue received from the sale of x units is $R(x) = 1600x$ dollars, the manufacturer's weekly profit is

$$P(x) = R(x) - C(x)$$
$$= 1600x - (10,000 + 350x + 25x^2)$$
$$= -25x^2 + 1250x - 10,000.$$

Factor $P(x)$.

Since

$$P(x) = -25(x^2 - 50x + 400)$$
$$= -25(x - 10)(x - 40)$$

we shall have $P(x) = 0$ when $x - 10 = 0$ or $x - 40 = 0$.

Set factors of $P(x)$ equal to zero and solve. Solutions are zeros of P.

The equation

$$x - 10 = 0 \text{ gives } x = 10$$

and the equation

$$x - 40 = 0 \text{ gives } x = 40.$$

The break-even levels are therefore $x_1 = 10$ units per week and $x_2 = 40$ units per week.

Figure 6.4 shows that the manufacturer will experience a true profit ($P(x) > 0$) for $10 < x < 40$, and losses ($P(x) < 0$) for $0 \le x < 10$ or $x > 40$. ■

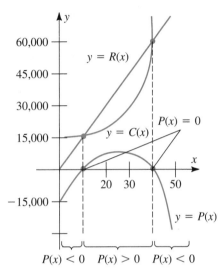

Figure 6.4 Zeros for profit function $P(x) = -25x^2 + 1250x - 10{,}000$ give break-even points $x_1 = 10$ and $x_2 = 40$.

□ **EXAMPLE 3**

Find the zeros of the function $f(x) = x^{5/3} - 4x$.

Solution: We factor the right-hand side as

$$f(x) = x^{5/3} - 4x$$
$$= x(x^{2/3} - 4).$$

Then $f(x) = 0$ if $x = 0$ or if $x^{2/3} - 4 = 0$. The equation

$$x^{2/3} - 4 = 0$$

gives

$$x^{2/3} = 4.$$

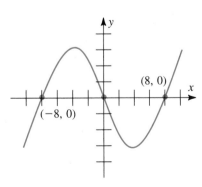

Figure 6.5 Zeros of $f(x) = x^{5/3} - 4x$ are $x_1 = -8$, $x_2 = 0$, and $x_3 = 8$.

Cubing both sides gives $x^2 = 4^3 = 64$, which has solutions $x = \pm 8$. The zeros of f are therefore $x_1 = -8$, $x_2 = 0$, and $x_3 = 8$. (See Figure 6.5.) ■

The Quadratic Formula

For the special case of quadratic functions of the form

$$f(x) = ax^2 + bx + c \tag{1}$$

the zeros are given by the **quadratic formula**

$$x = \frac{-b \pm \sqrt{b^2 - 4ac}}{2a}. \tag{2}$$

The quadratic formula is particularly useful when factors of a quadratic expression are not easily recognized.

□ **EXAMPLE 4**

Find the zeros of the function $f(x) = 2x^2 + x - 3$.

Solution: This function has the form of the quadratic function in equation (1) with $a = 2$, $b = 1$, and $c = -3$. Thus by the quadratic formula (2) the zeros are

$$x = \frac{-1 \pm \sqrt{1 - 4(2)(-3)}}{2 \cdot 2}$$

$$= \frac{-1 \pm \sqrt{1 + 24}}{4}$$

$$= -\frac{1}{4} \pm \frac{\sqrt{25}}{4}.$$

The zeros are therefore $x_1 = -\frac{1}{4} - \frac{5}{4} = -\frac{3}{2}$ and $x_2 = -\frac{1}{4} + \frac{5}{4} = 1$.   ■

Equality of Function Values

Closely related to the problem of finding the zeros of a single function is the problem of finding the numbers for which two given functions have the same values. Note that finding the numbers x for which $f(x) = g(x)$ is the same as finding the zeros of the function $h = g - f$. The following example requires just this observation.

□ **EXAMPLE 5**

The population of town A is currently 20 thousand people. It is projected by demographers that the population of town A will have grown to $P(t) = \sqrt{400 + 200t}$ thousand after t years. The neighboring town B currently has 10 thousand people and is projected to have $Q(t) = (10 + 8t)$ thousand after t years. When will the towns have equal populations?

Strategy · · · · · · · **Solution**

Set $P = Q$.

The two towns have equal populations if $P(t) = Q(t)$, or

$$\sqrt{400 + 200t} = 10 + 8t.$$

Eliminate radical by squaring both sides.

Squaring both sides of this equation gives

$$400 + 200t = 100 + 160t + 64t^2$$

so

$$64t^2 - 40t - 300 = 0.$$

Collect all terms on one side of the equation.

Find the zeros of this function using the quadratic formula.

By the quadratic formula the solutions are

$$t = \frac{40 \pm \sqrt{(40)^2 - 4(64)(-300)}}{2(64)}$$

$$= \frac{40 \pm \sqrt{1600 + 76{,}800}}{128}$$

$$= \frac{40 \pm 280}{128}.$$

Since time must be positive, disregard any negative values for t.

Now the time $t_1 = \dfrac{40 - 280}{128} = -\dfrac{15}{8}$ is meaningless in this application, so the only time at which the two towns will have equal populations is

$$t_2 = \frac{40 + 280}{128} = \frac{320}{128} = \frac{5}{2}$$

Verify that $P(t) = Q(t)$ at the time $t = \frac{5}{2}$ years.

years from the present. At this time the populations will be

$$P\left(\frac{5}{2}\right) = \sqrt{400 + 200\left(\frac{5}{2}\right)} = \sqrt{900} = 30 \text{ thousand}$$

which is the same as

$$Q\left(\frac{5}{2}\right) = 10 + 8\left(\frac{5}{2}\right) = 10 + 20 = 30 \text{ thousand}.$$

These population curves are graphed in Figure 6.6. ■

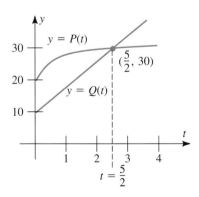

Figure 6.6 Population curves in Example 5.

Average Cost

Often a manufacturer is concerned with knowing not only the total cost, $C(x)$, of producing x items, but also with knowing the *average cost per item*. The average cost per item, of producing x items at a total cost $C(x)$, is simply the quotient $c(x) = \dfrac{C(x)}{x}$. Knowing the average cost per item is often helpful in decisions concerning the selling price, since both concern the individual item rather than the entire lot.

□ **EXAMPLE 6**

A producer of golf shoes has determined that the total cost of producing x pairs of golf shoes per week is

$$C(x) = 7500 + 20x + 0.01x^2.$$

The producer wishes to price the shoes as little above $40 per pair as possible, due to marketing concerns. For which weekly production levels x will the average cost per pair be less than $40?

Strategy · · · · · · · ·

Find the average cost function

$$c(x) = \frac{C(x)}{x}.$$

Solution

We have the average cost function

$$c(x) = \frac{C(x)}{x} = \frac{7500 + 20x + 0.01x^2}{x}$$

$$= \frac{7500}{x} + 20 + 0.01x.$$

Set $c(x) = 40$ and solve to determine where average cost *equals* $40.

To determine when average cost *equals* $40 per pair we get $c(x) = 40$:

$$\frac{7500}{x} + 20 + 0.01x = 40$$

gives

$$7500 + 20x + 0.01x^2 = 40x$$

so

$$0.01x^2 - 20x + 7500 = 0.$$

Solve the quadratic equation by using the quadratic formula. (Or by factoring—can you find the factors?)

By the quadratic formula, the zeros are

$$x = \frac{20 \pm \sqrt{400 - 4(0.01)(7500)}}{2(0.01)}$$

$$= 1000 \pm 500.$$

Thus, the two production levels at which average cost equals $40 per pair are

$$x_1 = 500 \quad \text{and} \quad x_2 = 1500$$

Examine values of $c(x)$ between the solutions of $c(x) = 40$ to ensure that $c(x) < 40$ in this interval.

pairs per week. Any production level between these two will yield an average cost per pair less than \$40, as you can see by graphing the equation for $c(x)$ or by checking various values. For example,

$$c(1000) = \frac{7500 + 20(1000) + 0.01(1000)^2}{1000}$$

$$= 37.50. \qquad \blacksquare$$

Demand and Supply Functions

Under certain market conditions the selling price p of a particular item (Brand X dishwashers, for example) determines the number of items that consumers will purchase in a given unit of time. If we let $D(p)$ denote the number of items that will be sold at price p during the unit of time, then D is called a **demand function.** Figure 6.7 shows the graph of a typical demand function. The property that higher prices correspond to lower demands is called the *law of demand.*

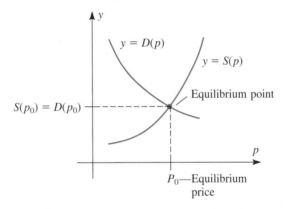

Figure 6.7 Graphs of typical demand and supply curves.

Similarly, the function S giving the number $S(p)$ of items that suppliers are willing to produce at selling price p in a unit of time is called the **supply function** for that item. In general, higher selling prices result in higher levels of supply, as reflected by the graph of a typical supply function in Figure 6.7.

For a given item and market the point where the graphs of the demand and supply functions intersect is called the *equilibrium* point. It indicates the price at which all who wish to purchase the item will be able to do so, and no surplus items will exist. The techniques of this section are useful in locating equilibrium points.

□ **EXAMPLE 7**

Market research indicates that when a certain type of alloy tennis racket is priced at p dollars per racket, consumers will purchase $D(p) = 50 - \dfrac{1}{2}p$ rackets per week and suppliers will produce $S(p) = \dfrac{2}{5}p - 4$ rackets per week. Find the equilibrium point for these demand and supply functions.

Solution: Setting the demand and supply functions equal to each other, we obtain the equation

$$\frac{2}{5}p - 4 = 50 - \frac{1}{2}p.$$

Thus

$$\left(\frac{2}{5} + \frac{1}{2}\right)p = 50 + 4$$

or

$$\frac{9}{10}p = 54.$$

Thus

$$p = \left(\frac{10}{9}\right)54$$

$$= 60.$$

The equilibrium price is therefore \$60, corresponding to a demand and supply of $D(60) = S(60) = 20$ rackets per week. The equilibrium point is therefore $(60, 20)$. (See Figure 6.8.) ■

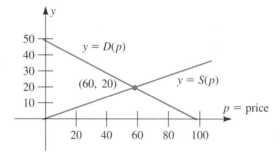

Figure 6.8 Demand and supply functions in Example 7.

☑ PRACTICE PROBLEMS 1.6

1. Find the zeros of the function $f(x) = x^3 + 2x^2 - 4x$.

2. Determine where the demand curve $D(x) = \dfrac{1}{4}(x - 10)^2$ and the supply curve $S(x) = \dfrac{1}{8}x^2$ intersect for $0 \le x \le 10$.

Exercise Set 1.6

In Exercises 1–10 find the zero(s) of the given function by factoring, if necessary.

1. $f(x) = x^2 - 4$

2. $f(x) = x - x^3$

3. $f(x) = x^2 + x - 6$

4. $f(x) = x^2 - 9x + 20$

5. $f(x) = x^2 - 2x - 35$

6. $f(x) = x^3 - 5x^2 - 36x$

7. $f(x) = \dfrac{\sqrt{x} - 2}{x + 1}$

8. $f(x) = \dfrac{x^{4/3} - 16}{x^2 + 1}$

9. $f(x) = x^{3/2} - 3\sqrt{x}$

10. $f(x) = x - 2\sqrt{x} + 1$

In Exercises 11–18 find the zeros of the given function by using the quadratic formula.

11. $f(x) = x^2 + x - 1$

12. $f(x) = x^2 + 3x + 1$

13. $f(x) = 2x^2 + 3x - 1$

14. $f(x) = 1 + 4x - x^2$

15. $f(x) = 3 + 2x - x^2$

16. $f(x) = 2x^2 - 2 - 2x$

17. $f(x) = x - 3x^2 + 4$

18. $f(x) = 3 - 3x - 2x^2$

In Exercises 19–28 find the point(s) of intersection of the graphs of f and g.

19. $f(x) = 2x + 1$
$g(x) = 7 - x$

20. $f(x) = 1 - \dfrac{x}{3}$
$g(x) = 8 + 2x$

21. $f(x) = x^2 - 2$
$g(x) = 2x + 1$

22. $f(x) = 4 - x^2$
$g(x) = 2 - x$

23. $f(x) = \sqrt{x}$
$g(x) = 4x - 3$

24. $f(x) = 7 - x^2$
$g(x) = x^2 - 1$

25. $f(x) = x^3 + 2$
$g(x) = x + 2$

26. $f(x) = \sqrt{x + 2}$
$g(x) = \dfrac{1}{2}x + 1$

27. $f(x) = 3x^2 - 12x$
$g(x) = 5x - 20$

28. $f(x) = \sqrt{x} + 1$
$g(x) = \dfrac{1}{3}x + 1$

29. Figure 6.9 shows typical demand and supply curves for an item selling at price p. Let p_0 denote the equilibrium price as indicated. Explain why a shortage of this item will exist if the selling price is set at price $p_1 < p_0$.

30. Refer to Exercise 29 and Figure 6.9. Explain why a surplus of the item will exist if the selling price is set at price $p_2 > p_0$.

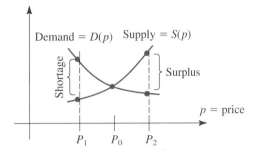

Demand $= D(p)$ Supply $= S(p)$

Figure 6.9 At other than equilibrium price, either a shortage or a surplus will exist.

31. A consumer's utility function (a measure of satisfaction) for dollars spent annually on leisure activities is $L(x) = 100\sqrt{x}$ while the same consumer's utility function for dollars spent annually on investments is $S(x) = \frac{5}{3}x$. Find the expenditure level x for which these two utility functions are equal.

32. A manufacturer's cost of producing x pairs of roller skates per week is $C(x) = 400 + 15x$. If the roller skates can be sold for \$25 per pair, what is the manufacturer's break-even production level?

33. The weekly cost of manufacturing x telephones per week is found by a manufacturer to be $C(x) = 500 + 20x + x^2$ dollars. The telephones can be sold at a price of $p = \$80$ each.
a. Find the manufacturer's break-even production level(s).
b. For what production levels will the manufacturer experience a profit?

34. The demand for a certain type of T-shirt is determined to be $D(p) = 20 - p$ T-shirts per week at price p. At this price suppliers are willing to produce $S(p) = p^2$ T-shirts per week. Find the equilibrium price.

35. Deaths from trauma after a serious injury are known to be of two types. Type A is due to severe damage to a major organ (heart, brain, etc.). Type B is due to blood loss, either through internal hemorrhages or through loss of blood from the body. Figure 6.10 shows typical graphs for the frequencies of each type of death from trauma. If

$$f(t) = \frac{25}{t} \quad \text{and} \quad g(t) = \frac{50}{1 + (t - 2)^2}$$

find the times t at which these functions have equal values.

36. The percentage of the U.S. labor force involved in farming fell linearly from 70% in 1830 to 20% in 1930. According to these data, when was it 40%?

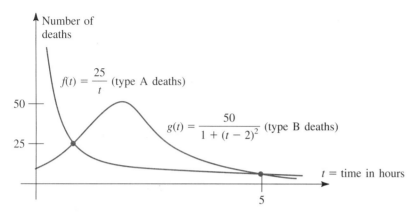

Figure 6.10 Distribution of deaths from two types of injuries associated with trauma. (See Exercise 35.)

37. A manufacturer of picnic tables finds that its total cost of producing x tables is given by the function $C(x) = 500 + 10x + x^2$ dollars. If the tables can be sold for $70 each, at what production level(s) does the selling price equal the average cost?

38. A producer of athletic jackets determines that its weekly cost in producing x jackets is given by the total cost function

$$C(x) = 400 + 10x + \frac{1}{2}x^2.$$

a. Find the production level x for which the average cost per jacket equals $40.
b. For which production levels x is the average cost per jacket *less* than $40?
c. Why does average cost increase beyond the interval computed in part (b)?

39. For the total cost function

$$C(x) = 2000 + 80\sqrt{x}$$

find the production levels at which average cost per item equals one. (*Hint:* View the resulting equation for $c(x)$, average cost, as a quadratic equation in $\sqrt{x}$.)

40. Explain the mistake in using the following procedure to find the zeros of the function $f(x) = x^{5/3} - 4x$. (See Example 3.)
   i. We seek the solutions of the equation $x^{5/3} - 4x = 0$
   ii. by writing it as $x^{5/3} = 4x$,
   iii. "canceling" the common factor x to obtain $x^{2/3} = 4$
   iv. and solving to obtain $x = \pm 8$.

41. Derive the quadratic formula by completing the square on the expression $ax^2 + bx + c$.

☑ **SOLUTIONS TO PRACTICE PROBLEMS 1.6**

1. We can write

$$f(x) = x^3 + 2x^2 - 4x$$
$$= x(x^2 + 2x - 4)$$

so the zeros occur at $x_1 = 0$ and at solutions of the quadratic equation

$$x^2 + 2x - 4 = 0.$$

Using the quadratic formula, we find these zeros as

$$x = \frac{-2 \pm \sqrt{2^2 - 4(1)(-4)}}{2(1)}$$

$$= \frac{-2 \pm \sqrt{20}}{2}$$

$$= -1 \pm \sqrt{5}.$$

The zeros are $x_1 = 0$, $x_2 = -1 - \sqrt{5}$, and $x_3 = -1 + \sqrt{5}$.

2. The curves intersect where $D(x) = S(x)$, or where

$$\frac{1}{4}(x - 10)^2 = \frac{1}{8}x^2$$

or

$$\frac{1}{4}(x^2 - 20x + 100) = \frac{1}{8}x^2$$

or

$$\frac{1}{8}x^2 - 5x + 25 = 0$$

which is equivalent to

$$x^2 - 40x + 200 = 0.$$

Using the quadratic formula we find the solutions to be

$$x = \frac{40 \pm \sqrt{(-40)^2 - 4(1)(200)}}{2(1)}$$

$$= \frac{40 \pm \sqrt{800}}{2}$$

$$= 20 \pm 10\sqrt{2}.$$

The solution satisfying the condition $0 \le x \le 10$ is

$$x = 20 - 10\sqrt{2} \approx 5.858.$$

1.7 Combinations of Functions

We have already seen several examples of ways in which certain functions are combined to form other functions of interest. Two such examples involve the revenue function $y = R(x)$ and the total cost function $y = C(x)$ per unit time associated with the manufacture and sale of x items. They are the profit and average cost functions:

$$P(x) = R(x) - C(x) \qquad \text{(profit function)}$$

$$c(x) = \frac{C(x)}{x}. \qquad \text{(average cost function)}$$

Figures 7.1 to 7.3 describe another such example. They are what industrial psychologists refer to as *work curves*. In such curves the horizontal axis represents time and the vertical axis represents productivity or efficiency of a worker performing a certain task. The curve in Figure 7.1 represents what is called the *warm-up effect*. This is the phenomenon of a worker's efficiency initially rising during the early part of the work period. Figure 7.2 shows the *fatigue effect*—as the work period drags on, the worker tires and becomes less efficient. Figure 7.3 shows how the warm-up and fatigue effects combine through addition to produce an *overall* work curve.

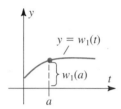

Figure 7.1 Warm-up curve.

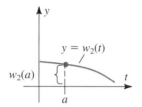

Figure 7.2 Fatigue curve.

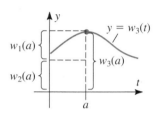

Figure 7.3 Overall work curve

$$w_3(t) = w_1(t) + w_2(t).$$

The Algebra of Functions

It is a simple matter to combine functions algebraically to form new functions that are sums, differences, multiples, products, or quotients of the given functions. It is done by calculating separately the values of the individual terms in the combination and then forming the given combination using these values.

Definition 7

Given the functions f and g, and the number c, the functions $f + g, f - g, cf, fg$, and $\dfrac{f}{g}$ are defined by the following equations:

$$(f + g)(x) = f(x) + g(x)$$
$$(f - g)(x) = f(x) - g(x)$$
$$(cf)(x) = c[f(x)]$$
$$(fg)(x) = f(x)g(x)$$
$$(f/g)(x) = f(x)/g(x). \quad \text{(provided } g(x) \neq 0)$$

Of course, these combinations can be formed only for numbers x that are in the domains of both functions. Although these definitions may seem obvious, we will need a clear understanding of these definitions in studying limits of functions in Chapter 2.

☐ **EXAMPLE 1**

Let $f(x) = x^3 + 2$ and $g(x) = \sqrt{x + 1}$. Then

(a) for $h_1 = f + g$, $h_1(x) = x^3 + 2 + \sqrt{x + 1}$

so

$$h_1(3) = f(3) + g(3) = (3^3 + 2) + \sqrt{3 + 1} = 29 + 2 = 31$$

and

$$h_1(1) = f(1) + g(1) = (1^3 + 2) + \sqrt{1 + 1} = 3 + \sqrt{2}$$

but

$h_1(-2)$ is undefined since $g(-2) = \sqrt{1 - 2}$ is undefined.

(b) for $h_2 = \dfrac{f}{3g}$, $h_2(x) = \dfrac{x^3 + 2}{3\sqrt{x + 1}}$

so

$$h_2(3) = \frac{f(3)}{3g(3)} = \frac{3^3 + 2}{3\sqrt{3 + 1}} = \frac{27 + 2}{3\sqrt{4}} = \frac{29}{6}$$

and

$$h_2(0) = \frac{f(0)}{3g(0)} = \frac{0^3 + 2}{3\sqrt{0 + 1}} = \frac{2}{3}.$$

■

☐ **EXAMPLE 2**

A manufacturer of computers uses two separate manufacturing facilities. Facility A produces chips and facility B uses the chips in making a finished product. The cost for facility A of producing chips for the manufacture of x computers per week is determined to be

$$C_A(x) = 10{,}000 + 500x + 2x^2 \text{ dollars}$$

and the cost for facility B of producing x finished products per week is

$$C_B(x) = 15{,}000 + 2000x + 5x^{2/3} \text{ dollars.}$$

The overall (total) cost $C(x)$ to the computer company in producing x computers per week is therefore found by adding these two cost functions:

$$\begin{aligned} C(x) &= C_A(x) + C_B(x) \\ &= 25{,}000 + 2500x + 5x^{2/3} + 2x^2 \end{aligned}$$

dollars per week.

■

Composite Functions

Often two functions are combined not by an algebraic operation such as addition, but by letting the second function act on the result (output) of the first. For example, Figure 7.4 shows how one would calculate the distance between an air controller at ground level and an airplane flying at an altitude of 2 miles:

(i) find the distance $d_1(t)$ from the control tower to the point on the ground directly beneath the plane;

(ii) use the Pythagorean theorem to find the actual distance $d_2(t)$ between the controller and the airplane as

$$d_2(t) = \sqrt{[d_1(t)]^2 + 2^2}. \tag{1}$$

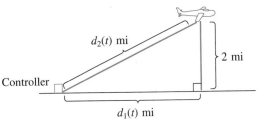

$d_2(t)$ mi

2 mi

Controller

$d_1(t)$ mi

Figure 7.4 Distance between controller and airplane is $d_2(t) = \sqrt{[d_1(t)]^2 + 2^2}$.

In this example we have written both distances $d_1(t)$ and $d_2(t)$ as functions of t (time), since both change in time (hopefully!) with the location of the airplane. Note in equation (1) that the square root function acts on the function $f(t) = [d_1(t)]^2 + 4$ to produce the value of the function d_2. This is an example of a *composite* function.

Definition 8

Given two functions f and g the **composite** function $g \circ f$ is the result of the function g acting on the values of the function f. That is

$$(g \circ f)(x) = g(f(x))$$

as illustrated in Figure 7.5.

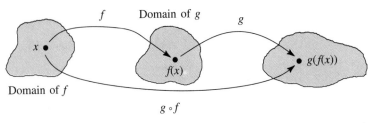

f Domain of g g

x

Domain of f

$f(x)$

$g(f(x))$

$g \circ f$

Figure 7.5 The composite function $g \circ f$ is the result of the function g acting on values of the function f.

The difference between composite functions, or functions formed by *composition,* and algebraic combinations of functions has to do with the order in which the operations are performed. In an algebraic combination the individual function values are found first and then combined. In the composite function $g \circ f$ we first find the value of the *inside* function $f(x)$ and then insert this number into the function g. Obviously, the number $f(x)$ must lie in the domain of the function g for the value $g(f(x))$ to be defined.

☐ **EXAMPLE 3**

Let $f(x) = x^2 + 3$ and $g(x) = \sqrt{x}$. Then

(a) $(g \circ f)(x) = g(f(x)) = g(x^2 + 3) = \sqrt{x^2 + 3}$

(b) $(f \circ g)(x) = f(g(x)) = f(\sqrt{x}) = (\sqrt{x})^2 + 3 = x + 3$

whenever $x \geq 0$. ■

☐ **EXAMPLE 4**

Let $f(x) = (3x + 1)^2$ and $g(x) = x - 2$. Then

(a) $(g \circ f)(x) = g((3x + 1)^2) = (3x + 1)^2 - 2$
$= (9x^2 + 6x + 1) - 2 = 9x^2 + 6x - 1$

(b) $(f \circ g)(x) = f(x - 2) = [3(x - 2) + 1]^2 = (3x - 5)^2 = 9x^2 - 30x + 25.$ ■

Notice in both Example 3 and Example 4 that $g(f(x)) \neq f(g(x))$ in general. The next example shows how we must be careful about order in determining the domain of a composite function.

☐ **EXAMPLE 5**

For $f(x) = \sqrt{x}$ and $g(x) = x + 4$ find

(a) the composite function $g \circ f$ and its domain.

(b) the composite function $f \circ g$ and its domain.

Solution: In (a) we have

$$g(f(x)) = g(\sqrt{x}) = \sqrt{x} + 4$$

and the domain of $g \circ f$ is $[0, \infty)$ since we must have $x \geq 0$. In part (b) we have

$$f(g(x)) = f(x + 4) = \sqrt{x + 4}.$$

The domain of $f \circ g$ is therefore all x with $x + 4 \geq 0$. This requires $x \geq -4$, so the domain is $[-4, \infty)$. ■

Split Functions

In certain applications we will need to work with functions that are defined differently for various numbers x. This occurs frequently in pricing structures where manufacturers wish to encourage volume purchases.

□ **EXAMPLE 6**

The producer of the Easy-as-Pie software product, which retails for $500 a copy, offers discounts of 20% on orders for 10 or more copies, and an additional 20% on orders for 25 or more copies. The total cost $C(x)$ of purchasing x copies of this software would then be:

(i) $500x$ if $1 \leq x < 10$

(ii) $(0.8)(500x) = 400x$ if $10 \leq x < 25$

(iii) $(0.6)(500x) = 300x$ if $25 \leq x$.

In this case we would write the *split function C* as

$$C(x) = \begin{cases} 500x & \text{if} \quad 1 \leq x < 10 \\ 400x & \text{if} \quad 10 \leq x < 25 \\ 300x & \text{if} \quad 25 \leq x. \end{cases} \qquad (2)$$

To find the value $C(x)$ for a particular number x, we would first determine which of the three inequalities in statement (2) the number x satisfies and then use the corresponding equation for the function. The graph of $y = C(x)$ appears in Figure 7.6. ■

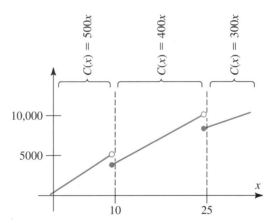

Figure 7.6 Graph of $C(x) = \begin{cases} 500x & \text{if} \quad 0 \leq x < 10 \\ 400x & \text{if} \quad 10 \leq x < 25 \\ 300x & \text{if} \quad 25 \leq x. \end{cases}$

□ **EXAMPLE 7**

For the function $f(x) = \begin{cases} 4 - x^2 & \text{if} \quad -\infty < x \leq 1 \\ x + 2 & \text{if} \quad 1 < x < \infty \end{cases}$

(a) find $f(-2)$
(b) find $f(3)$
(c) graph f.

Solution:

(a) Since $x = -2$ satisfies $-\infty < x \le 1$, we have

$$f(-2) = 4 - (-2)^2 = 4 - 4 = 0.$$

(b) Since $x = 3$ satisfies $1 < x < \infty$, we have

$$f(3) = 3 + 2 = 5.$$

(c) The graph of f appears in Figure 7.7. ■

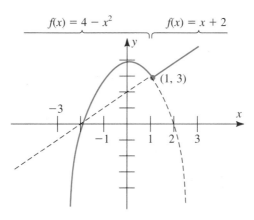

Figure 7.7 Graph of $f(x) = \begin{cases} 4 - x^2 & \text{if} \quad -\infty < x \le 1 \\ x + 2 & \text{if} \quad 1 < x < \infty. \end{cases}$

The Absolute Value Function

An important split function is the **absolute value** function. It is defined as follows:

$$|x| = \begin{cases} x & \text{if} \quad x \ge 0 \\ -x & \text{if} \quad x < 0. \end{cases}$$

In words, the absolute value of a number is just the number itself if the number is nonnegative. If the number is negative, its absolute value is found by changing its sign. Thus

$$|3| = 3, \quad |0| = 0, \quad |-7| = 7, \quad \text{and} \quad |-\sqrt{2}| = \sqrt{2}.$$

The graph of the absolute value function appears in Figure 7.8. In working with absolute values in composite functions, we must be careful to note the sign of the expression inside the absolute value signs as the following example shows.

☐ **EXAMPLE 8**

Graph the function $f(x) = |4 - x^2|$.

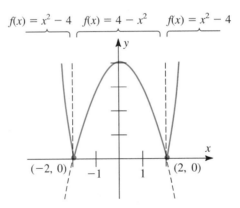

Figure 7.8 Graph of the absolute value function.

Strategy · · · · · · ·

Determine where the expression inside absolute value signs is nonnegative.

Rewrite f as a split function.

Graph each branch corresponding to one part of the split function separately.

Solution

We shall have $4 - x^2 \geq 0$ if $4 \geq x^2$, which requires $-2 \leq x \leq 2$. Thus

$$f(x) = \begin{cases} -(4 - x^2) = x^2 - 4 & \text{if } -\infty < x < -2 \\ 4 - x^2 & \text{if } -2 \leq x \leq 2 \\ -(4 - x^2) = x^2 - 4 & \text{if } 2 < x < \infty. \end{cases}$$

The graph appears in Figure 7.9. Note that the effect of the absolute value signs is to turn the "legs" of the graph of $4 - x^2$ that extend below the x-axis upward.

$$f(x) = x^2 - 4 \quad f(x) = 4 - x^2 \quad f(x) = x^2 - 4$$

Figure 7.9 Graph of $f(x) = |4 - x^2|$.

□ **EXAMPLE 9**

Graph the function $f(x) = \dfrac{|x - 1|}{x - 1}$.

Solution: Since $x - 1 \geq 0$ if $x \geq 1$, we have

$$|x - 1| = \begin{cases} x - 1 & \text{if } x \geq 1 \\ 1 - x & \text{if } x < 1 \end{cases}$$

by the definition of the absolute value of the quantity $x - 1$. We can therefore write f as the split function

$$f(x) = \begin{cases} \dfrac{x - 1}{x - 1} = 1 & \text{if } x > 1 \\[2mm] \dfrac{1 - x}{x - 1} = -1 & \text{if } x < 1. \end{cases}$$

The graph of f appears in Figure 7.10. Note that $f(1)$ is not defined.

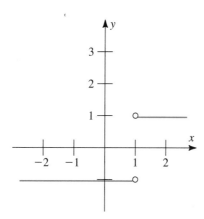

Figure 7.10 Graph of $f(x) = \dfrac{|x - 1|}{x - 1}$.

✓ **PRACTICE PROBLEMS 1.7**

1. For the functions $f(x) = \dfrac{x^2}{x + 3}$ and $g(x) = \sqrt{x + 2}$, find the following:

    a. $f(g(2))$
    b. $g(f(6))$
    c. $g \circ f$

2. Graph the function $f(x) = |x^2 + 2x - 3|$.

Exercise Set 1.7

In Exercises 1–6 let $f(x) = x - 7$, $g(x) = x^2 + 2$, $h_1 = f + g$, and $h_2 = \dfrac{f}{g}$. Find

1. $h_1(x)$ **2.** $h_2(x)$

3. $h_1(5)$ **4.** $h_2(-1)$

5. $h_2(-4)$ **6.** $h_1(-3)$

In Exercises 7–12 let $f(x) = \dfrac{1}{x + 2}$, $g(x) = \sqrt{3 + x}$, $h_1 = f - 2g$, and $h_2 = \dfrac{g}{f}$. Find

7. $h_1(x)$ **8.** $h_2(x)$

9. $h_2(-3)$ **10.** $h_1(-3)$

11. $h_1(1)$ **12.** $h_2(6)$

13. Let $f(x) = x^2 - x$. Find g so that $(f + g)(x) = 4 - x$.

14. Let $f(x) = \sqrt{x} - 2$. Find g so that $(fg)(x) = x - 4$.

In Exercises 15–22 use the functions

$$f(x) = 3x + 1 \qquad g(x) = x^3$$
$$h(x) = \frac{1}{x + 1} \qquad u(x) = \sqrt{x}$$

to find equations for the indicated composite function.

15. $f \circ u$ **16.** $u \circ h$

17. $g \circ f$ **18.** $u \circ 2g$

19. $h^2 \circ u$ **20.** $h \circ f \circ u$

21. $f \circ g \circ u$ **22.** $u \circ g \circ f$

23. Let $u(x) = x - 3$. Find a function f so that $f(u(x)) = x^3 + 5$.

24. Let $u(x) = x^2$. Find a function f so that $f(u(x)) = \sqrt{x^2 + 1}$.

25. Let $f(x) = x + 4$ and $g(x) = (x - 2)^2$. Find a function u so that $f(g(u(x))) = 4x^2 - 8x + 8$.

In each of Exercises 26–31 match the split function with the correct graph among figures a–f.

26. $f(x) = \begin{cases} x + 1, & x \le 2 \\ 9 - 3x, & x > 2 \end{cases}$ **a.**

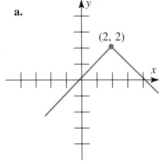

27. $f(x) = \begin{cases} x, & x \le 2 \\ 4 - x, & x > 2 \end{cases}$ **b.**

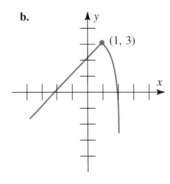

28. $f(x) = \begin{cases} 4 - x^2, & x \le 1 \\ 4 - x, & x > 1 \end{cases}$ **c.**

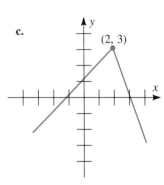

29. $f(x) = \begin{cases} x + 2 & x \le 1 \\ 4 - x^2, & x > 1 \end{cases}$ **d.**

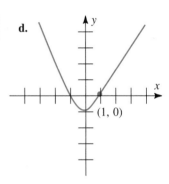

30. $f(x) = \begin{cases} 4 - 2x, & x \le 1 \\ \dfrac{2}{x}, & x \ge 1 \end{cases}$ **e.**

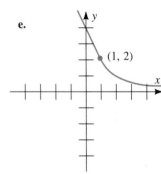

31. $f(x) = \begin{cases} x^2 - 1, & x \le 1 \\ x - 1, & x > 1 \end{cases}$ **f.**

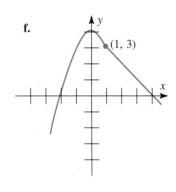

In Exercises 32–35 match the function written with absolute value notation with its equivalent split function form a–d.

32. $f(x) = |2x - 4|$

33. $f(x) = |4 + 2x|$

34. $f(x) = |4 - 2x|$

35. $f(x) = |4x - 2|$

a. $f(x) = \begin{cases} -4 - 2x, & x < -2 \\ 4 + 2x, & x \geq -2 \end{cases}$

b. $f(x) = \begin{cases} 4 - 2x, & x < 2 \\ 2x - 4, & x \geq 2 \end{cases}$

c. $f(x) = \begin{cases} 4 - 2x, & x \leq 2 \\ 2x - 4, & x > 2 \end{cases}$

d. $f(x) = \begin{cases} 2 - 4x, & x < \dfrac{1}{2} \\ 4x - 2, & x \geq \dfrac{1}{2} \end{cases}$

In Exercises 36–41 graph the given function.

36. $f(x) = \begin{cases} x^2 - 2, & x \leq 2 \\ 4 - x, & x > 2 \end{cases}$

37. $f(x) = \begin{cases} \sqrt{4 - x}, & x \leq 0 \\ 2 - x^2, & x > 0 \end{cases}$

38. $f(x) = |x^2 - x - 6|$

39. $f(x) = x - |x|$

40. $f(x) = |x^2 - 4|$

41. $f(x) = |x^2 - x - 2|$

42. A manufacturing plant can produce one dishwasher every 30 minutes. The total variable costs associated with the production of x dishwashers are $C(x) = 30x + 0.02x^2$. Write a composite function C giving the total variable costs resulting from t hours of dishwasher production.

43. A producer of a certain software product sells the product according to a price structure that encourages volume purchases. For orders of up to five copies the price is $500 per copy. On orders of more than five copies the price per copy is reduced by $10 for each copy in excess of five, except that all orders for more than 25 copies are filled at $300 per copy.

a. Write a function p giving the price per copy in purchasing x copies of this software.

b. Graph the function p.

44. Find the function R giving the total revenue received from a single order of x copies of the software described in Exercise 43.

45. Foxes and rabbits coexist in a certain ecological niche. The number of rabbits r is determined by the number of carrots according to the function $r(c) = 10 + 0.2c + 0.01c^2$. The number of foxes, which prey on the rabbits, is given by the function $f(r) = \sqrt{r + 5}$. Find the composite function f giving the number of foxes as a function of the number of carrots.

46. A delivery truck depreciates in value at the rate of 30% per year. Comprehensive theft and damage insurance on the truck costs 8% of its value per year. Find a function C giving the cost of the comprehensive insurance policy on the truck after t years if the original cost of the truck is $20,000.

47. A lawnmower manufacturer sells mowers to a certain retailer for $200 each, plus a handling charge of $75 on each order. The retailer applies a markup of 40% to the total price paid to the manufacturer.

a. Find the function C giving the retailer's total cost of a single order of x lawnmowers.

b. Find the function R giving the retailer's total revenues from the sale of these x lawnmowers.

c. If the retailer sells all these lawnmowers at the same price, what is the retail price per lawnmower?

48. The computer manufacturer in Example 2 produces its computers in a country that charges a value-added tax of 5%, which is applied to the total cost of production. The computer company sells its computers for $5000 each.

a. Express its profit function as a composite function involving the total cost, $C(x)$, of production, its revenue, and its tax.

b. Express its profit function solely in terms of x, the weekly production level.

✓ **SOLUTIONS TO PRACTICE PROBLEMS 1.7**

1. a. $f(g(2)) = f(\sqrt{2 + 2}) = f(2) = \dfrac{2^2}{2 + 3} = \dfrac{4}{5}$.

b. $g(f(6)) = g\left(\dfrac{6^2}{6 + 3}\right) = g(4) = \sqrt{4 + 2} = \sqrt{6}$

c. $(g \circ f)(x) = g\left(\dfrac{x^2}{x+3}\right) = \sqrt{\dfrac{x^2}{x+3} + 2}$

2. Since $f(x) = |x^2 + 2x - 3| = |(x+3)(x-1)|$, we have

$$f(x) = \begin{cases} x^2 + 2x - 3 & \text{if } x \le -3 \\ -(x^2 + 2x - 3) & \text{if } -3 \le x \le 1 \\ x^2 + 2x - 3 & \text{if } x > 1. \end{cases}$$

(See Figure 7.11.)

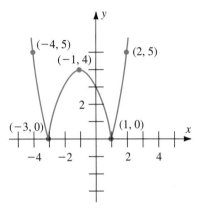

Figure 7.11 Graph of $f(x) = |x^2 + 2x - 3|$.

Summary Outline of Chapter 1

▌ The **inequality** $a < b$ means a lies to the left of b on the number line. (Page 3)

▌ *Interval notation* (Page 4)

$[a, b]$ means $\{x \,|\, a \le x \le b\}$
(a, b) means $\{x \,|\, a < x < b\}$
$[a, b)$ means $\{x \,|\, a \le x < b\}$
$(a, b]$ means $\{x \,|\, a < x \le b\}$
(a, ∞) means $\{x \,|\, a < x\}$, etc.

▌ *Theorem (Properties of Inequalities):* Let a, b, and c be real num- (Page 5)
bers.

(i) If $a < b$ then $a + c < b + c$.
(ii) If $a < b$ and $c > 0$, then $ac < bc$.
(iii) If $a < b$ and $c < 0$, then $ac > bc$.
(iv) If $a < b$ and $b < c$, then $a < c$.

▌ The **slope** of the line through the points (x_1, y_1) and (x_2, y_2) is the (Page 13)
number

$$m = \frac{y_2 - y_1}{x_2 - x_1}.$$

▌ The **point-slope** form of the equation for the line with slope m containing the point (x_1, y_1) is   (Page 14)

$$y - y_1 = m(x - x_1).$$

▌ The **slope-intercept** form of the equation for the line with slope m and y-intercept b is   (Page 15)

$$y = mx + b.$$

▌ An equation for the horizontal line through the point (a, b) is $y = b$.   (Page 20)

▌ An equation for the vertical line through the point (a, b) is $x = a$.   (Page 20)

▌ *Theorem:* Let ℓ_1: $y = m_1 x + b_1$ and ℓ_2: $y = m_2 x + b_2$ be equations for lines ℓ_1 and ℓ_2. Then   (Page 21)

  (i) ℓ_1 and ℓ_2 are **parallel** if $m_1 = m_2$.
  (ii) ℓ_1 and ℓ_2 are **perpendicular** if $m_1 m_2 = -1$.

▌ *Definition:* A **function** from set A to set B is a rule that assigns to each element of set A one and only one element of set B. Set A is called the **domain** of the function.   (Page 32)

▌ If, for a given manufacturer, C, R, and P denote the total cost, revenues, and profit from the production and sale of x items, then   (Page 37)

$$P(x) = R(x) - C(x) \qquad \text{(profit equation)}.$$

▌ *Definition:* Let x and y be real numbers and let n and m be positive integers. Then   (Page 46)

  (a) x^n means $x \cdot x \cdot x \cdot \ldots \cdot x$ (n factors)
  (b) x^{-n} means $\dfrac{1}{x^n}$ whenever $x \neq 0$.
  (c) $x^{1/n} = y$ means $y^n = x$.   ($x \geq 0$ if n is even.)
  (d) $x^{m/n}$ means $(x^{1/n})^m$.   ($x \geq 0$ if n is even.)
  (e) x^0 means 1 whenever $x \neq 0$.

▌ *Theorem (Laws of Exponents):* Let x and y be real numbers and let n and m be integers. Then   (Page 47)

  (a) $x^n x^m = x^{n+m}$
  (b) $x^n / x^m = x^{n-m}$, $x \neq 0$
  (c) $(x^n)^m = x^{nm}$
  (d) $x^{m/n} = (x^{1/n})^m = (x^m)^{1/n}$
  (e) $(xy)^n = x^n y^n$.

▌ The **quadratic formula** gives the zeros of the function $f(x) = ax^2 + bx + c$:   (Page 54)

$$x = \frac{-b \pm \sqrt{b^2 - 4ac}}{2a}.$$

▌The **demand function** D gives the number of items that consumers will purchase in a unit of time at price p. The **supply function** S gives the number of items that producers will supply in a unit of time at price p. The **equilibrium price** p_0 is the price for which   (Page 57)

$$D(p_0) = S(p_0) \quad \text{(equilibrium price equation)}.$$
If $C(x)$ gives the total cost of producing x items, the **average cost** per item is

$$c(x) = \frac{C(x)}{x}.$$

▌The **composite function** $g \circ f$ has values $(g \circ f)(x) = g(f(x))$.   (Page 64)

▌The **absolute value** function $f(x) = |x|$ is defined by   (Page 67)

$$|x| = \begin{cases} x & \text{if } x \geq 0 \\ -x & \text{if } x < 0. \end{cases}$$

Review Exercises—Chapter 1

1. Write each of the following sets of real numbers as an interval.
  a. $\{x \mid -6 < x \leq 3\}$
  b. $\{x \mid x < 4\}$
  c. $\{x \mid 2 \leq x\}$

In Exercises 2–5 solve the given inequality

2. $2x - 6 \leq 4$ **3.** $3 - x \geq 4 + x$

4. $6x - 6 < x + 3$ **5.** $2 - x \leq 4 - 4x$

In Exercises 6–9 sketch the graph of the given function by plotting points.

6. $f(x) = (x - 2)^3$ **7.** $f(x) = 2\sqrt{x} + 1$

8. $f(x) = \dfrac{1}{x - 3}$ **9.** $f(x) = \dfrac{x}{x^2 + 1}$

10. Find the slope of the line through the points $(-3, 2)$ and $(4, 1)$.

11. Find the slope of a line parallel to the line with equation $x - 6y = 24$.

12. Find an equation of the line perpendicular to the line $x - 6y = 24$ that contains the point $(2, -3)$.

13. Find an equation for the horizontal line containing the point $(-3, 5)$.

14. Find an equation for the vertical line containing the point $(-6, -3)$.

15. Find b if the point $(b, 4)$ lies on the line with no slope that contains the point $(7, -2)$.

16. Find an equation for the line containing the points $(2, -6)$ and $(-3, 4)$.

In Exercises 17–20 state the slope and y-intercept for the line determined by the given equation. Graph the line.

17. $x - 2y = 6$ **18.** $3x - y = -4$

19. $2x + 2y = 8$ **20.** $3 - y = 4x + 6$

In Exercises 21–24 state the domain of the given function.

21. $f(x) = \dfrac{x - 7}{x}$ **22.** $f(x) = \dfrac{x - 2}{x^2 - 4}$

23. $f(x) = \sqrt{8 - x^3}$ **24.** $f(x) = \dfrac{x + 3}{x^2 - 2x - 15}$

25. For the function $f(x) = \dfrac{\sqrt{x - 2}}{x + 3}$ find
  a. $f(6)$ **b.** $f(11)$

26. For the function $f(x) = x^{3/2} + 2x$ find
  a. $f(4)$ **b.** $f(9)$

In Exercises 27–30 simplify the given expression as much as possible.

27. $16^{3/4}$ **28.** $27^{-4/3}$

29. $\dfrac{(x^2y^4)^2}{xy^2}$ **30.** $\dfrac{3\sqrt{xy}}{x^2\sqrt{y}}$

In Exercises 31–36 graph the circle whose equation is given.

31. $x^2 + y^2 = 9$ **32.** $x^2 + y^2 = 16$

33. $x^2 + 2x + y^2 = 7 + 2y$ **34.** $x^2 + y^2 + 6y = 13$

35. $x^2 + 4x + y^2 + 2y = 14$ **36.** $x^2 - 2x + y^2 - 9y = 22$

In Exercises 37–42 find all zeros of the given function.

37. $f(x) = x^2 - 3x + 2$ **38.** $f(x) = x^2 - 8x + 16$

39. $f(x) = \dfrac{x - 3}{x + 2}$ **40.** $f(x) = \sqrt{x} - x^{3/2}$

41. $f(x) = \dfrac{x^2 + 9}{x - 2}$ **42.** $f(x) = 6 - 2x - x^2$

In Exercises 43–46 find the point(s) of intersection of the graphs of f and g.

43. $f(x) = x - 6$ **44.** $f(x) = \sqrt{x + 2}$
$g(x) = 2x + 2$ $g(x) = x$

45. $f(x) = 2 - x^2$ **46.** $f(x) = \dfrac{1}{x + 2}$
$g(x) = 4x^2 - 3$ $g(x) = x + 2$

In Exercises 47–50 let $f(x) = x^3 + 2$, $g(x) = x + 4$, $h_1 = fg$, and $h_2 = f/g$. Find

47. $h_1(x)$ **48.** $h_2(x)$

49. $h_1(0)$ **50.** $h_2(1)$

In Exercises 51–54 let $f(x) = x^2 - 7$, $g(x) = \sqrt{x + 3}$, and $u(x) = 4x$. Find equations for the indicated composite functions.

51. $g \circ f$ **52.** $g \circ u$

53. $u \circ f$ **54.** $u \circ f \circ g$

In Exercises 55–58 graph the given function.

55. $f(x) = |x + 3|$

56. $f(x) = |x^2 - 2x - 3|$

57. $f(x) = \begin{cases} x - 4, & x < 2 \\ -\dfrac{1}{2}x^2 & x \geq 2 \end{cases}$

58. $f(x) = \begin{cases} \sqrt{2 - x}, & x \leq 1 \\ 2x^2 - 1, & x > 1 \end{cases}$

59. Market research indicates that the demand for 12-inch color television sets is $D(p) = 2000 - 6p$ sets per month if the sets sell for p dollars each. Producers are willing to supply $S(p) = 4p$ sets per month at price p. What is the equilibrium price $[D(p_0) = S(p_0)]$ for this market?

60. After x repetitions a worker can perform a task in $T(x) = 10\left(1 + \dfrac{4}{\sqrt{x + 2}}\right)$ seconds. Graph this learning curve.

61. Which of Figures (a)–(d) are graphs of functions?

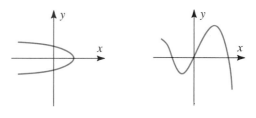

(a)   (b)

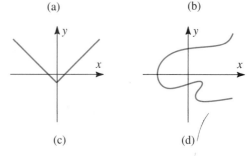

(c)   (d)

62. Find the lowest point on the graph of $f(x) = 3(x - 2)^2 + 4$.

63. True or false? The graph of $y = 3x^2 + 2x - 1$ opens downward.

64. Find an equation for the line with slope $m = -4$ and containing the point $(2, -3)$.

65. A restaurant agrees to serve a banquet at a cost of $20 per person for the first 50 people and $15 per person for each additional person. Find the function C giving the total cost of the meal.

66. Cotton production in the United States increased from 12.2 million bales (480 pounds each) in 1989 to 18.0 million bales in 1991. Assuming production of cotton to follow a linear equation, find the production level predicted by these data for the year 1995.

67. Refer to Exercise 66. In India, cotton production fell from 10.7 million bales in 1989 to 9.5 million bales in 1991. If the production rate for India is also assumed to be a linear function of time, what production level is predicted for India in 1996 according to these data?

68. Air quality engineers predict that the level of air pollutants in the center of a particular city will be $c(n) = \sqrt{1 + 0.2n}$ parts per million, where n is the average number of automobiles in the center city area. Traffic engineers predict that the average number of automobiles in the center of the city after t years will be $n(t) = 10{,}000 + 50t^{2/3}$. Write a composite function $c \circ n$ giving the level of air pollutants after t years.

69. The average daily temperature in a certain city rose from 58°F in 1940 to 59.2°F in 1980. If the relationship between temperature and time is assumed to be linear, what temperature do these data project for this city's average daily temperature in 2000?

70. Cab fare in a certain city is $2 per ride plus $1.20 per mile. How far can you ride for $10?

71. The *disposable annual income* for an individual is defined by the equation $D = (1 - r)T$ where T is total income and r is the net tax rate applied to his income.
a. Find the disposable income for an individual with a total income of $30,000 subject to a net tax rate of $r = 30\% = 0.30$.
b. What net tax rate gives a disposable income of $16,000 from a total income of $20,000?
c. Under a net tax rate of 40%, what total income is required to yield a disposable income of $30,000?

72. If a piece of equipment originally valued at V_0 dollars is assumed to have a useful life of N years, after which it will have a salvage value of V_s dollars, the *straight line* (constant rate) method of depreciation gives its value after n years as $V(n) = V_s + (V_0 - V_s)\left(1 - \dfrac{n}{N}\right)$. Find m and b so that this linear function can be written in the form $V(n) = mn + b$.

73. Refer to Exercise 72. If a computer originally valued at $30,000 is to be depreciated by the straight line method to a salvage value of $5000 over a period of five years, find its assumed value at the end of three years.

74. Market research shows that the demand for a particular type of mechanical pencil will be $D(p) = \dfrac{400}{p^2 + 2p + 5}$ thousand pencils per year at a selling price of p dollars per pencil. At what price will demand equal 20 thousand pencils per year?

75. Agricultural research shows that a certain type of apple tree will yield 400 pounds of apples per year minus 2 pounds for each tree planted per acre. Write a function Y giving the annual yield in pounds of a one-acre plot containing x such apple trees.

76. A 6-inch thick blanket of glass fiber insulation has an R-value of $R(6) = 19$. If R-value is a linear function of the thickness w of the insulation, what R-value is produced by 15 inches of glass fiber insulation? (*Hint:* $R(0) = 0$.)

77. A manufacturer of smoke detectors finds that its total cost in producing x units per day is $C(x) = C_0 + 16x + 0.02x^2$ dollars where C_0 represents fixed daily costs. The alarms are sold to retailers for $24 each. Find C_0 if the manufacturer's break-even production level (total costs equal total revenue) is to be $x = 100$ units per day.

78. Write a linear function giving the total cost C of leasing a car for x months if a driver travels 800 miles per month and the leasing fees are $100 per month plus 20¢ per mile for each mile over 500 per month.

79. For tax purposes a building that originally cost $100,000 is to be fully depreciated by the straight line method over a period of $N = 20$ years. This means that its value after n years is assumed to be $V(n) = (100{,}000)\left(1 - \dfrac{n}{20}\right)$.
a. Find $V(5)$, its value after five years.
b. Find an expression for $V(n)$ if the depreciation period is changed to $N = 30$ years.
c. Find $V(5)$ if $N = 30$ years.

80. Demand for a certain type of dishwasher is known to be $D(p) = \dfrac{154}{p}$ units per month at selling price p hundred dollars. If producers are willing to supply $S(p) = 2p - 8$ units per month at selling price p hundred dollars ($p \geq 4$), find the equilibrium price p_0 at which $S(p_0) = D(p_0)$.

81. The following table shows world production levels of sugar for three years (in millions of metric tons). For which countries/regions did production follow a linear function of time?

Country/region	1989	1990	1991
a. U.S.A.	6.0	6.3	6.6
b. Mexico	3.1	3.6	3.5
c. Argentina	0.9	1.2	1.4
d. Eastern Europe	4.9	4.7	4.5
e. U.S.S.R.	9.5	9.2	8.7
f. South Africa	2.3	2.3	2.3
g. Australia	3.8	3.5	3.2

82. Japan's domestic automobile production level increased from approximately 4.5 million automobiles in 1970 to 13 million in 1990. During the same period, United States' domestic automobile production increased from approximately 7.3 million in 1970 to approximately 8.3 million automobiles in 1990. Use these data to answer the following questions:

a. What linear equation is determined by the data for Japanese auto production? (Use $t = 0$ for 1970.)

b. What linear equation is determined by the U.S. data?

c. Do the two lines corresponding to these equations intersect? If so, at what time?

d. What production levels are predicted by these models for the year 2000?

83. Average manufacturing costs for small cars increased in Japan from $4200 in 1982 to $7200 in 1992. In the United States, average manufacturing costs for small cars increased from $6400 in 1982 to $7400 in 1992. (All numbers are approximations.) Use these data to answer the following questions:

a. Find linear models for these data, using $t = 0$ as 1982.

b. Which linear model has the larger slope? For which model is cost increasing more rapidly?

c. Do the two lines corresponding to these models intersect? If so, where? What does this mean?

d. Use these models to predict average manufacturing costs for small autos for the two countries in 1997.

2

Population growth and decline, for humans, as well as for other animals and plants, is affected by information given by "survivorship curves," one type of mathematical model concerning population growth. *(Michael Coyne/ The Image Bank)*

The Derivative

Much of both natural and social science has to do with the study of change. How does climatic fluctuation affect the growth of vegetation in an ecological niche? How will an increase in excise taxes affect the consumption of gasoline? Or, what increase in sales will result from a 20% reduction in the price of a personal computer?

For example, Figure 1.0 shows three "survivorship curves" used by demographers and ecologists to describe survivorship among animal and human populations as functions of time:

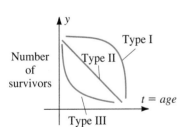

Figure 1.0 Three types of survivorship curves. The corresponding functions have greatly different rates of change.

Type I is common to developed countries, where a large percentage of the population lives into old age.

Type II is common to less-developed countries, where malnutrition and disease cause mortality to occur more frequently at younger ages.

Type III is common to animals that produce large numbers of offspring and quickly abandon them.

These three types of curves represent three very different types of functions. These differences are primarily in the *rates* at which these functions change as time increases.

The **derivative** is a new function that we can use to measure rates of change for a given function. Although a powerful tool, this concept can best be understood by beginning with the slope of a straight line as a simple example of a rate of change and then extending the notion to more general types of functions.

2.1   The Slope of a Curve

Figure 1.1 shows how the slope of a straight line may be interpreted as a **rate of change.** Since the definition of slope is

$$m = \frac{y_2 - y_1}{x_2 - x_1} \quad \left(= \frac{\text{change in } y\text{-coordinate}}{\text{change in } x\text{-coordinate}} \right) \tag{1}$$

when m is known, we may choose $x_2 - x_1 = 1$ and use equation (1) to conclude that the y-coordinate of a point on ℓ changes by $m = \dfrac{y_2 - y_1}{1} = y_2 - y_1$ units whenever the x-coordinate increases by 1 unit. (See Figure 1.2.) This is what is meant by the *rate* at which the y-coordinate changes with respect to change in the x-coordinate.

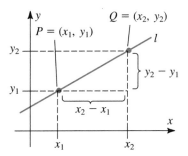

Figure 1.1 Slope of ℓ is $m = \dfrac{y_2 - y_1}{x_2 - x_1}$.

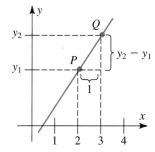

Figure 1.2 When $x_2 - x_1 = 1$, we have $m = \dfrac{y_2 - y_1}{1} = y_2 - y_1$, the rate at which y changes with respect to change in x.

For example, if the linear demand function $D(p) = 40 - 2p$ gives the number of hair dryers that consumers will purchase per week at price p, the slope $m = -2$ signifies that demand will decrease by two hair dryers per week for each one dollar increase in price. (See Figure 1.3.) That is, demand will decrease at a *rate* of two items per week for each one dollar increase in price.

But many of the functions of interest in business and other applications are not linear functions. As Figure 1.4 suggests, we would like to be able to determine the

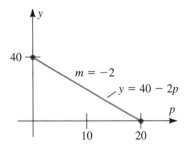

Figure 1.3 For $D(p) = 40 - 2p$, demand changes by $m = -2$ for each \$1 increase in price.

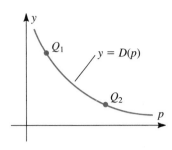

Figure 1.4 At what rate is demand changing at points Q_1 or Q_2?

rate at which values of a demand function, for example, change with respect to change in price even though its graph is not a straight line. Since the graph is not a straight line, we should expect to find different rates of change associated with different prices.

We shall answer this question in terms of *tangents* to a given curve. After resolving the question in this geometric setting, we shall return to the discussion of rates of change and the economic and physical interpretations of this concept.

The Tangent to a Curve

Intuitively, the line **tangent** to a curve C at a point P is the straight line that most resembles the curve at P. Figure 1.5 shows one way to visualize this concept. By repeatedly magnifying a small region surrounding the point P, we should observe the part of the curve "near" P flattening out and resembling a straight line. This line is what we mean by the tangent to the curve C at P.

Figure 1.5 By magnifying an increasingly small region near P we observe the curve C looking more and more like a straight line. This straight line is the *tangent* to the curve C at P.

Figure 1.6 shows both the curve C and its tangent at point P. The reason why we are so interested in this tangent is that its slope, which we can compute because a tangent is a straight line, is what we shall mean by the slope of the curve C at point P.

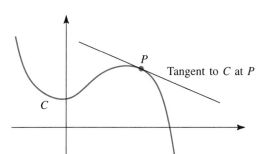

Figure 1.6 The slope of a curve C at point P is the slope of the line *tangent* to the curve C at P.

The difficulty with the preceding discussion is that it does not provide a precise meaning for the concept of a line tangent to a curve. Here is a more careful description of what a tangent really is, one that also provides a means for actually calculating the slope of the tangent that is defined.

We begin by assuming that the curve C is actually the graph of a function $y = f(x)$ and that the point P has coordinates $P = (x_0, y_0)$ with $y_0 = f(x_0)$. If we let $Q = (x_1, y_1)$ be a second point on this graph, then the line ℓ_{sec} through P and Q is called a **secant** to the graph of $y = f(x)$ at P. (See Figure 1.7.)

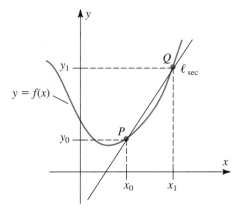

Figure 1.7 Secant ℓ_{sec} through $P = (x_0, y_0)$ and $Q = (x_1, y_1)$ on the graph of $y = f(x)$.

Figure 1.8 shows how these secants yield a tangent at point P. By moving point Q toward point P along the graph of $y = f(x)$, we generate an entire family of secant lines through P, which approach a "limiting position" as Q approaches P. This "limiting position" is our tangent, ℓ_{tan}, to the graph of $y = f(x)$ at point $P = (x_0, y_0)$.

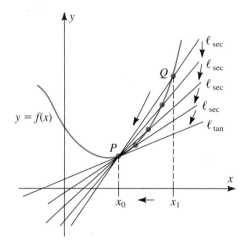

Figure 1.8 Tangent ℓ_{tan} is limiting position of secants as Q approaches P.

The Slope of a Tangent to a Curve

By examining this process a bit more critically, we can see how to find the slope of ℓ_{tan}. With $h = x_1 - x_0$ we can write $x_1 = x_0 + h$ and $f(x_1) = f(x_0 + h)$. Then, as Figure 1.9 shows, the slope of the secant through P and Q is

$$\text{slope of } \ell_{\text{sec}} = \frac{f(x_0 + h) - f(x_0)}{h}, \qquad h \neq 0.$$

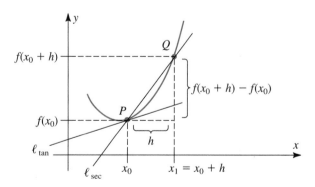

Figure 1.9 Slope of tangent to graph of $y = f(x)$ at the point $P = (x_0, y_0)$ is

$$m = \lim_{h \to 0} \frac{f(x_0 + h) - f(x_0)}{h}.$$

Since the tangent ℓ_{tan} is the limiting position of ℓ_{sec} as Q approaches P (that is, as h approaches zero), we say that

$$\text{slope of } \ell_{tan} = \{\text{``limit'' of slope of } m_{sec} \text{ as } h \to 0\}$$

$$= \lim_{h \to 0} \frac{f(x_0 + h) - f(x_0)}{h}$$

in the sense that the number $\dfrac{f(x_0 + h) - f(x_0)}{h}$ can be made as close as desired to the slope of ℓ_{tan} simply by taking h sufficiently close to 0.

Combining this observation with the point-slope form for the equation of a line, we may summarize our findings about ℓ_{tan} as follows:

If ℓ is the line tangent to the graph of $y = f(x)$ at the point $(x_0, f(x_0))$, then the slope of ℓ is

$$m = \lim_{h \to 0} \frac{f(x_0 + h) - f(x_0)}{h} \tag{2}$$

and an equation for ℓ is

$$y - y_0 = m(x - x_0) \tag{3}$$

where $y_0 = f(x_0)$.

The symbol "$\lim\limits_{h \to 0}$" in equation (2) is read, "the *limit* as h approaches zero of."

The meaning of this, roughly speaking, is the result of allowing the number h to "shrink to zero" in the expression that follows. For example, we would write

$$\lim_{h \to 0} (2 + h) = 2$$

read, "the limit of the expression $2 + h$ as h approaches zero is 2," since the number $2 + h$ "approaches" the number 2 as the number h "approaches" zero. Similarly, we would write

$$\lim_{h \to 0} (x + 4h) = x$$

since, as h approaches zero, the number $4h$ approaches zero but the number x remains unchanged. We shall discuss the concept of *limit* more generally in Section 2.2.

The following examples show how equation (2) may be applied to actually calculate the slope of a tangent to a particular curve at a given point when a certain key factorization can be accomplished.

☐ **EXAMPLE 1**

Use equation (2) to find the slope of the line tangent to the graph of the function $f(x) = x^2$ at the point $(2, 4)$.

Strategy · · · · · · · · · · · **Solution**

Identify the number x_0.

Here the specified value of x_0 is

$$x_0 = 2$$

so a nearby value of x is

$$x_0 + h = 2 + h.$$

From the equation for $f(x)$ determine $f(x_0)$ and $f(x_0 + h)$.

Since $f(x) = x^2$, we have

$$f(x_0) = f(2) = 2^2 = 4$$

and

$$f(x_0 + h) = f(2 + h) = (2 + h)^2.$$

Set up the expression for m from equation (2).

Simplify this expression as much as possible.

Substituting each of these expressions in equation (2), we find that

$$m = \lim_{h \to 0} \frac{f(2 + h) - f(2)}{h} \qquad (4)$$

$$= \lim_{h \to 0} \frac{(2 + h)^2 - 2^2}{h}$$

$$= \lim_{h \to 0} \frac{(4 + 4h + h^2) - 4}{h}$$

$$= \lim_{h \to 0} \frac{4h + h^2}{h}$$

Factor h from each term in the numerator.

$$= \lim_{h \to 0} \frac{h(4 + h)}{h}$$

$$= \lim_{h \to 0} \left(\frac{h}{h}\right)(4 + h)$$

Use $\dfrac{h}{h} = 1$.

$$= \lim_{h \to 0} (4 + h) \qquad \left(\frac{h}{h} = 1, \text{ provided } h \neq 0\right)$$

Evaluate the limit by letting h approach zero.

$$= 4.$$

Thus $m = 4$ at the point $(2, 4)$. (See Figure 1.10.) ■

It is important to note that we cannot evaluate the expression for m in equation (2) by simply setting $h = 0$, since this will produce a factor of zero in its denominator. In particular, setting $h = 0$ in equation (4) of Example 1 would have given the meaningless expression

$$\frac{f(2 + 0) - f(2)}{0}. \qquad \text{(undefined)}$$

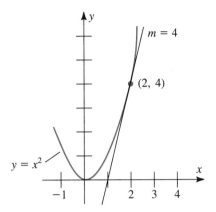

Figure 1.10 Slope of tangent to graph of $f(x) = x^2$ at $(2, 4)$ is $m = 4$.

To evaluate properly the expression for m, we must follow the steps outlined in Example 1.

Method for finding m, the slope of ℓ_{tan} at $x = x_0$:

(1) Set up the expression

$$m = \lim_{h \to 0} \frac{f(x_0 + h) - f(x_0)}{h}.$$

(2) Using algebra, simplify the numerator and attempt to identify a factor h in each of its terms.

(3) If successful in identifying a common factor h in the numerator, simplify the common factors of h in the numerator and denominator to the number 1. $\left(\text{That is, use the fact that } \dfrac{h}{h} = 1 \text{ when } h \neq 0.\right)$

(4) Finally, determine the limit by allowing the remaining factors of h to approach zero.

Here is another example of how these steps are followed in calculating the slope of a curve.

☐ **EXAMPLE 2**

Find the slope of the line tangent to the graph of the function $f(x) = 1 + 2x - x^2$ at the point where $x = 1$.

Strategy · · · · · · · ·

Identify x_0.

Set up expression for m.

Substitute expressions for $f(x_0 + h)$, $f(x_0)$.

Simplify by algebra.

Use $\dfrac{h}{h} = 1$.

Let h approach zero.

Solution

With $x_0 = 1$ we have

$$m = \lim_{h \to 0} \frac{f(1 + h) - f(1)}{h}$$

$$= \lim_{h \to 0} \frac{[1 + 2(1 + h) - (1 + h)^2] - [1 + 2 \cdot 1 - 1^2]}{h}$$

$$= \lim_{h \to 0} \frac{[1 + 2(1 + h) - (1 + 2h + h^2)] - 2}{h}$$

$$= \lim_{h \to 0} \frac{(2 - h^2) - 2}{h}$$

$$= \lim_{h \to 0} \frac{-h^2}{h}$$

$$= \lim_{h \to 0} - \left(\frac{h}{h}\right)h$$

$$= \lim_{h \to 0} - h$$

$$= 0.$$

Thus $m = 0$ when $x = 1$. (See Figure 1.11.) ∎

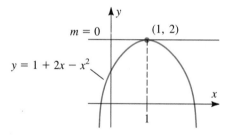

Figure 1.11 Slope of tangent to graph of $f(x) = 1 + 2x - x^2$ at $(1, 2)$ is $m = 0$.

The following examples show how equations (2) and (3) can be used together to find an *equation* for the line tangent to the graph of $y = f(x)$ at the point $P = (x_0, y_0)$.

□ **EXAMPLE 3**

Find an equation for the line tangent to the graph of $f(x) = x^2$ at the point $(2, 4)$.

Solution: The slope of this tangent line was found in Example 1 to be $m = 4$. Using equation (3) with $x_0 = 2$ and $y_0 = 4$, we obtain the equation

$$y - 4 = 4(x - 2)$$

or

$$y = 4x - 4.$$

∎

☐ **EXAMPLE 4**

Find an equation for the line tangent to the graph of the function $f(x) = \dfrac{3}{x + 1}$ at the point where $x = 2$. (See Figure 1.12.)

Strategy · · · · · · ·
Set up the expression for m.

Solution
Using $x_0 = 2$, we first calculate the slope of this tangent line as

$$m = \lim_{h \to 0} \frac{f(2 + h) - f(2)}{h}$$

Substitute for $f(x_0 + h)$, $f(x_0)$.

$$= \lim_{h \to 0} \frac{\dfrac{3}{(2 + h) + 1} - \dfrac{3}{2 + 1}}{h}$$

Simplify the expression by

$$= \lim_{h \to 0} \left(\frac{1}{h}\right)\left[\frac{3}{3 + h} - 1\right]$$

1. finding a common denominator

$$= \lim_{h \to 0} \left(\frac{1}{h}\right)\left[\frac{3}{3 + h} - \left(\frac{3 + h}{3 + h}\right)\right]$$

2. combining terms

$$= \lim_{h \to 0} \left(\frac{1}{h}\right)\left[\frac{3 - (3 + h)}{3 + h}\right]$$

$$= \lim_{h \to 0} \left(\frac{1}{h}\right)\left(\frac{-h}{3 + h}\right)$$

3. factoring h from the numerator

$$= \lim_{h \to 0} \left(\frac{h}{h}\right)\left(\frac{-1}{3 + h}\right)$$

4. using $\dfrac{h}{h} = 1$.

$$= \lim_{h \to 0} \left(\frac{-1}{3 + h}\right)$$

Evaluate the limit.

$$= -\frac{1}{3}.$$

The desired slope is therefore $m = -\dfrac{1}{3}$.

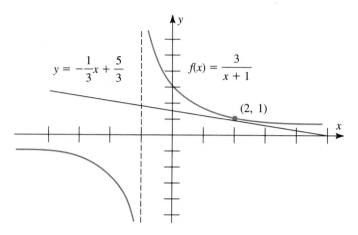

Figure 1.12 Tangent to graph of $f(x) = \dfrac{3}{x+1}$ at (2, 1) has equation $y = -\dfrac{1}{3}x + \dfrac{5}{3}$.

Use equation (3) to write the equation for the tangent line.

Now when $x_0 = 2$, $y_0 = f(2) = \dfrac{3}{2+1} = 1$.

Equation (3) then gives the equation for the desired tangent line as

$$y - 1 = -\frac{1}{3}(x - 2)$$

or

$$y = -\frac{1}{3}x + \frac{5}{3}.$$

(See Figure 1.12.)

■

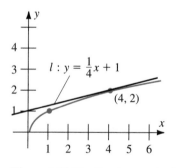

Figure 1.13 The line tangent to the graph of $f(x) = \sqrt{x}$ at (4, 2) has slope $m = \dfrac{1}{4}$.

□ **EXAMPLE 5**

Plant ecologists report that, among certain species of plants, the relationship between precipitation (rainfall or other sources of water) and overall plant growth is generally of the type represented by the square root function, $f(x) = \sqrt{x}$. (See Figure 1.13.)

(a) Find an equation for the line tangent to the graph of $f(x) = \sqrt{x}$ at the point (4, 2).

(b) What does the answer to part (a) say about the rate at which plant size will increase as precipitation increases at (4, 2) if x represents the amount of precipitation per unit time and $f(x)$ represents plant size?

Strategy · · · · · · · ·

(a) Identify x_0.

Set up the expression for m using equation (2).

Simplify, using algebra, to eliminate radical from the numerator using the observation that

$$\sqrt{a} - \sqrt{b}$$
$$= (\sqrt{a} - \sqrt{b})\left(\frac{\sqrt{a} + \sqrt{b}}{\sqrt{a} + \sqrt{b}}\right)$$
$$= \frac{a - b}{\sqrt{a} + \sqrt{b}}.$$

Use $\dfrac{h}{h} = 1$.

Let h approach zero.

Use equation (3) to write equation for tangent.

(b) Interpret slope of the tangent as rate of change (increase).

Solution

(a) Here $f(x) = \sqrt{x}$ and $x_0 = 4$. Thus,

$$m = \lim_{h \to 0} \frac{\sqrt{4 + h} - \sqrt{4}}{h}$$

$$= \lim_{h \to 0} \left[\frac{\sqrt{4 + h} - 2}{h} \cdot \frac{\sqrt{4 + h} + 2}{\sqrt{4 + h} + 2} \right]$$

$$= \lim_{h \to 0} \left[\frac{(4 + h) - 4}{h(\sqrt{4 + h} + 2)} \right]$$

$$= \lim_{h \to 0} \frac{h}{h(\sqrt{4 + h} + 2)}$$

$$= \lim_{h \to 0} \frac{1}{\sqrt{4 + h} + 2}$$

$$= \frac{1}{\sqrt{4} + 2} = \frac{1}{4}.$$

The desired tangent therefore has slope $m = \dfrac{1}{4}$. Since it contains the point $(4, 2)$, its equation is

$$y - 2 = \frac{1}{4}(x - 4)$$

or

$$y = \frac{1}{4}x + 1.$$

(b) Since the tangent to the graph of $f(x) = \sqrt{x}$ at $(4, 2)$ has slope $\dfrac{1}{4}$, we conclude that the y-coordinate, representing plant size, is increasing at only one-fourth the rate of increase of the x-coordinate, representing rainfall. (We note also that further increases in rainfall bring diminishing increases in plant size. This will be discussed further in Chapter 3.) ∎

In this section we have defined the slope of a curve at a point P to be the slope of the line *tangent* to the curve at P. To find the slope of this tangent, we have introduced the concept of *limit*. The notion of the slope of a tangent will lead us in Section 2.4 to the more general concept of the *derivative* of a function, one of the principal objects of interest in the calculus. Before taking up the study of derivatives, we need to develop a better understanding of the idea of the *limit* of a function. This is the agenda for Sections 2.2 and 2.3.

☑ **PRACTICE PROBLEMS 2.1**

1. Find an equation for the line tangent to the graph of $f(x) = 2x^2 + 3$ at the point $(1, 5)$.

2. Find the slope of the demand curve $D(p) = \dfrac{20}{p + 2}$ at the point where $p = 2$.

Exercise Set 2.1

In Exercises 1–6, estimate the slope m_{tan} of the line tangent to the graph of the given function at point P by positioning a straight edge in the position of the tangent and determining the slope by inspection.

1. $f(x) = 9 - x^2$

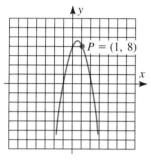

2. $f(x) = x^3$

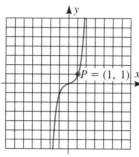

3. $f(x) = \sqrt{x}$

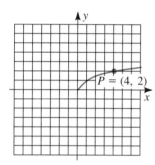

4. $f(x) = \dfrac{1}{x - 2}$

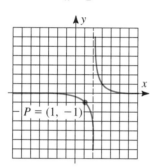

5. $f(x) = \dfrac{1}{1 + x^2}$

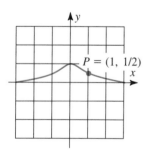

6. $f(x) = x^2 + 2x - 3$

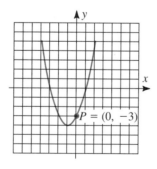

In Exercises 7–21, use the method of this section to find the slope of the line tangent to the graph of the given function at point P.

7. $f(x) = x^2$, $P = (1, 3)$

8. $f(x) = 3x^2 - 1$, $P = (2, 11)$

9. $f(x) = 2 - x^2$, $P = (1, 1)$

10. $f(x) = x^2 + x$, $P = (-1, 0)$

11. $f(x) = x^3$, $P = (1, 1)$

12. $f(x) = x^2 + x - 2$, $P = (2, 4)$

13. $f(x) = x^3 + x$, $P = (-1, -2)$

14. $f(x) = x^4$, $P = (2, 16)$

15. $f(x) = x^4 + x$, $P = (1, 2)$

16. $f(x) = \dfrac{1}{x}$, $P = (1, 1)$

17. $f(x) = \dfrac{1}{x + 3}$, $P = (-2, 1)$

18. $f(x) = \dfrac{x}{1 + x}$, $P = \left(2, \frac{2}{3}\right)$

19. $f(x) = \sqrt{x + 1}$, $P = (3, 2)$

20. $f(x) = 2 - \sqrt{x}$, $P = (4, 0)$

21. $f(x) = x^{3/2}$, $P = (4, 8)$

22. Find an equation for the line tangent to the graph of $f(x) = 4x^2 - 3$ at the point $(1, 1)$.

23. Find an equation for the line tangent to the graph of $f(x) = 9 - x^2$ at the point where $x = -2$.

24. Find an equation for the line tangent to the graph of $f(x) = \dfrac{2}{3 + x}$ at the point $\left(1, \frac{1}{2}\right)$.

25. Use the method of this section to show that the line tangent to the graph of $f(x) = mx + b$ at any point P on the graph is just the line $y = mx + b$.

26. Find the slope of the supply curve $S(p) = \frac{1}{4}p^2 + 4$, $p > 0$, at the point where $p = 4$.

27. What is the slope of the demand curve $D(p) = \dfrac{10}{p + 4}$, $p > 0$, at the point where $p = 6$?

28. Find the slope of the graph of

$$f(x) = \begin{cases} 4 - x^2, & x \le 1 \\ 2x + 1, & x > 1 \end{cases} \quad \text{at the point}$$

a. $P = (-1, 3)$.

b. $P = (2, 5)$.

29. Find the slope of the graph of the function $f(x) = |x - 3|$ at the point $P = (a, f(a))$ for

a. $a < 3$.

b. $a > 3$.

30. For the supply function $S(p) = \frac{1}{4}p^2$ and the demand function $D(p) = 12 - 2p$, find

    a. the equilibrium price p_0, where $S(p_0) = D(p_0)$.

    b. the slope of the supply curve at the equilibrium point $(p_0, S(p_0))$.

    c. the slope of the demand curve at the point $(p_0, D(p_0))$.

31. The quadratic function $y = a + bt + ct^2$ is used to model human length during certain periods of growth. Find the slope of the line tangent to the graph of this function at the point where $t = 1$.

32. During the first 50 days following the outbreak of influenza on a college campus the number $N(t)$ of students infected after t days is given by the function

$$N(t) = 25t - \left(\frac{1}{2}\right)t^2, \qquad 0 \le t \le 50.$$

    a. Graph the function $y = N(t)$ for $0 \le t \le 50$.

    b. Find the slope of the line tangent to this graph at the point where $t = 1$.

    c. Find the slope of the line tangent to this graph at the point where

$$t = a, \qquad 0 \le a \le 50.$$

    d. At what time t, between 0 and 50, is the slope of the tangent to this graph horizontal?

33. Refer to the survivorship curves in Figure 1.14.

    a. What would be the sign of the slope of the line tangent to the curve labeled Type I? Type III?

    b. Do the answers to part (a) distinguish one curve from the other? Why or why not?

    c. What can you say about the slopes of the lines tangent to the curves of Type I and Type II that distinguishes one

curve from the other? (*Hint:* Consider what happens to these tangents as the time variable increases.)

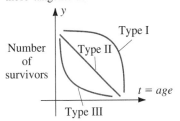

Figure 1.14 Survivorship curves.

34. A manufacturer's total cost in producing x tennis rackets weekly is determined to be

$$C(x) = 2000 + 20x + 2x^2.$$

    a. Find the slope of the line tangent to the graph of this function at the point where $x = 4$.

    b. Find the equation of this line.

35. Consider the manufacturer in Exercise 34.

    a. Find the average cost function $c(x) = \dfrac{c(x)}{x}$.

    b. Find the slope of the line tangent to the graph of $y = c(x)$ at the point where $x = 10$. Do you think average cost per racket is increasing or decreasing at this level of production? Why?

    c. Find the slope of the line tangent to the graph of $y = c(x)$ at the point where $x = 100$. Do you think average cost is increasing or decreasing at this level of production? Why?

    d. Find the number x_0 for which the slope of the line tangent to the graph of $y = c(x)$ at $(x_0, c(x_0))$ equals zero.

☑ **SOLUTIONS TO PRACTICE PROBLEMS 2.1**

    1. We first find the slope of the line tangent to the graph of $f(x) = 2x^2 + 3$ at $(1, 5)$. With $x_0 = 1$, we obtain

$$m = \lim_{h \to 0} \frac{[2(1 + h)^2 + 3] - [2(1)^2 + 3]}{h}$$

$$= \lim_{h \to 0} \frac{2(1 + 2h + h^2) + 3 - 5}{h}$$

$$= \lim_{h \to 0} \frac{4h + 2h^2}{h}$$

$$= \lim_{h \to 0} \frac{h(4 + 2h)}{h}$$

$$= \lim_{h \to 0} (4 + 2h)$$

$$= 4.$$

Using the point $(1, 5)$ and the slope $m = 4$, an equation for the tangent line is

$$y - 5 = 4(x - 1)$$

or

$$y = 4x + 1.$$

2. To find the slope of the demand curve $D(p) = \dfrac{20}{p + 2}$ at the point where $p_0 = 2$, we evaluate the limit

$$m = \lim_{h \to 0} \frac{D(2 + h) - D(2)}{h}$$

$$= \lim_{h \to 0} \left\{ \frac{\dfrac{20}{(2 + h) + 2} - \dfrac{20}{2 + 2}}{h} \right\}$$

$$= \lim_{h \to 0} \frac{20}{h} \left(\frac{1}{4 + h} - \frac{1}{4} \right)$$

$$= \lim_{h \to 0} \frac{20}{h} \left[\frac{4 - (4 + h)}{4(4 + h)} \right]$$

$$= \lim_{h \to 0} \left(\frac{20}{h} \right) \left[\frac{-h}{4(4 + h)} \right]$$

$$= \lim_{h \to 0} \left(\frac{h}{h} \right) \left[\frac{-20}{16 + 4h} \right]$$

$$= -\frac{20}{16}$$

$$= -\frac{5}{4}.$$

2.2 Limits of Functions

In Section 2.1 we determined that the slope of the line tangent to the graph of $y = f(x)$ at the point $(x_0, f(x_0))$ is

$$m = \lim_{h \to 0} \frac{f(x_0 + h) - f(x_0)}{h}. \tag{1}$$

The purpose of this section is to take a closer look at the meaning of the *limit* concept used in equation (1). You will discover that the notion of limit is a central theme in the calculus, one that is used in studying many ideas in addition to the slope of a tangent line.

Before addressing the more general notion of the limit of a function, let's take one additional look at the limit that arises in calculating the slope of a tangent to a

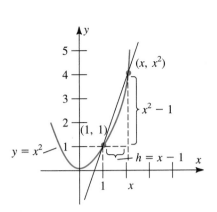

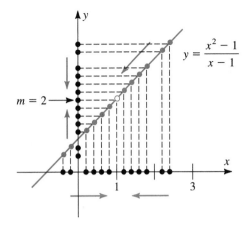

Figure 2.1 Slope of secant is $m = \dfrac{x^2 - 1}{x - 1}$.

Figure 2.2 As the numbers x approach 1, values of $\dfrac{x^2 - 1}{x - 1}$ approach 2. Thus

$$\lim_{x \to 1} \frac{x^2 - 1}{x - 1} = 2.$$

curve. Figure 2.1 shows the graph of the function $f(x) = x^2$ and one of the secant lines used in defining the tangent at the point $(1, 1)$. According to the way we have labeled Figure 2.1, the slope of this secant is

$$m_{\text{sec}} = \frac{f(x) - f(1)}{x - 1} = \frac{x^2 - 1}{x - 1}. \tag{2}$$

Since $h = x - 1$ in this example, to find the slope of the tangent at $(1, 1)$ we want to find the limit of the expression for m_{sec} in equation (2) as x approaches 1 (which is the same as h approaching zero):

$$m = \lim_{x \to 1} \frac{x^2 - 1}{x - 1}.$$

Figure 2.2 shows the graph of this quotient $g(x) = \dfrac{x^2 - 1}{x - 1}$ and what happens as we choose x "closer and closer" to $x = 1$. Some examples of such choices are listed in Table 2.1.

Table 2.1

Number x	2.0	1.5	1.1	1.01	1.001	0.999	0.99	0.9	0.5	0
Value of $g(x) = \dfrac{x^2 - 1}{x - 1}$	3.0	2.5	2.1	2.01	2.001	1.999	1.99	1.9	1.5	1

Note that as x approaches the number 1 from either direction, the values $g(x)$ approach the number $m = 2$. That is why we conclude that

$$m = \lim_{x \to 1} g(x) = \lim_{x \to 1} \frac{x^2 - 1}{x - 1} = 2.$$

There are two important observations concerning this result:

1. We *cannot* determine the limit $\lim_{x \to 1} g(x)$ by simply setting $x = 1$ since $g(1)$ is not defined. (Indeed, setting $x = 1$ in $g(x) = \dfrac{x^2 - 1}{x - 1}$ gives $\dfrac{1^2 - 1}{1 - 1} = \dfrac{0}{0}$, which is not defined. That is why there is a "hole" in the graph of $y = g(x)$ at location $(1, 2)$ in Figure 2.2.)

2. In this example, however, we could have used algebra to factor the numerator and simplify, thus allowing the limit to be obtained "by inspection," as in Section 2.1, as follows:

$$m = \lim_{x \to 1} \frac{x^2 - 1}{x - 1}$$

$$= \lim_{x \to 1} \frac{(x - 1)(x + 1)}{x - 1}$$

$$= \lim_{x \to 1} \left(\frac{x - 1}{x - 1} \right)(x + 1)$$

$$= \lim_{x \to 1} (x + 1) \qquad \left(\left(\frac{x - 1}{x - 1} \right) = 1, \text{ provided } x \neq 1 \right)$$

$$= (1 + 1)$$

$$= 2.$$

This is an example of the more general notion of the limit of a function.

The Limit of a Function

The example of finding the slope of a tangent to a curve is one case of needing to know what happens to the values of a function, say, $f(x)$, as x approaches a particular number, say, $x = a$, *even though $f(a)$ itself may not be defined.* Figure 2.3 shows such a situation, one where the values $f(x)$ approach the number $y = L$ as x approaches the number $x = a$. This is what we mean by writing $L = \lim_{x \to a} f(x)$.

Definition 1

We say that the number L is the *limit of the function f as x approaches a,* written

$$L = \lim_{x \to a} f(x)$$

if the values $f(x)$ approach the unique number L as x approaches a from either direction. (See Figure 2.3.)

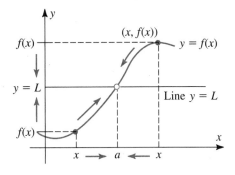

(*Note:* An open dot on a graph means that the point is *not* included in the graph.)

Figure 2.3 $L = \lim_{x \to a} f(x)$; values $f(x)$ approach the number L as x approaches a.

The following examples illustrate various typical situations in which limits of functions are determined.

☐ **EXAMPLE 1**

Since we have already mastered the techniques for graphing quadratic functions, it is clear from the graph of a quadratic function $f(x) = Ax^2 + Bx + C$ that

$$\lim_{x \to a} (Ax^2 + Bx + C) = Aa^2 + Ba + C.$$

That is, the limit as x approaches a of a quadratic function f is just the value $f(a)$. Figure 2.4 shows the particular case

$$\lim_{x \to 3} (4 + 3x - x^2) = 4.$$

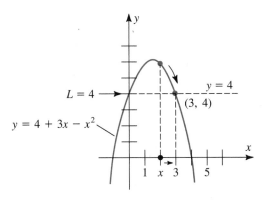

Figure 2.4 $\lim_{x \to 3} (4 + 3x - x^2) = 4$.

Functions that have the property that $\lim\limits_{x \to a} f(x) = f(a)$ are called *continuous* at the number $x = a$. We will have more to say about continuous functions in the next section. ∎

☐ **EXAMPLE 2**

The limit $\lim\limits_{x \to 2} \dfrac{x^2 + x - 6}{x - 2}$ cannot be evaluated by simply letting $x = 2$ since the rational function $f(x) = \dfrac{x^2 + x - 6}{x - 2}$ is not defined for $x = 2$. We must apply the method of Section 2.1. That is, we must try to remove the "offending" factor $(x - 2)$ from the numerator as follows:

$$\lim_{x \to 2} \frac{x^2 + x - 6}{x - 2} = \lim_{x \to 2} \frac{(x - 2)(x + 3)}{x - 2}$$

$$= \lim_{x \to 2} \left(\frac{x - 2}{x - 2}\right)(x + 3)$$

$$= \lim_{x \to 2} (x + 3)$$

$$= 2 + 3$$

$$= 5.$$

In this case we have used the fact that values of the rational function $f(x) = \dfrac{x^2 + x - 6}{x - 2}$ equal those of the linear function $g(x) = x + 3$ except when $x = 2$, because $f(2)$ is undefined. (See Figure 2.5.) ∎

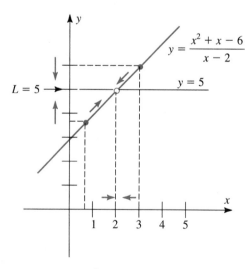

Figure 2.5 $\lim\limits_{x \to 2} \dfrac{x^2 + x - 6}{x - 2} = 5.$

□ **EXAMPLE 3**

If we change the numerator of the function in Example 2 to $x^2 + x + 6$, we find that
the limit

$$\lim_{x \to 2} \frac{x^2 + x + 6}{x - 2}$$

does not exist. This is because $(x - 2)$ is no longer a factor of the numerator, so it
cannot be ''canceled.'' As x approaches 2, the numerator approaches $2^2 + 2 + 6 = 12$ while the denominator approaches zero. Thus the quotient ''blows up.'' Table
2.2 shows the result of using BASIC Program 1 in Appendix I to calculate values
$f(x) = \dfrac{x^2 + x + 6}{x - 2}$ for various numbers x near $x_0 = 2$. You can see the phenomenon described here in these data. Figure 2.6, the graph of $y = f(x)$, illustrates graphically why this limit does not exist. We shall have more to say about limits that fail
to exist in Section 2.9, infinite limits.   ■

Table 2.2. Values $f(x) = \dfrac{x^2 + x + 6}{x - 2}$ near $x_0 = 2$

x	$f(x) = \dfrac{x^2 + x + 6}{x - 2}$
3	18
2.5	29.5
2.1	125
2.01	1205
2.001	12005
2.0001	120005
1	−8
1.5	−19.5
1.9	−115
1.99	−1195
1.999	−11995
1.9999	−119995

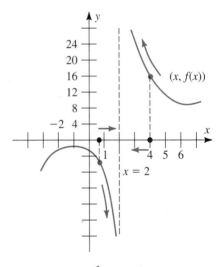

Figure 2.6 $\lim\limits_{x \to 2} \dfrac{x^2 + x + 6}{x - 2}$ does not
exist.

Properties of Limits

In Section 1.7 we reviewed the ways in which functions may be combined using
algebra to form new functions. When limits of each of these individual functions
exist, the limits of the resulting combinations of functions can be calculated from the
limits of the original functions. The following theorem shows how this is done.

Theorem 1
Properties of Limits

Let f and g be functions for which

$$\lim_{x \to a} f(x) = L, \quad \text{and} \quad \lim_{x \to a} g(x) = M$$

and let c be any real number. Then

(i) $\lim_{x \to a} (f + g)(x) = \lim_{x \to a} f(x) + \lim_{x \to a} g(x) = L + M$

(ii) $\lim_{x \to a} (cf)(x) = c[\lim_{x \to a} f(x)] = cL$

(iii) $\lim_{x \to a} (fg)(x) = [\lim_{x \to a} f(x)] \cdot [\lim_{x \to a} g(x)] = L \cdot M$

(iv) $\lim_{x \to a} (f/g)(x) = [\lim_{x \to a} f(x)]/[\lim_{x \to a} g(x)] = L/M$, provided $M \neq 0$.

The following examples show how Theorem 1 may be used.

☐ **EXAMPLE 4**

Find $\lim_{x \to 3} (2x^2 + 4x + 9)$.

Strategy · · · · · · ·
Apply Theorem 1, part (i).

Solution

$$\lim_{x \to 3} (2x^2 + 4x + 9) = \lim_{x \to 3} (2x^2) + \lim_{x \to 3} (4x) + \lim_{x \to 3} (9)$$

Apply Theorem 1, part (ii).

$$= 2 \lim_{x \to 3} (x^2) + 4 \lim_{x \to 3} (x) + \lim_{x \to 3} (9)$$

$$= 2 \cdot 3^2 + 4 \cdot 3 + 9$$

$$= 39.$$

■

☐ **EXAMPLE 5**

Find $\lim_{x \to 2} \dfrac{x^2 - 4x}{3x + 6}$.

Strategy · · · · · · ·
Apply Theorem 1, part (iv).

Solution

$$\lim_{x \to 2} \frac{x^2 - 4x}{3x + 6} = \frac{\lim_{x \to 2} (x^2 - 4x)}{\lim_{x \to 2} (3x + 6)}$$

Apply Theorem 1, part (i).

$$= \frac{\lim_{x \to 2} (x^2) + \lim_{x \to 2} (-4x)}{\lim_{x \to 2} (3x) + \lim_{x \to 2} (6)}$$

Apply Theorem 1, part (ii).

$$= \frac{\lim_{x \to 2} (x^2) - 4 \lim_{x \to 2} (x)}{3 \lim_{x \to 2} (x) + \lim_{x \to 2} (6)}$$

$$= \frac{2^2 - 4 \cdot 2}{3 \cdot 2 + 6}$$

$$= -\frac{4}{12}$$

$$= -\frac{1}{3}.$$ ∎

The next two examples show how the technique of "removing the offending factor" may be used in conjunction with Theorem 1.

☐ **EXAMPLE 6**

Find $\lim\limits_{x \to 9} \dfrac{x^2 - 81}{\sqrt{x} - 3}$.

Strategy · · · · · · ·

Examine the numerator and denominator individually to determine their limits as $x \to 9$.

Try to factor numerator into a product involving a factor of $\sqrt{x} - 3$.

Factor as difference of squares in x.

Factor first term as difference of squares in $\sqrt{x}$.

Apply Theorem 1, part (iii).

Solution

We observe first that both $\lim\limits_{x \to 9} (x^2 - 81) = 0$ and $\lim\limits_{x \to 9} (\sqrt{x} - 3) = 0$, so we obtain no information about the limit of the quotient in this manner.

We next try factoring the numerator and applying Theorem 1 as follows:

$$\lim_{x \to 9} \frac{x^2 - 81}{\sqrt{x} - 3} = \lim_{x \to 9} \frac{(x - 9)(x + 9)}{\sqrt{x} - 3}$$

$$= \lim_{x \to 9} \frac{(\sqrt{x} - 3)(\sqrt{x} + 3)(x + 9)}{\sqrt{x} - 3}$$

$$= \lim_{x \to 9} (\sqrt{x} + 3)(x + 9)$$

$$= 6 \cdot 18$$

$$= 108.$$ ∎

☐ **EXAMPLE 7**

Find $\lim\limits_{x \to 1} \dfrac{x^{3/2} - 1}{1 - x}$.

Strategy · · · · · · ·

First, examine limits of numerators and denominator separately.

Next, try factoring by viewing $1 - x$ as a difference of squares of 1 and $\sqrt{x}$.

Apply Theorem 1.

Solution

The limits of the numerator and denominator are both equal to zero, as you can verify.

We therefore attempt to factor the numerator and denominator, and to apply Theorem 1:

$$\lim_{x \to 1} \frac{x^{3/2} - 1}{(1 - x)} = \lim_{x \to 1} \frac{(\sqrt{x} - 1)(\sqrt{x^2} + \sqrt{x} + 1)}{(1 - \sqrt{x})(1 + \sqrt{x})}$$

$$= \lim_{x \to 1} (-1)\left(\frac{x + \sqrt{x} + 1}{1 + \sqrt{x}} \right)$$

$$= (-1)\left(\frac{1 + 1 + 1}{1 + 1} \right)$$

$$= -\frac{3}{2}.$$

∎

☑ **PRACTICE PROBLEMS 2.2**

1. Find the limit: $\displaystyle \lim_{x \to 3} \frac{x - 3}{x^2 - 2x - 3}$.

2. Find the limit: $\displaystyle \lim_{x \to 9} \frac{x - 9}{\sqrt{x} - 3}$.

Exercise Set 2.2

In Exercises 1–18, find the indicated limit if it exists.

1. $\displaystyle \lim_{x \to 3} (2x - 6)$

2. $\displaystyle \lim_{x \to 3} \frac{2x - 1}{x + 5}$

3. $\displaystyle \lim_{x \to 1} (x^2 - 4x)$

4. $\displaystyle \lim_{x \to 2} \frac{x^2 - 4}{x - 2}$

5. $\displaystyle \lim_{x \to -3} \frac{x^2 - 9}{x + 3}$

6. $\displaystyle \lim_{x \to 0} \frac{x^3 - x}{x}$

7. $\displaystyle \lim_{x \to 4} \frac{x - 4}{x^2 - x - 12}$

8. $\displaystyle \lim_{x \to 6} \frac{36 - x^2}{x - 6}$

9. $\displaystyle \lim_{x \to 1} \frac{x^3 - 1}{x - 1}$

10. $\displaystyle \lim_{x \to 0} |x|$

11. $\displaystyle \lim_{h \to 0} \frac{(4 + h)^2 - 16}{h}$

12. $\displaystyle \lim_{x \to -1} \frac{x^2 - 2x - 3}{x + 1}$

13. $\displaystyle \lim_{x \to 4} \frac{x - 4}{\sqrt{x} - 2}$

14. $\displaystyle \lim_{x \to -3} \frac{x^2 - 6x - 27}{x^2 + 3x}$

15. $\displaystyle \lim_{x \to -3} \frac{x^2 - 4x - 21}{x + 3}$

16. $\displaystyle \lim_{x \to 4} \frac{|x - 4| + 2x}{x + 3}$

17. $\displaystyle \lim_{x \to 1} \frac{1 - x^4}{x^2 - 1}$

18. $\displaystyle \lim_{x \to -1} \frac{x^3 + 2x^2 - 5x - 6}{x + 1}$

19. $\displaystyle \lim_{x \to 0} \frac{\sqrt{x + 1} - 1}{x}$

20. $\displaystyle \lim_{x \to 2} \frac{\sqrt{x + 2} - 2}{x - 2}$

21. $\displaystyle \lim_{x \to 1} \frac{1 - \sqrt{x}}{x + 1}$

22. $\displaystyle \lim_{x \to 4} \frac{4 - x}{\sqrt{x} - 2}$

23. $\displaystyle \lim_{x \to 3} \frac{\sqrt{x + 1} - \sqrt{x}}{1 - x}$

24. $\displaystyle \lim_{x \to 4} \frac{\sqrt{x} - 2}{x - 4}$

25. $\displaystyle \lim_{x \to 1} \frac{1 - \sqrt{x}}{x^{3/2} - \sqrt{x}}$

26. $\displaystyle \lim_{x \to 1} \frac{\sqrt{x} - x}{x^2 - x}$

☑ **SOLUTIONS TO PRACTICE PROBLEMS 2.2**

1. $\lim\limits_{x\to 3} \dfrac{x-3}{x^2-2x-3} = \lim\limits_{x\to 3} \dfrac{x-3}{(x-3)(x+1)}$

$\qquad\qquad\qquad = \lim\limits_{x\to 3} \dfrac{1}{x+1}$

$\qquad\qquad\qquad = \dfrac{1}{4}.$

2. $\lim\limits_{x\to 9} \dfrac{x-9}{\sqrt{x}-3} = \lim\limits_{x\to 9} \dfrac{(\sqrt{x}-3)(\sqrt{x}+3)}{\sqrt{x}-3}$

$\qquad\qquad\qquad = \lim\limits_{x\to 9} (\sqrt{x}+3)$

$\qquad\qquad\qquad = 6.$

2.3 One-Sided Limits and Continuity

Many functions of interest in business and other applications have *discontinuities* that are important to understand. We shall define this term formally later in this section. Intuitively, a discontinuity is a "break" or "tear" in the graph of a function. At such locations, for example, the function values may experience a sudden jump, or become infinite.

In order to understand the properties of *continuity* and *discontinuity* for functions, we need first to develop the concept of *one-sided* limits. We begin with an illustration.

Figure 3.1 shows the graph of the "postage function," which gives the postage $P(x)$ required to mail a letter weighing x ounces, for $0 < x < 3$. We can write this function formally as

$$P(x) = \begin{cases} 29 \text{ cents} & \text{for} \quad 0 < x < 1 \\ 52 \text{ cents} & \text{for} \quad 1 < x < 2 \\ 75 \text{ cents} & \text{for} \quad 2 < x < 3. \end{cases}$$

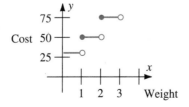

Figure 3.1 Postage stamp function.

In this example we would say that $\lim_{x \to 1} P(x)$ fails to exist because as x approaches 1 *from the right* all values $P(x)$ eventually equal 52, while as x approaches 1 *from the left* all values $P(x)$ eventually equal 29. Thus, $P(x)$ does not approach a *unique* value as x approaches 1, as required by the definition of limit.

When we restrict our considerations to just one side of $x = 1$ or the other, however, we can use the terminology of limit to report a limit in this restricted sense. This is the notion of *one-sided limit,* as defined below.

Definition 2

We say that L is the **left-hand limit** of f as x approaches a, written

$$L = \lim_{x \to a^-} f(x)$$

if the values $f(x)$ approach the unique number L as x approaches *a from the left only.* Similarly, we say that M is the **right-hand limit** of f as x approaches a, written

$$M = \lim_{x \to a^+} f(x)$$

if the values $f(x)$ approach the unique number M as x approaches *a from the right only.* (See Figure 3.2.)

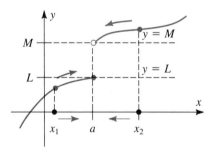

Figure 3.2 $\lim_{x \to a^-} f(x)$ does not exist, but

$$\lim_{x \to a^-} f(x) = L$$

$$\lim_{x \to a^+} f(x) = M.$$

With these one-sided limits we may refer to the postage stamp function $P(x)$ and say that

$$\lim_{x \to 1^-} P(x) = 29 \qquad \text{and} \qquad \lim_{x \to 1^+} P(x) = 52.$$

Finally, we note that our original (two-sided) limit, $\lim\limits_{x \to a} f(x)$, can exist if and only if both one-sided limits exist and are equal. That is

$$L = \lim_{x \to a} f(x) \quad \text{if and only if} \quad \lim_{x \to a^-} f(x) = L = \lim_{x \to a^+} f(x).$$

Thus, for example, $\lim\limits_{x \to 1} P(x)$ does not exist.

□ **EXAMPLE 1**

The *greatest integer* function is defined by

$$[x] = \text{the largest integer } n \text{ with } n \le x.$$

(See Figure 3.3.) We have

$$\lim_{x \to 2^+} [x] = 2; \qquad \lim_{x \to 2^-} [x] = 1$$

$$\lim_{x \to -2^-} [x] = -3; \qquad \lim_{x \to -2^+} [x] = -2.$$

But neither $\lim\limits_{x \to 2} [x]$ nor $\lim\limits_{x \to -2} [x]$ exists.   ■

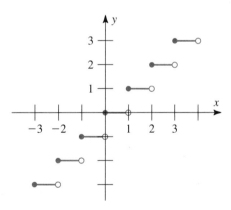

Figure 3.3 Graph of the greatest integer function $f(x) = |x|$.

□ **EXAMPLE 2**

For the split function $f(x) = \begin{cases} \dfrac{1}{x} & \text{if } x > 0 \\[2mm] -x^2 & \text{if } x \le 0 \end{cases}$

the left-hand limit at $a = 0$ is

$$\lim_{x \to 0^-} f(x) = \lim_{x \to 0^-} (-x^2) = 0.$$

However, the right-hand limit fails to exist since the values $f(x)$ become increasingly large as x approaches zero from the right. (See Figure 3.4.) ∎

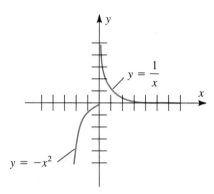

Figure 3.4 For $f(x) = \begin{cases} \dfrac{1}{x} & \text{if } x > 0 \\ -x^2 & \text{if } x \leq 0. \end{cases}$

Continuity

Figure 3.2 shows that when the two one-sided limits for f at $x = a$ exist but are not equal, the graph of f has a "jump" or a "tear" at $x = a$. Such phenomena are referred to as *discontinuities* of f. Other ways in which discontinuities can occur are that $\lim_{x \to a} f(x)$ fails to exist (Figure 3.5), that $f(a)$ fails to exist (Figure 3.6), or that $f(a)$ does not equal $\lim_{x \to a} f(x)$ (Figure 3.7). The property of *continuity*, defined here, rules out all such "tears" or "holes" in the graph of f.

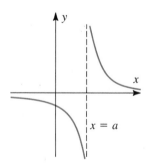

Figure 3.5 $\lim_{x \to a} f(x)$ does not exist.

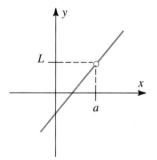

Figure 3.6 $f(a)$ does not exist.

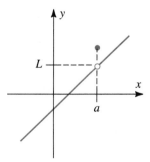

Figure 3.7 $f(a) \neq \lim_{x \to a} f(x)$.

Definition 3

The function f is said to be **continuous** at $x = a$ if each of the following conditions holds:

(i) $\lim_{x \to a} f(x)$ exists.

(ii) $f(a)$ is defined.

(iii) $f(a) = \lim_{x \to a} f(x)$.

The function f is said to be continuous on the interval (a, b) if it is continuous at each x in (a, b). It is said to be **discontinuous** at $x = c$ if it is not continuous at $x = c$.

All polynomial functions are continuous for all x. Discontinuities of the kind readers of this book will encounter almost always occur because a factor in the denominator of a function becomes zero, or because two components of a "split" function do not agree at the common number x.

□ **EXAMPLE 3**

Find the intervals on which the function

$$f(x) = \frac{x}{x^2 - x - 2}$$

is continuous.

Strategy · · · · · · · ·

Factor the denominator and find its zeros.

Solution

The denominator of this function is

$$x^2 - x - 2 = (x + 1)(x - 2).$$

It equals zero for $x = -1$ and $x = 2$. The function

Discontinuities occur at each zero of the denominator.

$$f(x) = \frac{x}{x^2 - x - 2} = \frac{x}{(x + 1)(x - 2)}$$

f is continuous at all other x.

will therefore be discontinuous at $x = -1$ and $x = 2$. There are no other zeros for the denominator. Thus, f is continuous on the intervals $(-\infty, -1)$, $(-1, 2)$, and $(2, \infty)$. (See Figure 3.8.) ■

A final remark: Many of the functions that we shall work with in this text are inherently discontinuous because they are defined only for integers, strictly speaking. Here we refer primarily to the functions of business and economics that involve the cost, price, revenues, profits, and losses associated with the production and sale of certain numbers (that is, integers) of items. However, unless we state otherwise we shall assume that these functions are defined for all real numbers (even though manufacturing $7\frac{1}{2}$ bicycles is not possible). This affords the advantage of working with continuous functions for the most part and allows us to associate discontinuities with truly dramatic behavior on the part of these models.

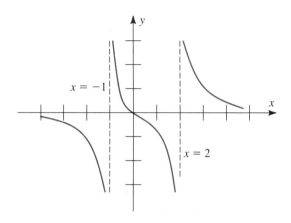

Figure 3.8 $f(x) = \dfrac{x}{(x+1)(x-2)}$ is discontinuous at $x = -1$ and $x = 2$.

☐ **EXAMPLE 4**

Where is the split function

$$f(x) = \begin{cases} x + 2, & x \le -1 \\ x^2, & -1 < x < 2 \\ \sqrt{2x + 3}, & 2 \le x \end{cases}$$

continuous and discontinuous?

Strategy · · · · · · · ·

First, examine the individual components (lines) of the split function to see if they are continuous.

Examine the behavior of f at any discontinuities in the components and at the transition numbers.

At x_1, check the one-sided limits for f.

If they exist, check that they are equal. If so, check that this (two-sided) limit equals the function value. Apply Definition 3.

Solution

The polynomials $x + 2$, x^2, and $2x + 5$ are all continuous functions, and the square root function has no discontinuities. Thus, $\sqrt{2x + 5}$ is a continuous function. When combined in a split function, therefore, these three functions should produce discontinuities only at the "transition numbers," where we change from one line to another in calculating the function values. These are the numbers $x_1 = -1$ and $x_2 = 2$.

At $x_1 = -1$, we have

$$\lim_{x \to -1^-} f(x) = \lim_{x \to -1^-} (x + 2) = 1$$

and

$$\lim_{x \to -1^+} f(x) = \lim_{x \to -1^+} (x^2) = 1.$$

Thus, $\lim_{x \to -1} f(x)$ exists, $f(-1)$ exists, and $f(-1) = 1 = \lim_{x \to -1} f(x)$. According to Definition 3, f is *continuous* at $x_1 = -1$.

Check $x_2 = 2$ in the same manner.

If the one-sided limits are unequal, the (two-sided) limit cannot exist and f is discontinuous.

At $x_2 = 2$, we have

$$\lim_{x \to 2^-} f(x) = \lim_{x \to 2^-} x^2 = 4$$

but

$$\lim_{x \to 2^+} f(x) = \lim_{x \to 2^+} \sqrt{2x + 5} = 3.$$

Thus, $\lim_{x \to 2^-} f(x) \neq \lim_{x \to 2^+} f(x)$, so $\lim_{x \to 2} f(x)$ does not exist.

According to Definition 3, f is *not* continuous, or is *discontinuous,* at $x_2 = 2$.

Thus, f is discontinuous at $x = 2$ and continuous at all other numbers x. (See Figure 3.9.) ■

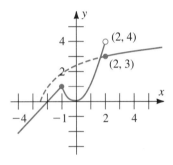

Figure 3.9 The split function in Example 4 is continuous at $x_1 = -1$ and discontinuous at $x_2 = 2$.

□ **EXAMPLE 5**

A state income tax schedule shows the following taxes due on these ranges of adjusted gross income for single taxpayers:

Income Range	Tax
$\$10,000 \leq x < \$15,000$	\$500 + 5% of amount over \$10,000
$\$15,000 \leq x < \$20,000$	\$800 + 6% of amount over \$15,000
$\$20,000 \leq x < \$25,000$	\$1200 + 7% of amount over \$20,000

If $T(x)$ denotes the tax due on income level x, is T a continuous function for all x? Why or why not?

Solution: The answer is no. In fact, T is discontinuous at $x = \$15{,}000$ and at $x = \$20{,}000$. To see this, note that

$$T(x) = 500 + 0.05(x - 10{,}000) \quad \text{if} \quad 10{,}000 \le x < 15{,}000.$$

Thus

$$\lim_{x \to 15{,}000^-} T(x) = \lim_{x \to 15{,}000^-} [500 + 0.05(x - 10{,}000)]$$

$$= 500 + 0.05(15{,}000 - 10{,}000)$$

$$= 750.$$

But $T(15{,}000) = 800$ according to the second line of the tax table. Thus $\lim_{x \to 15{,}000^-} T(x) \ne T(15{,}000)$, so T is discontinuous at $x = 15{,}000$. A similar calculation shows that T is discontinuous at $x = \$20{,}000$. The graph of $y = T(x)$ appears in Figure 3.10. ∎

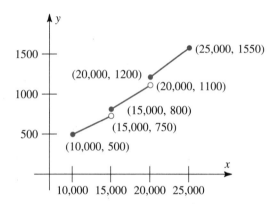

Figure 3.10 Tax schedule in Example 4 is discontinuous at income levels $x_1 = \$15{,}000$ and $x_2 = \$20{,}000$.

☑ **PRACTICE PROBLEMS 2.3**

1. Evaluate the one-sided limit $\lim_{x \to 3^-} \dfrac{|x - 3|}{x - 3}$.

2. Local income taxes in Sunrise City are assessed according to the following scheme, where $T(x)$ is the tax on an income of x dollars per year:

$$T(x) = \begin{cases} 0, & 0 \le x \le 5000 \\ 0.02(x - 5000), & 5000 < x \le 20{,}000 \\ 0.04(x - 10{,}000), & 20{,}000 < x. \end{cases}$$

Is this tax function discontinuous? If so, where?

Exercise Set 2.3

1. For the function $y = f(x)$ in Figure 3.11,

  a. $f(1)$

  b. $\lim\limits_{x \to 1^-} f(x)$

  c. $\lim\limits_{x \to 1} f(x)$

  d. $\lim\limits_{x \to 0} f(x)$

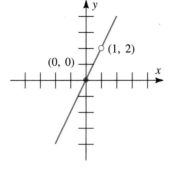

Figure 3.11

2. For the function $y = f(x)$ in Figure 3.12 find

  a. $f(1)$

  b. $\lim\limits_{x \to 1^-} f(x)$

  c. $\lim\limits_{x \to 1^+} f(x)$

  d. $\lim\limits_{x \to 1} f(x)$

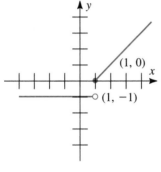

Figure 3.12

3. For the function $y = f(x)$ in Figure 3.13 find

  a. $\lim\limits_{x \to 0^-} f(x)$

  b. $\lim\limits_{x \to 0^+} f(x)$

  c. $\lim\limits_{x \to -2} f(x)$

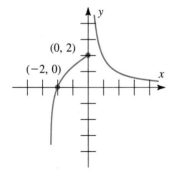

Figure 3.13

4. For the function $y = f(x)$ in Figure 3.14, find

  a. $\lim\limits_{x \to -2^+} f(x)$

  b. $\lim\limits_{x \to 2^-} f(x)$

  c. $\lim\limits_{x \to 2^+} f(x)$

  d. $f(2)$

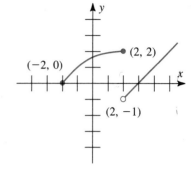

Figure 3.14

In Exercises 5–10, find the indicated one-sided limit.

5. $\lim\limits_{x \to 0^-} \dfrac{|x|}{x}$

6. $\lim\limits_{x \to 0^+} \dfrac{|x|}{x}$

7. $\lim\limits_{x \to 0^+} \sqrt{\dfrac{x}{x + 2}}$

8. $\lim\limits_{x \to 2^-} \dfrac{|1 - x^2|}{1 + x^2}$

9. $\lim\limits_{x \to 1^-} \dfrac{|x - 2|}{x + 2}$

10. $\lim\limits_{x \to 6^+} \dfrac{\sqrt{x^2 - 5x - 6}}{x - 3}$

In Exercises 11–20, find the numbers x at which the given function is discontinuous.

11. $f(x) = \dfrac{1}{1 - x^2}$

12. $f(x) = \dfrac{x + 2}{x^2 - x - 2}$

13. $f(x) = \dfrac{x^2 - x - 6}{x + 3}$

14. $f(x) = \dfrac{x^3 + 4x^2 - 7x - 10}{x - 2}$

15. $f(x) = \dfrac{x + 3}{x^3 + 3x^2 - x - 3}$

16. $f(x) = \dfrac{|x + 2|}{x + 2}$

17. $f(x) = \begin{cases} 1 - x, & x \le 2 \\ x - 1, & x > 2 \end{cases}$

18. $f(x) = \begin{cases} x^2 - 4, & x < 0 \\ 9 - \sqrt{x + 16}, & x \geq 0 \end{cases}$

19. $f(x) = \begin{cases} x^2 - 2x - 15, & x < -3 \\ 9 - x^2, & -3 < x < 5 \\ x^2 - 2x - 15, & x > 5 \end{cases}$

20. $f(x) = \begin{cases} \dfrac{\sqrt{x^2 + 1}}{x + 2}, & x < 0 \\ \dfrac{1 + x}{2 - 3x}, & x \geq 0 \end{cases}$

In Exercises 21–23, find the constant k that makes the function continuous at $x = a$.

21. $f(x) = \begin{cases} x^k, & x \leq 2 \\ 10 - x, & x > 2 \end{cases} \quad a = 2$

22. $f(x) = \begin{cases} k, & x \geq 1 \\ \dfrac{1}{\sqrt{kx^2 + k}}, & x < 1 \end{cases} \quad a = 1$

23. $f(x) = \begin{cases} (x - k)(x + k), & x \leq 2 \\ kx + 5, & x > 2 \end{cases} \quad a = 2$

24. The supply $S(p)$ of electric razors that manufacturers will supply weekly at price p is given by the function

$$S(p) = \begin{cases} \dfrac{1}{2}p & 0 \leq p < 20 \\ \dfrac{2}{3}p - 10 & 20 \leq p < 40 \\ \dfrac{4}{3}p - \dfrac{110}{3} & 40 \leq p \end{cases}$$

For what values of p is this function discontinuous?

25. A manufacturer of electric hedge trimmers offers reduced prices (that is, discounts) for volume purchases according to the following schedule.

Quantity Purchased	Price per Trimmer $p(q)$
$0 \leq q < 50$	$p(q) = 40$
$50 \leq q < 100$	$p(q) = 35$
$100 \leq q$	$p(q) = 30$

For what values of q is this price function p discontinuous?

26. Graph the total revenue function $R(q) = q \cdot p(q)$ where $p(q)$

is the price per trimmer in Exercise 25. Is the revenue function R discontinuous at $q = 50$? Why or why not?

27. A national income tax schedule provides the following taxes for single taxpayers, in part.

Income Range	Tax
$15,000–18,200	$2097 + 24% of amount over $15,000
$18,200–23,500	A + 28% of amount over $18,200

Find A if the tax T was a continuous function of income at level $x = \$18,200$.

28. A television salesman receives a monthly salary and commission payment $S(x)$, in dollars, according to the following schedule, where x represents the number of television sets sold:

$$S(x) = \begin{cases} 500 + 150x, & 0 \leq x \leq 5 \\ 1230 + 100(x - 5), & 5 < x \leq 10 \\ 1800 + 50(x - 10), & 10 < x. \end{cases}$$

Assuming the function S to be defined for all nonnegative real numbers x, find any numbers where S is discontinuous.

29. The function f defined by

$$f(x) = \begin{cases} ax^2 + 2, & 0 \leq x \leq 3 \\ 3x + 11, & x > 3 \end{cases}$$

is continuous at $x = 3$. Find a.

30. Extend the definition of the postage stamp function according to the following rule: postage on letters up to one ounce is 29 cents; for each full ounce, postage increases by 23 additional cents, up to, but not including, 11 ounces.
a. What is the domain of this function?
b. For what numbers does the limit at such numbers of this function fail to exist?
c. Call this function $p(x)$; find $\lim\limits_{x \to 7^-} p(x)$.
d. Find $\lim\limits_{x \to 7^+} p(x)$.

31. Paula wants to impress her younger sister by using the calculus to inform her that the price she must pay for a movie ticket will increase on her twelfth birthday. If the ticket prices are $2.50 for children under 12 years of age and $4.50 for those 12 and older, how can Paula use one-sided limits to explain this fact of life?

☑ **SOLUTIONS TO PRACTICE PROBLEMS 2.3**

1. $\lim\limits_{x \to 3^-} \dfrac{|x-3|}{x-3} = \lim\limits_{x \to 3^-} \left(\dfrac{3-x}{x-3} \right)$

$\qquad\qquad\qquad = \lim\limits_{x \to 3} (-1)$

$\qquad\qquad\qquad = -1.$

2. T is continuous at $x = 5000$ because

$$\lim_{x \to 5000^-} T(x) = \lim_{x \to 5000^-} (0)$$

$$= \lim_{x \to 5000^+} [0.02(x - 5000)]$$

$$= \lim_{x \to 5000^+} T(x).$$

But T is discontinuous at $x = 20{,}000$ because

$$\lim_{x \to 20{,}000^-} T(x) = \lim_{x \to 20{,}000^-} [0.02(x - 5000)]$$

$$= (0.02)(20{,}000 - 5000)$$

$$= 300$$

while

$$\lim_{x \to 20{,}000^+} T(x) = \lim_{x \to 20{,}000^+} [0.04(x - 10{,}000)]$$

$$= \lim_{x \to 20{,}000^+} (0.04)(10{,}000)$$

$$= 400$$

and, therefore, $\lim\limits_{x \to 20{,}000^-} T(x) \neq \lim\limits_{x \to 20{,}000^+} T(x).$

2.4 The Derivative

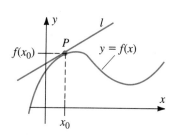

Figure 4.1 The slope of the line tangent to the graph of f at $P = (x_0, f(x_0))$ is the rate of change of f at $x = x_0$.

In Section 2.1 we saw that the *slope* of the line tangent to the graph of a function f at a point $(x_0, f(x_0))$ is the measure of the *rate of change* of the function f at $x = x_0$. (See Figure 4.1.) In most applications we will want to be able to find the rate of change of f at more than one number x_0, however. We therefore extend the procedure for finding the rate of change of f at a *single* point by developing a tool that can calculate rates of change at *many* different points. This tool is called the *derivative* of the function f.

In other words, the *derivative* of the function f will tell us the rate of change of f at *any* number x for which it is defined. Thus, the derivative of f is another *function*, which we denote by f' (read ''f prime'').

Figures 4.2 and 4.3 illustrate the basic idea that we have developed so far for the interpretation of the rate of change of f as the slope of the line tangent to its graph. For each number x_0, the derivative value $f'(x_0)$ is the *slope* of the line tangent to

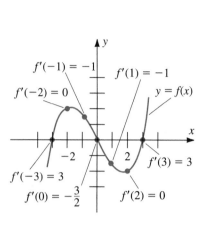

Figure 4.2 The derivative $f'(x_0)$ gives the slope of the graph of $y = f(x)$ at (x_0, y_0).

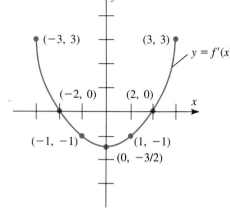

Figure 4.3 "Slope function" f' for f in Figure 4.2. Slopes for f are values of the function f'.

the graph of f at the point $(x_0, f(x_0))$. The graph of the derivative function f' can be sketched by estimating the values $f'(x_0)$ as slopes of tangents to the graph f (Figure 4.3).

Obviously, we need a more precise way to calculate values of the derivative function f'. This is found by recalling that the slope of the line tangent to the graph of the function f at the point where $x = x_0$ is given by the limit

$$m = \lim_{h \to 0} \frac{f(x_0 + h) - f(x_0)}{h}. \tag{1}$$

This is the value $f'(x_0)$ of the derivative function f' at the number $x = x_0$. We generalize this by defining the derivative $f'(x)$ at *any* number $x = x_0$ by equation (1).

Definition 4

The **derivative** of the function f with respect to x is the function f' whose value at x is

$$f'(x) = \lim_{h \to 0} \frac{f(x + h) - f(x)}{h}.$$

provided this limit exists.
The domain of f' is the set of all x for which this limit exists.

In Section 2.1 we determined that the slope of the line tangent to the graph of $f(x) = x^2$ at the point $P = (2, 4)$ was $m = 4$. In the notation of Definition 4 we would write this conclusion, "$f'(2) = 4$ if $f(x) = x^2$." The following example shows how to find the derivative of $f(x) = x^2$ for all x. (The process of finding a derivative is called differentiation.)

☐ **EXAMPLE 1**

Find the derivative of the function $f(x) = x^2$.

Strategy · · · · · · · **Solution**

If $f(x) = x^2$, then $f(x + h) = (x + h)^2$. Thus the definition of $f'(x)$ gives

Set up expression for $f'(x)$ using Definition 4.

$$f'(x) = \lim_{h \to 0} \frac{f(x + h) - f(x)}{h}$$

Substitute expressions for $f(x + h)$, $f(x)$, and simplify, using algebra.

$$= \lim_{h \to 0} \frac{(x + h)^2 - x^2}{h}$$

$$= \lim_{h \to 0} \frac{(x^2 + 2xh + h^2) - x^2}{h}$$

$$= \lim_{h \to 0} \frac{2xh + h^2}{h}$$

Factor h from terms of numerator and use $\dfrac{h}{h} = 1$, $h \neq 0$.

$$= \lim_{h \to 0} \left(\frac{h}{h}\right)(2x + h)$$

$$= \lim_{h \to 0} (2x + h)$$

Evaluate limit by letting h approach zero.

$$= 2x.$$

Thus $f'(x) = 2x$. In terms of the slope of the graph of $f(x) = x^2$ this means, for instance, that

$$\begin{array}{llll}
\text{if } x = -2, & m = f'(-2) = 2(-2) = -4 \\
\text{if } x = -1, & m = f'(-1) = 2(-1) = -2 \\
\text{if } x = 0, & m = f'(0) \;\;\; = 2(0) \;\;\;\; = \;\;\, 0 \\
\text{if } x = 1, & m = f'(1) \;\;\; = 2(1) \;\;\;\; = \;\;\, 2 \\
\text{if } x = 2, & m = f'(2) \;\;\; = 2(2) \;\;\;\; = \;\;\, 4
\end{array}$$

etc. (See Figure 4.4.)

☐ **EXAMPLE 2**

Find the derivative of the function $f(x) = \dfrac{1}{x}$.

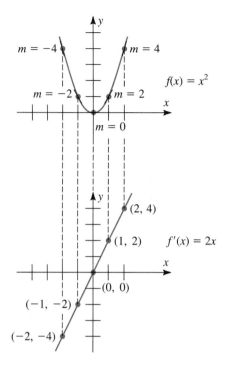

Figure 4.4 Graph of $f(x) = x^2$ (upper) and its "slope function" $f'(x) = 2x$ (lower).

Solution: Following the same steps as in Example 1, we find that

$$f'(x) = \lim_{h \to 0} \frac{f(x+h) - f(x)}{h}$$

$$= \lim_{h \to 0} \frac{\dfrac{1}{x+h} - \dfrac{1}{x}}{h}$$

$$= \lim_{h \to 0} \left[\frac{\dfrac{1}{x+h} - \dfrac{1}{x}}{h} \right] \left[\frac{x(x+h)}{x(x+h)} \right]$$

$$= \lim_{h \to 0} \left(\frac{1}{h} \right) \left[\frac{x - (x+h)}{x(x+h)} \right]$$

$$= \lim_{h \to 0} \left(\frac{h}{h} \right) \left[\frac{-1}{x(x+h)} \right]$$

$$= \lim_{h \to 0} \frac{-1}{x(x+h)}$$

$$= -\frac{1}{x^2}.$$

Thus $f'(x) = -\dfrac{1}{x^2}$. Note that neither $f(x)$ nor $f'(x)$ is defined if $x = 0$. Graphs of both functions appear in Figure 4.5.

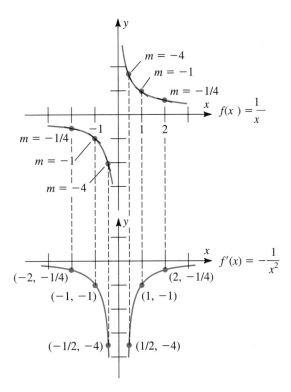

Figure 4.5 Graph of $f(x) = \dfrac{1}{x}$ (upper) and its "slope function" $f'(x) = -\dfrac{1}{x^2}$ (lower).

☐ **EXAMPLE 3**

Find the derivative of the function $f(x) = \sqrt{x}$. ($\sqrt{x} = x^{1/2}$).

Strategy · · · · · · ·

Form the "difference quotient"
$$\frac{f(x + h) - f(x)}{h}.$$

Use algebra to eliminate the factor h from the denominator, as in Section 2.2.

Solution

By Definition 4 the derivative is

$$f'(x) = \lim_{h \to 0} \frac{\sqrt{x + h} - \sqrt{x}}{h}$$

$$= \lim_{h \to 0} \frac{\sqrt{x + h} - \sqrt{x}}{h}\left(\frac{\sqrt{x + h} + \sqrt{x}}{\sqrt{x + h} + \sqrt{x}}\right)$$

$$= \lim_{h \to 0} \frac{(x + h) - x}{h(\sqrt{x + h} + \sqrt{x})}$$

$$= \lim_{h \to 0} \frac{h}{h(\sqrt{x + h} + \sqrt{x})}$$

Use $\dfrac{h}{h} = 1$.

$$= \lim_{h \to 0} \frac{1}{\sqrt{x + h} + \sqrt{x}}$$

Evaluate the limit as in Section 2.2.

$$= \frac{1}{2\sqrt{x}}.$$

Thus, for $f(x) = \sqrt{x}$, $f'(x) = \dfrac{1}{2\sqrt{x}}$. ∎

Other Notation for Derivatives

When a function is written in the form of an equation, $y = f(x)$, the notation $\dfrac{dy}{dx}$ is sometimes used to denote the derivative function. (This notation is due to the German mathematician Gottfried Leibniz.)

For example, if we consider the function $f(x) = \sqrt{x}$ as described simply by the equation $y = \sqrt{x}$, we could write either

$$f'(x) = \frac{1}{2\sqrt{x}}$$

or

$$\frac{dy}{dx} = \frac{1}{2\sqrt{x}}$$

to summarize the result of the calculation in Example 3.

Leibniz's notation is applied a bit more loosely to interpret the symbol "$\dfrac{d}{dx}$" as meaning "the derivative of." Thus, all of the following denote the derivative of the function $y = f(x)$:

$$f'(x), \quad \frac{dy}{dx}, \quad \frac{d}{dx}f(x) \quad \text{and} \quad \frac{df}{dx}.$$

Using this notation, we can write the results of Examples 1 and 2 as

(1) $\dfrac{d}{dx}(x^2) = 2x;$ or $\dfrac{dy}{dx} = 2x$ if $y = x^2$

(2) $\dfrac{d}{dx}\left(\dfrac{1}{x}\right) = -\dfrac{1}{x^2};$ or $\dfrac{dy}{dx} = -\dfrac{1}{x^2}$ if $y = \dfrac{1}{x}.$

Rules for Calculating Derivatives

Our next objective is to free ourselves from the tedium of using the formal definition in calculating the derivative of each function with which we intend to work. We do so by trying to determine derivatives for entire classes of functions of similar types.

The simplest functions are the constant functions, $f(x) \equiv c$. (The meaning of the symbol "$\equiv$" is that $f(x)$ equals c for every x.) Since the graph of any constant function is a horizontal line (with slope zero), the derivative of any constant function should be zero. This is our first rule.

Rule 1: If f is a constant function $f(x) \equiv c$, then $f'(x) \equiv 0$. That is

$$\frac{d}{dx}(c) \equiv 0.$$

The proof of this is almost as easy as the intuition. Since $f(x) = c$ for all x, we have from the definition of the derivative that, for any x,

$$f'(x) = \lim_{h \to 0} \frac{f(x + h) - f(x)}{h} = \lim_{h \to 0} \frac{c - c}{h}$$

$$= \lim_{h \to 0} \left(\frac{0}{h} \right)$$

$$= \lim_{h \to 0} (0)$$

$$= 0.$$

Again, drawing on the fact that $f'(x)$ is the slope of the graph of $y = f(x)$, we would expect the derivative of a linear function $f(x) = mx + b$ to be its slope, $f'(x) = m$. This is our next rule.

Rule 2: If $f(x) = mx + b$, then $f'(x) \equiv m$. That is, for all x

$$\frac{d}{dx}(mx + b) \equiv m.$$

☐ **EXAMPLE 4**

Using Rule 2, we find that

$$\frac{d}{dx}(3x + 6) = 3$$

$$\frac{d}{dx}(4 - 2x) = -2,$$

etc.

■

The proof of Rule 2 is straightforward. With $f(x) = mx + b$ the definition of $f'(x)$ gives

$$f'(x) = \lim_{h \to 0} \frac{f(x + h) - f(x)}{h}$$

$$= \lim_{h \to 0} \frac{[m(x + h) + b] - [mx + b]}{h}$$

$$= \lim_{h \to 0} \frac{mx + mh + b - mx - b}{h}$$

$$= \lim_{h \to 0} m\left(\frac{h}{h}\right) = \lim_{h \to 0} m = m$$

as required.

Powers of x

From Example 1, Example 2, Rule 2 (with $m = 1$, $b = 0$), and Exercises 4 and 5 in this section the following derivatives of powers of x are obtained:

If $f(x) = x^{-1}$, $f'(x) = -x^{-2}$, or $\dfrac{d}{dx}(x^{-1}) = -x^{-2}$.

If $f(x) = x$, $f'(x) = 1 \ (= x^0)$, or $\dfrac{d}{dx}(x) = 1$.

If $f(x) = x^2$, $f'(x) = 2x$, or $\dfrac{d}{dx}(x^2) = 2x$.

If $f(x) = x^3$, $f'(x) = 3x^2$, or $\dfrac{d}{dx}(x^3) = 3x^2$.

If $f(x) = x^4$, $f'(x) = 4x^3$, or $\dfrac{d}{dx}(x^4) = 4x^3$.

Indeed, this pattern holds for all powers of x, as the following rule states.

Rule 3 (Power Rule): Let n be any real number with $n \neq 0$.
If $f(x) = x^n$, then $f'(x) = nx^{n-1}$.
That is

$$\frac{d}{dx}(x^n) = nx^{n-1}. \qquad \text{(provided } x \neq 0 \text{ if } n < 0)$$

A proof of the Power Rule for the case where n is a positive integer is outlined in Exercise Set 2.4. Ideas developed later in the text will allow us to prove this rule for all real powers of x.

REMARK: Up to this point, we have defined power functions, $f(x) = x^n$, only for rational exponents n. Later in the text we shall extend this definition to include irrational exponents as well, for which the Power Rule is also valid.

According to the Power Rule, we have the following examples:

$$\frac{d}{dx}(x^7) = 7x^6 \qquad (n = 7)$$

$$\frac{d}{dx}(x^{-2}) = -2x^{-3} \qquad (n = -2)$$

$$\frac{d}{dx}(x^{1/2}) = \frac{1}{2}x^{-1/2} \qquad \left(n = \frac{1}{2}\right).$$

☐ **EXAMPLE 5**

Find an equation for the line tangent to the graph of $f(x) = \sqrt[3]{x}$ at the point where $x = 8$.

Solution: Since $\sqrt[3]{x}$ means $x^{1/3}$, we have $f'(x) = \frac{1}{3}x^{-2/3}$ by the power rule. The slope of the tangent is therefore

$$m = f'(8) = \frac{1}{3}(8^{-2/3}) = \frac{1}{3(8^{2/3})} = \frac{1}{3(8^{1/3})^2} = \frac{1}{3 \cdot 2^2} = \frac{1}{12}.$$

Since $(8, f(8)) = (8, \sqrt[3]{8}) = (8, 2)$, the line has equation

$$y - 2 = \frac{1}{12}(x - 8), \quad \text{or} \quad 12y - x = 16.$$

■

Properties of the Derivative

Two important properties of the derivative enable us to use Rules 1 to 3 to differentiate polynomials. In stating them, we use the terminology "f is differentiable on an interval" to mean that $f'(x)$ exists for each x in that interval.

Theorem 2
Properties of the Derivative

Let the functions f and g be differentiable on an interval I, and let c be a constant. Then, on I

(i) the function $h = f + g$ is differentiable, and

$$h'(x) = f'(x) + g'(x).$$

That is,

$$\frac{d}{dx}(f + g) = \frac{df}{dx} + \frac{dg}{dx}. \tag{2}$$

(ii) the function $r = cf$ is differentiable, and

$$r'(x) = cf'(x).$$

That is,

$$\frac{d}{dx}(cf) = c\frac{df}{dx}. \tag{3}$$

Here are some examples of how these rules are used.

☐ **EXAMPLE 6**

Find $f'(x)$ for $f(x) = x^3 + x^{2/3}$.

Solution: Using equation (2), we find

$$\frac{d}{dx}(x^3 + x^{2/3}) = \frac{d}{dx}(x^3) + \frac{d}{dx}(x^{2/3})$$

$$= 3x^2 + \frac{2}{3}x^{-1/3}.$$

Thus, $f'(x) = 3x^2 + \frac{2}{3}x^{-1/3}$.   ■

☐ **EXAMPLE 7**

For $y = 3x^5$ find $\frac{dy}{dx}$.

Solution: By equation (3) we obtain

$$\frac{d}{dx}(3x^5) = 3\frac{d}{dx}(x^5) = 3(5x^4) = 15x^4.$$

Thus, $\frac{dy}{dx} = 15x^4$.   ■

☐ **EXAMPLE 8**

Find $f'(x)$ for $f(x) = 6x^3 - 2x^{-3/4} + 8$.

Strategy · · · · · · ·   **Solution**

Apply equation (2).
$$\frac{d}{dx}(6x^3 - 2x^{-3/4} + 8) = \frac{d}{dx}(6x^3) + \frac{d}{dx}(-2x^{-3/4}) + \frac{d}{dx}(8)$$

Apply equation (3).
$$= 6 \cdot \frac{d}{dx}(x^3) + (-2)\frac{d}{dx}(x^{-3/4}) + \frac{d}{dx}(8)$$

Apply Rules 1 and 3.
$$= 6(3x^2) + (-2)\left(-\frac{3}{4}x^{-7/4}\right) + 0.$$

Simplify.
Thus, $f'(x) = 18x^2 + \frac{3}{2}x^{-7/4}.$ ∎

□ **EXAMPLE 9**

Here are two additional examples whose solutions are more typical of how you will actually apply these rules and theorems:

(i) $\dfrac{d}{dx}[3x^5 - 7x^2 + x^{-2}] = 3(5x^4) - 7(2x) + (-2x^{-3})$

$$= 15x^4 - 14x - 2x^{-3}.$$

(ii) $\dfrac{d}{dx}[4x^{5/3} + 6x^{-1/4} + 5] = 4\left(\frac{5}{3}x^{2/3}\right) + 6\left(-\frac{1}{4}x^{-5/4}\right) + 0$

$$= \frac{20}{3}x^{2/3} - \frac{3}{2}x^{-5/4}.$$ ∎

Proof of Theorem 2:   The first part of Theorem 2 is proved by using the basic definition of the derivative and the first part of Theorem 1 (the limit of a sum is the sum of the limits):

$$\frac{d}{dx}(f + g)(x) = \lim_{h \to 0} \frac{(f + g)(x + h) - (f + g)(x)}{h}$$

$$= \lim_{h \to 0} \frac{[f(x + h) + g(x + h)] - [f(x) + g(x)]}{h}$$

$$= \lim_{h \to 0} \frac{[f(x + h) - f(x)] + [g(x + h) - g(x)]}{h}$$

$$= \lim_{h \to 0} \left\{\frac{f(x + h) - f(x)}{h} + \frac{g(x + h) - g(x)}{h}\right\}$$

$$= \lim_{h \to 0} \frac{f(x + h) - f(x)}{h} + \lim_{h \to 0} \frac{g(x + h) - g(x)}{h}$$

$$= f'(x) + g'(x).$$

The second part of Theorem 2 is proved in a similar way and is left for you as Exercise 44.   □

☑ **PRACTICE PROBLEMS 2.4**

1. Find $f'(x)$ for $f(x) = \dfrac{1}{x+4}$.

2. Find an equation for the line tangent to the graph of $f(x) = 3x^2 - 6$ at the point $(2, 6)$.

Exercise Set 2.4

In Exercises 1–8, use the basic definition of the derivative to find $f'(x)$.

1. $f(x) = 2x + 5$

2. $f(x) = 3 - x$

3. $f(x) = x^2 + 4$

4. $f(x) = x^3 + 7$

5. $f(x) = x^4$

6. $f(x) = \sqrt{x+2}$

7. $f(x) = \dfrac{2}{x+3}$

8. $f(x) = \dfrac{1}{\sqrt{x+1}}$

In Exercises 9–26, use Rules 1 to 3 and properties of the derivative to find $f'(x)$ or $\dfrac{dy}{dx}$.

9. $f(x) = 3x^2 + 4x + 2$

10. $y = 4x^3 - x + 5$

11. $y = 3x^4 - 4x + 2$

12. $f(x) = 6 - 3x + 4x^2 + x^5$

13. $f(x) = x^3 - x^5$

14. $f(x) = x^2 + x^{-2} + 7x^{-1}$

15. $f(x) = 3x^4 - 6x - 1$

16. $y = 4x^{-2} - 6x^3 + \dfrac{4}{x}$

17. $y = 2x^5 - 3x^{-2}$

18. $f(x) = 4 + \sqrt{x}$

19. $f(x) = 2x^{2/3} + 3x^{5/3}$

20. $y = 3\sqrt{x} - 5x^{-3/2}$

21. $y = 9x^{-2} + 3\sqrt{x} - 6$

22. $f(x) = 9 - 4x^{-2} + 10x^{2/3}$

23. $y = 5x^9 - 10\sqrt{x} + 3x^{11/2}$

24. $f(x) = (x - 3)^2$ (*Hint:* square first)

25. $f(x) = 4x^{-2/3} - 7x^{-1/4}$

26. $f(x) = 6 + 3\sqrt{x} - 5x^{-4/3}$

In Exercises 37–32, find $f'(a)$ for the given function $f(x)$ and number $x = a$.

27. $f(x) = 4x^3 - 2x^2$, $a = 2$

28. $f(x) = x^3 - \sqrt{x}$, $a = 4$

29. $f(x) = 3x^4 - 6x^2 + 4x + 9$, $a = -3$

30. $f(x) = 4x^3 - 3x^4$, $a = -1$

31. $f(x) = 7 - 6\sqrt{x} + 5x^{2/3}$, $a = 8$

32. $f(x) = 4x^3 + 5x^{-2}$, $a = -2$

33. Find an equation for the line tangent to the graph of $f(x) = 4x^2 - 2x + 1$ at the point $(1, 3)$.

34. Find an equation for the line tangent to the graph of $y = \sqrt{x}$ at the point $(4, 2)$.

35. Find the slope of the graph of $f(x) = x^{1/2} - x^{-1/2}$ at the point $\left(4, \dfrac{3}{2}\right)$.

36. Find the slope of the graph of $y = 3x^4 - 4x^3$ at the point $(1, -1)$.

37. Find a if the line tangent to the graph of $f(x) = x^2 + ax - 6$ at the point where $x = 2$ has slope $m = 9$.

38. Find b if the graph of $y = \dfrac{b}{x^2}$ has tangent $4y - bx - 21 = 0$ when $x = -2$.

39. Find the number a so that the line tangent to the graph of $f(x) = \sqrt{x} + 5$ has slope $\dfrac{1}{4}$ at $x = a$.

40. The graphs of the functions $f(x) = A + x - x^2$ and $g(x) = 10 - 3x$ are tangent at a common point.
   a. Find the point of tangency.
   b. Find A.

41. A company's profit function, at production level x units per week, is given by $P(x) = 32x - 2x^2 - 120$.
   a. For which numbers x is $P(x)$ positive?
   b. For which numbers x is profit increasing as production increases?

c. What is the largest possible profit? At what level of production?

d. How does the interpretation of $P'(x)$ as the rate of change in profit help answer these questions?

42. Growth of a particular species of plant occurs with precipitation according to the function $P(x) = a\sqrt{x}$ where a is a constant, x is the amount of precipitation per unit time, and $P(x)$ is the biomass of the plant. (See Section 2.1.)

a. Find the derivative function, $P'(x)$.

b. Find the value $P'(4)$ for the derivative.

c. Find an equation for the line tangent to the graph of $P(x)$ at the point where $x = 4$.

d. What does the answer to part b tell you about the rate at which biomass increases with increasing precipitation?

43. A Type III survival curve (see Section 2.1) is represented by the graph of the function $f(t) = t^{-3/2}$ for $t > 0$.

a. Find the derivative, $f'(t)$.

b. Find the value $f'(2)$ of the derivative.

c. Find an equation for the line tangent to the survival curve at the point where $t = 2$.

44. Prove statement (ii) of Theorem 2.

45. Prove the Power Rule as follows:

a. For $f(x) = x^n$, n a positive integer, show that

$$f'(x) = \lim_{h \to 0} \frac{(x + h)^n - x^n}{h}.$$

b. Use the Binomial Theorem

$$(a + b)^n = a^n + na^{n-1}b + \cdots + nab^{n-1} + b^n$$

to write

$$(x + h)^n = x^n + nx^{n-1}h + \cdots + nxh^{n-1} + h^n.$$

c. Use part b to show that $f'(x)$ in part a can be written

$$f'(x) = \lim_{h \to 0} \{nx^{n-1} + \text{terms involving factors of } h\}.$$

d. Conclude that $f'(x) = nx^{n-1}$.

☑ **SOLUTIONS TO PRACTICE PROBLEMS 2.4**

1. For $f(x) = \dfrac{1}{x + 4}$,

$$f'(x) = \lim_{h \to 0} \frac{1}{h} \left\{ \frac{1}{(x + h) + 4} - \frac{1}{x + 4} \right\}$$

$$= \lim_{h \to 0} \frac{1}{h} \left\{ \frac{x + 4 - (x + h + 4)}{(x + h + 4)(x + 4)} \right\}$$

$$= \lim_{h \to 0} \frac{1}{h} \left\{ \frac{-h}{(x + h + 4)(x + 4)} \right\}$$

$$= \frac{-1}{(x + 4)^2}.$$

2. The derivative of $f(x) = 3x^2 - 6$ is

$$f'(x) = \lim_{h \to 0} \frac{[3(x + h)^2 - 6] - (3x^2 - 6)}{h}$$

$$= \lim_{h \to 0} \frac{(3x^2 + 6xh + 3h^2 - 6) - (3x^2 - 6)}{h}$$

$$= \lim_{h \to 0} \frac{6xh + 3h^2}{h}$$

$$= \lim_{h \to 0} (6x + 3h)$$

$$= 6x.$$

Thus, the *slope* of the line tangent to the graph of f at $x_0 = 2$ is $f'(2) = 6(2) = 12$, and an equation for this line is

$$y - 6 = 12(x - 2)$$

or

$$y = 12x - 18.$$

2.5 Applications of the Derivative: Position and Velocity

The derivative has an interpretation as the *velocity* of a moving object. This interpretation gives insight into the derivative as the rate of change of a function, and it also provides a tool for solving certain applied problems about objects in motion.

Imagine an object moving along a line, such as an automobile on a highway or a jogger on a footpath. For a given interval of time the *velocity* of the object is defined to be the ratio

$$\text{velocity} = \frac{\text{change in distance}}{\text{change in time}}. \tag{1}$$

Of course, what is meant by equation (1) is really an *average* velocity for the time interval in question. For example, if a jogger travels 6 miles in 45 minutes, the average velocity for this period is

$$\text{velocity} = \frac{6 \text{ miles}}{3/4 \text{ hour}} = 8 \text{ miles/hour}$$

However, at various times during the run the jogger will quite likely have been moving either faster or slower than 8 miles/hour.

There is a special setting in which we can use the theory of the derivative to define the velocity of an object *at each instant,* rather than having to settle for the average velocity over a time interval. First, the motion must be along a straight line (we call this rectilinear motion), rather than along a general curve. Second, we must have available a **position function,** usually denoted by s, giving the location $s(t)$ of the object along the line at each time t. (See Figure 5.1.)

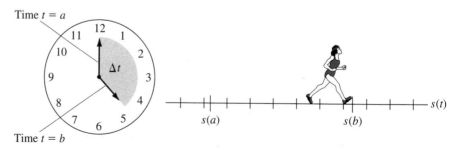

Figure 5.1 A position function $s(t)$ gives the location of an object along a line at time t.

With this notation, the *average* velocity of an object whose position is given by the function s between times $t = t_1$ and $t = t_2$ is

$$\bar{v} = \frac{s(t_2) - s(t_1)}{t_2 - t_1} \tag{2}$$

☐ EXAMPLE 1

A group of physics students conducts an experiment by firing a water-propelled plastic rocket upward from ground level, recording its flight on a videotape that can later by analyzed to determine the rocket's height at various elapsed times. After having completed the experiment, the students report the following data:

t = elapsed time 0	0	1/2	1	3/2	2	5/2	3
s = height	0	20	32	36	32	20	0

Find the average velocity for the rocket on each of the time intervals of length $\frac{1}{2}$ second, beginning at time $t = 0$.

Solution Using equation (2) and these data, we find these values.

(a) On the interval $\left[0, \frac{1}{2}\right]$, the average velocity is

$$\bar{v} = \frac{s\left(\frac{1}{2}\right) - s(0)}{\frac{1}{2} - 0} = \frac{20 - 0}{\frac{1}{2}} = 40 \text{ feet per second.}$$

(b) On the interval $\left[\frac{1}{2}, 1\right]$, the average velocity is

$$\bar{v} = \frac{s(1) - s\left(\frac{1}{2}\right)}{1 - \frac{1}{2}} = \frac{32 - 20}{\frac{1}{2}} = 24 \text{ feet per second.}$$

(c) Similarly, on the remaining intervals, the average velocities are as follows:

Interval	Average Velocity (feet per second)
$\left[1, \frac{3}{2}\right]$	8
$\left[\frac{3}{2}, 2\right]$	-8
$\left[2, \frac{5}{2}\right]$	-24
$\left[\frac{5}{2}, 3\right]$	-40

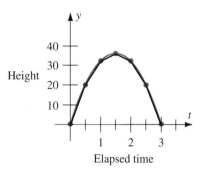

Figure 5.2 Graph of height as a function of time.

Figure 5.2 shows the points (t, s) for the given data, with height as a function of time. The slopes of the line segments connecting the successive points are just the average velocities found above, because equation (2) is precisely the definition of the slope of the line through the points $(t_1, s(t_1))$ and $(t_2, s(t_2))$. The *curve* drawn through these points is the graph of the function

$$s(t) = 48t - 16t^2$$

to which these data correspond. ∎

To calculate *instantaneous* velocity (velocity at a given instant, not over an interval of time) we designate the desired time as t_0, and consider a small interval of time beginning at t_0: $[t_0, t_0 + h]$ where $h > 0$. According to equation (2), the *average* velocity of an object whose position is $s(t)$, over the time interval $[t_0, t_0 + h]$, is

$$\bar{v} = \frac{s(t_0 + h) - s(t_0)}{(t_0 + h) - t_0} = \frac{s(t_0 + h) - s(t_0)}{h}.$$

We now argue that, as $h \to 0$, the average velocity corresponding to the (shrinking) time interval from t_0 to $t_0 + h$ becomes an increasingly accurate approximation to the velocity at the instant $t = t_0$. For this reason we *define* the velocity $v(t_0)$ to be this limit. That is, we define the velocity $v(t_0)$ as

$$v(t_0) = \lim_{h \to 0} \frac{s(t_0 + h) - s(t_0)}{h} \qquad (3)$$

whenever this limit exists. Comparing equation (3) with the definition of the derivative of a function, you can see that we have simply defined velocity as the derivative of the position function.

Definition 5

If s is a differentiable function giving the position at time t of an object moving along a line, then the velocity $v(t)$ at time t is the derivative

$$v(t) = s'(t).$$

That is

$$v(t) = \frac{d}{dt} s(t).$$

☐ **EXAMPLE 2**

Starting at time $t = 0$, a particle moves along a line so that its position after t seconds is $s(t) = t^2 - 6t + 8$. The unit of measurement along the line is feet.

(a) What is its velocity at time t?
(b) When is its velocity zero?

Strategy · · · · · · · ·

Use equation for $v(t)$ to find the velocity.

Solution

Since the position function is

$$s(t) = t^2 - 6t + 8$$

the velocity function is

$$v(t) = s'(t)$$
$$= 2t - 6 \text{ feet per second.}$$

Set $v(t) = 0$ and solve to find time when velocity equals zero.

Setting the velocity function equal to zero gives

$$v(t) = 2t - 6 = 0$$
$$2t = 6$$
$$t = 3 \text{ seconds.} \qquad \blacksquare$$

Figure 5.3 is the graph of the position function in Example 2. Notice that the distance $s(t)$ decreases from time $t = 0$ until time $t = 3$, which is reflected in the sign of the velocity function $v(t) = 2t - 6$: for $0 \le t \le 3$, $-6 \le 2t - 6 \le 0$ so $v(t) \le 0$. After $t = 3$ seconds the position function is increasing, and this corresponds to positive velocity: $t > 3$ implies $2t - 6 > 0$, so $v(t) > 0$. Figure 5.4 shows another way of thinking about motion along a line and its relation to velocity. The point here is that *velocity indicates both a speed and a direction*. The *sign* of $v(t)$ determines the direction in which the object is moving.

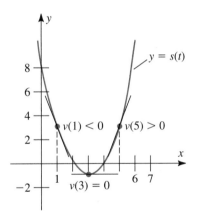

Figure 5.3 Position function $s(t) = t^2 - 6t + 8$ and several values of velocity $v(t) = s'(t)$.

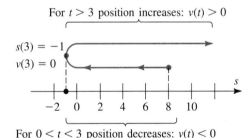

Figure 5.4 Position of an object at various times with s as in Figure 5.3.

☐ **EXAMPLE 3**

When an object is launched vertically upward from ground level with an initial velocity of 72 feet per second, its location after t seconds will be

$$s(t) = 72t - 16t^2$$

feet above ground level.

(a) When does the object stop rising?
(b) What is its maximum height?

Strategy · · · · · · · ·

Solution

The velocity function is

Find $v(t)$.

$$v(t) = \frac{d}{dt}(72t - 16t^2)$$

$$= 72 - 32t.$$

Set $v(t_0) = 0$ and solve to find the *time* when object stops rising.

The object stops rising when $v(t_0) = 0$. That is, when

$$72 - 32t_0 = 0$$

or

$$t_0 = \frac{72}{32} = \frac{9}{4} \text{ seconds.}$$

At this time its height is

Find $s(t_0)$, the height at this time.

$$s(t_0) = 72\left(\frac{9}{4}\right) - 16\left(\frac{9}{4}\right)^2$$

$$= 81 \text{ feet.}$$

(See Figure 5.5.)   ■

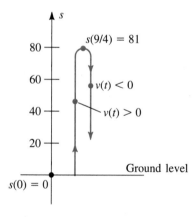

Figure 5.5 Object in Example 3.

☐ EXAMPLE 4

A diver springs from a board located over a swimming pool. If the height of the diver above the water level t seconds after leaving the board is given by the position function

$$s(t) = 24 + 32t - 16t^2.$$

Find the following:

(a) The height of the board above water level.
(b) The diver's velocity at time t.
(c) When the velocity equals zero.
(d) The highest point in the diver.
(e) The velocity with which the diver hits the water.

Strategy · · · · · · · ·

(a) Height of board is $s(0)$.

Solution

(a) The board is located at the diver's rest position

$$s(0) = 24 + 32(0) - 16(0)^2 = 24$$

feet above the water.

(b) $v(t) = s'(t)$.

(b) The diver's velocity at time t is

$$v(t) = s'(t) = 32 - 32t.$$

(c) Solve $v(t) = 0$.

(c) Setting $v(t) = 0$ gives

$$32 - 32t = 0 \quad \text{or} \quad t = 1 \text{ (second)}.$$

(d) Find $s(t)$ when $v(t) = 0$.

(d) The highest point in the dive occurs when $v(t) = 0$, or after $t = 1$ second. It is

$$s(1) = 24 + 32(1) - 16(1)^2 = 40 \text{ feet}.$$

(e) Find time when $s(t) = 0$; then find velocity.

(e) The diver hits the water when $s(t) = 0$, or

$$24 + 32t - 16t^2 = 0.$$

The quadratic equation gives these times as:

$$t = \frac{-32 \pm \sqrt{(32)^2 - 4(-16)(24)}}{2(-16)}$$

$$= 1 \pm \frac{\sqrt{10}}{2}.$$

The time $t_1 = 1 - \dfrac{\sqrt{10}}{2}$ is negative, and therefore meaningless in this example.

The diver therefore hits the water after $t_2 = 1 + \dfrac{\sqrt{10}}{2} \approx 2.58$ seconds, at a velocity of

$$v\left(1 + \frac{\sqrt{10}}{2}\right) = 32 - 32\left(1 + \frac{\sqrt{10}}{2}\right)$$

$$= -16\sqrt{10}$$

$$\approx -50.6 \text{ feet per second}.$$

Note that the sign of this velocity is negative, indicating that the direction is downward. (See Figure 5.6.) ∎

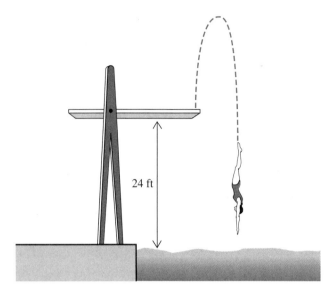

24 ft

Figure 5.6 Diver hits water with negative velocity, 40 feet below maximum height of dive.

☑ **PRACTICE PROBLEMS 2.5**

1. A particle moves along a line so that at time t its location is $s(t) = t^3 + 3t^2 - 18t + 4$. Find
   a. $v(0)$.
   b. $v(2)$.
2. Assuming that the particle in Problem 1 begins its motion when $t = 0$, when does it change direction?

Exercise Set 2.5

In Exercises 1–6, find the average velocity for a particle moving with position function $s(t)$ from time t_1 to time t_2.

1. $s(t) = 7 + 3t^2$, $t_1 = 0$, $t_2 = 3$

2. $s(t) = t^2 - 2t + 5$, $t_1 = 1$, $t_2 = 3$

3. $s(t) = \dfrac{10t}{1 + t^2}$, $t_1 = 0$, $t_2 = 3$

4. $s(t) = 50 - \dfrac{3\sqrt{t}}{t + 5}$, $t_1 = 1$, $t_2 = 9$

5. $s(t) = 40 + 64t - 3t^2$, $t_1 = 1$, $t_2 = 2$

6. $s(t) = 64 + 24t - 8t^2$, $t_1 = 1$, $t_2 = 3$

In Exercises 7–16, find the velocity function for the given position function.

7. $s(t) = t^2 + 2t - 6$

8. $s(t) = 9 - t^3$

9. $s(t) = t^3 - 5t^2 + 3t - 6$

10. $s(t) = 2t^4 - 8t^2 + 35$

11. $s(t) = 3\sqrt{t} + 5t^{3/2}$

12. $s(t) = t^{2/3} + 6t^{5/2}$

13. $s(t) = 2\sqrt{t} + 5t^{-2/3}$

14. $s(t) = t(t - 1)(t + 2)$

15. $s(t) = \dfrac{(t + 6)(t - 2)}{\sqrt{t}}$

16. $s(t) = \dfrac{t^2 + 9t + 20}{t + 4}$

17. An object moves along a line so that its position at time t is $s(t) = (t^2 + 2)(t + 1)$ units. Find its velocity at time $t = 3$.

18. A particle moves along a line so that after t seconds its position is $s(t) = 6 + 5t - t^2$. Find its position when its velocity equals zero.

19. A particle moves along the number line so that at time $t \geq 0$ its position is $s(t) = 6t - t^2$.
    a. What is its initial velocity, $v(0)$?
    b. When does it change direction?
    c. How fast is it moving when it crosses the origin the second time?

20. The physics students repeat their experiment, this time setting the rocket controls so as to launch the rocket upward with an initial velocity of 32 feet per second. Thus, after t seconds its height is $s(t) = 32t - 16t^2$ feet.

a. What is its velocity at time t?
b. At what time does it reach its maximum height?
c. What is its maximum height?
d. How fast is it moving when it strikes the ground?

21. Carol, one of the physics students in Example 1, conducts another experiment, dropping a water balloon from her dormitory window. Her roommate, waiting below, determines that the balloon strikes the ground with velocity -96 feet per second.
    a. From what height did Carol drop the balloon?
    b. How long did it fall?

22. A flare is launched vertically from a tower 256 feet above ground level with an initial velocity of $v_0 = 256$ feet per second. Its position function, as height above the ground after t seconds, is therefore $s(t) = 100 + 256t - 16t^2$.
    a. When does it reach its maximum height?
    b. What is its maximum height?

23. Consider the particle in Exercise 18. Find its maximum distance from position $s = 0$ in the time interval $[0, 6]$.

☑ **SOLUTIONS TO PRACTICE PROBLEMS 2.5**

1. For the position function $s(t) = t^3 + 3t^2 - 18t + 4$ the velocity function is

$$v(t) = s'(t) = 3t^2 + 6t - 18.$$

Thus,
   a. $v(0) = 3(0)^2 + 6(0) - 18 = -18$.
   b. $v(2) = 3 \cdot 2^2 + 6 \cdot 2 - 18 = 6$.
2. The velocity function $v(t) = 3t^2 + 6t - 18$ is zero when (according to the quadratic formula)

$$t = \frac{-6 \pm \sqrt{6^2 - 4(3)(-18)}}{2 \cdot 3}$$

$$= -1 \pm \frac{1}{6}\sqrt{252}$$

$$= -1 \pm \sqrt{7}.$$

Since we require $t > 0$, the velocity changes sign (and, therefore, the particle changes direction) only at the time $t = -1 + \sqrt{7} \approx 1.6458$.

2.6 Business Applications of the Derivative

This brief section shows how the derivative can be used to calculate the *rate* at which a business' costs, revenues, and profits will change with changes in the production level of certain products. While not all readers may be interested in business applications, these topics apply the same idea involved with the interpretation of the derivative as the slope of a tangent or the velocity of a particle: If the ratio

$$\frac{f(x_0 + h) - f(x_0)}{h}$$

gives the *average change* in values of a function between x_0 and $x_0 + h$, then the derivative

$$f'(x_0) = \lim_{h \to 0} \frac{f(x_0 + h) - f(x_0)}{h}$$

gives the *rate of change* of the function f, with respect to change in x, at $x = x_0$.

Marginal Cost

Let $C(x)$ be a manufacturer's total cost in producing x items per unit time (such as, say, per week). Then the change in total cost between production level x_0 and production level $x_0 + h$ is $C(x_0 + h) - C(x_0)$. Thus the ratio

$$\frac{C(x_0 + h) - C(x_0)}{h} \qquad \text{(average rate of change of cost)}$$

is the average rate of change of total cost between production levels x_0 and $x_0 + h$. Letting h approach zero, and assuming C to be a differentiable function, we conclude that the derivative

$$MC(x_0) = C'(x_0) = \lim_{h \to 0} \frac{C(x_0 + h) - C(x_0)}{h} \qquad \text{(marginal cost)}$$

is the rate at which total cost will change with change in x at production level x_0. The derivative C' is called the **marginal cost** function associated with the total cost function C.

When the production level x is restricted to integer values only (such as 2 cars or 3 cars, but not 2.7 cars), economists use the term "marginal cost at production level x_0" to mean the change in total cost caused by an increase in production of one unit to level $x_0 + 1$. For a differentiable cost function C this is not quite the same as the marginal cost $C'(x_0)$, although the approximation is usually quite close. For the purposes of this section we will work exclusively with differentiable cost functions and marginal cost as defined by the derivative C'.

☐ **EXAMPLE 1**

A manufacturer of billfolds determines that the total cost of producing x billfolds per week is

$$C(x) = 40 + 5x + \frac{1}{4}x^2. \qquad \text{(See Figure 6.1.)}$$

In this case the manufacturer's marginal cost function is

$$MC(x) = C'(x) = 5 + \frac{1}{2}x. \qquad \text{(See Figure 6.2.)}$$

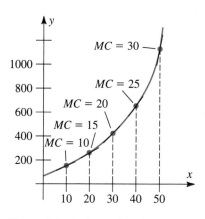

Figure 6.1 Total cost function
$C(x) = 40 + 5x + \frac{1}{4}x^2$ and
various marginal costs (slopes).

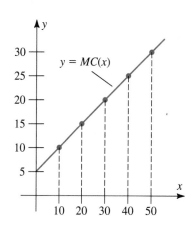

Figure 6.2 Marginal cost function
$MC(x) = C'(x) = 5 + \frac{1}{2}x$ for $y = C(x)$ in Figure 6.1.

Thus at production level $x_0 = 10$ billfolds per week the marginal cost $C'(10) = 10$ means that total cost will increase at a rate of \$10 per additional billfold. Compare this with production level $x_1 = 40$ billfolds per week, where total cost will increase at a rate of $C'(40) = 25$ dollars per additional billfold. ∎

Marginal Revenue

If $R(x)$ represents the total revenue received by a merchant for the sale of x items in a unit of time, then the quotient

$$\frac{R(x_0 + h) - R(x_0)}{h} \quad \text{(average rate of change of revenue)}$$

gives the average rate of change of total revenues between sales levels $x = x_0$ and $x = x_0 + h$. If we assume R to be differentiable and let the change in sales level h approach zero, we obtain the derivative

$$MR(x_0) = R'(x_0) = \lim_{h \to 0} \frac{R(x_0 + h) - R(x_0)}{h} \quad \text{(marginal revenue)}$$

as the rate at which total revenue will change with change in x at sales level x_0. As in the case of marginal cost, we refer to this rate of change of revenue as the **marginal revenue function.** The value $MR(x_0) = R'(x_0)$ provides a close approximation to the increase (or decrease) in total revenue resulting from the sale of one additional item at sales level x_0.

Revenue and Demand

When the number of items that a particular merchant or company sells in a unit of time is small relative to the total consumer demand, the selling price per item is often a fixed price p regardless of the number x of items sold. In this case the total revenue function is simply

$$R(x) = px$$

and the marginal revenue function is just

$$MR(x) = R'(x) = p$$

the selling price. However, when a company's position in a market approaches a monopoly, the selling price p and sales level x are often related to each other via a *demand* equation. Among the simplest of these is the linear demand equation of the form $p(x) = a - bx$. The next example shows how in such cases an increase in sales volume can actually correspond to a decrease in total revenue.

☐ EXAMPLE 2

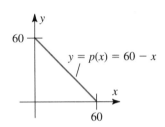

Figure 6.3 Demand curve
$p(x) = 60 - x$.

Market research by the manufacturer in Example 1 shows that the selling price p and expected weekly sales levels x for billfolds are related by the demand equation

$$p(x) = 60 - x. \quad \text{(See Figure 6.3.)}$$

Thus total revenue from the sale of x billfolds per week will be

$$\begin{aligned} R(x) &= xp(x) \\ &= x(60 - x) \\ &= 60x - x^2 \text{ dollars.} \end{aligned}$$

In this case the marginal revenue function is

$$MR(x) = R'(x) = 60 - 2x$$

dollars per billfold at sales level x. Thus,

(a) at sales level $x = 10$ the marginal revenue is $MR(10) = 60 - 2(10) = 40$ dollars per billfold. This means that the additional revenue resulting from the sale of the eleventh billfold per week will be *approximately* \$40. Note that we can use the expression for $R(x)$ to calculate the *actual* additional revenue as

$$\begin{aligned} R(11) - R(10) &= [60(11) - 11^2] - [60(10) - 10^2] \\ &= 39 \text{ dollars.} \end{aligned}$$

(b) At sales level $x = 30$ we have $MR(30) = 60 - 2(30) = 0$. This means that the additional revenue resulting from the sale of the 31st billfold per week will be *approximately* zero. The *actual* additional revenue, according to the equation $R(x) = 60x - x^2$, will be

$$\begin{aligned} R(31) - R(30) &= [60(31) - 31^2] - [60(30) - 30^2] \\ &= -1 \text{ dollar.} \end{aligned}$$

Note from Figures 6.4 and 6.5 that total revenue actually *decreases* as sales levels increase beyond 30 billfolds per week. This happens, for example, when a market becomes so "flooded" with a product that to sell additional quantities requires that the price be lowered so far as to more than offset the effect of additional sales. ∎

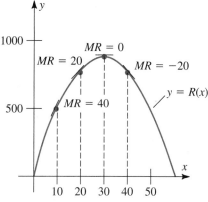

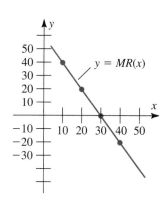

Figure 6.4 Revenue function $R(x) = 60x - x^2$ and various marginal revenues (slopes).

Figure 6.5 Marginal revenue function $MR(x) = R'(x) = 60 - 2x$.

REMARK: It is important to note that the marginal rates $MR(x)$ provide only *approximations* to the actual change in revenue as sales levels are increased from x to $x + 1$. However, since "models" for revenue functions themselves are usually only approximations, these marginal rates provide valuable insight into how values of the revenue function change over small intervals of the form $[x, x + 1]$. The same observation holds for the other economic models for cost, profit, etc.

The Profit Equation

The profit from the production and sale of x items in a unit of time is given by the equation

$$P(x) = R(x) - C(x) \quad \text{(profit equation)}$$

where $R(x)$ and $C(x)$ are the total revenue and total cost, respectively, at sales level x. Thus the rate at which profits are changing at production level x is given by the derivative

$$MP(x) = P'(x) = R'(x) - C'(x).$$

That is,

$$MP(x) = MR(x) - MC(x).$$

Thus, **marginal profit,** $MP(x)$, is simply the difference between marginal revenue and marginal cost.

☐ **EXAMPLE 3**

For the manufacturer of billfolds in Examples 1 and 2 the total revenue and costs are

$$R(x) = 60x - x^2 \quad \text{and} \quad C(x) = 40 + 5x + \frac{1}{4}x^2.$$

The profit function P is therefore

$$P(x) = (60x - x^2) - \left(40 + 5x + \frac{1}{4}x^2\right)$$

$$= -40 + 55x - \frac{5}{4}x^2 \text{ dollars.}$$

The marginal profit at production level x is

$$MP(x) = P'(x) = 55 - \frac{5}{2}x \text{ dollars per billfold.}$$

Thus at production level $x = 20$, profits are increasing at the rate of $MP(20) = 55 - \frac{5}{2}(20) = 5$ dollars per additional billfold, while at production level $x = 30$ profits change by $MP(30) = 55 - \frac{5}{2}(30) = -20$ dollars per additional billfold.

The two functions R and C are graphed on a common set of axes in Figure 6.6. Their difference, P, is graphed in Figure 6.7. ■

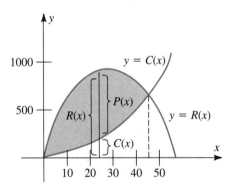

Figure 6.6 Profit is revenue minus cost.

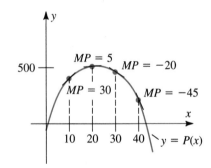

Figure 6.7 $P(x) = R(x) - C(x)$
$$= -40 + 55x - \frac{5}{4}x^2.$$

Recall, from Section 1.5, that the *average cost* in producing x items with total cost $C(x)$ is the quotient

$$c(x) = \frac{C(x)}{x} \qquad \text{(average cost)}$$

Both the average cost and the marginal cost are useful in analyzing options for increasing or decreasing levels of production.

☐ **EXAMPLE 4**

A manufacturer determines that its total cost in producing x radios per week is given by the function

$$C(x) = 10{,}000 + 30x + 3x^{2/3}.$$

Find

(a) The marginal cost function $MC(x)$.
(b) The average cost function $c(x)$.
(c) The values of these two functions at production level $x = 1000$ radios per week.

What conclusions might you draw from your answer to these questions?

Strategy · · · · · · · ·

(a) Find $MC(x) = C'(x)$.

(b) Find $c(x) = \dfrac{C(x)}{x}$.

(c) Evaluate $MC(x)$ and $c(x)$ for $x = 1000$.

Solution

(a) The marginal cost function is

$$MC(x) = 30 + 2x^{-1/3}$$

$$= 30 + \frac{2}{\sqrt[3]{x}}.$$

(b) The average cost per radio is

$$c(x) = \frac{C(x)}{x} = \frac{10{,}000 + 30x + 3x^{2/3}}{x}$$

$$= \frac{10{,}000}{x} + 30 + \frac{3}{\sqrt[3]{x}}.$$

(c) At production level $x = 1000$, we have

$$MC(1000) = 30 + \frac{2}{\sqrt[3]{1000}} = 30 + \frac{2}{10} = \$30.20$$

and

$$c(1000) = \frac{10{,}000}{1000} + 30 + \frac{3}{\sqrt[3]{1000}} = \$40.30.$$

Conclusions might include the following

1. Conclusion that marginal cost applies *only* to 1001st radio.

1. The cost of producing the next radio, at production level $x = 1000$, is approximately \$30.20. If *it* can be sold for more than this amount, a profit would result *on this sale alone*.

2. Conclusion about average cost applies to all 1000 radios.

2. But the *average cost* per radio, in producing 1000 radios per week, is \$40.30. If all 1000 are sold at the same price p (say, to a wholesaler), we must have $p > \$40.30$ for a profit to result. ∎

☑ **PRACTICE PROBLEMS 2.6**

1. A manufacturer of air-conditioners finds that the total cost in producing x units of model A per week is

$$C(x) = 10,000 + 400x + 2x^2.$$

If the units can be sold for $p = \$1000$ each without delay, find the manufacturer's
a. marginal cost function,
b. revenue function,
c. marginal revenue function,
d. profit function, and
e. marginal profit function.

2. Find the production level x for which marginal cost equals marginal revenue in Problem 1.

Exercise Set 2.6

In Exercises 1–8 a revenue function R and a total cost function C are given. In each exercise find
a. the marginal revenue function R',
b. the marginal cost function C', and
c. the profit function $P = R - C$, and
d. the marginal profit function P'.

1. $R(x) = 10x$
$C(x) = 50 + 6x$

2. $R(x) = 100x$
$C(x) = 400 + 40x + x^2$

3. $R(x) = 100x - 2x^2$
$C(x) = 20x + x^{3/2} + 400$

4. $R(x) = 20\sqrt{x}$
$C(x) = 10x + \sqrt{x} + 30$

5. $R(x) = 40x + 50\sqrt{x}$
$C(x) = 150 + 20x + x^{2/3}$

6. $R(x) = 40(20 - x)$
$C(x) = 250 + 20x + 3x^{4/3}$

7. $R(x) = 400x - 10x^{2/3}$
$C(x) = \dfrac{5000}{x} + 40$

8. $R(x) = 100(x - 40) - \dfrac{30}{x}$
$C(x) = 200 + 3x^{2/3} - \dfrac{10}{x^2}$

9. Kate and Jerry decide to open a business producing a special type of soccer ball. Their business plan predicts that profit from the production and sale of x balls per week will be

$$P(x) = 160x - x^2$$

dollars.
a. Find the marginal profit at production level $x = 40$ balls per week.
b. For what sales levels of x is marginal profit positive?

10. Paula and Frank decide to start a business together in which they intend to produce plastic tennis racquets. According to their business plan, the revenue obtained from the sale of x racquets will be $R(x) = 200x - 4x^2$ dollars for $0 \le x \le 25$ while the cost of producing these x racquets will be $C(x) = 900 + 40x$. Find the output level x for which marginal revenue equals marginal cost.

11. Kate and Jerry (from Exercise 9) are considering an opportunity to expand their business by purchasing a company that manufactures dishwashers. The following information is important to their decision.

 The dishwasher company can produce up to 100 dishwashers per week. Sales experience indicates that the manufacturer can sell x dishwashers per week at price p where $p + 3x = 600$ dollars. Production records show that the cost of producing x dishwashers per week is

$$C(x) = 4000 + 150x + 0.5x^2.$$

a. Find the weekly revenue function $R(x) = xp(x)$. (*Hint:* Here $p(x) = 600 - 3x$.)

b. Find the weekly profit function.

c. Find the marginal cost and marginal revenue functions.

d. Find the weekly production level x for which marginal cost equals marginal revenue.

12. Paula and Frank (from Exercise 10) are evaluating the opportunity to expand their business through part ownership in a camera company. In analyzing the business profile of the camera company, they learn that the price at which it can sell x cameras per week is roughly $p(x) = (500 - x)$ dollars. Furthermore, the total cost of producing x cameras per week is $C(x) = 150 + 4x + x^2$ dollars.

a. Find the weekly revenue function $R(x) = xp(x)$.

b. Find the profit $P(x)$ obtained from selling x items per week.

c. Find the marginal revenue and marginal cost functions.

d. Find the production level x for which marginal cost will equal marginal revenue.

e. If the manufacturer is currently producing $x = 125$ cameras per week, should the level of production be increased or decreased? Why?

13. Sarah, a foreign language student, has learned $N(t) = 20t - t^2$ vocabulary terms after t hours of uninterrupted study.

a. How many terms are learned between times $t = 2$ and $t = 3$ hours?

b. What is the rate in terms per hour at which Sarah is learning at time $t = 2$ hours?

14. Allan can master $5\sqrt{t} - \frac{1}{4}t$ basic skills after t continuous hours of practice.

a. What is the rate of basic skills per hour at which he is learning?

b. Does this rate ever become negative? If so, when?

15. A city's population t years after 1980 is predicted to be $P(t) = 40{,}000 + 2000\sqrt{t}$.

a. Find the rate, in terms of people per year, at which the city is growing.

b. Does the population of the city in 1990 affect its growth rate?

16. A manufacturer's total weekly cost in producing x items can be written $C(x) = F + V(x)$ where F, a constant, represents fixed costs (space, light, heat, etc.) and $V(x)$ represents the variable costs that depend on the production level x. Show that the marginal cost is independent of fixed costs.

17. Suppose that the demand for an item is such that its selling price p and weekly sales level x are related by the equation

$p(x) = a - bx$ where a and b are constants. Show that the marginal revenue function is a linear function with slope $m = -2b$ (which is twice the slope of the demand curve $p = a - bx$).

18. The *total utility* $U(x)$ attained by a consumer from a commodity is the amount of satisfaction the consumer receives by consuming x units of the commodity in a unit of time. Marginal utility, $U'(x)$, is the rate of change of utility. Figure 6.8 shows a consumer's utility function $U(x) = x(6 - x)$ associated with the consumption of x ice cream cones per day.

a. Find the consumer's marginal utility function $MU(x) = U'(x)$.

b. For what value of x is $MU(x) = 0$?

c. According to this model, would the person wish to consume another ice cream cone if she had already eaten four cones that day?

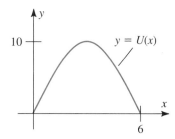

Figure 6.8 Utility curve for daily consumption of ice cream cones.

19. The quadratic function $y = At^2 + Bt + C$ is sometimes used to model human growth during certain time intervals, with t representing time since birth, in years, and with A, B, and C being constants. In such growth models the *velocity* of the growth curve is the derivative $v(t) = 2At + B$. For this growth model, find the constants A, B, and C if $y(0) = 40$, $y(5) = 315$, and $v(5) = 105$.

20. A manufacturer of men's dress shirts finds that its cost in producing x shirts per week is $C(x) = 400 + 10x + 20\sqrt{x}$ dollars, while its revenue from the sale of x shirts is $R(x) = 30x$ dollars.

a. Does the manufacturer earn a profit at production level $x_0 = 16$ shirts per week?

b. Does the manufacturer earn a profit at production level $x_0 = 100$?

c. At what production level x_0 does cost equal revenue? (*Hint:* Obtain a quadratic equation in x_0.)

d. Find the profit function P and the values $P(16)$, $P(25)$, $P(49)$, and $P(100)$.

21. A manufacturer of air conditioners finds that its total cost in producing x units per week is

$$C(x) = 10,000 + 400x + 25x^2.$$

A market study shows that it can sell the units at the price $p(x) = 1600 - 5x$ dollars per unit.
a. Find the revenue function $R(x)$.
b. Find the profit function $P(x)$.
c. Find the marginal profit function $MP(x)$.
d. Where is the marginal profit function equal to zero?
e. Compare the values of the marginal cost and marginal revenues at the production level where marginal profit equals zero.
f. What can you conclude about the manufacturer's maximum possible profit? Why?

22. A manufacturer of baseball bats has a total cost of $C(x) = A + Bx + Cx^2$ in producing x bats per week. If A, B, and C are constants, show the following relationships.
a. The fixed cost of production (which does not depend on the number of bats produced) is A.
b. The marginal cost of production, at any production level, does not depend on A. That is, marginal costs are independent of fixed costs.
c. For any profit function, the marginal profit at any production level is independent of fixed costs, A.

23. Demand for a new television system is predicted by the equation

$$p = 10,000 - 5x$$

where p is the unit price, in dollars, and x is the number of units produced and sold in a specified period of time.
a. Find $R(x)$, the total revenue as a function of x.
b. Find $MR(x)$, the marginal revenue function.
c. Find $MR(500)$, $MR(1000)$, and $MR(1500)$.
d. At what production level do you think revenues are the largest? Why?

24. For a profit function $P(x) = R(x) - C(x)$, is it possible for marginal profit to be negative at the same production level x where marginal revenue is positive? Why or why not?

25. Refer to Exercise 24. Is it possible for marginal profit to be positive at the same production level where marginal revenue is negative? Why or why not?

26. The growth of plant life as a function of precipitation is another application of the notions of utility and marginal utility. (See Exercise 18.) Consider the model where overall plant biomass, $B(x)$, is related to the amount of precipitation, x, per unit area and per unit time, by the equation

$$B(x) = \sqrt{x + 9} - 3, \qquad x > 0.$$

In this model we can think of $B(x)$ as the *utility* of precipitation.
a. Find the marginal utility function, $B'(x)$.
b. Sketch the graphs of both $B(x)$ and $B'(x)$.
c. Is marginal utility ever negative? Why or why not?
d. Do you think the answer to part (c) is realistic? Why or why not?

☑ SOLUTIONS TO PRACTICE PROBLEMS 2.6

1. a. If $C(x) = 10,000 + 400x + 2x^2$,

$$MC(x) = C'(x) = 400 + 4x.$$

b. $R(x) = px = 1000x$.
c. $MR(x) = R'(x) = 1000$.
d. $P(x) = R(x) - C(x)$
$$= 1000x - (10,000 + 400x + 2x^2)$$
$$= 600x - 10,000 - 2x^2.$$
e. $MP(x) = P'(x) = 600 - 4x$.
2. $MR(x) = MC(x)$ if $400 + 4x = 1000$, or if $4x = 600$. Thus, $x = 150$ units.

2.7 The Product and Quotient Rules

In this section and the next, we develop a number of additional rules for calculating derivatives. These will speed your calculations when we return to applications of the derivative in the next chapter.

We can paraphrase Theorem 2 of Section 2.4 by saying, ''The derivative of a sum is the sum of the derivatives.'' This simple relationship may lead you to suspect a similar rule for products. However, the following example shows that the derivative of a product is *not* simply the product of the individual derivatives, in general. Let

$$f(x) = x \quad \text{and} \quad g(x) = x^3.$$

Then

$$f'(x) = 1 \quad \text{and} \quad g'(x) = 3x^2.$$

Now the product $p(x) = (fg)(x) = x \cdot x^3 = x^4$ has derivative

$$p'(x) = \frac{d}{dx}(x^4) = 4x^3$$

while the product of the individual derivatives is

$$f'(x)g'(x) = (1)(3x^2) = 3x^2.$$

Since $4x^3 \neq 3x^2$, we see that $\dfrac{d}{dx}(fg) \neq \left(\dfrac{df}{dx}\right)\left(\dfrac{dg}{dx}\right)$.

The correct rule for differentiating a product is the following:

Rule 4 (Product Rule): Let f and g be differentiable at x. Then the product function $p = fg$ is differentiable at x, and

$$p'(x) = f'(x)g(x) + f(x)g'(x).$$

That is

$$\frac{d}{dx}(fg) = \left(\frac{df}{dx}\right)g + f\left(\frac{dg}{dx}\right).$$

We shall defer the proof of the Product Rule to the end of this section. The following examples illustrate the use of this rule.

☐ **EXAMPLE 1**

For $f(x) = (2x + 7)(x - 9)$ find $f'(x)$.

Solution: One way to find $f'(x)$ is to first multiply the two binomial factors in $f(x)$ to find that

$$f(x) = (2x + 7)(x - 9)$$
$$= 2x^2 - 11x - 63.$$

Then

$$f'(x) = 4x - 11.$$

Now let's rework the problem using the Product Rule:

$$f(x) = (2x + 7)(x - 9)$$

so

$$f'(x) = \left[\frac{d}{dx}(2x + 7)\right](x - 9) + (2x + 7)\left[\frac{d}{dx}(x - 9)\right]$$
$$= 2(x - 9) + (2x + 7)(1)$$
$$= 2x - 18 + 2x + 7$$
$$= 4x - 11.$$

Of course, the result must be the same by either method. ■

☐ **EXAMPLE 2**

For $f(x) = (3x^3 - 6x)(9x^{-2} + x^{1/2})$ find $f'(x)$.

Solution: This time we proceed directly by the Product Rule:

$$f'(x) = \left[\frac{d}{dx}(3x^3 - 6x)\right](9x^{-2} + x^{1/2}) + (3x^3 - 6x)\left[\frac{d}{dx}(9x^{-2} + x^{1/2})\right]$$

$$= (9x^2 - 6)(9x^{-2} + x^{1/2}) + (3x^3 - 6x)\left(-18x^{-3} + \frac{1}{2}x^{-1/2}\right)$$

$$= (81 - 54x^{-2} + 9x^{5/2} - 6x^{1/2}) + \left(-54 + 108x^{-2} + \frac{3}{2}x^{5/2} - 3x^{1/2}\right)$$

$$= \frac{21}{2}x^{5/2} - 9x^{1/2} + 54x^{-2} + 27.$$ ■

☐ **EXAMPLE 3**

Find the slope of the line tangent to the graph of the function $f(x) = (\sqrt{x} - 2)$ $(x^3 - 6)$ at the point $(4, 0)$.

Strategy · · · · · · · ·

First, find the derivative, $f'(x)$.

Solution

By the Product Rule we have

$$f'(x) = \left[\frac{d}{dx}(x^{1/2} - 2)\right](x^3 - 6) + (x^{1/2} - 2)\left[\frac{d}{dx}(x^3 - 6)\right]$$

$$= \frac{1}{2}x^{-1/2}(x^3 - 6) + (x^{1/2} - 2)(3x^2)$$

$$= \frac{7}{2}x^{5/2} - 6x^2 - 3x^{-1/2}.$$

Thus,

Evaluate $f'(x)$ to find the desired slope.

$$m = f'(4) = \frac{7}{2}(4)^{5/2} - 6(4)^2 - 3(4)^{-1/2}$$

$$= \frac{7}{2}(32) - 6(16) - 3\left(\frac{1}{2}\right)$$

$$= \frac{29}{2}.$$

The Quotient Rule

The rule for differentiating the quotient of two functions is even more surprising than the Product Rule.

Rule 5 (Quotient Rule): Let f and g be differentiable at x with $g(x) \neq 0$. Then the quotient $q = f/g$ is differentiable at x, and

$$q'(x) = \frac{g(x)f'(x) - f(x)g'(x)}{[g(x)]^2}.$$

That is

$$\frac{d}{dx}\left(\frac{f}{g}\right) = \frac{g \cdot \dfrac{df}{dx} - f \cdot \dfrac{dg}{dx}}{g^2}.$$

☐ **EXAMPLE 4**

For $f(x) = \dfrac{2x}{x + 3}$ find $f'(x)$.

Solution: Using the Quotient Rule, we obtain

$$f'(x) = \frac{(x + 3)\left[\dfrac{d}{dx}(2x)\right] - (2x)\left[\dfrac{d}{dx}(x + 3)\right]}{(x + 3)^2}$$

$$= \frac{(x + 3)(2) - (2x)(1)}{(x + 3)^2}$$

$$= \frac{6}{(x + 3)^2}.$$

□ **EXAMPLE 5**

Find $f'(x)$ for $f(x) = \dfrac{3x^2 + 7x + 1}{9 - x^3}$.

Solution: By the Quotient Rule we have

$$f'(x) = \frac{(9 - x^3)\left[\dfrac{d}{dx}(3x^2 + 7x + 1)\right] - (3x^2 + 7x + 1)\left[\dfrac{d}{dx}(9 - x^3)\right]}{(9 - x^3)^2}$$

$$= \frac{(9 - x^3)(6x + 7) - (3x^2 + 7x + 1)(-3x^2)}{(9 - x^3)^2}$$

$$= \frac{3x^4 + 14x^3 + 3x^2 + 54x + 63}{(9 - x^3)^2}. \qquad \text{(as above)}$$

□ **EXAMPLE 6**

For $f(x) = \dfrac{x^{-2} + 3\sqrt{x}}{4 - \sqrt{x}}$ find $f'(x)$.

Solution: Again applying the Quotient Rule, we obtain

$$f'(x) = \frac{(4 - x^{1/2})\left[\dfrac{d}{dx}(x^{-2} + 3x^{1/2})\right] - (x^{-2} + 3x^{1/2})\left[\dfrac{d}{dx}(4 - x^{1/2})\right]}{(4 - x^{1/2})^2}$$

$$= \frac{(4 - x^{1/2})\left(-2x^{-3} + \dfrac{3}{2}x^{-1/2}\right) - (x^{-2} + 3x^{1/2})\left(-\dfrac{1}{2}x^{-1/2}\right)}{(4 - x^{1/2})^2}$$

$$= \frac{\left(-8x^{-3} + 2x^{-5/2} + 6x^{-1/2} - \dfrac{3}{2}\right) - \left(-\dfrac{1}{2}x^{-5/2} - \dfrac{3}{2}\right)}{(4 - x^{1/2})^2}$$

$$= \frac{-8x^{-3} + \dfrac{5}{2}x^{-5/2} + 6x^{-1/2}}{(4 - x^{1/2})^2}$$

Differentiability and Continuity

In order to prove the Product and Quotient Rules we need to use the following theorem that we can paraphrase by saying, "If f is differentiable at x then f must be continuous at x."

Theorem 3

If f is differentiable at x, then

$$\lim_{h \to 0} f(x + h) = f(x).$$

Proof of Theorem 3: Since f is differentiable at x the limit

$$\lim_{h \to 0} \frac{f(x + h) - f(x)}{h} \tag{1}$$

exists and equals $f'(x)$. Since $\lim_{h \to 0} h = 0$ in the denominator of (1), we must also have $\lim_{h \to 0} [\, f(x + h) - f(x)] = 0$ in the numerator; otherwise the limit (1) would not exist. Thus

$$0 = \lim_{h \to 0} [\, f(x + h) - f(x)]$$

$$= [\lim_{h \to 0} f(x + h)] - f(x)$$

so

$$\lim_{h \to 0} f(x + h) = f(x). \qquad \square$$

Proof of the Product Rule: By the definition of the derivative we have, for $p = fg$, that

$$p'(x) = \lim_{h \to 0} \frac{f(x + h)g(x + h) - f(x)g(x)}{h}.$$

In order to factor the numerator, we introduce the term

$$-f(x)g(x + h) + f(x)g(x + h)$$

which is simply zero, and use the properties of limits as follows:

$$p'(x) = \lim_{h \to 0} \frac{[\, f(x + h)g(x + h) - f(x)g(x + h)] + [\, f(x)g(x + h) - f(x)g(x)]}{h}$$

$$= \lim_{h \to 0} \left[\left(\frac{f(x + h) - f(x)}{h} \right) g(x + h) + f(x) \left(\frac{g(x + h) - g(x)}{h} \right) \right]$$

$$= \left[\lim_{h \to 0} \frac{f(x + h) - f(x)}{h} \right] \left[\lim_{h \to 0} g(x + h) \right] + f(x) \left[\lim_{h \to 0} \frac{g(x + h) - g(x)}{h} \right]$$

$$= f'(x)g(x) + f(x)g'(x). \tag{2}$$

In equation (2) we have used the definition of $f'(x)$ and $g'(x)$ and Theorem 3 in the form $\lim_{h \to 0} g(x + h) = g(x)$. ☐

Proof of the Quotient Rule: The technique is the same as in the proof of the Product Rule except that the algebra is a bit trickier. For $q = f/g$ we have

$$q'(x) = \lim_{h \to 0} \frac{\dfrac{f(x + h)}{g(x + h)} - \dfrac{f(x)}{g(x)}}{h}$$

$$= \lim_{h \to 0} \frac{f(x + h)g(x) - f(x)g(x + h)}{hg(x + h)g(x)}$$

$$= \lim_{h \to 0} \frac{[\, f(x + h)g(x) - f(x)g(x)] + [\, f(x)g(x) - f(x)g(x + h)]}{hg(x + h)g(x)}$$

$$= \lim_{h \to 0} \frac{\left[\dfrac{f(x + h) - f(x)}{h}\right]g(x) - f(x)\left[\dfrac{g(x + h) - g(x)}{h}\right]}{g(x + h)g(x)}$$

$$= \frac{\left[\lim_{h \to 0}\dfrac{f(x + h) - f(x)}{h}\right]g(x) - f(x)\left[\lim_{h \to 0}\dfrac{g(x + h) - g(x)}{h}\right]}{\lim_{h \to 0} g(x + h)g(x)}$$

$$= \frac{g(x)f'(x) - f(x)g'(x)}{[g(x)]^2} \tag{3}$$

Note, once again we have used Theorem 3 in equation (3) to conclude that $\lim_{h \to 0} g(x + h) = g(x)$. ☐

☑ **PRACTICE PROBLEMS 2.7**

1. Find the derivative $f'(x)$ for the following functions.
   a. $f(x) = x^{-2/3}(x - x^{-2})$
   b. $f(x) = \dfrac{1 + \sqrt{x}}{4 - x^2}$

2. For the utility function $U(t) = \dfrac{20t}{1 + t^2}$, find the marginal utility function $MU(t) = U'(t)$.

Exercise Set 2.7

In Exercises 1–10, use the Product Rule to find $f'(x)$.

1. $f(x) = (x - 1)(x + 1)$

2. $f(x) = (x^2 - 1)(2 - x)$

3. $f(x) = (3x^2 - 8x)(x^2 + 2)$

4. $f(x) = (x^2 - 6x + 10)(7 - x)$

5. $f(x) = (x^3 - x)^2$

6. $f(x) = \left(x^2 - \dfrac{3}{x^2}\right)^2$

7. $f(x) = \sqrt{x}(x^3 + x^{-2/3})$

8. $f(x) = (x^2 - x)(x^{2/3} + 2x^{1/3})$

9. $f(x) = (3x^{-2} + x^{-1})(x - 4)$

10. $f(x) = (x^{4/3} - x^{-2})^2$

In Exercises 11–20, use the Quotient Rule to find $f'(x)$.

11. $f(x) = \dfrac{x + 2}{x - 2}$

12. $f(x) = \dfrac{x^2 - 6}{3 - x}$

13. $f(x) = \dfrac{(8x + 2)(x + 1)}{x - 3}$

14. $f(x) = \dfrac{x^4 + 4}{1 - x^3}$

15. $f(x) = \dfrac{x^2 - 4}{x + 2}$

16. $f(x) = \dfrac{(x^2 + 7)(x + 2)}{x(x - 3)}$

17. $f(x) = \dfrac{1 - x}{(1 + x)^2}$

18. $f(x) = \dfrac{\sqrt{x} + 1}{1 + x^2}$

19. $f(x) = \dfrac{x^2 - x^{2/3}}{\sqrt{x} + 1}$

20. $f(x) = \dfrac{x - 4 + x^2}{x^2 - \sqrt{x} + 1}$

In Exercises 21–26, find the derivative.

21. $f(x) = x^{1/3}(x^2 + 2)$

22. $f(x) = \dfrac{x^2}{1 + x^3}$

23. $f(x) = \left(\dfrac{1}{x + 1}\right)\left(\dfrac{x - 3}{x}\right)$

24. $f(x) = \sqrt{x}\left(\dfrac{1 - x^3}{1 + x}\right)$

25. $f(x) = (ax + b)(cx^2 + d)$

26. $f(x) = \dfrac{C(x)}{x}$ (assume $C'(x)$ exists)

27. Find the points at which the tangent to the graph of $f(x) = \dfrac{3x}{2x - 4}$ has slope $m = -3$.

28. Find the constant a so that the graph of $y = \dfrac{1}{ax + 2}$ has tangent $4y + 3x - 2 = 0$ at $\left(0, \frac{1}{2}\right)$.

29. Verify the Product Rule for three functions

$$\dfrac{d}{dx}(fgh) = \left(\dfrac{df}{dx}\right)gh + f\left(\dfrac{dg}{dx}\right)h + fg\left(\dfrac{dh}{dx}\right)$$

by applying the Product Rule for two functions to the function fv where $v = gh$.

In Exercises 30–33, use the result of Exercise 29 to find $f'(x)$.

30. $f(x) = x(x + 1)(x + 2)$

31. $f(x) = (x - 3)(1 - x)(x^3 - x)$

32. $f(x) = \sqrt{x}(1 + x)(1 - x)$

33. $f(x) = (x - x^2)(x^3 - x^{-2})(x^{-1} - x^{-3})$

34. A manufacturer's total weekly cost in producing x bicycles is $C(x) = 500 + (1 + \sqrt{x})(20x + x^2)$.
 a. Find the marginal cost $MC(x) = C'(x)$.
 b. Find $MC(16)$.

35. An automobile dealer finds that the total monthly revenue from the sale of x automobiles of a certain model is

$$R(x) = \dfrac{10{,}000x^{3/2}}{2 + \sqrt{x}}.$$

 a. Find the marginal revenue $MR(x) = R'(x)$.
 b. Find $MR(9)$.

36. Find an equation for the line tangent to the graph of $f(x) = \dfrac{x}{1 + x^2}$ at the point $\left(2, \frac{2}{5}\right)$.

37. If $C(x)$ gives a manufacturer's total weekly cost for the production of x items, the *average* weekly cost per item is defined to be the ratio $c(x) = \dfrac{C(x)}{x}$. The *marginal average cost* per item is defined to be the derivative $c'(x)$. If $C(x) = 400 + 20x + x^2$, find
 a. the marginal cost $MC(x) = C'(x)$,
 b. the average cost $c(x)$, and
 c. the marginal average cost $c'(x)$.

38. Refer to Exercise 37. Show that marginal average cost can be written as

$$c'(x) = \dfrac{xMC(x) - C(x)}{x^2}.$$

39. A typing instructor finds that after t hours of instruction a typical student can type

$$W(t) = \dfrac{50t^2}{10 + t^2}$$

words per minute. Find $W'(t)$, the rate at which the student's skill is improving after t hours.

40. An object moves along a line so that after t seconds its position is

$$s(t) = \frac{t^2 - 6t + 4}{t + 3}.$$

a. Find the object's velocity $v(t) = s'(t)$.
b. Find $v(3)$.

41. For the utility curve $U(x) = \dfrac{x}{x^2 + 9}$ find

a. the marginal utility function $MU = \dfrac{dU}{dx}$ and
b. the value of $x > 0$ for which $MU(x) = 0$.

42. The price that Paula and Frank, producers of tennis racquets, expect to receive for their new model is

$$p(x) = \frac{8000}{10 + x}$$

where x is the number of sets produced and sold per week.

a. Find the weekly revenue function $R(x) = xp(x)$.
b. Find the marginal revenue function $MR(x) = R'(x)$.
c. What is the marginal revenue at production level $x = 10$ and $x = 90$?
d. Does marginal revenue ever become negative?

43. Ring-necked pheasants were introduced onto a North American island and observed to grow in number according to the equation

$$P(t) = 10 + \frac{100t}{t^2 + 9}, \qquad t > 0.$$

a. Find the rate $P'(x)$ at which the population changes as a function of time.
b. Initially, does the population increase or decrease? Why?
c. Does the population ever decline in size? Why or why not?
d. Can you speculate on the eventual size of the population? What is your reason?

☑ **SOLUTIONS TO PRACTICE PROBLEMS 2.7**

1. a. Using the Product Rule, we find that for $f(x) = x^{-2/3}(x - x^{-2})$

$$f'(x) = -\frac{2}{3}x^{-5/3}(x - x^{-2}) + x^{-2/3}(1 + 2x^{-3})$$

$$= -\frac{2}{3}x^{-2/3} + \frac{2}{3}x^{-11/3} + x^{-2/3} + 2x^{-11/3}$$

$$= \frac{1}{3}x^{-2/3} + \frac{8}{3}x^{-11/3}.$$

The same result can be obtained by first writing

$$f(x) = x^{-2/3}(x - x^{-2}) = x^{1/3} - x^{-8/3}$$

and differentiating.

b. Using the Quotient Rule, we obtain for

$$f(x) = \frac{1 + \sqrt{x}}{4 - x^2} = \frac{1 + x^{1/2}}{4 - x^2}$$

that

$$f'(x) = \frac{(4 - x^2)\left(\frac{1}{2}x^{-1/2}\right) - (1 + x^{1/2})(-2x)}{(4 - x^2)^2}$$

$$= \frac{\frac{3}{2}x^{3/2} + 2x + 2x^{-1/2}}{(4 - x^2)^2}.$$

2. For $U(t) = \dfrac{20t}{1 + t^2}$,

$$U'(t) = \frac{(1 + t^2)(20) - (20t)(2t)}{(1 + t^2)^2}$$

$$= \frac{20 - 20t^2}{(1 + t^2)^2}.$$

2.8 The Chain Rule

This section is about *composite* functions, which occur when one function acts on values of another function. For example, if a corporation is required to pay a tax of 3% on all profits earned in a given period, then the calculation of the company's tax bill would involve applying the tax function $T(P) = 0.03P$ to the company's profit function P. If profits are determined from revenues, costs and production levels by an equation of the form

$$P(x) = R(x) - C(x)$$

then the tax function can be written as

$$\text{total tax} = T(P) = 0.03P$$

$$= 0.03[R(x) - C(x)].$$

This is an example of one function (the tax function) acting on values of another (the profit function). (See Figure 8.1.)

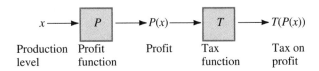

Production level   Profit function   Profit   Tax function   Tax on profit

Figure 8.1 The tax on profits is an example of a *composite* function.

The tax-on-profits function is a simple example of the general situation of a function g acting on values of a function f, as illustrated in Figure 8.2. We refer to this as the *composition* of the function g with the function f, which we denote by $g \circ f$. That is,

$$(g \circ f)(x) \qquad \text{means} \qquad g(f(x)).$$

As reviewed in Section 1.6, the *domain* of the composite function $g \circ f$ is the set of numbers x for which *both* $f(x)$ is defined *and* $f(x)$ is in the domain of g.

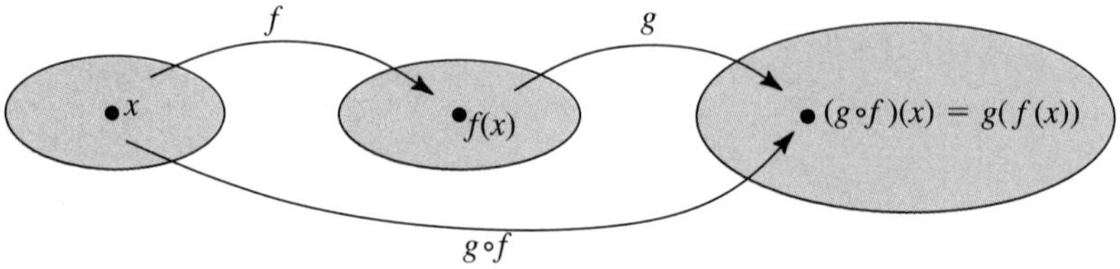

Figure 8.2 The composite function $g \circ f$ is defined by the equation $(g \circ f)(x) = g(f(x))$.

□ **EXAMPLE 1**

Here are two examples of composite functions.

(a) The function $h(x) = (2x^2 - 7)^4$ is a composite function of the form

$$h(x) = g(f(x))$$

where the "inside" function is

$$f(x) = 2x^2 - 7$$

and the "outside" function is

$$g(u) = u^4.$$

(b) The function $h(x) = \sqrt{4 - \dfrac{1}{x}}$ is composite with "inside" function

$$f(x) = 4 - \frac{1}{x}$$

and "outside" function

$$g(u) = \sqrt{u}.$$ ■

Derivatives of Composite Functions

A key to knowing what to expect as the derivative of a composite function of the form $h = g \circ f$ is to think of our interpretation of the derivative as the rate at which a function is changing with respect to its independent variable at a specified value (number) for that variable: "If $h(x) = g(f(x))$, if f is changing n times as fast as x, and if g is changing m times as fast as $f(x)$, then h must be changing $m \cdot n$ times as fast as x."

This is basically the outcome, but we must establish the result with greater care. We do so by beginning with the special case of *power* functions.

The Power Rule

When a given function is the square of another function, $f(x) = [u(x)]^2$, we can find $f'(x)$ using the Product Rule.

$$\frac{d}{dx}[u(x)]^2 = \frac{d}{dx}[u(x)u(x)]$$

$$= u'(x)u(x) + u(x)u'(x)$$

$$= 2u(x)u'(x).$$

Similarly, we can use the Product Rule for three functions (See Exercise 29, Section 2.7) to find the derivative of $f(x) = [u(x)]^3$.

$$\frac{d}{dx}[u(x)]^3 = \frac{d}{dx}[u(x)u(x)u(x)]$$

$$= u'(x)u(x)u(x) + u(x)u'(x)u(x) + u(x)u(x)u'(x)$$

$$= 3[u(x)]^2u'(x).$$

Each of these results is a special case of the rule for differentiating a power of a function.

Rule 6 (General Power Rule): Let n be any nonzero real number. If the function u is differentiable at x and if both $f(x) = [u(x)]^n$ and $[u(x)]^{n-1}$ exist, then the derivative of the power function

$$f(x) = [u(x)]^n \quad \text{is} \quad f'(x) = n[u(x)]^{n-1} \cdot u'(x).$$

That is

$$\frac{d}{dx}[u(x)]^n = n[u(x)]^{n-1} \cdot u'(x).$$

(In stating the Power Rule, we assume that $u(x) \neq 0$ if $n < 0$.)

Rule 6 states that the function $f(x) = [u(x)]^n$ is differentiated just as if the function u itself were the independent variable (multiply by n and reduce the exponent by one) except that an additional factor $u'(x)$ appears. When $u(x) = x$, Rule 6 reduces to our earlier Power Rule for differentiating $f(x) = x^n$.

The General Power Rule is itself a special case of the Chain Rule, which we will discuss later in this section.

□ **EXAMPLE 2**

For $f(x) = (x^2 - 6x + 2)^5$ find $f'(x)$.

Solution: Here $f(x)$ has the form $f(x) = [u(x)]^5$ where the "inside" function is $u(x) = x^2 - 6x + 2$. Thus by the General Power Rule

$$\frac{d}{dx}(x^2 - 6x + 2)^5 = 5(x^2 - 6x + 2)^4 \cdot \frac{d}{dx}(x^2 - 6x + 2)$$

$$= 5(x^2 - 6x + 2)^4(2x - 6)$$

$$= 10(x - 3)(x^2 - 6x + 2)^4. \qquad \blacksquare$$

☐ **EXAMPLE 3**

For $f(x) = \sqrt{9 - x^3}$, find $f'(x)$.

Strategy · · · · · · ·

Identify the inside function u.

Solution

In this case the inside function is

$$u(x) = 9 - x^3$$

so

Express $f(x)$ as $f(x) = [u(x)]^n$.

$$f(x) = \sqrt{9 - x^3} = \sqrt{u(x)} = [u(x)]^{1/2}.$$

Thus,

Apply General Power Rule.

$$f'(x) = \frac{1}{2}[u(x)]^{-1/2} \cdot u'(x)$$

$$= \frac{1}{2}(9 - x^3)^{-1/2} \cdot \frac{d}{dx}(9 - x^3)$$

$$= \frac{1}{2}(9 - x^3)^{-1/2}(-3x^2)$$

$$= -\frac{3}{2}x^2(9 - x^3)^{-1/2}. \qquad \blacksquare$$

☐ **EXAMPLE 4**

For $f(x) = \left(\dfrac{x - 3}{x^2 + 7}\right)^9$, find $f'(x)$.

Strategy · · · · · · ·

Identify the inside function u.

Solution

In this case we let

$$u(x) = \frac{x - 3}{x^2 + 7}.$$

Since $u(x)$ is somewhat complicated, calculate $u'(x)$ before applying the Power Rule to $f(x)$.

Using the Quotient Rule we find that

$$u'(x) = \frac{(x^2 + 7)(1) - (x - 3)(2x)}{(x^2 + 7)^2}$$

$$= \frac{7 + 6x - x^2}{(x^2 + 7)^2}.$$

Write $f(x)$ as $f(x) = [u(x)]^n$.

We can now apply the Power Rule. Since

$$f(x) = \left(\frac{x - 3}{x^2 + 7}\right)^9 = [u(x)]^9$$

Apply the General Power Rule.

we have

$$f'(x) = 9[u(x)]^8 \cdot u'(x)$$

$$= 9\left(\frac{x - 3}{x^2 + 7}\right)^8\left[\frac{7 + 6x - x^2}{(x^2 + 7)^2}\right]$$

$$= \frac{9(7 + 6x - x^2)(x - 3)^8}{(x^2 + 7)^{10}}. \qquad \blacksquare$$

Composite Functions: The Chain Rule

A power function $f(x) = [u(x)]^n$ is one type of *composite* function of the form $f(x) = (g \circ u)(x) = g(u(x))$. For power functions the ''outside'' function is $g(u) = u^n$.

The **Chain Rule** specifies the derivative of a composite function whether or not the outside function g is a power function. Thus it is a more general differentiation rule than the General Power Rule. Although we will not encounter outside functions other than power functions until Chapter 4, it is important to begin thinking of power functions as composite functions now so that the transition in Chapter 4 will be less abrupt.

Rule 7 (Chain Rule): If u is a differentiable function of x, and if g is a differentiable function of u, then the composite function

$$(g \circ u)(x) = g(u(x))$$

is differentiable at x, and its derivative is

$$(g \circ u)'(x) = g'(u(x)) \cdot u'(x). \qquad (1)$$

That is

$$\frac{d}{dx}[g(u(x))] = g'(u(x)) \cdot u'(x). \qquad (2)$$

The Chain Rule says this: ''To differentiate the composite function $f(x) = g(u(x))$, first differentiate g as a function of u (as if u were the independent variable). Then multiply the result by the derivative of u.''

Before looking at why the Chain Rule is true, we apply it in several examples.

☐ **EXAMPLE 5**

For $f(x) = (x^2 - 3x)^{2/3}$ find $f'(x)$.

Strategy · · · · · · · ·
Identify f as a composite function. Specify the inside and outside functions, and their derivatives.

Solution

Here $f(x) = g(u(x))$ where the inside function is

$$u(x) = x^2 - 3x, \qquad \text{with } u'(x) = 2x - 3$$

and the outside function is

$$g(u) = u^{2/3}, \qquad \text{with } g'(u) = \frac{2}{3}u^{-1/3}, \qquad u \neq 0.$$

Apply the Chain Rule to these components.

Thus by the Chain Rule, as stated in equation (2), we obtain

$$\frac{d}{dx}(x^2 - 3x)^{2/3} = \frac{d}{dx}g(u(x))$$

$$= g'(u(x)) \cdot u'(x)$$

$$= \frac{2}{3}(x^2 - 3x)^{-1/3} \cdot (2x - 3)$$

$$= \frac{2(2x - 3)}{3(x^2 - 3x)^{1/3}}, \qquad x \neq 0, 3.$$

☐ **EXAMPLE 6**

For $f(x) = \dfrac{1}{(6x^3 - x)^4}$, find $f'(x)$.

Solution: In this example the inside function is

$$u = 6x^3 - x, \qquad \text{with } u'(x) = 18x^2 - 1$$

and the outside function is

$$g(u) = \frac{1}{u^4} = u^{-4}, \qquad \text{with } g'(u) = -4u^{-5}.$$

Using the Chain Rule, as stated in equation (2), we have

$$\frac{d}{dx}\left[\frac{1}{(6x^3 - x)^4}\right] = \frac{d}{dx}[g(u(x))]$$

$$= g'(u(x)) \cdot u'(x)$$

$$= -4(6x^3 - x)^{-5}(18x^2 - 1)$$

$$= \frac{-4(18x^2 - 1)}{(6x^3 - x)^5}.$$

□ **EXAMPLE 7**

For $f(x) = \sqrt{\dfrac{x^2 - 1}{x^2 + 1}}$, find $f'(x)$.

Strategy · · · · · · · ·

Solution

Identify the inside function u.

We let $u(x) = \dfrac{x^2 - 1}{x^2 + 1}$ be the inside function u. Then, using the Quotient Rule, we have that

Find $u'(x)$.

$$u'(x) = \frac{(x^2 + 1)(2x) - (x^2 - 1)(2x)}{(x^2 + 1)^2}$$

$$= \frac{4x}{(x^2 + 1)^2}.$$

Identify the outside function g.

The outside function is $g(u) = \sqrt{u} = u^{1/2}$, so

Find $g'(u)$.

$$g'(u) = \frac{1}{2}u^{-1/2}.$$

Apply the Chain Rule:

$f'(x) = g'(u(x)) \cdot u'(x).$

By the Chain Rule we have, for $f(x) = g(u(x))$, that

$$f'(x) = g'(u(x)) \cdot u'(x)$$

$$= \frac{1}{2}\left[\frac{x^2 - 1}{x^2 + 1}\right]^{-1/2} \cdot \left[\frac{4x}{(x^2 + 1)^2}\right]$$

$$= \frac{2x}{(x^2 + 1)^{3/2}(x^2 - 1)^{1/2}}.$$ ■

Justifying the Chain Rule

Here is an informal explanation of why the Chain Rule works. According to the definition of the derivative, we have

$$\frac{d}{dx}g(u(x)) = \lim_{h \to 0} \frac{g(u(x + h)) - g(u(x))}{h}.$$

If we assume that $u(x + h) - u(x) \neq 0$, we may rewrite this limit as

$$\frac{d}{dx}g(u(x)) = \lim_{h \to 0}\left[\frac{g(u(x + h)) - g(u(x))}{u(x + h) - u(x)}\right] \cdot \left[\frac{u(x + h) - u(x)}{h}\right]. \qquad (3)$$

Now if we let $v = u(x + h) - u(x)$, we can write the first factor on the right-hand side of equation (3) as

$$\frac{g(u(x + h)) - g(u(x))}{u(x + h) - u(x)} = \frac{g(u + v) - g(u)}{v}. \qquad (4)$$

Also, since u is differentiable at x, Theorem 3 guarantees that

$$\lim_{h \to 0}[u(x + h) - u(x)] = 0.$$

That is, $v \to 0$ as $h \to 0$. Thus we may combine equations (3) and (4) and use properties of limits to write

$$\frac{d}{dx} g(u(x)) = \left[\lim_{v \to 0} \frac{g(u + v) - g(u)}{v} \right] \cdot \left[\lim_{h \to 0} \frac{u(x + h) - u(x)}{h} \right]$$

$$= \frac{dg}{du} \cdot \frac{du}{dx}.$$

as desired. However, this argument is not an entirely rigorous proof because we have not insured that the denominator $v = u(x + h) - u(x)$ is nonzero for $h \neq 0$. A rigorous proof that treats this difficulty can be given, but it is beyond the scope of this text.

☑ **PRACTICE PROBLEMS 2.8**

Use the Chain Rule to find the derivative $f'(x)$ for these functions.

1. $f(x) = x^3 \sqrt{1 + x^4}$

2. $f(x) = \dfrac{(x^3 - 4x)^{2/3}}{1 + \sqrt{1 + x^2}}$

Exercise Set 2.8

In each of Exercises 1–30, find $f'(x)$.

1. $f(x) = (x + 4)^3$

2. $f(x) = (3x - 2)^4$

3. $f(x) = (3x^2 - 2x)^5$

4. $f(x) = (x^2 + 8x + 8)^9$

5. $f(x) = \sqrt{x^4 - 2x^2}$

6. $f(x) = x^3(x^2 - 7)^4$

7. $f(x) = \dfrac{x}{(x^2 - 9)^3}$

8. $f(x) = \dfrac{x + 3}{(x^2 - 6x + 3)^2}$

9. $f(x) = (3\sqrt{x} - 2)^4$

10. $f(x) = (x^6 - x^2 + 2)^{-3}$

11. $f(x) = (x^{2/3} - x^{1/4})^4$

12. $f(x) = \sqrt{x^2 - 6x + 6}$

13. $f(x) = \left(\dfrac{x - 3}{x + 3} \right)^4$

14. $f(x) = \left(\dfrac{1 + \sqrt{x}}{1 - \sqrt{x}} \right)^6$

15. $f(x) = \left(\dfrac{x + 2}{\sqrt[3]{x}} \right)^3$

16. $f(x) = \sqrt{x^{-2/3} - 2x^{1/3}}$

17. $f(x) = (4x^{-1/4} + 6)^{-3}$

18. $f(x) = (3 - 2x - x^4)^{1/4}$

19. $f(x) = \dfrac{(x^3 + 1)^3 + 1}{1 - x}$

20. $f(x) = \dfrac{x + 2}{3 + (x^2 + 1)^3}$

21. $f(x) = \dfrac{1}{1 + (x^2 + 2)^2}$

22. $f(x) = \left(\dfrac{1 + x}{1 - x} \right)^6$

23. $f(x) = \left(\dfrac{x^{2/3}}{1 + \sqrt{x}} \right)^3$

24. $f(x) = \dfrac{x}{(1 + \sqrt{x})^4}$

25. $f(x) = \left(\sqrt{x} - \dfrac{1}{\sqrt{x}} \right)^3$

26. $f(x) = \dfrac{\sqrt{x^2 + 1}}{(x + 5)^3}$

27. $f(x) = \dfrac{(x - 4)^5}{\sqrt{x^3 + 6}}$

28. $f(x) = (x^{1/4} - x^{3/4})^3(x^{-2/3} + x^{-4/3})^5$

29. $f(x) = (x^{1/3} - 4)^3(x - \sqrt{x})^{-2/3}$

30. $f(x) = \dfrac{\sqrt{1 - x^2}}{1 + \sqrt{x}}$

In Exercises 31–34, find an equation for the line tangent to the graph of $y = f(x)$ at point P.

31. $f(x) = (1 - x^2)^3$; $P = (1, 0)$

32. $f(x) = \left(\dfrac{x}{x + 1} \right)^2$; $P = (0, 0)$

33. $f(x) = x\sqrt{1 + x^3}$; $P = (2, 6)$

34. $f(x) = \sqrt{\dfrac{1 - x}{1 + x}}$; $P = (0, 1)$

35. A manufacturer's total monthly cost in producing x items is $C(x) = 500 + \sqrt{40 + 16x^2}$. Find the marginal cost $MC(x)$.

36. A manufacturer's monthly revenue from the sale of x items is $R(x) = 20\sqrt{100x - x^2}$.
   a. Find the marginal revenue $MR(x)$.
   b. For which values of $x \geq 0$ is $MR(x) \geq 0$?

37. Ajax Corporation determines that its weekly profit from the sale of x dishwashers is

$$P(x) = (x^3 + 10x + 125)^{1/3} - 15.$$

   a. Find its marginal weekly profit.
   b. Do increasing sales always correspond to increasing profit in this example? Why or why not?

38. An object moves along a line so that after t seconds its position is $s(t) = (t^3 - 9t + 2)^3$.
   a. Find its velocity $v(t)$.
   b. For which values of $t \geq 0$ is $v(t)$ negative?

39. A grocery store determines that after t hours on the job a new cashier can ring up $N(t) = 20 - \dfrac{30}{\sqrt{9 + t^2}}$ items per minute.

   a. Find $N'(t)$, the rate at which the cashier's speed is increasing.
   b. According to this model, does the cashier ever stop improving? Why?

40. The demand for a new type of toothbrush is predicted to be $D(p) = \left(\dfrac{20}{2 + p}\right)^{2/3}$ toothbrushes per week at price p, while producers are predicted to be willing to supply $S(p) = (p^2 + 1)^{2/3}$ toothbrushes per week at price p.
   a. Verify that $p = 2$ is the equilibrium price for this model.
   b. Find $D'(2)$, the rate at which demand is decreasing at equilibrium.
   c. Find $S'(2)$, the rate at which supply is increasing at equilibrium.

41. Find the marginal average monthly cost for the manufacturer in Exercise 35.

42. Foxes and rabbits coexist in a certain ecological niche. The number of rabbits, r, is determined by the number of carrots, c, according to the function $r(c) = 10 + 0.2c + 0.01c^2$. The number of foxes, which prey on the rabbits, is given by the function $f(r) = (r^2 + 5)^{1/3}$. Find $\dfrac{df}{dc}$, the derivative of f with respect to c.

☑ **SOLUTIONS TO PRACTICE PROBLEMS 2.8**

1. For $f(x) = x^3(1 + x^4)^{1/2}$,

$$f'(x) = 3x^2(1 + x^4)^{1/2} + x^3\left[\frac{1}{2}(1 + x^4)^{-1/2}(4x^3)\right]$$

$$= 3x^2\sqrt{1 + x^4} + \frac{2x^6}{\sqrt{1 + x^4}}.$$

2. For $f(x) = \dfrac{(x^3 - 4x)^{2/3}}{1 + (1 + x^2)^{1/2}}$,

$$f'(x) =$$

$$\frac{[1 + (1 + x^2)^{1/2}]\left[\frac{2}{3}(x^3 - 4x)^{-1/3}(3x^2 - 4)\right] - (x^3 - 4x)^{2/3}\left[\frac{1}{2}(1 + x^2)^{-1/2}(2x)\right]}{[1 + (1 + x^2)^{1/2}]^2}.$$

2.9   Limits at Infinity

In some applications we shall want to ask about the limiting behavior of a function as the independent variable becomes infinitely large, rather than as it approaches a finite number.

For example, suppose that a manufacturer determines that the cost of manufacturing x of its items per week is given by the cost function

$$C(x) = 1000 + 40x.$$

In this example the average cost per item is

$$c(x) = \frac{C(x)}{x} = \frac{1000}{x} + 40.$$

The graph of the average cost function appears in Figure 9.1. As you can see, the values of this function approach "limiting value" of average cost, $c_0 = 40$, as x increases without bound. We shall write this conclusion as the "infinite limit"

$$\lim_{x \to \infty} \left(\frac{1000}{x} + 40 \right) = 40$$

in a sense that is made more precise in the following discussion.

Another example of an infinite limit is shown in Figure 9.2 the graph of the function

$$f(x) = \frac{x + 2}{x}.$$

Notice that as x increases in the positive direction, the values of the function $f(x)$ approach the number 1. We can see why this happens by writing $f(x)$ as

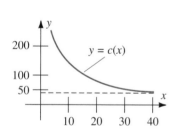

Figure 9.1 The average cost function $c(x) = \dfrac{1000}{x} + 40$ has limit $c_0 = 40$ as x increases without bound.

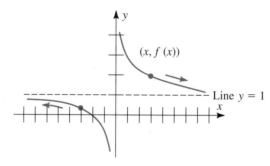

Figure 9.2 $\displaystyle\lim_{x \to \infty} \frac{x+2}{x} = 1; \quad \lim_{x \to -\infty} \frac{x+2}{x} = 1.$

$$f(x) = \frac{x + 2}{x}$$

$$= \frac{x}{x} + \frac{2}{x}$$

$$= 1 + \frac{2}{x}.$$

Since the number $\frac{2}{x}$ ''shrinks toward zero'' as x becomes large, the values $f(x)$ approach the number $1 + 0 = 1$. In this case we would write

$$\lim_{x \to \infty} \frac{x + 2}{x} = 1.$$

The meaning of this *limit at infinity* is the following.

Definition 6

We say that the number L is the *limit of the function f as x approaches infinity,* written

$$L = \lim_{x \to \infty} f(x)$$

if the values $f(x)$ approach the unique number L as x increases without bound.

We say that the number M is the *limit of the function f as x approaches negative infinity,* written

$$M = \lim_{x \to -\infty} f(x)$$

if the values $f(x)$ approach the number M as x decreases without bound.

Figure 9.2 also shows that

$$\lim_{x \to -\infty} \frac{x + 2}{x} = 1.$$

That is, the values of the function $f(x) = \frac{x + 2}{x}$ approach the number 1 as x decreases without bound through negative numbers.

The following example shows how we can use the technique of *dividing the numerator and denominator by the highest power of x present to evaluate a limit at infinity.*

☐ **EXAMPLE 1**

To evaluate the limit

$$\lim_{x \to \infty} \frac{3x^2 + 2x + 1}{x^2 + 4x + 5}$$

we divide both numerator and denominator by x^2, the highest power of x in both the numerator and denominator, to obtain

$$\lim_{x \to \infty} \frac{3x^2 + 2x + 1}{x^2 + 4x + 5} = \lim_{x \to \infty} \frac{3x^2 + 2x + 1}{x^2 + 4x + 5} \left\{ \frac{\dfrac{1}{x^2}}{\dfrac{1}{x^2}} \right\}$$

$$= \lim_{x \to \infty} \left\{ \frac{\dfrac{3x^2}{x^2} + \dfrac{2x}{x^2} + \dfrac{1}{x^2}}{\dfrac{x^2}{x^2} + \dfrac{4x}{x^2} + \dfrac{5}{x^2}} \right\}$$

$$= \lim_{x \to \infty} \left\{ \frac{3 + \dfrac{2}{x} + \dfrac{1}{x^2}}{1 + \dfrac{4}{x} + \dfrac{5}{x^2}} \right\}$$

$$= \frac{3 + 0 + 0}{1 + 0 + 0}$$

$$= 3$$

since $\lim\limits_{x \to \infty} \dfrac{2}{x} = 0$, $\lim\limits_{x \to \infty} \dfrac{1}{x^2} = 0$, $\lim\limits_{x \to \infty} \dfrac{4}{x} = 0$, and $\lim\limits_{x \to \infty} \dfrac{5}{x^2} = 0$. ∎

The idea behind the technique of Example 1 is that once we have divided all terms by the highest power of x present, we will be left with only constants and terms of the form $\dfrac{c}{x^n}$, $n > 0$, for which

$$\lim_{x \to \infty} \frac{c}{x^n} = 0$$

since the denominator "blows up" while the numerator remains constant.

☐ EXAMPLE 2

Using this technique, we find that

$$\lim_{x \to \infty} \frac{x-3}{2x+x^3} = \lim_{x \to \infty} \frac{x-3}{2x+x^3} \left\{ \frac{\dfrac{1}{x^3}}{\dfrac{1}{x^3}} \right\}$$

$$= \lim_{x \to \infty} \left\{ \frac{\dfrac{1}{x^2} - \dfrac{3}{x^3}}{\dfrac{2}{x^2} + 1} \right\}$$

$$= \frac{0-0}{0+1}$$

$$= 0. \qquad ■$$

Not all functions have limits at infinity. For example, the quadratic function $f(x) = x^2$ has the property that

$$\lim_{x \to \infty} x^2 = +\infty; \qquad \lim_{x \to -\infty} x^2 = +\infty. \qquad (1)$$

The meaning of the statements in line (1) is that as x increases without bound, so do the values of the function $f(x) = x^2$. (See Figure 9.3.) In such cases we say that the limit does not exist since the symbol ∞ is not a number.

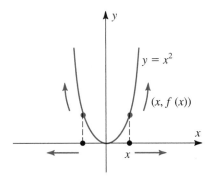

Figure 9.3 $\lim_{x \to \infty} x^2 = \infty$ and $\lim_{x \to -\infty} x^2 = \infty$.

☐ EXAMPLE 3

Find $\lim_{x \to \infty} \dfrac{4x^3 + 3x + 3}{2x^2 + x}$.

Solution: Here we divide numerator and denominator by x^3 to obtain

$$\lim_{x \to \infty} \frac{4x^3 + 3x + 3}{2x^2 + x} = \lim_{x \to \infty} \left\{ \frac{4 + \dfrac{3}{x^2} + \dfrac{3}{x^3}}{\dfrac{2}{x} + \dfrac{1}{x^2}} \right\}.$$

In the numerator we obtain

$$\lim_{x \to \infty} \left(4 + \frac{3}{x^2} + \frac{3}{x^3} \right) = 4 + 0 + 0 = 4$$

while in the denominator

$$\lim_{x \to \infty} \left(\frac{2}{x} + \frac{1}{x^2} \right) = 0 + 0 = 0.$$

Since the denominator "shrinks" to zero while the numerator approaches 4, the quotient "blows up," that is, increases without bound through positive numbers. Thus

$$\lim_{x \to \infty} \frac{4x^3 + 3x + 3}{2x^2 + x} = +\infty. \qquad \blacksquare$$

☑ **PRACTICE PROBLEMS 2.9**

1. Evaluate the limits:
   a. $\displaystyle \lim_{x \to \infty} \frac{3 - \sqrt{x} + 4x^2}{3x^2 + 2x - 5}$
   b. $\displaystyle \lim_{x \to \infty} \frac{\sqrt{x} + 3x}{5x^{2/3} + 3x^{3/2}}$

2. A manufacturer's total cost in producing x air conditioners per week is
   $$C(x) = 10{,}000 + 400x + 6\sqrt{x}.$$
   a. Find the average cost, $c(x) = \dfrac{C(x)}{x}$.
   b. Find $\displaystyle \lim_{x \to \infty} c(x)$.

Exercise Set 2.9

In Exercises 1–12, find the indicated limit at infinity if it exists.

1. $\displaystyle \lim_{x \to \infty} \frac{3x^2 + 2}{10x^2 - 3x}$

2. $\displaystyle \lim_{x \to \infty} \frac{2x^4 - 6x}{7 - 3x^4}$

5. $\displaystyle \lim_{x \to -\infty} \frac{2x^2 + 7}{3 - 4x^2}$

6. $\displaystyle \lim_{x \to -\infty} \frac{2x + 6}{x^2 + 1}$

3. $\displaystyle \lim_{x \to \infty} \frac{x(4 - x^3)}{3x^4 + 2x^2}$

4. $\displaystyle \lim_{x \to \infty} \frac{(x - 3)(x + 4)}{2x^2 + 2}$

7. $\displaystyle \lim_{x \to \infty} \frac{3x^2 + 7x}{1 - x^4}$

8. $\displaystyle \lim_{x \to \infty} \frac{x^4 - 4x^2}{x^3 + 7x^2}$

9. $\lim\limits_{x\to\infty} \dfrac{\sqrt{x-1}}{x^2}$

10. $\lim\limits_{x\to\infty} \dfrac{x^{2/3} + x^{4/3}}{x^2}$

11. $\lim\limits_{x\to\infty} \dfrac{x + 7 - x^3}{10x^2 + 18}$

12. $\lim\limits_{x\to\infty} \dfrac{3x^{2/3} - x^{5/2}}{6 + x^{3/2}}$

13. A manufacturer's total cost in producing x items per week is $C(x) = 3000 + 24x$.
    a. Find the average cost per item, $c(x)$.
    b. Find $\lim\limits_{x\to\infty} c(x)$.

14. A manufacturer's total cost in producing x items per week is $C(x) = 500 + 30x + 16\sqrt{x}$.
    a. Find the average cost per item, $c(x)$.
    b. Find $\lim\limits_{x\to\infty} c(x)$.

15. A company's profit function is determined to be $P(x) = \dfrac{1000 + 30x + \sqrt{x}}{10 + 2x}$ where x is the number of items produced and sold per day. Find $\lim\limits_{x\to\infty} P(x)$. Is the company profitable at high production levels?

16. Ecologists studying a certain ecological niche determine that overall plant size, $B(x)$, is related to the precipitation level x by the model

$$B(x) = \dfrac{40x}{\sqrt{1 + x^2}} + 20.$$

    a. Find the marginal utility of precipitation, $B'(x)$, for this model.
    b. What is the long-term behavior of this marginal utility function? What does this mean for the relationship between precipitation and plant growth?

17. Patrick is a demographer working on population models for a major metropolitan area. He reports to his supervisor, Ellen, that the long-term behavior of the marginal population function, $P'(t)$, is to approach a constant value, D.
    a. Describe this statement using a limit at infinity.
    b. Will the population function $P(t)$ also "level off" in the long run? Why or why not?
    c. Ellen's task is to report to the city fathers on the long-run expectations for population size. What should she say, depending on the sign of D?

18. An ecologist has written, "It is infinitely cheaper to dispose of toxic waste safely in the first place than to clean it up later." Regardless of your position on the underlying issue, the ecologist has misused the notion of the infinite. Comment on this statement in the context of the discussion of infinite limits in this section.

☑ **SOLUTIONS TO PRACTICE PROBLEMS 2.9**

1. a. $\lim\limits_{x\to\infty} \dfrac{3 - \sqrt{x} + 4x^2}{3x^2 + 2x - 5} = \lim\limits_{x\to\infty} \dfrac{\dfrac{3}{x^2} - \dfrac{1}{x^{3/2}} + 4}{3 + \dfrac{2}{x} - \dfrac{5}{x^2}}$

$$= \dfrac{4}{3}.$$

b. $\lim\limits_{x\to\infty} \dfrac{\sqrt{x} + 3x}{5x^{2/3} + 3x^{3/2}} = \lim\limits_{x\to\infty} \dfrac{x^{-1} + 3x^{-1/2}}{5x^{-5/6} + 3} = 0.$

2. a. $c(x) = \dfrac{10{,}000}{x} + 400 + \dfrac{6}{\sqrt{x}}.$

b. $\lim\limits_{x\to\infty} c(x) = \lim\limits_{x\to\infty} \left(\dfrac{1000}{x} + 400 + \dfrac{6}{\sqrt{x}} \right)$

$$= 400.$$

Summary Outline of Chapter 2

▌ The **derivative** of the function f at $x = x_0$ is $f'(x_0) =$ (Page 112)
$$\lim_{h \to 0} \frac{f(x_0 + h) - f(x_0)}{h}.$$

▌ The **slope** of the line tangent to the graph of $y = f(x)$ at the point   (Page 83)
$(x_0, f(x_0))$ is the derivative $f'(x_0)$.

▌ An **equation** for the line tangent to the graph of $y = f(x)$ at the point   (Page 83)
$(x_0, f(x_0))$ is
$$y - f(x_0) = f'(x_0)(x - x_0)$$

▌ The statement $L = \lim_{x \to a} f(x)$, read, "the **limit** of f as x approaches a is   (Page 94)
L," means that the values $f(x)$ approach the unique number L as x approaches the number a.

▌ *Theorem* (Properties of Limits)   (Page 98)
$$\lim_{x \to a} (f + g)(x) = \lim_{x \to a} f(x) + \lim_{x \to a} g(x)$$
$$\lim_{x \to a} (cf)(x) = c \cdot \lim_{x \to a} f(x)$$
$$\lim_{x \to a} (fg)(x) = [\lim_{x \to a} f(x)] \cdot [\lim_{x \to a} g(x)]$$
$$\lim_{x \to a} (f/g)(x) = [\lim_{x \to a} f(x)]/[\lim_{x \to a} g(x)] \quad \text{if} \quad \lim_{x \to a} g(x) \neq 0$$

▌ The **one-sided limit,** $\lim_{x \to a^+} f(x) = L$, means that $f(x)$ approaches L as x (Page 102)
approaches a *from the right only*. The one-sided limit, $\lim_{x \to a^-} f(x) = L$,
means that $f(x)$ approaches L as x approaches a from the left only.

▌ The function f is continuous at $x = a$ if both $f(a)$ and $\lim_{x \to a} f(x)$ exist,   (Page 105)
and if $f(a) = \lim_{x \to a} f(x)$.

▌ *Rules for Calculating Derivatives*   (Page 117)

$$\frac{d}{dx}(c) = 0$$

$$\frac{d}{dx}(mx + b) = m$$

$$\frac{d}{dx}(x^n) = nx^{n-1} \quad \text{(Power Rule)}$$

$$\frac{d}{dx}[f(x) + g(x)] = \frac{d}{dx}f(x) + \frac{d}{dx}g(x)$$

$$\frac{d}{dx}[cf(x)] = c\frac{d}{dx}f(x)$$

$$\frac{d}{dx}[f(x)g(x)] = \left[\frac{d}{dx}f(x)\right]g(x) + f(x)\left[\frac{d}{dx}g(x)\right] \quad \text{(Product Rule)}$$

$$\frac{d}{dx}[\,f(x)/g(x)] = \frac{g(x)\left[\dfrac{d}{dx}f(x)\right] - f(x)\left[\dfrac{d}{dx}g(x)\right]}{[g(x)]^2} \qquad \text{(Quotient Rule)}$$

$$\frac{d}{dx}[u(x)]^n = n \cdot u(x)^{n-1}u'(x) \qquad \text{(Power Rule)}$$

$$\frac{d}{dx}g(u(x)) = g'(u(x))u'(x) \qquad \text{(Chain Rule)}$$

▌ *Applications*   (Page 132)

If $C(x)$ = total cost, then $MC(x) = C'(x)$ = marginal cost.
If $R(x)$ = total revenue, then $MR(x) = R'(x)$ = marginal revenue.
If $P(x)$ = total profit, then $MP(x) = P'(x)$ = marginal profit.
$MP(x) = MR(x) - MC(x)$

▌ If $s(t)$ is the position at time t of an object moving along a line and if   (Page 126)
$v(t)$ is the object's velocity at time t, then

$$v(t) = s'(t).$$

▌ If $U(x)$ is the utility associated with the consumption of x units of a   (Page 139)
quantity per unit time, then $MU(x) = U'(x)$ is the marginal utility
function.

Review Exercises—Chapter 2

In Exercises 1–14, find the indicated limit.

1. $\lim\limits_{x\to 2}(3x - 1)$

2. $\lim\limits_{x\to 2}\dfrac{2x - 1}{x + 6}$

3. $\lim\limits_{x\to 3}(x^4 - 4)$

4. $\lim\limits_{x\to 5}\dfrac{x^2 - 25}{x - 5}$

5. $\lim\limits_{x\to 3}\dfrac{x^2 - 9}{x - 3}$

6. $\lim\limits_{x\to 3}\dfrac{x - 3}{x^2 - 9}$

7. $\lim\limits_{x\to -2}\dfrac{x^2 + x - 2}{x + 2}$

8. $\lim\limits_{x\to 1}\dfrac{x^2 + 6x - 7}{x - 1}$

9. $\lim\limits_{x\to 1}\dfrac{x^2 + 2x - 3}{x^2 + x - 2}$

10. $\lim\limits_{x\to -2}\dfrac{x^2 + 4x + 4}{x^2 + x - 2}$

11. $\lim\limits_{t\to -1^+}\sqrt{\dfrac{1 - t^2}{1 - t}}$

12. $\lim\limits_{x\to 8}\sqrt{\dfrac{x - 7}{x + 2}}$

13. $\lim\limits_{x\to 0}\dfrac{(2 + x)^2 - 4}{x}$

14. $\lim\limits_{x\to 0}\dfrac{3x + 5x^2}{x}$

In Exercises 15–20, find those values of x for which $f(x)$ is discontinuous.

15. $f(x) = \dfrac{x^2 - 4}{x - 2}$

16. $f(x) = \dfrac{x^2 - 7}{x - 3x - 4}$

17. $f(x) = \dfrac{x + 2}{x^2 - x - 6}$

18. $f(x) = \dfrac{x}{|x|}$

19. $f(x) = \begin{cases} 2 - x^2, & x \le 2 \\ -x & x > 2 \end{cases}$

20. $f(x) = \begin{cases} \sqrt{x}, & x \le 4 \\ x - 1, & x > 4 \end{cases}$

In Exercises 21–46, find the derivative of the given function.

21. $f(x) = x^2 - x + 3$

22. $f(x) = 9 - x^3$

23. $f(x) = \sqrt{x} + 4$

24. $f(x) = \sqrt{x} - 3$

25. $f(x) = \dfrac{1}{x^2}$

26. $f(x) = \dfrac{9}{x^3}$

27. $f(x) = \dfrac{1}{x - 2}$

28. $f(x) = x^{1/3} - x$

29. $f(x) = mx + b$

30. $f(x) = \sqrt{1 - x}$

31. $f(x) = \dfrac{1}{3x - 7}$

32. $f(x) = \dfrac{1}{1 + \sqrt{x}}$

33. $f(x) = \dfrac{x - 1}{x + 3}$

34. $f(x) = \dfrac{\sqrt{x}}{1 + x}$

35. $f(x) = \dfrac{1}{x^2 + 6}$

36. $f(x) = \dfrac{1}{(x + 3)^3}$

37. $f(x) = (x^2 + 4x + 4)^2$

38. $f(x) = \sqrt{9 + x^2}$

39. $f(x) = (x^2 + 3)^{-2/3}$

40. $f(x) = x^{-4} + (x - 6)^{-3/4}$

41. $f(x) = \dfrac{1}{\sqrt{1 + x^2}}$

42. $f(x) = \dfrac{(x + 1)^2}{x^3 - 3}$

43. $f(x) = x^4\sqrt{1 + x^2}$

44. $f(x) = (x - 2)^3(x^2 + 9)^4$

45. $f(x) = (1 - x^2)^3(6 + 2x + 5x^3)^{-3}$

46. $f(x) = (x^2 - 9)\sqrt{3 - x}$

47. Find the slope of the demand curve $D(p) = \dfrac{200}{40 + p^2}$, at the point where $p = 10$.

48. Find the slope of the line tangent to the graph of $f(x) = (9 - x^2)^{2/3}$ at the point $(1, 4)$.

49. Find an equation for the line in Exercise 48.

50. The graph of the function $f(x) = x^2 - 1$ has two tangents that pass through the point $(0, -2)$. Find equations for these lines.

51. For the demand curve $D(p) = \dfrac{12}{p - 1}$, $p > 1$, and the supply curve $S(p) = p - 5$, $p > 5$, find
  a. the equilibrium price p_0 where $S(p_0) = D(p_0)$
  b. the slope of the demand curve at $(p_0, D(p_0))$
  c. the slope of the supply curve at $(p_0, S(p_0))$.

52. Excise taxes on automobiles in a certain state are levied according to the following schedule:

Value of Automobile	Excise Tax
$0 \le x < 5000$	$(10 + 0.02x)$ dollars
$5{,}000 \le x < 10{,}000$	$(A + 0.03(x - 2000))$ dollars
$10{,}000 \le x$	$(B + 0.04(x - 5000))$ dollars

Find A and B if the function $y = T(x)$, given that the tax as a function of x is continuous at $x_1 = 2000$ and $x_2 = 5000$.

53. The demand for lawnmowers in a certain market sector is determined to be

$$D(p) = \begin{cases} 2p - 5 & 50 \le p < 200 \\ p + 400, & 200 \le p < 400 \\ \dfrac{1}{2}p + 800, & 400 \le p \end{cases}$$

where $D(p)$ is the number of lawnmowers sold per week during the month of April at price p. For which prices p is D discontinuous?

54. a. Graph the revenue function

$$R(x) = \begin{cases} 4x, & 0 \le x < 10 \\ 140 - (x - 20)^2, & 10 \le x < 20 \\ 160 - x, & 20 \le x \end{cases}$$

  b. For what value of x is marginal revenue equal to 10?
  c. For which value(s) of x is marginal revenue equal to 4?

55. A manufacturer finds that the cost of producing x tennis racquets per week is $C(x) = 500 + 30x + \frac{1}{2}x^2$.
  a. Find the marginal cost $MC(x)$.
  b. Find the production level x for which $MC(x) = 60$.

56. A rug weaver makes a weekly revenue from the sale of x rugs of a certain type to be $R(x) = 450x - \dfrac{x^2}{4}$.
  a. Find the marginal revenue $MR(x)$.
  b. Find $MR(40)$.
  c. For which values of $x > 0$ is $MR(x) > 0$?
  d. For which values of $x > 0$ is $MR(x) < 0$?

57. An athletic equipment supplier experiences weekly costs of $C(x) = 700 + 40x + \frac{1}{3}x^3$ in producing x baseball gloves per week.
  a. Find the marginal cost $MC(x)$.
  b. Find the production level x for which marginal cost is \$76 per glove.

58. A manufacturer of kitchen appliances experiences revenues from the sale of x refrigerators per month of

$$R(x) = 750x - \dfrac{x^2}{6} - \dfrac{2x^3}{3} \text{ dollars.}$$

  a. Find the marginal revenue $MR(x)$.
  b. Find the marginal revenue at sales level $x = 10$ refrigerators per month.

59. A manufacturer of cameras finds that the number x of cameras that can be sold per month at price p is given by the demand equation $x = 500 - 2p$.
   a. Find price $p(x)$ as a function of x.
   b. Find the monthly revenue function $R(x) = xp(x)$.
   c. Find the marginal revenue function $MR = \dfrac{dR}{dx}$.
   d. For what production level x is $MR(x) = 0$?

60. The manufacturer in Exercise 59 finds that the total cost of producing x cameras per month is $C(x) = 40 + 50x$ dollars.
   a. Find the marginal cost $MC(x)$.
   b. Find the monthly profit $P(x) = R(x) - C(x)$.
   c. Find the marginal profit $MP(x)$.
   d. Find the production level at which $MP(x) = 0$.

61. A manufacturer experiences total costs of producing x items per day of $C(x) = 400 + 50x$ dollars.
   a. Find the average daily cost per item $c(x) = \dfrac{C(x)}{x}$.
   b. Find the marginal average daily cost per item $c'(x)$.

62. For the utility curve $U(x) = 20\sqrt{x^2 + 9}$ find
   a. marginal utility $MU(x) = U'(x)$
   b. marginal utility for $x = 4$, $MU(4)$.

63. Compensation consultants for Bong Airlines advise management that an employee's total utility (satisfaction) resulting from a salary of x thousand dollars per month is modelled by the utility function
$$u(x) = \sqrt{x(x + 24)}.$$
   Find the associated marginal utility function $mu(x) = u'(x)$.

64. For the utility function $u(x)$ in Exercise 63, find the value of the marginal utility function $u'(x)$ at
   a. $x = 1$ ($1000 per month)
   b. $x = 3$ ($3000 per month).

65. For the utility function in Exercises 63 and 64, which employee will appreciate more an increase of an equal amount in salary:
   a. an employee earning $1000 per month, or
   b. an employee earning $3000 per month? Why?

3

Designing highways for optimal "traffic flow" involves finding the maximum value of the function modelling the traffic behavior resulting from given speeds and densities of automobiles on the highway. These and other applications of the derivatives are discussed in this chapter.
(Guido Alberto Rossi/The Image Bank)

Applications of the Derivative

3.1 Increasing and Decreasing Functions

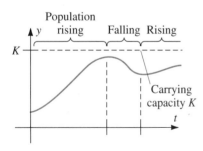

Figure 1.1 Population size $P(t)$ rises and falls as it approaches the system's carrying capacity.

Figure 1.1 shows the graph of a population function $P(t)$ of the kind often experienced when a species of plants or animals is placed in an environment with a limited "carrying capacity." Previously cited examples of such situations are pine trees in a woodlot or fish in a fishery.

Note that the graph of $P(t)$ first rises toward the carrying capacity, then falls, then rises again, and so on. Such changes, from rising to falling, may occur because of interactions between the population and its environment or for more intrinsic reasons (mating and reproductive issues are included in this category).

In this chapter we shall study the properties of functions that cause their graphs to rise or fall. The corresponding behavior of functions is referred to as "increasing" or "decreasing." Understanding how to analyze this type of behavior will enable us to find the maximum and minimum values of given functions, something that is useful in business applications (maximizing revenues and profits and minimizing costs) as well as in more biologically oriented settings (maximizing yield from a vegetable crop or minimizing the energy loss in a ''food chain'' leading from grain crops to processed poultry products, for example).

We begin with a precise definition for two key terms.

Definition 1

Let I be an open interval. Then

(i) The function f is said to be **increasing** on I if

$$f(x_2) > f(x_1) \qquad \text{whenever} \qquad x_1 < x_2$$

for any numbers x_1 and x_2 in I.

(ii) The function f is said to be **decreasing** on I if

$$f(x_2) < f(x_1) \qquad \text{whenever} \qquad x_1 < x_2$$

for any numbers x_1 and x_2 in I.

Definition 1 says that f is increasing if the values $f(x)$ increase when x does. Thus the graph of an increasing function ''runs uphill.'' (See Figure 1.2.) And a decreasing function has the property that its values $f(x)$ *decrease* when x increases. Graphs of decreasing functions ''run downhill.'' (See Figure 1.3.)

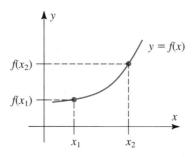

Figure 1.2 f is increasing if $f(x_2) > f(x_1)$ whenever $x_1 < x_2$.

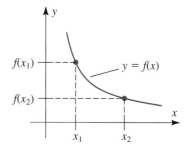

Figure 1.3 f is decreasing if $f(x_2) < f(x_1)$ whenever $x_1 < x_2$.

Figure 1.4 indicates how we can use the derivative to determine the intervals on which a function is either increasing or decreasing. Since the derivative $f'(x)$ measures the slope of the graph of f at x, f is increasing (running uphill) when $f'(x)$ is positive, and f is decreasing (running downhill) when $f'(x)$ is negative. Theorem 1 formalizes this observation. While its truth should seem obvious from the geometric interpretation of the derivative as a slope, we shall actually prove this theorem in Section 3.9, using the Mean Value Theorem.

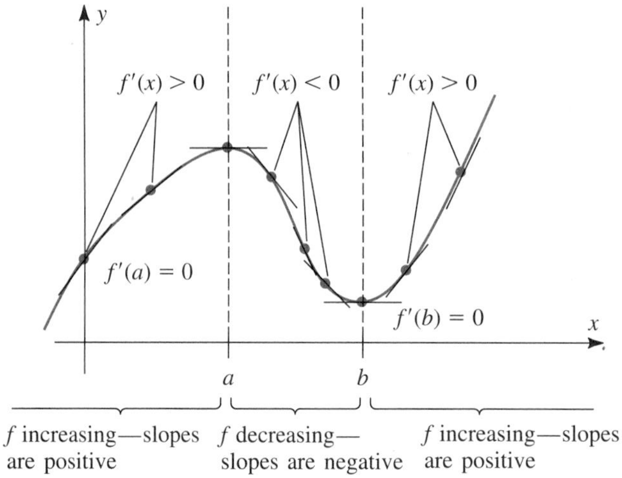

Figure 1.4 Sign of $f'(x)$ determines whether f is increasing or decreasing at x.

Theorem 1	Let f be differentiable on an open interval I.

(i) If $f'(x) > 0$ for all x in I, then f is increasing on I.

(ii) If $f'(x) < 0$ for all x in I, then f is decreasing on I.

How can we use Theorem 1 to find the intervals on which a function is either increasing or decreasing? The idea is really very simple. Notice in Figure 1.4 that f changes from increasing to decreasing at $x = a$ *and $f'(a)$ equals zero.* Also, f changes from decreasing to increasing at $x = b$ *and $f'(b)$ equals zero.* More generally, when f' is a continuous function, f can change from increasing to decreasing (or vice versa) only where $f'(x) = 0$. (This is because the *continuous* function f' cannot ''skip'' the value zero in changing sign from positive to negative, or vice versa, without actually equaling zero for some number x.) So we simply find the zeros of f' and check the sign of f' on the resulting intervals between the zeros.

☐ **EXAMPLE 1**

For the function $f(x) = x(20 - x)$ find the open intervals on which f is (a) increasing and (b) decreasing.

Strategy

Find f'.

Solution

For the function $f(x) = x(20 - x) = 20x - x^2$, we have

$$f'(x) = 20 - 2x.$$

Set $f'(x) = 0$ and solve to find the zero(s) of f'.

Setting $f'(x) = 0$ gives

$$20 - 2x = 0$$

or

$$x = 10.$$

Identify the intervals determined by the zeros of f'.

This single zero of f' gives the two intervals $(-\infty, 10)$ and $(10, \infty)$ on which we must determine the sign of f'. We do this by checking the sign of $f'(x)$ at an arbitrarily chosen "test number" t in each interval:

Determine the sign of f' on each interval by checking its sign at any particular number of t.

(i) In the interval $(-\infty, 10)$, we pick, say, $t_1 = 5$. Since

$$f'(5) = 20 - 2(5) = 10 > 0$$

we conclude that f is *increasing* on $(-\infty, 10)$.

Apply Theorem 1: f is increasing if $f'(t) > 0$; decreasing if $f'(t) < 0$.

(ii) In the interval $(10, \infty)$ we pick, say, $t_2 = 15$. Since

$$f'(15) = 20 - 2(15) = -10 < 0$$

we conclude that f is *decreasing* on $(10, \infty)$.
(See Table 1.1 and Figure 1.5.)   ■

Table 1.1 Sign of $f'(x)$ Determines Whether f is Increasing or Decreasing

Interval I	Test Number t in I	Sign of $f'(t)$	Conclusion
$(-\infty, 10)$	$t_1 = 5$	$f'(5) = 10 > 0$	f is increasing
$(10, \infty)$	$t_2 = 15$	$f'(15) = -10 < 0$	f is decreasing

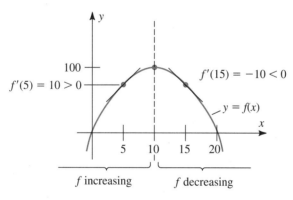

Figure 1.5 $f(x) = x(20 - x)$.

☐ EXAMPLE 2

Find the open intervals on which the function $f(x) = 2x^3 + 3x^2 - 12x + 1$ is (a) increasing and (b) decreasing.

Strategy · · · · · · · ·

Find f'.

Solution

The derivative is

$$f'(x) = 6x^2 + 6x - 12$$
$$= 6(x^2 + x - 2)$$
$$= 6(x + 2)(x - 1).$$

Set $f'(x) = 0$ and solve to find the zeros of f.

Check the sign of $f'(t)$ on each of the resulting intervals and apply Theorem 1.

Setting $f'(x) = 0$ gives $x = -2$ and $x = 1$. We must therefore check the sign of f' on each of the intervals $(-\infty, -2)$, $(-2, 1)$, and $(1, \infty)$.

(i) Choosing $t_1 = -3$ in the interval $(-\infty, -2)$, we find

$$f'(-3) = 6(-3)^2 + 6(-3) - 12 = 24 > 0.$$

Thus f is increasing on $(-\infty, -2)$.

(ii) Choosing $t_2 = 0$ in the interval $(-2, 1)$ gives

$$f'(0) = 6(0)^2 + 6(0) - 12 = -12 < 0$$

so f is decreasing on $(-2, 1)$.

(iii) Choosing $t_3 = 2$ in the interval $(1, \infty)$ gives

$$f'(2) = 6(2)^2 + 6(2) - 12 = 24 > 0$$

so f is increasing on $(1, \infty)$. (See Table 1.2 and Figure 1.6.) ∎

Table 1.2 Analysis of $f(x) = 2x^3 + 3x^2 - 12x + 1$

Interval I	Test Number t in I	Sign of $f'(t)$	Conclusion
$(-\infty, -2)$	$t_1 = -3$	$f'(-3) = 24 > 0$	f increasing
$(-2, 1)$	$t_2 = 0$	$f'(0) = -12 < 0$	f decreasing
$(1, \infty)$	$t_3 = 2$	$f'(2) = 24 > 0$	f increasing

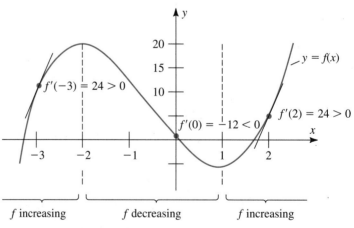

Figure 1.6 $f(x) = 2x^3 + 3x^2 - 12x + 1$.

When $f'(x)$ Fails to Exist

In Examples 1 and 2 the functions f each had a continuous derivative. Thus the only place at which f could change from increasing ($f'(x) > 0$) to decreasing ($f'(x) < 0$), or vice versa, was at a zero of f'. However, when the derivative $f'(x)$

fails to exist at a number $x = x_0$ it is possible that f may change from increasing to decreasing, or vice versa, at $x = x_0$. The next two examples show that this can happen when $f(x_0)$ itself is undefined, or when $f'(x_0)$ fails to exist because of a factor of zero in its denominator.

☐ **EXAMPLE 3**

For the function $f(x) = \dfrac{1}{x^2} = x^{-2}$, the derivative is $f'(x) = -2x^{-3} = \dfrac{-2}{x^3}$. Note that

(i) $f'(0)$ is undefined, as is $f(0)$.

(ii) If $x < 0$, $f'(x) = \dfrac{-2}{x^3}$ is positive, so f is increasing on $(-\infty, 0)$.

(iii) But if $x > 0$, $f'(x) = \dfrac{-2}{x^3}$ is negative, so f is decreasing on $(0, \infty)$.

Thus f changes from increasing to decreasing at $x_0 = 0$ where $f'(x_0)$ is undefined. (See Figure 1.7.) ■

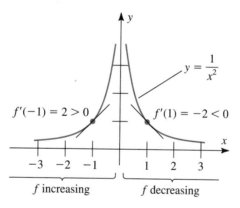

Figure 1.7 $f(x) = \dfrac{1}{x^2}$ changes from increasing to decreasing at $x = 0$ where $f'(x)$ is undefined.

☐ **EXAMPLE 4**

The function $f(x) = x^{2/3}$ is defined for all x. But the derivative $f'(x) = \dfrac{2}{3} x^{-1/3} = \dfrac{2}{3\sqrt[3]{x}}$ fails to exist at $x = 0$. Moreover,

(i) If $x < 0$, $f'(x) = \dfrac{2}{3\sqrt[3]{x}}$ is negative, so f is decreasing on $(-\infty, 0)$.

(ii) If $x > 0$, $f'(x) = \dfrac{2}{3\sqrt[3]{x}}$ is positive, so f is increasing on $(0, \infty)$.

Here f changes from decreasing to increasing at $x_0 = 0$ where $f'(x_0)$ is undefined. (See Figure 1.8.) ■

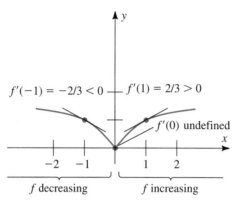

$f'(-1) = -2/3 < 0$ $f'(1) = 2/3 > 0$

$f'(0)$ undefined

f decreasing f increasing

Figure 1.8 $f(x) = x^{2/3}$ changes from decreasing to increasing where $f'(x)$ is undefined.

The following procedure summarizes our findings.

Procedure for Determining the Open Intervals on Which f Is Either Increasing or Decreasing:

(1) Find all numbers x for which $f'(x) = 0$.
(2) Find all numbers x for which $f'(x)$ fails to exist.
(3) Identify all intervals I in the domain of f determined by the numbers in steps (1) and (2).
(4) In each interval I select one "test number" t_0 and determine the sign of $f'(t_0)$:
    (a) If $f'(t_0) > 0$, f is increasing on I.
    (b) If $f'(t_0) < 0$, f is decreasing on I.

□ **EXAMPLE 5**

A manufacturer of motorcycles finds that its weekly revenue from the sale of x motorcycles is approximately

$$R(x) = 1440x - 54x^2 - 3x^3 \text{ dollars.}$$

At which production levels x will revenue increase as production increases?

Solution: Here the derivative is

$$R'(x) = MR(x) = 1440 - 108x - 9x^2$$
$$= (20 + x)(72 - 9x).$$

Thus $R'(x) = 0$ when $(20 + x) = 0$ or when $(72 - 9x) = 0$. Since only nonnegative levels of production make sense, the domain of R is $[0, \infty)$ and the only zero of R' that lies in this domain occurs when $72 - 9x = 0$, that is, at $x = 8$. Also, there are no numbers x for which $R'(x)$ is undefined. We must therefore examine the sign of R' on the intervals $(0, 8)$ and $(8, \infty)$.

(i) On the interval $(0, 8)$ we choose the test number $t_1 = 4$, and we find

$$R'(4) = 1440 - 108(4) - 9(4^2) = 864 > 0.$$

Since $R'(4) > 0$, revenue is increasing for $0 < x < 8$.

(ii) On the interval $(8, \infty)$ we choose the test number $t_2 = 10$, and we find

$$R'(10) = 1440 - 108(10) - 9(10^2) = -540 < 0.$$

Since $R'(10) < 0$, revenue is decreasing for $x > 8$.

Figure 1.9 shows the graph of the revenue function $y = R(x)$.   ∎

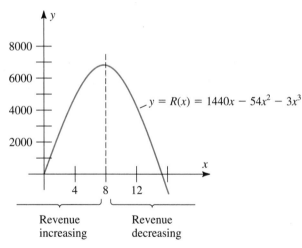

Figure 1.9 Revenue function $R(x) = 1440x - 54x^2 - 3x^3$ in Example 5.

☑ **PRACTICE PROBLEMS 3.1**

1. Find the open intervals on which the function

$$f(x) = 2x^3 + 3x^2 - 120x + 30$$

is either increasing or decreasing.

2. A manufacturer's total cost in producing x items per day is given by the function

$$C(x) = 500 + 20x + 5x^2, \qquad x \geq 0$$

dollars. Find the intervals on which the average cost function, $c(x) = \dfrac{C(x)}{x}$, is either increasing or decreasing.

Exercise Set 3.1

In Exercises 1–20, find the open intervals on which f is (a) increasing and (b) decreasing.

1. $f(x) = 7 + 3x$

2. $f(x) = 9 - x$

3. $f(x) = 9 - x^2$

4. $f(x) = x^2 - 7x + 6$

5. $f(x) = x - x^3$

6. $f(x) = x^3 + 3x^2 - 24x + 10$

7. $f(x) = x^3 - 3x + 6$

8. $f(x) = 2x^3 - 3x^2 - 12x + 6$

9. $f(x) = x^3 - 12x^2 + 48x + 12$

10. $f(x) = x^3 + 3x^2 - 9x + 6$

11. $f(x) = 2x^3 - 3x^2 - 36x + 6$

12. $f(x) = x^4 - 18x^2 + 8$

13. $f(x) = 3x^4 + 4x^3 - 12x^2 + 12$

14. $f(x) = \dfrac{1}{x - 3}$

15. $f(x) = x^{4/3} + 3$

16. $f(x) = \sqrt{x^2 + 2}$

17. $f(x) = |4 - x^2|$

18. $f(x) = (x + 3)^{2/3}$

19. $f(x) = \sqrt[3]{8 - x^3}$

20. $f(x) = |9 - x^2|$

21. The function $f(x) = 2x^3 - 3ax^2 + 6$ decreases only on the interval $(0, 3)$. Find a.

22. Profits for the XYZ Corporation during the 10 years of its existence were given by the function $P(t) = \dfrac{50}{1 + (t - 6)^2}$. During which periods were profits (a) increasing, (b) decreasing?

23. The sum of two numbers is 50. If x denotes one of these numbers, for which numbers x is the product of the two numbers increasing?

24. The total cost of producing x reading lamps per week is determined by a manufacturer to be $C(x) = 100 + 5x + 0.02x^2$.
a. For which numbers $x > 0$ is total cost $C(x)$ increasing?
b. For which numbers $x > 0$ is average per unit cost $c(x) = \dfrac{C(x)}{x}$ increasing?

25. A manufacturer of sofas finds that its total cost in producing x sofas per week is $C(x) = 20 + 200x + 0.01x^3$. For which numbers x is average weekly per item cost $c(x) = \dfrac{C(x)}{x}$
a. increasing?
b. decreasing?

26. A producer of graphics software finds that the selling price p for its software is related to its annual sales level x by the demand equation $x = 10{,}000 - 200p$, while its total annual cost of producing x copies of its software is given by the function $C(x) = 450{,}000 + 5x$.
a. Find $C(p)$, its total annual cost as a function of selling price p.
b. Is $C(p)$ an increasing or decreasing function of p? Why?
c. Find $R(p) = xp$, its annual revenue as a function of p.
d. For which numbers $p > 0$ is $R(p)$ an increasing function of p?
e. Find $P(p) = R(p) - C(p)$, its annual profit as a function of p.
f. For which numbers $p > 0$ is P increasing?
g. For which numbers $p > 0$ is P decreasing?

27. For the revenue function $R(x) = 1500x - 60x^2 - x^3$
a. For which numbers $x > 0$ is R increasing?
b. For which numbers $x > 0$ is marginal revenue decreasing?

28. For the utility function $U(x) = \sqrt{40 - 10x + x^2}$
a. Find the marginal utility function $MU(x) = U'(x)$.
b. For which numbers $x > 0$ is utility increasing?
c. For which numbers $x > 0$ is utility decreasing?

29. A producer of art prints finds that it can sell $x = 1000 - 2p$ prints monthly at retail price p. The total monthly cost of producing these x prints is $C(x) = 400 + 2x$ dollars.
 a. Find the producer's monthly revenue $R(x) = xp$.
 b. For which numbers $x > 0$ is monthly revenue increasing?
 c. Find the producer's monthly profit $P(x) = R(x) - C(x)$.
 d. For which numbers $x > 0$ is P increasing?
 e. For which numbers $x > 0$ is P decreasing?

30. A tool rental company can achieve 500 daily rentals of jack-hammers per month at a daily rate of $30 per jackhammer. For each $1 increase in price 10 fewer daily rentals are achieved.
 a. Find $R(p)$, the company's monthly revenue from renting jackhammers at p dollars per day.
 b. For which numbers $p > 0$ is R increasing as a function of p?
 c. For which numbers $p > 0$ is R decreasing as a function of p?

31. Demographers predict that the population of a certain urban region will follow the model

$$P(t) = \frac{Kt}{100 + t^2}, \quad t > 0$$

for the next 20 years, where K is a positive constant. For which values of $t = $ time will $P(t)$ increase? Decrease?

32. A city is hit by an epidemic of winter colds. Public health officials report that t days after the epidemic is declared, the number of infected citizens is given by $N(t)$ where

$$N(t) = 20{,}000 + 20t^2 - 2t^3, \quad t > 0.$$

 a. During which times is the epidemic growing?
 b. During which times is the epidemic declining?

33. Sketch the graph of the function f in Practice Problem 1.

34. Sketch the graph of the total cost function C in Practice Problem 2. On what intervals is it increasing or decreasing?

35. Explain why the *average cost* function c in Practice Problem 2 changes from decreasing to increasing at $x = 10$, but the total cost function does not.

36. Graph the average cost function c in Practice Problem 2.

✔ SOLUTIONS TO PRACTICE PROBLEMS 3.1

1. The derivative of $f(x) = 2x^3 + 3x^2 - 120x + 30$ is

$$\begin{aligned} f'(x) &= 6x^2 + 6x - 120 \\ &= 6(x^2 + x - 20) \\ &= 6(x + 5)(x - 4) \end{aligned}$$

which equals zero at $x_1 = -5$ and $x_2 = 4$. Checking the sign of f' at a test number in each of the resulting intervals gives the conclusions listed below.

Interval I	Test Number $t \in I$	Sign of $f'(t)$	Conclusion
$(-\infty, -5)$	$t_1 = -6$	$f'(-6) = 60 > 0$	f increasing
$(-5, 4)$	$t_2 = 0$	$f'(0) = -120 < 0$	f decreasing
$(4, \infty)$	$t_3 = 5$	$f'(5) = 60 > 0$	f increasing

2. The average cost function is

$$\begin{aligned} c(x) = \frac{C(x)}{x} &= \frac{1}{x}(500 + 20x + 5x^2) \\ &= \frac{500}{x} + 20 + 5x \end{aligned}$$

Its derivative is

$$c'(x) = -\frac{500}{x^2} + 5.$$

Setting $c'(x) = 0$ gives the equation

$$-\frac{500}{x^2} + 5 = 0$$

or

$$5x^2 = 500$$

which has solutions $x = \pm 10$. Since $c(x)$ is not defined for $x < 0$ in this application, we must check the sign $c'(x)$ on the intervals $(0, 10)$ and $(10, \infty)$. The results are as follows:

Interval I	Test Number $t \in I$	Sign of $c'(t)$	Conclusion
$(0, 10)$	$t_1 = 5$	$c'(5) = -15 < 0$	$c(x)$ decreasing
$(10, \infty)$	$t_2 = 20$	$c'(20) = \dfrac{15}{4} > 0$	$c(x)$ increasing

3.2 Relative Maxima and Minima

We can use the basic facts about increasing and decreasing functions to determine the high and low points on the graph of a function. Figure 2.1 shows one reason why we would want to do this: The profit function $y = P(x)$ has its largest value at the sales level x_0 for which $(x_0, P(x_0))$ is the highest point on the graph of $y = P(x)$.

Figure 2.2 shows a more general situation for the graph of a function $y = f(x)$ with several "relative" high and low points. We refer to these values as *relative maxima and minima*, which we define as follows.

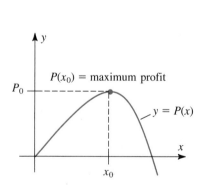

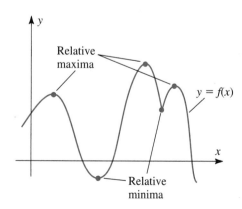

Figure 2.1 Profit $P(x)$ is a maximum at sales level $x = x_0$.

Figure 2.2 Several relative maxima and minima for $y = f(x)$.

Definition 2

The value $M = f(c)$ is a **relative maximum** for the function f if there exists a number $h > 0$ so that

$$f(c) \geq f(x)$$

for all x in the interval $(c - h, c + h)$.

The value $m = f(d)$ is a **relative minimum** for the function f if there exists a number $h > 0$ so that

$$f(d) \leq f(x)$$

for all x in the interval $(d - h, d + h)$.

In other words, $M = f(c)$ is a relative maximum if $f(c)$ is the largest value of f for all x "near" c. Similarly, $m = f(d)$ is a relative minimum if $f(d)$ is the smallest value of f for x "near" d. (See Figures 2.3 and 2.4.) We use the term **relative extremum** to refer to either a relative maximum or a relative minimum.

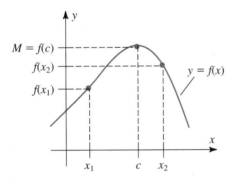

Figure 2.3 $M = f(c)$ is a relative maximum if $f(c) \geq f(x)$ for all x near c.

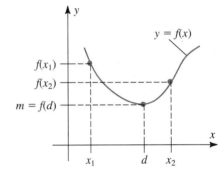

Figure 2.4 $m = f(d)$ is a relative minimum if $f(d) \leq f(x)$ for all x near d.

The following theorem is our basic tool in finding relative extrema.

Theorem 2

Let f be a continuous function defined on some open interval containing the number c. If $f(c)$ is a relative maximum or minimum value of the function f, then either

(i) $f'(c) = 0$, or else
(ii) $f'(c)$ fails to exist.

Theorem 2 is proved using Theorem 1 in an argument that we shall only sketch. The idea is simply to rule out the possibilities that $f'(c) > 0$ or $f'(c) < 0$ when $f(c)$ is a relative extremum. This will leave only the possibilities (i) $f'(c) = 0$ or (ii) $f'(c)$ fails to exist.

The possibility $f'(c) > 0$ is ruled out by showing that if $f'(c) > 0$, then $f(x) > f(c)$ for sufficiently small x with $x > c$. But this would mean that $f(c)$ could not be a relative maximum. Also, we would have $f(x) < f(c)$ for sufficiently large x with $x < c$, so $f(c)$ could not be a relative minimum. Thus the possibility $f'(c) > 0$ leads to the contradiction that $f(c)$ is not a relative extremum, so it cannot be true and must be ruled out. A similar argument rules out the possibility $f'(c) < 0$.

☐ **EXAMPLE 1**

Figure 2.5 shows one example of the condition $f'(c) = 0$ at a relative maximum. From our study of the quadratic function $f(x) = 2 - (x - 1)^2$ we know that its graph is a parabola whose highest point occurs at the point $(1, 2)$. Since $f'(x) = -2(x - 1)$, we have $f'(x) = 0$ when $x = 1$, the x-coordinate of the "high point." ∎

☐ **EXAMPLE 2**

Figure 2.6 shows an example of the condition of $f'(c)$ failing to exist at a relative minimum. The function $f(x) = (x - 2)^{2/3}$ has derivative $f'(x) = \dfrac{2}{3}(x - 2)^{-1/3} = \dfrac{2}{3(x - 2)^{1/3}}$. This derivative fails to exist at $x = 2$, which corresponds to the relative minimum value $f(2) = 0$. Note the "cusp" or "point" on the graph of $y = f(x)$ at $(2, 0)$. ∎

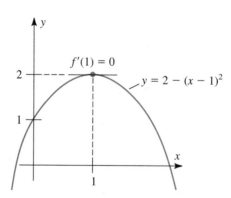

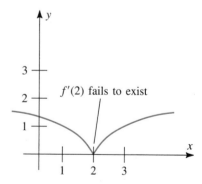

Figure 2.5 For $f(x) = 2 - (x - 1)^2$ the relative maximum if $f(1) = 2$, the "high point" of the parabola, and $f'(1) = 0$.

Figure 2.6 For $f(x) = (x - 2)^{2/3}$, the relative minimum is $f(2) = 0$ where $f'(x)$ is undefined.

Critical Numbers

Since the only numbers x for which $f(x)$ can be a relative extremum are those for which $f'(x) = 0$ or $f'(x)$ is undefined, we give these numbers a special name.

Definition 3

The **critical numbers** for the function f are those numbers x for which $f(x)$ exists and either

(i) $f'(x) = 0$, or
(ii) $f'(x)$ fails to exist.

Using this terminology we may paraphrase Theorem 2 by stating that *relative extrema can occur only at critical numbers*. This is the point of Figure 2.7.

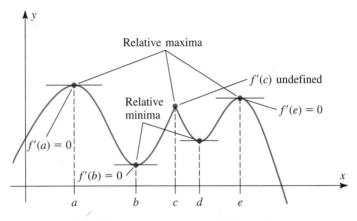

Figure 2.7 All relative extrema occur at critical numbers.

Identifying Relative Extrema

To find the relative maxima and minima for f, we obviously begin by finding the critical numbers for f. But if c is such a critical number, how can we determine if $f(c)$ is indeed a relative maximum or minimum? The answer is suggested by Figures 2.8 and 2.9:

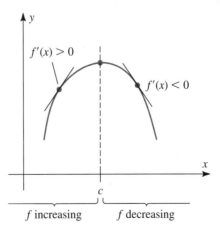

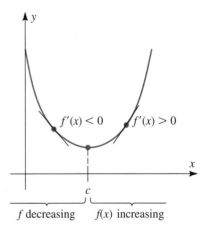

Figure 2.8 If $f'(x) > 0$ for $x < c$ and $f'(x) < 0$ for $x > c$, then $f(c)$ is a relative maximum.

Figure 2.9 If $f'(x) < 0$ for $x < c$ and $f'(x) > 0$ for $x > c$, then $f(c)$ is a relative minimum.

(i) If f is increasing for $x < c$ and decreasing for $x > c$, then $f(c)$ is a relative maximum (i.e., a high point on the graph of $y = f(x)$).

(ii) If f is decreasing for $x < c$ and increasing for $x > c$, then $f(c)$ is a relative minimum (i.e., a low point on the graph of $y = f(x)$).

Since the sign of f' determines whether f is increasing or decreasing, the following theorem formalizes these observations. It is called the *First Derivative Test for relative extrema.*

Theorem 3

First Derivative Test

Let c be a critical number for f and let I be an interval containing c but no other critical numbers for f. Then, for x in the interval I

(i) If $f'(x) > 0$ for $x < c$ and $f'(x) < 0$ for $x > c$, then $f(c)$ is a relative maximum.

(ii) If $f'(x) < 0$ for $x < c$ and $f'(x) > 0$ for $x > c$, then $f(c)$ is a relative minimum.

(iii) If f' does not change sign at $x = c$, then $f(c)$ is neither a relative maximum nor a relative minimum.

□ **EXAMPLE 3**

Find the relative extrema for the function $f(x) = 2x^3 - 3x^2 - 12x + 1$.

Strategy   ·   ·   ·   ·   ·   ·   ·

Find f'.

Solution

The derivative is

$$f'(x) = 6x^2 - 6x - 12$$
$$= 6(x^2 - x - 2)$$
$$= 6(x + 1)(x - 2).$$

Set $f'(x) = 0$ to find the critical numbers.

Check the sign of f' on each of the intervals determined by the critical numbers.

Thus $f'(x) = 0$ if $x = -1$ or $x = 2$. Since $f'(x)$ is defined for all x, the only critical numbers are $c_1 = -1$ and $c_2 = 2$. We must therefore check the sign of f' on the intervals $(-\infty, -1)$, $(-1, 2)$, and $(2, \infty)$. We do so by selecting one "test number" in each interval. Table 2.1 shows the results.

Table 2.1

Interval I	Test Number t	Value of $f'(t)$	Sign of $f'(t)$
$(-\infty, -1)$	$t = -2$	$f'(-2) = 24$	$+$
$(-1, 2)$	$t = 0$	$f'(0) = -12$	$-$
$(2, \infty)$	$t = 3$	$f'(3) = 24$	$+$

Figure 2.10 shows the results of Table 2.1 as a "sign analysis" of f' on the number line.

Figure 2.10 Sign of f'.

Apply the First Derivative Test to the information about the sign of f'.

According to the First Derivative Test

$$f(-1) = 8 \text{ is a relative maximum.}$$

$$f(2) = -19 \text{ is a relative minimum.}$$

The graph of $y = f(x)$ appears in Figure 2.11. ■

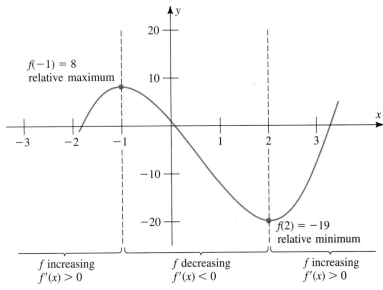

Figure 2.11 Graph of $f(x) = 2x^3 - 3x^2 - 12x + 1$.

☐ **EXAMPLE 4**

The function $f(x) = x^3$ provides an example of a critical number that yields neither a relative maximum nor a relative minimum. Here $f'(x) = 3x^2$, so setting $f'(x) = 0$ gives the single critical number $c = 0$. But since $f'(x) = 3x^2$ is positive on both the intervals $(-\infty, 0)$ and $(0, \infty)$, the derivative does not change sign at the critical number $c = 0$. In fact, $f(x) = x^3$ is increasing for all x. (See Figure 2.12.) ■

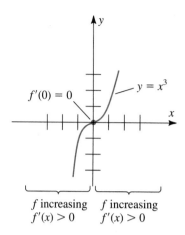

Figure 2.12 $f(x) = x^3$ has a critical number at $c = 0$ but no relative extrema.

☐ **EXAMPLE 5**

For $f(x) = 4x^2(1 - x^2)$, find all relative extrema.

Solution: Since $f(x) = 4x^2 - 4x^4$, we have

$$f'(x) = 8x - 16x^3$$
$$= 8x(1 - 2x^2).$$

Setting $f'(x) = 0$ gives $8x(1 - 2x^2) = 0$, so either

$$8x = 0 \quad \text{or} \quad 1 - 2x^2 = 0.$$

Thus either

$$x = 0 \quad \text{or} \quad x^2 = \frac{1}{2}.$$

The three critical numbers are therefore $c_1 = 0$, $c_2 = -\dfrac{\sqrt{2}}{2}$, and $c_3 = \dfrac{\sqrt{2}}{2}$. Table 2.2 shows the result of checking the sign of $f'(x)$ on each of the resulting intervals.

Table 2.2

Interval I	Test Number t	Value $f'(t)$	Sign of $f'(t)$
$\left(-\infty, -\dfrac{\sqrt{2}}{2}\right)$	$t = -1$	$f'(-1) = 8$	$+$
$\left(-\dfrac{\sqrt{2}}{2}, 0\right)$	$t = -\dfrac{1}{2}$	$f'\left(-\dfrac{1}{2}\right) = -2$	$-$
$\left(0, \dfrac{\sqrt{2}}{2}\right)$	$t = \dfrac{1}{2}$	$f'\left(\dfrac{1}{2}\right) = 2$	$+$
$\left(\dfrac{\sqrt{2}}{2}, \infty\right)$	$t = 1$	$f'(1) = -8$	$-$

Figure 2.13 shows the result of this sign analysis on the number line. From the First Derivative Test we conclude that

$$f\left(-\frac{\sqrt{2}}{2}\right) = 1 \text{ is a relative maximum.}$$

$$f(0) = 0 \text{ is a relative minimum.}$$

$$f\left(\frac{\sqrt{2}}{2}\right) = 1 \text{ is a relative maximum.}$$

The graph of $f(x) = 4x^2(1 - x^2)$ appears in Figure 2.14. ■

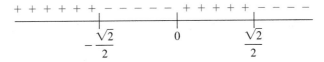

Figure 2.13 Sign analysis for $f'(x) = 8x(1 - 2x^2)$.

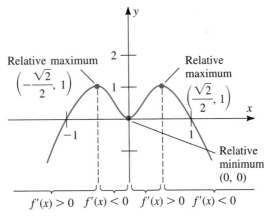

Figure 2.14 Relative extrema for $f(x) = 4x^2(1 - x^2)$.

☑ **PRACTICE PROBLEMS 3.2**

1. Find all relative extrema for the function

$$f(x) = x^3 - 6x^2 - 36x - 20.$$

2. In Practice Problem 2, Section 3.1, a manufacturer's total cost function was given as

$$C(x) = 500 + 20x + 5x^2, \ x \ge 0.$$

Find the relative extrema for the manufacturer's average cost function $c(x) = \dfrac{C(x)}{x}$ and graph this function.

Exercise Set 3.2

In Exercises 1–22, find all critical numbers for f. Then classify each critical number as corresponding to a relative maximum, a relative minimum, or neither. Use this information to sketch the graph of f, where possible.

1. $f(x) = x^2 - 2x$

2. $f(x) = x^2 + 3x + 2$

3. $f(x) = 3x^2 - 6x + 3$

4. $f(x) = x^2 - x - 6$

5. $f(x) = 9 - 4x - x^2$

6. $f(x) = (x - 3)(2 + x)$

7. $f(x) = \sqrt{x^2 + 2}$

8. $f(x) = x^3 - 3x^2 + 6$

9. $f(x) = x^3 - 3x + 7$

10. $f(x) = 2x^3 + 3x^2 - 36x + 4$

11. $f(x) = x^{3/2} - 3x + 7$

12. $f(x) = x^{4/3} - 4x - 3$

13. $f(x) = 4x^3 + 9x^2 - 12x + 7$

14. $f(x) = x^4 + 4x^3 - 8x^2 - 48x + 9$

15. $f(x) = 3x^4 - 8x^3 - 18x^2 + 36$

16. $f(x) = \dfrac{x - 1}{x + 1}$

17. $f(x) = 9x - x^{-1}$

18. $f(x) = x^{1/3}(x - 7)^2$

19. $f(x) = x^{5/3} - 5x^{2/3} + 3$

20. $f(x) = \dfrac{x - 1}{x^2 + 2}$

21. $f(x) = \sqrt{x^2 + 4x + 6}$

22. $f(x) = (x^2 + 2x + 2)^{1/3}$

23. A company determines that its profit resulting from the sale of x items per week is $P(x) = 160 - 96x + 18x^2 - x^3$ thousand dollars. Find all relative extrema for this profit function.

24. Find all relative extrema for the profit function $P(x) = 500 - 60(3x - 27)^{2/3}$.

25. Explain why a function of the form $f(x) = ax + b$ has no relative extrema.

26. Explain why a function of the form $f(x) = x^2 + bx + c$ always has precisely one relative minimum and no relative maximum.

27. The function $f(x) = x^2 - ax + b$ has a relative minimum at $x = 2$. Find a.

28. A manufacturer has total cost function $C(x) = 20 + 200x + 0.01x^3$. Find the relative extrema, if any, for
  a. the total cost function C, and
  b. the average cost function $c(x) = \dfrac{C(x)}{x}$.

29. The sum of two positive numbers is 50. For which pair is the product a maximum?

30. The function $f(x) = 2x^3 - ax^2 + 6$ decreases only on the interval $(0, 3)$.
  a. Find the number a.
  b. Find its relative maximum value.
  c. Find its relative minimum value.

31. Find the maximum value of the population function

$$P(t) = \frac{Kt}{100 + t^2}, \qquad t > 0$$

from Exercise 31, Section 3.1.

32. Find the maximum value of the epidemic model function

$$N(t) = 20{,}000 + 20t^2 - 2t^3, \qquad t > 0$$

from Exercise 32, Section 3.1.

☑ **SOLUTIONS TO PRACTICE PROBLEMS 3.2**

1. For $f(x) = x^3 - 6x^2 - 36x - 20$ the derivative is

$$
\begin{aligned}
f'(x) &= 3x^2 - 12x - 36 \\
&= 3(x^2 - 4x - 12) \\
&= 3(x + 2)(x - 6).
\end{aligned}
$$

The critical numbers are therefore $x = -2$ and $x = 6$. Using test numbers from each of the resulting intervals we reach the following conclusions about f.

Table 2.3

Interval I	Test Number $t \in I$	Sign of $f'(t)$	Conclusion about f
$(-\infty, -2)$	$t = -3$	$f'(-3) = 27 > 0$	f increasing
$(-2, 6)$	$t = 0$	$f'(0) = -36 < 0$	f decreasing
$(6, \infty)$	$t = 7$	$f'(7) = 27 > 0$	f increasing

Using the First Derivative Test, we conclude that

$$f(-2) = 20 \text{ is a relative maximum,} \quad \text{and}$$
$$f(6) = -236 \text{ is a relative minimum.}$$

2. In the solution to Practice Problem 2, Section 3.1, we saw that the average cost function is

$$c(x) = \frac{500}{x} + 20 + 5x, \ x \geq 0$$

and that the function $y = c(x)$ is
a. decreasing on $(0, 10)$, and
b. increasing on $(10, \infty)$.
The First Derivative Test therefore tells us that, for the single critical number $x = 10$, the value

$$c(10) = \frac{500}{10} + 20 + 5(10) = 120$$

is a relative minimum. (See Figure 2.15.)

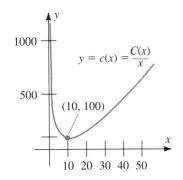

Figure 2.15 Average cost function $c(x) = \dfrac{C(x)}{x}$.

3.3 Concavity and the Second Derivative

The following example shows that in analyzing the behavior of a function we often need to know more than simply whether the function is increasing or decreasing on a particular interval.

☐ **EXAMPLE 1**

Figures 3.1 and 3.2 show total monthly cost functions for two computer software companies, Alphaware and Betaware. Although both cost functions are increasing functions of production, these functions are very different for reasons we shall now describe.

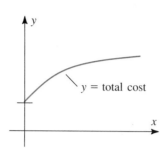

Figure 3.1 Total cost function for Alphaware increases slowly as production increases.

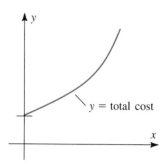

Figure 3.2 Total cost function for Betaware increases rapidly as production increases.

Alphaware produces only one software product, its Allpurpose software, so its costs associated with producing x software systems per month are primarily just the costs of copying and distributing its single product. Thus total costs rise slowly as production increases, as indicated in Figure 3.1.

Betaware, on the other hand, produces only custom software. Every software system that it ships is individually written to a customer's specifications. Since the manpower required to produce software is known to increase rapidly as the amount of software increases, total costs for Betaware rise rapidly as the monthly production level increases. (See Figure 3.2.) ∎

Note that the graph of the slowly increasing cost function in Figure 3.1 has a "cupped down" shape, while the graph of the rapidly increasing cost function in Figure 3.2 is "cupped up." Figures 3.3 and 3.4 explain in more detail why this happens. Figure 3.3 shows both the cost function $y = C_A(x)$ and its derivative, the marginal cost function $MC_A = C'_A$. Since marginal cost is just the slope of the cost curve, *the graph of $y = C_A(x)$ is cupped down because marginal cost MC_A is a decreasing function.* Similarly, *the graph of the cost function $y = C_B(x)$ in Figure 3.4 is cupped up because the marginal cost function $MC_B = C'_B$ is an increasing function.*

The Second Derivative

This simple example of cost curves suggests that whether the graph of a function f is cupped up or cupped down is determined by whether the derivative (i.e., slope) is an increasing or a decreasing function. To determine whether f' itself is increasing or decreasing, we must examine the derivative of f', if it exists, which we denote by f''. That is,

$$f''(x) \quad \text{means} \quad \frac{d}{dx}f'(x).$$

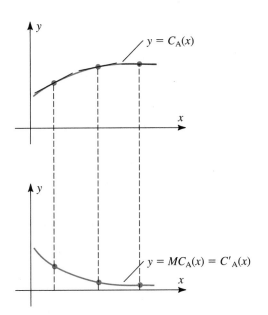

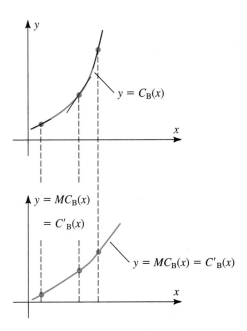

Figure 3.3 Graph of $y = C_A(x)$ is cupped downward and derivative $C'_A = MC_A$ is decreasing.

Figure 3.4 Graph of $y = C_B(x)$ is cupped downward and derivative $C'_B = MC_B$ is increasing.

We refer to f'' as the *second derivative* of f since it is obtained by differentiating $f(x)$ twice. Another notation for the second derivative is $\dfrac{d^2f}{dx^2}$. That is,

$$\frac{d^2}{dx^2}f(x) \quad \text{means} \quad f''(x), \quad \text{or} \quad \frac{d}{dx}f'(x).$$

☐ **EXAMPLE 2**

For $f(x) = 3x^4 - x^2 - x^{-1}$ we have

$$f'(x) = 12x^3 - 2x + x^{-2}$$

so

$$f''(x) = \frac{d}{dx}(12x^3 - 2x + x^{-2})$$
$$= 36x^2 - 2 - 2x^{-3}.$$

□ **EXAMPLE 3**

Since $\dfrac{d}{dx}\sqrt{9-x^2} = \dfrac{1}{2}(9-x^2)^{-1/2}(-2x)$

$$= -x(9-x^2)^{-1/2}$$

we have

$$\frac{d^2}{dx^2}\sqrt{9-x^2} = \frac{d}{dx}[-x(9-x^2)^{-1/2}]$$

$$= -(9-x^2)^{-1/2} - x\left[-\frac{1}{2}(9-x^2)^{-3/2}(-2x)\right]$$

$$= -(9-x^2)^{-1/2} - x^2(9-x^2)^{-3/2}.$$　∎

Concavity and the Second Derivative

Mathematicians prefer the terminology *concave up* when referring to graphs that we have called "cupped upward" and *concave down* for graphs that are "cupped downward." Since the function f' is increasing when $\dfrac{d}{dx}(f'(x)) = f''(x)$ is positive, it follows that the graph of f is concave up when $f''(x)$ is positive. Similarly, the graph of f is concave down when $f''(x)$ is negative. (See Figures 3.5 and 3.6.) This observation is the basis for our formal definition of concavity.

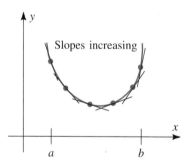

Figure 3.5 The graph of f is concave up if f' is an increasing function on (a, b), that is, if $f''(x) > 0$ for all x in (a, b).

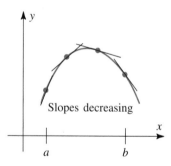

Figure 3.6 The graph of f is concave down if $f'(x)$ is a decreasing function on (a, b), that is, if $f''(x) < 0$ for all x in (a, b).

Definition 4

Let f be twice differentiable (i.e., let $f'(x)$ and $f''(x)$ exist) for all x in (a, b). Then

(i) The graph of f is said to be **concave up** on (a, b) if $f''(x) > 0$ for all x in (a, b).
(ii) The graph of f is said to be **concave down** on (a, b) if $f''(x) < 0$ for all x in (a, b).

Points on the graph of f that separate arcs of opposite concavity are called **inflection points**.

Definition 4 gives *a procedure for determining the intervals on which the graph of* $y = f(x)$ *is concave up or concave down:*

(i) Find all numbers x for which $f''(x) = 0$ or $f''(x)$ fails to exist.
(ii) Check the sign of f'' on each of the resulting intervals to determine concavity.

☐ **EXAMPLE 4**

Determine the concavity for the graph of the function $f(x) = x^4 - 6x^2 + 2$.

Strategy · · · · · · ·
Find $f''(x)$.

Find numbers x for which $f''(x) = 0$
or $f''(x)$ undefined.

Check the sign of f'' on each of the
resulting intervals.

Solution
For $f(x) = x^4 - 6x^2 + 2$ we have

$$f'(x) = 4x^3 - 12x$$

and

$$f''(x) = 12x^2 - 12.$$

Setting $f''(x) = 0$ gives $x^2 = 1$, so the zeros of the second derivative are $x_1 = -1$ and $x_2 = 1$. There are no numbers x for which $f''(x)$ is undefined.

We therefore proceed to determine the sign of f'' on each of the intervals $(-\infty, -1)$, $(-1, 1)$, and $(1, \infty)$ by choosing one "test number" t in each interval and calculating $f''(t)$. The results are given in Table 3.1.

Table 3.1

Interval	Test Number t	$f''(t)$	Sign of $f''(t)$
$(-\infty, -1)$	$t = -2$	$f''(-2) = 36$	+
$(-1, 1)$	$t = 0$	$f''(0) = -12$	−
$(1, \infty)$	$t = 2$	$f''(2) = 36$	+

Apply Definition 4.

Applying Definition 4 to the results in the last column of Table 3.1, we conclude that the graph of $f(x) = x^4 - 6x^2 + 2$ is

(i) concave up on $(-\infty, -1)$.
(ii) concave down on $(-1, 1)$.
(iii) concave up on $(1, \infty)$.

Identify inflection points where $f''(x)$
changes sign.

Since the concavity of the graph changes both at $(-1, f(-1)) = (-1, -3)$ and $(1, f(1)) = (1, -3)$, these are inflection points. The graph appears in Figure 3.7. ■

☐ **EXAMPLE 5**

Determine the concavity and find the inflection points for the graph of $f(x) = x^{2/3} - \dfrac{1}{5}x^{5/3}$.

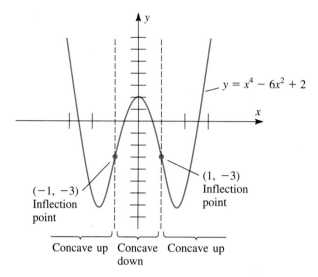

$$y = x^4 - 6x^2 + 2$$

$(-1, -3)$
Inflection
point

$(1, -3)$
Inflection
point

Concave up Concave Concave up
down

Figure 3.7 Graph of $f(x) = x^4 - 6x^2 + 2$ showing intervals of concavity.

Solution: Here $f'(x) = \dfrac{2}{3}x^{-1/3} - \dfrac{1}{3}x^{2/3}$, so

$$f''(x) = -\frac{2}{9}x^{-4/3} - \frac{2}{9}x^{-1/3}$$

$$= -\frac{2(1 + x)}{9x^{4/3}}.$$

Thus $f''(x) = 0$ for $x = -1$ and $f''(x)$ is undefined for $x = 0$. We must therefore check the sign of f'' on each of the intervals $(-\infty, -1)$, $(-1, 0)$, and $(0, \infty)$ to determine concavity. The results of doing so are given in Table 3.2.

Table 3.2

Interval	Test Number t	$f''(t)$	Sign of $f''(t)$
$(-\infty, -1)$	$t = -2$	$f''(-2) = \dfrac{2}{9}$	$+$
$(-1, 0)$	$t = -\dfrac{1}{2}$	$f''\left(-\dfrac{1}{2}\right) = -\dfrac{2^{4/3}}{9}$	$-$
$(0, \infty)$	$t = 1$	$f''(1) = -\dfrac{4}{9}$	$-$

From Table 3.2 and Theorem 4 we conclude that the graph of $f(x) = x^{2/3} - \frac{1}{5}x^{5/3}$ is

(i) concave up on $(-\infty, -1)$.
(ii) concave down on $(-1, 0)$.
(iii) concave down on $(0, \infty)$.

Thus the point $(-1, f(-1)) = \left(-1, \frac{6}{5}\right)$ is an inflection point but the point $(0, f(0)) = (0, 0)$ is not. (See Figure 3.8.) ∎

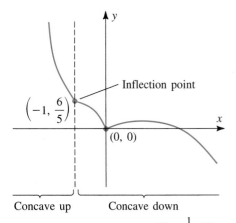

Figure 3.8 Graph of $f(x) = x^{2/3} - \frac{1}{5}x^{5/3}$ showing intervals of concavity.

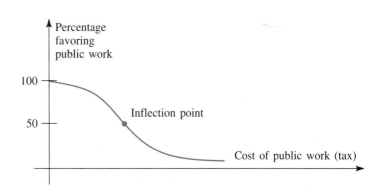

Figure 3.9 A typical "political supply curve" showing percentage of voters favoring a public work at various levels of required tax.

☐ **EXAMPLE 6**

Figure 3.9 shows a typical example of a "political supply curve." The values of the function represented by this graph are the percentages of voters supporting various levels of proposed expenditures in support of a "public good." For example, this graph might represent the percentage of voters favoring various tax increases proposed to support the construction of a new public library. The fact that $P(0) = 100$ means that everyone would support construction of a new library if it cost the taxpayers nothing. But as the size of the required tax increases, the percentage of voters favoring construction of the new library decreases. Typically such curves change from concave down to concave up at an inflection point somewhere in the vicinity of $P = 50\%$. Can you think of reasons why such a political supply curve might have this shape? ∎

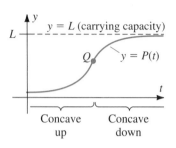

Figure 3.10 A logistic growth curve and its inflection point Q.

◻ **EXAMPLE 7**

Figure 3.10 shows a typical "logistic growth curve" for a biological population growing in a limited environment. The function $P(t)$ represents the size of the population at time t, and the horizontal line $y = L$ represents the "carrying capacity," or maximum population size that the environment can sustain. (Examples would include fruit flies in a bell jar, rabbits on an island, fish in an aquarium, etc.)

We will study the functions associated with such graphs in a later chapter. For now, notice the existence of an inflection point Q and its geometric significance. When the population is small relative to its environment's carrying capacity, there is little restraint on population growth, which is rapid. As population grows, however, the limits associated with the carrying capacity (such as limits on food, water, and space) dampen the population's tendency to grow. ■

◻ **EXAMPLE 8**

Figure 3.11 shows the graph of the *average* cost function

$$c(x) = \frac{500}{x} + 20 + 5x, \qquad x > 0$$

of Practice Problem 2 in Section 3.1. Its first derivative is

$$c'(x) = -\frac{500}{x^2} + 5$$

and its second derivative is

$$c''(x) = \frac{1000}{x^3}.$$

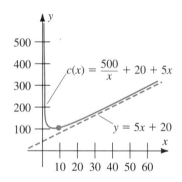

Figure 3.11 Graph of average cost function $c(x) = \dfrac{500}{x} + 20 + 5x$.

Since the second derivative is positive for all $x > 0$, we conclude that the graph of $y = c(x)$ is concave up for all $x > 0$. (Even though the graph is concave up for all $x > 0$, we will see in Section 3.4 that this graph becomes much like the graph of $y = 5x + 20$, a straight line, as x becomes large. Can you explain why?) ■

The Second Derivative Test for Extrema

The second derivative provides us with a very straightforward test for determining whether certain critical numbers for the function f yield relative extrema. It is often easier to apply than the First Derivative Test.

Theorem 4
Second Derivative Test

Let f be differentiable on an open interval containing the critical number $x = c$ with $f'(c) = 0$. Suppose also that $f''(x)$ exists throughout this interval.

(i) If $f''(c) < 0$, then $f(c)$ is a relative maximum.
(ii) If $f''(c) > 0$, then $f(c)$ is a relative minimum.
(iii) If $f''(c) = 0$, there is no conclusion from this test.

Although we shall not provide a formal proof of Theorem 4, Figures 3.12 and 3.13 indicate why it is true. If $f''(x) > 0$ near $x = c$, then the point $(c, f(c))$ must be a "low point," since the graph is concave up. Similarly, if $f''(x) < 0$ near $x = c$, the graph is concave down, so $(c, f(c))$ must be a high point.

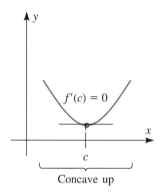

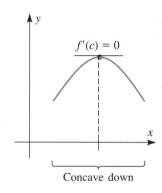

Figure 3.12 If $f'(c) = 0$ and $f''(c) > 0$, then $f(c)$ is a relative minimum.

Figure 3.13 If $f'(c) = 0$ and $f''(c) < 0$, then $f(c)$ is a relative maximum.

In applying the Second Derivative Test, be sure to note statement (iii): if $f''(c) = 0$, we obtain no conclusion as to whether $f(c)$ is a relative extremum. Exercise 50 presents several examples of just this situation. Also, note that the Second Derivative Test applies only to critical numbers c with $f'(c) = 0$. It does *not* apply to critical numbers c for which $f'(c)$ fails to exist. In either case we must resort to the First Derivative Test to classify $f(c)$.

☐ **EXAMPLE 9**

Find all relative extrema for the function $f(x) = x^4 - 8x^2 + 2$.

Strategy · · · · · · · ·
Set $f'(x) = 0$ to find the critical numbers.

Solution
Setting $f'(x) = 4x^3 - 16x = 0$, we obtain the equation

$$4x(x^2 - 4) = 0$$

so $f'(x) = 0$ if $x = 0$ or if $x^2 = 4$. The three critical numbers are therefore $x = 0$, $x = -2$, and $x = 2$. Since the second derivative is

Find f''.

$$f''(x) = 12x^2 - 16$$

we may apply the Second Derivative Test to each of the three critical numbers as follows:

Check the sign of $f''(c)$ for each critical number c and apply the Second Derivative Test.

(i) $f''(0) = 12(0)^2 - 16 = -16 < 0$,
  so $(0, f(0)) = (0, 2)$ is a relative maximum.
(ii) $f''(-2) = 12(-2)^2 - 16 = 32 > 0$,
  so $(-2, f(-2)) = (-2, -14)$ is a relative minimum.

(iii) $f''(2) = 12(2)^2 - 16 = 32 > 0$,
     so $(2, f(2)) = (2, -14)$ is a relative minimum.

The graph of $f(x) = x^4 - 8x^2 + 2$ appears in Figure 3.14.

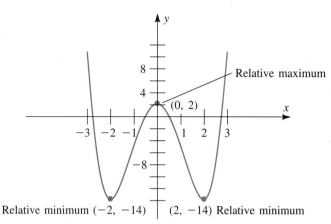

Figure 3.14 Graph of $f(x) = x^4 - 8x^2 + 2$.

Higher Order Derivatives

There is no reason why we cannot differentiate a given function more than twice, although we shall have little practical reason to do so in this text. The notation for such "higher order" derivatives is this:

$$f'''(x), \qquad \text{or} \qquad \frac{d^3}{dx^3}f(x), \qquad \text{means} \qquad \frac{d}{dx}(f''(x))$$

$$f^{(4)}(x), \qquad \text{or} \qquad \frac{d^4}{dx^4}f(x), \qquad \text{means} \qquad \frac{d}{dx}(f'''(x))$$

and, in general,

$$f^{(n)}(x), \qquad \text{or} \qquad \frac{d^n}{dx^n}f(x), \qquad \text{means} \qquad \frac{d}{dx}(f^{(n-1)}(x)), \qquad n = 4, 5, 6, \cdots.$$

□ **EXAMPLE 10**

For $f(x) = x^5 - 2x^3 + x^{2/3} - 6$,   we have

$$f'(x) = 5x^4 - 6x^2 + \frac{2}{3}x^{-1/3}$$

$$f''(x) = 20x^3 - 12x - \frac{2}{9}x^{-4/3}$$

$$f'''(x) = 60x^2 - 12 + \frac{8}{27}x^{-7/3}$$

$$f^{(4)}(x) = 120x - \frac{56}{81}x^{-10/3}$$

and so on.

☑ **PRACTICE PROBLEMS 3.3**

1. Find the intervals on which the graph of

$$f(x) = x^4 - 4x^3 - 18x^2 + 48x - 24$$

is either concave up or concave down.

2. Find all relative extrema for the function

$$f(x) = x^4 - 2x^2.$$

Exercise Set 3.3

In Exercises 1–24, find $f'(x)$ and $f''(x)$.

1. $f(x) = x^2 + 6x + 9$

2. $f(x) = 7x^2 - 5x + 14$

3. $f(x) = x^3 - 4x^2 + 10x - 7$

4. $f(x) = x - x^3 + 6$

5. $f(x) = 4x^4 - 3x^3 + 9x^2 - x + 6$

6. $f(x) = x^4 - 4x^2 + 3$

7. $f(x) = 9x^3 - x^6$

8. $f(x) = x^{-2} - 2x^3$

9. $f(x) = 3x^6 - 6x^4 + 3$

10. $f(x) = 4x - x^{-1} + 3x^{-2}$

11. $f(x) = 3x^{5/3} - 2x^{-2/3} + x^{-2}$

12. $f(x) = 4(2x - 3)^{5/3}$

13. $f(x) = \dfrac{1}{x - 1}$

14. $f(x) = \dfrac{x}{x + 3}$

15. $f(x) = \sqrt{x + 2}$

16. $f(x) = (x - 6)^{2/3}$

17. $f(x) = 2(x^3 - 3x)^3$

18. $f(x) = \sqrt{x^2 + 4x + 3}$

19. $f(x) = \dfrac{2x + 1}{9 - 3x}$

20. $f(x) = x\sqrt{4 + x^3}$

21. $f(x) = x(x - 1)^{2/3}$

22. $f(x) = \dfrac{x}{1 + x^2}$

23. $f(x) = (1 - x^2)^3$

24. $f(x) = \sqrt{1 + x^3}$

In Exercises 25–40, describe the concavity of the graph of f and find the inflection points. Use this information to sketch the graph of f, where possible.

25. $f(x) = x^3 - 3x + 2$

26. $f(x) = 9 - x^3$

27. $f(x) = x^3 - 9x^2 + 12x - 6$

28. $f(x) = x^2 - x^3 + 3x - 6$

29. $f(x) = \dfrac{1}{x}$

30. $f(x) = \dfrac{1}{x - 4}$

31. $f(x) = \dfrac{x}{x + 1}$

32. $f(x) = (x + 2)^{1/3}$

33. $f(x) = (2x + 1)^3$

34. $f(x) = \sqrt{x + 4}$

35. $f(x) = 2x^3 - 3x^2 + 18x - 12$

36. $f(x) = \dfrac{x + 4}{x - 4}$

37. $f(x) = (x - 2)^{1/3}$

38. $f(x) = |4 - x^2|$

39. $f(x) = \dfrac{x}{1 - x}$

40. $f(x) = x^{5/3} - 5x^{2/3} + 3$

In Exercises 41–45, use the Second Derivative Test to determine whether f has a relative extremum at the given value of x. If so, identify the relative extremum as a relative maximum or a relative minimum.

41. $f(x) = x^2 + \dfrac{2}{x};\quad x = 1$

42. $f(x) = 2x^3 - 3x^2;\quad x = 1$

43. $f'(x) = \dfrac{x - 1}{x + 1};\quad x = 1$

44. $f'(x) = (x - 1)(x + 2)$; $x = -2$

45. $f'(x) = (x^3 - 4x)^{4/3}$; $x = 2$

46. Translate each of the following into a statement about the first and second derivative of the relevant function:
   a. The rate of inflation is slowing.
   b. There was no change in the inflation rate last year.
   c. The rate of decay of the radioactive isotope is constant.
   d. The rate of growth of the population of Sioux City is increasing.
   e. The fall in real estate prices is accelerating.
   f. Home prices are rising at a slower rate.
   g. Her weight loss is increasing.
   h. His weight gain is slowing.

47. a. What can you say about the concavity of the graph of the total revenue function $y = R(x)$ if marginal revenue is decreasing for all $x > 0$?
   b. What can you say about the concavity of the graph of the total cost function $y = C(x)$ if marginal cost is increasing for all $x > 0$?

48. Figure 3.15 is a graph of a function $y = U(x)$ giving total utility U as a function of quantity x. On which interval is
   a. utility U increasing but marginal utility $MU = U'$ decreasing?

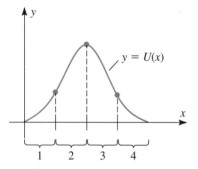

Figure 3.15 Utility function U.

b. both utility and marginal utility increasing?
c. both utility and marginal utility decreasing?
d. utility decreasing but marginal utility increasing?

49. Figure 3.16 shows the graphs of two utility curves $y = U_1(x)$ and $y = U_2(x)$.
   a. For which curve is marginal utility an increasing function of x?
   b. If the two utility curves represent the amount of annual returns that two individual investors can achieve investing x dollars, which investor "knows how to make money work for him"? Why?
   c. With assumptions as in part b, which investor would be more inclined to risk an additional dollar on his investments
      (i) at $x = a$?
      (ii) at $x = b$?

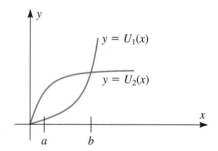

Figure 3.16 Two utility curves.

50. Verify for each of the following functions that the number $a = 0$ is a critical number for f, that $f''(a) = 0$, and that the value $f(a)$ satisfies the stated property:
   a. $f(x) = x^3$; $f(0) = 0$ is neither a relative maximum nor a relative minimum.
   b. $f(x) = x^4$; $f(0) = 0$ is a relative minimum.
   c. $f(x) = -x^4$; $f(0) = 0$ is a relative maximum.

☑ **SOLUTIONS TO PRACTICE PROBLEMS 3.3**

1. The first two derivatives of $f(x) = x^4 - 4x^3 - 18x^2 + 48x - 24$ are

$$f'(x) = 4x^3 - 12x^2 - 36x + 48$$

and

$$f''(x) = 12x^2 - 24x - 36$$
$$= 12(x^2 - 2x - 3)$$
$$= 12(x + 1)(x - 3).$$

Setting $f''(x) = 0$ gives $x_1 = -1$ and $x_2 = 3$ as possible inflection points. Checking the sign of f'' on the resulting intervals gives the following information:

Interval I	Test Number $t \in I$	Sign of $f''(t)$	Conclusion about Graph of f
$(-\infty, -1)$	$t_1 = -2$	$f''(-2) = 48 > 0$	Concave up
$(-1, 3)$	$t_2 = 0$	$f''(0) = -36 < 0$	Concave down
$(3, \infty)$	$t_3 = 4$	$f''(4) = 60 > 0$	Concave up

2. For the function $f(x) = x^4 - 2x^2$, the derivative is

$$\begin{aligned} f'(x) &= 4x^3 - 4x \\ &= 4x(x^2 - 1) \\ &= 4x(x + 1)(x - 1). \end{aligned}$$

Setting $f'(x) = 0$ gives the critical numbers $x = -1$, 0, and 1.
To test these critical numbers we calculate

$$\begin{aligned} f''(x) &= \frac{d}{dx}(4x^3 - 4x) \\ &= 12x^2 - 4 \end{aligned}$$

and use the Second Derivative Test:
a. $f''(-1) = 12(-1)^2 - 4 = 8 > 0$, so $f(-1) = -1$ is a relative minimum;
b. $f''(0) = 12(0)^2 - 4 = -4 < 0$, so $f(0)$ is a relative maximum; and
c. $f''(1) = 12(1)^2 - 4 = 8 > 0$, so $f(1) = -1$ is a relative minimum.

3.4   Curve Sketching I: Asymptotes

Our next objective is to use what we have learned about graphs of functions in Sections 3.1–3.3 to give you a fairly complete "tool kit" for sketching the graphs of functions. Even though graphing calculators and personal computers are now able to plot graphs of functions with good accuracy, understanding the relationships between certain *properties* of a given function and the corresponding properties of its graph is an important ability in understanding, criticizing, and constructing mathematical models for phenomena of interest in business, science, or the social sciences.

Our general strategy for curve sketching is presented in Section 3.5. This section is devoted to the topic of *asymptotes*. An asymptote is just a line approached by one or more branches of the graph of a function. Thus, an **asymptote** is not part of the graph of a function, but it is a line that the graph of a function resembles for certain ranges of the independent variable.

Asymptotes in Business Models

Before turning to a rather precise mathematical analysis of asymptotes, let's use a business setting to see how asymptotes can arise in mathematical models.

Previously, we have seen that a producer's total cost $C(x)$ of producing and marketing x items per unit time (per day, for example, or per week) is related to its average cost per item, $c(x)$, by the equation

$$c(x) = \frac{C(x)}{x} \qquad \left(\text{average cost} = \frac{\text{total cost}}{\text{production}}\right) \tag{1}$$

Let's examine the graph of $y = c(x)$ for three typical kinds of total cost functions.

CASE I: Suppose the total cost function has the form

$$C_1(x) = A + Bx, \qquad x \geq 0$$

where A and B are constants. (Here we call A the *fixed cost* of production, and B is the *variable,* or per-unit cost.) Then equation (1) gives the average cost per item as

$$c_1(x) = \frac{A}{x} + B, \qquad x > 0. \tag{2}$$

This function is graphed in Figure 4.1. Notice that as x approaches zero from the right, the graph more nearly resembles the y-axis. In this case we say that the y-axis is a *vertical asymptote* for the function $y = c_1(x)$ in equation (2). (The *practical* implication of this asymptote is that equation (2) is not a good model for average cost when x is very small. This is not surprising, because average cost for production levels between, say, zero and two is virtually meaningless.)

There is more to say about the graph of c, however. Note that as production levels (x) become very large, the values $c_1(x)$ of average cost more nearly equal the constant B. In the notation of Section 2.9 we say that we have the limit at infinity

$$\lim_{x \to \infty} c_1(x) = B.$$

This means that the line $y = B$ is a *horizontal* asymptote for the function $y = c_1(x)$, as illustrated in Figure 4.1 also. (The *practical* meaning of this observation is that for very high production levels the *fixed* cost of production (A) is divided among so many units that the only significant factor in the calculation of average cost is the variable, or per-unit cost.)

CASE II: Now let us assume a different form for the total cost function, say

$$C_2(x) = A + Bx + Dx^2, \qquad x \geq 0$$

where D is a constant. In this case, there has been added another factor, Dx^2, which grows faster than just the production level. (This occurs, for example, when expen-

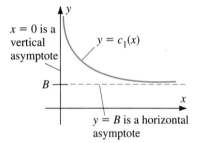

$x = 0$ is a vertical asymptote

$y = c_1(x)$

B

$y = B$ is a horizontal asymptote

Figure 4.1 Graph of average cost function $c_1(x) = \dfrac{A}{x} + B$ has *both* a vertical and a horizontal asymptote.

sive marketing costs, such as rebates or other incentive programs, are necessary to generate sales.) Here the average cost function is

$$c_2(x) = \frac{A}{x} + B + Dx. \tag{3}$$

The graph of $y = c_2(x)$ appears in Figure 4.2. Like the graph of $y = c_1(x)$, this graph has a vertical asymptote, which is the y-axis. Unlike the graph of $y = c_1(x)$, however, this graph does not approach a horizontal line as x becomes very large. The reason for this can be seen from equation (3): For very large numbers x, the term $\dfrac{A}{x}$ is nearly zero, and the value $c_2(x)$ is almost entirely determined by the terms B and Dx. That is, for large x the graph of $y = c_2(x)$ closely resembles the graph of the *linear* function

$$c_2(x) = B + Dx. \tag{4}$$

In this case, we refer to the line that is the graph of the linear function in equation (4) as an *oblique** asymptote for the graph of $y = c_2(x)$. (The practical meaning of an oblique asymptote with positive slope for an average cost function is that average cost will continue to increase, at the rate (slope) D, as production rises.)

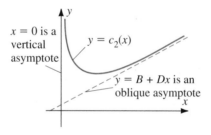

Figure 4.2 Graph of average cost function $c_2(x) = \dfrac{A}{x} + B + Dx$ has a vertical asymptote and an *oblique asymptote.*

We are now ready for a mathematical treatment of the topic of asymptotes.

Vertical Asymptotes

A **vertical asymptote** occurs in the graph of f at $x = a$ when the values $f(x)$ become infinite (with either positive or negative sign) as x approaches a. This phenomenon may occur as x approaches a from one side only or as x approaches a from either direction (as in Figure 4.3).

Vertical asymptotes are fairly easy to spot. Many functions that have vertical asymptotes do so because their denominator approaches zero as x approaches a, while their numerator does not. Consider the following examples.

---

*"Oblique," as used here, simply means neither vertical nor horizontal.

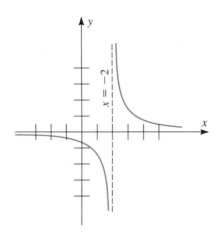

Figure 4.3 Graph of $f(x) = \dfrac{1}{x-2}$ has a vertical asymptote at $x = 2$.

☐ **EXAMPLE 1**

The graph of $f(x) = \dfrac{1}{x-2}$ has a vertical asymptote at $x = 2$ because as x approaches 2 the denominator $(x - 2)$ approaches zero. Since the numerator (1) is fixed, this causes the values $f(x)$ to ''blow up'' as x approaches 2, for they are the result of dividing the constant 1 by increasingly tiny numbers. (See Figure 4.3.) ∎

☐ **EXAMPLE 2**

To find the vertical asymptotes for the graph of $f(x) = \dfrac{x^2}{4-x^2}$, we set the denominator equal to zero and solve for x: $4 - x^2 = 0$ gives $x^2 = 4$ so $x = \pm 2$. This graph has vertical asymptotes at both $x = -2$ and $x = 2$ since the denominator approaches zero as x approaches either of these numbers but the numerator approaches $x^2 = 4$. (See Figure 4.4.) ∎

☐ **EXAMPLE 3**

By way of comparison with Examples 1 and 2, we note that the graph of $f(x) = \dfrac{x^2 - 4}{x - 2}$ does *not* have a vertical asymptote at $x = 2$ since both its numerator and denominator approach zero as x approaches 2. In fact, we can write f as

$$f(x) = \frac{x^2 - 4}{x - 2} = \frac{(x - 2)(x + 2)}{(x - 2)} = x + 2, \qquad x \neq 2$$

so the graph of f is the line with equation $y = x + 2$, minus the single point $(2, 4)$. (See Figure 4.5.) ∎

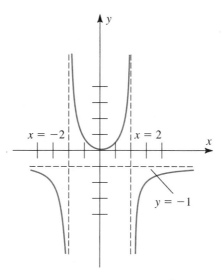

Figure 4.4 Graph of $f(x) = \dfrac{x^2}{4 - x^2}$ has vertical asymptotes at $x = 2$ and $x = -2$.

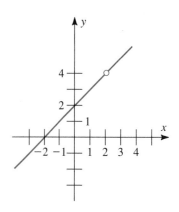

Figure 4.5 The graph of $f(x) = \dfrac{x^2 - 4}{x - 2}$ has no asymptote at $x = 2$, even though $f(2)$ is undefined.

Once a vertical asymptote for f has been located at $x = a$, sketching the graph of f in the vicinity of the asymptote requires knowledge of the one-sided limits (defined in Section 2.3)

$$\lim_{x \to a^+} f(x) \qquad \text{and} \qquad \lim_{x \to a^-} f(x).$$

We use the statement "$\lim_{x \to a^+} f(x) = +\infty$" to mean that the values $f(x)$ "increase without bound" as x approaches a from the right. This is the case in Example 1 where

$$\lim_{x \to 2^+} \frac{1}{x - 2} = +\infty. \tag{5}$$

In comparison, the statement "$\lim_{x \to a^-} f(x) = -\infty$" means that the values $f(x)$ decrease through negative values without bound as x approaches a from the left. Again referring to Example 1, we find that

$$\lim_{x \to 2^-} \frac{1}{x - 2} = -\infty. \tag{6}$$

Taken together, statements (5) and (6) tell us how to sketch the graph of $f(x) = \dfrac{1}{x-2}$ near the vertical asymptote $x = 2$. In general, the sign of these one-sided limits will indicate how the graph of f approaches an asymptote.

☐ **EXAMPLE 4**

Find the vertical asymptotes and corresponding one-sided limits for the function
$$f(x) = \frac{x+1}{9-x^2}.$$

Solution: By factoring the denominator as $9 - x^2 = (3-x)(3+x)$, we can write f as

$$f(x) = \frac{x+1}{(3-x)(3+x)}.$$

Clearly, the denominator has zeros at $x = \pm 3$. Since the numerator is not zero at either of these numbers, the graph of f has vertical asymptotes at both $x = -3$ and $x = 3$. Figure 4.6 shows a method of keeping track of the sign of each factor of $f(x)$, from which we can determine the sign of f on each of the three intervals $(-\infty, -3)$, $(-3, 3)$, and $(3, \infty)$:

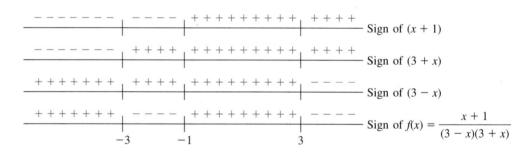

Figure 4.6 Sign analysis for $f(x) = \dfrac{x+1}{9-x^2}$.

From the sign of $f(x)$ as illustrated in Figure 4.6 we conclude that

$$\lim_{x \to -3^-} \frac{x+1}{9-x^2} = +\infty$$

$$\lim_{x \to -3^+} \frac{x+1}{9-x^2} = -\infty$$

$$\lim_{x \to 3^-} \frac{x+1}{9-x^2} = +\infty$$

$$\lim_{x \to 3^+} \frac{x+1}{9-x^2} = -\infty$$

The graph of f in Figure 4.7 reflects these results. ■

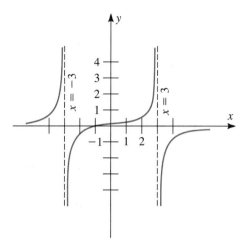

Figure 4.7 The graph of $f(x) = \dfrac{x+1}{9-x^2}$ has vertical asymptotes at $x = -3$ and $x = 3$.

Horizontal Asymptotes

We say that the line $y = L$ is a **horizontal asymptote** for the graph of f if the values $f(x)$ approach the number L as x increases without bound or as x decreases without bound. That is, $y = L$ is a horizontal asymptote for the graph of f if either

$$\lim_{x \to \infty} f(x) = L \qquad \text{or} \qquad \lim_{x \to -\infty} f(x) = L. \tag{7}$$

Thus the problem of finding horizontal asymptotes boils down to that of evaluating the *limits at infinity* appearing in equation (7). (Recall, these limits at infinity were discussed in Section 2.9.)

☐ **EXAMPLE 5**

For the function $y = \dfrac{1-x}{1+x}$ the limit

$$\lim_{x \to \infty} \frac{1-x}{1+x}$$

is not easy to evaluate since x appears in both the numerator and denominator. However, using the technique of Section 2.9, we divide both the numerator and denominator by x $\left(\text{i.e., multiply both by } \dfrac{1}{x}\right)$ and use the fact that $\lim\limits_{x \to \infty} \dfrac{1}{x} = 0$ to find that

$$\lim_{x \to \infty} \left(\frac{1-x}{1+x}\right) = \lim_{x \to \infty} \left(\frac{1-x}{1+x}\right)\left(\frac{1/x}{1/x}\right)$$

$$= \lim_{x \to \infty} \frac{\dfrac{1}{x} - 1}{\dfrac{1}{x} + 1}$$

$$= \frac{0-1}{0+1}$$

$$= -1.$$

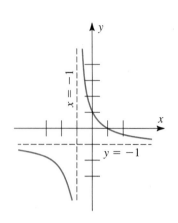

Figure 4.8 Graph of $y = $ $\dfrac{1-x}{1+x}$ approaches line $x = -1$ as x approaches -1, and line $y = -1$ as $|x|$ becomes large.

Thus the line $y = -1$ is a horizontal asymptote. Examining the other limit at infinity $\lim\limits_{x \to -\infty} \left(\dfrac{1-x}{1+x}\right)$ by this technique leads to the same result. (See Figure 4.8.) ∎

□ **EXAMPLE 6**

Find the horizontal asymptotes for the graph of $f(x) = \dfrac{x^2 - 9}{x^2}$.

Strategy · · · · · · ·
Identify highest power of x.

Solution
The highest power of x present is x^2. We therefore divide numerator and denominator by x^2 to evaluate the limit at infinity:

Divide numerator and denominator by this power of x.

$$\lim_{x \to \infty} \left(\frac{x^2 - 9}{x^2}\right)\left(\frac{1/x^2}{1/x^2}\right) = \lim_{x \to \infty} \frac{1 - 9/x^2}{1}$$

Evaluate limit using fact that

$$\lim_{x \to \infty} \frac{1}{x^2} = 0.$$

$$= \frac{1 - 0}{1}$$

$$= 1.$$

Horizontal asymptote is $y = \lim\limits_{x \to \infty} f(x)$.

Thus the graph of f has the horizontal asymptote $y = 1$. (See Figure 4.9.) ∎

Horizontal asymptotes often occur in economic models when a variable such as total cost has a fixed component and a component that varies proportionally with an independent variable such as production or sales level. In the "long run" the average value of such a variable will sometimes approach a constant value, which is then a horizontal asymptote for its graph.

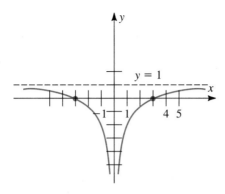

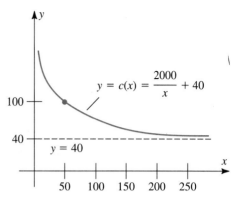

Figure 4.9 Graph of $f(x) = \dfrac{x^2 - 9}{x^2}$ has horizontal asymptote $y = 1$.

Figure 4.10 Average cost function $c(x) = \dfrac{2000}{x} + 40$ has horizontal asymptote $y = 40$.

☐ **EXAMPLE 7**

A manufacturer of bicycles experiences fixed weekly costs of \$2000 plus variable costs of \$40 per bicycle.

(a) Find the manufacturer's *average* cost per bicycle $c(x)$ for the production of x bicycles per week.
(b) Find the "long run" value of $c(x)$, that is, $\lim\limits_{x \to \infty} c(x)$.

Solution: We are given that the total weekly costs are

$$C(x) = 2000 + 40x \text{ dollars}$$

so the *average* weekly cost per bicycle is

$$c(x) = \frac{2000 + 40x}{x} = \frac{2000}{x} + 40 \text{ dollars per bicycle.}$$

The horizontal asymptote $y = 40$ arises from the limit

$$\lim_{x \to \infty} c(x) = \lim_{x \to \infty} \left(\frac{2000}{x} + 40 \right)$$
$$= 0 + 40$$
$$= 40.$$

(See Figure 4.10.) ∎

Oblique Asymptotes

Some functions have the form

$$f(x) = g(x) + L(x) \tag{8}$$

where $L(x)$ denotes a linear function, and $g(x)$ is a function whose values become very small as $|x|$ becomes very large. That is, both

$$L(x) = ax + b \tag{9}$$

and either

$$\lim_{x \to \infty} g(x) = 0 \quad \text{or} \quad \lim_{x \to -\infty} g(x) = 0. \tag{10}$$

In such cases, portions of the graph of f in equation (8) will resemble the graph of the linear function $L(x) = a + bx$. This line is called an *oblique asymptote* for f.

The technique for identifying oblique asymptotes is to try to write the function f in the form of equation (8) where both conditions (9) and (10) are satisfied.

□ **EXAMPLE 8**

Identify any asymptotes for the function

$$f(x) = \frac{x^2 - 3x + 3}{x - 2}.$$

Solution: By performing a polynomial long division

$$
\begin{array}{r}
x - 1 \\
x - 2 \overline{\smash{)}x^2 - 3x + 3} \\
\underline{x^2 - 2x} \\
-x + 3 \\
\underline{-x + 2} \\
1
\end{array}
$$

we can write the given function in reduced form as

$$f(x) = x - 1 + \frac{1}{x - 2}.$$

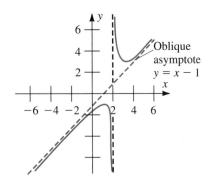

Figure 4.11 Graph of $f(x) = \dfrac{x^2 - 3x + 3}{x - 2}$.

Since $\displaystyle\lim_{x \to \infty} \frac{1}{x - 2} = 0$ and $\displaystyle\lim_{x \to -\infty} \frac{1}{x - 2} = 0$, the graph of the linear function $L(x) = x - 1$ is an oblique asymptote for the graph of f. (See Figure 4.11.) ■

□ **EXAMPLE 9**

A producer of extension ladders determines that its total cost in producing and marketing x stepladders per week is

$$C(x) = 2000 + 24x + 0.5x^2.$$

Find the average cost per stepladder, $c(x)$, and any asymptotes for the graph of $y = c(x)$.

Strategy · · · · · · · ·

Find c from the equation

$$c(x) = \frac{C(x)}{x}.$$

Solution

Here

$$c(x) = \frac{2000 + 24x + 0.5x^2}{x}$$

$$= \frac{2000}{x} + 24 + 0.5x.$$

Note that the first term *both* yields a vertical asymptote at $x = 0$ and approaches zero as $x \to \infty$.

The function $g(x) = \dfrac{2000}{x}$ has the property that

$$\lim_{x \to 0^+} g(x) = +\infty$$

and

$$\lim_{x \to \infty} g(x) = 0.$$

Thus, the remaining *linear* part,

$$L(x) = 0.5x + 24,$$

is an oblique asymptote.

Thus, the line $x = 0$ is a vertical asymptote, and the line $y = 0.5x + 24$ is an *oblique asymptote*. (See Figure 4.12). ■

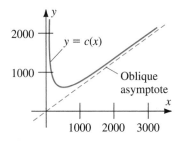

Figure 4.12 Graph of average cost function $c(x) = \dfrac{2000}{x} + 24 + 0.5x$ has vertical asymptote $x = 0$ and oblique asymptote $y = 0.5x + 24$.

☑ **PRACTICE PROBLEMS 3.4**

1. Find all asymptotes for the graph of

$$f(x) = \frac{x^3 + 2}{x^2 - 2}.$$

2. A condominium developer decides to install central air conditioning in a new complex containing x units, where x is yet to be determined. The cost of air conditioning the complex is known to be $20,000 for the common utility plus $2500 per unit.
   a. Find $c(x)$, the average cost per unit of the entire air conditioning project.
   b. Find any asymptotes to the graph of $y = c(x)$.

Exercise Set 3.4

In Exercises 1–10, identify all horizontal asymptotes, if any, for the given functions.

1. $f(x) = \dfrac{3}{x + 5}$

2. $f(x) = \dfrac{1 + x}{3 - x}$

3. $f(x) = \dfrac{3x^2}{1 + x^2}$

4. $f(x) = \dfrac{\sqrt{x}}{1 + x^2}$

5. $f(x) = \dfrac{x^3}{9 - x^3}$

6. $f(x) = \dfrac{4x^2}{1 + 3x + 2x^2}$

7. $f(x) = \sqrt{\dfrac{1 + 7x^2}{x^2 + 3}}$

8. $f(x) = \dfrac{4x - \sqrt{x}}{x^{2/3} + x}$

9. $f(x) = 6 - 4x^{-2/3}$

10. $f(x) = \dfrac{x^{2/3} - x^{-1/3}}{x^{1/4} + x^{1/2}}$

In Exercises 11–20, find the vertical asymptotes.

11. $y = \dfrac{1}{x - 4}$

12. $f(x) = \dfrac{1}{(x + 2)^2}$

13. $f(x) = \dfrac{x^2 + 4}{x^2 - 4}$

14. $y = \dfrac{x^2 + 1}{x^2 - 1}$

15. $y = \dfrac{4}{4 + 5x + x^2}$

16. $f(x) = \dfrac{x + 3}{x^2 - 4x + 3}$

17. $f(x) = \dfrac{x + 3}{x^2 + x - 6}$

18. $f(x) = \dfrac{x^2 + x - 6}{x^2 + 3x - 10}$

19. $f(x) = \dfrac{x^2 + 5x + 6}{x^2 - 5x + 6}$

20. $f(x) = \dfrac{x^3 + 2x^2 - 5x - 6}{x^2 - x - 2}$

In Exercises 21–26, find all asymptotes, including oblique asymptotes.

21. $f(x) = 3 + x + \dfrac{\sqrt{x}}{1 + \sqrt{x}}$

22. $f(x) = 6 - x + \dfrac{x + 3}{1 - x^2}$

23. $f(x) = \dfrac{2x^3 + 3x + 5}{x^2 + 1}$

24. $f(x) = \dfrac{x^2 + x + 3}{x + 1}$

25. $f(x) = \dfrac{2x - 2x^3 + 1}{1 - x^2}$

26. $f(x) = \dfrac{x^3 + x^2 - 3x - 3}{x + 1}$

27. Can a function have both an oblique asymptote and a horizontal asymptote? If so, give an example. If not, why not?

28. Can a function have both an oblique asymptote and a vertical asymptote? If so, give an example. If not, why not?

29. A manufacturing company finds that its weekly fixed costs are $2500 and that its variable costs of production for its single product are $80 per item. Find
  a. $C(x)$, its total weekly cost in producing x items.
  b. $c(x) = \dfrac{C(x)}{x}$, its average cost per item.
  c. Any asymptotes for the graph of c.

30. A manufacturer of picnic tables has total cost $C(x) = 500 + 20\sqrt{x} + 40x$ in producing x picnic tables per week. Find any asymptotes for the average cost function $c(x) = \dfrac{C(x)}{x}$.

31. A manufacturer has total cost function $C(x) = 2000 + 500x^{1/3} + Ax$. Find A if, for the average cost function $c(x) = \dfrac{C(x)}{x}$, $\lim\limits_{x \to \infty} c(x) = 35$.

32. A firm determines that the average cost per apple of supplying x apples per week to a certain grocery chain is $c(x) = \dfrac{22 + 10x + 20x^2}{1 + x^2}$ cents. Does this average cost function have a horizontal asymptote? If so, what?

33. A public relations firm determines that the demand for a certain product, as a function of the amount x spent per month on advertising the product, is

$$d(x) = \frac{72 + 96x^{1/3}}{10x^{1/5} + 6x^{1/3}}$$

thousand sales per month. Does this demand function have a horizontal asymptote? If so, what?

34. Suppose that the supply of uranium available on world markets is related to the price per pound by the function

$$S(p) = \frac{100}{200 - p}$$

where p is the price per pound, $0 \le p < 200$. Sketch the graph of $S(p)$ and identify the vertical asymptote.

✅ **SOLUTIONS TO PRACTICE PROBLEMS 3.4**

1. A polynomial long division reduces $\dfrac{x^3 + 2}{x^2 - 2}$.

$$x^2 - 2 \overline{)\begin{array}{l} x \\ x^3 + 2 \\ \underline{x^3 - 2x} \\ 2x + 2 \end{array}}$$

Thus,

$$f(x) = x + \frac{2x + 2}{x^2 - 2}$$

$$= x + \frac{2x + 2}{(x - \sqrt{2})(x + \sqrt{2})}$$

and we conclude that the graph of f has

a. Vertical asymptotes at $x = \pm\sqrt{2}$ because

$$\lim_{x \to -\sqrt{2}^-} f(x) = -\infty \qquad \text{and} \qquad \lim_{x \to -\sqrt{2}^+} f(x) = +\infty.$$

This is similar for $x = \sqrt{2}$.

b. An oblique asymptote $y = x$ because

$$\lim_{x \to \infty} \left(\frac{2x + 2}{x^2 - 2} \right) = 0.$$

(See Figure 4.13.)

2. a. Here the per unit average cost is

$$c(x) = \frac{20{,}000 + 2500x}{x}$$

$$= \frac{20{,}000}{x} + 2500$$

b. This function has a horizontal asymptote at $y = 2500$, the per-unit cost, because

$$\lim_{x \to \infty} c(x) = \lim_{x \to \infty} \left(\frac{20{,}000}{x} + 2500 \right)$$

$$= 2500,$$

and a vertical asymptote at $x = 0$ because

$$\lim_{x \to 0^+} c(x) = +\infty.$$

(See Figure 4.14.)

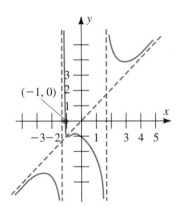

Figure 4.13

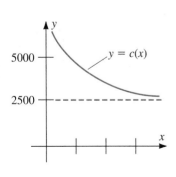

Figure 4.14

3.5   Curve Sketching II

In this section we present a complete "tool kit" for sketching the graph of a given function.

Before doing so, there is one additional topic that we wish to mention. Although it does not involve the calculus, it is often a handy aid in sketching the types of graphs that follow.

Symmetry: Even and Odd Functions

Symmetry in a graph means that one part of the graph is congruent with another part:

> A graph of a function is symmetric with respect to the y-axis if the part of the graph in the left half-plane is the mirror image of the part in the right half-plane.

For example, the graphs of $f(x) = x^2$ and $g(x) = \dfrac{1}{x^2 - 4}$ in Figures 5.1 and 5.2 are symmetric with respect to the y-axis.

In order for the graph of a function f to be symmetric with respect to the y-axis, it is necessary that $f(-x_0)$ be the same value as $f(x_0)$ for all x_0 in the domain of f. (See Figure 5.3.) Functions with this property include all even power functions, $f(x) = x^{2n}$, $n = \pm 1, \pm 2, \ldots$, as well as many others. Such functions are called even functions.

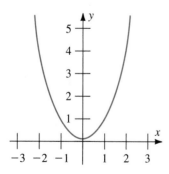

Figure 5.1 Graph of $f(x) = x^2$.

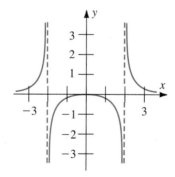

Figure 5.2 Graph of $f(x) = \dfrac{1}{x^2 - 4}$.

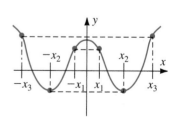

Figure 5.3 For the graph of f to be symmetric with respect to the y-axis we must have $f(-x_0) = f(x_0)$ for all x.

Definition 5	A function f is called **even** if

$$f(-x) = f(x)$$

for all x in the domain of f. The graph of an even function is symmetric with respect to the y-axis.

☐ **EXAMPLE 1**

The function $f(x) = \dfrac{1}{x^2 - 4}$ in Figure 5.2 is an even function because

$$f(-x) = \frac{1}{(-x)^2 - 4} = \frac{1}{x^2 - 4} = f(x)$$

for all x in its domain. We have already seen that its graph is symmetric with respect to the y-axis. ■

☐ **EXAMPLE 2**

The function $f(x) = x^4 - 3x^2 + 7$ is an even function because

$$f(-x) = (-x)^4 - 3(-x)^2 + 7 = x^4 - 3x^2 + 7 = f(x)$$

for all x. ■

☐ **EXAMPLE 3**

The function $f(x) = x^3$ is *not* an even function, however, because

$$f(-x) = (-x)^3 = (-1)^3 x^3 = -x^3 = -f(x).$$

Thus, except for the single number $x = 0$, we have $f(-x) \neq f(x)$. ■

Odd Functions

Even though the function $f(x) = x^3$ is not an even function, its graph (Figure 5.4) does possess a kind of symmetry. It has the property that the entire graph is congruent with itself if rotated 180° about the origin. This is called symmetry with respect to the origin. As Figure 5.5 illustrates, the graph of a function f will be symmetric with respect to the origin if $f(-x) = -f(x)$ for all x in the domain of f. This is a property shared by all odd power functions $f(x) = x^{2n-1}$, $n = \pm 1, \pm 2, \ldots$, as well as many other functions.

Definition 6	A function is called **odd** if

$$f(-x) = -f(x)$$

for all x in the domain of f. The graph of an odd function is symmetric with respect to the origin.

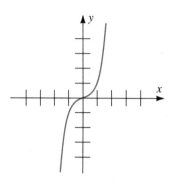

Figure 5.4 Graph of $f(x) = x^3$ is symmetric with respect to the origin.

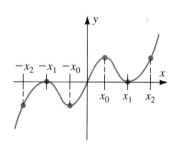

Figure 5.5 The graph of f is symmetric with respect to the origin if $f(-x) = -f(x)$ for all x.

☐ **EXAMPLE 4**

The function $f(x) = x^5 - 5x^3 + x^{1/3}$ is an odd function since

$$f(-x) = (-x)^5 - 5(-x)^3 + (-x)^{1/3} = -(x^5 - 5x^3 + x^{1/3}) = -f(x).$$ ■

☐ **EXAMPLE 5**

The function $f(x) = x^3 + 5$ is *not* an odd function. To see this we note that

$$f(-x) = (-x)^3 + 5 = -x^3 + 5$$

but

$$-f(x) = -(x^3 + 5) = -x^3 - 5.$$

Since these expressions are unequal, in general, we do not have the essential property $f(-x) = -f(x)$. ■

The advantage in identifying a function as either an even or an odd function is that only half its graph need be sketched. The other half can then be obtained easily by application of the relevant symmetry property.

Curve Sketching

We now have available to us the following steps to use in sketching the graph of a function. The examples that follow illustrate how these steps are executed.

Steps to Follow in Sketching the Graph of f

(1) Determine the domain of f.
(2) Identify any symmetry in the graph by checking to see if f is an even or odd function.
(3) If possible, locate the zeros of f by solving the equation $f(x) = 0$.

(4) Find all vertical asymptotes by finding the numbers a for which $\lim\limits_{x \to a^+} f(x)$

or $\lim\limits_{x \to a^-} f(x)$ is infinite.

(5) Find all horizontal asymptotes by examining $\lim\limits_{x \to \pm\infty} f(x)$.

(6) Find all critical numbers, determine whether f is increasing or decreasing on the resulting intervals, and classify the extrema. (Sections 3.1, 3.2.)

(7) Determine the concavity and locate the inflection points. (Section 3.3.)

(8) Calculate the values of the function at a few convenient numbers and locate the corresponding points on the graph. Then sketch the graph according to the above information.

□ **EXAMPLE 6**

Sketch the graph of the function $f(x) = 2x^3 + 3x^2 - 12x + 3$.

Solution: We follow the steps outlined above.

(1) The domain of f is all real numbers since f is a polynomial.

(2) f is neither an odd nor an even function, so there is no symmetry of the corresponding types.

(3) Since f is a polynomial of degree 3, it is not easy to find its zeros. We therefore skip this step since the point here is to obtain a quick sketch.

(4,5) The graph of f has no vertical or horizontal asymptotes since f is a polynomial.

(6) To find the critical numbers, we set $f'(x) = 0$:

$$\begin{aligned} f'(x) &= 6x^2 + 6x - 12 \\ &= 6(x^2 + x - 2) \\ &= 6(x + 2)(x - 1) \end{aligned}$$

so the equation $f'(x) = 0$ has solutions $x = -2$ and $x = 1$. These are the only critical numbers. Table 5.1 shows the results of testing the sign of $f'(x)$ on each of the resulting intervals.

Table 5.1

Interval	Test Number t	$f'(t)$	Conclusion
$(-\infty, -2)$	$t = -3$	$f'(-3) = 24 > 0$	f increasing
$(-2, 1)$	$t = 0$	$f'(0) = -12 < 0$	f decreasing
$(1, \infty)$	$t = 2$	$f'(2) = 24 > 0$	f increasing

From these conclusions we know that

$$f(-2) = 2(-2)^3 + 3(-2)^2 - 12(-2) + 3 = 23$$

is a relative maximum for f, and that

$$f(1) = 2(1)^3 + 3(1)^2 - 12(1) + 3 = -4$$

is a relative minimum.

(7) The second derivative of f is

$$f''(x) = 12x + 6$$

so setting $f''(x) = 0$ gives $12x = -6$, or $x = -\dfrac{1}{2}$. We test the sign of $f''(x)$ on the resulting intervals to determine the concavity as indicated in Table 5.2.

Table 5.2

Interval	Test Number t	$f''(t)$	Conclusion
$\left(-\infty, -\dfrac{1}{2}\right)$	$t = -1$	$f''(-1) = -6 < 0$	f concave down
$\left(-\dfrac{1}{2}, \infty\right)$	$t = 0$	$f''(0) = 6 > 0$	f concave up

Thus the point $\left(-\dfrac{1}{2}, f\left(-\dfrac{1}{2}\right)\right) = \left(-\dfrac{1}{2}, \dfrac{19}{2}\right)$ is an inflection point.

(8) Table 5.3 shows several points $(x, f(x))$, which we use to plot the graph of f in Figure 5.6. ∎

Table 5.3

x	-2	-1	0	1	2
$y = f(x)$	23	16	3	-4	7
(x, y)	$(-2, 23)$	$(-1, 16)$	$(0, 3)$	$(1, -4)$	$(2, 7)$

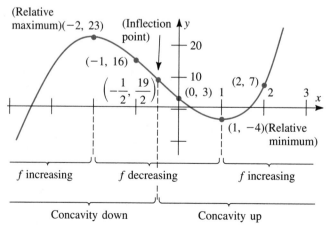

Figure 5.6 Graph of $f(x) = 2x^3 + 3x^2 - 12x + 3$ in Example 6.

□ **EXAMPLE 7**

Sketch the graph of $f(x) = \dfrac{x}{1 - x^2}$.

Solution: Following the outline, we find that

(1) The *domain* of f is all real numbers except $x = -1$ and $x = 1$. That is because the zeros of the denominator are $x = \pm 1$.

(2) f is an odd function, because

$$f(-x) = \frac{-x}{1 - (-x)^2} = \frac{-x}{1 - x^2} = -f(x).$$

The graph is therefore symmetric with respect to the origin.

(3) The equation $f(x) = 0$ has the single solution $x = 0$. Thus the point $(0, 0)$ is on the graph.

(4) Since the zeros of the denominator are $x = \pm 1$, we check for vertical asymptotes at these numbers. Because of symmetry, we need only check $x = 1$:

$$\lim_{x \to 1^-} \left(\frac{x}{1 - x^2} \right) = \infty \quad \text{and} \quad \lim_{x \to 1^+} \left(\frac{x}{1 - x^2} \right) = -\infty.$$

Thus, both $x = -1$ and $x = 1$ are vertical asymptotes.

(5) Checking for horizontal asymptotes, we find that

$$\lim_{x \to \infty} \left(\frac{x}{1 - x^2} \right) = \lim_{x \to \infty} \left(\frac{x}{1 - x^2} \right) \left(\frac{1/x^2}{1/x^2} \right) = \lim_{x \to \infty} \left[\frac{1/x}{(1/x^2) - 1} \right] = \frac{0}{0 - 1} = 0.$$

Thus the line $y = 0$ (i.e., the x-axis) is a horizontal asymptote.

(6) To find the critical numbers, we calculate the derivative using the Quotient Rule:

$$f'(x) = \frac{d}{dx} \left(\frac{x}{1 - x^2} \right) = \frac{(1 - x^2)(1) - x(-2x)}{(1 - x^2)^2} = \frac{1 + x^2}{(1 - x^2)^2}.$$

Since $1 + x^2 \geq 1$ for all x, this derivative is never zero. However, $f'(x)$ is undefined for $x = \pm 1$, but so is $f(x)$. Thus there are no critical numbers. Finally, since both the numerator and denominator of f' are positive for all $x \neq \pm 1$, f is increasing on each of the intervals $(-\infty, -1)$, $(-1, 1)$, and $(1, \infty)$.

(7) The second derivative of $f(x)$ is

$$f''(x) = \frac{d}{dx} \left[\frac{1 + x^2}{(1 - x^2)^2} \right] = \frac{(1 - x^2)^2(2x) - (1 + x^2) \cdot 2(1 - x^2)(-2x)}{(1 - x^2)^4}$$

$$= \frac{2x^3 + 6x}{(1 - x^2)^3}$$

$$= \frac{2x(x^2 + 3)}{(1 - x^2)^3}.$$

Thus the concavity of the graph of f may change at $x = 0$ ($f''(x) = 0$) and $x = \pm 1$ ($f''(x)$ undefined). The sign of $f''(x)$ on each of the resulting intervals is shown in Figure 5.7, which also shows the sign of each factor of $f''(x)$. From the sign of $f''(x)$ we conclude that the graph of f is

concave up on $(-\infty, -1)$,
concave down on $(-1, 0)$,
concave up on $(0, 1)$,   and
concave down on $(1, \infty)$.

The point $(0, f(0)) = (0, 0)$ is therefore an inflection point.

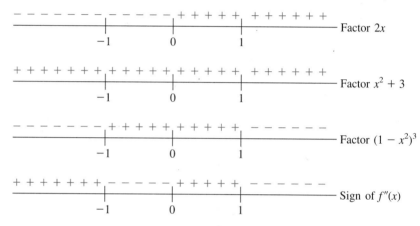

Figure 5.7 Sign analysis for $f''(x) = \dfrac{2x(x^2 + 3)}{(1 - x^2)^3}$.

(8) Since $f(0) = 0$, and $f(2) = -\dfrac{2}{3}$, the points $\left(-2, \dfrac{2}{3}\right)$, $(0, 0)$, and $\left(2, -\dfrac{2}{3}\right)$ are on the graph. The graph is sketched in Figure 5.8. ■

☑ **PRACTICE PROBLEMS 3.5**

1. Determine whether f is odd or even:
   a. $f(x) = \dfrac{x^4 + 4x^2}{x^3 - x}$

   b. $f(x) = \dfrac{x}{x^3 + x^5}$

2. Sketch the graph of $f(x) = x^2(1 - x^2)$.

Figure 5.8 Graph of $f(x) = \dfrac{x}{1-x^2}$ is symmetric with respect to the origin.

Exercise Set 3.5

In each of Exercises 1–10, determine if f is an odd function, an even function, or neither.

1. $f(x) = 9 - x^2$

2. $f(x) = 3 + 5x^4$

3. $f(x) = x - x^5$

4. $f(x) = 3 + x + 5x^3$

5. $f(x) = x(9 - x^2)$

6. $f(x) = x^4(5 + x^2)$

7. $f(x) = \dfrac{1 + x^2}{9 - x}$

8. $f(x) = \dfrac{x^2 + 2x + 1}{\sqrt{3 + x^2}}$

9. $f(x) = \dfrac{1 - x^{2/3}}{1 + x^{4/3}}$

10. $f(x) = 3(x^3 + x^5)^{1/3}$

In each of Exercises 11–30, sketch the graph of the given function.

11. $f(x) = x^2 - 2x - 8$

12. $f(x) = x^2 - 3x + 10$

13. $f(x) = 2x^3 - 3x^2$

14. $f(x) = x^3 - 12x + 6$

15. $f(x) = x^3 + x^2 - 8x + 8$

16. $f(x) = 9x - \dfrac{1}{x}$

17. $f(x) = \dfrac{x + 4}{x - 4}$

18. $f(x) = 4 - x^{2/3}$

19. $f(x) = |4 - x^2|$

20. $f(x) = x^{5/3} - x^{2/3}$

21. $f(x) = \dfrac{1}{x(x - 4)}$

22. $f(x) = x^2 - \dfrac{9}{x^2}$

23. $f(x) = \dfrac{x}{(2x + 1)^2}$

24. $f(x) = 1 + (x - 3)^{2/3}$

25. $f(x) = \dfrac{1}{3}x^3 - x^2 - 3x + 4$

26. $f(x) = \dfrac{x^2 - 4x + 5}{x - 2}$

27. $f(x) = 4x^2(1 - x^2)$

28. $f(x) = \dfrac{x^2}{9 - x^2}$

29. $f(x) = 16 - 20x^3 + 3x^5$

30. $f(x) = x^4 - 8x^2 + 10$

31. True or false? The graph of an odd function must contain the origin. Why?

32. True or false? The graph of an even function must contain the origin. Why or why not?

33. Let $h(x) = \sqrt{g(x)}$ where $g(x)$ is defined for all x. Can h be an even function? If so, give an example. If not, why not?

34. Let $g(x) = h^3(x)$ where $h(x)$ is defined for all x. Must g be an odd function? Why or why not?

35. True or false? The product of two odd functions is an even function. Why or why not?

36. True or false? The product of an odd function and an even function is an odd function. Why or why not?

37. The graph of a function can be symmetric with respect to vertical lines other than the y-axis. Explain the symmetry associated with the graph of a function of the form $f(x) = (x - a)^2 + b$.

38. Is there any symmetry in the graph of the function $f(x) = x^2 - 4x - 2$? If so, what?

39. Is there any symmetry in the graph of the function $f(x) = x^5 + 2$? If so, what?

40. Can the graph of a function be symmetric with respect to the x-axis? Why or why not?

☑ **SOLUTIONS TO PRACTICE PROBLEMS 3.5**

1. a. $f(-x) = \dfrac{(-x)^4 + 4(-x)^2}{(-x)^3 - (-x)} = \dfrac{x^4 + 4x^2}{-(x^3 - x)} = -f(x)$.

Therefore, f is odd.

b. $f(-x) = \dfrac{-x}{(-x)^3 + (-x)^5} = \dfrac{-x}{-(x^3 + x^5)} = \dfrac{x}{x^3 + x^5} = f(x)$.

Therefore, f is even.

2. For $f(x) = x^2(1 - x^2)$:

(a) $f(x) = 0$ implies $x = -1$, 0, or 1.

(b) f is even since $f(-x) = (-x)^2[1 - (-x)^2] = x^2(1 - x^2) = f(x)$.

(c) $f(x) = x^2 - x^4$, so $f'(x) = 2x - 4x^3 = 2x(1 - 2x^2)$.

Thus, $f'(x) = 0$ for $x = -\dfrac{\sqrt{2}}{2}$, 0, and $\dfrac{\sqrt{2}}{2}$ (critical numbers).

(d) $f''(x) = 2 - 12x^2 = 2(1 - 6x^2)$, so $f''(x) = 0$ for $x = \pm\dfrac{\sqrt{6}}{6}$.

(e) The critical points yield extrema as follows:

$$f''(0) = 2 - 12(0) = 2 > 0, \text{ so } f(0) = 0 \text{ is a relative minima.}$$

$$f''\left(\dfrac{\sqrt{2}}{2}\right) = 2 - 12\left(\dfrac{\sqrt{2}}{2}\right)^2 = -4 < 0$$

so $f\left(\dfrac{\sqrt{2}}{2}\right)$ and $f\left(-\dfrac{\sqrt{2}}{2}\right)$ are relative maxima.

(f) f'' changes sign on either side of $x = \pm\dfrac{\sqrt{6}}{6}$, so $\left(\dfrac{\sqrt{6}}{6}, f\left(\dfrac{\sqrt{6}}{6}\right)\right)$ and $\left(-\dfrac{\sqrt{6}}{6}, f\left(-\dfrac{\sqrt{6}}{6}\right)\right)$ are inflection points.

(See Figure 5.9.)

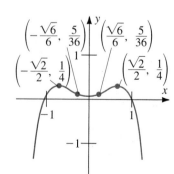

Figure 5.9 Graph of $f(x) = x^2(1 - x^2)$.

3.6 Finding Absolute Extrema

Many applications of the derivative have to do with finding the *absolute maximum* or *absolute minimum* value of a given function. For example, we may wish to find the maximum value of a company's profits, a college's enrollment, or a crop's yield, or the minimum value of a company's total costs, a college's attrition rate, or a farmer's crop loss due to a plant disease.

By the **absolute maximum** value of a function f we simply mean the largest value of $f(x)$ for all x in the domain of f. Similarly, the **absolute minimum** value of f is just the smallest value of $f(x)$ for all x in the domain of f. We use the term **absolute extremum** to refer to either an absolute maximum or an absolute minimum. (When we use the terms maximum or minimum value we are referring to an *absolute* maximum or minimum, rather than a *relative* maximum or minimum.)

While a relative maximum or minimum value of a function may also be an absolute maximum or minimum value for that function, the two concepts are not the same, and the procedure for finding absolute extrema is somewhat different from that for finding relative extrema. In this section we highlight the differences between these two types of extrema and develop a procedure for finding absolute extrema.

We begin with two examples in which absolute extrema either occur at relative extrema or fail to exist.

☐ **EXAMPLE 1**

For the function $f(x) = 4x^2 - 2x^4$ graphed in Figure 6.1, the absolute maximum value $f(x) = 2$ occurs both at $x = -1$ and at $x = 1$. Both of these numbers x are critical numbers since the derivative is

$$f'(x) = 8x - 8x^3 = 8x(1 - x^2)$$

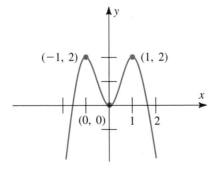

Figure 6.1 $f(x) = 4x^2 - 2x^4$ has absolute and relative maxima $f(-1) = f(1) = 2$, but no absolute minimum value. Relative minimum at $(0, 0)$ is not an absolute minimum.

which equals zero for $x = \pm 1$. Also, since

$$f''(x) = 8 - 24x^2$$

we have $f''(-1) = f''(1) = -16 < 0$, so both $f(-1)$ and $f(1)$ are relative maxima by the Second Derivative Test.

However, f has no absolute minimum value since this function takes on increasingly large negative values as $|x|$ increases. (Note that a relative minimum exists at $x = 0$, but this is *not* an absolute minimum.) ■

□ **EXAMPLE 2**

The function $f(x) = \sqrt{x}$ has an absolute minimum value $f(x) = 0$ at $x = 0$. However, since $f(x) = \sqrt{x}$ is an increasing function for all $x > 0$, this function has no absolute maximum value. (See Figure 6.2.) ■

Endpoint Extrema

The point of these first two examples is that absolute extrema may exist at relative extrema, but that an absolute maximum or minimum may not exist even though relative extrema are present. Figures 6.3 and 6.4 show another way in which absolute extrema can occur—at endpoints of the domain of a function. It is important to note that when the domain of a function is restricted to a closed interval $[a, b]$, the endpoint values $f(a)$ and $f(b)$ may become absolute extrema, even though they are not relative extrema when the domain of f is unrestricted.

The following theorem states that when a continuous function is restricted to a closed bounded interval $[a, b]$, there will always exist precisely one maximum and one minimum value for the function (although either of them may occur at more than one point in the interval). Its proof is beyond the scope of this text.

Theorem 5

If the function f is continuous on the closed interval $[a, b]$, then f has both a maximum and a minimum value on $[a, b]$.

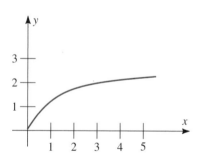

Figure 6.2 $f(x) = \sqrt{x}$ has an absolute minimum at $x = 0$ but no absolute maximum.

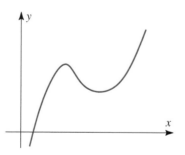

Figure 6.3 Function f has no absolute extrema.

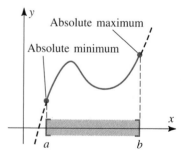

Figure 6.4 When restricted to the domain $[a, b]$, the function f has an absolute minimum at endpoint $x = a$ and an absolute maximum at endpoint $x = b$.

Most problems in which we shall need to find maximum or minimum values of a function will involve closed intervals of the form $[a, b]$ as the domain of the function. (When this is not the case, we shall need to keep in mind the fact that extrema need not exist, as in Examples 1 and 2.)

When the domain of f is restricted to the closed interval $[a, b]$, we have seen that maximum or minimum values can exist

(a) at relative extrema, or
(b) at the endpoints $x = a$ and $x = b$.

These are the only possibilities. Since relative extrema can exist only at critical numbers, we have the following procedure for finding absolute extrema.

Procedure for Finding the Maximum and Minimum Values of a Continuous Function f on a Closed Interval $[a, b]$:

(1) Find all critical numbers c in $[a, b]$. (These are the numbers c for which $f'(c) = 0$ or $f'(c)$ is undefined.)
(2) Compute the endpoint values $f(a)$ and $f(b)$ and all values $f(c)$ where c is a critical number in $[a, b]$.
(3) The largest of the values found in step 2 is the absolute maximum value of f on $[a, b]$. The smallest is the absolute minimum value of f on $[a, b]$.

□ **EXAMPLE 3**

Find the maximum and minimum values for the function $f(x) = x^3 - 3x^2 - 24x + 5$ for x on the interval $[-3, 8]$.

Strategy · · · · · · · ·   **Solution**

Find f'.

For $f(x) = x^3 - 3x^2 - 24x + 5$ the derivative is

$$f'(x) = 3x^2 - 6x - 24$$
$$= (3x + 6)(x - 4).$$

Set $f'(x) = 0$ to find the critical numbers.

Thus $f'(x) = 0$ if $3x + 6 = 0$ or if $x - 4 = 0$. These two equations give the critical numbers $x = -2$ and $x = 4$. Since $f'(x)$ exists for all x, there are no other critical numbers.

Calculate $f(x)$ for each critical number and endpoint of the interval $[-3, 8]$.

Calculating $f(x)$ for each critical number and both endpoints of the interval $[-3, 8]$, we find

$$f(-3) = (-3)^3 - 3(-3)^2 - 24(-3) + 5 = 23$$
$$f(-2) = (-2)^3 - 3(-2)^2 - 24(-2) + 5 = 33$$
$$f(4) = 4^3 - 3(4)^2 - 24(4) + 5 = -75$$
$$f(8) = 8^3 - 3(8)^2 - 24(8) + 5 = 133.$$

Select the largest and smallest of these values.

The maximum value of f is therefore $f(8) = 133$ and the minimum value is $f(4) = -75$. Note from Figure 6.5 that the maximum value of f occurs at an endpoint while the minimum value of f occurs at a critical number. ■

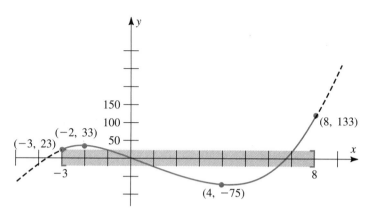

Figure 6.5 For $f(x) = x^3 - 3x^2 - 24x + 5$, the maximum value is $f(8) = 133$ and the minimum value is $f(4) = -75$ on the interval $[-3, 8]$.

□ **EXAMPLE 4**

Find the maximum and minimum values for the function $f(x) = x^{2/3}$ for $-1 \le x \le 8$.

Strategy   · · · · · · ·

Find f'.

Solution

For the function $f(x) = x^{2/3}$ the derivative is

$$f'(x) = \frac{2}{3}x^{-1/3} = \frac{2}{3x^{1/3}}.$$

Find all critical numbers.

Calculate $f(x)$ for all critical numbers and endpoints.

Now $f'(x)$ is nonzero for all x, but $f'(x)$ fails to exist for $x = 0$. Thus the only critical number for f is $x = 0$. Checking the values $f(x)$ at this critical number and at both endpoints of $[-1, 8]$ gives

$$f(-1) = (-1)^{2/3} = 1$$
$$f(0) = (0)^{2/3} = 0$$
$$f(8) = 8^{2/3} = (8^{1/3})^2 = 2^2 = 4.$$

Select the largest and smallest of these values.

Thus the maximum value $f(8) = 4$ occurs at an endpoint and the minimum value $f(0) = 0$ occurs at the critical number. (See Figure 6.6.)   ■

Occasionally, we do not have a closed finite interval $[a, b]$ to work with, and we must do our analysis somewhat differently. In the following example the function to be maximized is defined on an *infinite* interval of the form $[a, \infty)$. In the absence of a (finite) right endpoint for this interval we must consider the behavior of the function for very large numbers x.

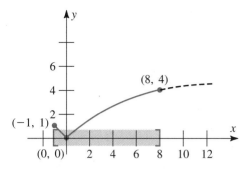

Figure 6.6 For $f(x) = x^{2/3}$ on the interval $[-1, 8]$, the maximum is $f(8) = 4$ and the minimum is $f(0) = 0$.

□ **EXAMPLE 5**

A manufacturer of pocket cameras finds that the total cost of producing and marketing x cameras per month is $C(x) = 400 + 10x + \dfrac{1}{2}x^2$ dollars. If the manufacturer can sell all cameras produced for \$50 each, what monthly production level yields the maximum profit for the manufacturer?

Solution: The revenue from the sale of x cameras is

$$R(x) = 50x$$

so the monthly profit to the manufacturer is

$$P(x) = R(x) - C(x)$$
$$= 50x - \left(400 + 10x + \frac{1}{2}x^2\right)$$
$$= 40x - 400 - \frac{1}{2}x^2.$$

Since negative production levels do not make sense, the problem is to find the maximum value of the profit function

$$P(x) = 40x - 400 - \frac{1}{2}x^2$$

for x in the interval $[0, \infty)$. Setting $P'(x) = 0$ gives

$$P'(x) = 40 - x = 0$$

so $x = 40$ is the only critical number. Since

$$P''(x) = -1 < 0$$

for all x, the Second Derivative Test verifies that

$$P(40) = 40(40) - 400 - \frac{1}{2}(40)^2 = 400$$

is a relative maximum value for P. Since

$$P(0) = 40(0) - 400 - \frac{1}{2}(0)^2 = -400$$

the relative maximum yields a larger value $P(x)$ than does the endpoint $x = 0$.

Since $P'(x)$ is negative for large x, $P(x)$ is a decreasing function for large x, so the possibility of a larger value for $P(x)$ than $P(40)$ occurring for $x > 40$ is ruled out. Thus the maximum profit of $P(40) = 400$ dollars per month occurs at the production level of 40 cameras per month. (See Figure 6.7.)

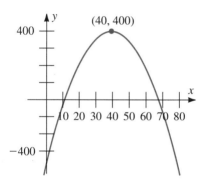

Figure 6.7 Maximum value of the profit function $P(x) = 40x - 400 - \frac{1}{2}x^2$ is $P(40) = 400$.

☑ **PRACTICE PROBLEMS 3.6**

1. Find the maximum and minimum values of the function

$$f(x) = x^3 - 6x^2 + 9x + 4$$

on the interval $[0, 4]$.

2. Find the maximum value of the slope of the line tangent to the graph of the function

$$f(x) = x^2(6 - x^2)$$

on the interval $[-2, 2]$.

Exercise Set 3.6

In each of Exercises 1–20, find the maximum and minimum values of the given function on the given interval.

1. $f(x) = 9 - x^2$, x in $[-1, 3]$

2. $f(x) = 9 - x^2 + 8x$, x in $[0, 5]$

3. $f(x) = x^2 - 2x + 3$, x in $[-1, 3]$

4. $f(x) = 7 - x^3 + 3x$, x in $[-2, 2]$

5. $f(x) = 3 + x + x^2 + 2x^3$ x in $[-2, 3]$

6. $f(x) = 3x - x^3$, x in $[-1, 1]$

7. $f(x) = x^2(x - 1)$, x in $[0, 3]$

8. $f(x) = |x - 2|$, x in $[0, 5]$

9. $f(x) = x^3 - 2x^2$, x in $[-1, 2]$

10. $f(x) = 5x^3 - x^5$, x in $[-1, 1]$

11. $f(x) = x + \dfrac{1}{x}$, x in $\left[\frac{1}{2}, 2\right]$

12. $f(x) = (\sqrt{x} + x)^2$, x in $[0, 4]$

13. $f(x) = x^{2/3} + 2$, x in $[0, \infty)$

14. $f(x) = 3 - x^{2/3}$, x in $[-1, 8]$

15. $f(x) = \dfrac{1}{x(x - 4)}$, x in $[1, 3]$

16. $f(x) = \dfrac{(x + 1)}{(x - 1)}$, x in $[-3, 0]$

17. $f(x) = 2x^3 - 15x^2 + 24x + 10$, x in $[0, 4]$

18. $f(x) = 8x^{1/3} - 2x^{4/3}$, x in $[-1, 8]$

19. $f(x) = \sqrt{x}(1 - x)$, x in $[0, 4]$

20. $f(x) = 3x^5 - 5x^3$, x in $[-2, 2]$

21. The population of a certain city is predicted to be $P(t) = 100{,}000 + 48t^{3/2} - 4t^2$ people t years after 1985. In what year will the population be a maximum according to this prediction?

22. A manufacturer of men's shoes experiences a total cost of $C(x) = 400 + 20x + x^2$ dollars in producing x pairs of shoes per week. If the manufacturer receives \$60 for each pair of shoes produced, what is the weekly production level that maximizes profit?

23. A company determines that the profit resulting from the sale of x of its products per week is $P(x) = 160 - 96x + 18x^2 - x^3$ thousand dollars. Find the maximum and minimum values for this function on the interval $[0, 10]$ and the sales level x at which each occurs.

24. Find the maximum and minimum values of the profit function

$$P(x) = 500 - 60(3x - 27)^{2/3}$$

on the interval $[0, 15]$.

25. A producer of picture frames finds that x frames can be sold per week at price p where $x = 400 - 4p$ for $0 \le p \le 100$. At what price will revenue be a maximum? $[R(x) = xp(x).]$

26. A large suburban community receives its electrical power supply from an urban power plant. A local engineer, after studying data on energy usage, determines that a good model for daily energy usage between 6:00 a.m. and 8:00 p.m. is given by the function

$$E(t) = 4 - 2\left(\frac{t - 13}{7}\right)^4, \qquad 6 \le t \le 20$$

where t represents hours after midnight. The engineer argues that through the use of solar generators the community could reduce its energy demand from the urban power plant by the amount $S(t)$ where

$$S(t) = 1 - \left(\frac{t - 13}{7}\right)^2, \qquad 6 \le t \le 20.$$

(See Figure 6.8.)

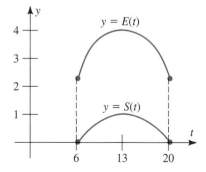

Figure 6.8

a. Find the peak demand for energy according to the engineer's model for present usage and the time when it occurs.

b. Find the resulting peak demand according to the model for the contribution due to solar power and the time(s) at which it occurs.

c. Calculate the amount by which peak demand from the power plant can be reduced according to this model. (See Figure 6.9.)

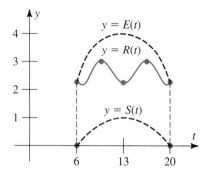

Figure 6.9 $R(t) = E(t) - S(t)$.

☑ **SOLUTIONS TO PRACTICE PROBLEMS 3.6**

1. For $f(x) = x^3 - 6x^2 + 9x + 4$,

$$f'(x) = 3x^2 - 12x + 9$$
$$= 3(x - 1)(x - 3).$$

Thus, $f'(x) = 0$ for $x = 1$ and $x = 3$. We therefore check:

$$f(0) = 4$$
$$f(1) = 8$$
$$f(3) = 4$$

and

$$f(4) = 8.$$

The maximum value of f is $f(1) = f(4) = 8$ and the minimum is $f(0) = f(3) = 4$ on $[0, 4]$. (See Figure 6.10.)

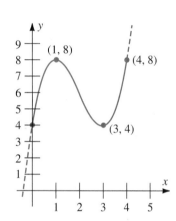

Figure 6.10

2. The slope of the tangent is given by the derivative of $f(x) = x^2(6 - x^2) = 6x^2 - x^4$

$$f'(x) = 12x - 4x^3.$$

This is the function (f) to be maximized, so we avoid confusion over notation by giving it its own name, $S(x)$:

$$S(x) = 12x - 4x^3.$$

To find its maximum on $[-2, 2]$ we calculate its derivative:

$$S'(x) = 12 - 12x^2$$
$$= 12(1 - x^2)$$

which equals zero for $x = \pm 1$. We therefore calculate the values

$$S(-2) = 12(-2) - 4(-2)^3 = 8$$
$$S(-1) = 12(-1) - 4(-1)^3 = -8$$
$$S(1) = 12(1) - 4(1)^3 = 8$$
$$S(2) = 12(2) - 4(2)^3 = -8.$$

The maximum value of the slope of the line tangent to the graph of f is $m = 8$, which occurs when $x = -2$ and $x = 1$. (See Figure 6.11.)

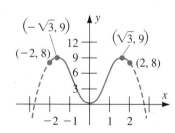

Figure 6.11

3.7 Applied Maximum–Minimum Problems

It is frequently the case that problems to which we would like to apply the techniques of the calculus are not stated for us mathematically, but rather, they are stated in the language of a particular field of application—business, the social sciences, and so on. It is important to develop the ability to reformulate such problems mathematically, so that appropriate mathematical techniques can be applied to solve the problem. This act is called *mathematical modelling*. The following diagram indicates the three basic steps in solving applied problems by this approach.

This section contains many applied problems. Each is stated in the language of some area of application, and the mathematical solution of each involves using the derivative to find the maximum or minimum value of a certain function on a particular interval. In each case you will need to begin by reformulating the given problem into a mathematical problem of finding extrema, as in Section 3.6, and in each case you will be executing the three basic steps below.

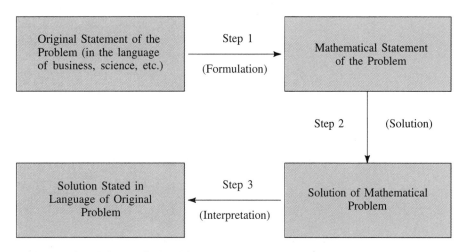

Basic steps in solving applied problems.

We begin with a typical example, following which we shall describe a general procedure for solving additional problems of this type.

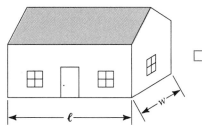

Figure 7.1 House in Example 1.

□ **EXAMPLE 1**

An individual is interested in building a rectangular one-story house containing 180 square meters of floor space. Due to energy conservation considerations, the perimeter of the house is to be as small as possible. Also, for aesthetic reasons neither the length nor the width of the house is to be less than 10 meters. What dimensions for the house meet all these requirements? (See Figure 7.1.)

Solution: We begin by identifying and naming the relevant variables. We let

$$\ell = \text{length of the house}$$
$$w = \text{width of the house}$$
$$P = \text{perimeter of the house}$$
$$A = \text{area of the floor space.}$$

We next identify all known relationships among the variables as well as any information concerning these variables. We have

$$P = 2\ell + 2w \qquad \text{(principal equation defining } P\text{)}$$
$$A = \ell w = 180 \qquad \text{(auxiliary equation giving condition on } A\text{)}$$
$$\ell \geq 10 \qquad \text{(constraint on variable } \ell\text{)}$$
$$w \geq 10 \qquad \text{(constraint on variable } w\text{)}$$

We can now state a precise formulation for our problem: "Find values for ℓ and w that minimize the expression $P = 2\ell + 2w$ given that $\ell w = 180$, $\ell \geq 10$, and $w \geq 10$."

However, this formulation is not yet in a form to which the techniques of Section 3.6 can be applied. The difficulty lies in the fact that the variable P to be minimized is not a function of a single independent variable. Indeed, the principal equation $P = 2\ell + 2w$ gives P as a function of *two* independent variables, ℓ and w. To overcome this difficulty, we use the auxiliary equation $\ell w = 180$ to solve for one of these variables in terms of the other:

$$\ell w = 180 \qquad \text{gives} \qquad w = \frac{180}{\ell}.$$

We may now substitute $w = \dfrac{180}{\ell}$ into the principal equation to obtain P as a function of the single variable ℓ:

$$P(\ell) = 2\ell + 2\left(\frac{180}{\ell}\right)$$
$$= 2\ell + \frac{360}{\ell}.$$

Finally, since it is given that neither ℓ nor w can be less than 10, and since $\ell w = 180$, it follows that ℓ cannot be greater than $\dfrac{180}{10} = 18$. That is, we must have $10 \leq \ell \leq 18$. We can therefore state our problem as follows:
"Find the minimum value of the function

$$P(\ell) = 2\ell + \frac{360}{\ell} \qquad \text{for } \ell \text{ in } [10, 18]."$$

To solve this problem, we proceed as in Section 3.6. The derivative of P is

$$P'(\ell) = 2 - \frac{360}{\ell^2}.$$

Setting $P'(\ell) = 0$ gives the equation $\dfrac{360}{\ell^2} = 2$, so $\ell^2 = 180$. Thus $\ell = \pm\sqrt{180} = \pm 6\sqrt{5}$.

Now $P'(\ell)$ is undefined for $\ell = 0$, but 0 lies outside the interval $[10, 18]$ as does the critical number $-6\sqrt{5}$. Thus the only critical number for P in the interval $[10, 18]$ is $\ell = 6\sqrt{5}$. The minimum value for P must therefore lie among the three values

$$P(10) = 2(10) + \frac{360}{10} = 56 \text{ meters} \qquad \text{(endpoint)}$$

$$P(6\sqrt{5}) = 2(6\sqrt{5}) + \frac{360}{6\sqrt{5}} \approx 53.67 \text{ meters} \qquad \text{(critical number)}$$

$$P(18) = 2(18) + \frac{360}{18} = 56 \text{ meters} \qquad \text{(endpoint)}$$

The dimensions that minimize the perimeter are therefore $\ell = 6\sqrt{5}$ and $w = \dfrac{180}{\ell} = \dfrac{180}{6\sqrt{5}} = 6\sqrt{5}$. In other words, the house should be built in the shape of a square $6\sqrt{5}$ meters on each side.   ∎

At this point you should look back over the solution of Example 1 to identify where each of the three basic steps (formulation, solution, interpretation) occurred. The following procedure breaks each of these three conceptual steps down into finer detail, corresponding more closely to the actual steps that you will follow in working the remaining problems in this section.

Procedure for Solving Applied Max–Min Problems

Step 1: Formulation

a. Draw a sketch, if appropriate, illustrating all variables and relevant constant quantities or dimensions.
b. Identify and label all variables.
c. Identify the variable for which the extremum is to be found.
d. Find an equation expressing this variable in terms of other variables and constants (principal equation).
e. Find all other equations among variables (auxiliary equations).
f. Identify any other constraints (e.g., intervals within which variables must lie).

Step 2: Mathematical Solution

a. Use auxiliary equations, if necessary, to substitute for variables in the principal equation until the principal equation expresses the variable for which the extremum is sought as a function of a single independent variable.
b. Determine the interval within which the independent variable lies.
c. Solve the resulting problem by the methods of Section 3.6.

Step 3: Interpretation

a. From the auxiliary equation(s), find the values of all remaining variables corresponding to the solution found above.
b. Describe the solution in the language of the original statement of the problem.

In the examples that follow, the comments in the *Strategy* column will point out which of the steps in the procedure are being applied. Use these comments as a guide to help you think through the basic steps required to solve a problem before actually beginning any of the calculations.

☐ **EXAMPLE 2**

A highway engineer has sampled the speed and density of automobiles along a particular section of highway and determined that a good model of the relationship between velocity and density is

$$v(\rho) = \frac{100}{1 + \rho^2} \text{ kilometers per hour,} \qquad 0 \le \rho \le 3.$$

(See Figure 7.2.)

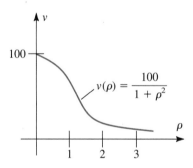

Figure 7.2 Velocity as a function of density.

Here ρ represents density in units of 100 automobiles per kilometer, and v represents velocity. Find the density at which *traffic flow* $q = \rho v$ will be a maximum according to this model.

Strategy · · · · · · · ·

Identify the relevant variables.

Solution

The relevant variables are

$$q = \text{traffic flow}$$
$$v = \text{traffic velocity}$$
$$\rho = \text{traffic density.}$$

Find the principal equation.	The principal equation for flow is given as

$$q = \rho v \tag{1}$$

Identify the auxiliary equation.	and the auxiliary equation for velocity is

$$v(\rho) = \frac{100}{1 + \rho^2}. \tag{2}$$

Use constraints to find the interval in which the independent variable lies.	Finally, we have the constraint that density must satisfy the inequality

$$0 \le \rho \le 3. \tag{3}$$

Use the auxiliary equation to eliminate one of the two variables on the right-hand side of the principal equation.	If we are to maximize flow as a function of density, we must work with ρ as the independent variable. Thus we use auxiliary equation (2) to substitute for v in principal equation (1):

$$q = \rho v$$
$$= \rho \left(\frac{100}{1 + \rho^2} \right).$$

The principal equation now gives flow q as a function of ρ alone:

$$q(\rho) = \frac{100\rho}{1 + \rho^2} \text{ hundred automobiles per hour.}$$

State the mathematical problem to be solved.	Our mathematical problem is therefore to find the maximum value of this function for ρ in the closed interval $[0, 3]$. (See Figure 7.3.)

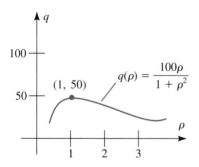

Figure 7.3 Traffic flow as a function of density.

Set the derivative equal to zero and solve to find critical numbers.	To solve this problem, we begin by calculating the derivative of q using the Quotient Rule:

$$q'(\rho) = \frac{100(1 + \rho^2) - 2\rho(100\rho)}{(1 + \rho^2)^2}$$
$$= \frac{100(1 - \rho^2)}{(1 + \rho^2)^2}.$$

Now $q'(\rho) = 0$ only if $1 - \rho^2 = 0$. Thus the critical numbers for q are $\rho = -1$ and $\rho = 1$. Since only $\rho = 1$ lies within the interval $[0, 3]$, the maximum flow lies among the values

Calculate values of flow at endpoints and critical numbers.

$$q(0) = \frac{100(0)}{1 + 0^2} = 0 \qquad \text{(endpoint)}$$

$$q(1) = \frac{100}{1 + 1^2} = 50 \qquad \text{(critical number)}$$

$$q(3) = \frac{100(3)}{1 + 3^2} = 30 \qquad \text{(endpoint)}$$

Select maximum value.
Interpret result.

The maximum flow is therefore $50 \times 100 = 5000$ automobiles per hour, which corresponds to a density of $\rho = 100$ automobiles per kilometer and a velocity of $v(1) = 50$ kilometers per hour. ■

□ **EXAMPLE 3**

A producer of computer graphics software finds that the selling price p of its software is related to the number x of copies of its software sold annually by the demand equation

$$x = 10,000 - 200p \qquad (4)$$

while its total cost in producing and marketing these x copies is given by the function

$$C(x) = 50,000 + 5x. \qquad (5)$$

Find the price p for which profits will be a maximum.

Strategy · · · · · · ·
Identify all relevant variables.

Solution
Since profits depend on price, quantity, costs, and revenues, the relevant variables are

$P =$ annual profits
$R =$ annual revenues
$C =$ annual costs
$p =$ selling price
$x =$ production level. (copies produced and sold annually)

Find principal equation for profit, the variable to be maximized.

We have seen earlier that profit is determined from revenues and costs by the equation

$$P = R - C. \qquad (6)$$

Find auxiliary equation for revenue.

Also, we know that revenues are determined from price and production level as $R = xp$. Using equation (4), we can express revenues as a function of price alone as

$$\begin{aligned} R(p) &= xp \\ &= (10,000 - 200p)p \\ &= 10,000p - 200p^2. \end{aligned} \qquad (7)$$

Identify constraints on independent variables. Use to determine interval for independent variable p.

Since neither price nor production level can be negative, we have the constraints

$$p \geq 0 \quad \text{and} \quad x \geq 0.$$

The constraint $x \geq 0$, together with equation (4), gives the inequality

$$10{,}000 - 200p \geq 0.$$

Thus

$$200p \leq 10{,}000$$

so

$$0 \leq p \leq 50.$$

(See Figure 7.4.)

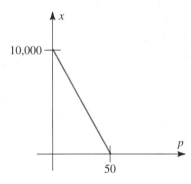

Figure 7.4 Demand equation $x = 10{,}000 - 200p$ gives the constraint $0 \leq p \leq 50$.

Use auxiliary equations to substitute for variables in the principal equation.

Using equations (5), (6), and (7) we can now express profit P as

$$\begin{aligned} P &= R - C \\ &= (10{,}000p - 200p^2) - (50{,}000 + 5x) \\ &= 10{,}000p - 200p^2 - 50{,}000 - 5x. \end{aligned}$$

Using equation (4), we can express profit P as a function of price alone as

Use auxiliary equation (4) to eliminate second independent variable in principal equation.

$$\begin{aligned} P(p) &= 10{,}000p - 200p^2 - 50{,}000 - 5(10{,}000 - 200p) \\ &= 11{,}000p - 200p^2 - 100{,}000. \end{aligned} \tag{8}$$

This is the function for which we seek a maximum value.

State the mathematical problem to be solved.

The mathematical problem is therefore to find the maximum value of the function

$$P(p) = 11{,}000p - 200p^2 - 100{,}000$$

for p in the closed interval $[0, 50]$.

Find critical numbers.

To do so, we set $P'(p) = 0$ and find the critical numbers

$$P'(p) = 11{,}000 - 400p = 0$$

gives

$$p = \frac{11{,}000}{400} = 27.5.$$

This is the only critical number, and it does lie in the interval $[0, 50]$. Using equation (8), we calculate the values

Calculate the values $P(p)$ at endpoints and critical numbers.

$$P(0) = 11{,}000(0) - 200(0)^2 - 100{,}000$$
$$= -100{,}000 \qquad \text{(endpoint)}$$
$$P(27.5) = 11{,}000(27.5) - 200(27.5)^2 - 100{,}000$$
$$= 51{,}250 \qquad \text{(critical number)}$$

Select maximum.

$$P(50) = 11{,}000(50) - 200(50)^2 - 100{,}000$$
$$= -50{,}000. \qquad \text{(endpoint)}$$

Interpret result.

The maximum profit of $51,250 will therefore occur at selling price $p = \$27.50$ per copy. (See Figure 7.5.) ∎

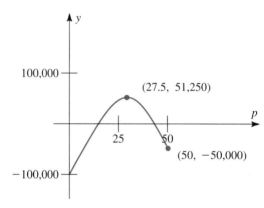

Figure 7.5 Maximum profit of $P = \$51{,}250$ occurs at selling price $p = \$27.50$.

☐ EXAMPLE 4

An orchard currently has 25 trees per acre. The average yield has been found to be 495 apples per tree. It is predicted that for each additional tree planted per acre the average yield will be reduced by 15 apples per tree. According to this information, how many additional trees per acre should be planted in order to maximize total yield per acre?

Solution: Let x be the number of additional trees to be planted per acre, N the total number of trees per acre, and Y the total yield per acre. Since

$$\left\{\begin{matrix} \text{total yield} \\ \text{per acre} \end{matrix}\right\} \text{ equals } \left\{\begin{matrix} \text{number of trees} \\ \text{per acre} \end{matrix}\right\} \text{ times } \{\text{yield per tree}\}$$

we have the principal equation

$$Y = N(495 - 15x).$$

The auxiliary equation $N = 25 + x$ may be combined with the principal equation to give yield as a function of x alone:

$$Y = (25 + x)(495 - 15x)$$
$$= 12{,}375 + 120x - 15x^2.$$

Finally, we note that the yield per tree will reach zero when $495 - 15x = 0$, or when $x = 33$. Thus, our problem is to find the maximum value of the function

$$Y(x) = 12{,}375 + 120x - 15x^2$$

for x in the interval $[0, 33]$. Since

$$Y'(x) = 120 - 30x$$

we shall have $Y'(x) = 0$ when $x = \dfrac{120}{30} = 4$. This is the only critical number for Y.

Since

$$
\begin{aligned}
Y(0) &= 12{,}375 + 120(0) - 15(0)^2 = 12{,}375 &\text{(endpoint)}\\
Y(4) &= 12{,}375 + 120(4) - 15(4)^2 = 12{,}615 &\text{(critical number)}\\
Y(33) &= 12{,}375 + 120(33) - 15(33)^2 = 0 &\text{(endpoint)}
\end{aligned}
$$

the maximum yield per acre of 12,615 apples will occur when $x = 4$ additional trees are planted per acre. ∎

☑ PRACTICE PROBLEMS 3.7

1. A bicycle manufacturer determines that the total cost of producing x bicycles weekly is

$$C(x) = 5000 + 40x + 2x^2.$$

   Find the production level that minimizes the *average* cost per bicycle.

2. An open box is to be made from a rectangular sheet of cardboard, measuring 16 inches by 10 inches, by cutting equal squares from each corner and folding up the resulting sides. (See Figure 7.6.) Find the dimensions for which volume is a maximum.

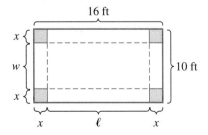

Figure 7.6

Exercise Set 3.7

1. The percentage of school age children attending private schools in a certain city is predicted to be $p(t) = \sqrt{24 + 10t - t^2}$ where t represents years after 1990. When will this percentage be the largest between 1990 and 2000?

2. A manufacturer finds that its total monthly costs in producing x hairdryers is $C(x) = 100 + 5x + 0.02x^2$. For what production level x is *average cost per item* a minimum? $\left(\text{Recall, average cost } c(x) \text{ is defined by } c(x) = \dfrac{C(x)}{x}.\right)$

3. Efficiency specialists determine that t hours after beginning a shift a plant worker's efficiency on the job is approximately $R(t) = 0.92 + 0.08t - 0.02t^2$ percent. When is efficiency a maximum?

4. The sum of two nonnegative numbers is 10. Find these numbers if their product is as large as possible.

5. The sum of two nonnegative numbers is 36. Find these numbers if the first plus the square of the second is a maximum.

6. A rectangular yard is to be constructed along the side of a house by erecting a fence on three sides, using the house as the fourth wall of the play yard. Find the dimensions that produce the play yard of maximum area if 20 meters of fence is available for the project.

7. A model for the spread of disease assumes that the rate at which disease spreads is proportional to the product of the number of people infected and the number not infected. Assume the size of the population to be a constant N. When is the disease spreading most rapidly? (*Hint:* Use the equation $R(t) = KI(t)[N - I(t)]$.)

8. A farmer has 120 meters of fencing with which to make a rectangular pen. The pen is to have one internal fence running parallel to the end fence that divides the pen into two sections. Find the dimensions that produce the pen of maximum area if the length of the larger section is to be twice the length of the smaller section.

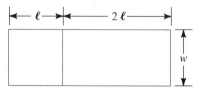

9. Find the minimum and maximum values of the slopes of the lines tangent to the graph of
$$f(x) = x^3 - 9x^2 + 7x - 6, \qquad 1 \le x \le 4$$
and the points where these slopes occur.

10. For the total cost function $C(x) = 16 + 4x + x^2$, find the production level x for which average cost per item, $\dfrac{C(x)}{x}$, is a minimum.

11. Demand for a certain type of electric appliance is related to its selling price p by the equation $x = 2000 - 100p$. Here x is the number of appliances that can be sold per month at price p. Find the selling price for which revenues received from sales will be a maximum.

12. For the appliance manufacturer in Exercise 11 the total cost of producing x appliances per month is $C(x) = 500 + 10x$. Find the selling price p at which profits are a maximum.

13. A tool rental company determines that it can achieve 500 daily rentals of jackhammers per year at a daily rental fee of $30. For each $1 increase in rental price 10 fewer jackhammers will be rented. What rental price maximizes revenue?

14. An open box is to be made from a square sheet of cardboard by cutting out squares of equal size from each of the four corners and bending up the flaps. The sheet of cardboard measures 20 cm on each side. Find the dimensions of the box of maximum volume that can be made in this way.

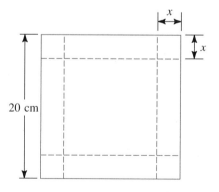

15. A rectangle is inscribed in a triangle with sides of length 6 cm, 8 cm, and 10 cm, respectively. Find the dimensions of the rectangle of maximum area if two sides of the rectangle lie along two sides of the triangle.

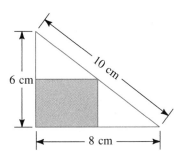

16. A pattern for a rectangular box with a top is cut from a sheet of cardboard measuring 10 cm by 16 cm. Find the dimensions of the box for which volume is a maximum.

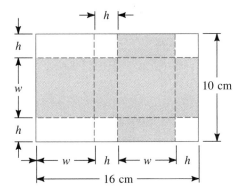

17. A window has the shape of a rectangle surmounted by a semicircle. Find the dimensions that provide maximum area if the perimeter of the window is 10 meters.

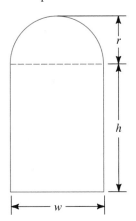

18. A hotel finds that it can rent 200 rooms per day if it charges $40 per room. For each $1 increase in rental rate 4 fewer rooms will be rented per day. What room rate maximizes revenues?

19. The level of antacid in a person's stomach t minutes after a certain brand of antacid tablet is taken is found to be $f(t) = \dfrac{6t}{t^2 + 2t + 1}$. When is the antacid level a maximum?

20. Utility is a measure of an individual's satisfaction due to the consumption of x units of a given quantity or commodity during a unit of time. For a utility function $U(x)$ the *saturation* quantity x_0 is the number for which $U(x_0)$ is the maximum value of the utility function. Find the saturation quantity for the utility function

$$U(x) = \frac{6x - x^2}{10x^2 - 60x + 100}.$$

21. For the utility function $U(x) = 2 - (x - 8)^{2/3}$, $x \geq 0$, for which x is utility, $U(x)$, a maximum?

22. The cost per hour of operating a truck is $C(v) = kv^{3/2}$ where v is velocity and k is a constant. If the cost per hour for the driver is a constant A, what is the most economical speed at which to operate the truck over a route of fixed distance?

23. A homeowner wishes to enclose 800 square feet of garden space, to be laid out in the shape of a rectangle. One side of the space is to have a stone wall costing $50 per foot. The other three sides are to have cedar fencing costing $20 per foot. Find the dimensions for the space that will minimize the total of these costs.

24. Promoters of a musical event can sell 4000 tickets at a price of $20 each. They wish to increase revenues by raising ticket prices. However, it is determined by market research that for each $1 increase in ticket prices, 100 fewer people will attend. What ticket price maximizes revenues?

25. A savings bank is permitted to loan half its receipts from savings deposits. It can loan funds at 10% interest, up to this limit. Its receipts from savings deposits will be $100,000$r$, where $0 \leq r \leq 0.10$ and r is the rate of interest paid on the savings deposits. What interest rate r maximizes profits for the bank, based on this information?

26. What is the answer to Exercise 25 if the bank is permitted to loan all of its receipts from savings deposits at 10% interest?

27. A summer camp determines that the cost of enrolling n students in its summer program is

$$C(n) = 3n^2 + 2000n + 7500$$

dollars. For what number n will the average cost per child be the smallest?

28. The summer camp in Exercise 27 determines that the price p (in dollars) that it can charge for its program and the number n of students who will enroll are related by the equation

$$p = 5000 - 27n.$$

What registration level n maximizes profits?

29. A baseball card company determines that the quantity x of its new card sets can be sold at price p, where x and p are related by the equation

$$p = 10 - 0.002x.$$

Here p is in dollars and x is units (sets of cards). If the total cost in producing x sets of these cards is

$$C(x) = 2000 + 2x$$

find the quantity x to be produced in order to maximize profits.

30. A rectangle is bounded by the x-axis, the y-axis, and the line $y = 10 - \dfrac{1}{2}x$. Find the maximum possible area for such a rectangle.

31. An orchard presently has 30 trees per acre. The average yield per tree has been found to be 300 apples. It is predicted that for each additional tree planted per acre the yield will be reduced by 5 apples per tree. According to this information, how many additional trees per acre should be planted in order to maximize yield per acre?

32. A rectangular beam is to be cut from a round log 20 cm in diameter. If the strength of the beam is proportional to the product of its width and the square of its depth, find the dimensions of the cross section for the beam of maximum strength.

33. Suppose that the density of automobiles along a section of highway between the hours of $t = 3$ p.m. and $t = 7$ p.m. is given by the function

$$\rho(t) = -10(t - 3)(t - 7)$$ automobiles per kilometer.

If the velocity $v(\rho)$ as a function of density is as given in Example 2, find the maximum and minimum velocities and the times at which they occur.

34. A wire 50 cm long is to be cut into two pieces, one of which is to be bent into the shape of a circle and the other of which is to be bent into the shape of a square. Find where the wire should be cut so that the combined area of the resulting figures is a maximum.

35. A supervisor has the option of scheduling a laborer for up to 4 hours per day of overtime work in addition to the regular 8-hour workday. For a certain job requiring 200 man-hours to complete, the supervisor has available only one laborer. The laborer is paid $10 per hour during regular hours and $15 per hour during overtime. In addition, the company incurs daily costs of $200 for each workday in which the job remains incomplete. How should the supervisor schedule the laborer's time in order to minimize costs? (That is, should overtime work be scheduled and, if so, how much?)

36. A swimmer is in the ocean 100 meters from a straight shoreline. A person in distress is located on the shoreline 300 meters from the point on the shoreline closest to the swimmer. If the swimmer can swim 3 meters per second and run 5 meters per second, what path should the swimmer follow in order to reach the distressed person as quickly as possible?

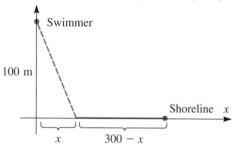

37. An underground telephone cable is to be laid between two boat docks on opposite sides of a straight river. One boathouse is 600 meters downstream from the other. The river is 200 meters wide. If the cost of laying the cable is $50 per meter under water and $30 per meter on land, how should the cable be laid to minimize cost?

38. Observations by plant biologists support the thesis that the survival rate for seedlings in the vicinity of a parent tree is proportional to the product of the density of the seeds on the ground and their probability of survival against herbivores. (The density of the herbivores tends to decrease as distance from the tree increases since the density of the food supply also decreases.) Let x denote the distance in meters from the trunk of the tree. The results of sampling indicate that the density of seeds on the ground for $0 \leq x \leq 10$ is given by

$$d(x) = \frac{1}{1 + (0.2x)^2}$$

and the probability of survival against herbivores is

$$p(x) = (0.1)x.$$

Find the distance, according to the model proposed here, at which the survival rate is a maximum.

39. In Exercise 38, suppose that the density of seeds for $1 \le x \le 9$ is given by the function

$$d(x) = \frac{1}{x}$$

and the probability of a seed surviving against herbivores is

$$p(x) = \frac{1}{(x - 10)^2}.$$

Find the distance from the parent tree at which seed survival will be a minimum.

40. Find the maximum possible area for a rectangle inscribed in a circle of radius $r = 6$.

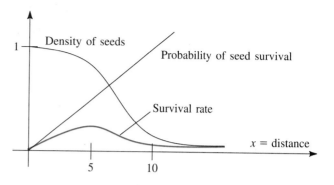

☑ SOLUTIONS TO PRACTICE PROBLEMS 3.7

1. The average cost function is

$$c(x) = \frac{C(x)}{x} = \frac{5000 + 40x + 2x^2}{x} = \frac{5000}{x} + 40 + 2x.$$

Its derivative is

$$c'(x) = -\frac{5000}{x^2} + 2.$$

Setting $c'(x) = 0$ gives $x^2 = 2500$, so $x = 50$ is the only (positive) critical number. We leave it to you to verify that $x = 50$ corresponds to the minimum cost per bicycle.

2. If we let x be the dimension of the square tabs cut from the corners, the resulting box has dimensions:

$$\text{length} = \ell = 16 - 2x$$
$$\text{width} = w = 10 - 2x$$
$$\text{height} = h = x.$$

The volume can be expressed as a function of x as follows:

$$V = \ell w h$$

so

$$V(x) = (16 - 2x)(10 - 2x)x$$
$$= 160x - 52x^2 + 4x^3.$$

Then

$$V'(x) = 160 - 104x + 12x^2$$
$$= 4(3x^2 - 26x + 40).$$

Setting $V'(x) = 0$ and using the quadratic formula to solve gives

$$x = \frac{26 \pm \sqrt{26^2 - 4 \cdot 3 \cdot 40}}{2 \cdot 3}$$
$$= \frac{26 \pm \sqrt{196}}{6}$$
$$= \frac{26 \pm 14}{6}$$
$$= 2 \text{ or } \frac{20}{3}.$$

The root $x = \dfrac{20}{3}$ is impossible in this case, since we must have $0 < x < 5$ (because the smaller dimension of the cardboard sheet is 10 inches). You can verify that $x = 2$ yields the maximum volume, with corresponding dimensions

$$\ell = 16 - 2 \cdot 2 = 12; \qquad w = 10 - 2 \cdot 2 = 6; \qquad h = 2.$$

3.8 Applications to Economics and Business

Our preceding examples have made frequent use of the concepts of production, cost, revenue, supply, demand, and profit. We briefly revisit these relationships here and consider several additional examples of how the derivative is useful in treating problems in business and economic theory.

Maximizing Profit

If $P(x)$, $R(x)$, and $C(x)$ represent the profit, revenue, and total cost associated with the production and sale of x items in a given period of time, the basic relationship among these three quantities is

$$P(x) = R(x) - C(x). \tag{1}$$

That is, profit equals revenues minus costs.

We have also made use of the rates at which revenue and cost change with respect to production level x. We have defined these marginal quantities as

$$\text{marginal revenue} = MR(x) = R'(x)$$

and

$$\text{marginal cost} = MC(x) = C'(x).$$

Of course, in defining marginal cost and marginal revenue we have assumed that the revenue and cost functions are differentiable functions of x. When this is the case, there exists an important relationship among the production level x_0 that maximizes profit and these two marginal quantities. To obtain this relationship, we differentiate the functions on both sides of equation (1) to obtain

$$\begin{aligned} P'(x) &= R'(x) - C'(x) \\ &= MR(x) - MC(x). \end{aligned} \tag{2}$$

When profit is a maximum, we have, in general, $P'(x_0) = 0$. Setting $P'(x_0) = 0$ in equation (2) gives $MR(x_0) - MC(x_0) = 0$, or $MR(x_0) = MC(x_0)$. That is, *marginal revenue equals marginal cost when profit is a maximum.* (The exception to this principle is that x_0 may be an endpoint, rather than a critical number.)

□ **EXAMPLE 1**

A monopoly exists when a single firm is the sole producer of a particular product or service. In this situation there is a direct relationship between the price the monopolist charges for the item and the number of items the public will purchase in a given

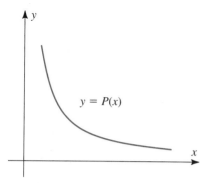

Figure 8.1 Typical demand curve.

period of time. Decreasing the price increases sales, and conversely. A typical demand curve appears in Figure 8.1.

Suppose that a monopolist can manufacture at most 175 items per week and that market research shows that the price at which the monopolist can sell x items per week is approximately $p(x) = (500 - x)$ dollars. Furthermore, suppose that the monopolist estimates that the cost of producing x items per week is $C(x) = 150 + 4x + x^2$ dollars. Then

(a) the revenue obtained from the sale of x items per week is

$$R(x) = xp(x) = x(500 - x) = 500x - x^2$$

(b) the profit obtained from selling x items per week is

$$\begin{aligned}
P(x) &= R(x) - C(x) \\
&= (500x - x^2) - (150 + 4x + x^2) \\
&= -2x^2 + 496x - 150 \text{ dollars}
\end{aligned}$$

(c) the maximum weekly profit corresponds to the maximum value of the function $P(x)$. To find this maximum, we set

$$P'(x) = -4x + 496 = 0$$

and obtain the single critical number $x_0 = \dfrac{496}{4} = 124$. Since the weekly production must satisfy the inequality $0 \le x \le 175$, the maximum profit must lie among the numbers

$$\begin{aligned}
P(0) &= -150 && \text{(endpoint)} \\
P(124) &= 30{,}602 && \text{(critical number)} \\
P(175) &= 25{,}400 && \text{(endpoint).}
\end{aligned}$$

The maximum profit of \$30,602 is therefore achieved at the production level $x_0 = 124$ items per week.

(d) The marginal revenue and cost functions are

$$MR(x) = R'(x) = \frac{d}{dx}(500x - x^2) = 500 - 2x$$

and

$$MC(x) = C'(x) = \frac{d}{dx}(150 + 4x + x^2) = 4 + 2x.$$

At the production level $x_0 = 124$ for which profit is maximized we have that

$$MR(124) = 500 - 2(124) = 252$$

and

$$MC(124) = 4 + 2(124) = 252$$

which shows that *marginal revenue equals marginal cost when profit is maximized.* ∎

Monopolists Versus Perfect Competitors

Example 1 concerned a monopoly. This is a market in which only one producer of a particular item exists, so there is no competition among sellers. In such situations the number of items the monopolist can sell is related to the price that is charged by a demand curve such as Figure 8.1. Since higher sales levels (values of x) correspond to lower prices, the corresponding revenue function eventually decreases to zero. Figure 8.2 shows the graphs of the revenue, cost, and profit functions for the monopoly in Example 1. Note that revenue increases to a maximum value (at $x = 250$) and then decreases to zero. Figure 8.2(a) also illustrates the principle that marginal revenue equals marginal cost when profit is a maximum. This translates into the fact that the line tangents to the revenue and cost curves are parallel for $x = 124$, the production level for which profit is a maximum.

At the opposite extreme from a monopoly is a purely competitive market. In this situation many suppliers are present, with none commanding a large enough share of the market to be able to affect price by increasing or decreasing production. The selling price p for the item is constant, so the revenue function for any supplier is just the linear function $R(x) = px$. This situation is illustrated in Figure 8.3. Since marginal revenue is just $MR(x) = R'(x) = p$, we must have $MC(x_0) = p = MR(x_0)$ at the output level x_0 for which profit is a maximum.

☐ **EXAMPLE 2**

A child-care center determines that its total weekly costs of operations are

$$C(x) = 1200 + 40x + 2x^2$$

where x is the number of children enrolled. If the center charges tuition of $200 per week per child, and can enroll any desired number of children, what enrollment will maximize profit for the center?

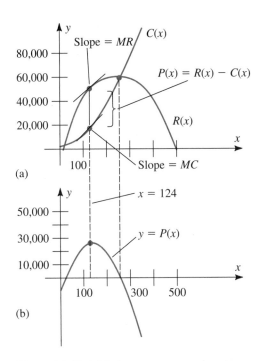

(a)

(b)

Figure 8.2 Part (a) shows revenue and cost curves in Example 1. Note $MR(x) = MC(x)$ when $P(x)$ is a maximum. Part (b) shows profit function $P(x) = R(x) - C(x)$.

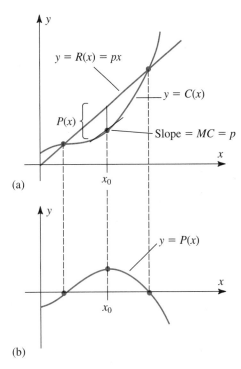

(a)

(b)

Figure 8.3 Part (a) shows revenue curve for a "perfect competitor." Note that revenue is a linear function. $MC(x)$ equals the slope of the revenue line when profit is a maximum. Part (b) shows the corresponding profit function.

Solution: Here the number of children (customers) does not affect the price. Thus, the total revenue $R(x)$ from the enrollment of x children per week at price $p = \$200$ is

$$R(x) = px = 200x.$$

The profit function is therefore

$$P(x) = R(x) - C(x)$$
$$= 200x - (1200 + 40x + 2x^2)$$
$$= 160x - 1200 - 2x^2.$$

To maximize P, we calculate

$$P'(x) = 160 - 4x.$$

Setting $P'(x) = 0$ gives $x = 40$. Since $P''(x) = -4$ is negative for all x, the enrollment $x = 40$ maximizes profit. ∎

Inventory Cost Control

Since a perfect competitor cannot affect the price at which an item will sell, minimizing costs is doubly important. The techniques used to do this are just those of Sections 3.6 and 3.7 if we can find an expression for the total cost function C.

For merchants, especially retailers, there is an important problem of how much inventory (supply of goods for sale) to keep in stock. This is essentially a question of how frequently to order stock, because there is no economic advantage in replenishing stock before it is depleted. Figure 8.4 illustrates a typical supply function for an individual item. It is assumed that orders of size x can be timed so that shipments arrive just as current stock is depleted.

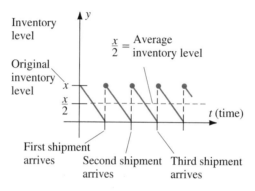

Figure 8.4 Inventory function for a product that is ordered in shipments of size x and sold at a constant rate.

Even granting the ability for perfect timing of shipments of stock, there remains the problem of deciding how frequently to place orders or, equivalently, of what size orders to place. (We shall assume the product is sold at a constant rate, so one of these quantities determines the other.) Since there are costs associated both with the placing of orders (ordering costs) and with the storage of inventory (storage costs), the answer is not obvious. Frequent ordering of small lots will mean larger ordering costs but smaller storage costs, while infrequent orders of large lots will have just the opposite tendencies.

Under the assumptions of equal order sizes and constant rates of sale, we can use the calculus to find the optimal order size (or optimal ordering schedule) by minimizing the total costs associated with the procurement (ordering) and storage of inventory:

$$\text{total inventory cost} = (\text{ordering costs}) + (\text{storage costs}). \qquad (3)$$

The following example shows how equation (3) can be applied to solve a typical problem in inventory cost control.

☐ **EXAMPLE 3**

A merchant sells brooms rather uniformly at a rate of about 1600 brooms a year. Accounting procedures determine that the cost of carrying a broom in stock is $2 per year. When ordering brooms, the merchant experiences a fixed order cost of $25 plus a variable order cost of 10¢ per broom. Assuming that orders can be placed so that delivery occurs precisely when stock is depleted, how often should the merchant order brooms so as to minimize yearly costs?

Strategy · · · · · · · ·
Write equation for cost in words, noting all contributing factors.

Solution

The merchant faces a trade-off between ordering brooms frequently, thereby reducing storage costs, and ordering infrequently, thus reducing ordering costs. To analyze this inventory cost control problem we first identify all cost components:

$$\text{total costs} = (\text{ordering costs}) + (\text{storage costs}). \tag{4}$$

Identify the independent variable.

The only independent variable in the problem is the number of orders placed per year, which we denote by x. Since brooms are sold at a constant rate, and there is no reason to vary the size of the orders, knowing x determines the size and timing of all orders, as well as all costs.

Develop algebraic expression for ordering costs.

The ordering costs are of two kinds. First, there is a charge of 10¢ per broom no matter how many orders are placed. Since 1600 brooms are required, this cost is ($1600)(0.10) = $160 annually.

The other ordering cost is the cost of $25 to place each order. In placing x orders per year this charge will be $25x$. Thus,

$$\text{ordering costs} = 160 + 25x.$$

Develop algebraic expression for storage costs.

To calculate storage costs, we note first that each broom will remain in storage, on average, for half the time between orders. If there are x orders per year, this duration is $\left(\dfrac{1}{2}\right)\left(\dfrac{1}{x}\right) = \dfrac{1}{2x}$ years. Since this is the "storage time" for a single broom, the total "storage time" for 1600 brooms is $1600\left(\dfrac{1}{2x}\right) = \dfrac{1600}{2x}$ broom-years. Finally, we are given that the cost of one broom-year in storage is $2. Thus,

$$\text{storage costs} = \left(\frac{1600}{2x}\right)(2) = \frac{1600}{x}.$$

Equation (4) now gives total cost as

Write equation (4) in algebraic terms.

$$C(x) = 1600 + 25x + \frac{1600}{x}.$$

(See Figure 8.5.)

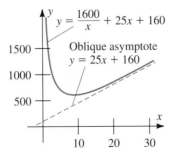

Figure 8.5 Graph of total inventory cost function C in Example 3.

Now x will be limited to an interval, say, $[1, 52]$. Then the problem of minimizing cost is simply the problem of finding the minimum value for the function C on the interval $[1, 52]$. We find that

$$C'(x) = 25 - \frac{1600}{x^2}$$

Set $C'(x) = 0$ to find critical numbers.

so setting $C'(x) = 0$ gives the equation

$$x^2 = \frac{1600}{25} = \left(\frac{40}{5}\right)^2 = 8^2$$

Remaining critical numbers occur where $C'(x)$ is undefined.

which yields the critical numbers $x = \pm 8$. In addition, $x = 0$ is also a critical number since $C'(0)$ is undefined. However, among these critical numbers only $x = 8$ lies within the interval of feasible solutions $[1, 52]$. Since

$$C(1) = 1600 + 25 + 160 = 1785 \text{ dollars}$$
$$C(8) = 200 + 200 + 160 = 560 \text{ dollars, and}$$
$$C(52) \approx 31 + 1300 + 160 = 1491 \text{ dollars}$$

Examine $C(x)$ at critical points and endpoints to find minimum.

the minimum cost occurs when brooms are ordered eight times per year.   ∎

Taxation and Other Policy Questions

In addition to serving the fundamental capitalist objective of maximizing profits, models such as those of the preceding examples can be helpful in analyzing policy questions such as the effect on output of taxation. For instance, if a government decides to impose a tax of t dollars on each item produced, the basic profit equation (1) becomes

$$P(x) = R(x) - C(x) - tx, \qquad x = \text{output}. \tag{5}$$

If, on the other hand, the tax is imposed as a percentage α of profits, the profit equation (1) becomes

$$P(x) = (1 - \alpha)[R(x) - C(x)]. \tag{6}$$

(In practice, a tax on profits rarely occurs, mainly because of the difficulty in establishing accurate figures on profit levels.)

☐ **EXAMPLE 4**

Suppose that the city in which the monopolist in Example 1 is located is contemplating a tax of $20 to be imposed on each item manufactured by the monopolist. How will the monopolist respond, given the objective of profit maximization?

Solution: Applying the taxed profit equation (5) to the calculations of Example 1 gives the monopolist's revised profit equation as

$$P(x) = R(x) - C(x) - 20x$$
$$= (-2x^2 + 496x - 150) - 20x$$
$$= -2x^2 + 476x - 150 \text{ dollars}.$$

The new maximum is obtained by setting

$$P'(x) = -4x + 476 = 0$$

which gives the new critical number $x = 119$. Inspection of endpoint values $P(0)$ and $P(175)$ shows that, indeed, the new maximum value of profit is $P(119) = \$28,172$, a reduction in profit of $2430 per week. Notice that the sale price corresponding to the new output level is $p = (500 - 119) = \$381$ per item, as opposed to $p = \$376$ per item at the original output level of 124 items per week. The results of the proposed tax will therefore be that:

(a) The monopolist will reduce output from 124 to 119 items per week, achieving a maximum profit of $28,172 weekly.
(b) The monopolist will sell the items at a price of $381, thus passing $5 of the $20 tax along to the consumer and absorbing the remaining $15.
(c) The tax will generate a weekly revenue of $119 \times 20 = \$2380$ to the city government.   ∎

Elasticity of Demand

When consumer demand for an item is related to its selling price, economists (and producers!) often ask about the relationship between a change in price and the corresponding change in demand. In the simplest terms, they are asking, ''If we increase (or decrease) the price, what will be the effect on sales?'' Figure 8.6 shows two different demand curves relating the price p at which an item sells to the quantity $Q(p)$ of that item that consumers will purchase in a given period of time. Note that because of the steepness of the graph of Q_1, a small change in price will result in a substantial change in demand. Economists refer to such demand curves as *elastic*. Because the slope of the demand curve Q_2 is relatively small, a small change in p will cause only a small change in demand. Demand curves with this property are called *inelastic*.

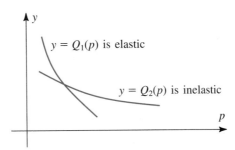

Figure 8.6 Two demand curves.

The concept *elasticity of demand* is designed to answer such questions. Before stating its definition, we illustrate by returning to Example 1 that this concept depends not only on the relationship (equation) between demand and price, but also on the particular price, p_0, at which the question is asked.

□ **EXAMPLE 5**

We return again to Example 1 where a producer of a certain commodity, say television sets, determined that the number of units that could be sold in a given period of time was related to the selling price p by the equation $x = 500 - p$. If we write the quantity x as a function $Q(p)$ of p, we have the demand function

$$Q(p) = 500 - p.$$

Table 8.1 shows the effect on the value $Q(p)$ of an increase in the selling price of 10%. Notice that for relatively small prices p, the effect of a 10% price increase has only a modest effect on demand. But at higher prices, a 10% increase in price can cause a huge percentage change in demand. At the price level $p = \$450$, for example, a 10% price increase leads to a reduction in demand by 90%.

Table 8.1

Price p_0 (Dollars)	p_0 Increased by 10% to $p_0 + h$	$Q(p_0)$	$Q(p_0 + h)$	Decrease in $Q(p_0)$
10	10 + 1 = 11	490	489	0.2%
50	50 + 5 = 55	450	445	1.1%
100	100 + 10 = 110	400	390	2.5%
200	200 + 20 = 220	300	280	6.6%
300	300 + 30 = 330	200	170	15.0%
400	400 + 40 = 440	100	60	40.0%
450	450 + 45 = 495	50	5	90.0%

Elasticity of demand measures the *relative* (or percent) change in demand compared to a small relative (percent) change in price, at a particular price p_0. That is, given the demand function $Q(p)$,

$$\text{elasticity of demand} = \frac{\text{relative change in } Q(p)}{\text{relative change in } p} \qquad (7)$$

at $p = p_0$. In order to make equation (7) more precise, we let p_0 be the price of interest and h be a small increment in p. Then equation (7) becomes

$$\text{elasticity of demand at } p = p_0 = \frac{\left[\dfrac{Q(p_0 + h) - Q(p_0)}{Q(p_0)}\right]}{\left[\dfrac{(p_0 + h) - p_0}{p_0}\right]}$$

$$= \left[\frac{Q(p_0 + h) - Q(p_0)}{h}\right]\left(\frac{p_0}{Q(p_0)}\right).$$

You can now see that the derivative, $Q'(p_0)$, plays a role here when Q is differentiable at p_0. In this case we can allow the increment h in p to approach zero, obtaining the limit

$$\lim_{h \to 0} \left[\frac{Q(p_0 + h) - Q(p_0)}{h} \right] \cdot \left(\frac{p_0}{Q(p_0)} \right) = Q'(p_0) \left[\frac{p_0}{Q(p_0)} \right].$$

This is essentially the definition of *elasticity of demand,* except that economists usually introduce a negative sign in the definition to ensure that elasticity is always a positive number. (Can you see why this will always be the case?)

Definition 7

Given the differentiable demand function $Q(p)$, the (point) **elasticity of demand** for Q at price p_0 is the number

$$E(p_0) = -\frac{p_0 Q'(p_0)}{Q(p_0)}. \tag{8}$$

When $E(p) > 1$, the demand curve is called **elastic** at p. This is because the relative change in demand is larger than the relative change in price $\left(\dfrac{h}{p} \right)$. When $E(p) < 1$, the demand curve is called **inelastic** at p because just the opposite is happening.

☐ **EXAMPLE 6**

Find the elasticity of the demand curve with equation

$$Q(p) = \frac{500}{(p + 1)^2}$$

at price level $p = 4$.

Solution: With $Q(p) = 500(p + 1)^{-2}$, we have

$$Q'(p) = -1000(p + 1)^{-3}$$

so

$$E(p) = \frac{-pQ'(p)}{Q(p)}$$

$$= \frac{-p[-1000(p + 1)^{-3}]}{500(p + 1)^{-2}}$$

$$= \frac{2p}{p + 1}.$$

When $p = 4$, the elasticity is

$$E(4) = \frac{(2)(4)}{4 + 1} = \frac{8}{5}.$$

Since $\frac{8}{5} > 1$, we say that this demand curve is *elastic* at price $p = 4$. ∎

□ **EXAMPLE 7**

The demand for an item is found to be roughly

$$Q(p) = 200 - p$$

for prices between $p = 25$ and $p = 200$ dollars. For which prices is this demand curve (a) elastic? (b) inelastic?

Solution: Here $Q'(p) = \frac{d}{dp}(200 - p) = -1$, so we have from equation (8) that

$$E(p) = \frac{-(-1)}{\left(\frac{200 - p}{p}\right)} = \frac{p}{200 - p}.$$

To determine for which p we shall have $E(p) > 1$ or $E(p) < 1$, we begin by finding the price for which $E(p) = 1$. Setting $E(p) = 1$ gives

$$\frac{p}{200 - p} = 1, \quad \text{or} \quad p = 200 - p.$$

Thus $2p = 200$, so $p = 100$. We must therefore check the magnitude of $E(p)$ on the intervals $[25, 100)$ and $(100, 200]$.

(i) Choosing the test point $p_1 = 50$ in $[25, 100)$, we find

$$E(50) = \frac{50}{200 - 50} = \frac{50}{150} = \frac{1}{3} < 1.$$

Thus $E(p) < 1$ and the demand curve is inelastic for $25 \le p < 100$.
(ii) Choosing the test point $p_2 = 150$ in $(100, 200]$, we find

$$E(150) = \frac{150}{200 - 150} = \frac{150}{50} = 3 > 1.$$

Thus $E(p) > 1$ and the demand curve is elastic for $100 < p \le 200$. ∎

Interest in the concept of elasticity has to do in part with its relation to marginal revenue. If $Q(p)$ denotes the demand for an item at price p, then the revenue function is $R(p) = pQ(p)$. The marginal revenue is therefore

$$MR(p) = R'(p) = \frac{d}{dp}[pQ(p)]$$

$$= Q(p) + pQ'(p)$$

$$= Q(p)\left[1 + p\frac{Q'(p)}{Q(p)}\right]$$

$$= Q(p)[1 - E(p)].$$

From this calculation we can conclude:

(1) If the demand curve is *elastic* at p (i.e., if $E(p) > 1$), revenue will decrease if price is increased since in this case $MR(p) = R'(p) < 0$.
(2) If the demand curve is *inelastic* at p, meaning $E(p) < 1$, then we shall have $MR(p) = R'(p) > 0$, so revenue will *increase* if price is increased.

REMARK: Do not underestimate the importance of these observations. It is *generally* true that an increase in price will bring a decrease (or, at best, no change) in demand. But with revenues, and therefore with profits, it is not such a bleak situation: An increase in price may bring an *increase* in revenues—*if* the demand curve is inelastic!

☐ **EXAMPLE 8**

A producer of alloy golf clubs finds that monthly demand for a new line of clubs is related to its selling price by the equation

$$p = 400 - 0.02x.$$

(a) Find the elasticity of demand at price p, $E(p)$.
(b) Find $E(300)$ and interpret the result.
(c) Contrast this with the situation for price $p = \$150$.

Solution: Solving the demand equation for x gives

$$x = 50(400 - p) = 20{,}000 - 50p$$

so the demand function is

$$Q(p) = 20{,}000 - 50p$$

with derivative

$$Q'(p) = -50.$$

(a) The elasticity of demand at price p is therefore

$$E(p) = \frac{-pQ'(p)}{Q(p)} = \frac{(-p)(-50)}{20{,}000 - 50p} = \frac{50p}{20{,}000 - 50p}.$$

(b) At price $p = 300$, the elasticity is

$$E(300) = \frac{50(300)}{20{,}000 - 50(300)} = \frac{15{,}000}{5000} = 3.0.$$

Thus, the demand curve is *elastic* at $p = 300$, and an increase in price will bring a *decrease* in revenues. This conclusion can be confirmed by examining the revenue function:

$$\begin{aligned} R(p) &= pQ(p) \\ &= p(20{,}000 - 50p) \\ &= 20{,}000p - 50p^2. \end{aligned}$$

Thus, marginal revenue is

$$MR(p) = R'(p) = 20{,}000 - 100p.$$

At price $p = 300$, we have

$$\begin{aligned} MR(300) &= 20{,}000 - 100(300) \\ &= 20{,}000 - 30{,}000 \\ &= -10{,}000 \end{aligned}$$

which is negative, as indicated by the elasticity.

(c) At price $p = \$150$, we have

$$E(150) = \frac{50(150)}{20{,}000 - 50(150)} = \frac{7500}{12{,}500} = 0.6.$$

Since $E(150) < 1$, the demand curve is *inelastic* at price $p = \$150$, and an increase in price will bring an *increase* in total revenues. (We leave it to you to confirm this conclusion by examining the marginal revenue function.) ∎

These observations illustrate the type of conclusion that can be drawn from general models such as the profit equation (1) and the preceding definition of elasticity, even though explicit equations for the demand function and its derivative are not known. The determining factor in these observations is the magnitude of elasticity, $E(p)$, which in turn depends on the relationship between the variables p and Q and the derivative $Q'(p)$. The study of relationships between marginal rates constitutes a significant part of modern economic theory, and the concept of the derivative clearly plays a central role in this subject.

☑ **PRACTICE PROBLEMS 3.8**

1. Suppose the demand for a new model of exercise equipment is related to its selling price by the equation

$$x = 1000 - 0.5p.$$

   a. Find the revenue function, $R(x)$.
   b. Find the marginal revenue at sales level $x = 400$.
   c. Find the elasticity $E(p)$ at price $p = \$400$ and interpret the result.

2. A retailer of golf clubs sells approximately 200 sets per year at a constant rate. Each order costs the retailer $100 plus $10 per set of clubs. How frequently should the retailer order clubs if the cost of storing one set of clubs for one year is $40, and the retailer wishes to minimize inventory costs?

Exercise Set 3.8

In Exercises 1–4, the cost $C(x)$ and revenue $R(x)$ from the manufacture and sale of x items per month for a company are given along with the range of possible production levels. In each case find the production level that most nearly maximizes profits, $P(x) = R(x) - C(x)$.

1. $C(x) = 500 + 4x$
   $R(x) = 100x - \frac{1}{4}x^2$
   $0 \le x \le 200$

2. $C(x) = 1000 + 30x + \frac{1}{2}x^2$
   $R(x) = 80x$
   $0 \le x \le 500$

3. $C(x) = 500 + 20x + x^2$
   $R(x) = 30x$
   $0 \le x \le 100$

4. $C(x) = 200 + 50x + \frac{1}{10}x^2$
   $R(x) = 100x - \frac{1}{10}x^2$
   $0 \le x \le 40$

5. Not all of the companies in Exercises 1–4 are profitable, even at the output level that maximizes profit. Which are profitable $(P(x_0) > 0)$?

6. The cost of operating a small aircraft is calculated to be $200 per hour plus the cost of fuel. Fuel costs are $\dfrac{s}{100}$ dollars per kilometer, where s represents speed in kilometers per hour. Find the speed that minimizes the cost per kilometer.

7. An automobile parts store sells 3000 headlight bulbs per year at a uniform rate. Orders can be placed from the distributor so that shipments arrive just as supplies run out. In ordering bulbs the parts store encounters costs of $20 per order plus 5¢ per bulb. How frequently should the parts store order bulbs if the cost of maintaining one bulb in stock for one year is estimated to be 48¢?

8. A chartered cruise requires a minimum of 100 persons. If 100 people sign up, the cost is $400 per person. For each additional person the cost per person decreases by $1.50. Find the number of passengers that maximizes revenue.

9. A merchant sells shirts uniformly at a rate of about 2000 per year. The cost of carrying a shirt in stock is $3 per year. The cost of ordering shirts is $50 per order plus 20¢ per shirt. Approximately how many times per year should the merchant order shirts to minimize his total yearly costs? (Assume that orders can be placed so that shipment arrives precisely when stock is depleted.)

10. Find the effect on the broom merchant's reorder scheme in Example 3 if sales fall to 1200 brooms per year and reorder costs increase by 20%.

11. A manufacturing company determines that the revenue obtained from the sale of x items will be $R(x) = 200x - 4x^2$ dollars for $0 \le x \le 25$ and that the cost of producing these x items will be $C(x) = 900 + 40x$. Find the output x at which profits will be a maximum.

12. A publisher can produce a certain book at a net cost of $4 per book. Market research indicates that 20,000 copies of the book can be sold at a price of $16 per book and that sales can be increased by 2000 copies for each $1 reduction in price.

a. What price maximizes revenue?
b. What is the marginal cost per book?
c. What price maximizes profit?

13. A manufacturer of dishwashers can produce up to 100 dishwashers per week. Sales experience indicates that the manufacturer can sell x dishwashers per week at price p where $p + 3x = 600$ dollars. Production records show that the cost of producing x dishwashers per week is

$$C(x) = 400 + 150x + 0.5x^2.$$

a. Find the weekly revenue function.
b. Find the weekly profit function.
c. Find the marginal cost and marginal revenue functions.
d. Find the weekly production level for which profit is a maximum.
e. What is the relationship between marginal cost and marginal revenue for the production level found in part d?

14. Suppose that the supply of uranium available on world markets is related to the price per pound by the function

$$S(p) = \frac{100}{200 - p}$$

where p is the price per pound, $0 \le p \le 180$.
a. Find the price at which the marginal supply equals 0.25 ton.
b. Explain why S is an increasing function.
c. What would be unrealistic about this model if p were to have the range $0 \le p < 200$?

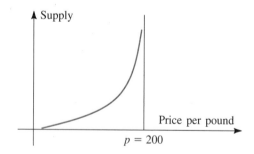

15. Let $C(x)$ denote the cost of producing x items. Then the *average cost per item* of production for these items is $c(x) = \frac{C(x)}{x}$. Assuming C and c to be differentiable functions of x, find the relationship between average cost and marginal cost when average cost is a minimum.

16. From equation (5), find the relationship between marginal cost and marginal revenue, in the presence of a tax of t dollars per item, when profit is a maximum.

17. A firm is called a *perfect competitor* if the price it can receive for its items is independent of production level (in other words, price is a fixed constant p beyond the control of the firm). In this case the revenue obtained from the sale of x items is simply $R(x) = px$. Show that for a perfect competitor subject to a per item tax, an increase in the tax rate will cause a decrease in output level.

18. Suppose a tax of $30 per dishwasher is imposed on the manufacturer in Exercise 13. Find
a. the output level that maximizes profit.
b. the resulting change in price per dishwasher.
c. the amount of tax absorbed by the manufacturer.

19. In Exercise 13, find the resulting production level, assuming the manufacturer will always schedule production so as to maximize profit, of the granting of a tax credit of $35 per dishwasher to the manufacturer.

In Exercises 20–27, find the elasticity of the given demand function Q at the given price level p_0.

20. $Q(p) = -\dfrac{3}{2}p + 10, \qquad p_0 = 3$

21. $Q(p) = -\dfrac{5}{4}p + 40, \qquad p_0 = 20$

22. $Q(p) = 169 - p^2, \qquad p_0 = 6$

23. $Q(p) = \sqrt{1000 - 4p}, \qquad p_0 = 40$

24. $Q(p) = \dfrac{1}{p^2}, \qquad p_0 = 5$

25. $Q(p) = \dfrac{1}{\sqrt{p}}, \qquad p_0 = 3$

26. $Q(p) = \dfrac{40}{(1 + p)^2}, \qquad p_0 = 5$

27. $Q(p) = \dfrac{10}{(p + 2)^2}, \qquad p_0 = 2$

For each of Exercises 28–31, determine for which numbers p the given demand curve is elastic or inelastic.

28. $Q(p) = \dfrac{1}{\sqrt{p}}$ \qquad\qquad **29.** $Q(p) = \dfrac{1}{p^2}$

30. $Q(p) = 500 - \frac{1}{2}p$

31. $Q(p) = \dfrac{\sqrt{p}}{1 + p}$, $p > 1$

32. For the demand curve $Q = 40 + 6p - p^2$, $0 < p < 10$, find
  a. the elasticity of demand $E(p)$.
  b. $E(4)$.

33. A producer in a monopoly faces a demand curve $Q(p) = 200 - p$ where p is the price per item of the manufactured item. Suppose that the cost of manufacturing Q items is given by the function $C(Q) = 2Q + 100$.
  a. Find the output Q that maximizes profits and the corresponding price.
  b. Find the elasticity of demand at the output that maximizes profit.

34. A retailer of premium razors determines that demand for a certain model is related to its selling price by the equation

$$x = 45 - 0.2p^2$$

where x is the quantity sold per week and p is the selling price.
  a. Find the demand function $Q(p)$.
  b. Is demand elastic or inelastic at $p = 4$?

c. What will be the effect on revenues of a price increase from $p_0 = \$10$ to $p_1 = \$11$?

35. Demand for a new portable stereo system is thought to be related to its selling price via the equation

$$x = \sqrt{1000 - 10p}.$$

According to this mathematical model,
  a. What is the demand function $Q(p)$?
  b. Is demand elastic or inelastic at $p = 50$?
  c. Is demand elastic or inelastic at $p = 70$?
  d. What is the first price p_0 above which further price increases will result in declining revenues?

36. The proprietor of a winter sports supply store determines that demand for a new model of hockey skate is related to the selling price by the equation

$$p = \sqrt{8000 - 4x^2}.$$

  a. Find the demand function $Q(p)$.
  b. Is this demand function elastic or inelastic at price $p = \$40$?
  c. To what point can the store increase the price of the skates before beginning to experience declining revenues?

☑ **SOLUTIONS TO PRACTICE PROBLEMS 3.8**

1. Solving the demand equation for p gives

$$p = 2000 - 2x.$$

Thus,
  a. The revenue is

$$\begin{aligned} R(x) = xp &= x(2000 - 2x) \\ &= 2000x - 2x^2. \end{aligned}$$

  b. The marginal revenue is

$$MR(x) = R'(x) = 2000 - 4x$$

so

$$\begin{aligned} MR(400) &= 2000 - 1600 \\ &= \$400. \end{aligned}$$

  c. The elasticity at price p, for $Q(p) = 1000 - 0.5p$, is

$$E(p) = -\frac{pQ'(p)}{Q(p)} = \frac{(-p)(-0.5)}{1000 - 0.5p} = \frac{0.5p}{1000 - 0.5p}.$$

At $p = \$400$, this is

$$E(400) = \frac{(0.5)(400)}{1000 - (0.5)400} = \frac{200}{800} = 0.25.$$

Since $E(400) < 1$, the demand function is inelastic at $p = \$400$. Increasing price will increase revenues.

2. The total cost of ordering and storing the inventory, ordering x times per year, is

$$C(x) = \text{(total ordering costs)} + \text{(storage costs)}$$

$$= 100x + (10)(200) + \left(\frac{200}{2x}\right)(40)$$

$$= 100x + 2000 + \frac{4000}{x}.$$

To minimize C, we calculate the derivative

$$C'(x) = 100 - \frac{4000}{x^2}.$$

Setting $C'(x) = 0$ and solving for x gives

$$x = \sqrt{40} = 2\sqrt{10} \approx 6.32.$$

Since x must be an integer, we compare the values of the total cost function at the two closest integers, $x = 6$ and $x = 7$:

$$C(6) = 100(6) + 2000 + \frac{4000}{6} = \$3266.67$$

$$C(7) = 100(7) + 2000 + \frac{4000}{7} = \$3271.43.$$

Cost is therefore minimized at the integer $x = 6$, corresponding to the critical number $x = 2\sqrt{10}$. The merchant should order clubs six times per year.

3.9 Related Rates and Implicit Differentiation

Often one encounters problems in which two or more variables are each functions of a third variable, usually time. For example, when an ice cube melts, its volume, its weight, and each of its dimensions change continuously as time passes. For any such variable the rate at which it changes is given by its derivative with respect to the independent variable. A *related rates* problem is one in which we are asked to find the rate at which one variable is changing in terms of the rate(s) of change of the other variable(s).

☐ **EXAMPLE 1**

Suppose that a child is inflating a spherical balloon. If V and r represent the volume and radius of the balloon, these two variables are related by the familiar formula for the volume of a sphere

$$V = \frac{4}{3}\pi r^3. \tag{1}$$

Now suppose we know that the balloon is being inflated at a rate of 100 cubic centimeters per second. Since this is the rate of change of volume, this means that

$$\frac{dV}{dt} = 100 \text{ cm}^3/\text{sec.} \tag{2}$$

Can we use this information to determine the rate at which the radius r is increasing?

We begin by taking the point of view that equation (1) states that V and $\frac{4}{3}(\pi r^3)$ are *the same function* of time. Thus the derivatives of these two functions must be the same. Now the derivative of the left-hand side of equation (1) with respect to t is just $\frac{dV}{dt}$. To find the derivative of the right-hand side, we must remember that r is a function of t and apply the Chain Rule:

$$\frac{d}{dt}\left(\frac{4}{3}\pi r^3\right) = \frac{4}{3}\pi \cdot \frac{d}{dt}r^3 = \frac{4}{3}\pi \cdot 3r^2 \cdot \frac{dr}{dt} = 4\pi r^2 \cdot \frac{dr}{dt}.$$

Thus by differentiating both sides of the equation

$$V = \frac{4}{3}\pi r^3$$

with respect to t we find that

$$\frac{dV}{dt} = 4\pi r^2 \cdot \frac{dr}{dt}. \tag{3}$$

We can now solve equation (3) for $\frac{dr}{dt}$:

$$\frac{dr}{dt} = \frac{1}{4\pi r^2} \cdot \frac{dV}{dt}. \tag{4}$$

Equation (4) gives the rate $\frac{dr}{dt}$ at which the radius is increasing for particular values of r and $\frac{dV}{dt}$. For example, when $r = 9$ cm and $\frac{dV}{dt} = 100 \text{ cm}^3/\text{sec}$, we have

$$\frac{dr}{dt} = \frac{1}{4\pi \cdot 9^2}(100)$$

$$= \frac{25}{81\pi} \approx 0.098 \text{ cm/sec.}$$

In general, when two or more functions of time are related by a single equation, we can find the relationship between the *rates* at which these variables are changing by simply differentiating both sides of the given equation with respect to t. Unless the basic equation is quite simple, this will require a careful application of the Chain Rule. ∎

☐ **EXAMPLE 2**

A manufacturer of insulated steel doors finds that the revenue received from the production and sale of x doors per month is

$$R(x) = 200x - 3x^{2/3}$$

dollars per month. If the production level x is increasing at the rate of 10 doors per month, at what rate is revenue changing at production level $x = 1000$ doors per month?

Solution: Since the production level x is changing in time, both x and the revenue function R are functions of $t = $ time. The principal equation relating revenue and production is given as

$$R = 200x - 3x^{2/3}. \tag{5}$$

Differentiating both sides of this equation with respect to t gives

$$\frac{dR}{dt} = \frac{d}{dt}[200x - 3x^{2/3}]$$

$$= 200\frac{d}{dt}(x) - 3\frac{d}{dt}(x^{2/3})$$

$$= 200\frac{dx}{dt} - 3\left(\frac{2}{3}x^{-1/3} \cdot \frac{dx}{dt}\right)$$

$$= (200 - 2x^{-1/3})\frac{dx}{dt}.$$

When $x = 1000$ and $\frac{dx}{dt} = 10$, this gives the rate

$$\frac{dR}{dt} = [200 - 2(1000)^{-1/3}](10)$$

$$= \left(200 - \frac{2}{\sqrt[3]{1000}}\right)(10)$$

$$= \$1998 \text{ per month.} \quad \blacksquare$$

In this example it is important to note that the particular value $x = 1000$ could not be substituted in equation (5) until the differentiations had been performed. That is because once we have substituted a particular value for the variable x, differentiation will simply produce zero. We must differentiate both sides of the basic equation *before* substituting particular values for the variables so that the desired rates (derivatives) will appear.

☐ EXAMPLE 3

At noon a truck leaves a depot in Columbus, Ohio, traveling east at a rate of 40 miles per hour. An hour later a second truck leaves the depot traveling north at a rate of 60 miles per hour. At what rate is the distance between the trucks increasing at 2:00 p.m. that day?

Strategy · · · · · · · ·

From a sketch name the variables.

Solution

Figure 9.1 shows that we may think of the trucks as moving along the x- and y-axes of a coordinate plane with the depot located at the origin. If we let x be the distance of the eastbound truck from the depot and y be the distance of the northbound truck from the depot, the Pythagorean theorem gives the distance between the trucks as

Find an equation relating the variables.

$$D = \sqrt{x^2 + y^2}. \tag{6}$$

Since each of the variables D, x, and y are functions of t we differentiate both sides of equation (6) with respect to t to obtain

Differentiate both sides of the principal equation to obtain equation relating the rates.

$$\frac{dD}{dt} = \frac{d}{dt}\sqrt{x^2 + y^2}$$

$$= \frac{1}{2}(x^2 + y^2)^{-1/2} \cdot \frac{d}{dt}(x^2 + y^2)$$

$$= \frac{1}{2}(x^2 + y^2)^{-1/2}\left(2x\frac{dx}{dt} + 2y\frac{dy}{dt}\right).$$

Determine values for all variables and rates on right-hand side from given data.

At 2:00 p.m. the eastbound truck has been traveling at 40 mph for two hours, so

$$x = 80 \quad \text{and} \quad \frac{dx}{dt} = 40$$

while the northbound truck has been traveling at 60 mph for one hour, so

$$y = 60 \quad \text{and} \quad \frac{dy}{dt} = 60.$$

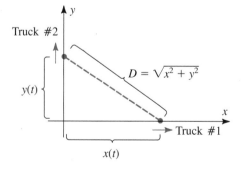

Figure 9.1 Distance between trucks in Example 3.

Substitute known values into rate equation to determine desired rate.

Substituting these values into the expression for $\dfrac{dD}{dt}$ gives

$$\frac{dD}{dt} = \frac{1}{2}(80^2 + 60^2)^{-1/2}[2(80)(40) + 2(60)(60)]$$

$$= \frac{6800}{\sqrt{10,000}}$$

$$= 68 \text{ miles per hour.} \qquad \blacksquare$$

Implicit Differentiation

The basic idea of differentiating both sides of an equation in order to find a relationship between the derivatives can also be applied to find the derivative $\dfrac{dy}{dx}$ when y is *implicitly* defined as a function of x by an equation in those two variables. For example, the equation

$$x^2 + y^2 = 25 \qquad (7)$$

does not specify y as an *explicit* function of x of the form $y = f(x)$. (This can be most easily seen from the graph of Figure 9.2, a circle that fails to have the vertical line property.) However, as Figure 9.3 illustrates, in the region of the plane near the point $(3, 4)$ the graph of equation (7) does appear to be the graph of a function. To find the

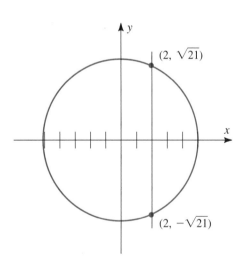

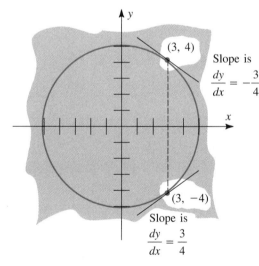

Figure 9.2 Graph of $x^2 + y^2 = 25$ does not have the vertical line property. For each x with $-5 < x < 5$ there are *two* points on the graph with this x-coordinate.

Figure 9.3 Near the point $(3, 4)$, the graph of $x^2 + y^2 = 25$ represents a function. The slope of the tangent is $\dfrac{dy}{dx} = -\dfrac{x}{y} = -\dfrac{3}{4}$.

derivative $\dfrac{dy}{dx}$ of this function, we simply differentiate both sides of equation (7) with respect to x, thinking of y as $f(x)$:

$$\frac{d}{dx}(x^2 + y^2) = \frac{d}{dx}(25)$$

gives $2x + 2y\dfrac{dy}{dx} = 0$, so

$$2y\frac{dy}{dx} = -2x$$

and

$$\frac{dy}{dx} = -\frac{2x}{2y}$$

$$= -\frac{x}{y}.$$

To find the value of this derivative at the point $(3, 4)$, we must substitute *both* coordinates $x = 3$ and $y = 4$ to obtain $\dfrac{dy}{dx} = -\dfrac{3}{4}$, the slope of the line tangent to the graph of equation (7). (See Figure 9.3.)

There are two important points to note concerning this example:

1. Since we differentiated both sides of equation (6) *with respect to x* we were *assuming* that the dependent variable y represented a differentiable function of x. Thus we were required to use the Chain Rule in differentiating the term y^2 to obtain

$$\frac{d}{dx}(y^2) = 2y \cdot \frac{dy}{dx}$$

just as we do when the function y is written in the form $y = f(x)$:

$$\frac{d}{dx}[f(x)]^2 = 2f(x) \cdot f'(x).$$

Note that, in contrast, $\dfrac{d}{dx}(x^2) = 2x$, as usual; you could think of this as

$\dfrac{d}{dx}(x^2) = 2x \cdot \dfrac{dx}{dx}$, because $\dfrac{dx}{dx} = 1$.

2. Since for many values of x the graph of equation (7) contains more than one point with the same x-coordinate, we must specify *both* the x- and y-coordinates of a particular point to find the value of the derivative at that point. For example, the point $(3, -4)$ is also on the graph of $x^2 + y^2 = 25$, and the derivative at that point is $\dfrac{dy}{dx} = -\dfrac{x}{y} = -\dfrac{3}{(-4)} = \dfrac{3}{4}$. (See Figure 9.3.)

In general, when an equation *implicitly* defines y as a function of x, we find the derivative $\dfrac{dy}{dx}$ by *implicit differentiation,* which involves the following steps:

(i) Differentiate all terms on both sides of the equation remembering that the derivative of any term involving y must include the factor $\dfrac{dy}{dx}$, according to the Chain Rule.

(ii) Solve the resulting equation for the term $\dfrac{dy}{dx}$.

(iii) To find the value of $\dfrac{dy}{dx}$ at a particular point (a, b), substitute the numbers $x = a$ and $y = b$ into the expression for $\dfrac{dy}{dx}$.

□ **EXAMPLE 4**

Assuming that the equation

$$y^2 + x^2y = 3x^2$$

defines y as a differentiable function of x near the point $(2, 2)$, find an expression for $\dfrac{dy}{dx}$ near $(2, 2)$ and the slope of the line tangent to the graph at this point.

Strategy · · · · · · · ·

Differentiate all terms with respect to x.

Solution

Differentiating both sides of the equation with respect to x gives

$$\underbrace{2y \frac{dy}{dx}}_{\frac{d}{dx}(y^2)} + \underbrace{2xy + x^2 \frac{dy}{dx}}_{\frac{d}{dx}(x^2y)} = \underbrace{6x}_{\frac{d}{dx}(3x^2)}$$

Collect all terms involving $\dfrac{dy}{dx}$.

so

Solve for $\dfrac{dy}{dx}$.

$$(x^2 + 2y) \frac{dy}{dx} = 6x - 2xy$$

and

$$\frac{dy}{dx} = \frac{6x - 2xy}{x^2 + 2y}.$$

Substitute $x = 2$ and $y = 2$ to find value of $\dfrac{dy}{dx}$ at $(2, 2)$.

At the point $(2, 2)$ the value of this derivative is

$$\frac{dy}{dx} = \frac{6(2) - 2(2)(2)}{2^2 + 2(2)} = \frac{4}{8} = \frac{1}{2}$$

which is the desired slope. ■

☐ **EXAMPLE 5**

Find $\dfrac{dy}{dx}$ if $\sqrt[3]{x} + \sqrt[3]{y} = 1$.

Solution: Differentiating all terms in the equation

$$x^{1/3} + y^{1/3} = 1$$

gives

$$\frac{1}{3}x^{-2/3} + \frac{1}{3}y^{-2/3} \cdot \frac{dy}{dx} = 0$$

so

$$\frac{dy}{dx} = \frac{-\dfrac{1}{3}x^{-2/3}}{\dfrac{1}{3}y^{-2/3}} = -\left(\frac{y}{x}\right)^{2/3}.$$

■

☐ **EXAMPLE 6**

A manufacturer of digital clocks determines that he can sell x clocks per week at price p where x and p are related by the equation

$$x^2 + 3xp + p^2 = 3600.$$

This equation determines demand as a function of price, $x = Q(p)$, near the point $(p_0, x_0) = (40, 20)$.

(a) If price is increasing at the rate of 50¢ per week, how fast is demand changing when $p = \$40$?

(b) Find $Q'(p) = \dfrac{dx}{dp}$ at the point $(p_0, x_0) = (40, 20)$.

(c) What is the elasticity of this demand curve at the point $(p_0, x_0) = (40, 20)$?

Strategy · · · · · · · ·

(a) Treat as a related rates problem, differentiating both sides of equation (7) and solving for $\dfrac{dx}{dt}$.
(Remember, *both* p and x are functions of t.)

Solution

(a) Treating both $p = p(t)$ and $x = x(t)$ as functions of t and differentiating all terms in the equation

$$x^2 + 3xp + p^2 = 3600$$

gives

$$2x \cdot \frac{dx}{dt} + 3p\frac{dx}{dt} + 3x\frac{dp}{dt} + 2p\frac{dp}{dt} = 0. \tag{8}$$

The rate of change in demand is $\dfrac{dx}{dt}$, so we solve equation (8) for this factor:

$$(2x + 3p)\frac{dx}{dt} = -(3x + 2p)\frac{dp}{dt}$$

or

$$\frac{dx}{dt} = -\left(\frac{3x + 2p}{2x + 3p}\right) \cdot \frac{dp}{dt}.$$

Substitute given values for x, p, and $\dfrac{dp}{dt}$.

Substituting $p = 40$, $x = 20$, and $\dfrac{dp}{dt} = 0.5$ then gives

$$\frac{dx}{dt} = -\left(\frac{3 \cdot 20 + 2 \cdot 40}{2 \cdot 20 + 3 \cdot 40}\right)(0.5) = -\frac{7}{16}.$$

Interpret the answer.

The negative value $\dfrac{dx}{dt} = -\dfrac{7}{16}$ means that demand is *decreasing* by slightly less than one-half sale per week (or, by about one sale in two weeks) when price is increasing by 50¢ per week at price level $p = \$40$.

(b) This time we use implicit differentiation and the Chain Rule, remembering that $x = Q(p)$ is treated as a function of p.

(b) To find $\dfrac{dx}{dp}$, we view x as a function of p (thus, p is regarded as the independent variable) and differentiate all terms in the equation

$$x^2 + 3xp + p^2 = 360$$

with respect to p. We obtain

$$2x \cdot \frac{dx}{dp} + 3p\frac{dx}{dp} + 3x + 2p = 0$$

so

$$(2x + 3p)\frac{dx}{dp} = -(3x + 2p)$$

and

$$\frac{dx}{dp} = -\frac{3x + 2p}{2x + 3p}.$$

At $(40, 20)$,

$$\frac{dx}{dp}(40, 20) = -\frac{3 \cdot 20 + 2 \cdot 40}{2 \cdot 20 + 3 \cdot 40} = -\frac{7}{8}.$$

(c) Recall definition of elasticity:

Substitute $Q'(p) = \dfrac{dx}{dp}$ and $Q(p) = x$ in the definition of elasticity.

(c) Since $x = Q(p)$, $\dfrac{dx}{dp} = Q'(p)$ and

$$E(p) = \frac{-pQ'(p)}{Q(p)}$$

the elasticity of this demand curve is

$$E(p) = \frac{-p \cdot \dfrac{dx}{dp}}{x}$$

$$= \frac{-p\left(-\dfrac{3x + 2p}{2x + 3p}\right)}{x}$$

$$= \frac{3px + 2p^2}{2x^2 + 3px}.$$

Substitute given values of x and p.

Evaluating this expression when $p = 40$ and $x = 20$ gives

$$E(40) = \frac{3(40)(20) + 2(40)^2}{2(20)^2 + 3(40)(20)}$$

$$= \frac{5600}{3200}$$

$$= \frac{7}{4}.$$

Since $E(40) > 1$, the curve is elastic, and price increases beyond $p = 40$ will lead to decreasing revenues. ■

Proof of the Power Rule

Proof: Up to this point we have been able to prove the Power Rule

$$\frac{d}{dx}(x^r) = rx^{r-1} \tag{9}$$

only for the case where r is an integer. Assuming x^r to be differentiable, we can use the technique of implicit differentiation to verify the Power Rule for all rational exponents r as follows. First, we write $r = \dfrac{p}{q}$ where p and q are integers with $q \neq 0$. Then if $y = x^r$ with $x \neq 0$, we have $y = x^{p/q} \neq 0$, so

$$y^q = (x^{p/q})^q = x^p.$$

Differentiating both sides of this equation gives

$$qy^{q-1} \cdot \frac{dy}{dx} = px^{p-1}.$$

Recalling that $y = x^{p/q} \neq 0$, we can now solve for $\dfrac{dy}{dx}$:

$$\frac{dy}{dx} = px^{p-1}\left(\frac{1}{q}\right)y^{1-q}$$

$$= \left(\frac{p}{q}\right)x^{p-1}(x^{p/q})^{1-q}$$

$$= \left(\frac{p}{q}\right)x^{p-1} \cdot x^{\frac{p}{q}-p}$$

$$= \left(\frac{p}{q}\right)x^{\left(p-1+\frac{p}{q}-p\right)}$$

$$= \left(\frac{p}{q}\right)x^{\frac{p}{q}-1}$$

which is equation (9), the Power Rule, with $r = {}^{p/q}$. ☐

☑ PRACTICE PROBLEMS 3.9

1. Find $\dfrac{dx}{dt}$ if $\dfrac{dy}{dt} = -2$, $x = 2$, $y = -3$, and

$$x^2 + 4xy + 3y^2 = 7.$$

2. Find $\dfrac{dy}{dx}$ if x and y are related by the equation in Problem 1.

Exercise Set 3.9

In Exercises 1–14, assume y to be a differentiable function of x and find an expression for $\dfrac{dy}{dx}$.

1. $x^2 + y^2 = 9$

2. $x^2 - y^2 = 16$

3. $xy^2 = 6$

4. $4x^2 + 2y^2 = 4$

5. $x^2 + 2xy + y^2 = 8$

6. $x^2 + 3xy + 6y + y^2 = 10$

7. $x^3 + 2xy^2 + x^2y + 2y^3 = 5$

8. $3x^2 - xy + 5xy^3 = 6$

9. $x^3 + 2x^2y + 5xy^2 - y^2 = 10$

10. $xy + 3\sqrt{x+y} - y^2 = 5$

11. $xy - y^4 + \sqrt{xy} = 10$

12. $\sqrt{x+y} = x - y$

13. $\sqrt{x} - xy + x^{2/3}y^{4/3} = 30$

14. $\dfrac{x+y}{x-y} = 3$

In Exercises 15–20, find the value of the derivative $\dfrac{dy}{dx}$ at the indicated point.

15. $xy = 9$ at $(3, 3)$

16. $x^2 + y^2 = 4$ at $(\sqrt{2}, \sqrt{2})$

17. $x^3 + y^3 = 16$ at $(2, 2)$

18. $x^2y^2 = 16$ at $(-1, 4)$

19. $\dfrac{x + y}{x - y} = 4$ at $(5, 3)$

20. $(y - x)^2 = x$ at $(9, 12)$

21. Find an equation for the line tangent to the curve $\sqrt{x} + \sqrt{y} = 4$ at the point $(4, 4)$.

22. Find an equation for the line tangent to the graph of the equation $x^2 + y^2 = 8$ at the point $(-2, 2)$.

23. Find the slope of the line tangent to the graph of $y^3 - x^2 = 7$ at the point $(1, 2)$.

24. Find the slope of the line tangent to the graph of the ellipse $\dfrac{x^2}{16} + \dfrac{y^2}{9} = 1$ at the point $\left(2, \dfrac{3\sqrt{3}}{2}\right)$.

25. When a pebble is tossed into a still pond, ripples move out in the shape of concentric circles from the point where the stone hits. Find the rate at which the area of the disturbed water is increasing when the radius of the outermost circle equals 10 meters if the radius is increasing at a rate of 2 meters per second.

26. A radio transmitter is located 3 kilometers from a straight section of interstate highway. A truck is traveling away from the transmitter along the highway at a speed of 80 kilometers per hour. How fast is the distance between the truck and the transmitter increasing when they are 5 kilometers apart?

27. Following the outbreak of an epidemic, a population of $N(t)$ people can be regarded as being made up of immunes, $I(t)$, and susceptibles, $S(t)$. That is, $N(t) = I(t) + S(t)$. $I(t)$ includes both those who have contracted the disease and those who cannot contract the disease. If the rate of decrease of susceptibles is 20 persons per day, and the rate of increase of immunes is 24 persons per day, how fast is the population growing?

28. An orchard has 100 apple trees. Currently the average yield per tree is 200 pounds of apples per year. This yield is increasing by 20 pounds per year. If the price of apples is expected to increase by 10¢ per pound per year for the next few years and the current price of apples is 60¢ per pound, find the rate at which the orchard's annual revenue from the sale of its apples will be increasing after one year.

29. A company determines that the demand for its product is related to its price by the equation

$$x^2 + 5xp + p^2 = 1500.$$

Find $\dfrac{dx}{dt}$, the rate of change in demand, if price is decreasing at the rate $\dfrac{dp}{dt} = -1$ when $p = 10$ and $x = 20$.

30. For the demand equation

$$x^2 + 4xp + 4p = 18,000$$

find $\dfrac{dx}{dt}$ if $\dfrac{dp}{dt} = -0.5$, $p = 100$, and $x = 40$.

31. A producer of instant cameras finds from market research that it can sell x cameras per day at price p, where

$$5x + 5xp + p^2 = 2100.$$

How fast is this rate of sales changing when $p = \$40$, $x = 20$ cameras per day, and price is increasing by 20¢ per camera per week?

32. Find the elasticity of demand for the demand equation

$$x^2 + 5xp + p^2 = 1500$$

at the point $(p_0, x_0) = (10, 20)$.

33. What is the elasticity of demand for the demand equation

$$x^2 + 4xp + 4p = 18,000$$

when $p = 100$ and $x = 40$?

34. The population of a certain city is predicted to be $P(t) = \sqrt{2 + t}$ million people t years after 1990. If the per capita income is expected to be $I(t) = 9 + 0.2t$ thousand dollars at this same time, and if the city has a tax on personal income of 5%, find the rate at which revenues from the city's personal income tax will be increasing in 1997.

35. Tuition at a small college is currently $8000 per year. The college currently has 1000 students. If tuition is increasing at the rate of $400 per year and enrollment is declining at the rate of 20 students per year, find the rate at which annual revenues from tuition will be changing two years from now.

36. A company estimates that it experiences a cost of $40 per day for each employee who misses work due to illness. It also estimates that t days after the outbreak of a certain type of flu among its employees $I(t) = \sqrt{4 + t^2}$ employees will be ill. At what rate is the company's total cost due to illness increasing 6 days after the outbreak?

37. The velocity at which a viscous fluid flows through a circular tube is not the same at all points of a cross-section. The flow is a maximum at the center of the cross-section and decreases to zero at the walls. For a point at a radial distance r from the center of the tube, the velocity of the flow is

$$v = \frac{\alpha}{L}(R^2 - r^2)$$

where R is the radius of the tube, L is its length, and α is a constant. Find the acceleration of the fluid moving at the center of the tube if $L = 25$ centimeters is fixed and R is increasing at a rate of 0.02 centimeter per minute at the instant when $R = 10$ centimeters.

☑ **SOLUTIONS TO PRACTICE PROBLEMS 3.9**

1. $x^2 + 4xy + 3y^2 = 7$ gives

$$2x \cdot \frac{dx}{dt} + 4y \cdot \frac{dx}{dt} + 4x \cdot \frac{dy}{dt} + 6y \cdot \frac{dy}{dt} = 0$$

$$(2x + 4y)\frac{dx}{dt} + (4x + 6y)\frac{dy}{dt} = 0$$

$$\frac{dx}{dt} = -\left(\frac{4x + 6y}{2x + 4y}\right)\frac{dy}{dt}.$$

When $\frac{dy}{dt} = -2$, $x = 2$, and $y = -3$ this gives

$$\frac{dx}{dt} = -\left(\frac{4 \cdot 2 + 6(-3)}{2 \cdot 2 + 4(-3)}\right)(-2) = \frac{5}{2}.$$

2. Treating y as a function of x gives from

$$x^2 + 4xy + 3y^2 = 7$$

that

$$2x + 4y + 4x\frac{dy}{dx} + 6y\frac{dy}{dx} = 0$$

$$(4x + 6y)\frac{dy}{dx} = -(2x + 4y)$$

$$\frac{dy}{dx} = -\left(\frac{2x + 4y}{4x + 6y}\right).$$

3.10 Linear Approximation and Differentials

Frequently, we would like to be able easily to approximate the change in the value of a function resulting from a small change in its independent variable. For example, if $Q(p)$ is the demand for an item when the selling price is p, what would be the effect on the demand of a small increase, or decrease, in the selling price?

Linear Approximations

The fact that the derivative $f'(x_0)$ of a differentiable function f determines a line tangent to the graph of f at $(x_0, f(x_0))$ gives the basis for a *linear approximation* to values $f(x)$ when x is "near" x_0. Figure 10.1 illustrates the basic idea. Once x_0, $f(x_0)$, and $f'(x_0)$ are known, we have determined the linear function

$$L(x) = f(x_0) + f'(x_0)(x - x_0)$$

to approximate values $f(x)$ of the function f for x near x_0, we will use the value of this linear (i.e., "tangent line") function as our approximations.

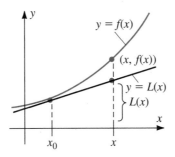

Figure 10.1 The tangent to the graph of f at $(x_0, f(x_0))$ provides a linear approximation to values $f(x)$ for x near x_0.

That is, we use the *linear approximation*

$$f(x) \approx f(x_0) + f'(x_0)(x - x_0) \tag{1}$$

for x near x_0.

We use the symbol $\approx$ to remind you that the expression on the right side of statement (1) is only an approximation to the value $f(x)$.

□ **EXAMPLE 1**

Use a linear approximation to approximate values of the function $f(x) = \sqrt{x}$ for x near $x_0 = 4$. Compare your results with actual values of the square root function (to four decimal place accuracy).

Strategy · · · · · · ·
Identify f and x_0; calculate $f(x_0)$ and $f'(x_0)$.

Set up linear approximation (1).

Solution

Here $f(x) = \sqrt{x}, f'(x) = \dfrac{1}{2\sqrt{x}}$, and $x_0 = 4$. The linear approximation (1) becomes

$$\sqrt{x} \approx \sqrt{4} + \frac{1}{2\sqrt{4}}(x - 4)$$

or

$$\sqrt{x} \approx 2 + \frac{1}{4}(x - 4). \tag{1a}$$

Substitute various values of x to obtain approximations to $\sqrt{x}$.

Compare with actual values obtained using a calculator.

Table 10.1 shows values of this approximation for several numbers near $x_0 = 4$, and it compares them with actual values of these square roots, to four decimal places.

■

Table 10.1

x	Linear Approximation from (1a)	Actual Square Root, $\sqrt{x}$, to Four Decimal Place Accuracy	Difference
4.01	2.0025	2.0025	0
4.1	2.0250	2.0248	0.0002
4.2	2.0500	2.0494	0.0006
4.3	2.0750	2.0736	0.0014
4.5	2.1250	2.1213	0.0037
5.0	2.2500	2.2361	0.0139
3.99	1.9975	1.9975	0.0000
3.95	1.9875	1.9875	0.0000
3.5	1.8750	1.8708	0.0042
3.0	1.7500	1.7321	0.0179

Example 1 and the preceding discussion should convince you that the linear approximation (1) can be useful, as long as the approximations are made for numbers x near the number x_0.

□ **EXAMPLE 2**

A manufacturer of VCRs determines that the cost of producing x units per day is given by the function

$$C(x) = 2000 + 75x + 2x^2.$$

Current, $x = 100$ units are being produced daily. Give the manufacturer a linear approximation to the total cost that would result from an increase from $x_0 = 100$ to $x = 105$ units per day. Compare this approximation with the actual value $C(105)$.

Solution: For $C(x) = 2000 + 75x + 2x^2$, we have

$$C'(x) = 75 + 4x.$$

At production level $x_0 = 100$, the total cost is

$$C(100) = 2000 + 75(100) + 2(100)^2 = 29,500$$

and

$$C'(100) = 75 + 4(100) = 475.$$

Using linear approximation (1), we have

$$C(x) \approx C(100) + C'(100)(x - 100)$$
$$= 29,500 + 475(x - 100).$$

For $x = 105$, the approximation is

$$C(105) \approx 29,500 + 475(5)$$
$$= \$31,875.$$

The actual value $C(105)$, from the cost function, is

$$C(105) = 2000 + 75(105) + 2(105)^2$$
$$= \$31,925. \qquad \blacksquare$$

Error Propagation

Up to this point you may have had difficulty in appreciating the value of the linear approximation (1). Especially when one has access to a calculator or a computer, what is the reason to *approximate* function values that are just as easy to compute?

Besides the more theoretical interpretation, which we shall take up later in the section, an understanding of linear approximation can provide insight on how measurement errors can propagate (and grow) through calculations involving them.

To see how this is done, we rewrite approximation (1) in the form

$$f(x) - f(x_0) \approx f'(x_0)(x - x_0) \qquad (2)$$

In this form, approximation (2) says, "the difference between the function value at a designated number (x_0) and at a nearby number (x) is approximately equal to the derivative at the designated number ($f'(x_0)$) multiplied by the difference between the numbers."

Thus, if a calculation $f(x_0)$ is based on the measurement x_0, while the actual number to have been measured is x, the resulting error in the calculation, $f(x) - f(x_0)$, is approximately $f'(x_0)(x - x_0)$. That is, a "measurement error" of magnitude $x - x_0$ will produce a "calculation error" of approximately $f'(x_0)(x - x_0)$.

☐ **EXAMPLE 3**

The measurement of the side of a cube is used to calculate its volume. If the measurement taken is $x_0 = 5$ inches, while the actual length of the side is $x = 5.2$ inches, use approximation (2) to estimate the error in the resulting calculation of volume.

Solution: The volume of a cube of side x is

$$V(x) = x^3.$$

Thus, $V'(x) = 3x^2$. With $x_0 = 5$ and $x = 5.2$, approximation (2) gives the estimate for the error in the calculation of the volume:

$$\begin{aligned}
\text{error} = V(5.2) - V(5.0) &\approx [V'(5.0)](5.2 - 5.0) \\
&= 3(5.0)^2(0.2) \\
&= 15.
\end{aligned}$$

In this case, the calculated volume would be

$$V(5.0) = (5.0)^3 = 125$$

while the actual volume is

$$V(5.2) = 140.608.$$

Thus, the *actual error* in the calculation is 15.608, while the *estimate* of the error, from using approximation (2), is 15.0. Notice how an error in measurement of only 0.2 inch produces an error in the calculation of volume of approximately 15 cubic inches. ■

Marginal Analysis

Approximation (2) gives some additional insight into our definitions of marginal cost, revenue, and profit.

We have defined marginal revenue, for example, to be the derivative of the revenue function, $MR(x) = R'(x)$, and we have said that:

(a) marginal revenue is the rate of change of revenue and
(b) the marginal revenue $MR(x_0)$ at production level x_0 is *approximately* the gain or loss in revenue resulting from an increase in production by one unit, from x_0 to $x_0 + 1$.

Statement (a) is just a recapitulation of what is measured by the derivative of any function. Statement (b), however, echoes approximation (2): with $f(x) = R(x)$, and with $x = x_0 + 1$, approximation (2) says that

$$\begin{aligned}
R(x_0 + 1) - R(x_0) &\approx R'(x_0)[(x_0 + 1) - x_0] \\
&= MR(x_0)(1) \\
&= MR(x_0).
\end{aligned}$$

That is, $MR(x_0)$ approximates the increase or decrease in revenue associated with an increase in production by one unit. Similar observations hold for marginal cost and marginal profit.

☐ **EXAMPLE 4**

A manufacturer of electric golf carts experiences annual profits of

$$P(x) = 400x - 10,000 - 0.2x^2$$

where x is the number of units produced annually. At the current production level of $x_0 = 500$ carts, profits are $P(500) = \$140{,}000$ annually. Estimate the change in profits associated with

(a) an increase in production by 1 cart.
(b) an increase in production by 50 carts.
(c) a decrease in production by 50 carts.

Solution: Here $P'(x) = 400 - 0.4x$ is the marginal profit function.

(a) According to our interpretation of marginal profit, the additional profit resulting from the production of one additional unit is

$$MP(500) = P'(500) = 400 - 0.4(500) = \$200.$$

Approximation (2) gives this same result:

$$\begin{aligned}
P(501) - P(500) &\approx P'(500)(501 - 500) \\
&= [500 - 0.4(500)](1) \\
&= \$200.
\end{aligned}$$

(b) To estimate the change in profit resulting from an increase from $x_0 = 500$ to $x = 550$ units per year we use approximation (2):

$$\begin{aligned}
P(550) - P(500) &\approx P'(500)(550 - 500) \\
&= [400 - 0.4(500)]50 \\
&= \$10{,}000.
\end{aligned}$$

Thus, we estimate

$$\begin{aligned}
P(550) &\approx P(500) + \$10{,}000 \\
&= \$150{,}000.
\end{aligned}$$

(c) Similarly, for a *decrease* from $x_0 = 500$ to $x = 450$, we estimate profit to change by

$$\begin{aligned}
P(450) - P(500) &= P'(500)(450 - 500) \\
&= [400 - 0.4(500)](-50) \\
&= \$-10{,}000
\end{aligned}$$

and we estimate $P(450)$ as $P(450) = \$130{,}000$.

By substituting directly into the equation for $P(x)$ you can verify that the *actual* values for these quantities are $P(550) = \$149{,}500$ and $P(450) = \$129{,}500$. ■

Relative and Percentage Change

In using approximation formulas (1) and (2) it is often helpful to refer to the *relative* or *percentage* change in the independent variable and the corresponding relative or percentage change estimated for the values of the function. This is especially helpful when the values of a function are of significantly different magnitude from the numbers specified for the independent variable.

□ **EXAMPLE 5**

(a) For the linear function $f(x) = 1000 + x$ a change in the independent variable from $x_0 = 2$ to $x = 3$, an increase of 50%, produces a change in the function value of

$$f(3) - f(2) = (1000 + 3) - (1000 + 2)$$
$$= 1003 - 1002$$
$$= 1$$

which is only $\dfrac{1}{1002}$, or about *one tenth of one percent* change in the function value.

(b) But for the function $g(x) = 5 + 10x^2$ a change from $x_0 = 5$ to $x = 6$, which is an increase of 20% in the independent variable, produces an increase in the function value of

$$f(6) - f(5) = (5 + 20 \cdot 6^2) - (5 + 20 \cdot 5^2) = 220$$

which is an increase of $\dfrac{220}{725}$, or about 30% in the function value.   ■

Definition 8

Let a and b be two numbers, with $a \neq b$.

(i) The **relative change**, from a to b, is the quotient $\dfrac{b - a}{a}$.

(ii) The **percent change,** from a to b, is the product $\left(\dfrac{b - a}{a}\right)(100\%)$.

□ **EXAMPLE 6**

Using this terminology, we can restate the conclusions from several previous examples as follows:

(a) In Example 1, a relative change in x from $x_0 = 4$ to $x = 5$, or $\dfrac{5 - 4}{4} = \dfrac{1}{4}$, produced a relative change in the square root function of

$$\frac{\sqrt{5} - \sqrt{4}}{\sqrt{4}} = \frac{2.2361 - 2.0}{2.0} = 0.1680.$$

That is, a *percent* increase of $\dfrac{1}{4} \times 100\% = 25\%$ in x produced a percent increase of $(0.1680) \times 100\% = 16.8\%$ in $f(x) = \sqrt{x}$.

(b) In Example 2, we estimated that a 5% increase in production, from $x_0 = 100$ units to $x = 105$ units, would produce a percent change in total costs of

$$\left(\frac{31{,}875 - 29{,}500}{31{,}875}\right) \times 100\% = 7.45\%.$$

(c) In Example 3, we used approximation (2) to estimate that a relative error in measuring the length of the side of the cube of

$$\frac{5.2 - 5}{5} = \frac{0.2}{5} = 0.04 \qquad \text{(or 4\%)}$$

would produce a relative error in the calculation of the volume of the cube of

$$\frac{V(5.2) - V(5)}{V(5)} \times \frac{15}{125} = 0.12 \qquad \text{(or 12\%).}$$

(d) In Example 4, a relative increase in production, from $x_0 = 500$ to $x = 550$, of

$$\frac{550 - 500}{500} = \frac{1}{10} \qquad \text{(or 10\%)}$$

led to an estimated increase in profits of

$$\frac{P(550) - P(500)}{P(500)} \approx \frac{10{,}000}{140{,}000} = \frac{1}{14} \qquad \text{(or 7.1\%).} \qquad \blacksquare$$

□ EXAMPLE 7

A producer of alloy tennis rackets determines that the weekly revenues resulting from the sale of its rackets are related to the price p by the equation

$$R(p) = 5000p - 40p^2.$$

Thus, at the current price $p_0 = 100$, weekly revenues are $R(100) = 5000(100) - 40(100)^2 = \$100{,}000$.

(a) Estimate the percentage change in revenues resulting from a 10% price increase.
(b) If the producer, unsure of the effect of a price increase, wishes to limit any resulting loss in revenues to 10%, within what range should any price increase be limited?

Strategy · · · · · · · ·

(a) First, find the derivative $R'(p)$.

Find the actual price p corresponding to the 10% increase. Use approximation (2) to estimate the actual change in R.

Solution

(a) For $R(p) = 5000p - 40p^2$, we have

$$R'(p) = 5000 - 80p.$$

Now, an increase in p of 10% from $p_0 = 100$ would be to price $p = 110$.

The corresponding change in R is approximately

$$\begin{aligned}
R(110) - R(100) &\approx R'(100)(110 - 100) \\
&= [5000 - (80)(100)](10) \\
&= -30{,}000
\end{aligned}$$

Use Definition 8 to calculate relative and percent change.

This is a relative decrease of

$$\frac{R(110) - R(100)}{R(100)} \approx \frac{-30,000}{100,000} = -\frac{3}{10}$$

or a percent decrease of

$$\left(-\frac{3}{10}\right) \times 100\% = -30\%.$$

(b) Translate the requirement of a 10% limit in revenue loss to an inequality involving relative change in R.

(b) To limit to 10% any change in revenue resulting from a change in price from $p_0 = 100$ to another price p requires that

$$\left| \frac{R(p) - R(100)}{R(100)} \right| < \frac{1}{10} \qquad \text{(or 10\%)}$$

or

$$|R(p) - R(100)| < \frac{1}{10}R(100).$$

Use approximation (2) to estimate the (unknown) change in revenue.

Using the approximation

$$R(p) - R(100) \approx R'(100)(p - 100) \qquad (3)$$

gives the requirement that

$$|R'(100)(p - 100)| < \frac{1}{10}R(100).$$

Substitute given values for p_0 and solve inequality for p.

Substituting $R(100) = 100,000$ and $R'(100) = -3000$ gives

$$|(-3000)(p - 100)| < \frac{1}{10}(100,000)$$

or

$$|p - 100| < \frac{100,000}{10(3000)} = \frac{10}{3}$$

which is equivalent to

This is the range of acceptable prices.

$$-\frac{10}{3} < p - 100 < \frac{10}{3}$$

or

$$\$96.67 < p < \$103.33.$$

Note the limitation caused by the use of the approximation.

Of course, this range is based on the approximation used in line (3). To be safe, we should check the revenue resulting from any *particular* potential new price. For example, at price $p = 103$ the revenue equation gives

$$R(103) = (5000)(103) - 40(103)^2 = 90,640$$

a decrease of 9.36% from $R(100)$.

The Differential *dy*

The term *differential,* and the notation *df,* or *dy,* is used to denote the *approximation* to actual changes in the value $f(x)$ given by approximation (2). That is, for a differentiable function f we write the *differential* for f as

$$df = f'(x)\,dx. \tag{4}$$

Thus, the differential *df* approximates the change in *y* corresponding to a change $dx = (x - x_0)$ in *x*, resulting from the linear approximation to *f*, rather than from *f* itself. (See Figure 10.2.) That is

$$f(x) - f(x_0) \approx df(x_0)$$
$$= f'(x_0)(x - x_0).$$

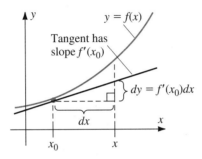

Figure 10.2 The differential $dy = f'(x)\,dx$.

The differential *df* in line (4) is a formal expression, reminding us that the derivative measures the change in *f* relative to change in *x* at each number *x* in the domain of *f*.

It is tempting to say that the differential $dy = f'(x)\,dx$ results from "multiplying the equation $\dfrac{dy}{dx} = f'(x)$ through by *dx*," but this is at best a memory device, since both $f'(x)$ and *dy* are symbols for concepts (one being rate of change, the other a linear approximation) rather than numbers. Nevertheless, for a given function $y = f(x)$ we can always form the differential $dy = f'(x)\,dx$ as a reminder of the linear approximation to *f*.

□ **EXAMPLE 8**

For the functions (a) $f(x) = \sqrt{x^2 + 7}$ and (b) $f(x) = \dfrac{1}{x + 2}$ the differentials are

(a) $df = \left[\dfrac{d}{dx}(\sqrt{x^2 + 7})\right] dx$

$\quad = \dfrac{x}{\sqrt{x^2 + 7}}\,dx$

and

(b) $df = \left[\dfrac{d}{dx} \left(\dfrac{1}{x+2} \right) \right] dx$

$\quad = \dfrac{-1}{(x+2)^2} \, dx.$ ∎

Limitations on Linear Approximations

It is important to remember that the linear approximation (2) is only an estimate, not a statement of fact. Its accuracy depends upon the rate at which f is changing slope (i.e., the second derivative) as well as the slope itself.

☐ **EXAMPLE 9**

As a final example, and as an illustration of the last remark, consider the functions

$$f(x) = 4 - x^2 \quad \text{and} \quad g(x) = \sqrt{16 + x} \quad \text{at} \quad x_0 = 0$$

(Figures 10.3 and 10.4).

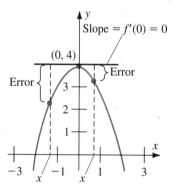

Figure 10.3 Linear approximation to $f(x) = 4 - x^2$ at $x_0 = 0$.

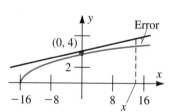

Figure 10.4 Linear approximation to $g(x) = \sqrt{16 + x}$ at $x_0 = 0$.

As you can see from Table 10.2, the linear approximation

$$f(x) \approx f(0) + f'(0)(x - 0)$$
$$= 4$$

provides a relatively poor estimate for values $f(x)$, even when x is within 1 unit of $x_0 = 0$.

Table 10.2

x	Linear Approximation to $4 - x^2$	Actual Value $4 - x^2$	Percent Error (%)
0.2	4	3.96	1
0.5	4	3.75	6.25
1.0	4	3	25
1.5	4	1.75	56.25
−0.2	4	3.96	1
−0.5	4	3.75	6.25
−1.0	4	3	25
−1.5	4	1.75	56.25

On the other hand, the linear approximation

$$g(x) \approx g(0) + g'(0)(x - 0)$$
$$= 4 + \frac{1}{2\sqrt{16 + 0}}(x - 0)$$
$$= 4 + \frac{x}{8}$$

gives much better estimates for similar choices of x. (See Table 10.3.)

Table 10.3

x	Linear Approximation to $\sqrt{16 + x}$	Actual Value $\sqrt{16 + x}$	Percent Error (%)
0.2	4.0250	4.0249	0.01
0.5	4.0625	4.0621	0.04
1.0	4.1250	4.1231	0.19
1.5	4.1875	4.1833	0.42
−0.2	3.9750	3.9749	0.01
−0.5	3.9375	3.9370	0.05
−1.0	3.8750	3.8730	0.20
−1.5	3.8125	3.8079	0.46

Thus, while the approximation ideas of the section are important for their expositional and conceptual value, they should be used with caution and compared to actual function values whenever possible. ■

☑ PRACTICE PROBLEMS 3.10

1. Find an approximation for $\sqrt[3]{128}$ and determine its accuracy.
2. The diameter of a spherical machine bearing is measured to be 4 centimeters. Estimate the percentage error in the calculation of the volume (and, therefore, the weight) of the bearing if the measurement of the diameter is in error by 10%.

Exercise Set 3.10

In each of Exercises 1–8, use approximation (1) to estimate the value of the given function at the given value of x, basing your approximation at the given number x_0.

1. $f(x) = 3x^2 + 7$, $x = 9.2$, $x_0 = 8$

2. $f(x) = x^3 + 5$, $x = 2.7$, $x_0 = 3$

3. $f(x) = 2x^2 + 3x$, $x = -5.4$, $x_0 = -6$

4. $f(x) = \sqrt{x + 3}$, $x = 6.2$, $x_0 = 6$

5. $f(x) = \sqrt{\dfrac{x + 2}{x - 1}}$, $x = 2.2$, $x_0 = 2$

6. $f(x) = \sqrt{x^2 + 11}$, $x = 6$, $x_0 = 5$

7. $f(x) = 5 + x^{2/3}$, $x = 120$, $x_0 = 125$

8. $f(x) = x^{1/3} + 3x$, $x = 25$, $x_0 = 27$

In Exercises 9–14, use a linear approximation to estimate the given quantity.

9. $\sqrt{38.6}$

10. $\sqrt[3]{124.3}$

11. $\dfrac{1}{\sqrt{17.2}}$

12. $(31)^{3/5}$

13. $(83.2)^{3/4}$

14. $\sqrt{123.5}$

15. A manufacturer of sewing machines finds that its revenue is related to the selling price of the machines by the equation

$$R(p) = 800p - 3p^2.$$

   a. Find $R(100)$, the revenue at price $p_0 = 100$.
   b. Find a linear approximation for the change in revenues resulting from an increase in p from $p_0 = 100$ to $p = 105$.
   c. Estimate the effect on revenues of an increase in the selling price of 20% from $p_0 = 100$.

16. The length of the edge of a cube is measured to be 10 inches. Use a linear approximation to estimate the percent error in the calculation of the volume if the measurement of the edge is in error by $\dfrac{1}{4}$ inch.

17. The demand equation for a certain brand of portable radio is

$$x = 1000 - 2p^{3/4}.$$

   Use a linear approximation to estimate the percent change in revenues resulting from an increase in price from $p_0 = \$81$ to $p = \$85$.

18. The amount of time required by a typist to complete a manuscript of length n pages is given by the equation

$$T(n) = \frac{1}{4}\sqrt{n^2 + 4n + 4}.$$

   a. Find $T(6)$, the time required to type a 6-page manuscript.
   b. Estimate the time required to type an 8-page manuscript.

19. The daily output of a certain factory is determined to be $f(K) = 500\sqrt{K}$ where K represents units of capital investment. The current daily input of capital is $\$640,000$. By approximately what percent will output increase if the daily capital input is increased to $\$700,000$?

20. A manufacturer's total cost in producing x items is

$$C(x) = 4000 + 40x + 3x^2$$

   per week. By approximately what percentage does total cost increase when production is increased by 10% from 100 to 110 units per week?

21. A producer of fashion watches determines that the demand x for one of its models is related to its selling price by the demand equation

$$x = 2000 - 40p$$

where x is weekly sales and p is selling price.
  a. Find the manufacturer's weekly revenue $R(x)$ as a function of x.
  b. Find the marginal revenue at demand level $x = 100$.
  c. What estimate does a linear approximation to the function R based at $x_0 = 100$ make for revenues associated with a demand level of $x = 80$?
  d. From the equation for $R(x)$, what is the *actual* value $R(80)$?
  e. Explain the difference between the answers to parts c and d.

22. Explain the relationship between marginal cost at production level x_0, the actual cost experienced at level $x_0 + 1$, and the linear approximation to $C(x_0 + 1)$ based at production level x_0.

23. What happens to the volume of a sphere when the radius is increased by 5%?

24. Wind resistance by an automobile (drag) increases with the square of the speed. What happens when speed is increased by 50%?

25. Water flows through a pipe at a rate of 3 liters per minute per square inch of cross-sectional area.
  a. Find the volume $V(r)$ per minute flowing through the pipe if the cross section is a circle of radius r.
  b. Find the volume per minute, $V(4)$, if the radius is $r = 4$ inches.
  c. Approximate the change in the volume per minute resulting from an increase in the radius from $r_0 = 4$ to $r = 4.5$ inches.

26. A roller bearing has the shape of a circular cylinder. The length is supposed to be 5 cm and the radius of the base is supposed to be 2 cm. Estimate the deviation of the volume from the intended volume if the length is precise but the radius is actually $r = 2.05$ cm.

27. A plot of ground is to be laid out in the shape of a square with sides of length $s = 200$ feet. Approximate the variation in the area of the plot, in square feet, resulting from variations in each of the sides of up to 2 feet.

28. Find an estimate for $f(9)$ if $f(10) = 6$ and $f'(10) = -3$.

☑ **SOLUTIONS TO PRACTICE PROBLEMS 3.10**

  1. The function is $f(x) = x^{1/3}$, with $f'(x) = \dfrac{1}{3}x^{-2/3}$. We use $x_0 = 125$, because it is a perfect cube. Then $x = 128$, $x - x_0 = 3$, $f(x_0) = \sqrt[3]{125} = 5$, and $f'(x_0) = \dfrac{1}{3(125)^{2/3}} = \dfrac{1}{75}$.

Using linear approximation (1) we obtain

$$\sqrt[3]{128} \approx f(125) + f'(125)(128 - 125)$$
$$= 5 + \frac{3}{75}$$
$$= 5.04.$$

To determine the accuracy we compare this estimate with the value of $\sqrt[3]{128}$ obtained from a calculator. It is $\sqrt[3]{128} = 5.0397$. The percent error is therefore

$$\left(\frac{5.04 - 5.0397}{5.0397}\right) \times 100\% = 0.006\%.$$

  2. The measured value $d_0 = 4$ cm of the diameter gives a measured value $r_0 = 2$ cm for the radius. To be in error by less than 10% the actual radius r must satisfy

$$\frac{r - 2}{2} < \frac{1}{10}$$

or

$$r - 2 < 0.2.$$

The volume corresponding to the measurement $r = 2$ is

$$V(2) = \frac{4}{3}\pi r^3 \Big|_{r=2} = \frac{32\pi}{3}$$

and the derivative of the function $V(r) = \frac{4}{3}\pi r^3$ at $r = 2$ is

$$V'(2) = 4\pi r^2 \Big|_{r=2} = 16\pi.$$

Approximation (2) then gives that

$$
\begin{aligned}
V(r) - V(2) &\approx V'(2)(r - 2) \\
&= (16\pi)(r - 2) \\
&< (16\pi)(0.2) \qquad (r - 2 < 0.2) \\
&= (3.2)\pi
\end{aligned}
$$

The relative and percent errors in the calculation of volume are therefore estimated as

$$\frac{V(r) - V(2)}{V(2)} \approx \frac{(3.2)\pi}{32\pi/3} = \frac{9.6}{32} = 0.3 \qquad \text{or} \qquad 30\%.$$

3.11 The Mean Value Theorem

The final theorem of this chapter has a very simple geometric interpretation, yet it is an important and powerful tool in establishing key theorems in both this chapter and others that follow.

   Figure 11.1 shows a portion of the graph of the function f corresponding to an interval $[a, b]$. There is also shown the secant line containing the points $(a, f(a))$ and $(b, f(b))$. The **Mean Value Theorem** guarantees that, under certain conditions on f,

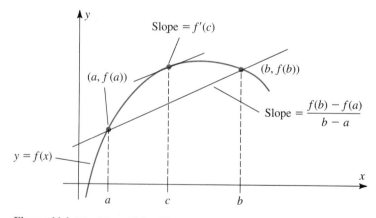

Figure 11.1 The Mean Value Theorem guarantees that there is a number c in (a, b) for which $f'(c) = \dfrac{f(b) - f(a)}{b - a}$.

there will always exist at least one number c in the interval (a, b) for which the line tangent to the graph of f at $(c, f(c))$ is parallel to the secant through $(a, f(a))$ and $(b, f(b))$.

The precise statement of this result is the following.

Theorem 6

(Mean Value Theorem)

If the function f is continuous on the closed interval $[a, b]$ and differentiable on the open interval (a, b), there exists at least one number c in (a, b) for which

$$f'(c) = \frac{f(b) - f(a)}{b - a}. \tag{1}$$

Comparing equation (1) with Figure 11.1, you will note that the left-hand side of equation (1) gives the slope of the tangent to the graph of f at $(c, f(c))$, while the right-hand side of equation (1) is the slope of the secant through $(a, f(a))$ and $(b, f(b))$. The terminology "Mean Value" refers to the slope of this secant, which we have referred to earlier as the average (mean) rate of change of the function f over the interval $[a, b]$. The Mean Value Theorem states that the derivative $f'(x)$ must equal this average rate of change for at least one number $x = c$ in (a, b).

A proof of the Mean Value Theorem is sketched in Exercise 12. Before giving an economic interpretation of this theorem and using it to prove an earlier result, we give one example showing how the number c in equation (1) may be found.

☐ **EXAMPLE 1**

Find the number c satisfying the Mean Value Theorem for the function $f(x) = \sqrt{x}$ on the interval $[0, 4]$.

Solution: Since $f(x) = \sqrt{x}$ is continuous on $[0, 4]$ and $f'(x) = \dfrac{1}{2\sqrt{x}}$ exists for all x in $(0, 4)$, the Mean Value Theorem applies. We therefore seek a number c for which

$$f'(c) = \frac{f(4) - f(0)}{4 - 0}$$

that is, for which

$$\frac{1}{2\sqrt{c}} = \frac{\sqrt{4} - \sqrt{0}}{4 - 0} = \frac{2}{4} = \frac{1}{2}.$$

This requires $2\sqrt{c} = 2$, or $\sqrt{c} = 1$. Thus $c = 1$ satisfies the Mean Value Theorem. (See Figure 11.2.) ■

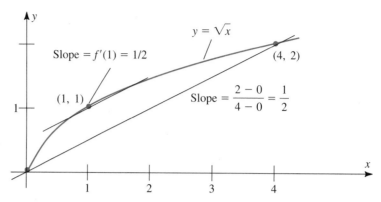

Figure 11.2 The number $c = 1$ satisfies the Mean Value Theorem for $f(x) = \sqrt{x}$ on $[0, 4]$.

An Economic Interpretation of the Mean Value Theorem

Figure 11.3 shows the graphs of a typical total cost function $y = C(x)$ and a total revenue function of the form $R(x) = px$, p constant. If we assume that these graphs intersect at $x = a$ and $x = b$, and that $R(x) > C(x)$ for $a < x < b$, then the profit function $P(x) = R(x) - C(x)$ is nonnegative for $a \le x \le b$. Thus if P is differentiable (it will be if C is), there must exist a number c in (a, b) for which $P(c)$ is the maximum value of P on $[a, b]$. This is because the differentiable, hence continuous, function P must have a maximum value on a closed, bounded interval, according to Theorem 5. This number c is shown in Figure 11.3.

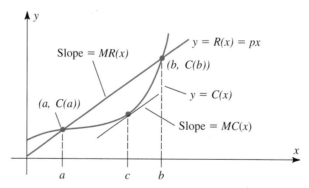

Figure 11.3 $P(x) = R(x) - C(x)$ has a maximum value at $x = c$ where $MR(c) = MC(c)$.

So far we are just reviewing the theory of extrema for the function P on the interval $[a, b]$, according to Sections 3.6 and 3.7. But now let us combine these observations with the principle from Section 3.8 that *marginal cost equals marginal revenue when profit is a maximum*. This means that

$$MC(c) = MR(c). \tag{2}$$

Now since the revenue function in Figure 11.3 is the linear function $R(x) = px$, the marginal revenue function is the constant function $MR(x) \equiv p$, *which is the slope of the straight line through $(a, C(a))$ and $(b, C(b))$*. That is

$$MR(x) \equiv p = \frac{C(b) - C(a)}{b - a}, \qquad x \text{ in } [a, b]. \tag{3}$$

Since the marginal cost function is just the derivative $MC(x) = C'(x)$, we can use equation (3) to rewrite equation (2) as

$$C'(c) = \frac{C(b) - C(a)}{b - a}. \tag{4}$$

What we have discovered in equation (4) may be stated as follows: "Given a differentiable cost function C on a closed interval $[a, b]$, there exists a number c in (a, b) where the slope of the *curve* $y = C(x)$ equals the slope of the *line* through $(a, C(a))$ and $(b, C(b))$." But this "discovery" is, of course, just the statement of the Mean Value Theorem applied to the cost function C.

Proof of Theorem 1, Chapter 3

Proof: Using the Mean Value Theorem we can prove one of our earlier results. We shall prove the first part of this theorem, which states that "if $f'(x) > 0$ for all x in (a, b), then f is increasing on (a, b)."

To show that f is increasing on (a, b), we let x_1 and x_2 be numbers in (a, b) with $x_1 < x_2$. We must show that $f(x_2) > f(x_1)$.

Since x_1 and x_2 are in (a, b), the closed interval $[x_1, x_2]$ is in (a, b). Thus f is differentiable, hence also continuous, on $[x_1, x_2]$. Then, by the Mean Value Theorem, there is a number c in (x_1, x_2) with

$$f'(c) = \frac{f(x_2) - f(x_1)}{x_2 - x_1}.$$

Now since $f'(x) > 0$ for *all* x in (a, b), we must have $f'(c) > 0$. Thus

$$\frac{f(x_2) - f(x_1)}{x_2 - x_1} > 0. \tag{5}$$

But since $x_2 > x_1$, the denominator $x_2 - x_1$ is positive. Thus for inequality (5) to hold, the numerator $f(x_2) - f(x_1)$ must also be positive. But $f(x_2) - f(x_1) > 0$ means that $f(x_2) > f(x_1)$, which is what we needed to show.

The other statement of Theorem 1, that "if $f'(x) < 0$ for all x in (a, b), then f is decreasing on (a, b)," is proved in a similar way. This task is left for you as an exercise. □

☑ **PRACTICE PROBLEM 3.11**

1. For the function $f(x) = \dfrac{1}{1 + x^2}$, determine whether the Mean Value Theorem applies on the interval $[-2, 2]$. If so, find a number c satisfying the Mean Value Theorem.

Exercise Set 3.11

1. Sketch the function $f(x) = |x|$ for $-1 \le x \le 1$. Does the Mean Value Theorem hold for this example? Why or why not?

In each of Exercises 2–8, find the value of c that satisfies the Mean Value Theorem for the given function and interval.

2. $f(x) = 2x^2 - 7$, x in $[-1, 5]$

3. $f(x) = 4 - x^2$, x in $[0, 2]$

4. $f(x) = x^2 + 2x$, x in $[0, 4]$

5. $f(x) = \sqrt{x + 5}$, x in $[-5, 4]$

6. $f(x) = \dfrac{1}{x}$, x in $[1, 3]$

7. $f(x) = x^2 + 2x - 3$, x in $[-3, 0]$

8. $f(x) = x^3 - 2x + 4$, x in $[0, 2]$

9. If an automobile travels 120 miles in two hours, at varying speeds, why can you conclude that the driver violated the 55 mph speed limit at least once?

10. A monopolist determines that its total revenue from the sale of 100 items per month is the same as its total revenue from the sale of 300 items per month.
   a. Does this necessarily mean that marginal revenue equals zero for all sales levels x with $100 < x < 300$? Why?
   b. Assuming the monopolist's total revenue function $y = R(x)$ to be differentiable, is there a sales level x with $100 \le x \le 300$ for which marginal revenue equals zero? Why?

11. Use the Mean Value Theorem to prove that if $f'(x) < 0$ for all x in (a, b) then f is decreasing on (a, b).

12. Prove the Mean Value Theorem as follows, referring to Figure 11.4.
   a. Let d be the function defined by

$$d(x) = f(x) - \left[f(a) + \frac{f(b) - f(a)}{b - a}(x - a) \right].$$

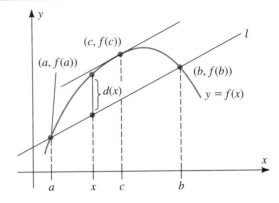

Figure 11.4

   b. Explain why d is differentiable on (a, b).
   c. Show that $d(a) = d(b) = 0$.
   d. Explain why either $d(x) = 0$ for all x in $[a, b]$ or else d has a relative extremum at some number c in (a, b).
   e. Using part d, explain why there must be a number c in (a, b) for which $d'(c) = 0$.
   f. Show that the equation $d'(c) = 0$ gives

$$f'(c) = \frac{f(b) - f(a)}{b - a}.$$

13. Use the Mean Value Theorem to explain why the following is true: If f is an even function satisfying the hypothesis of the Mean Value Theorem, then $c = 0$ will always satisfy the Mean Value Theorem on an interval of the form $[-a, a]$, $a > 0$.

14. True or false? If f is a differentiable, even function, then $f'(0) = 0$. If true, explain why. If not, give a counterexample. (*Hint:* Refer to Exercise 13.)

15. Use the Mean Value Theorem to explain why the following statement is true: If $f'(x) = 0$ for all x in the interval (a, b), then f is a constant function on (a, b).

☑ **SOLUTION TO PRACTICE PROBLEM 3.11**

1. For the function $f(x) = \dfrac{1}{1 + x^2}$, the derivative

$$f'(x) = \frac{-2x}{(1 + x^2)^2}$$

exists for all $x \in [-2, 2]$. Thus, f is continuous on $[-2, 2]$ also, and the Mean Value Theorem applies.

To find c we must solve the equation

$$f'(c) = \frac{f(2) - f(-2)}{2 - (-2)}$$

or

$$\frac{-2c}{(1 + c^2)^2} = \frac{\dfrac{1}{5} - \dfrac{1}{5}}{4} = 0.$$

Obviously, the choice $c = 0$ suffices. (*Note:* Can you see the relationship between the fact that f is an even function and the outcome $c = 0$? See Exercise 13.)

Summary Outline of Chapter 3

■ ***Theorem:***   If $f'(x) > 0$ for all x in I, then f is increasing on the open   (Page 170)
interval I.
            If $f'(x) < 0$ for all x in I, then f is decreasing on I.

■ $M = f(c)$ is a **relative maximum** for f if $f(c) \geq f(x)$ for all x near c.   (Page 179)

■ $m = f(d)$ is a **relative minimum** for f if $f(d) \leq f(x)$ for all x near d.   (Page 179)

■ ***Theorem:***   If $f(c)$ is a relative maximum or minimum, then either   (Page 179)
$f'(c) = 0$ or else $f'(c)$ fails to exist.

■ A **critical number** for f is a number x in the domain of f for which   (Page 181)
either $f'(x) = 0$ or else $f'(x)$ fails to exist.

■ ***Theorem:***   If c is a critical number for f, then   (Page 182)

    (i) If $f'(x) > 0$ for $x < c$ and $f'(x) < 0$ for $x > c$, then $f(c)$ is a relative maximum.
    (ii) If $f'(x) < 0$ for $x < c$ and $f'(x) > 0$ for $x > c$, then $f(c)$ is a relative minimum.

■ $f''(x)$, the **second derivative** of $f(x)$, is $\dfrac{d}{dx} f'(x)$.   (Page 188)

■ The graph of f is   (Page 190)

    (i) **concave up** on (a, b) if $f''(x) > 0$ for all x in (a, b).
    (ii) **concave down** on (a, b) if $f''(x) < 0$ for all x in (a, b).

■ Points on the graph of f that separate arcs of opposite concavity are   (Page 190)
called **inflection points.**

■ ***Theorem:***   Let c be a critical number for f with $f'(c) = 0$.   (Page 194)

    (i) If $f''(c) < 0$, then $f(c)$ is a relative maximum.
    (ii) If $f''(c) > 0$, then $f(c)$ is a relative minimum.
    (iii) If $f''(c) = 0$, there is no conclusion.

▌ $f'''(x)$ means $\dfrac{d}{dx} f''(x)$, $f^{(4)}(x)$ means $\dfrac{d}{dx} f'''(x)$, etc.   (Page 196)

▌ The line $x = a$ is a **vertical asymptote** for the graph of $y = f(x)$ (Page 200)
if $\lim\limits_{x \to a^-} f(x) = \pm\infty$ or if $\lim\limits_{x \to a^+} f(x) = \pm\infty$.

▌ The line $y = a$ is a **horizontal asymptote** for the graph of $y = f(x)$ if   (Page 200)
$\lim\limits_{x \to \infty} f(x) = a$ or if $\lim\limits_{x \to -\infty} f(x) = a$.

▌ $m = f(c)$ is the **absolute maximum** value of f for x in $[a, b]$ if   (Page 221)
$f(c) \geq f(x)$ for all x in $[a, b]$. The number $m = f(d)$ is the **absolute
minimum** for x in $[a, b]$ if $f(d) \leq f(x)$ for all x in $[a, b]$.

▌ The **elasticity** $E(p)$ of the demand curve $Q(p)$ at price level p is   (Page 251)

$$E(p) = -\frac{pQ'(p)}{Q(p)}.$$

▌ *Theorem (Mean Value Theorem):* If f is differentiable on (a, b) and   (Page 285)
continuous on $[a, b]$, there exists at least one number c in (a, b) for
which

$$f'(c) = \frac{f(b) - f(a)}{b - a}.$$

Review Exercises—Chapter 3

In Exercises 1–12, find the intervals on which f is increasing or decreasing and all relative extrema.

1. $f(x) = 4x - x^2$

2. $f(x) = x^2 - 6x - 16$

3. $f(x) = x^2 - 2x + 3$

4. $f(x) = \dfrac{1 - x}{x}$

5. $f(x) = \dfrac{x - 3}{x + 3}$

6. $f(x) = \dfrac{x}{x^2 + 1}$

7. $f(x) = x\sqrt{16 - x^2}$

8. $f(x) = x^4 - 2x^2$

9. $f(x) = x^3 - 3x^2 + 2$

10. $f(x) = x^2 + \dfrac{2}{x}$

11. $f(x) = 4 - 2x^{2/3}$

12. $f(x) = |x^2 - 4x - 5|$

In Exercises 13–22, find the maximum and minimum values of the function on the given interval and the corresponding values of x.

13. $f(x) = \dfrac{1}{x^2 - 4}$, x in $[-1, 1]$

14. $f(x) = x^3 - 3x^2 + 1$, x in $[-1, 1]$

15. $f(x) = x\sqrt{1 - x^2}$, x in $[-1, 1]$

16. $f(x) = x + x^{2/3}$, x in $[-1, 1]$

17. $f(x) = x - \sqrt{1 - x^2}$, x in $[-1, 1]$

18. $f(x) = \sqrt[3]{x} - x$, x in $[-1, 1]$

19. $f(x) = x - 4x^{-2}$, x in $[-3, -1]$

20. $f(x) = \dfrac{x}{1 + x^2}$, x in $[-2, 2]$

21. $f(x) = x^4 - 2x^2$, x in $[-2, 2]$

22. $f(x) = \dfrac{x - 1}{x^2 + 3}$, x in $[-2, 4]$

In Exercises 23–32, find all horizontal and vertical asymptotes.

23. $f(x) = \dfrac{1}{7 - x}$

24. $f(x) = \dfrac{x - 2}{x + 2}$

25. $y = \dfrac{x^2}{4 - x^2}$

26. $f(x) = \dfrac{x^2 + 5}{3 - x^2}$

27. $y = \dfrac{x^2 + 9}{x^2 - 9}$

28. $y = \dfrac{x - 1}{x^2 + x - 2}$

29. $y = \dfrac{x}{|x|}$

30. $f(x) = \dfrac{9 + 2x^4}{x^2 + 3x + 2}$

31. $y = 4 + 6x^{-3}$

32. $f(x) = \dfrac{x^3}{(x^2 + 6)^2}$

In Exercises 33–42, find the indicated limit.

33. $\lim\limits_{x \to \infty} \dfrac{2x + 6}{9 - x}$

34. $\lim\limits_{x \to \infty} \dfrac{x^2 + 3x + 5}{3x^2 + 6}$

35. $\lim\limits_{x \to \infty} \dfrac{7}{3x - x^{-3/2}}$

36. $\lim\limits_{x \to \infty} \dfrac{7}{3 - x^{-3}}$

37. $\lim\limits_{x \to 4^-} \dfrac{x^2 + 5\sqrt{x}}{x^2 - 16}$

38. $\lim\limits_{x \to 3^+} \left| \dfrac{x^2 - 4x - 3}{x - 3} \right|$

39. $\lim\limits_{x \to 2^-} \dfrac{6}{x^2 - 4}$

40. $\lim\limits_{x \to \infty} \dfrac{(x - 6)(x + 3)}{2x^3 + 8}$

41. $\lim\limits_{x \to 1^-} \dfrac{5x^2}{1 - x}$

42. $\lim\limits_{x \to \infty} \dfrac{1 - x^{-2}}{2 + x^{-2}}$

In Exercises 43–52, sketch the graph of the given function.

43. $y = 4x - x^2$

44. $y = x(x - 1)(x + 3)$

45. $f(x) = x^2 - 2x - 3$

46. $f(x) = \dfrac{1 - x}{x}$

47. $y = \dfrac{x - 3}{x + 3}$

48. $f(t) = \dfrac{t^2}{t^2 - 1}$

49. $f(x) = x\sqrt{16 - x^2}$

50. $y = \dfrac{\sqrt{x}}{1 + \sqrt{x}}$

51. $y = \dfrac{x^2}{x^2 + 9}$

52. $f(x) = x^2 + \dfrac{2}{x}$

53. The sides of a square are increasing at a rate of 2 cm/sec. At what rate is the area increasing when the length of a side equals 10 cm?

54. A peach orchard has 25 trees per acre, and the average yield is 300 peaches per tree. For each additional tree planted per acre the average yield per tree will be reduced by 10 peaches. How many trees per acre give the largest peach crop?

55. A volume V of oil is spilled at sea. The spill takes the shape of a disc whose radius is increasing at a rate of $a/\sqrt{t}$ m/sec where a is a constant. Find the rate at which the thickness of the layer of oil is decreasing after 9 seconds if the radius at that time is $r(9) = 6a$.

56. A fertilizer company can sell x pounds of fertilizer per week at a price of $p(x)$ cents per pound where

$$p(x) = 90 - \frac{x}{500}.$$

a. Find the total weekly revenue.
b. Find the marginal revenue function.
c. If weekly production is limited to 50 tons, what sales level maximizes revenue?

57. The cost of producing x wastebaskets per week is found by a manufacturer to be $C(x) = 5000 + 2x$ dollars. Market research shows that the relationship between the number x of wastebaskets that can be sold and the selling price p is $p(x) = 5 + \dfrac{200}{x}$. If production is limited to 1000 wastebaskets per week, what production level maximizes profit?

58. The cost per hour of driving a particular automobile at speed v is calculated to be $C(v) = 10 + 0.004v^2$ dollars per hour. What is the most economical speed at which to operate this automobile? (Assume v to be in units of miles per hour.)

59. A truck traveling 80 kilometers per hour is heading north on highway X, which crosses east–west highway Y at point P. A car traveling east on highway Y at 60 kilometers per hour passed point P when the truck was 20 kilometers south of point P. At what rate is the distance between the truck and the car increasing when the truck passes point P?

60. A student 1.6 meters tall walks directly away from a street light 8 meters above the ground at a rate of 1.2 meters per second. Find the rate at which the student's shadow is increasing when the student is 20 meters from the point directly beneath the light.

61. An appliance dealer sells 150 dishwashers per year at a uniform rate. The storage costs are $15 per year per dishwasher. The ordering costs are $2 per dishwasher, plus an additional $25 per order. How many times per year should the store order dishwashers so as to minimize costs?

62. A monopolist can manufacture at most 200 items per week. The price at which the monopolist can sell x items per week is $p(x) = 800 - 2x$ dollars, while the cost of producing x items per week is $C(x) = 100 + 6x + x^2$ dollars. Find the output level x_0 that maximizes profits.

63. How would the imposition of a $30 per item manufacturing tax change the optimal output level in Exercise 62?

64. A publisher currently sells 2000 subscriptions annually for a professional journal at a rate of $40 per year. Its marketing department predicts that for each $1 reduction in subscription price an additional 50 subscriptions can be sold. Under this assumption what subscription rate maximizes revenues?

65. The price p and demand x for a certain commodity are related by the equation $p = \sqrt{100 - x^2}, 0 \le x \le 10$. Find the price that maximizes revenue.

66. Find the slope of the line tangent to the circle with equation $(x + 2)^2 + (y - 3)^2 = 4$ at the point $(-1, 3 + \sqrt{3})$.

67. A pebble that is thrown vertically upward from ground level is at a height of $s(t) = 96t - 16t^2$ feet t seconds after it is thrown.
  a. Find its velocity function v.
  b. When is height $s(t)$ a maximum? At what height?
  c. When is velocity a maximum? At what height?
  d. What is its speed when it strikes the ground?

68. A lawn care service experiences the following profit function in contracting to service x lawns per week:
$$P(x) = 40x - 300 - 0.5x^2.$$
  a. Find the interval on which P is increasing.
  b. How many lawns should the service handle per week in order to maximize profit?

69. A tire manufacturer finds that its total cost of producing x tires per day is
$$C(x) = 30x + 200 + 0.5x^2 \text{ dollars.}$$
  a. Find its average daily cost per tire, $c(x) = \dfrac{C(x)}{x}$.
  b. For what production level x will average cost be a minimum?

70. A bicycle merchant finds that the combined annual cost of ordering and storing x bicycles at a time is
$$C(x) = 8x + \frac{3200}{x} \text{ dollars.}$$
Find the lot size x that minimizes this cost.

In Exercises 71 and 72 find $\dfrac{dy}{dx}$.

71. $x^2y + xy^2 = -4$ **72.** $x^3y - xy^3 = 10$

In Exercises 73 and 74 find the value of the derivative $\dfrac{dy}{dx}$ at the indicated point.

73. $\sqrt[3]{xy} - y = -6$ at $(3, 9)$

74. $\sqrt{x} - \sqrt{y} = 1$ at $(25, 16)$

75. The function modeling the total utility of salary for employees at Bong Airlines is determined by a compensation consultant to be
$$u(x) = \sqrt{x(x + 24)}$$
where x is in thousands of dollars per month.
  a. On what interval(s) is u increasing?
  b. On what interval(s) is u decreasing?
  c. Does u have any relative extrema? If so, what?
  d. Determine the concavity of the graph of u.
  e. Interpret these answers in terms of employee satisfaction (utility) with salary.

76. Demand for a new type of videotape recorder is predicted to follow the model
$$D(p) = \frac{500}{10 + \sqrt{p(p + 24)}}$$
  a. Find the marginal demand, $D'(p)$.
  b. Does demand increase or decrease as price increases?
  c. Determine the convexity of the graph of D for $p > 0$.
  d. Compare the marginal demand at $p = 1$ with the marginal demand at $p = 3$. Which is larger? Why?

77. Marketing experts believe that in certain unusual situations, increasing the price of an item can actually increase the demand for it, up to a point. (This can happen, for example, when higher prices are associated with status or when additional price increases are anticipated or feared.) If the demand for a new brand of cologne is predicted by the model
$$D(p) = \frac{10\sqrt{p}}{16 + p}, \qquad p > 0$$
where p is the price in dollars and D is in units of thousands of ounces per month, find the price at which demand will be a maximum. Explain why this model reflects the counterintuitive situation described above.

CHAPTER

4

Renewing woodlands is key to preserving many species of plants and animals. Rates at which populations of plants and animals grow and decline are often modelled by exponential functions. *(Grant Heilman/Grant Heilman Photography, Inc.)*

Exponential and Logarithmic Functions

4.1 Exponential Functions

Many models of interest in economics and business, as well as in the life sciences, involve quantities whose rate of growth depends on their current size. In business the amount of interest that a sum of money will earn depends, in part, on the size of the sum, and in the biology lab the rate at which a population of bacteria increases depends on the number of bacteria present. Such situations are often modelled using **exponential functions.**

Before briefly reviewing exponential functions, we introduce the idea of **compound interest** as one example of where the exponential function occurs as an important mathematical model.

□ **EXAMPLE 1**

Thrifty Savings Bank offers an investment account guaranteed to pay the depositor 10% annually on all funds that have been on deposit for the entire year. If all earnings are reinvested in the account, find the annual balances resulting from a single, initial deposit of $1000.

Solution: At the end of the first year, $10\% = 0.10$ of the initial deposit $P_0 = 1000$ is added to the account to produce a new balance

$$P(1) = P_0 + (0.10)P_0$$
$$= (1.10)P_0.$$

At the end of the second year, 10% of the amount $P(1)$ is added to give a new balance

$$P(2) = P(1) + (0.10)P(1)$$
$$= (1.10)P(1)$$
$$= (1.10)[(1.10)P_0]$$
$$= (1.10)^2 P_0.$$

Similarly, at the end of the third year the balance is increased by another factor of 1.10 to give

$$P(3) = (1.10)^3 P_0$$

in the account. Continuing in this way we find the amount in the account after n years to be

$$P(n) = (1.10)^n P_0 \text{ for } n = 1, 2, 3, \ldots, \qquad ∎$$

Generalizing from Example 1 we say that an amount P is increased by annual compounding of interest at rate r (in decimal form) if the value of the increased amount after n years is

$$P(n) = (1 + r)^n P_0.$$

This expression is called the nth **power** of the constant base $1 + r$; it is a simple example of using variables in exponents of expressions, which leads directly to our discussion of exponential functions.

Exponential Functions

If n is a positive integer and a is a nonzero number, we define the expression a^n by

$$a^n = \overbrace{a \cdot a \cdot a \cdot \ldots \cdot a}^{n \text{ factors}}.$$

Further, we define $a^0 = 1$ for all $a \neq 0$, and we define

$$a^{-n} = \frac{1}{a^n}, \qquad a \neq 0.$$

These definitions determine the values of the *exponential function*

$$f(n) = a^n \tag{1}$$

for all integers n. This function has the following properties:

(E1) $a^n a^m = a^{n+m}$

(E2) $\dfrac{a^n}{a^m} = a^{n-m}$

(E3) $[a^n]^m = a^{nm}$.

Properties (E1)–(E3) hold for all integers n and m. Proofs of these properties are direct applications of the above definitions. For example, to prove property (E1), we note that

$$a^n a^m = \overbrace{a \cdot a \cdot a \cdots a}^{n \text{ factors}} \cdot \overbrace{a \cdot a \cdot a \cdots a}^{m \text{ factors}}$$

$$= \overbrace{a \cdot a \cdot a \cdot \ldots \cdot a}^{(n+m) \text{ factors}}$$

$$= a^{n+m}.$$

Figure 1.1 shows the graph of the exponential function $f(n) = 2^n$.

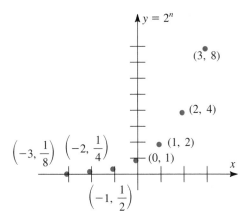

Figure 1.1 Graph of $f(n) = 2^n$ for n an integer.

We have already seen in Chapter 1 that the domain of the exponential function $f(n) = a^n$ can be extended to include rational numbers. We do so in two steps.

(i) We define the nth root function by saying that

$$a^{1/n} = y \quad \text{means} \quad a = y^n. \tag{2}$$

For example, $9^{1/2} = 3$ since $3^2 = 9$, and $(-8)^{1/3} = -2$ since $(-2)^3 = -8$. (Recall, however, that we must require $a > 0$ if n is even. That is, even roots of negative numbers are not defined.)

(ii) Then, we use composition of functions to define the exponential function for rational exponents by saying that

$$a^{n/m} \quad \text{means} \quad (a^{1/m})^n. \tag{3}$$

For example, $8^{2/3} = (8^{1/3})^2 = 2^2 = 4$, and $(-27)^{4/3} = [(-27)^{1/3}]^4 = (-3)^4 = 81$. (Again, we must require that $a > 0$ if the denominator m of the exponent is even.)

Equations (2) and (3) together allow us to define the exponential function $f(x) = a^x$ for all rational numbers x when $a > 0$. Using these definitions, we can show that properties (E1)–(E3) hold for rational exponents. The following example shows how these properties are used.

☐ **EXAMPLE 2**

According to the above definitions and properties (E1)–(E3), we have:

(i) $2^5 = 2 \cdot 2 \cdot 2 \cdot 2 \cdot 2 = 32$.

(ii) $\dfrac{3^2}{3^5} = 3^{2-5} = 3^{-3} = \dfrac{1}{3^3} = \dfrac{1}{27}$.

(iii) $27^{1/3} = 3$ since $3^3 = 27$.

(iv) $64^{-5/6} = 1/(64^{1/6})^5 = \dfrac{1}{2^5} = \dfrac{1}{32}$. ∎

Graphs of Exponential Functions

Figure 1.2 shows the graph of $f(x) = 2^x$. Figure 1.3 shows the graph of the exponential functions $f(x) = 3^x$ and $g(x) = -2^x$. Compare these graphs with those of Figure 1.4 for the functions $f(x) = 2^{-x}$ and $g(x) = 10^x$.

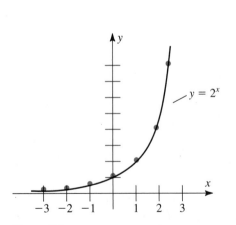

Figure 1.2 Graph of $f(x) = 2^x$ for x rational.

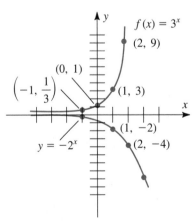

Figure 1.3 Graphs of $f(x) = 3^x$ and $g(x) = -2^x$.

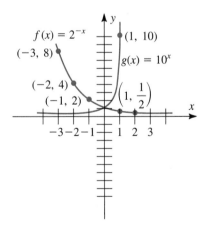

Figure 1.4 Graphs of $f(x) = 2^{-x}$ and $g(x) = 10^x$.

Irrational Exponents

Although the graphs of the exponential functions in Figures 1.2–1.4 suggest that these functions have been defined for all x, this is not the case, because we have defined the expression a^x only when x is a rational number. Thus when x is an irrational number, such as $\sqrt{2}$ or π, the expression a^x is as yet undefined.

Since, for $a > 0$, we would like our exponential functions $f(x) = a^x$ to be not only defined but also continuous and differentiable for all values of x, we wish to extend the domain of our exponential functions to include all real numbers, both irrational and rational. We shall do so here quite informally by saying that we define the values of $f(x) = a^x$ for x irrational "by continuity" from the values of $f(x) = a^x$ for x rational. That is, if x_0 is an irrational number, we define $f(x_0) = a^{x_0}$ to be the number that makes $f(x) = a^x$ continuous at x_0 given the values of a^x for x rational. Geometrically, this simply says that we draw the graph of $f(x) = a^x$ by sketching a smooth curve through the points (x, a^x) for x rational, thus producing the values of a^x for x irrational "by continuity."

More advanced mathematical texts present a formal extension of the domain of the exponential function $f(x) = a^x$ to irrational numbers. We shall not pursue such formalities here. Rather, we shall henceforth assume that, for $a > 0$, the exponential function $f(x) = a^x$ is defined, continuous, and differentiable for all values of x.

Compound Interest: An Application of Exponential Functions

As we have seen, exponential functions occur naturally in formulas for the periodic compounding of interest. For example, if an annual rate of interest of r percent is applied to a principal amount P_0 placed in a savings account, the amount $P(1)$ on deposit at the end of 1 year is

$$P(1) = P_0 + rP_0$$

where P_0 is the original deposit and rP_0 is the interest

$$= (1 + r)P_0.$$

At the end of the second year the interest rate is again applied to this amount, giving a total $P(2)$ on deposit after 2 years of

$$P(2) = (1 + r)P_0 + r[(1 + r)P_0]$$

where $(1+r)P_0$ is the amount on deposit after 1 year and $r[(1+r)P_0]$ is the interest

$$= (1 + r)[(1 + r)P_0]$$
$$= (1 + r)^2 P_0.$$

Continuing in this manner, we find that the amount on deposit after 3 years is

$$P(3) = (1 + r)^2 P_0 + r[(1 + r)^2 P_0]$$
$$= (1 + r)^3 P_0$$

and, after n years, the amount on deposit is

$$P(n) = (1 + r)^n P_0. \tag{4}$$

Equation (4) involves the exponential function $f(n) = a^n$ with $a = (1 + r)$.

□ **EXAMPLE 3**

Sarah deposits $100 in a savings account that pays 8% interest compounded annually. No additional deposits or withdrawals are made. Find the amount in this account after 1, 2, and 4 years.

Solution: With $r = 0.08$, equation (4) gives

$$P(1) = (1.08)(100) = \$108$$
$$P(2) = (1.08)^2(100) = \$116.64$$
$$P(4) = (1.08)^4(100) = \$136.05.$$ ■

More Frequent Compounding of Interest

If a *nominal* interest rate r is used by a bank that compounds interest k times per year, rather than once per year, this means that on each of k days equally spaced throughout the year an interest payment of $\dfrac{r}{k}$ percent is added to the current balance in an account. Thus if interest is compounded semiannually ($k = 2$), at the end of 6 months $\left(\dfrac{1}{2} \text{ year}\right)$ an original deposit of P_0 dollars will have grown to

$$P\left(\frac{1}{2}\right) = \left(1 + \frac{r}{2}\right)P_0 \text{ dollars}$$

and at the end of the first year the balance in the account will be

$$P(1) = \left(1 + \frac{r}{2}\right)P\left(\frac{1}{2}\right) = \left(1 + \frac{r}{2}\right)\left[\left(1 + \frac{r}{2}\right)P_0\right] = \left(1 + \frac{r}{2}\right)^2 P_0 \text{ dollars.}$$

Similarly, if interest is compounded quarterly ($k = 4$), the balances on deposit at the end of the four quarters of the first year would be

$$P\left(\frac{1}{4}\right) = \left(1 + \frac{r}{4}\right)P_0$$

$$P\left(\frac{1}{2}\right) = \left(1 + \frac{r}{4}\right)^2 P_0$$

$$P\left(\frac{3}{4}\right) = \left(1 + \frac{r}{4}\right)^3 P_0$$

$$P(1) = \left(1 + \frac{r}{4}\right)^4 P_0.$$

In general, it follows that compounding k times per year at a nominal interest rate r gives an amount on deposit at the end of one year of

$$P(1) = \left(1 + \frac{r}{k}\right)^k P_0. \tag{5}$$

☐ **EXAMPLE 4**

If Sarah, in Example 3, deposited the $100 in a savings account paying 8% interest *compounded quarterly,* the amounts on deposit after 3, 6, 9, and 12 months would be as follows:

(a) Amount after 3 months (one quarter):

$$P\left(\frac{1}{4}\right) = \left(1 + \frac{0.08}{4}\right)(100) = \$102.$$

(b) Amount after 6 months (two quarters):

$$P\left(\frac{1}{2}\right) = \left(1 + \frac{0.08}{4}\right)P\left(\frac{1}{4}\right)$$
$$= \left(1 + \frac{0.08}{4}\right)^2 (100) = \$104.04.$$

(c) Amount after 9 months (three quarters):

$$P\left(\frac{3}{4}\right) = \left(1 + \frac{0.08}{4}\right)^3 (100) = \$106.12.$$

(d) Amount after 12 months (four quarters):

$$P(1) = \left(1 + \frac{0.08}{4}\right)^4 (100) = \$108.24.$$

(Part (d) can be calculated directly from equation (5) with $r = 0.08$, $k = 4$.) The quarterly compounding outperforms annual compounding in the first year by 24¢!

■

Applying equation (5), we find that the amount on deposit after 2 years of compounding k times per year is

$$P(2) = \underbrace{\left(1 + \frac{r}{k}\right)^k}_{} \underbrace{\left[\left(1 + \frac{r}{k}\right)^k P_0\right]}_{}$$

——— amount on deposit after 1 year

——— annual compounding factor from equation (6)

$$= \left(1 + \frac{r}{k}\right)^{2k} P_0$$

and more generally, the amount on deposit after n years is

$$P(n) = \left(1 + \frac{r}{k}\right)^{nk} P_0. \qquad (6)$$

By experimenting with various values of k using a calculator or a computer, you can obtain results such as those in Table 1.1. Notice that the amount $P(1)$ increases as k increases, but that the rate at which $P(1)$ increases seems to slow considerably as k increases. This raises the question of whether there exists a "limiting value" for $P(1)$ as the number of compoundings per year becomes infinitely large.

Table 1.1 Annual Growth Due to Interest Using Program 3, Appendix I.

k = Number of Compoundings per Year		$P(1) = \left(1 + \dfrac{r}{k}\right)^k P_0$ = Amount on Deposit After One Year ($P_0 = 100$, $r = 0.08$)
$k = 1$	(annual)	108.00
$k = 2$	(semiannual)	108.16
$k = 4$	(quarterly)	108.24
$k = 12$	(monthly)	108.30
$k = 365$	(daily)	108.33

Generalizing to Infinitely Many Compoundings

If we were to allow the number of compoundings in equation (6) to become infinite, we would find the amount $P(1)$ on deposit after one year to be

$$P(1) = \lim_{k \to \infty} \left(1 + \frac{r}{k}\right)^k P_0. \tag{7}$$

To analyze the limit in equation (7), we let $x = \dfrac{k}{r}$. Then x is a rational number with the property that $x \to \infty$ as $k \to \infty$ because r is fixed. We can write

$$P(1) = \lim_{k \to \infty} \left(1 + \frac{r}{k}\right)^k P_0$$

$$= \lim_{k \to \infty} \left(1 + \frac{r}{k}\right)^{(k/r)r} P_0 \qquad \left[\left(\frac{k}{r}\right)r = k\right]$$

$$= \lim_{x \to \infty} \left[\left(1 + \frac{1}{x}\right)^x\right]^r P_0 \qquad \left[x = \frac{k}{r}\right]. \tag{8}$$

The Number e

We now pause for a moment to study the limit

$$\lim_{x \to \infty} \left(1 + \frac{1}{x}\right)^x, \qquad x \text{ rational}$$

in line (8). By using a calculator or a computer, you can examine values of the expression $\left(1 + \dfrac{1}{x}\right)^x$ for large numbers x. Table 1.2 shows the results of doing so, for several choices for x.

Table 1.2 Approximation to $\lim_{x \to \infty} \left(1 + \dfrac{1}{x}\right)^x$, Using Program 2, Appendix I.

x	$\left(1 + \dfrac{1}{x}\right)^x$
10	2.593742
20	2.653297
100	2.704813
200	2.711517
1000	2.716925
2000	2.717603
10,000	2.718146

As suggested by these numerical "experiments," this limit does exist. In fact, it is a famous number in mathematics, called "e," and its first 12 digits are as follows:

$$e = \lim_{x \to \infty} \left(1 + \frac{1}{x}\right)^x \approx 2.71828182845. \tag{9}$$

As with any real number, we can use e as a base for defining the exponential function $f(x) = e^x$. Values of this function have been calculated to great precision. Good approximations to these values are contained in Table 1 in Appendix II and can be obtained from most calculators and computers.

Using the approximation in line (9), we can plot values of the exponential function for various rational exponents and sketch the graph as in Figure 1.5. Later in this chapter, and throughout the remainder of this book, we shall encounter many applications of the exponential function.

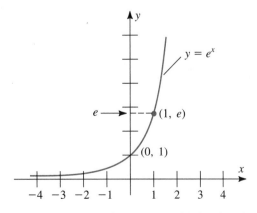

Figure 1.5 Graph of the exponential function $f(x) = e^x$.

Continuous Compounding of Interest

Using the definition of e in line (9), we may now return to equation (7) and allow the number of compoundings of interest to become infinite. We obtain

$$P(1) = \lim_{k \to \infty} \left(1 + \frac{r}{k}\right)^k P_0 \qquad \text{(equation (7))}$$

$$= \lim_{x \to \infty} \left[\left(1 + \frac{1}{x}\right)^x\right]^r P_0 \qquad \text{(equation (8))}$$

$$= e^r \cdot P_0. \qquad \text{(by equation (9))} \qquad (10)$$

That is, the amount on deposit after 1 year, under "infinitely many" compoundings, is just the value of the exponential function $P(1) = e^r P_0$. Such compounding is called "continuous" compounding of interest, reflecting the notion that interest is being compounded at each instant of time.

Extending this result, we find that the amount $P(2)$ on deposit after 2 years resulting from continuous compounding of interest at a nominal rate of r percent on an initial deposit of P_0 dollars would be

$$P(2) = e^r[e^r P_0]$$

— amount $P(1)$ on deposit after 1 year

— annual compounding factor from equation (10)

$$= e^{2r} P_0$$

and, in general, that the amount on deposit after t years will be

$$P(t) = e^{rt} P_0. \qquad (11)$$

Equation (11) is the formula used by banks and other institutions in calculating the value of an initial investment of P_0 dollars compounded continuously at a nominal rate of interest of r percent for a period of t years.

□ **EXAMPLE 5**

Find the amount that Sarah will have on deposit 5 years after making a single deposit of $1000 in a savings account paying 8% nominal interest if interest is compounded:

(a) quarterly
(b) continuously.

Solution

(a) Under quarterly compounding of interest we have $k = 4$ compoundings per year. Using equation (6) with $r = 0.08$, $n = 5$, and $P_0 = 1000$, we obtain

$$P(5) = \left(1 + \frac{0.08}{4}\right)^{5 \cdot 4} (1000)$$

$$= (1.02)^{20}(1000)$$

$$= \$1485.95.$$

(The last step requires use of a calculator or computer to evaluate the expression a^x with $a = 1.02$ and $x = 20$, in order to avoid a very lengthy calculation.)

(b) Under continuous compounding of interest we apply equation (11) with $t = 5$, $r = 0.08$, and $P_0 = 1000$ to obtain

$$\begin{aligned} P(5) &= e^{5(0.08)}(1000) \\ &= 1000e^{0.4} \\ &= 1000(1.49182) \\ &= \$1491.82. \end{aligned}$$

(The value $e^{0.4} \approx 1.49182$ was obtained from the table of values for e^x in Appendix II.)

Note in this example that continuous compounding of interest produced a yield $\$1491.82 - \$1485.95 = \$5.87$ larger than quarterly compounding of interest. ∎

Present Value

The concept of compound interest is used to answer the question, "How much will I have later if I deposit a specified amount now?" The concept of *present value* answers the opposite question: "How much do I need to have *now* in order that it will grow, under compounding of interest, to a specified amount at a specified later time?"

☐ **EXAMPLE 6**

Under annual compounding of interest at 5%:

(a) The value of a deposit of \$1000 *after one year* is

$$P(1) = \$1000 + (\$1000)(0.05) = \$1050.$$

(b) The *present value* of a single payment of \$1000 to be made one year in the future is the amount P_0 that satisfies the equation

$$P_0 + (0.05)P_0 = 1000$$

Thus $(1.05)P_0 = 1000$ so $P_0 = \dfrac{1000}{1.05} = 958.38$.

This shows that having \$958.38 on hand today will guarantee, under annual compounding of interest at 5%, that \$1000 will be available 1 year from now. ∎

From equation (11) for continuous compounding of interest, we can see, by multiplying both sides of the equation by e^{-rt}, that the equation for the *present value* P_0 of an amount $P(t)$ in t years, under continuous compounding of interest at the rate r (in decimal form) is

$$P_0 = e^{-rt}P(t) = \frac{P(t)}{e^{rt}}. \tag{12}$$

□ **EXAMPLE 7**

Roger receives an inheritance and wishes to create a trust fund that will provide $50,000 for his nephew's education. If this amount is intended to be available in 10 years, what amount will Roger need to deposit now, under continuous compounding of interest at rate 8%, in order that the value of his account will have grown to $50,000 in 10 years?

Solution: This question involves the concept of present value. We need to find the present value of an amount $P(t) = 50,000$ that will be available in $n = 10$ years under continuous compounding at rate $r = 0.08$. Using equation (12), we determine this to be

$$P_0 = e^{-(0.08)(10)}(50,000) = e^{-0.8}(50,000) \approx (0.45)(50,000) = \$22,500. \quad ■$$

☑ **PRACTICE PROBLEMS 4.1**

1. Paul, a high school sophomore, inherits $1000 that his parents urge him to place in a savings account for later use in college. The available accounts pay 6% interest. Find the amount on deposit, assuming all interest payments are added to the principal, after 3 years under
   a. annual compounding,
   b. quarterly compounding,
   c. monthly compounding, and
   d. continuous compounding.
2. What rate of interest is required for annual compounding to achieve the same result after one year as continuous compounding at a nominal rate of 6%?

Exercise Set 4.1

1. Simplify the following expressions.
   a. $9^{3/2}$ **b.** $16^{1/4}$
   c. $49^{3/2}$ **d.** $4^{-3/2}$

2. Simplify the following expressions.
   a. $36^{-3/2}$ **b.** $81^{-3/4}$
   c. $8^{5/3}$ **d.** $125^{-2/3}$

3. Simplify the following expressions.
   a. $\left(\frac{1}{4}\right)^{3/2}$ **b.** $\left(\frac{27}{8}\right)^{2/3}$
   c. $\left(\frac{1}{16}\right)^{-3/4}$ **d.** $\left(\frac{81}{36}\right)^{-3/2}$

In Exercises 4–11, sketch the graph of the given exponential function.

4. $f(x) = 2^x$
5. $f(x) = 3^{-x}$
6. $f(x) = \left(\frac{1}{2}\right)^x$
7. $f(x) = 10^{-x}$

8. $f(x) = 2^{2x}$
9. $f(x) = e^{-x}$
10. $f(x) = -2e^x$
11. $f(x) = -3e^{-x}$

In Exercises 12–21, use properties (E1)–(E3) of exponents to simplify the given expression.

12. $2^3 \cdot 4^{-2}$
13. $\dfrac{27^{4/3} \cdot 4^3}{9^{3/2} \cdot 32}$
14. $\dfrac{3^{-6} \cdot 3^5}{3^2}$
15. $\dfrac{(2^3 \cdot 3^{-2})^2}{\frac{1}{3}(8)}$
16. $e^2 e^{-2}$
17. $e^3 \cdot e^x$
18. $\dfrac{e^3 e^{-2x}}{e^{-x}}$
19. $\sqrt{16e^{4x}}$
20. $(27e^{-6}e^{3x})^{1/3}$
21. $\dfrac{(4e^{3x})^{2/3}}{\sqrt{8e^4}}$

22. What if Paul, the high school sophomore in Practice Problem 1, were able to find a bank paying 10% nominal interest rather than 6%? Find the value of his investment, assuming all interest payments to be credited to his account, under
    a. annual compounding,
    b. semiannual compounding,
    c. quarterly compounding, and
    d. continuous compounding of interest.

23. During the summer, Pam earned $500 by caring for her younger brother while her parents were at work. Rather than pay her cash, however, her parents promised to pay her in the future an amount determined by what the $500 would earn if placed in a savings account paying 8% annual interest, compounded semiannually. How much will Pam receive, under these terms, if the debt is paid
    a. after 1 year?
    b. after 2 years?
    c. in 18 months?

24. Find the payments provided in Exercise 23 if interest is compounded continuously rather than semiannually.

25. A *zero coupon bond* is a bond that pays its face amount at the stated maturity date with no dividends at any time. Thus zero coupon bonds sell at a discount from the face value, depending on what their present value is believed to be. Find the present value of a zero coupon bond with a face amount of $1000 and a maturity date 4 years hence, assuming continuous compounding of interest at the nominal rate $r = 10\%$.

26. Carol wishes to guarantee that she will have $20,000 available in 10 years to supplement her mother's retirement fund. She will accomplish this by purchasing a zero coupon bond with a face amount of $20,000 maturing in 10 years. If she believes that the prevailing interest rate, compounded continuously, during this period will be 8%, what should she expect to pay for the bond? (See Exercise 25.)

27. Paul has a trust that will pay him $10,000 in 5 years. What is the present value of this trust, assuming continuous compounding of interest at rate $r = 8\%$?

28. What is the present value of a zero coupon bond with a face amount of $5000 and a maturity period of 5 years if the rate of interest, compounded continuously, is assumed to be $r = 6\%$? (See Exercise 25.)

29. What is the value of $10,000 after 7 years of continuous compounding at the rate $r = 7\%$?

30. Use the result of Exercise 29 and equation (11) to explain the sayings: "Money doubles in 7 years at 10%; it doubles in 10 years at 7%."

31. Paul asks you for a loan, saying that he has a trust fund that will pay $10,000 to him in 6 years. He is desperate for you to loan him as much as possible, and you want to help him by lending him the full "fair" amount that is possible. If he agrees to deed to you his entire trust fund, and if you believe the prevailing rate of interest for the next 6 years will be 5%, how much should you lend him today in exchange for ownership of the trust?

32. A case of wine is offered for sale. You are told that the wine will be worth $20 per bottle when it is ready for drinking in 6 years. What is the present value of the case (12 bottles) under the assumption of continuous compounding of interest
    a. at the rate $r = 4\%$?
    b. at the rate $r = 7\%$?

33. What rate of interest, compounded continuously, will produce an *effective annual yield* of 8%? (Effective annual yield is the rate required under *annual* compounding of interest to obtain the specified yield. *Hint:* Do this by trial and error using a calculator.)

34. What is the present value of an investment that will be worth $1000 5 years from now if the prevailing rate of interest, compounded continuously, is 10%?

35. Find the effective annual yield (see Exercise 33) on
    a. an interest rate of 10% compounded semiannually.
    b. an interest rate of 10% compounded continuously.

✓ **SOLUTIONS TO PRACTICE PROBLEMS 4.1**

1. Using equation (6) with $P_0 = 1000$ and $r = 0.06$:
   a. With $k = 1$ and $n = 3$, we have

$$P(3) = (1 + 0.06)^3(1000) = \$1191.02.$$

b. With $k = 4$ and $n = 3$, we obtain

$$P(3) = \left(1 + \frac{0.06}{4}\right)^{3 \cdot 4} (1000) = \$1195.62.$$

c. With $k = 12$ and $n = 3$, we obtain

$$P(3) = \left(1 + \frac{0.06}{12}\right)^{3 \cdot 12} (1000) = \$1196.68$$

For continuous compounding we use a calculator or Table 1 in the Appendix and equation (11) to find

d. $P(3) = e^{3(0.06)}(1000) = \$1197.22.$

2. Compounding continuously for 1 year gives

$$P(1) = e^{(0.06)(1)}(1000) = \$1061.84.$$

The interest rate required to produce this result under one annual compounding is $r = 6.184\%$.

4.2 Logarithm Functions

In many applied problems we will need to solve equations of the form $e^x = C$ where the constant C is given and the exponent x is to be found. This involves the concept of the *logarithm.*

Before addressing the situation concerning the exponential function with base e, we recall the notion of *common logarithm* from precalculus mathematics: The number x that satisfies the equation $10^x = C$ is called the common logarithm of C, because it is the power to which the "base" 10 must be raised to obtain C.

Common logarithms are written with the notation "log." Thus, we can write:

$$\log 100 = 2 \qquad \text{since} \qquad 10^2 = 100;$$
$$\log 1000 = 3 \qquad \text{since} \qquad 10^3 = 1000;$$

and

$$\log (0.01) = -2 \qquad \text{since} \qquad 10^{-2} = 0.01.$$

Logarithms can be defined for bases other than 10 (or e) as the following definition provides.

If b and y are positive numbers, we define the **logarithm of y to the base b** by the statement

$$\log_b y = x \qquad \text{if and only if} \qquad y = b^x. \tag{1}$$

Thus

$$\log_2 8 \quad = 3 \qquad \text{since} \qquad 2^3 = 8$$

and

$$\log_{27} 3 \quad = \frac{1}{3} \qquad \text{since} \qquad 27^{1/3} = 3.$$

In other words, $\log_b y$ is just the *exponent* that we must apply to the *base b* in order to obtain y.

For any base b we say that the logarithm function $g(y) = \log_b y$ is the *inverse* of the exponential function $f(x) = b^x$, because if $y = b^x$ then $x = \log_b y$ and vice versa. That is, the logarithm function reverses the effect of the exponential function and vice versa, as illustrated in Figure 2.1.

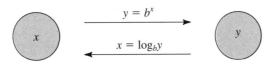

Figure 2.1 The logarithm function $x = \log_b y$ is the inverse of the function $y = b^x$.

Two important identities summarize the fact that the logarithm and exponential functions are inverses of each other:

$$\log_b(b^y) = y, \qquad b^{\log_b x} = x. \tag{2}$$

☐ **EXAMPLE 1**

Here are some values of various logarithm functions.

$$
\begin{array}{llll}
\log_2 16 & = 4 & \text{since} & 2^4 = 16 \\
\log_5 25 & = 2 & \text{since} & 5^2 = 25 \\
\log_{81} 3 & = \dfrac{1}{4} & \text{since} & 81^{1/4} = 3 \\
\log_2\left(\dfrac{1}{8}\right) & = -3 & \text{since} & 2^{-3} = \dfrac{1}{8} \\
\log_{16}\left(\dfrac{1}{4}\right) & = -\dfrac{1}{2} & \text{since} & 16^{-1/2} = \dfrac{1}{4}.
\end{array}
$$

∎

☐ **EXAMPLE 2**

The Beer–Lambert law relates the absorption of light traveling in a material to the concentration and thickness of the material. If I_0 and I denote the intensities of light of a particular wavelength before and after passing through the material, respectively, and if x denotes the length of the path followed by the beam of light passing through the material, then

$$\log_{10}\left(\frac{I}{I_0}\right) = kx$$

where k is a constant depending on the material. To express I as a function of x, we use equation (1):

$$\log_{10}\left(\frac{I}{I_0}\right) = kx \qquad \text{if and only if} \qquad 10^{kx} = \frac{I}{I_0}.$$

Thus $I = I_0 \cdot 10^{kx}$. ∎

Figure 2.2 shows the graphs of the functions $f(x) = 2^x$ and $g(x) = \log_2 x$. Since the graph of $f(x) = 2^x$ consists of points of the form (x, y) with $y = 2^x$, the graph of $g(x) = \log_2 x$ consists of points of the form $(y, x) = (2^x, x)$. That is, the graph of $g(x) = \log_2 x$ is obtained from the graph of $f(x) = 2^x$ by interchanging x- and y-coordinates, or by *reflecting* the graph of $f(x) = 2^x$ about the line $y = x$. (Note that since the exponential function b^x can have only positive values, $\log_b x$ is defined only for positive numbers.)

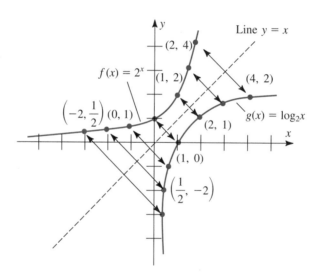

Figure 2.2 Graphs of $f(x) = 2^x$ and $g(x) = \log_2 x$.

Properties of Logarithms

Logarithms have three algebraic properties that are due to properties (E1)–(E3) of exponential functions. Here x, y, and b are positive numbers and r is any real number:

$$\text{(L1)} \qquad \log_b(xy) = \log_b x + \log_b y$$

$$\text{(L2)} \qquad \log_b\left(\frac{x}{y}\right) = \log_b x - \log_b y$$

$$\text{(L3)} \qquad \log_b x^r = r \log_b x.$$

Proofs of these properties follow from properties (E1)–(E3) for exponential functions. (See Exercises 37–39.)

☐ **EXAMPLE 3**

Simplify the following expressions.

(a) $\log_2\left(\dfrac{16}{4^x}\right)$ (b) $\log_3(x^2 \cdot 3^x)$

Strategy · · · · · · · ·

Apply property (L2),
property (L3),
and equation (1).

Apply property (L1),
property (L3), and equation (2).

Solution

(a) $\log_2\left(\dfrac{16}{4^x}\right) = \log_2 16 - \log_2 4^x$

$\qquad\qquad = 4 - x\log_2 4$

$\qquad\qquad = 4 - 2x.$

(b) $\log_3(x^2 \cdot 3^x) = \log_3 x^2 + \log_3 3^x$

$\qquad\qquad = 2\log_3 x + x.$ ∎

Common Logarithms vs. Natural Logarithms

Common logarithms once played an important role in mathematics and engineering. This was due to properties (L1)–(L3), which allowed multiplications and divisions involving very large or very small numbers to be carried out as additions or subtractions. The development of modern calculating devices has all but eliminated this role for the logarithm function. However, the *natural* logarithm function, which is the logarithm to the base e, plays an important role in modelling various phenomena that are characterized by certain *rates of growth.*

We shall address the applications of the natural logarithm function in Section 4.5, after we have determined its derivative and related properties.

Definition 1

The natural logarithm function, $y = \ln x$, is the logarithm function with base e. That is,

$$\ln x = \log_e x, \qquad x > 0.$$

It is important to note that the natural logarithm function satisfies properties (L1)–(L3) of logarithms, even though the abbreviated notation $\ln x$ does not display the base e. For the natural logarithm function, equation (1) becomes

$$\ln y = x \qquad \text{if and only if} \qquad y = e^x. \tag{3}$$

and the identities in equation (2) become

$$\ln(e^x) = x \qquad \text{and} \qquad e^{\ln x} = x. \tag{4}$$

The following example illustrates how the natural logarithm function is useful in simplifying expressions involving the exponential function. (Values of the natural logarithm function are listed in Appendix II and may be obtained on most hand calculators.)

◻ **EXAMPLE 4**

Solve the equation $e^{x+3} = 1$.

Solution: Taking the natural logarithm of both sides gives

$$\ln(e^{x+3}) = \ln(1).$$

Using the first identity in equation (4), we may simplify the left-hand side as

$$\ln(e^{x+3}) = x + 3.$$

Since $e^0 = 1$, we must have $\ln(1) = 0$ by equation (3). Thus, we obtain

$$x + 3 = 0, \quad \text{or} \quad x = -3. \qquad ■$$

Fitting Exponential Models to Data

In many applied settings, mathematical models for functions of interest involve the (natural) exponential function $y = Ce^{kt}$ where C and k are constants. "Fitting" this exponential model to the given information about the particular application involves substituting the given data and using the natural logarithm function to determine the constants C and k. The following example is typical of this step. A number of the particular applications of exponential models are discussed later in the chapter.

◻ **EXAMPLE 5**

Environmentalists estimate that approximately 6 million hectares (a hectare is 10,000 square meters, or about 2.5 acres) of land were reforested (planted with new trees) worldwide in 1990; they predict that 17 million acres will be reforested in the year 2000. Assume that the trend in reforestation follows the exponential model

$$N(t) = Ce^{kt}.$$

(a) Find the constants C and k.
(b) Find the number of hectares, according to this model, that will be reforested in the year 2010.

Solution

(a) Using t to represent time beginning in year 1990, the given data may be organized as follows:

t = Years after 1990	$N(t)$ = Acres Reforested
0	6
10	17

Substituting $t = 0$ and $N(0) = 6$ into the expression $N(t) = Ce^{kt}$ gives the result

$$6 = N(0) = Ce^{k \cdot 0} = Ce^0 = C$$

so

$$C = 6.$$

Then, using this value for C and the data $N(0) = 17$, we obtain

$$17 = 6e^{k \cdot 10} = 6e^{10k}.$$

Thus,

$$e^{10k} = \frac{17}{6}.$$

Taking the natural logarithms of both sides and using equation (4) now gives

$$\ln(e^{10k}) = 10k = \ln\left(\frac{17}{6}\right) \approx 1.04.$$

Thus,

$$k \approx \left(\frac{1}{10}\right)(1.04) = 0.104.$$

(b) With these values for C and k, the model predicts the number of hectares to be reforested in the year 2010 ($t = 20$) as

$$N(20) = 6e^{20(0.104)} = 6e^{2.08} = (6)(8) = 48$$

million hectares. (While this result is valid *mathematically,* its validity as a prediction depends on whether the given model turns out accurately to describe the rate of reforestation worldwide during the period in question.) ■

□ **EXAMPLE 6**

Scientists who study human growth often model human body parameters, such as length, by functions involving polynomials and logarithmic and exponential functions. One such example would be

$$f(t) = a + 3t + 4e^{bt}$$

where a and b are constants. For this function, find a and b if it is known that

$$f(0) = 9 \quad \text{and} \quad f(2) = 23.$$

Solution: Substituting $t = 0$ in the equation for f and using the given information that $f(0) = 9$ gives

$$\begin{aligned}
f(0) &= a + (3)(0) + 4e^{(b)(0)} \\
&= a + 4 \\
&= 9
\end{aligned}$$

so

$$a = 5.$$

Next, with $a = 5$ we substitute $t = 2$ in the equation for f and use the fact that $f(2) = 23$ to obtain

$$\begin{aligned}
f(2) &= 5 + (3)(2) + 4e^{2b} \\
&= 11 + 4e^{2b} \\
&= 23
\end{aligned}$$

so

$$4e^{2b} = 12$$

or

$$e^{2b} = 3.$$

To solve for b, we take natural logarithms of both sides and apply equation (4):

$$\ln (e^{2b}) = \ln 3$$
$$2b = \ln 3$$
$$b = \frac{1}{2} \ln 3 \cong 0.54930.$$

∎

Effective Annual Yields on Investments

The comparison between interest compounded annually and continuous compounding of interest provides excellent insight into the practical effect of the exponential and logarithm functions being inverses of each other.

For interest computed on any basis other than annually, the *effective annual yield* of the interest scheme is the rate r_A required to produce the same total interest in 1 year by a single compounding. For example, an interest rate of 10% compounded semiannually has an effective annual yield of 10.25%, because it produces a total on deposit after 1 year of $P(1) = \left(1 + \dfrac{0.10}{2}\right)^2 P_0 = (1.1025)P_0$ (equation (5), Section 4.1).

□ **EXAMPLE 7**

Find the effective annual yield on a savings account paying a nominal interest rate of $r = 8\%$ compounded continuously.

Solution: At the end of 1 year, an initial deposit of P_0 dollars grows under continuous compounding of interest, to the amount

$$P(1) = e^{(0.08)(1)}P_0$$
$$= (1.083287)P_0. \qquad \text{(equation (11), Section 4.1)}$$

This is the same as a single compounding by the rate $r_A = 8.3287\%$, which is the effective annual yield. ∎

The next example asks the opposite question, and requires the use of the *inverse* of the exponential function.

□ **EXAMPLE 8**

Find the rate of interest that, when compounded continuously, produces an effective annual yield of 10%.

Solution: The effective annual yield of 10% on an investment of P dollars is just 110% of P, or $(1.1)P$ dollars. Continuous compounding of P dollars for 1 year at r

percent interest produces the amount $e^{1r}P = e^{r}P$. Thus we must solve the equation

$$e^{r}P = (1.1)P$$

for r. Dividing both sides by P gives

$$e^{r} = 1.1.$$

Taking the natural logarithm of both sides of this equation and using the first identity in equation (4) gives

$$\ln(e^{r}) = \ln(1.1)$$

or

$$r = \ln(1.1)$$
$$= 0.09531 \quad \text{(from Table 2, Appendix II).}$$

Thus the rate 9.531%, when compounded continuously, gives an effective annual yield of 10%. ∎

The Natural Exponential Function

Using the natural logarithm function, we can express any exponential b^{x} in the form e^{ax} for some constant a. To do so, we begin with the identity $b = e^{\ln b}$ from equation (4). This gives

$$b^{x} = [e^{\ln b}]^{x} \tag{5}$$
$$= e^{x \ln b}$$

by property (E3) of exponents. Thus $b^{x} = e^{ax}$ with $a = \ln b$. For example

$$2^{x} = e^{x \ln 2}$$
$$10^{x} = e^{x \ln 10}$$

etc. For this reason we shall henceforth work exclusively with exponential functions with base e. These are sometimes referred to as *natural* exponential functions, although we shall simply refer to $f(x) = e^{x}$ as "the" exponential function in what follows.

☑ **PRACTICE PROBLEMS 4.2**

1. Solve the equation

$$e^{x+5} = 75.$$

2. A stock, purchased originally for $40, is sold after 2 years for $48. At what rate, compounded continuously, did the stock appreciate?

Exercise Set 4.2

1. Use the definition of the logarithm $\log_{b} y$ in equation (1) to find the value of each of the following.

   a. $\log_{10} 100$ **d.** $\log_{4} 64$
   b. $\log_{10} 10$ **e.** $\log_{3} 81$
   c. $\log_{2} 16$ **f.** $\ln e^{2}$

2. Use the definition of the logarithm in equation (1) to find the value of each of the following.

   a. $\log_{8} 2$ **d.** $\log_{10}\left(\frac{1}{100}\right)$
   b. $\log_{2} \sqrt{2}$ **e.** $\log_{10}(0.001)$
   c. $\log_{9}\left(\frac{1}{3}\right)$ **f.** $\log_{4}\left(\frac{1}{8}\right)$

3. Use Table 2, Appendix II, where necessary, to find the value of the following natural logarithms.

a. $\ln e$ **d.** $\ln(0.3)$

b. $\ln 1$ **e.** $\ln(e^3)$

c. $\ln(2.2)$ **f.** $\ln\left(\dfrac{1}{e^2}\right)$

4. Complete the following steps to establish the formulas

$$\log_a x = \frac{\ln x}{\ln a} \qquad \text{and} \qquad \ln x = (\ln a)\log_a x$$

for converting natural logarithms to logarithms to the base a and vice versa.

a. Let $y = \log_a x$. Explain why $x = a^y$ follows.

b. Take natural logs of both sides of the equation $x = a^y$ to show that

$$\ln x = \ln(a^y) = y \ln a.$$

c. Solve the equation in part b for y to obtain

$$y = \frac{\ln x}{\ln a}.$$

d. Use part a to show that both formulas follow from part c.

5. Use the formulas in Exercise 4 to find formulas for converting between common and natural logarithms:

$$\log_{10} x = \frac{\ln x}{\ln 10} \qquad \text{and} \qquad \ln x = (\ln 10)\log_{10} x.$$

6. Use the results of Exercises 4 and 5 together with Table 2, Appendix II (or a hand calculator) to find values for the following logarithms.

a. $\log_{10} 5$ **d.** $\log_8 4$

b. $\log_3 8$ **e.** $\log_3 \dfrac{1}{2}$

c. $\log_2 12$ **f.** $\log_4 6$

In Exercises 7–16, use properties of logarithms and exponents to solve for x.

7. $e^x = 1$ **8.** $e^x = 3$

9. $e^{x^2 - 3} = 5$ **10.** $\ln x^2 = 2$

11. $e^{x + \ln x} = 2x$ **12.** $2^{x-2} = 8$

13. $\ln x^2 = 8$ **14.** $e^{x^2 - 2x - 3} = 1$

15. $e^{\ln(2x+3)} = 7$ **16.** $e^{2x} + e^x - 2 = 0$

17. The Antoine equation for the relationship between the vapor pressure P and temperature t of a pure liquid is

$$\log_{10} P = \frac{-A}{t + C} + B$$

where A, B, and C are empirically determined constants and t is in units of degrees centigrade. Use Exercise 4 to rewrite this equation in terms of $\ln P$.

18. Use Exercise 4 and the definition of the natural logarithm to solve the equation in Exercise 17 for P.

19. The selling price p and quantity sold per month x for a certain product are related by the equation $p = 100e^{-x}$. Solve this equation for x as a function of p.

20. Under continuous compounding of interest at a nominal rate r, an initial amount P_0 will grow to the amount $P_T = e^{rT}P_0$ after T years. Use the natural logarithm to show that this equation may be solved for T to give

$$T = \frac{1}{r} \ln\left(\frac{P_T}{P_0}\right).$$

21. Use the result of Exercise 20 to find the number of years required for an initial deposit of $1000 to grow to $1500 under continuous compounding of interest at nominal rate $r = 10\%$.

22. Repeat Exercise 21 with $r = 5\%$.

23. Use the result of Exercise 20 to find the number of years required for an investment to double under continuous compounding at a nominal rate of $r = 10\%$.

24. Suppose that the selling price p and the number x of items that can be sold per month at price p are related by the equation $p(x) = 100e^{-0.02x}$. What price will be required in order to sell 100 items per month?

25. For the price–demand equation in Exercise 24, find the number of items that can be sold per month at price $p = \$50$.

26. For the growth model $f(t) = 10 + 3t + 6\ln t$, find
a. $f(1)$
b. $f(2)$
c. $f(e)$.

27. In the growth model $f(t) = a + b\ln t$ assume that $f(1) = 15$ and $f(e) = 20$. Find a and b.

28. The growth model $f(t) = a + b(1 - e^{2t})$ has the property that $f(0) = 10$ and $f(\ln 2) = 4$. Find the constants a and b.

29. Gerry is in business with his father, an owner of a chain of convenience stores. They buy a particular store for $1 million and sell it 5 years later for $2 million. What is their annual rate of return, compounded continuously, on this investment?

30. Gerry, the businessman in Exercise 29, becomes intrigued with the notion of continuous compounding of interest and he wonders, at the nominal rate of 5%, how long it would take an investment to double, assuming no additions or deletions were made to the principal during the growth period. What is the answer to his question?

31. Sally decides to purchase a vacant lot in a nice area as an investment. She pays $100,000 for it, holds it for 5 years, and then sells it. She tells her friends that she achieved a rate of return of 15% annually, compounded continuously, on the transaction. What was the selling price?

32. Judy, Sally's friend (see Exercise 31) became interested in real estate investing after hearing about Sally's success. She bought another piece of property, held it for 4 years, sold it for $250,000 and claimed a rate of return equal to 12% on an annual basis, compounded continuously. What did Judy pay for the property originally?

33. A college fraternity receives a gift of cash from the estate of an alumnus. The members decide to invest the full amount in a savings account in order to allow it to grow by continuous compounding of interest. What nominal interest rate is required in order that the amount double in 6 years?

34. The population of a small, tropical region increased from 10 million people in 1980 to 16 million in 1990. Assume that the population is growing according to the exponential population model $N(t) = Ce^{kt}$.
a. Find the value of the growth constant, k.
b. Find the predicted population size in the year 2000.

35. Time catches up with Sally (Exercise 31), and the real estate market takes a plunge. The speculative house she constructed in 1990 at a cost of $200,000 takes until 1994 to sell, and it brings a selling price of only $140,000. At what annual rate, compounded continuously, did the house depreciate during this period?

36. True or false? Under continuous compounding of interest, doubling the interest rate will reduce the time required for an investment to double in value by one half. Why?

37. Prove property (L1) of logarithms as follows.
a. Let $u = \log_b x$ and $v = \log_b y$. Then
$$x = b^u \quad \text{and} \quad y = b^v. \quad \text{(Why?)}$$
b. Then $\log_b(xy) = \log_b(b^u b^v) = \log_b b^{u+v} = u + v$. (Why?)
c. Finally, since $u = \log_b x$ and $v = \log_b y$ it follows that $\log_b(xy) = \log_b x + \log_b y$.

38. Prove property (L2) of logarithms using the method of Exercise 37.

39. Prove property (L3) of logarithms using the method of Exercise 37.

☑ **SOLUTIONS TO PRACTICE PROBLEMS 4.2**

1. Taking natural logarithms of both sides and using a hand calculator, we obtain
$$\ln(e^{x+5}) = \ln 75$$
or
$$x + 5 = 4.3175$$
so
$$x = -0.6825.$$

2. We need to find r so that
$$(e^{2r})(40) = 48.$$
Thus
$$e^{2r} = \frac{48}{40}$$
so
$$\ln(e^{2r}) = \ln\left(\frac{48}{40}\right)$$

or

$$2r = 0.1823$$

and

$$r = .0912 = 9.12\%.$$

4.3 Differentiating the Natural Logarithm Function

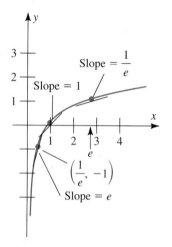

Figure 3.1 Graph of $y = \ln x$ is increasing and concave down for all $x > 0$. Slope decreases as x increases in the domain of $\ln x$.

The natural logarithm function has a very simple derivative, one that is very important in applications. We shall show at the end of the section that it is simply the reciprocal function.

> For $f(x) = \ln x,$ then $f'(x) = \dfrac{1}{x}$ (1)
>
> or, in Leibniz notation,
>
> $$\frac{d}{dx} \ln x = \frac{1}{x}, \qquad x > 0.$$

This result is not all that surprising when we think about the graph of $f(x) = \ln x$ (see Figure 3.1). Recall that the logarithm function $\ln x$ is defined only for $x > 0$, and that its graph rises quickly at first, increasing more slowly as x increases. This property is verified by its derivative $f'(x) = \dfrac{1}{x}$, which measures the slope of the tangents to its graph (see Figure 3.2), because $f'(x) = \dfrac{1}{x}$ is *positive* for all x in the domain of $\ln x$. In the language of Section 3.1, this says that the function $f(x) = \ln x$ is an increasing function for all x.

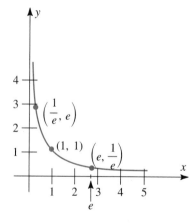

Figure 3.2 Graph of $f'(x) = \dfrac{1}{x}$. This derivative is positive and decreasing for all $x > 0$.

We can say more about the graph of $\ln x$. The second derivative is

$$\frac{d^2}{dx^2}(\ln x) = \frac{d}{dx}\left(\frac{1}{x}\right) = -\frac{1}{x^2}$$

which is negative for all x. Thus, the graph of $y = \ln x$ is concave down for all x in the domain of $\ln x$.

Differentiating Composite Functions

Most logarithm functions that we encounter in applications are actually composite functions of the form $\ln u$ where u is a function of x. When u is differentiable, we can differentiate such functions using equation (1) together with the Chain Rule:

If $\quad f(x) = \ln[u(x)]$, $\qquad$ then $f'(x) = \dfrac{1}{u(x)} \cdot u'(x)$ $\qquad\qquad$ (2)

or, in Leibniz notation,

$$\frac{d}{dx}\ln u = \frac{1}{u} \cdot \frac{du}{dx}.$$

We shall establish the differentiation formula for $\ln x$ at the end of this section. Before doing so, we consider several examples involving equation (2).

☐ **EXAMPLE 1**

For $f(x) = \ln(3x + 5)$ find $f'(x)$.

Solution: Here $f(x) = \ln[u(x)]$ with $u(x) = 3x + 5$. Using equation (2), we obtain

$$f'(x) = \underbrace{\frac{1}{3x + 5}}_{\frac{1}{u(x)}} \cdot \underbrace{3}_{u'(x)} = \frac{3}{3x + 5}.$$

☐ **EXAMPLE 2**

For $f(x) = \ln(3x^{2/3} - 6x^2 + \sqrt{x})$, find $f'(x)$.

Strategy · · · · · · · ·

Here $u(x) = 3x^{2/3} - 6x^2 + \sqrt{x}$.

Use equation (2).

Solution

By equation (2) we have

$$f'(x) = \frac{1}{3x^{2/3} - 6x^2 + \sqrt{x}}\left(2x^{-1/3} - 12x + \frac{1}{2}x^{-1/2}\right)$$

$$= \frac{2x^{-1/3} - 12x + \frac{1}{2}x^{-1/2}}{3x^{2/3} - 6x^2 + \sqrt{x}}.$$

☐ **EXAMPLE 3**

Find $\dfrac{dy}{dx}$ for $y = \sqrt{x+3}\,\ln(4+x^2)$.

Solution: Here we must use the Product Rule. We obtain

$$\frac{dy}{dx} = \left[\frac{d}{dx}(x+3)^{1/2}\right]\ln(4+x^2) + (x+3)^{1/2}\left[\frac{d}{dx}\ln(4+x^2)\right]$$

$$= \frac{1}{2}(x+3)^{-1/2}\ln(4+x^2) + (x+3)^{1/2}\left(\frac{1}{4+x^2}\right)(2x)$$

$$= \frac{\ln(4+x^2)}{2\sqrt{x+3}} + \frac{2x\sqrt{x+3}}{4+x^2}.$$

☐ **EXAMPLE 4**

For $y = \ln(x^2 + 2x + 1)^5$, find $\dfrac{dy}{dx}$.

Solution: This function has the form $y = \ln u$ with $u = (x^2 + 2x + 1)^5$. Since $\dfrac{du}{dx} = 5(x^2 + 2x + 1)^4(2x + 2)$, the derivative of y is

$$\frac{dy}{dx} = \underbrace{\frac{1}{(x^2 + 2x + 1)^5}}_{\dfrac{1}{u}}\underbrace{[5(x^2 + 2x + 1)^4](2x + 2)}_{\dfrac{du}{dx}}$$

$$= \frac{5(2x + 2)}{x^2 + 2x + 1}$$

$$= \frac{10x + 10}{x^2 + 2x + 1}$$

$$= \frac{10(x + 1)}{(x + 1)^2}$$

$$= \frac{10}{x + 1}.$$

☐ **EXAMPLE 5**

For $f(x) = \ln\dfrac{\sqrt{x+3}}{x^2 - x + 2}$, find $f'(x)$.

Solution: Here it simplifies matters to use properties of logarithms to first rewrite $f(x)$ as

$$f(x) = \ln \frac{(x+3)^{1/2}}{(x^2 - x + 2)} = \ln(x+3)^{1/2} - \ln(x^2 - x + 2) \qquad \text{(Property L2)}$$

$$= \frac{1}{2} \ln(x+3) - \ln(x^2 - x + 2). \qquad \text{(Property L3)}$$

Differentiation gives

$$f'(x) = \frac{1}{2}\left(\frac{1}{x+3}\right) - \left(\frac{1}{x^2 - x + 2}\right)(2x - 1)$$

$$= \frac{1}{2x+6} - \frac{2x-1}{x^2 - x + 2}.$$

■

Logarithmic Differentiation

There are two general types of situations in which the derivative of a given function is more easily found by first differentiating the **natural logarithm** of the function and then solving the resulting expression for the desired derivative. This technique is called **logarithmic differentiation.**

The first of these situations involves a function that has the form of a variable base expression raised to a power that is also variable. Examples of such functions are x^x, $(x^2 + 4)^{1/x}$, and so on. Note, in the following example, how the natural logarithm of such a function will involve a **product** of such factors, rather than an exponentiation.

□ **EXAMPLE 6**

Find $\dfrac{dy}{dx}$ for $y = x^{\sqrt{x}}, \quad x > 0$.

Solution: Note that we have no differentiation formula available to use in calculating $\dfrac{dy}{dx}$ directly because the exponent $\sqrt{x}$ is not a *fixed* real number. But if we first take natural logarithms of both sides of the equation

$$y = x^{\sqrt{x}}$$

we obtain

$$\ln y = \ln (x^{\sqrt{x}})$$

$$= \sqrt{x} \ln x. \qquad \text{(by property (L3) of logarithms)}$$

Differentiating both sides of the equation $\ln y = \sqrt{x}\,\ln x$ and remembering that y is a function of x gives

$$\left(\frac{1}{y}\right)\frac{dy}{dx} = \left(\frac{d}{dx}\sqrt{x}\right)\ln x + \sqrt{x}\left(\frac{d}{dx}\ln x\right)$$

$$= \frac{1}{2\sqrt{x}}\ln x + \sqrt{x}\left(\frac{1}{x}\right)$$

$$= \frac{\ln x + 2}{2\sqrt{x}}.$$

Solving for $\dfrac{dy}{dx}$ now gives

$$\frac{dy}{dx} = y\left(\frac{\ln x + 2}{2\sqrt{x}}\right)$$

or, since $y = x^{\sqrt{x}}$,

$$\frac{dy}{dx} = x^{\sqrt{x}}\left(\frac{\ln x + 2}{2\sqrt{x}}\right)$$

■

☐ EXAMPLE 7

Find $\dfrac{dy}{dx}$ for $y = (2x^2 + 3)^x$, $\qquad x > 0$.

Strategy · · · · · · · ·
Take natural logs of both sides to eliminate the variable exponent.

Solution

Taking natural logs of both sides of the equation

$$y = (2x^2 + 3)^x$$

gives

$$\ln y = \ln\left[(2x^2 + 3)^x\right]$$

$$= x\ln(2x^2 + 3).$$

Use Property (L3).
Differentiate both sides.

Differentiating both sides of this equation gives

$$\frac{1}{y}\frac{dy}{dx} = \ln(2x^2 + 3) + x\left[\frac{4x}{2x^2 + 3}\right]$$

$$= \ln(2x^2 + 3) + \frac{4x^2}{2x^2 + 3}$$

so

Solve for $\dfrac{dy}{dx}$.

$$\frac{dy}{dx} = y\left[\ln(2x^2 + 3) + \frac{4x^2}{2x^2 + 3}\right]$$

$$= (2x^2 + 3)^x\left[\ln(2x^2 + 3) + \frac{4x^2}{2x^2 + 3}\right].$$

■

The other situation in which logarithmic differentiation is sometimes useful is in differentiating a rational expression involving products and exponentiations. Because logarithms can convert exponentiations, multiplications, and divisions into products, sums, and differences, it is sometimes useful to differentiate the **natural logarithm** of the given function, as the following example shows.

☐ **EXAMPLE 8**

Find the derivative of the function

$$y = \frac{x^3(x^4 + 6)^5}{\sqrt{1 + x^3}}.$$

Strategy · · · · · · · ·
Because of the powers, products, and quotient, first take natural log and simplify.

Solution

Taking natural logs of both sides of the equation for y gives

$$\ln y = \ln \frac{x^3(x^4 + 6)^5}{\sqrt{1 + x^3}}$$

$$= \ln x^3 + \ln(x^4 + 6)^5 - \ln(1 + x^3)^{1/2}$$

$$= 3 \ln x + 5 \ln(x^4 + 6) - \left(\frac{1}{2}\right) \ln(1 + x^3).$$

Differentiate both sides.

Differentiating both sides, and recalling that y is a function of x, gives

$$\left(\frac{1}{y}\right) \frac{dy}{dx} = \frac{3}{x} + \frac{20x^3}{x^4 + 6} - \frac{3x^2}{2(1 + x^3)}$$

Solve for $\dfrac{dy}{dx}$ and substitute for y.

so

$$\frac{dy}{dx} = \frac{x^3(x^4 + 6)^5}{\sqrt{1 + x^3}} \left[\frac{3}{x} + \frac{20x^3}{x^4 + 6} - \frac{3x^2}{2(1 + x^3)}\right].$$ ∎

The Rate of Growth of a Function

Economists define the **rate of growth** of a function as the ratio

$$G(x) = \frac{f'(x)}{f(x)}$$

of the rate of change of f (i.e., its derivative) to its current size $f(x)$. This ratio is sometimes called the *relative rate of change* of f.

For example, if a company's profit P as a function of its production level x is

$$P(x) = 400x + 5000 - x^2$$

then its marginal profit is

$$P'(x) = 400 - 2x$$

and at production level $x = 50$ its rate of increase in profits per unit increase in production is the marginal profit

$$P'(50) = 300 \text{ dollars.}$$

But what does this really mean? By calculating its *rate of growth* in profits

$$G(50) = \frac{P'(50)}{P(50)} = \frac{300}{22,500} \approx 0.0133$$

we can say that the *relative* rate of increase in profits is 0.0133, or $0.0133 \times 100 \approx 1.3\%$. Thus an increase in production of 2% (from $x = 50$ to $x = 51$) will result in an increase in profits of roughly 1.3%.

Notice that the growth function $G(x)$ can be written as a *logarithmic derivative*:

$$G(x) = \frac{f'(x)}{f(x)} = \frac{d}{dx} \ln[f(x)].$$

This interpretation sheds some light on the definition of elasticity of demand discussed in Section 3.8. Recall, if $Q(p)$ is the number of items that can be sold per unit time at price p, elasticity of demand is defined as the quantity

$$E(p) = -\frac{pQ'(p)}{Q(p)}.$$

Note that we can write elasticity as

$$E(p) = -\frac{\left(\dfrac{Q'(p)}{Q(p)}\right)}{\left(\dfrac{1}{p}\right)}$$

$$= -\frac{\dfrac{d}{dp} \ln[Q(p)]}{\dfrac{d}{dp} \ln p}$$

$$= -\frac{\text{rate of growth of } Q(p)}{\text{rate of growth of } p}.$$

We may therefore interpret elasticity as the (negative of the) ratio of the *relative* change in demand to the *relative* change in price at price level p.

Proof of the Differentiation Formula (1)

Proof: Assuming the function $y = \ln x$ to be differentiable for all $x > 0$, we establish the differentiation formula for $\ln x$ using the basic definition of the derivative

$$\frac{d}{dx} f(x) = \lim_{h \to 0} \frac{f(x + h) - f(x)}{h}.$$

We obtain

$$\frac{d}{dx} \ln x = \lim_{h \to 0} \frac{\ln(x + h) - \ln x}{h}$$

$$= \lim_{h \to 0} \left(\frac{1}{h}\right) \ln\left(\frac{x + h}{x}\right) \qquad \text{(by property (L2) of logarithms)}$$

$$= \lim_{h \to 0} \ln\left(1 + \frac{h}{x}\right)^{1/h}. \qquad \text{(by property (L3) of logarithms)}$$

We now let $t = \dfrac{x}{h}$. Then since x is fixed, we have that $t \to \infty$ as $h \to 0^+$ and vice versa.

(Similarly, $t \to -\infty$ as $h \to 0^-$, but we shall consider only the case of the right-hand limit.) The above limit can be written as

$$\frac{d}{dx} \ln x = \lim_{t \to \infty} \ln\left(1 + \frac{1}{t}\right)^{t/x}$$

$$= \lim_{t \to \infty} \ln\left[\left(1 + \frac{1}{t}\right)^{t}\right]^{1/x}$$

$$= \lim_{t \to \infty} \frac{1}{x} \cdot \ln\left(1 + \frac{1}{t}\right)^{t} \qquad \text{(property (L3) of logarithms again)}$$

$$= \left(\frac{1}{x}\right)\left[\lim_{t \to \infty} \ln\left(1 + \frac{1}{t}\right)^{t}\right].$$

But since $\lim_{t \to \infty} \left(1 + \dfrac{1}{t}\right)^{t} = e$, it follows from our assumption that $\ln x$ is a continuous function that

$$\lim_{t \to \infty} \ln\left(1 + \frac{1}{t}\right)^{t} = \ln\left[\lim_{t \to \infty} \left(1 + \frac{1}{t}\right)^{t}\right] = \ln e = 1.$$

Thus

$$\frac{d}{dx} \ln x = \left(\frac{1}{x}\right)(1) = \frac{1}{x}$$

as stated. □

☑ PRACTICE PROBLEMS 4.3

1. Find the derivative of the following functions.
   a. $f(x) = \sqrt{x} \ln^3(x^2 + 1)$
   b. $f(x) = (x + 3)^{x+1}$
2. Find the relative extrema for the function

$$f(x) = \ln(x^2 + 4x + 6).$$

Exercise Set 4.3

In Exercises 1–22, find the derivative of the given function.

1. $y = \ln 2x$

2. $f(x) = \ln ax$

3. $f(x) = 10 \ln(x^2 + 5)$

4. $f(x) = 4 \ln(9 - x^2)$

5. $y = x \ln x$

6. $y = \ln \sqrt{x + 6}$

7. $f(x) = \ln \sqrt{x^3 - x}$

8. $f(x) = \ln(x^2 - 2x)^3$

9. $f(x) = [\ln(x^2 - 2x)]^3$

10. $f(x) = \ln \sqrt{1 + \sqrt{x}}$

11. $y = \ln(\ln(t))$

12. $y = x\sqrt{1 + \ln x}$

13. $f(x) = \dfrac{x^3}{1 + \ln x}$

14. $f(x) = x^2 \ln^2 x$ ($\ln^2 x$ means $[\ln x]^2$.)

15. $y = (3 \ln \sqrt{x})^4$

16. $f(x) = \dfrac{\ln(a + bx)}{\ln(c + dx)}$

17. $f(x) = x^2 \ln(3x - 6)$

18. $y = \ln\left(\dfrac{x^2 + 3}{x + 5}\right)$

19. $f(x) = \ln x \ln \sqrt{x}$

20. $f(x) = \dfrac{1 + \ln x}{1 - \ln x}$

21. $f(x) = \dfrac{x + \ln^2(3x)}{\sqrt{1 + \ln x}}$

22. $f(x) = (x^2 - x \ln x)\sqrt{x + \ln x}$

In Exercises 23–26, use properties of logarithms to simplify as much as possible before finding $f'(x)$.

23. $f(x) = \ln(x^3 + 3)^{4/3}$

24. $f(x) = \ln[\sqrt{x}(x^2 + 3)]$

25. $f(x) = \ln \dfrac{(x - 6)^{2/3}}{\sqrt{1 + x}}$

26. $f(x) = \ln \dfrac{\sqrt{x}(x^2 + 2)}{\sqrt[3]{x}(1 + x^2)}$

In Exercises 27–34, find $\dfrac{dy}{dx}$ by logarithmic differentiation.

27. $y = (x + 3)^x$

28. $y = x^{\sqrt{x+2}}$

29. $y = x^{\sqrt{x+1}}$

30. $y = (x^2 + 3)^{\sqrt{x+1}}$

31. $y = \dfrac{x(x + 1)(x + 2)}{(x + 3)(x + 4)}$

32. $y = \dfrac{\sqrt{1 + x^2}}{x(1 - x^5)}$

33. $y = \dfrac{(x^2 + 3)(1 - x)^{2/3}}{x\sqrt{1 + x}}$

34. $y = \dfrac{x(x^3 + 6)^4}{\sqrt{1 + x^2}}$

In Exercises 35 and 36, find $\dfrac{dy}{dx}$ by implicit differentiation.

35. $\ln(xy) = x + y$

36. $x \ln y + y^2 \ln x = 1$

37. Find an equation for the line tangent to the graph of the equation $y = x(\ln x)^2 + \dfrac{x}{\ln x}$ at the point $(e, 2e)$.

In Exercises 38–41, find all relative extrema.

38. $y = x \ln x$

39. $y = x - \ln x$

40. $y = x^2 \ln x$

41. $y = \ln(x^2 - x)$

In Exercises 42 and 43, sketch the graph of the given function.

42. $y = \ln x^3$

43. $y = \ln(4 - x)$

44. Paul and Janice own a bicycle-manufacturing company. They determine that the total cost in manufacturing x bicycles per month is $C(x) = 2000 + 200x + x^2$ dollars.
 a. What is their marginal cost at production level $x = 20$ bicycles per month?
 b. What is the company's growth in cost at production level $x = 20$ bicycles per month?

45. Carol inherits a tennis-racquet manufacturing company and decides to run the business herself. She finds that the total cost in producing x tennis racquets per month is $C(x) = 20x + 300$ dollars. The total revenues from the sale of x tennis racquets per month are given by $R(x) = 60x - x^2$ dollars.
 a. Find the growth in costs at production level $x = 20$.
 b. Find the growth in revenues at production level $x = 20$.
 c. Find the growth in profits at production level $x = 20$.

46. After a period of streamlining, Carol (Exercise 45) manages to reduce costs at her company by a significant amount, although the revenue picture changes for her also. If her total monthly costs are now $C(x) = 200 + 10x$ dollars and total monthly revenues are $R(x) = 50x$ dollars at production level x,
 a. Find her break-even point, x_0.
 b. Show that growth in profits is increasing for $0 < x < x_0$ and decreasing for $x > x_0$.
 c. Does the result of part b mean that profits are decreasing for $x > x_0$? Why or why not?

47. The population of a certain metropolitan region is growing according to the population model

$$P(t) = 750{,}000 + 30{,}000t + 10{,}000e^{-t}$$

where $t = 0$ corresponds to 1990. Find the relative and percent rates of growth predicted by this model for the years
 a. 1992, and
 b. 1995.

48. A stand of timber is increasing in value according to the model

$$V(t) = 5000e^{\frac{1}{2}\sqrt{t}}$$

where $t = 0$ corresponds to 1990. Find the relative and percent rates of growth of this value in
a. 1995, and
b. 2000.

49. Land bought for speculation turns out to be worth

$$V(t) = 10{,}000te^{-0.5t}$$

t years after it is purchased. Find the relative and percent rates of decline 4 years after the purchase.

50. For the utility function $U(x) = \ln \sqrt{x}$ show that marginal utility is positive but decreasing for all $x > 0$.

51. Complete the following argument to show that the graph of the natural logarithm function has no horizontal asymptote. (That is, $y = \ln x$ is increasing but unbounded for $x > 0$.)
a. Recall that $\ln 2^n = n \ln 2$ for all $n > 0$.
b. Note that $\ln 2 > 0$.
c. Show that $\lim_{n \to \infty} \ln 2^n = \lim_{n \to \infty} n \cdot \ln 2 = +\infty$.
d. Conclude that $y = \ln x$ has no horizontal asymptote.

52. Use an argument similar to that of Exercise 51 to show that $\lim_{x \to 0^+} \ln x = -\infty$. That is, show that the y-axis is a vertical asymptote for $y = \ln x$.

☑ **SOLUTIONS TO PRACTICE PROBLEMS 4.3**

1. a. $f'(x) = \left(\dfrac{1}{2\sqrt{x}}\right) \ln^3(x^2 + 1) + [3\sqrt{x}\,\ln^2(x^2 + 1)]\left(\dfrac{2x}{x^2 + 1}\right)$

$$= \dfrac{\ln^3(x^2 + 1)}{2\sqrt{x}} + \dfrac{6x^{3/2}\ln^2(x^2 + 1)}{x^2 + 1}$$

b. $\ln f(x) = \ln[(x + 3)^{x+1}]$

$$= (x + 1)\ln(x + 3)$$

Then

$$\dfrac{1}{f(x)} \cdot f'(x) = \ln(x + 3) + \dfrac{x + 1}{x + 3}$$

so

$$f'(x) = (x + 3)^{x+1}\left[\ln(x + 3) + \dfrac{x + 1}{x + 3}\right]$$

2. For $f(x) = \ln(x^2 + 4x + 6)$ the derivative is

$$f'(x) = \dfrac{2x + 4}{x^2 + 4x + 6}.$$

Setting $f'(x) = 0$ gives $2x + 4 = 0$, or $x = -2$. This is the only critical value, since the denominator of $f'(x)$ is defined (and positive) for all x.

The second derivative is

$$f''(x) = \dfrac{2(x^2 + 4x + 6) - (2x + 4)^2}{(x^2 + 4x + 6)^2}$$

$$= -\dfrac{2x^2 + 8x + 4}{(x^2 + 4x + 6)^2}$$

so

$$f''(-2) = 1 > 0.$$

Thus, $f(-2) = \ln 2$ is a relative minimum. This is the only relative extremum.

4.4 Differentiating the Exponential Function

The identity linking the natural logarithm and exponential functions

$$\ln(e^x) = x \qquad (1)$$

provides us almost immediately with the derivative of the function $y = e^x$. Differentiating both sides of equation (1) with respect to x (using the Chain Rule formula $\dfrac{d}{dx} \ln u = \dfrac{1}{u} \cdot \dfrac{du}{dx}$ with $u = e^x$ on the left-hand side) gives

$$\frac{1}{e^x} \cdot \frac{d}{dx} e^x = 1.$$

Multiplying both sides of this equation by e^x gives the surprisingly simple result that

> If $f(x) = e^x$, then $f'(x) = e^x$
> or, in Leibniz notation,
> $$\frac{d}{dx} e^x = e^x. \qquad (2)$$

Thus the function $f(x) = e^x$ is its own derivative! It and its multiples are the only functions that have this property, which turns out to make them very useful in applications.

The Graph of $y = e^x$

Figure 4.1 shows the graph of $f(x) = e^x$. Since $f'(x) = e^x$ also, this means that the y-coordinate of any point on the graph of $y = e^x$ is the same as the slope of the line tangent to the graph at that point. Since the values of e^x are positive for all x, the

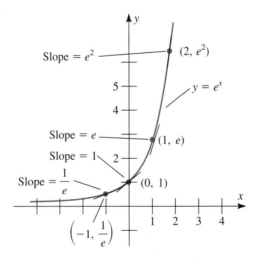

Figure 4.1 Graph of $y = e^x$. Since $\dfrac{d}{dx} e^x = e^x$, slope at each point equals its y-coordinate.

slopes of these tangents are always positive. Moreover, these slopes increase as x increases. Finally, since

$$\frac{d^2}{dx^2}e^x = \frac{d}{dx}\left(\frac{d}{dx}e^x\right) = \frac{d}{dx}e^x = e^x > 0$$

the graph of $y = e^x$ is concave up for all x.

Combining equation (2) with the Chain Rule, we obtain the following rule for differentiating composite functions of the form e^u where u is a differentiable function of x.

> If $f(x) = e^{u(x)}$,   then $f'(x) = e^{u(x)} \cdot u'(x)$ (3)
>
> or, in Leibniz notation,
>
> $$\frac{d}{dx}e^u = e^u \cdot \frac{du}{dx}.$$

The following examples illustrate the use of equation (3).

□ **EXAMPLE 1**

The function $f(x) = e^{3x}$ has the form $f(x) = e^u$ with $u = 3x$. Thus by equation (3)

$$f'(x) = \underbrace{e^{3x}}_{e^{u(x)}} \cdot \underbrace{3}_{u'(x)} = 3e^{3x}.$$

More generally, if a is any constant, we have

$$\frac{d}{dx}e^{ax} = e^{ax} \cdot \frac{d}{dx}(ax)$$

$$= e^{ax} \cdot a$$

$$= ae^{ax}. \qquad ■$$

□ **EXAMPLE 2**

Find $f'(x)$ for $f(x) = e^{\sqrt{x}}$.

Strategy · · · · · · · ·

Identify $u(x) = \sqrt{x}$.

Find $u'(x) = \dfrac{1}{2\sqrt{x}}$.

Solution

With $u(x) = \sqrt{x}$ we have, from equation (3), that

$$f'(x) = \underbrace{e^{\sqrt{x}}}_{e^{u(x)}} \cdot \underbrace{\frac{1}{2\sqrt{x}}}_{u'(x)} = \frac{1}{2\sqrt{x}}e^{\sqrt{x}}. \qquad ■$$

□ **EXAMPLE 3**

For $f(x) = \dfrac{e^{x^2}}{1+x}$, find $f'(x)$.

Solution: Since this function is a quotient, we must begin by applying the Quotient Rule:

$$\frac{d}{dx}\left(\frac{e^{x^2}}{1+x}\right) = \frac{(1+x)\left[\dfrac{d}{dx}e^{x^2}\right] - e^{x^2}\left[\dfrac{d}{dx}(1+x)\right]}{(1+x)^2}$$

$$= \frac{(1+x)[e^{x^2}\cdot 2x] - e^{x^2}(1)}{(1+x)^2}$$

$$= \frac{2xe^{x^2}(1+x) - e^{x^2}}{(1+x)^2}$$

$$= \frac{(2x^2 + 2x - 1)e^{x^2}}{(1+x)^2}.$$ ∎

□ **EXAMPLE 4**

For the function $f(x) = xe^x$, find all relative extrema, determine the intervals on which f is increasing or decreasing, find all inflection points, and determine the concavity.

Strategy

Find f'.

Solution

Using the Product Rule, we find that

$$f'(x) = \left[\frac{d}{dx}(x)\right]e^x + x\left[\frac{d}{dx}e^x\right]$$

$$= (1)e^x + xe^x$$

$$= (1+x)e^x.$$

Set $f'(x) = 0$ to find critical numbers.

Since e^x is never zero, the only zero of f' occurs when $x = -1$. This is the only critical number.

Test the critical number using the Second Derivative Test to determine whether it is a relative maximum or minimum.

To test this number, we find the second derivative:

$$f''(x) = \frac{d}{dx}[(1+x)e^x]$$

$$= \left[\frac{d}{dx}(1+x)\right]e^x + (1+x)\left[\frac{d}{dx}e^x\right]$$

$$= 1\cdot e^x + (1+x)e^x$$

$$= (2+x)e^x.$$

Since $f''(-1) = (2-1)e^{-1} = \dfrac{1}{e} > 0$, the Second Derivative Test shows that the value $f(-1) = \dfrac{-1}{e}$ is a relative minimum. Thus f must be decreasing on $(-\infty, -1)$ and increasing on $(-1, \infty)$. (Why?)

Find the zeros of the second
derivative.

The second derivative $f''(x) = (2 + x)e^x$ equals zero only when $x = -2$. In the
interval $(-\infty, -2)$ we use the test point $t = -3$ for which

$$f''(-3) = (2 - 3)e^{-3} = \frac{-1}{e^3} < 0$$

Check the sign of $f''(x)$ on each of
the resulting intervals to determine
the concavity.

so the graph is concave down on $(-\infty, -2)$. On the interval $(-2, \infty)$ we use the test
point $t = 0$:

Identify inflection points where
concavity changes.

$$f''(0) = (2 + 0)e^0 = 2 > 0$$

so the graph is concave up on $(-2, \infty)$. Since the concavity changes at $x = -2$, the
point $(-2, -2e^{-2})$ is an inflection point. The graph appears in Figure 4.2. ■

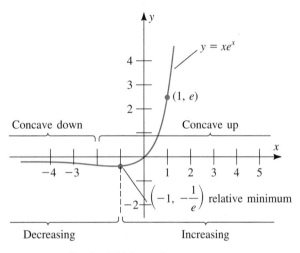

Figure 4.2 Graph of $f(x) = xe^x$.

☐ **EXAMPLE 5**

Sketch the graph of the function $f(x) = e^{-x^2}$.

Solution: Proceeding as in Example 4, we note first that $f(x)$ is never zero, but that f
is an *even* function. Thus, its graph will be symmetric with respect to the y-axis.
     The derivative is $f'(x) = -2xe^{-x^2}$, so setting $f'(x) = 0$ gives the single critical
number $x = 0$. Checking the sign of $f'(x)$ we see that:

(a) if $x < 0$, $f'(x) > 0$; and
(b) if $x > 0$, $f'(x) < 0$.

This shows that f is increasing on $(-\infty, 0)$; that f is decreasing on $(0, \infty)$; and
therefore, that $f(0) = e^0 = 1$ is a relative maximum.
     The second derivative is

$$f''(x) = \frac{d}{dx}(-2xe^{-x^2}) = (4x^2 - 2)e^{-x^2}$$

Setting $f''(x) = 0$ gives $x = \pm\dfrac{\sqrt{2}}{2}$. We observe that

(c) if $x < -\dfrac{\sqrt{2}}{2}$, $f''(x) > 0$;

(d) if $-\dfrac{\sqrt{2}}{2} < x < \dfrac{\sqrt{2}}{2}$, $f''(x) < 0$; and

(e) if $x > \dfrac{\sqrt{2}}{2}$, $f''(x) > 0$.

Thus, the graph of f is concave up on $\left(-\infty, -\dfrac{\sqrt{2}}{2}\right)$ and $\left(\dfrac{\sqrt{2}}{2}, \infty\right)$, and concave down on $\left(-\dfrac{\sqrt{2}}{2}, \dfrac{\sqrt{2}}{2}\right)$.

Finally,

$$\lim_{x \to \infty} e^{-x^2} = \lim_{x \to \infty}\left(\frac{1}{e^{x^2}}\right) = 0.$$

So, the line $y = 0$ is a horizontal asymptote. (See Figure 4.3.) ∎

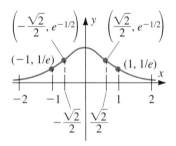

Figure 4.3 Graph of $f(x) = e^{-x^2}$.

☐ **EXAMPLE 6**

Figure 4.4 shows the graph of the function

$$N(t) = \frac{30}{1 + 5e^{-t}}, \qquad t \geq 0$$

which is proposed as a mathematical model for the size of a population of deer to be introduced into an animal preserve in a state forest.

(a) What is the initial size of the population?
(b) What is the rate of increase of population size, $N'(t)$, predicted by this model?
(c) What is the long-term size for the population, according to this model?

Solution

(a) The initial population size corresponds to $t = 0$:

$$N(0) = \frac{30}{1 + 5e^0} = \frac{30}{6} = 5 \text{ deer.}$$

(b) The rate of increase of population size is the derivative:

$$N'(t) = \frac{(1 + 5e^{-t}) \cdot (0) - 30(-5e^{-t})}{(1 + 5e^{-t})^2}$$

$$= \frac{150e^{-t}}{(1 + 5e^{-t})^2}.$$

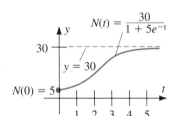

Figure 4.4 Graph of the population model for deer in a wildlife preserve.

(c) The long-term population size is the limit at infinity:

$$\lim_{t \to \infty} \frac{30}{1 + 5e^{-t}} = \frac{30}{1} = 30.$$

Since $\lim_{t \to \infty} e^{-t} = \lim_{t \to \infty} \dfrac{1}{e^t} = 0.$ ∎

□ **EXAMPLE 7**

The owner of a stand of timber estimates that the timber is currently worth \$5000 and that it will increase in value with time (as the trees continue to grow) according to the formula

$$V(t) = 5000e^{\sqrt{t}/2}$$

where t is time in years. But prevailing interest rates are expected to remain at 12%, and the owner worries that by waiting longer to convert the timber to cash considerable interest income will be forgone. When should the owner sell the timber so as to maximize revenue?

Solution: Since dollars received in the future have different values today depending on when they are to be received, it is helpful to convert the revenue to be received in the future into its *present value* using the formula $P_0 = e^{-rt}P(t)$. With $P(t) = V(t)$ and $r = 0.12$, this gives the present value of the revenue received in selling the timber after t years as

$$R(t) = e^{-0.12t}V(t)$$
$$= (5000e^{\sqrt{t}/2})e^{-0.12t}$$
$$= 5000e^{\sqrt{t}/2 - 0.12t}.$$

To find the maximum value of R, we set $R'(t) = 0$:

$$R'(t) = \underbrace{5000e^{(\sqrt{t}/2 - 0.12t)}}_{e^{u(t)}} \underbrace{\left[\frac{1}{4\sqrt{t}} - 0.12 \right]}_{u'(t)} = 0.$$

Since the exponential function $e^{u(t)}$ is never zero, we must have

$$\frac{1}{4\sqrt{t}} - 0.12 = 0 \qquad (4)$$

or

$$\sqrt{t} = \frac{1}{4(0.12)} = \frac{1}{0.48}.$$

Thus

$$t = \left(\frac{1}{0.48}\right)^2 = 4.34 \text{ years}$$

or approximately 4 years and 4 months. (You can verify that this critical number actually yields the maximum value of $R(t)$ by applying the Second Derivative Test.)

■

More on the Rate of Growth of a Function: Applications to Optimal Harvesting

Example 7 is typical of many situations in which the value of an asset $P(t)$ is growing in time. The question of when to sell the asset is called an *optimal harvest* problem because it applies to harvesting fish from a fishery, trees from a woodland, wine from an aging facility, and so on. What makes the question of when to harvest interesting is that while the value of the asset $P(t)$ is growing in time, the owner is missing the opportunity to invest these dollars at the prevailing interest rate r. This means that $P(t)$ must be *discounted* by the factor e^{-rt} used to calculate *present value*. As in Example 7, the present value of the revenue received from harvesting after t years is thus

$$R(t) = P(t)e^{-rt}.$$

To determine the *optimal* harvest time, we maximize $R(t)$ by setting $R'(t) = 0$. Since

$$R'(t) = P'(t)e^{-rt} + P(t)[e^{-rt}(-r)]$$
$$= [P'(t) - rP(t)]e^{-rt}$$

we will have $R'(t) = 0$ when

$$P'(t) - rP(t) = 0$$

or when

$$r = \frac{P'(t)}{P(t)}. \qquad \text{(rate of growth of } P(t)) \qquad (5)$$

Now recall that the ratio $\dfrac{P'(t)}{P(t)}$ is what we have defined as the *rate of growth* of the function P. Thus, under a constant prevailing rate of interest r, *the optimal time to harvest the asset whose value is given by the function* P *is when the rate of growth of* P *equals the prevailing interest rate*.

In Example 7 we had $P(t) = e^{\sqrt{t}/2}$ and $r = 0.12$, so this principle (equation (5)) would have required that we harvest when

$$0.12 = \frac{P'(t)}{P(t)} = \frac{e^{\sqrt{t}/2}\left(\frac{1}{4\sqrt{t}}\right)}{e^{\sqrt{t}/2}} = \frac{1}{4\sqrt{t}}.$$

This is precisely the condition in equation (4) that led to the solution $t = 4.34$ years.

Derivatives of Other Exponential and Logarithm Functions

In Section 4.2 we obtained a formula equivalent to

$$a^x = e^{x \ln a} \qquad \text{(equation (5), Section 4.2)}$$

which shows how to express exponential functions in other bases in terms of the natural exponential function. Differentiating both sides of this equation using equation (3) gives

$$\frac{d}{dx} a^x = \frac{d}{dx} e^{x \ln a}$$

$$= e^{x \ln a} \cdot \left\{ \frac{d}{dx} (x \ln a) \right\}$$

$$= e^{x \ln a} \cdot \ln a$$

$$= a^x \ln a.$$

Combining this result with the Chain Rule gives the formula for differentiating a^u when u is a differentiable function of x:

If $f(x) = a^{u(x)},$ then $f'(x) = a^{u(x)} \cdot u'(x) \cdot \ln a$ \qquad (6)

or

$$\frac{d}{dx} a^u = a^u \cdot \frac{du}{dx} \cdot \ln a$$

Similarly, we may differentiate both sides of the equation

$$\log_a x = \frac{\ln x}{\ln a} \qquad \text{(Exercise 4, Section 4.2)}$$

to obtain the rule for differentiating logarithm functions to the base a:

$$\frac{d}{dx} \log_a x = \frac{d}{dx} \left(\frac{1}{\ln a} \cdot \ln x \right)$$

$$= \left(\frac{1}{\ln a} \right) \left(\frac{d}{dx} \ln x \right)$$

$$= \frac{1}{\ln a} \cdot \frac{1}{x}$$

$$= \frac{1}{x \ln a}.$$

If $u = u(x)$ is a differentiable function, the Chain Rule combines with the above result to give the following:

$$\text{If} \quad f(x) = \log_a u(x), \quad \text{then} \ f'(x) = \frac{1}{u(x) \ln a} \cdot u'(x) \quad\quad (7)$$

or

$$\frac{d}{dx} \log_a u = \frac{1}{u \ln a} \cdot \frac{du}{dx}.$$

☐ **EXAMPLE 8**

Using differentiation formulas (6) and (7), we obtain the following results:

(a) $\dfrac{d}{dx} 3^x = 3^x \ln 3$

(b) $\dfrac{d}{dx} (7^{x^2 - \sqrt{x}}) = 7^{x^2 - \sqrt{x}} \cdot \left(2x - \dfrac{1}{2\sqrt{x}}\right) \ln 7$

(c) $\dfrac{d}{dx} (\log_{10} x) = \dfrac{1}{x \ln 10}$

(d) $\dfrac{d}{dx} \{[\log_2(9 - x^3)]^4\} = 4[\log_2(9 - x^3)]^3 \cdot \dfrac{1}{(9 - x^3) \ln 2} (-3x^2)$

$$= \frac{-12x^2 [\log_2(9 - x^3)]^3}{(9 - x^3) \ln 2}.$$ ■

☑ **PRACTICE PROBLEMS 4.4**

1. Find $f'(x)$ for the following functions.
 a. $f(x) = xe^{x^2 + 2x + 5}$
 b. $f(x) = 10^{\sqrt{3x}}$

2. Find an equation for the line tangent to the graph of $f(x) = e^{-1/x}$ at the point $\left(1, \dfrac{1}{e}\right)$.

Exercise Set 4.4

In Exercises 1–20, find the derivative of the given function.

1. $f(x) = e^{6x}$

2. $f(x) = e^{9-x}$

3. $f(x) = e^{x^2 - 4}$

4. $f(x) = 3e^{2\sqrt{x}}$

5. $f(x) = \dfrac{e^x}{x^2 + 2}$

6. $f(x) = x^2 e^{-x+5}$

7. $f(x) = \sqrt{x + e^{-x}}$

8. $f(x) = \dfrac{e^x + 1}{e^x - 1}$

9. $f(x) = e^{x^2 - \sqrt{x}}$

10. $f(x) = xe^{-2\ln x}$

11. $f(x) = \ln \dfrac{e^x + 1}{x^3 + 1}$

12. $y = \dfrac{e^x - 1}{e^{-x} + 1}$

13. $y = \dfrac{1}{2}(e^x + e^{-x})$

14. $y = (x^2 + x - 1)e^{x^2+3}$

15. $f(x) = (x - e^{-2x})^4$

16. $y = e^{\sqrt{x}+\ln x}$

17. $f(x) = xe^{1/x^2}$

18. $y = \ln(x + e^{x^2})$

19. $f(x) = \dfrac{xe^{-x}}{1 + x^2}$

20. $y = \ln^2 xe^{\sqrt{1+x^2}}$

In Exercises 21 and 22, find $\dfrac{dy}{dx}$ by implicit differentiation.

21. $e^{xy} = x$

22. $e^{x-y} = y^2e^{x^2}$

In Exercises 23–28, find the derivative.

23. $f(x) = x2^x$

24. $f(x) = 7^{x^3-6x}$

25. $y = \sqrt{1 + 4^x}$

26. $f(x) = \log_{10}(x^2 - 10^x)$

27. $f(x) = [\log_2 \sqrt{x}]^2$

28. $y = \log_8(x^2 - 4)^3$

29. Find the maximum value of the function $f(x) = (3 - x^2)e^x$.

30. Find all relative extrema for the function $y = x^2e^{1-x^2}$.

31. Find all relative extrema for the function $y = xe^{1-x^3}$.

32. The line $y = -\dfrac{1}{e}$ is tangent to the graph of $y = xe^x$ at the point P. Find P.

33. The selling price p and the number of items x that can be sold per month are related by the equation $p(x) = 100e^{-0.5x}$. Find the price p for which revenue is a maximum.

34. The population of a certain city is projected to be $P(t) = 100{,}000(1 + 5t)e^{-0.05t}$ in t years. When will the city's population be a maximum?

35. A manufacturer experiences weekly costs of $C(x) = 500 + 40x + e^{0.5x}$ in producing x hundred items. If the items can be sold for \$100 each, find the weekly production level x that maximizes profits.

36. The owner of a valuable oil painting estimates that the value of the painting will be approximately $V(t) = 5000(2)^{\sqrt{t}}$ dollars t years from now. At what rate will the value of the painting be increasing in 4 years?

37. Find the rate of *growth* of the value of the painting in Exercise 36 after 4 years.

38. The value of a case of a certain French wine t years after being imported into the United States is $V(t) = 100(1.5)^{\sqrt{t}}$. If interest rates under continuous compounding are expected

to remain constant at 12.5% nominally, when should the wine be sold so as to maximize profits? (Assume storage costs to be negligible.)

39. Land bought for speculation is expected to be worth $V(t) = 10{,}000(1.2)^{\sqrt{t}}$ dollars after t years. If the cost of money remains constant at 10% per year, when should the land be sold so as to maximize revenue to the owner?

40. Find the x-coordinate of the equilibrium point P for the supply curve $S(x) = 10e^{0.5x}$ and the demand curve $D(x) = 20e^{-0.5(x-10)}$. (P is where the curves intersect.)

41. Human growth in height from age 1 year to adulthood typically looks like the graph in Figure 4.5. A function that has been used to model this kind of growth is the *double-logistic*

$$y(t) = \frac{a}{1 + e^{-b_1(t-c_1)}} + \frac{f - a}{1 + e^{-b_2(t-c_2)}}$$

where the parameters a_1, b_1, a_2, b_2, c_1, c_2, and f are different for each individual.

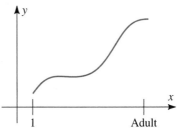

Figure 4.5 Typical double-logistic.

a. Show that the parameter f is adult height. That is, show that

$$f = \lim_{t \to \infty} y(t).$$

b. If $b_1 = b_2 = b$ and $c_1 = c_2 = c$, show that the time of most rapid growth is $t = c$.

42. The function $L(t) = a + b(1 - e^{-ct})$ is used to model the length of human infants as a function of time. Here a, b, and c are nonzero constants.

a. Find the velocity function $v(t) = L'(t)$ associated with this model by finding the first derivative of L.

b. Does the function L have a maximum value on $(0, \infty)$? Why or why not?

c. Find the acceleration function $a(t) = L''(t)$ associated with this model.

d. Show that the model has constant negative acceleration if $b > 0$.

43. The function

$$f(x) = \frac{1}{\sigma\sqrt{2\pi}} e^{-x^2/2\sigma^2}$$

is called the normal probability density function. Comparing this function with that of Example 5, show that f has a maximum value at $x = 0$ and inflection points where $x = \pm\sigma$. (The constant σ is called the *standard deviation* for the normal curve. See Figure 4.6.)

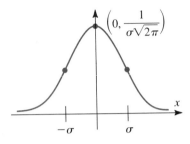

Figure 4.6 Graph of $f(x) = \frac{1}{\sigma\sqrt{2\pi}} e^{-x^2/2\sigma^2}$.

☑ **SOLUTIONS TO PRACTICE PROBLEMS 4.4**

1. a. Using the Product Rule first, we obtain

$$\begin{aligned} f'(x) &= (1)e^{x^2+2x+5} + x(2x + 2)e^{x^2+2x+5} \\ &= (2x^2 + 2x + 1)e^{x^2+2x+5}. \end{aligned}$$

b. Using equation (6) we obtain

$$f'(x) = 10^{\sqrt{3x}}\left(\frac{3}{2\sqrt{3x}}\right)\ln 10$$

$$= \left(\frac{3\ln 10}{2\sqrt{3x}}\right)10^{\sqrt{3x}}$$

2. The derivative of $f(x) = e^{-1/x}$ is

$$f'(x) = e^{-1/x}\left(\frac{1}{x^2}\right)$$

$$= \frac{e^{-1/x}}{x^2}.$$

Thus, $f'(x) = e^{-1} = \dfrac{1}{e}$ is the desired slope. The equation is

$$y - \frac{1}{e} = \left(\frac{1}{e}\right)(x - 1)$$

or

$$x - ey = 0.$$

4.5 Exponential Growth and Decay

Imagine the following experiment conducted in a biology course. On a certain day a number n of fruit flies is placed in an enclosed environment such as a large bell jar. If the environment is supportive (e.g., sufficient food supply and proper temperature), the number of flies will increase as time passes. The experiment is to record the number of fruit flies $N(t)$ present after t days, and to find a mathematical relationship between time and population size. In experiments of this kind, data such as those in Table 5.1 are often obtained. (These data are plotted in Figure 5.1.)

Table 5.1. Typical Data on the Growth of Fruit Flies

t (Days)	0	4	8	12	16	20	24
$N(t)$ Fruit Flies	10	18	35	72	107	208	361

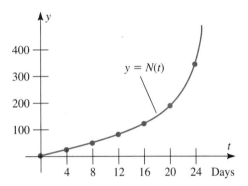

Figure 5.1 Plot of typical data on fruit flies.

On examining these data, we observe that $N(t)$ increases more rapidly as the population size itself grows. That is, the larger the population the faster it grows. Biologists refer to this phenomenon as the **Law of Natural Growth,** which is often stated as

{rate of change of population size} $\propto$ {current size of population}.

The symbol "$\propto$" means "is proportional to." The statement of proportionality, $A \propto B$, is expressed mathematically by the equation $A = kB$ where k is a constant.

If we assume the population size N to be a differentiable function of t, the derivative $N'(t)$ is the rate of change of the population size. We may then write the *Law of Natural Growth* as the equation

$$N'(t) = kN(t) \qquad (1)$$

or

$$\frac{dN}{dt} = kN.$$

The constant k in equation (1) is called the **growth constant.** Equation (1) itself is called a **differential equation*** because it is an equation involving an unknown function N and its derivative N'. Solving equation (1) involves finding a differentiable function N for which equation (1) is true.

Fortunately, the solution of equation (1) is quite straightforward. If we let $N(t) = Ce^{kt}$ where C is any constant, then

$$N'(t) = \frac{d}{dt} Ce^{kt}$$

$$= C\left(\frac{d}{dt} e^{kt}\right)$$

$$= C(ke^{kt})$$

$$= k(Ce^{kt})$$

$$= kN(t)$$

so the function $N(t) = Ce^{kt}$ is a solution of equation (1). Moreover, it can be shown that *every* solution of equation (1) must be of this form.

For example, the differential equation

$$N'(t) = 2N(t) \tag{2}$$

has the form of equation (1) with $k = 2$, so it has solutions $N_1(t) = 3e^{2t}$, $N_2(t) = 40e^{2t}$, $N_3(t) = -6e^{2t}$, $N_4(t) = \pi e^{2t}$, and, in general, $N(t) = Ce^{2t}$ for any number C (including zero!).

Similarly, the differential equation

$$\frac{dy}{dt} = 6y \tag{3}$$

has the form of equation (1), so its solutions all have the form $y = Ce^{6t}$.

Finally, we can say a bit more about the constant C. Setting $t = 0$ in the function $N(t) = Ce^{kt}$ gives

$$N(0) = Ce^{k \cdot 0} = Ce^0 = C.$$

Thus, given any solution Ce^{kt} of equation (1), the constant C is just the value of this solution when $t = 0$. For this reason the constant C is called the **initial value** of the solution Ce^{kt}. If we specify a particular initial value $N(0) = N_0$ that a solution of equation (1) must have, we then obtain the *unique* solution $N(t) = N_0 e^{kt}$ since both constants k and C are known. For example, if we specify $N(0) = 10$ in the differen-

---

* Recall, from Section 3.10, that the terms differential and derivative are nearly synonymous. We could just as easily refer to equation (1) as a *derivative* equation, but convention is to use the terminology *differential equation*.

tial equation (2), we obtain the unique solution $N(t) = 10e^{2t}$, since $k = 2$ and $C = 10$. Specifying the initial value $y(0) = -5$ in equation (3) gives the unique solution $y = -5e^{6t}$ since $k = 6$ and $C = -5$.

The following theorem summarizes our findings.

Theorem 1 Law of Natural Growth	If a differentiable function of time, N, has the property that its rate of change is proportional to its present size at each instant of time, then it satisfies the differential equation

$$N'(t) = kN(t) \qquad (4)$$

for some constant k. The *general solution* of equation (4) is

$$N(t) = Ce^{kt} \qquad (5)$$

where C is an arbitrary constant. If, in addition, one specifies the *initial condition*

$$N(0) = N_0$$

for some number N_0, then equation (4) has the *unique* solution

$$N(t) = N_0 e^{kt}. \qquad (6)$$

Figure 5.2 shows the graphs of two typical functions of the form $N(t) = Ce^{kt}$, one with $k > 0$ (exponential growth) and one with $k < 0$ (exponential decay). The advantage of having taken the trouble to develop the statement of Theorem 1 is that we now know that any quantity that grows or decays in time at a rate proportional to its present size can be represented by an exponential function as in equations (5) or (6).

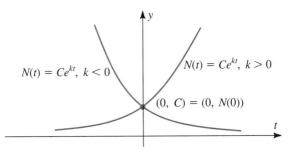

Figure 5.2 Graphs of the natural growth function $N(t) = Ce^{kt}$.

☐ **EXAMPLE 1**

(**Population Growth**) Assume that the rate of increase of a population of fruit flies is proportional to the population size at each instant of time. If 100 fruit flies are present initially and 300 are present after 10 days, how many will be present after 15 days?

Strategy   ·   ·   ·   ·   ·   ·   ·   ·

Apply Law of Natural Growth to find the form of $N(t)$.

Solution

Since it is stated that the population function N satisfies the differential equation

$$N'(t) = kN(t)$$

the solution $N(t)$ must have the form

$$N(t) = Ce^{kt}.$$

Use the initial value $N(0) = 100$ to find C.

We are given that $N(0) = 100$, so $C = N(0) = 100$. The solution therefore has the form

$$N(t) = 100e^{kt} \tag{7}$$

Substitute in other given data to obtain an equation in k alone.

but we do not as yet know k. To find k, we use the fact that $N(10) = 300$. Substituting $t = 10$ and $N(10) = 300$ in equation (7) gives

$$300 = 100e^{k \cdot 10}$$

or

$$e^{10k} = \frac{300}{100} = 3.$$

Take natural logs of both sides to solve for k.

To solve for k we take natural logs of both sides:

$$\ln e^{10k} = \ln 3$$

or

$$10k = \ln 3 \text{ (since } \ln e^{10k} = 10k\text{).}$$

Write $N(t)$ using known values for C and k.

Thus $k = \dfrac{1}{10} \ln 3$, and our population function is

$$N(t) = 100e^{(1/10 \ln 3)t}.$$

Set $t = 15$ and solve to find the desired population size.

The size of the population after $t = 15$ days is therefore

$$\begin{aligned} N(15) &= 100e^{(1/10 \ln 3)(15)} \\ &= 100e^{(3/2) \ln 3} \\ &= 100e^{\ln(3^{3/2})} \\ &= 100 \cdot 3^{3/2} \\ &\approx 520 \text{ fruit flies.} \end{aligned}$$

■

□ **EXAMPLE 2**

World population increased from approximately 2 billion in 1930 to approximately 4 billion in 1975. Assuming that world population size follows an exponential growth model, where the rate of increase of population is proportional to the present size of the population, what world populations do these data predict for the years

(a) 1990?
(b) 2000?

What factors might lead to questions about the assumption of true exponential growth?

Solution: As in Example 1, the population function must have the form $N(t) = Ce^{kt}$. Using time $t = 0$ to correspond to the year 1930, we may substitute $t = 0$ and $N(0) = 2$ (billion) to obtain

$$2 = Ce^{k \cdot 0} = C.$$

Thus, our population function must have the form

$$N(t) = 2e^{kt}.$$

To determine k we use the second datum, with the year 1975 corresponding to the time $t = 1975 - 1930 = 45$ and the population size $N(45) = 4$ (billion). Then,

$$4 = N(45) = 2e^{k \cdot 45}$$

so

$$e^{45k} = 2.$$

Taking natural logs of both sides of this equation and using the fact that $\ln(e^{45k}) = 45k$ gives

$$45k = \ln 2$$

so

$$k = \frac{\ln 2}{45}.$$

For the year 1990, which corresponds to $t = 1990 - 1930 = 60$, the exponential model predicts a population of size

$$N(60) = 2e^{60\left(\frac{\ln 2}{45}\right)} = 2e^{\frac{4 \ln 2}{3}} \approx 5.04 \text{ billion.}$$

For the year 2000, which corresponds to $t = 2000 - 1930 = 70$, the exponential model predicts a population of size

$$N(70) = 2e^{70\left(\frac{\ln 2}{45}\right)} = 2e^{\frac{14 \ln 2}{9}} \approx 5.89 \text{ billion.}$$

Actual data show that the prediction for year 1990 is not far from the actual observed world population in that year. Whether the prediction for year 2000 will prove accurate, however, depends on the extent to which the rather simple assumptions associated with the model for exponential growth are satisfied. Issues such as famine, overcrowding, and changing social attitudes toward childbearing can affect these dynamics. (We will have more to say about modifications to the exponential population model due to certain constraints in the next section.) ∎

☐ **EXAMPLE 3**

(Radioactive Decay) Certain radioactive isotopes, such as uranium, decay at a rate proportional to the amount present. If a block of 50 grams of such material decays to 40 grams in 5 days, what is the half-life of this material? (The half-life is the amount of time required for the material to decay to half the original amount.)

Strategy · · · · · · · ·	**Solution**
Label variables. State form $A(t)$ using Theorem 1.	Let $A(t)$ denote the amount present after t days. Since $A(t)$ satisfies the Law of Natural Growth, we have

$$A(t) = Ce^{kt}.$$

| Apply initial condition $A(0) = 50 = C$. | We are given that $A(0) = C = 50$ grams, so |

$$A(t) = 50e^{kt}. \tag{8}$$

| Substitute in other data to obtain equation for k. | To find k, we substitute the given data $A(5) = 40$ to obtain |

$$40 = 50e^{k \cdot 5}.$$

Thus,

| Take ln's of both sides to solve for k. | |

$$e^{5k} = \frac{40}{50} = \frac{4}{5}$$

so

$$5k = \ln\left(\frac{4}{5}\right), \quad \text{or} \quad k = \frac{1}{5}\ln\left(\frac{4}{5}\right).$$

| Write down half-life condition. | We seek a time T so that |

$$A(T) = \frac{1}{2}A(0).$$

With $A(t)$ as in equation (8) this equation becomes

$$50e^{kT} = \frac{1}{2} \cdot 50e^{0}$$

| Solve for T. | so |

$$e^{kT} = \frac{1}{2}$$

or

$$kT = \ln\left(\frac{1}{2}\right) = -\ln 2.$$

| Substitute known value for k. | Using the value for k found above, we have |

$$T = \frac{1}{k}(-\ln 2) = \frac{-\ln 2}{\frac{1}{5}\ln\left(\frac{4}{5}\right)}$$

$$= \frac{-5\ln 2}{\ln 4 - \ln 5}$$

$$\approx 15.53 \text{ days.}$$

Compound Interest

We have previously seen that the value of an initial investment of $P(0) = P_0$ dollars compounded continuously for t years at a nominal interest rate of r percent is

$$P(t) = P_0 e^{rt}. \tag{9}$$

That this function has the form of the solution to the differential equation

$$P'(t) = rP(t)$$

with initial condition $P(0) = P_0$ confirms our earlier interpretation of continuous compounding of interest: The rate of growth of the investment (i.e., the addition of interest due to compounding) is the constant $k = r$ times the current size of the investment at each instant of time.

☐ **EXAMPLE 4**

Paula's grandmother gave her a check for $500 when she graduated from high school. Paula told her grandmother that she intended to place the $500 in a savings account paying 10% interest, compounded continuously, to save for use when she graduated from college 4 years later. Under Paula's plan, what will be the value of this account in 4 years?

Solution: With $P_0 = 500$, $r = 0.10$, and $t = 4$ in equation (9) we obtain

$$P(4) = 500e^{(0.10)4} = 500e^{0.4} = 500(1.49182) = \$745.91. \qquad \blacksquare$$

☐ **EXAMPLE 5**

Susan, a high-school classmate of Paula (see Example 4) also received a cash gift on her graduation. It, however, was in the amount of $10,000. Susan has already decided to major in business in college, and to open her own business when she graduates. She intends to double the $10,000 gift in 4 years so as to have $20,000 available for launching her business. If she wishes to accomplish this by placing the $10,000 in a savings account for which interest is compounded continuously, what nominal interest rate is required to accomplish her goal?

Solution: We again use equation (9), this time with $P_0 = 10,000$, $t = 4$, and $P(t) = P(4) = 20,000$. We obtain

$$P(4) = P_0 e^{r \cdot 4}$$

or

$$20,000 = 10,000 e^{4r}.$$

Thus,

$$e^{4r} = \frac{20,000}{10,000} = 2$$

so

$$4r = \ln 2$$

and

$$r = \frac{\ln 2}{4} = \frac{0.69315}{4} = 0.17329.$$

Thus a rate of $r = 17.329\%$ is required.   ■

Present Value

Equation (9) for continuously compounded interest can be used to determine the *present value* P_0 of an asset that will have value $P(t)$ in t years. Since P_0 and $P(t)$ must satisfy equation (9), we may multiply both sides of this equation by e^{-rt} to obtain the equation for

> the present value of an asset worth $P(t)$ dollars in t years, assuming a rate of interest r compounded continuously:
>
> $$P_0 = e^{-rt}P(t) \tag{10}$$

□ **EXAMPLE 6**

Paul, a biology major, receives as a gift from his uncle a zero-coupon bond with a face value of $5000 that will mature in 8 years. What is the present value of this bond, assuming a prevailing rate of interest of $r = 6\%$?

Solution: Since zero-coupon bonds pay no interest or dividends, the entire value of the bond is determined by its face value, its maturity date, and our expectations for interest rates until the expiration date. Thus, the present value of this bond, using its face value of $P(8) = \$5000$, which will be available in $t = 8$ years, is found using equation (10) with $r = 0.06$:

$$P_0 = e^{-(0.06)}(5000)$$
$$= \$3093.92.$$ ■

□ **EXAMPLE 7**

It turns out that the best rate Susan in Example 5 can find is $r = 10\%$. How much *additional* money must she add to her initial deposit of $10,000 in order to reach her goal via continuous compounding of interest?

Solution: This time we use equation (10) with $r = 0.10$, $t = 4$, and $P(t) = P(4) = 20,000$ to find the *present value*

$$P_0 = e^{-(0.10)(4)}20,000$$
$$= e^{-0.40}(20,000)$$
$$= (0.67032)(20,000)$$
$$= 13,406.40.$$

Thus she will require an additional $3406.40.   ■

□ **EXAMPLE 8**

All living matter contains two types of carbon, ^{14}C and ^{12}C, in its molecules. While the organism is alive the ratio of ^{14}C to ^{12}C is constant, as the ^{14}C is interchanged with fixed levels of ^{14}C in the atmosphere. However, when a plant or animal dies, this replenishment ceases and the radioactive ^{14}C present decays exponentially with a half-life of 5760 years. By examining the $^{14}C/^{12}C$ ratio, archaeologists can determine the percentage of the original ^{14}C level remaining and thereby date a once living fossil.

(a) What percentage of the original ^{14}C will exist after 2000 years?
(b) If a fossil contains 10% of its original amount, what is its age?

Solution: Let $A(t)$ be the percentage amount of ^{14}C remaining t years after the fossil's death. Since $A(t)$ decays exponentially, we know that $A(t)$ has the form

$$A(t) = A_0 e^{kt}.$$

Clearly $A(0) = 100\%$, so $A_0 = 100$. To find k, we use the fact that the half-life is 5760 years. That is

$$A(5760) = \frac{1}{2}A_0.$$

Thus

$$A_0 e^{5760k} = \frac{1}{2}A_0$$

so

$$e^{5760k} = \frac{1}{2}$$

$$5760k = \ln\left(\frac{1}{2}\right) = \ln 1 - \ln 2 = -\ln 2$$

and

$$k = \frac{-\ln 2}{5760}.$$

The function $A(t)$ is therefore

$$A(t) = 100e^{\left(\frac{-\ln 2}{5760}t\right)}.$$

(a) After $t = 2000$ years the percent of ^{14}C remaining will be

$$A(2000) = 100e^{\left(\frac{-\ln 2}{5760}\right)(2000)}$$

$$= 100e^{-0.24}$$

$$\approx 79\%.$$

(b) To find the number of years T after which 10% of the original ^{14}C will remain, we set up the equation

$$A(T) = 0.10A(0)$$

which gives

$$100e^{\left(\frac{-\ln 2}{5760}T\right)} = 0.10(100)$$

or

$$e^{\left(\frac{-\ln 2}{5760}T\right)} = 0.10.$$

Thus

$$\left(\frac{-\ln 2}{5760}\right)T = \ln 0.1$$

so

$$T = \frac{5760(\ln 0.1)}{-\ln 2}$$

$$\approx 19{,}134 \text{ years.}$$

☑ PRACTICE PROBLEMS 4.5

1. Find the solution of the initial-value problem

$$\frac{dy}{dt} + 3y = 0, \qquad y(0) = 30.$$

2. A biological population of rabbits is growing exponentially. At the time of the first census there were 20 rabbits in the population. One year later there were 50. According to these data, how many rabbits would we expect to find after a second year?

Exercise Set 4.5

In Exercises 1–6, find the general solution of the differential equation.

1. $N'(t) = 4N(t)$

2. $\dfrac{dN}{dt} = -3N$

3. $f'(x) = -2f(x)$

4. $\dfrac{dy}{dt} = \pi y$

5. $\dfrac{dy}{dt} + 3y = 0$

6. $f'(t) - 6f(t) = 0$

In Exercises 7–10, find the unique solution of the differential equation satisfying the given initial condition.

7. $N'(t) = 4N(t), \qquad N(0) = 4$

8. $\dfrac{dy}{dx} = -2y, \qquad y(0) = -4$

9. $\dfrac{dN}{dt} + 10N = 0, \qquad N(0) = 6$

10. $\dfrac{dy}{dt} - 5y = 0,$ $y(0) = 4.$

11. A savings account pays 10% interest, compounded continuously. What amount of money deposited today will have grown to $2500 in 8 years?

12. What rate of interest, compounded continuously, will produce an effective annual yield of 8%? (Effective annual yield is the rate required under *annual* compounding of interest to obtain the specified yield.)

13. Show that the effective annual rate of interest, i, for continuous compounding of interest is $i = e^r - 1$.

14. True or false? If the population $P(t)$ of a city is increasing at a rate of 5% per year, then the function $P(t)$, if differentiable, satisfies the equation $P'(t) = 0.05P(t)$. If this is false, what is the correct equation?

15. How long does it take for a deposit of P_0 dollars to double at 5% interest compounded continuously?

16. True or false? The half-life of an isotope depends on the amount present. Why?

17. A radioactive isotope decays exponentially with a half-life of 20 days. Assume that 50 mg of the isotope remain after 10 days.
   a. How much of the isotope was present initially?
   b. How much will remain after 30 days?

18. For the isotope in Exercise 17, when will 90% of the initial amount have disintegrated?

19. The number of bacteria in a certain culture grows from 50 to 400 in 12 hours. Assume that the rate of increase is proportional to the number of bacteria present.
   a. How long does it take for the number of bacteria present to double?
   b. How many bacteria will be present after 16 hours?

20. Show that the relative rate of growth of an investment of P_0 dollars compounded continuously at a rate of r percent per year is r.

21. Bacteria grow rapidly in a certain rich culture, at a rate proportional to their current number. If 100,000 bacteria grow in number to 150,000 in 2 hours, how many bacteria will be present after 5 hours?

22. The half-life of radium is approximately 1600 years. How long will it take 10 grams of radium to decay to 6 grams?

23. After 3 years a deposit of $1000 has earned a total of $400 in accrued interest compounded continuously at a nominal rate of r percent. Find r.

24. How long will it be until a deposit of P dollars triples under continuous compounding of interest at a nominal interest rate of 8%?

25. When a certain drug is injected into a patient the amount of the drug present in the patient's bloodstream t hours after the injection satisfies the differential equation $A'(t) = -0.10A(t)$. Find the amount present 6 hours after an injection of 10 milligrams.

26. After 2 years, 80% of an original amount of a radioactive isotope remains. What is its half-life?

27. A start-up company's sales increased from $10,000 in year one to $150,000 in year two. If the growth in sales is exponential, what sales level will result in year three?

28. In a simple model of the growth of a biological population the rate of increase of N, the number of individuals, is proportional to the difference between the birthrate, b, and the death rate, d. That is, the simple birth–death model of population growth is

$$\frac{dN}{dt} = bN - dN.$$

   a. Find an expression for population size, N, as a function of the birthrate b, the death rate d, and the initial population size N_0.
   b. In a population modelled by this process there are 20 births and 10 deaths per year per 100 individuals. Find the anticipated size of the population in 20 years if its current size is $N_0 = 200$ individuals.

29. When a foreign substance is introduced into the body, the body's defense mechanisms move to break down the substance and excrete it. The rate of excretion is usually proportional to the concentration in the body, and the half-life of the resulting exponential decay is referred to as the *biological half-life* of the substance. If, after 12 hours, 30% of a massive dosage of a substance has been excreted by the body, what is the biological half-life of the substance?

30. What differential equation describes the biological half-life described in Exercise 29?

31. A fossil contains 80% of its original amount of ^{14}C. What is its age? (See Example 8.)

32. The body concentrates iodine in the thyroid gland. This observation leads to the treatment of thyroid cancer by the injection of radioactive iodine into the bloodstream. One isotope used has a half-life of approximately 8 days and decays exponentially in time. If 50 micrograms of this isotope are injected, what amount remains in the body after 3 weeks?

33. For the radioactive iodine injections described in Exercise 32, suppose it is desired that the amount of iodine in the bloodstream be maintained at no less than 20 micrograms. When should a second injection be scheduled so that it occurs precisely when the original injection has decayed to this amount?

34. A chemical dissolves in water at a rate proportional to the amount still undissolved. If 20 grams of the chemical are placed in water and 10 grams remain undissolved 5 minutes later, when will 90% of the chemical be dissolved?

☑ **SOLUTIONS TO PRACTICE PROBLEMS 4.5**

1. Here $\dfrac{dy}{dt} = -3y$. This is a differential equation for exponential decay. The general solution, by Theorem 1, is

$$y = Ce^{-3t}$$

where $C = y(0)$. Since we are given $y(0) = 30$, the specific solution is

$$y = 30e^{-3t}.$$

2. We are given that the population size $P(t)$ is growing exponentially. Thus, $P(t) = P_0 e^{kt}$ for some constants P_0 and k. But P_0 is the initial size of the population, which is given to be $P_0 = 20$. Thus,

$$P(t) = 20e^{kt}.$$

Substituting the given data $P(1) = 50$ gives

$$50 = 20e^{k \cdot 1}$$

so $e^k = \dfrac{50}{20} = 2.5$.

Thus $k = \ln 2.5$, and the population function is completely determined: $P(t) = 20e^{(\ln 2.5)t}$. After $t = 2$ years, we expect to observe

$$P(2) = 20e^{2 \ln(2.5)} = 20(e^{\ln 2.5})^2 = 20(2.5)^2 = 125 \text{ rabbits.}$$

4.6 Mathematical Modelling (Optional)

Up to this point we have made use of a number of *mathematical* models for various physical, biological, social, and economic phenomena. For example, the differential equation

$$P'(t) = kP(t)$$

and the corresponding solution $P(t) = Ce^{kt}$ were referred to as a mathematical model for the exponential growth, or decay, of a population or an amount of a substance of some kind.

What is a mathematical model, how is one developed, and how is one used? We shall comment briefly on each of these questions in this section.

What Is a Mathematical Model? A mathematical model is just a mathematical expression that *predicts* the values of one or more outputs (dependent variables) based on the data (values of the independent variable) supplied by the user of the model (see Figure 6.1).

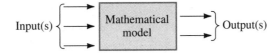

Input(s) { → [Mathematical model] → } Output(s)

Figure 6.1 A mathematical model provides predictions (outputs) when provided sufficient data (inputs).

Frequently, a mathematical model is an explicit function, such as the population growth function $P(t) = Ce^{kt}$: Once C, k, and t are specified, the population size $P(t)$ is determined by the equation for P.

Here are some other examples of mathematical models, in the form of explicit functions, that we have already seen:

$$V(t) = P - t\left(\frac{P - S}{N}\right) \qquad \text{(straight-line depreciation)}$$

$$P(t) = P_0 e^{rt} \qquad \text{(compound interest)}$$

$$P(0) = P(T)e^{-rT} \qquad \text{(present value)}$$

$$N(t) = I(t) + S(t) \qquad \text{(epidemic spread)}$$

$$v = \frac{\alpha}{L}(R^2 - r^2) \qquad \text{(fluid flow)}$$

(see Figure 6.2).

Mathematical models need not be in the form of explicit functions like these, however. Often a model consists of a differential equation, and the outputs are specific functions (solutions) rather than numbers (See Figure 6.3). Other kinds of mathematical models are statistical distributions, computer programs, and even graphical displays and motion pictures. Indeed, one of the newest branches of mathematics, called fractal geometry, is often best described by graphical images. This is also true for the closely related subject of chaos theory.

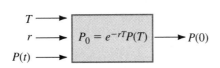

$T \rightarrow$
$r \rightarrow$ $\boxed{P_0 = e^{-rT}P(T)}$ $\rightarrow P(0)$
$P(t) \rightarrow$

Figure 6.2 Mathematical model for present value predicts present value based on assumptions (inputs) of interest rate, time, and future value.

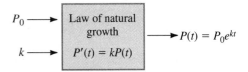

$P_0 \rightarrow$ $\boxed{\begin{array}{c}\text{Law of natural growth} \\ P'(t) = kP(t)\end{array}}$ $\rightarrow P(t) = P_0 e^{kt}$
$k \rightarrow$

Figure 6.3 The differential equation $P'(t) = kP(t)$ modelling the Law of Natural Growth produces a population function P as its output.

How Do Mathematical
Models Arise?

There are several general ways in which mathematical models arise. In many instances, especially in the physical sciences, there is an underlying scientific principle, or law, that becomes translated into mathematical statements. The model for natural (exponential) growth is one such example. Another is the model for logistic growth, which we describe later in this section. Yet another is the still-impressive discovery of Johannes Kepler: by discovering three simple geometric properties describing the motion of the planets about the sun, he was able to work out precise equations for their orbits.

In the life sciences, models are less likely to result from the direct translation of a biological principle into a mathematical statement. It is more often the case, especially in questions about human physiology and health, that large amounts of data must first be collected (very carefully, according to well-established principles) and analyzed to determine patterns of behavior. When such patterns are observed, models (equations, often) are developed that seem to "fit" the observed data. These models are then tested against additional data to be refined, accepted, or rejected. Here is one such example.

□ **EXAMPLE 1**

Human growth in height from age one year to adulthood has been modelled by a number of researchers using the double logistic function

$$y(t) = \frac{a}{1 + e^{-b_1(t - c_1)}} + \frac{d - a}{1 + e^{-b_2(t - c_2)}}$$

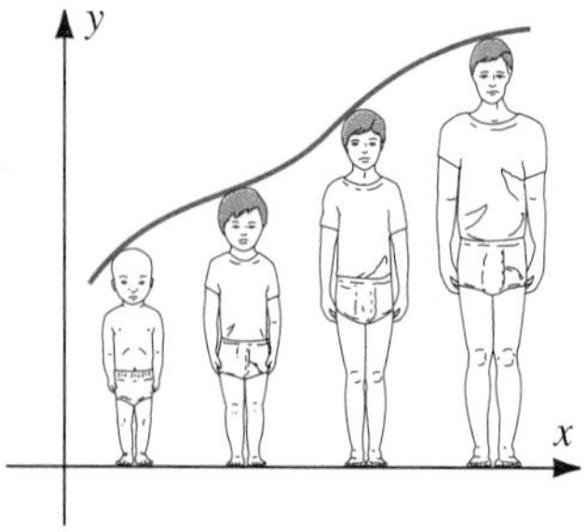

where the constants a, b_1, b_2, c_1, c_2, and d are different for each individual.

A typical graph of a double-logistic curve, which contains two "growth spurts," appears in Figure 6.4. Sophisticated statistical techniques are required to "fit" this model to growth data on a particular individual.

Note, however, that we can see that the constant d represents mature adult height in this model, assuming $b_1 > 0$ and $b_2 > 0$, because

$$\lim_{t \to \infty} \left[\frac{a}{1 + e^{-b_1(t - c_1)}} + \frac{d - a}{1 + e^{-b_2(t - c_2)}} \right] = \frac{a}{1 + 0} + \frac{d - a}{1 + 0}$$

$$= d. \quad \blacksquare$$

Figure 6.4 Double-logistic model for human growth.

Still other mathematical models, such as those for air flow about aircraft wings or the analysis of financial markets, contain such high degrees of complexities that they can be described and used only with the aid of computers, even supercomputers.

How Are Mathematical
Models Used?

The value of a mathematical model is in its ability to *predict*. Given certain inputs, the model should predict, with an acceptable degree of precision, what the result (output) will be in the system or phenomenon being modelled.

The advantage of mathematical models over less formal predictors lies in the precision of the predictions.

The precision of mathematical models also is a factor in their limitations, however. The precision of the particular model itself, especially if it is in the simple form of an equation, may be of little value if the model is not a ''good fit'' for the phenomenon being modelled. For example, economic theory often proceeds by trying to observe, in complex situations, certain underlying motivations of behavior. While reducing a complex problem to a smaller number of simpler principles can yield more tractable models, their accuracy in describing the original complex problem can leave room for improvement.

It is often the case that mathematical models are less complex than the phenomenon they model, due to necessary ''simplifying assumptions'' made in constructing the model. There is almost always some trade-off between accuracy and complexity in such cases, which makes the concern about accuracy of predictions all the more important.

These remarks on mathematical models have been general in nature, because mathematical modelling is a complex subject that itself cannot be modelled simply. We conclude with two examples of simple but particularly useful mathematical models, to illustrate how these observations apply in particular settings.

A Model for Bounded Growth: The Logistic Curve

In developing the mathematical model for natural growth, we assumed no limit on the eventual size of the population and proceeded from the *Law of Natural Growth*

$$\{\text{growth rate}\} \propto \{\text{present size of population}\}$$

to develop the mathematical model for natural growth,

$$N'(t) = kN(t).$$

An unstated assumption in this model was that there is no limit on the size of the population. The assumption of unlimited growth is unrealistic for many populations, however, even for fruit flies in a bell jar. Often there is a natural limit, or *carrying capacity,* to the environment (or, ecological niche) in which the population exists. When this is the case, we must adapt the Law of Natural Growth (or, *refine* our model) to acknowledge the limit on population size. One growth law that does this is called the *Law of Limited Growth,* which states that the rate at which the population grows is proportional to the product of *two* factors: as before, one factor is the present size of the population; the other factor is *the unutilized capacity for growth* in the environment. That is

$$\{\text{growth rate}\} \propto \left\{\begin{array}{c}\text{present size}\\ \text{population}\end{array}\right\}\left\{\begin{array}{c}\text{unutilized capacity}\\ \text{for \ \ growth}\end{array}\right\} \qquad (1)$$

To convert this biological law into a mathematical model, we again let the function $P(t)$ denote the size of the population at time t. Then the growth rate is $P'(t)$, as before. We must introduce a term representing the maximum possible size for the population, for which we use the letter M. Then the unutilized capacity for growth, when the population is of size $P(t)$, is $M - P(t)$, or, as a proportion, $\dfrac{[M - P(t)]}{M}$.

With this notation, and using k as the constant of proportionality as in Section 4.5, we can write the biological law (1) as a mathematical model as follows:

$$P'(t) = kP(t)\left[\frac{M - P(t)}{M}\right] \qquad (2)$$

Solving this differential equation requires techniques beyond what we have developed at this point. However, the solution is known to be

$$P(t) = \frac{M}{1 + Ce^{-kt}} \qquad (3)$$

where C is a constant determined by an initial condition. (You can verify that $P(t)$ in (3) is a solution of equation (2) by differentiating and substituting into equation (3).)

Figure 6.5 shows a typical graph of the function P. It is called a *logistic* curve, and it has the following properties:

a. For small t, it resembles an exponential growth curve (because a population that is very small relative to its environment's capacity is largely unaffected by this limit).
b. It has an inflection point Q (essentially, this represents the "crossover" between early exponential growth and a population size beginning to approach its limit).
c. It has a horizontal asymptote at its carrying capacity, $y = M$, that can be seen from the limit

$$\lim_{t \to \infty} P(t) = \lim_{t \to \infty}\left[\frac{M}{1 + Ce^{-kt}}\right] = M, \qquad k > 0.$$

Logistic curves, and the logistic model for bounded growth, occur in many situations where there is an upper limit on the size to which a quantity can grow. Some such examples are learning curves (rapid early learning that slows as mastery is obtained), the effects of public relations promotional efforts (where the phenomenon of consumer "saturation" is an upper limit on effectiveness), and the spread of rumors.

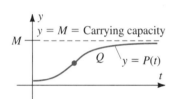

Figure 6.5 A typical logistic curve.

☐ **EXAMPLE 2**

A population of mice is growing in a limited environment according to the logistic growth model in equation (2). If 20 mice are present initially and 45 are observed after 60 days, find the population size predicted by the logistic model after 120 days, given that the maximum possible size for the population is $M = 180$.

Solution: Using $M = 180$, we substitute the given initial data $P(0) = 20$ into the form

$$P(t) = \frac{M}{1 + Ce^{-kt}}$$

of the solution to obtain

$$20 = P(0) = \frac{180}{1 + Ce^{-k(0)}} = \frac{180}{1 + C}.$$

Thus, $1 + C = \frac{180}{20} = 9$, so $C = 8$.

Next, we substitute the data $P(60) = 45$ to obtain

$$45 = P(6) = \frac{180}{1 + 8e^{-k(60)}}$$

so

$$1 + 8e^{-60k} = \frac{180}{45} = 4.$$

Then

$$e^{-60k} = \frac{4 - 1}{8} = \frac{3}{8}$$

and, on taking natural logarithms of both sides,

$$k = \frac{\ln\left(\dfrac{3}{8}\right)}{60}.$$

Finally, to determine the population size predicted after 120 days, we substitute $t = 120$ and all known quantities, to obtain

$$P(120) = \frac{180}{1 + 8e^{\left(\frac{\ln(3/8)}{60}\right)(120)}}$$

$$= \frac{180}{1 + 8e^{2\ln(3/8)}}$$

$$= \frac{180}{1 + 8\left(\dfrac{3}{8}\right)^2} = \frac{180}{1 + \dfrac{9}{8}} = \frac{180 \cdot 8}{17} = 84.7.$$

Of course, a population of 84.7 mice makes no sense. But a population of size 84 or 85 is the intended *prediction* in this case. ■

□ **EXAMPLE 3**

What would the answer to Example 2 have been had we assumed exponential growth of the population (i.e., the Law of Natural Growth) rather than logistic (limited) growth?

Solution: For natural growth, we assume a population function $P(t) = P_0 e^{kt}$ and we ignore the carrying capacity M.

Since $P_0 = P(0) = 20$ is given, we know that $P(t) = 20e^{kt}$. Substituting the data $P(60) = 45$ into this equation gives

$$45 = P(60) = 20e^{60k}$$

so

$$e^{60k} = \frac{45}{20} = \frac{9}{4}$$

and

$$k = \frac{1}{60} \ln \frac{9}{4}.$$

With this value for k, the prediction for $P(120)$ is

$$P(120) = 20e^{\left[\frac{1}{60} \ln(9/4)\right](120)}$$
$$= 20e^{2 \cdot \ln(9/4)}$$
$$= 20\left(\frac{9}{4}\right)^2$$
$$= 101.25.$$

Thus, rather than the prediction 84 or 85 from the model for limited growth, we obtain the prediction 101 or 102. Note the significant effect of the assumption about a limit on the eventual size of the population! ■

The Normal Distribution

Another important mathematical model, and one that is not simply in the form of an equation, is the familiar "bell-shaped curve" that describes the distribution of IQ scores, physical characteristics of large populations (height, weight, etc.), and a host of other properties of people and events.

Mathematically, the normal distribution is associated with a function of the form

$$f(x) = \frac{1}{\sigma\sqrt{2\pi}} e^{-\frac{1}{2}\left(\frac{x-\mu}{\sigma}\right)^2}$$

(called the normal probability density function (pdf)) that is to be used in a way that we shall describe below. Before doing so, however, we note several properties of the graph of the normal distribution (see Figure 6.6):

(i) The graph is symmetric with respect to the line $x = \mu$. (That is, $f(\mu + x) = f(\mu - x)$ for all x.) The constant μ (mu) is called the *mean* (middle) of the distribution.

(ii) The graph has inflection points at $x = \mu \pm \sigma$. (You are asked to show this in Exercise 26). The constant σ is called the *standard deviation* for the normal distribution.

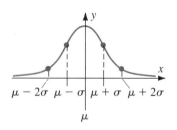

Figure 6.6 Graph of normal distribution $f(x) =$

$$\frac{1}{\sigma\sqrt{2\pi}} e^{-\frac{1}{2}\left(\frac{x-\mu}{\sigma}\right)^2}$$

(iii) The constants μ and σ completely determine the shape of the graph. Once these two numbers are chosen, we can compute $f(x)$ for any real number x.

The normal distribution is used as follows. When it is known (through statistical validation using methods beyond the scope of the text here) that a population (such as a group of measurements of human height) is "distributed normally," with mean μ and standard deviation σ, the normal probability density function can be used to determine what proportion of the entire population falls between any two measurements. This is done by comparing the area of the region under the graph of the probability density function lying between the two measurements to the area of the entire region bounded by the curve.

Figure 6.7 illustrates this principle for IQ scores, which are (by design of the tests) normally distributed with mean $\mu = 100$ and standard deviation 16. The proportion of all scores falling between $x_1 = 105$ and $x_2 = 120$ is the same as the proportion of the shaded region to the entire region bounded by the graph of the normal distribution $f(x) = \dfrac{1}{16\sqrt{2\pi}} e^{-\frac{1}{2}\left(\frac{x-100}{16}\right)^2}$.

In more advanced courses it is shown that, for a probability density function with mean μ and standard deviation σ,

(i) Approximately 68% of the area of the entire region bounded by the graph lies within one standard deviation of the mean, that is, between $\mu - \sigma$ and $\mu + \sigma$.

(ii) Approximately 95% of the area of the entire region bounded by the graph lies within two standard deviations of the mean, that is, between $\mu - 2\sigma$ and $\mu + 2\sigma$. (See Figure 6.8.)

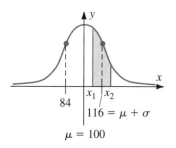

Figure 6.7 Proportion of IQ scores falling between $x_1 = 105$ and $x_2 = 120$ equals the proportion of the area of the shaded region to the area of the entire region under the curve.

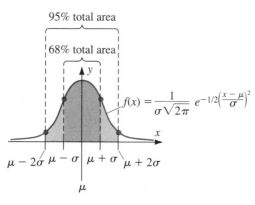

Figure 6.8 Areas corresponding to one and two standard deviations.

☐ **EXAMPLE 4**

Assuming that IQ scores are normally distributed with $\mu = 100$ and $\sigma = 16$, what percent of the scores fall between $x_1 = 100$ and $x_2 = 116$?

Solution: Using the symmetry of the normal probability density function, and the fact that approximately 68% of the scores fall in the interval $[\mu - \sigma, \mu + \sigma]$ = [84, 116], we conclude that half this number, or approximately 34%, will lie in the interval [100, 116] = $[\mu, \mu + \sigma]$. (See Figure 6.9.) ▪

☐ **EXAMPLE 5**

Again referring to IQ scores, what percent of all scores are

(a) greater than 84?
(b) less than 84?

Solution: Since the score $x = 84$ lies exactly one standard deviation to the left of the mean, that is, $84 = \mu - \sigma$, we can see from Figure 6.10 that

(a) the area of the region to the right of $x = 84$ consists of two pieces, one (from $x = 84$ to $x = 100$) containing 34% total area (as in Example 4); the other being the entire right half of the region, containing 50% total area. Thus, scores above 84 constitute $(34 + 50)\% = 84\%$ of all scores.
(b) The remaining region is $(100 - 84)\% = 16\%$ of the entire region, so the percent of scores below 84 is 16%. ▪

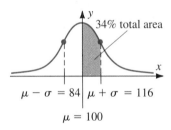

Figure 6.9 34% of the area lies between $\mu = 100$ and $\mu + \sigma = 116$.

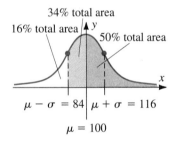

Figure 6.10 16% of the total area lies to the left of 84 = $\mu - \sigma$.

Obviously, this topic is too complex for an adequate treatment to be given here. In order to work with normal distributions for populations we need to be able to calculate areas of regions bounded by the graphs of exponential functions, for example, and to have some notion of what it means to calculate the area of a region of infinite extent. (All of these topics will be covered in later chapters, however.)

Nevertheless, we have mentioned the normal distribution here because it is a somewhat different kind of mathematical model. It is not just a function. It is a more sophisticated package, where the area of region bounded by the graph of a probability density function provides the prediction, not just the function itself.

Mathematical models can have many different forms and degrees of sophistication. The successful pursuit of mathematical modelling involves both a comprehensive understanding of the subject area in which the modelling is being done and a mastery of the mathematics associated with the model. This book is primarily focused on the latter, with as much attention to particular models as is appropriately useful.

Exercise Set 4.6

1. A population of bats grows in an environment with a carrying capacity of $M = 500$ bats. If 10 bats are present initially and 40 are present after 6 months, how many will be present, according to the logistic model for limited growth,
   a. after 1 year?
   b. after 3 years?

2. Fruit flies are growing in a bell jar that can sustain at most 1000 flies. If 50 are present at one observation and 120 two days later, what number are predicted after another two days by the model for limited growth?

3. What is the answer for Exercise 1 if the assumption on limited growth is changed to an assumption of unlimited growth?

4. What is the answer to Exercise 2 if the assumption of limited growth is dropped and the model for natural growth is assumed?

5. What are the coordinates of the inflection point on the graph of the logistic function $f(t) = \dfrac{100}{1 + 5e^{-2t}}$?

6. Sketch the graph of the logistic function
   $$f(t) = \frac{20}{1 + 10e^{-t}}.$$

7. Verify that the graph of the normal probability density function is symmetric about the line $x = \mu$ by showing that $f(\mu - x) = f(\mu + x)$ for all x.

In Exercises 8–14, let $f(x) = \dfrac{1}{16\sqrt{2x}} e^{-\frac{1}{2}\left(\frac{x - 100}{16}\right)^2}$ be the normal probability density function with mean $\mu = 100$ and standard deviation $\sigma = 16$. Consider a set of test scores (such as IQ scores) that have this distribution. Using the information summarized in Figure 6.8, determine approximately what percent of the scores fall in the following places:

8. below 116

9. above 116

10. above 132

11. below 132

12. between 84 and 132

13. between 68 and 100

14. between 68 and 132

Let $g(x) = \dfrac{1}{\sqrt{2x}} e^{-\frac{1}{2}x^2}$ be the normal probability density function with mean $\mu = 0$ and standard deviation $\sigma = 1$. (This is called the *standard* normal probability density function.) For measurements (such as scores) with this distribution, find the approximate percent falling:

15. above $x = 0$

16. above $x = -1$

17. between $x = -1$ and $x = 1$

18. between $x = 0$ and $x = 2$

19. below $x = -2$

20. between $x = -1$ and $x = 2$

21. Graph the standard normal probability density function
   $$g(x) = \frac{1}{\sqrt{2\pi}} e^{-x^2/2}.$$

22. Find the inflection points for the standard normal probability density function in Exercise 21.

23. Give an example of a mathematical model from physics.

24. Give an example of a mathematical model where we know that the prediction is very precise. (*Hint:* Consider our earlier work on velocity of objects, for example.)

25. Give an example of a mathematical model that could not be entirely precise in its predictions. What is the reason for the imprecision?

26. Show that the graph of the normal probability density function has inflection points at $x = \mu \pm \sigma$.

Summary Outline of Chapter 4

▮ *Definition:* $a^n = a \cdot a \cdot a \cdots \cdot a$ (n factors) (Page 294)

$$a^{-n} = \frac{1}{a^n}, \quad a \neq 0$$

$$a^0 = 1$$

▮ *Properties of Exponents* (Page 295)

$$(E1) \quad a^n a^m = a^{n+m}$$

$$(E2) \quad \frac{a^n}{a^m} = a^{n-m}$$

$$(E3) \quad [a^n]^m = a^{nm}$$

▮ *Definition:* $a^{1/n} = y$ means $y^n = a$ ($a > 0$ if n is even). (Page 295)

▮ *Formula for Compound Interest* (Page 299)

$$P(n) = \left(1 + \frac{r}{k}\right)^{nk} P_0$$

where P_0 = original amount, r = interest rate, k = number of compoundings annually, n = years.

▮ *Definition:* $e = \lim\limits_{x \to \infty} \left(1 + \frac{1}{x}\right)^x$ (Page 301)

$$e \approx 2.718281828.\ldots$$

▮ *Formula for Continuous Compounding of Interest:* $P(t) = e^{rt} P_0$. (Page 302)

▮ *Definition:* $\log_b y = x$ if and only if $y = b^x$. (Page 306)

▮ *Properties of Logarithms* (Page 308)

$$(L1) \quad \log_b(xy) = \log_b x + \log_b y$$

$$(L2) \quad \log_b\left(\frac{x}{y}\right) = \log_b x - \log_b y$$

$$(L3) \quad \log_b x^r = r \log_b x$$

▮ *Definition:* $\ln x = \log_e x$. Thus $\ln y = x$ if and only if $y = e^x$. (Page 309)

▮ *Definition:* $b^x = e^{x \ln b}$ (Page 313)

▮ For $f(x) = \ln x$, $f'(x) = \dfrac{1}{x}$; $\dfrac{d}{dx} \ln x = \dfrac{1}{x}$. (Page 316)

▮ For $f(x) = \ln u(x)$, $f'(x) = \dfrac{u'(x)}{u(x)}$; $\dfrac{d}{dx} \ln u = \dfrac{1}{u} \cdot \dfrac{du}{dx}$. (Page 317)

▮ The **rate of growth** of f at $x = x_0$ is $G(x_0) = \dfrac{f'(x_0)}{f(x_0)}$. (Page 321)

■ For $f(x) = e^x$, $f'(x) = e^x$; $\dfrac{d}{dx} e^x = e^x$.   (Page 326)

■ For $f(x) = e^{u(x)}$, $f'(x) = e^{u(x)} u'(x)$; $\dfrac{d}{dx} e^u = e^u \cdot \dfrac{du}{dx}$.   (Page 327)

■ For $f(x) = a^x$, $f'(x) = a^x \ln a$; $\dfrac{d}{dx} a^x = a^x \ln a$.   (Page 333)

■ For $f(x) = \log_a x$, $f'(x) = \dfrac{1}{x \ln a}$; $\dfrac{d}{dx} \log_a x = \dfrac{1}{x \ln a}$.   (Page 334)

■ A function that satisfies the **Law of Natural Growth**   (Page 338)

$$P'(t) = kP(t)$$

must have the form $P(t) = P_0 e^{kt}$, where $P_0 = P(0)$.

Review Exercises—Chapter 4

1. Simplify the following.

   a. $49^{-3/2}$

   b. $8^{-4/3}$

   c. $\left(\dfrac{8}{27}\right)^{2/3}$

   d. $\left(\dfrac{36}{81}\right)^{-3/2}$

2. Simplify the given expression.

   a. $e^6 e^{-2}$

   b. $\dfrac{(2^{-3} \cdot 3^{-2})^3}{\frac{1}{3}(16)^{3/4}}$

   c. $\dfrac{\{8e^{3x}\}^{-2/3}}{\sqrt{9e^2}}$

   d. $\{16e^{-4}2^{8x}\}^{3/4}$

3. Find the value of a deposit of $400 after 3 years in a savings account paying 6% nominal interest compounded semiannually.

4. Find the value of the investment in Exercise 3 if the interest is compounded continuously.

5. Find the present value of an investment that will yield a sum of $10,000 in 5 years if the prevailing rate of interest is expected to be 10%.

6. Find $\log_b x$.

   a. $\log_{10} \dfrac{1}{100}$

   b. $\log_3 243$

   c. $\log_2 \dfrac{1}{4}$

   d. $\ln(e^{-3})$

7. Solve for x:

   a. $e^{3x} = 1$

   b. $e^{x^2+x-2} = 1$

   c. $e^{3x} = e^{2x+5}$

   d. $e^{2x} - e^x - 2 = 0$

8. The selling price p and quantity sold x per month for a particular item are related by the equation $p = 50e^{-2x}$. Solve this equation for x as a function of p.

9. For the item in Exercise 8, find the selling price p for which revenue is a maximum.

10. For the price–demand model in Exercise 8, how many items will be sold per month at price $p = 2$ dollars?

In Exercises 11–30, find the derivative of the given function.

11. $y = \ln 6x$

12. $f(x) = xe^{-3x}$

13. $y = e^{6-x^2}$

14. $f(x) = 4 \ln(3x^2 + 2)$

15. $f(t) = e^{t^3-3t+2}$

16. $y = te^{1-t}$

17. $f(x) = \ln \sqrt{x + 1}$

18. $f(x) = \sqrt{1 - \ln^2 x}$

19. $y = x^2 e^{\sqrt{x}}$

20. $f(x) = \ln(e^{2x} - 2)$

21. $y = \ln\left(\dfrac{x}{x + 2}\right)$

22. $y = e^{\sqrt{x}} \ln x$

23. $f(x) = \ln \ln \sqrt{x}$

24. $y = x \ln(\sqrt{x} - e^{-x})$

25. $y = xe^{x-\sqrt{x}}$

26. $y = e^{t+\ln t}$

27. $y = \ln^2(1 - e^{-2x})$

28. $y = \sqrt{e^x - e^{-x}}$

29. $f(t) = e^{\sqrt{t} - \ln t}$ **30.** $f(x) = x^2 e^{1 - \sqrt{x}}$

In Exercises 31–34, find $\dfrac{dy}{dx}$ by implicit differentiation.

31. $x \ln y + y \ln x = 4$ **32.** $x^2 + e^{xy} - y = 2$

33. $e^{xy} = 3xy$ **34.** $\ln xy = x - y$

35. Find all relative extrema for the function $y = x^2 \ln x$.

36. Find the maximum and minimum values of the function $f(x) = e^{x^2/3}$ for x in the interval $[-1, \sqrt{8}]$.

37. On what intervals is the graph of the function $y = \ln(1 + x^2)$ concave up?

38. Find all relative extrema for the function $y = x^2 - \ln x^2$.

39. Find r if $2^x = e^{rx}$ for all x.

40. Find the equation of the line tangent to the graph of $y = xe^{2x}$ at the point $(\ln 2, 4 \ln 2)$.

41. A cylindrical jar 12 centimeters in diameter is leaking water at a rate of $\ln(t^2)$ cubic centimeters per minute. How fast is the water level in the jar falling?

Find the solutions of the differential equation.

42. $\dfrac{dy}{dx} = 2y$ **43.** $\dfrac{dy}{dx} + y = 0$

44. Find the solution of the initial value problem.

$$2y' + 4y = 0$$
$$y(0) = \pi$$

45. The population of the United States in 1970 was 203 million. By 1980 the population had grown to 227 million. Assuming exponential growth, what was the population in 1990?

46. In the chemical reaction called the inversion of raw sugar, the inversion rate is proportional to the amount of raw sugar remaining. If 100 kilograms of raw sugar is reduced to 75 kilograms in 6 hours, how long will it be until
a. half the raw sugar has been inverted?
b. 90% of the raw sugar has been inverted?

47. A population of fruit flies grows exponentially. If initially there were 100 flies and if after 10 days there were 500 flies, how many flies were present after 4 days?

48. 100 grams of a radioactive substance is reduced to 40 grams in 6 hours. If the decay is exponential, what is the half-life?

49. Show that the exponential function $f(x) = Ce^{kx}$ satisfies the differential equation $f'(x + a) = kf(x + a)$ for every real number a.

50. Find the numbers k for which the functions $f(x) = \ln kx$ and $g(x) = \ln x$ have the same derivative. Explain your answer.

51. Paul, a pre-med major, inherits a zero-coupon bond that will mature in 4 years with a redemption value of $2000. What is the present value of this bond, assuming a prevailing interest rate of 5% during this period?

52. The Clark family wishes to create an education fund for its children by depositing equal amounts D every January 1 into a savings account paying 5% interest compounded continuously. If this plan is followed for 5 years,
a. Show that the value of the account after 5 years is

$$T = D(e^{0.25} + e^{0.20} + e^{0.15} + e^{0.10} + e^{0.05}).$$

b. What must D equal in order that the total T equal $20,000?
c. What is the answer to part b if the interest rate r is changed to $r = 8\%$?

CHAPTER

5

These deer provide an example of a natural population whose growth over time can be measured using the definite integral. The theory and applications of the definite integral are discussed in this chapter.
(Carl R. Sams II/Peter Arnold, Inc.)

Antiderivatives and the Definite Integral

In this chapter we develop two major themes—reversing the process of differentiation (antidifferentiation) and calculating the areas of certain types of regions in the plane. While these two issues may seem unrelated, we shall see, using the Fundamental Theorem of Calculus, that they are intimately related, and that both yield important applications in business and economics.

5.1 Antiderivatives: Reversing the Process of Differentiation

We have seen that the derivative of a function may be interpreted as the rate at which it changes. For example, if the function $y = C(x)$ gives a company's total cost in producing x lawnmowers per week, the derivative $C'(x)$ gives the rate at which total cost changes with respect to change in the production level x. In this case we have referred to the derivative C' as the *marginal cost* function. In short, marginal cost is obtained from total cost by the process of differentiation.

Now consider just the reverse situation. Suppose you were told that the company's marginal cost in producing lawnmowers was $100 per lawnmower, regardless of current production level. That is, suppose

$$C'(x) = MC(x) = 100$$

is given. What can you say about the total cost function C? Obviously, it must be a function C whose derivative is $C'(x) = 100$. One such function that comes to mind immediately is

$$C_1(x) = 100x.$$

But there are others, including

$$C_2(x) = 500 + 100x$$
$$C_3(x) = 10,000 + 100x$$

and

$$C_4(x) = K + 100x$$

where K is any constant. Each of these functions has the property that its derivative is $MC(x) = 100$. For this reason each is called an *antiderivative* of the marginal cost function $MC(x)$.

Definition 1

The function F is called an **antiderivative** for the function f if F is differentiable and if

$$F'(x) = f(x).$$

In other words, an antiderivative for f is just any function whose derivative is f. The following examples show that a given function has many antiderivatives.

□ **EXAMPLE 1**

An antiderivative for $f(x) = 2x + 1$ is the function $F(x) = x^2 + x$, since

$$F'(x) = \frac{d}{dx}(x^2 + x) = 2x + 1 = f(x).$$

Other antiderivatives for f are

$$G(x) = x^2 + x + 7$$

and

$$H(x) = x^2 + x - 45. \qquad ■$$

□ **EXAMPLE 2**

An antiderivative for $f(x) = e^{2x} + \dfrac{1}{x}$ is $F(x) = \dfrac{1}{2}e^{2x} + \ln x + 5$, since

$$F'(x) = \frac{d}{dx}\left(\frac{1}{2}e^{2x} + \ln x + 5\right) = e^{2x} + \frac{1}{x} = f(x).$$

Other antiderivatives for f are

$$G(x) = \frac{1}{2}e^{2x} + \ln x + 100$$

and

$$H(x) = \frac{1}{2}e^{2x} + \ln x - e. \qquad \blacksquare$$

Examples 1 and 2 suggest that whenever F is an antiderivative for f so is $F + C$ where C is any constant. This is true because the derivative of a constant is zero. That is

$$\frac{d}{dx}(F(x) + C) = \frac{d}{dx}F(x) + \frac{d}{dx}C$$

$$= \frac{d}{dx}F(x) + 0$$

$$= \frac{d}{dx}F(x).$$

The following theorem states that once we have found a particular antiderivative F, any other antiderivative for f has the form $F + C$ for some constant C.

Theorem 1

Let F and G be antiderivatives for the function f. Then there exists a constant C so that

$$G(x) = F(x) + C.$$

We shall prove Theorem 1 at the end of this section using the Mean Value Theorem.

Notation for Antiderivatives

The notation used to denote the antiderivatives of f is

$$\int f(x)\, dx, \qquad \text{or just} \qquad \int f\, dx.$$

It consists of an elongated s preceding the function and the letters dx following $f(x)$. The symbol $\int$ is called the **integral sign,** and the function f is called the **integrand.**

The symbol dx identifies the independent variable for f. We shall say more about the meanings associated with these symbols in Section 5.4. For now, we simply think of $\int$ and dx as pieces of notation used to denote the antiderivative of a given function.

According to Theorem 1, once we have found a particular antiderivative F for f, we can express all others as $F + C$. Accordingly, we write

$$\int f(x)\, dx = F(x) + C \tag{1}$$

as the **general form** of the antiderivative for f.

The term **indefinite integral** is synonymous with antiderivative, and we speak of the process of finding an antiderivative as **antidifferentiation** or **integration.** Finally, the constant C in equation (1) is called the **constant of integration.**

At this point the only technique available to you for finding antiderivatives is to try to recognize the given function f as the derivative of a familiar function—in other words, to "think backward" through the differentiation process. In Section 5.3 we shall begin to develop a systematic approach to antidifferentiation.

☐ **EXAMPLE 3**

Using the notation of equation (1), we write

$$\int \frac{1}{2\sqrt{x}}\, dx = \sqrt{x} + C$$

since $\dfrac{d}{dx}(\sqrt{x} + C) = \dfrac{1}{2\sqrt{x}}$. ■

☐ **EXAMPLE 4**

For $x > 0$, we have

$$\int \frac{1}{x}\, dx = \ln x + C$$

since $\dfrac{d}{dx}(\ln x + C) = \dfrac{1}{x}, \qquad x > 0$. ■

☐ **EXAMPLE 5**

The rule for differentiating a polynomial tells us that

$$\int (5x^4 + 4x^3 + 3x^2 + 2x + 1)\, dx = x^5 + x^4 + x^3 + x^2 + x + C$$

as you can verify by differentiation. ■

☐ **EXAMPLE 6**

Using equation (2) of Section 4.4, we have $\dfrac{d}{dx}(e^x + C) = e^x$, so

$$\int e^x\, dx = e^x + C$$ ■

☐ **EXAMPLE 7**

Verify that

$$\int e^{ax}\, dx = \frac{1}{a} e^{ax} + C$$

for any constant $a \neq 0$.

Solution: To show that $F(x) = \dfrac{1}{a} e^{ax} + C$ is an antiderivative for $f(x)$, we differentiate $F(x)$:

$$F'(x) = \frac{d}{dx}\left[\frac{1}{a} e^{ax} + C \right]$$

$$= \frac{1}{a}\left[\frac{d}{dx} e^{ax} \right] + \frac{d}{dx}(C)$$

$$= \frac{1}{a}(e^{ax} \cdot a) + 0$$

$$= e^{ax}$$

$$= f(x).$$

This shows that $\displaystyle\int e^{ax}\, dx = \frac{1}{a} e^{ax} + C.$ ■

The Power Rule

One of the most basic differentiation rules is that for differentiating a power of x: $\dfrac{d}{dx} x^n = nx^{n-1}$. Reversing this operation gives the Power Rule for antiderivatives:

$$\int x^n\, dx = \frac{x^{n+1}}{n+1} + C, \qquad n \neq -1. \tag{2}$$

Equation (2) is easy to verify:

$$\frac{d}{dx}\left[\frac{x^{n+1}}{n+1} + C \right] = \frac{1}{n+1}(n+1)x^n + 0 = x^n.$$

Thus, for example

$$\int x^3\, dx = \frac{x^4}{4} + C$$

$$\int x^{3/2}\, dx = \frac{x^{5/2}}{\frac{5}{2}} + C = \frac{2}{5} x^{5/2} + C \qquad \text{(Here we must require } x \geq 0.\text{)}$$

$$\int x^{-2/3}\, dx = \frac{x^{1/3}}{\frac{1}{3}} + C = 3x^{1/3} + C \qquad \text{(Here we require } x \neq 0.)$$

and

$$\int x^{-5}\, dx = \frac{x^{-4}}{-4} + C = -\frac{1}{4}x^{-4} + C. \qquad \text{(Here we require } x \neq 0.)$$

It is important to note that we must *divide by the new exponent* as well as increase the old exponent by 1 in finding $\int x^n\, dx$. It is also important to note that *the Power Rule does not apply in the case n = −1*. This is because, as seen in Example 4

$$\int x^{-1}\, dx = \int \frac{1}{x}\, dx = \ln x + C, \qquad x > 0.$$

Properties of Antiderivatives

Since finding antiderivatives is just a matter of reversing the process of differentiation, the same algebraic laws govern both operations. Thus both equations

$$\int [\, f(x) + g(x)]\, dx = \int f(x)\, dx + \int g(x)\, dx \qquad (3)$$

and

$$\int kf(x)\, dx = k \int f(x)\, dx, \qquad k = \text{constant} \qquad (4)$$

are true. They simply restate properties of the derivative: The derivative (antiderivative) of the sum of two functions equals the sum of the individual derivatives (antiderivatives); and constants may be "factored out" of the differentiation (antidifferentiation) process.

Equations (3) and (4), together with the Power Rule (2), allow us to find the antiderivative of any polynomial.

□ **EXAMPLE 8**

Find $\int (6x^3 + 12x^2 - 4x + 5)\, dx$.

Strategy · · · · · · · **Solution**

Using equations (2), (3), and (4), we find that

$$\int (6x^3 + 12x^2 - 4x + 5)\, dx$$

Break integral into sum of simpler terms using equation (3).

$$= \int 6x^3 \, dx + \int 12x^2 \, dx + \int (-4x) \, dx + \int 5 \, dx$$

"Factor out" constants using equation (4).

$$= 6 \int x^3 \, dx + 12 \int x^2 \, dx - 4 \int x \, dx + 5 \int 1 \, dx$$

Apply Power Rule, equation (2), to each integral.

$$= 6 \left(\frac{x^4}{4} \right) + 12 \left(\frac{x^3}{3} \right) - 4 \left(\frac{x^2}{2} \right) + 5x + C$$

$$= \frac{3}{2} x^4 + 4x^3 - 2x^2 + 5x + C.$$

(Note that we write the constant of integration C only once, even though one could have been written for each integral. Since each is arbitrary, we have collected them all in one constant C.) ■

Just as the Power Rule for differentiation applies to all real exponents, so does the Power Rule for antiderivatives. Pay careful attention to the treatment of fractional and negative exponents in the next example.

☐ **EXAMPLE 9**

Find $\int (2x^{3/2} - 4x^{1/2} + 2x^{-2/3} - 3x^{-7/3}) \, dx.$

Solution: $\int (2x^{3/2} - 4x^{1/2} + 2x^{-2/3} - 3x^{-7/3}) \, dx$

$$= \int 2x^{3/2} \, dx + \int (-4x^{1/2}) \, dx + \int 2x^{-2/3} \, dx + \int (-3x^{-7/3}) \, dx$$

$$= 2 \int x^{3/2} \, dx - 4 \int x^{1/2} \, dx + 2 \int x^{-2/3} \, dx - 3 \int x^{-7/3} \, dx$$

$$= 2 \left(\frac{x^{5/2}}{\frac{5}{2}} \right) - 4 \left(\frac{x^{3/2}}{\frac{3}{2}} \right) + 2 \left(\frac{x^{1/3}}{\frac{1}{3}} \right) - 3 \left(\frac{x^{-4/3}}{-\frac{4}{3}} \right) + C$$

$$= \frac{4}{5} x^{5/2} - \frac{8}{3} x^{3/2} + 6x^{1/3} + \frac{9}{4} x^{-4/3} + C.$$

Proof of Theorem 1

The main step in the proof of Theorem 1 involves the following fact, whose proof involves the Mean Value Theorem of Section 3.11.

Lemma

The only antiderivatives for the zero function are the constant functions. That is, if $F'(x) = 0$ for all x, then $F(x) = C$ for some constant C and all x.

Proof of Lemma: Let x and a be any two numbers with $x > a$. Then by the Mean Value Theorem there is a number c in $[a, x]$ so that

$$F'(c) = \frac{F(x) - F(a)}{x - a}.$$

But $F'(c) = 0$ by assumption, so we must have $F(x) - F(a) = 0$. That is, $F(x) = F(a)$ whenever $x > a$. Taking $x < a$ and repeating the argument on $[x, a]$ gives the same conclusion. Thus, with $C = F(a)$, we have determined that $F(x) = C$ for all x. □

Proof of Theorem 1: We now proceed to prove Theorem 1, "If F and G are antiderivatives for f, then there exists a constant C so that $G(x) = F(x) + C$ for all x."

Given antiderivatives F and G for f, we know that

$$F'(x) = G'(x) = f(x).$$

Thus if we let $H(x) = (G - F)(x) = G(x) - F(x)$, we have

$$H'(x) = G'(x) - F'(x) = 0$$

for all x. Since $H'(x) = 0$ for all x, the lemma guarantees that $H(x) = C$ for some constant C and all x. Since $H(x) = G(x) - F(x)$, this gives

$$G(x) - F(x) = C$$

or $G(x) = F(x) + C$ for all x, as desired. □

☑ **PRACTICE PROBLEMS 5.1**

1. Find the general antiderivative for

$$f(x) = 6x^2 + 2x - e^{2x}.$$

2. Find $\displaystyle\int \left(3x^{1/2} - x^2 + \frac{3}{x}\right) dx$, $\quad x > 0$.

Exercise Set 5.1

In each of Exercises 1–22, find the general form of the antiderivative.

1. $\displaystyle\int 5\, dx$

2. $\displaystyle\int 3x^2\, dx$

3. $\displaystyle\int (2x^3 + 5x)\, dx$

4. $\displaystyle\int (4 - 4x^3)\, dx$

5. $\displaystyle\int (x^3 - 6x^2 + 2x - 1)\, dx$

6. $\displaystyle\int (9 - x^3 + 5x^4)\, dx$

7. $\displaystyle\int (x^{2/3} - 3x^{1/2})\, dx$

8. $\displaystyle\int e^{3x}\, dx$

9. $\displaystyle\int \frac{4}{x}\, dx, \; x > 0$

10. $\displaystyle\int \frac{1}{x + 2}\, dx$

11. $\displaystyle\int e^{5x}\, dx$

12. $\displaystyle\int 3e^{-x/2}\, dx$

13. $\displaystyle\int (x^{1/3} - 2x^{-2/3} + x^{-5/3})\, dx$

14. $\int (\sqrt{x} - 4x^{2/3} + 5)\, dx$

15. $\int \left(4e^{-x} - \dfrac{1}{x} + \sqrt{x}\right) dx, \; x > 0$

16. $\int (x - 1)(x + 2)\, dx$

17. $\int (4x^{-6} - 6x^{-4})\, dx$

18. $\int (\sqrt{x} - x^{1/3})\, dx$

19. $\int (\sqrt{x} - x^{1/3})^2\, dx$

20. $\int \dfrac{x^2 - 3x + 2}{x - 1}\, dx$

21. $\int (\sqrt{x} - e^{-x})\, dx$

22. $\int \sqrt{x}(x - 4)\, dx$

23. Find two functions, f and g, with the common derivative $f'(x) = g'(x) = 6x + 3x^2 + 5$. What is $[f(x) - g(x)]$ for any x?

24. The function $f(x) = x^2 + Ax + 6$ has the same derivative as the function $g(x) = Bx^2 + 10x - 9$.
   a. What is A?
   b. What is B?

25. The function $f(x) = Ae^{2x} + \sqrt{x} + 5$ has the same deriva-tive as the function $g(x) = 6e^{2x} + 3Bx^{1/2} + C$.
   a. What is A?
   b. What is B?
   c. What can we conclude about C?

26. A manufacturer's marginal revenue function, $MR(x) = R'(x)$, is constant and nonzero. Is it possible for the corre-sponding revenue function to have a relative maximum or minimum? Why or why not?

27. A population of deer in a wildlife preserve has a rate of change in size of $P'(t) = 4 + 2t$ deer per year, $t > 0$.
   a. What can you say about the function $P(t)$ giving the pop-ulation size as a function of t?
   b. Is the size of the population increasing or decreasing? Why?

28. After being introduced into an ecological niche, a family of ring-necked pheasants grows in size at the rate $P'(t) = 4\sqrt{t} - 6, \quad t > 0$.
   a. What can you say about the population function $P(t)$?
   b. Does the population always increase? Why or why not?
   c. What happens to the population size just after the pheas-ants are introduced to the niche?

☑ **SOLUTIONS TO PRACTICE PROBLEMS 5.1**

1. $\displaystyle \int (6x^2 + 2x - e^{2x})\, dx = 6\int x^2\, dx + 2\int x\, dx - \int e^{2x}\, dx$

$$= 6\left(\frac{x^3}{3}\right) + 2\left(\frac{x^2}{2}\right) - \left(\frac{1}{2}e^{2x}\right) + C$$

$$= 2x^3 + x^2 - \frac{1}{2}e^{2x} + C.$$

2. $\displaystyle \int \left(3x^{1/2} - x^2 + \frac{3}{x}\right) dx = 3\int x^{1/2}\, dx - \int x^2\, dx + 3\int \frac{1}{x}\, dx$

$$= 3\left(\frac{2}{3}\right)x^{3/2} - \left(\frac{x^3}{3}\right) + 3\ln x + C$$

$$= 2x^{3/2} - \frac{x^3}{3} + 3\ln x + C, \qquad x > 0.$$

5.2 More on Antiderivatives

Figure 2.1 reminds us that we may interpret differentiation as the operation of beginning with the graph of a function and finding the *slope function* $f'(x)$. Antidif-ferentiation is just the reverse. We begin with the slope function g and find the function $G(x) = \int g(x)\, dx$ whose slope at each number x is $g(x)$. (See Figure 2.2.)

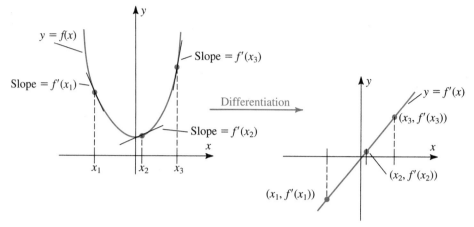

Figure 2.1 Differentiating f produces a slope function f'.

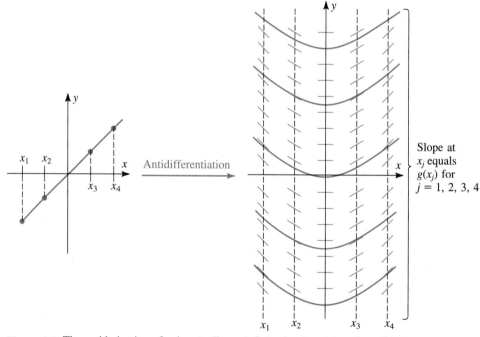

Figure 2.2 The antiderivative of g is actually an infinite family of functions $G(x) = \int g(x)\,dx$ each of which has slope function g.

Figure 2.2 also shows the difficulty that arises in trying to pass from values $g(x)$ as slopes to the antiderivative $G(x) = \int g(x)\, dx$, which has g as its slope function. Specifying the slope of a graph at each value of x produces not one graph but an entire family of graphs, each with slope function g.

But this should not be surprising since we already know that the antiderivative for g is actually a family of functions of the form

$$\int g(x)\, dx = G_1(x) + C \tag{1}$$

where G_1 is any particular antiderivative of g. Figure 2.3 shows the interpretation of equation (1) for the particular case $g(x) = x$. Antidifferentiation produces a family of congruent curves, all of which have equation $y = \dfrac{1}{2}x^2 + C$ and slope function $g(x) = x$. The various values for the constant C are just the y-intercepts of these curves.

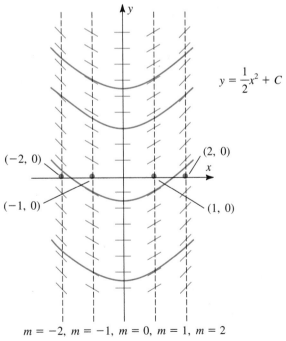

$$y = \frac{1}{2}x^2 + C$$

$m = -2,\ m = -1,\ m = 0,\ m = 1,\ m = 2$

Figure 2.3 Graphs of antiderivatives $G(x) = \dfrac{1}{2}x^2 + C$ of $g(x) = x$.

□ **EXAMPLE 1**

Find the family of curves that have slopes given by the function $f(x) = e^{3x} + 4x^2 - \dfrac{3}{x^2}$ at each value of $x \neq 0$.

Solution: The solution is simply the antiderivative for f, which is

$$F(x) = \int (e^{3x} + 4x^2 - 3x^{-2})\, dx$$

$$= \int e^{3x}\, dx + 4 \int x^2\, dx - 3 \int x^{-2}\, dx$$

$$= \frac{1}{3} e^{3x} + \frac{4}{3} x^3 + 3x^{-1} + C.$$ ∎

Particular Antiderivatives

When a particular value of the antiderivative

$$\int f(x)\, dx = F(x) + C$$

is specified, we may substitute this information into the general form of the antiderivative to determine the constant C. The next example shows how this is done.

□ **EXAMPLE 2**

Find the particular antiderivative F of the function $f(x) = 2x + e^{-x}$ that satisfies the condition $F(0) = 3$.

Solution: The general form of the antiderivative for f is

$$F(x) = \int (2x + e^{-x})\, dx$$

$$= x^2 - e^{-x} + C$$

as you can verify. Substituting $x = 0$ and using the condition that $F(0) = 3$ gives

$$3 = F(0) = 0^2 - e^{-0} + C = -1 + C.$$

Thus

$$3 = -1 + C$$

so

$$C = 4.$$

The desired antiderivative is $F(x) = x^2 - e^{-x} + 4$.
  This solution can be easily verified, as follows:

$$F'(x) = \frac{d}{dx}(x^2 - e^{-x} + 4)$$

$$= 2x - (-e^{-x}) + 0$$
$$= 2x + e^{-x}$$
$$= f(x)$$

and that

$$F(0) = 0^2 - e^{-0} + 4 = 0 - 1 + 4 = 3$$

as required. (It is a good idea to always check the results of antidifferentiation by differentiating the answer. This must bring you back to the function with which you began.) ■

Marginal Analysis

Since marginal cost and marginal revenue have been defined as the derivatives of total cost and total revenue, respectively (that is, $MC(x) = C'(x)$; $MR(x) = R'(x)$), we can determine total cost and revenue from these marginal rates by antidifferentiation:

$$\int MC(x) \, dx = C(x) + A \qquad (A \text{ constant}) \qquad (2)$$

$$\int MR(x) \, dx = R(x) + B. \qquad (B \text{ constant}) \qquad (3)$$

Of course, equations (2) and (3) determine total cost and revenue only to within a constant of integration. In each case a particular value of the antiderivative is needed to determine the function completely.

□ **EXAMPLE 3**

A manufacturer has a marginal revenue function

$$MR(x) = 200 - 2x.$$

Find the manufacturer's total revenue function $R(x)$.

Strategy · · · · · · · ·
Recall that $MR(x) = R'(x)$, so $R(x) = \int MR(x) \, dx$.

Find $R(x)$ by integrating $MR(x)$.

Solution
Since marginal revenue is the *derivative* of total revenue, that is, $MR(x) = R'(x)$, we know that total revenue is an antiderivative for marginal revenue. That is

$$R(x) = \int MR(x) \, dx$$

$$= \int (200 - 2x) \, dx$$

$$= 200x - x^2 + K.$$

Thus, the general antiderivative for $MR(x) = 200 - 2x$ is

$$R(x) = 200x - x^2 + K.$$

Recall, we must have $R(0) = 0$ for *any* revenue function.

Substitute this data to determine K.

To determine the constant K, we recall that $R(0) = 0$ for any revenue function, because we always have $R(x) = xp(x)$ where $p(x)$ is the price associated with sales level x. (In other words, no sale–no revenue.)

Substituting $x = 0$ and $R(x) = 0$ into the general antiderivative of $MR(x)$ gives

$$0 = 200(0) - 0^2 + K$$

so $K = 0$. The total revenue function is therefore

$$R(x) = 200x - x^2.$$

Check answer by differentiation.

To verify this, we check that

$$R'(x) = 200 - 2x = MR(x)$$

and that $R(0) = 0$. ∎

☐ EXAMPLE 4

Find a manufacturer's total cost in producing x items per month if its marginal cost per item is

$$MC(x) = 400 + 2x$$

and it is known that total monthly costs are \$60,000 when $x = 100$ items are produced per month.

Solution: We begin by finding the antiderivative for $MC(x)$:

$$C(x) = \int MC(x)\, dx = \int (400 + 2x)\, dx$$

$$= 400x + x^2 + K.$$

To find K, we insert the given data $C(100) = 60,000$ and obtain the equation

$$C(100) = 60,000 = 400(100) + (100)^2 + K$$
$$= 50,000 + K.$$

Thus

$$K = 60,000 - 50,000$$
$$= 10,000$$

is the fixed monthly cost. Total monthly cost is therefore

$$C(x) = 400x + x^2 + 10,000 \text{ dollars.}$$ ∎

□ **EXAMPLE 5**

A company that produces lawnmowers determines that the marginal cost at production level x lawnmowers per week is

$$MC(x) = 200 + 10e^{-0.1x}.$$

Find the company's total weekly costs at production level x, if $C(0) = 5000$. (That is, if the *fixed* costs of production, assuming *no* lawnmowers are produced, is $5000 per week.)

Solution: Since $MC(x) = C'(x)$, we must have

$$C(x) = \int MC(x)\, dx$$

$$= \int (200 + 10e^{-0.1x})\, dx$$

$$= \int 200\, dx + 10 \int e^{-0.1x}\, dx$$

$$= 200x + 10\left[\left(\frac{1}{-0.1}\right)e^{-0.1x}\right] + K$$

$$= 200x - 100e^{-0.1x} + K.$$

Substituting the given data $C(0) = 5000$ into the above equation for $C(x)$ gives

$$C(0) = 5000 = 200(0) - 100e^0 + K$$
$$= -100 + K.$$

Thus, $K = 5000 + 100 = 5100$, and the total cost function is

$$C(x) = 200x - 100e^{-0.1x} + 5100.$$

We verify this by differentiation:

$$C'(x) = 200 - 100(-0.1)e^{-0.1x}$$
$$= 200 + 10e^{-0.1x}. \qquad ■$$

☑ **PRACTICE PROBLEMS 5.2**

1. Find the antiderivative $F(x)$ of the function

$$f(x) + 4x^3 + \frac{2}{\sqrt{x}} + 4e^{-2x} + \frac{7}{x}, \qquad x > 0$$

for which $F(1) = \dfrac{3}{e^2} + 8$.

2. Find a manufacturer's total cost in producing x items per week if its marginal cost per item is $MC(x) = \$100$ and its fixed costs are \$500 per week.

Exercise Set 5.2

In Exercises 1–4, match the given function with the correct slope portrait for its antiderivative.

1.

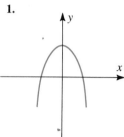

i.

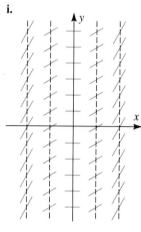

2.

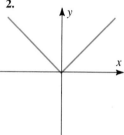

ii.

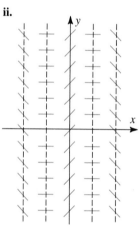

3.

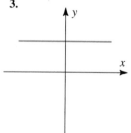

iii.

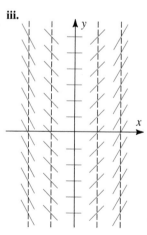

4.

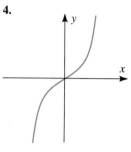

iv.

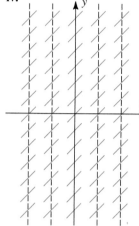

5.

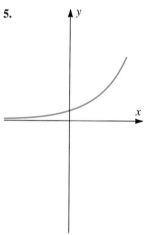

vi.

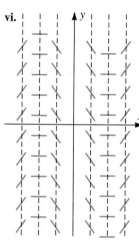

6.

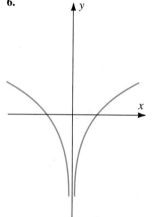

vi.

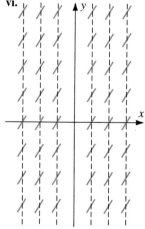

In Exercises 7–18, find the function F that has the given derivative and that has the specified value.

7. $F'(x) = 4;$ $F(0) = 3$

8. $F'(x) = x - 2;$ $F(0) = 6$

9. $F'(x) = x^2 - 2x;$ $F(0) = -3$

10. $F'(x) = \sqrt{x};$ $F(4) = 7$

11. $F'(x) = \dfrac{1}{x};$ $F(e) = 5$

12. $F'(x) = 4e^x + 5;$ $F(1) = 4e + 8$

13. $F'(x) = x^{2/3} - x^{-1/3};$ $F(0) = 5$

14. $F'(x) = x^2 - 4 + 3x^{-7/2};$ $F(0) = -4$

15. $F'(x) = 5e^{2x} + 4;$ $F(0) = 10$

16. $F'(x) = \sqrt{x} - \dfrac{1}{x};$ $F(1) = 3$

17. $F'(x) = \dfrac{3}{x + 5} + 2e^{-3x};$ $F(0) = 0$

18. $F'(x) = \dfrac{x - 1}{x + 1};$ $F(0) = 1$

19. A manufacturer of typewriters finds that its marginal cost per typewriter is $250. Find its total weekly cost in producing x typewriters if its fixed costs are $700 per week.

20. For the manufacturer in Exercise 19, suppose that fixed costs are unknown, but that the total cost in producing 20 typewriters per week is known to be $7000.
a. Find weekly fixed costs.
b. Find total weekly cost, $C(x)$.

21. A manufacturer of dishwashers experiences marginal costs of

$$MC(x) = 400 + \frac{1}{4}x \text{ dollars}$$

at a production level of x dishwashers per month. If the total cost in producing ten dishwashers per month is known to be $5200,
a. Find the manufacturer's fixed monthly cost.
b. Find the total monthly cost function $C(x)$.

22. A manufacturer's marginal cost function is

$$MC(x) = 50 + 2x$$

and its average cost per item is

$$c(x) = \frac{1000}{x} + A + x$$

where A is a constant.
a. Find A.
b. Find the total cost function, $C(x)$.

23. A manufacturer's marginal cost function is

$$MC(x) = 100 + 4x$$

and the total cost at production level $x = 100$ is $35,000. Find the total cost function.

24. A company's marginal revenue function is

$$MR(x) = 400 - 2x.$$

Find the revenue function R.

25. Marginal revenue from the sale of x cameras per month is known to be

$$MR(x) = 250 - \frac{1}{2}x \text{ dollars}.$$

Find the total revenue function R. (*Hint:* Use the fact that $R(0) = 0$ to find the value of the constant of integration.)

26. If a person has a marginal utility function of $MU(x) = \sqrt{x}$ for a particular commodity, find the utility function U. (Recall, $MU(x) = U'(x)$. Use the condition that $U(0) = 0$ to evaluate the constant.)

27. A population of deer in a wildlife preserve has a rate of change of $P'(t) = 4 + 2t$ deer per year, $t > 0$. Find the population function $P(t)$ if there were 12 deer initially.

28. After being introduced into an ecological niche, a family of ring-necked pheasants grows in size at the rate of $P'(t) = 4\sqrt{t} - 6$, $t > 0$. Find the population function $P(t)$ if there were 40 pheasants initially.

29. Match the survival curves I–III with the graphs of the *rates* of survival, a–c, in the following figure.

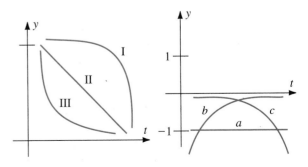

Three survival curves.　　　　Rates of survival.

30. A manufacturer of a certain product finds that it has a marginal cost of $MC(x) = 40 + \frac{1}{2}x$ dollars, marginal revenue of $60, and a fixed cost of $800 per month, where x is the number of items produced per month.

  a. Find the manufacturer's monthly cost, $C(x)$.
  b. Find the manufacturer's monthly revenue, $R(x)$.
  c. Find the manufacturer's monthly profit, $P(x)$.
  d. How can marginal profit, $MP(x) = P'(x)$, be obtained from marginal cost and marginal revenue?

31. Recall that if an object moves along a line so that after t seconds its position on the line is given by the differentiable function $s(t)$, then the velocity of the object at time t is the derivative $v(t) = s'(t)$ of the position function. Thus,

$$\int v(t)\, dt = s(t) + C.$$

That is, we can recover $s(t)$ from $v(t)$ by integration.

  Suppose that an object moves along a line with velocity $v(t) = 3t^2 + 6t + 2$ and that its location at time $t = 0$ is $s(0) = 4$.

  a. Find its location after t seconds, $s(t)$.
  b. Find its location after 4 seconds, $s(4)$.

32. An object dropped from rest achieves a velocity of $v(t) = -32t$ feet per second t seconds after it is released. How far has such an object fallen

  a. 4 seconds after release?
  b. 8 seconds after release?
  c. t seconds after release?

33. An epidemiologist estimates that the rate at which influenza is spreading throughout a city is

$$\frac{dN}{dt} = 20 + 24\sqrt{t}$$

persons per day t days after its outbreak. Assuming that $N(0) = 2$,

  a. Find $N(t)$, the number of people who have contracted influenza t days after its outbreak.
  b. Find $N(16)$.

☑ **SOLUTIONS TO PRACTICE PROBLEMS 5.2**

1. The general antiderivative for f is

$$F(x) = \int \left(4x^3 + \frac{2}{\sqrt{x}} + 4e^{-2x} + \frac{7}{x}\right) dx = x^4 + 4\sqrt{x} - 2e^{-2x} + 7\ln x + C.$$

The requirement that $F(1) = \dfrac{3}{e^2} + 8$ implies that

$$\frac{3}{e^2} + 8 = 1^4 + 4\sqrt{1} - 2e^{-2(1)} + 7\ln(1) + C$$

$$= 1 + 4 - \frac{2}{e^2} + 7(0) + C$$

$$= 5 - \frac{2}{e^2} + C.$$

Thus,

$$C = 3 + \frac{5}{e^2}$$

and the particular antiderivative satisfying the condition $F(1) = \dfrac{3}{e^2} + 8$ is

$$F(x) = x^4 + 4\sqrt{x} - 2e^{-2x} + 7\ln x + 3 + \frac{5}{e^2}.$$

2. Marginal cost equaling $100 means that
$$MC(x) = C'(x) = 100$$

so

$$C(x) = \int (100)\, dx$$

$$= 100x + K.$$

The fact that fixed costs equal \$500 means that $C(0) = 500$. Substituting this value into the equation for $C(x)$ above gives

$$C(0) = 500 = 100(0) + K$$

$$= K.$$

Thus, $K = 500$, and the cost function is

$$C(x) = 100x + 500.$$

5.3 Finding Antiderivatives by Substitution

Having seen a very limited glimpse at the potential applications of antiderivatives, we next wish to develop just a bit more technique for finding them. Later in this text there is an entire chapter (Chapter 7) devoted to finding antiderivatives. For our immediate purposes, however, we will need only the *method of substitution*, which we develop in this section.

Before beginning a discussion of substitution, we list the antidifferentiation rules that we have developed thus far. This is basically just a list of differentiation facts and the reverse statements about antiderivatives.

Differentiation Rule	Antidifferentiation Rule	
$\dfrac{d}{dx}(ax) = a$	$\displaystyle\int a\, dx = ax + C$	(1)
$\dfrac{d}{dx}(x^n) = nx^{n-1}$	$\displaystyle\int x^n\, dx = \dfrac{1}{n+1}x^{n+1} + C, \quad n \neq -1$	(2)
$\dfrac{d}{dx}\ln x = \dfrac{1}{x}, \quad x > 0$	$\displaystyle\int \dfrac{1}{x}\, dx = \ln x + C, \quad x > 0$	(3)
$\dfrac{d}{dx}e^x = e^x$	$\displaystyle\int e^x\, dx = e^x + C$	(4)

The Idea Behind the Method of Substitution

Like the antidifferentiation problems you have encountered so far, the method of substitution attempts to recognize the integrand (that is, the function for which we seek the antiderivative) as the derivative of some known function. It takes into account, however, the fact that the Chain Rule, when used to differentiate a composite function, produces a second factor (the "derivative of the inside function").

Using the method of substitution, we look for functions that are *products of two functions:* $g(x) = f(x) u(x)$. When we find such a function, we ask: "Is it possible that *one* of the factors came from differentiating a function *inside the other?*" If the answer is "yes," there is a possibility that what we are dealing with resulted from the Chain Rule acting on a composite function, and we have a strong clue as to how to work backwards to find an antiderivative.

The tipoff? Look for *products* of two functions, where one is the derivative of the inside of the other. We will now develop this idea more formally.

Inverting the Chain Rule

The Chain Rule for differentiating a composite function is

$$\frac{d}{dx} F(u(x)) = F'(u(x)) \cdot u'(x). \tag{5}$$

Now suppose f is the derivative of F. That is, let $f = F'$. Then $F'(u(x)) = f(u(x))$, and we can write equation (5) as

$$\frac{d}{dx} F(u(x)) = f(u(x)) \cdot u'(x). \tag{6}$$

Now let's interpret equation (6) as an antidifferentiation formula. We obtain

$$\int f(u(x)) \cdot u'(x)\, dx = F(u(x)) + C$$

where $F'(x) = f(x)$. $\tag{7}$

Equation (7) is really just a reminder that the derivative of a composite function $F \circ u$ has two factors: $F'(u(x))$ and $u'(x)$. When we are faced with the problem of integrating a function that is the product of two factors, we should check to see if this product has the form $f(u(x)) \cdot u'(x)$. If so, an antiderivative is $F \circ u$, where F is an antiderivative of f.

A special case of equation (7) involving the power function $f(x) = x^n$ occurs frequently enough to warrant special attention. In this case we have $f(u(x)) = [u(x)]^n$ and $F(x) = \frac{1}{n+1} x^{n+1} + C$, according to equation (2). Thus

$$\int [u(x)]^n\, u'(x)\, dx = \frac{1}{n+1} [u(x)]^{n+1} + C. \qquad (n \neq -1) \tag{8}$$

□ **EXAMPLE 1**

Find $\int (x^2 + 1)^5 \cdot 2x\, dx.$

Solution: We let $u(x) = x^2 + 1$. Then $u'(x) = 2x$, so the integral has the form of that in equation (8) with $n = 5$. Thus

$$\int \underbrace{(x^2 + 1)^5}_{[u(x)]^5} \cdot \underbrace{2x \cdot dx}_{u'(x)} = \underbrace{\frac{1}{6}(x^2 + 1)^6}_{\frac{1}{6}[u(x)]^6} + C.$$

■

□ **EXAMPLE 2**

Find $\int 2xe^{x^2+5}\, dx$.

Solution: We let $u(x) = x^2 + 5$. Then $u'(x) = 2x$, and the integral has the form $\int e^{u(x)} u'(x)\, dx$. Using equation (7) with $f(u) = e^u$, and equation (4), we obtain

$$\int \underbrace{e^{x^2+5}}_{e^{u(x)}} \cdot \underbrace{2x\, dx}_{u'(x)} = \underbrace{e^{x^2+5}}_{e^{u(x)}} + C.$$

■

□ **EXAMPLE 3**

Find $\int \dfrac{3x^2 + 4}{x^3 + 4x}\, dx$, $\quad x > 0$.

Solution: If we let $u(x) = x^3 + 4x$, we note that $u'(x) = 3x^2 + 4$, which is precisely the numerator of the integrand. Thus using equation (7), with $f(u) = \dfrac{1}{u}$, and equation (3), we obtain

$$\int \frac{3x^2 + 4}{x^3 + 4x}\, dx = \int \underbrace{\frac{1}{x^3 + 4x}}_{\frac{1}{u(x)}}\underbrace{(3x^2 + 4)\, dx}_{u'(x)} = \underbrace{\ln(x^3 + 4x)}_{\ln u(x)} + C.$$

■

□ **EXAMPLE 4**

Find $\int (x^2 + 6)^4 x\, dx$.

Solution: If we take $u(x) = x^2 + 6$, we shall need to have the factor $u'(x) = 2x$ present in the integral. But the integral contains only the factor of x, not the required

$2x$. However, we can multiply x by $\dfrac{2}{2}(=1)$ and "pull the factor of $\dfrac{1}{2}$ in front of the integral sign'' as follows:

$$\int (x^2 + 6)^4 x \, dx = \int (x^2 + 6)^4 \left(\frac{2}{2}\right) x \, dx$$

$$= \frac{1}{2} \int \underbrace{(x^2 + 6)^4 2x \, dx}$$
$$\hspace{5cm} [u(x)]^4 u'(x)$$

$$= \frac{1}{2} \cdot \frac{1}{5} (x^2 + 6)^5 + C$$

$$= \frac{1}{10} (x^2 + 6)^5 + C.$$ ∎

□ **EXAMPLE 5**

Find $\displaystyle\int (x^3 - 6x + 2)^3 (x^2 - 2) \, dx.$

Solution: With $u(x) = x^3 - 6x + 2$ we require $u'(x) = 3x^2 - 6 = 3(x^2 - 2)$. Since only the factor $(x^2 - 2)$ is present in the integrand, we multiply by $\dfrac{3}{3}$ and proceed as in Example 4:

$$\int (x^3 - 6x + 2)^3 (x^2 - 2) \, dx = \int (x^3 - 6x + 2)^3 \left(\frac{3}{3}\right)(x^2 - 2) \, dx$$

$$= \frac{1}{3} \int \underbrace{(x^3 - 6x + 2)^3 (3x^2 - 6) \, dx}$$
$$\hspace{6cm} [u(x)]^3 u'(x)$$

$$= \frac{1}{3} \cdot \frac{1}{4} (x^3 - 6x + 2)^4 + C$$

$$= \frac{1}{12} (x^3 - 6x + 2)^4 + C.$$ ∎

Differential Notation

The notation of differentials allows us to formalize these techniques a bit further. We have already made reference to the symbol dx as the differential for the independent variable x. If u is a differentiable function of x, we define the differential du as

$$du = u'(x) \, dx \tag{9}$$

or, in Leibniz notation

$$du = \frac{du}{dx} \cdot dx. \qquad \text{(See Section 3.10.)} \qquad (10)$$

For example, if $u = x^3 - 2x + 1$, then $du = (3x^2 - 2)\, dx$.

In other words, the differential for u is just its derivative multiplied by the differential dx. Note that equation (10) suggests that we may think of the derivative symbol $\frac{du}{dx}$ as a quotient of the differentials du and dx, whereby canceling common factors of dx on the right-hand side leaves us with the tautology $du = du$.

Differentials actually have a deeper meaning than just what we have described. Their usefulness to us here, however, is purely as a notational device; when we rewrite equation (7) using the definition of du in equation (9) we obtain the following:

> The equation
>
> $$\int \underbrace{f(u(x))}_{f(u)} \cdot \underbrace{u'(x)\, dx}_{du} = \underbrace{F(u(x))}_{F(u)} + C \qquad (11)$$
>
> becomes simply
>
> $$\int f(u)\, du = F(u) + C. \qquad (12)$$

The Method of Substitution

The point of equations (11) and (12) is that through the use of the differential notation $du = u'(x)\, dx$ we can rewrite the composite integrand in equation (11) as the simple function $f(u)$ of the independent variable u in equation (12). This greatly simplifies the integration to be performed.

□ **EXAMPLE 6**

Find $\int x\sqrt{x^2 + 4}\, dx$.

Strategy · · · · · · ·

Substitute u for the expression under the radical.

Solution

We let $u = x^2 + 4$. Then

$$du = \left[\frac{d}{dx}(x^2 + 4) \right] dx = 2x\, dx.$$

Find du by $du = u'(x)\, dx$.

Since only the factors x and dx are present in the integrand, we solve this last equation for $x\, dx$:

Solve equation involving du for factors actually present in the integrand.

$$x\, dx = \frac{1}{2}\, du.$$

Substituting these expressions involving u and du into the integrand gives

$$\int x\sqrt{x^2 + 4}\, dx = \int (x^2 + 4)^{1/2} x\, dx$$

Substitute expressions for u and du:
$$x^2 + 4 = u;$$

$$dx = \frac{1}{2}\, du.$$

$$= \int u^{1/2} \cdot \frac{1}{2}\, du$$

$$= \frac{1}{2}\int u^{1/2}\, du$$

Integrate with respect to u.

$$= \frac{1}{2} \cdot \frac{2}{3} u^{3/2} + C$$

Substitute back.

$$= \frac{1}{3}(x^2 + 4)^{3/2} + C.$$

☐ **EXAMPLE 7**

Find $\displaystyle\int \frac{e^{\sqrt{x}}}{\sqrt{x}}\, dx$.

Solution: The integral can be written

$$\int \frac{e^{\sqrt{x}}}{\sqrt{x}}\, dx = \int e^{\sqrt{x}} \cdot \frac{1}{\sqrt{x}}\, dx.$$

Letting $u = \sqrt{x}$, we have $du = \dfrac{1}{2\sqrt{x}}\, dx$. Solving this equation for the factor $\dfrac{1}{\sqrt{x}}\, dx$ in the integrand gives

$$\frac{1}{\sqrt{x}}\, dx = 2\, du.$$

With these substitutions the integral becomes

$$\int e^{\sqrt{x}} \cdot \frac{1}{\sqrt{x}}\, dx = \int e^u \cdot 2\, du$$

$$= 2\int e^u\, du$$

$$= 2e^u + C$$

$$= 2e^{\sqrt{x}} + C.$$

☐ **EXAMPLE 8**

Find $\displaystyle\int \frac{x^2 + e^{3x}}{x^3 + 6 + e^{3x}}\, dx, \qquad x > 0.$

Solution: Since the numerator of the integrand resembles the derivative of the denominator, we suspect that the integral can be brought into the form $\int \dfrac{du}{u}$. We therefore try the substitution

$$u = x^3 + 6 + e^{3x}$$

for the denominator. Then

$$du = (3x^2 + 3e^{3x})\, dx$$
$$= 3(x^2 + e^{3x})\, dx.$$

Thus,

$$(x^2 + e^{3x})\, dx = \frac{1}{3}\, du.$$

With these substitutions the integral becomes

$$\int \frac{x^2 + e^{3x}}{x^3 + 6 + e^{3x}}\, dx = \int \frac{1}{x^3 + 6 + e^{3x}}(x^2 + e^{3x})\, dx$$

$$= \int \frac{1}{u} \cdot \frac{1}{3}\, du$$

$$= \frac{1}{3} \int \frac{1}{u}\, du$$

$$= \frac{1}{3} \ln u + C$$

$$= \frac{1}{3} \ln(x^3 + 6 + e^{3x}) + C.$$ ∎

More on $\int \dfrac{1}{u}\, du$

The integration formula

$$\int \frac{1}{x}\, dx = \ln x + C, \qquad x > 0 \tag{13}$$

has thus far been restricted to $x > 0$ since $\ln x$ is defined only for $x > 0$. We shall now show that this formula can be extended to the formula

$$\int \frac{1}{x}\, dx = \ln |x| + C, \qquad x \neq 0 \tag{14}$$

valid for all $x \neq 0$.

If $x > 0$ formula (14) is the same as formula (13) since $|x| = x$, so we need only address the case $x < 0$. But then $-x > 0$, so $|x| = -x$. Thus $\ln |x|$ is defined, and

$$\frac{d}{dx}\ln|x| = \frac{d}{dx}\ln(-x) = \frac{1}{-x}\cdot\frac{d}{dx}(-x) = \frac{1}{-x}(-1) = \frac{1}{x} \qquad \text{for } x < 0.$$

Since $\dfrac{d}{dx}\ln|x| = \dfrac{1}{x}$, we have $\displaystyle\int \frac{1}{x}\,dx = \ln|x| + C$ as claimed.

□ **EXAMPLE 9**

Find $\displaystyle\int \frac{x}{9 - 4x^2}\,dx$.

Solution: We let $u = 9 - 4x^2$. Then $du = -8x\,dx$, so $x\,dx = -\dfrac{1}{8}\,du$. Thus,

$$\int \frac{x}{9 - 4x^2}\,dx = \int \frac{1}{9 - 4x^2}x\,dx = \int \frac{1}{u}\left(-\frac{1}{8}\right)du$$

$$= -\frac{1}{8}\int \frac{1}{u}\,du$$

$$= -\frac{1}{8}\ln|u| + C$$

$$= -\frac{1}{8}\ln|9 - 4x^2| + C. \qquad ■$$

☑ **PRACTICE PROBLEMS 5.3**

1. Find $\displaystyle\int (x + 3)(x^2 + 6x + 7)^4\,dx$.

2. Find $\displaystyle\int \frac{xe^{x^2}}{4 + e^{x^2}}\,dx$.

Exercise Set 5.3

In Exercises 1–26, find the antiderivative.

1. $\displaystyle\int x(3 + x^2)^3\,dx$

2. $\displaystyle\int x\sqrt{x^2 + 1}\,dx$

3. $\displaystyle\int 5x\sqrt{9 + x^2}\,dx$

4. $\displaystyle\int x^2(4 + x^3)^{-1/2}\,dx$

5. $\displaystyle\int xe^{x^2}\,dx$

6. $\displaystyle\int \frac{x^2\,dx}{\sqrt{1 + x^3}}$

7. $\displaystyle\int \frac{(\sqrt{x} + 5)^6}{\sqrt{x}}\,dx$

8. $\displaystyle\int \frac{x - 1}{x^2 - 2x}\,dx$

9. $\displaystyle\int \frac{x}{1 + 3x^2}\,dx$

10. $\displaystyle\int \frac{\ln^3 x}{x}\,dx$

11. $\displaystyle\int e^{2x}(1 + e^{2x})^3\,dx$

12. $\displaystyle\int \frac{e^x}{1 + e^x}\,dx$

13. $\displaystyle\int \frac{e^x}{\sqrt{e^x + 1}}\,dx$

14. $\displaystyle\int \frac{1}{x\ln x}\,dx$

15. $\displaystyle\int \frac{2x + 3}{(x^2 + 3x + 6)^3}\,dx$

16. $\displaystyle\int \frac{3x + 3}{(x^2 + 2x - 3)^3}\,dx$

17. $\displaystyle\int \left(1 - \frac{1}{x}\right)^3\left(\frac{1}{x^2}\right)dx$

18. $\displaystyle\int \frac{x^2 + 2x + 3x^{3/2}}{\sqrt{x}}\,dx$

19. $\int \dfrac{x^3}{\sqrt{5 + x^4}}\, dx$

20. $\int \dfrac{x}{x^2 + 5}\, dx$

21. $\int \dfrac{4 \ln x^2}{x}\, dx$

22. $\int \dfrac{1}{\sqrt{x}(1 - \sqrt{x})}\, dx$

23. $\int \dfrac{(x^{2/3} - 5)^{2/3}}{\sqrt[3]{x}}$

24. $\int \dfrac{e^{-3x} - x^2}{x^3 + e^{-3x}}\, dx$

25. $\int \dfrac{(1 + e^{\sqrt{x}})e^{\sqrt{x}}}{\sqrt{x}}\, dx$

26. $\int (x^{5/3} - 2x)^{3/2}(5x^{2/3} - 6)\, dx$

27. A manufacturer finds that its marginal cost at production level x in the production of a certain product is

$$MC(x) = C'(x) = 40 + \frac{20x}{1 + x^2} \text{ dollars.}$$

a. Find $\lim\limits_{x \to \infty} MC(x)$.

b. Find the total cost function C if $C(0) = 500$ dollars.

28. The manufacturer in Exercise 27 sells its products for $100 each.

a. Find the revenue function R giving the revenue from the sale of x items.

b. What is $R(0)$?

29. The marginal revenue from the sale of picnic tables at sales level x per month is

$$MR(x) = R'(x) = \frac{10,000x}{100 + 0.2x^2}.$$

a. Find $\lim\limits_{x \to \infty} MR(x)$.

b. Find the total revenue function R.

30. An individual's marginal utility function for the consumption of x items per unit time is $MU(x) = U'(x) = 4x(4 + x^2)^{-2/3}$. Find the utility function $U(x)$ assuming that $U(0) = 0$.

31. A city's population is predicted to grow at a rate of $P'(t) = \dfrac{100e^{20t}}{1 + e^{20t}}$ people per year where t is time in years from the present. Find the city's population $P(t)$ t years from now if its current population is $P(0) = 40,000$ people.

32. The rate at which a typist improves in speed is modelled by the mathematical function

$$S'(t) = \frac{5t}{t^2 + 1} + 0.10te^{-t^2}$$

words per minute per day.

a. Find the rate at which a novice ($t = 0$) typist improves in speed, according to this model.

b. If the novice typist is assumed to type 10 words per minute, find the function $S(t)$.

33. The size of a population of ring-necked pheasants is growing at the rate $P'(t) = \sqrt{t}e^{t^{3/2}}$. Initially there were 20 ring-necked pheasants in the flock. Find the population function $P(t)$.

34. The diameter of a Canadian elm tree is growing in size at the rate $D'(t) = \dfrac{4}{t} + te^{-t^2}$. Find the function $D(t)$ giving the size of the diameter if the diameter measured 30 centimeters when the tree was 10 years old.

✔️ **SOLUTIONS TO PRACTICE PROBLEMS 5.3**

1. In $\int (x + 3)(x^2 + 6x + 7)^4\, dx$, we let $u = x^2 + 6x + 7$. Then,

$$du = (2x + 6)\, dx$$

$$= 2(x + 3)\, dx$$

so

$$(x + 3)\, dx = \frac{1}{2}\, du.$$

With these substitutions we obtain

$$\int (x + 3)(x^2 + 6x + 7)^4 \, dx = \int u^4 \left(\frac{1}{2}\right) du$$

$$= \frac{1}{2} \int u^4 \, du$$

$$= \frac{1}{2} \cdot \frac{1}{5} u^5 + C$$

$$= \frac{1}{10} (x^2 + 6x + 7)^5 + C.$$

2. In $\int \dfrac{xe^{x^2}}{4 + e^{x^2}} \, dx$, we let $u = 4 + e^{x^2}$. Then $du = 2xe^{x^2} \, dx$ so $xe^{x^2} \, dx = \dfrac{1}{2} \, du$. Making these substitutions gives

$$\int \frac{xe^{x^2}}{4 + e^{x^2}} \, dx = \int \left(\frac{1}{4 + e^{x^2}}\right)(xe^{x^2}) \, dx = \int \frac{1}{u} \cdot \frac{1}{2} \, du$$

$$= \frac{1}{2} \int \frac{1}{u} \, du$$

$$= \frac{1}{2} \ln |u| + C$$

$$= \frac{1}{2} \ln(4 + e^{x^2}) + C.$$

(We may drop the absolute value signs since the function $4 + e^{x^2}$ is never negative.)

5.4 The Area Problem and the Definite Integral

Almost all of what was developed in Chapters 1–4 was related, in one way or another, to the *tangent line problem*. We come now to the second principal problem of the calculus, the *area problem*:

> **Area Problem:**
>
> Given the continuous nonnegative function f, find the area of the region R bounded by the x-axis, the graph of $y = f(x)$, the vertical line $x = a$, and the vertical line $x = b$. (See Figure 4.1.)

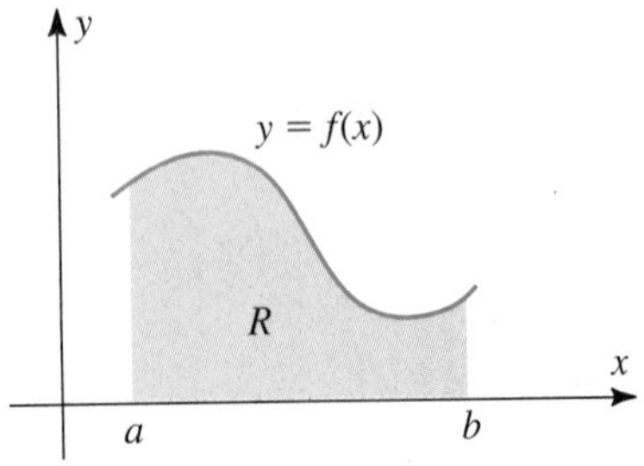

Figure 4.1 Area Problem: Find the area of region R.

Although the area problem is stated in purely geometrical terms, there are many practical situations in which we would like to be able to solve it. For example, Figure 4.2 shows the graphs of the interest paid by two money-market mutual funds over a common period of time. Although both funds experienced the same maximum and minimum interest rates, the fact that Fund B paid a higher rate of return over the period in question is reflected in the fact that the area of region R_B appears

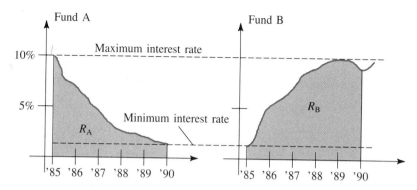

Figure 4.2 Interest rates as functions of time for two money-market funds.

to be larger than the area of region R_A. This is because Fund B's rate of interest was higher than Fund A's during most of the period.

Approximating the Area of R

Formulas from plane geometry enable us to calculate the area of a region R corresponding to a square, a circle, a triangle, or a trapezoid. But when R is bounded by the graph of an arbitrary continuous function f, as in Figure 4.1, no formula from geometry prescribes (or even defines) the area of R.

Figure 4.3 shows how we can use the formula for the area of a rectangle to *approximate* the area of such a region R when $f(x) \geq 0$ for all x in $\{a, b\}$. To do so, we

(i) Divide the interval $[a, b]$ into n subintervals of equal length $\Delta x = \dfrac{b - a}{n}$.

(ii) In each subinterval select one "test number" t; then approximate the area of the region lying over this subinterval by the area of the *rectangle* with width Δx and height $f(t)$.

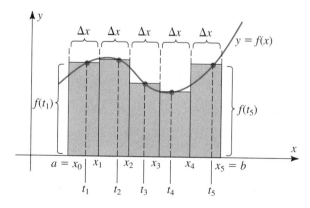

Figure 4.3 An approximation to the area of the region R bounded by the graph of $y = f(x)$ and the x-axis between $x = a$ and $x = b$ using five subintervals of equal length.

(iii) Sum the approximations associated with the subintervals to obtain the approximation

$$\text{Area of } R \approx f(t_1)\,\Delta x + f(t_2)\,\Delta x + \cdots + f(t_n)\,\Delta x$$
$$= \{f(t_1) + f(t_2) + \cdots + f(t_n)\}\,\Delta x. \tag{1}$$

Of course, the approximation in equation (1) will not give the exact value of the area of R because the rectangles do not fit "exactly" under the graph of f. However, as we increase the number n of rectangles used in the approximation, thereby decreasing their widths $\Delta x = \dfrac{b - a}{n}$, we might expect the region determined by the rectangles to "better fit" the region R, as illustrated in Figure 4.4.

□ **EXAMPLE 1**

Figure 4.5 shows how we can use this scheme to approximate the area of the region R bounded by the graph of $f(x) = x^2$ and the x-axis between $a = 0$ and $b = 4$.

(i) If we use $n = 4$ subintervals of equal width, we have

$$\Delta x = \frac{b - a}{n} = \frac{4 - 0}{4} = 1.$$

If we arbitrarily choose the "test point" t_j to be the left endpoint of each subinterval, we have

$$t_1 = 0, \qquad t_2 = 1, \qquad t_3 = 2, \qquad \text{and} \qquad t_4 = 3.$$

The approximation given by (1) is then

$$\text{Area of } R \approx \{f(0) + f(1) + f(2) + f(3)\}\,\Delta x$$
$$= \{0^2 + 1^2 + 2^2 + 3^2\}(1)$$
$$= 14.$$

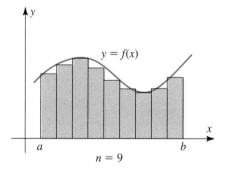
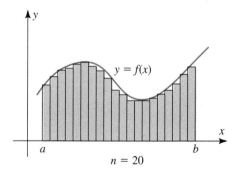

Figure 4.4 Increasing the number of rectangles while decreasing their common width provides an increasingly accurate approximation to the area of R, in general.

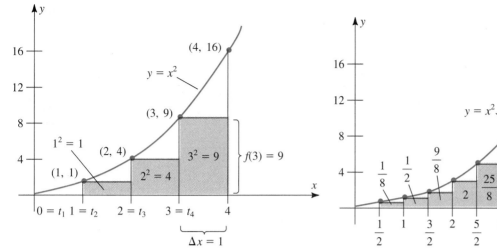

Figure 4.5 Approximating the area of the region bounded by graph of $y = x^2$ and x-axis, for $0 \le x \le 4$, by rectangles of width $\Delta x = 1$.

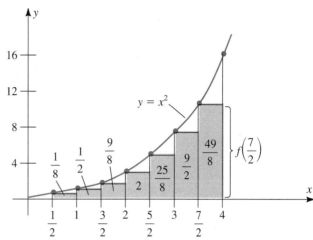

Figure 4.6 Approximating the area of the region in Figure 4.5 using $n = 8$ rectangles.

As you can see from Figure 4.5, this approximation is too small, since the corresponding rectangles lie within R but do not fill R entirely.

(ii) Figure 4.6 illustrates the approximation of the area of this same region using $n = 8$ subintervals rather than 4. In this case the width of each subinterval is

$$\Delta x = \frac{4 - 0}{8} = \frac{1}{2}.$$

If we again take left endpoints as our "test points" t_j, we have

$$t_1 = 0, \quad t_2 = \frac{1}{2}, \quad t_3 = 1, \quad t_4 = \frac{3}{2}, \quad t_5 = 2, \quad t_6 = \frac{5}{2}, \quad t_7 = 3, \quad t_8 = \frac{7}{2}.$$

Our approximation is then

$$\text{Area of } R \approx \left\{ f(0) + f\left(\frac{1}{2}\right) + f(1) + \cdots + f\left(\frac{7}{2}\right) \right\} \left(\frac{1}{2}\right)$$

$$= \left\{ 0^2 + \left(\frac{1}{2}\right)^2 + 1^2 + \left(\frac{3}{2}\right)^2 + 2^2 + \left(\frac{5}{2}\right)^2 + 3^2 + \left(\frac{7}{2}\right)^2 \right\} \left(\frac{1}{2}\right)$$

$$= \left\{ \frac{1}{4} + 1 + \frac{9}{4} + 4 + \frac{25}{4} + 9 + \frac{49}{4} \right\} \left(\frac{1}{2}\right)$$

$$= \frac{140}{8}$$

$$= 17.5.$$

(iii) Continuing in this way we could increase the value of n and recalculate the approximation given in (1). Although a tedious chore by hand calculation, such approximations are easily carried out for large values of n by computers. Table 4.1 shows the result of using BASIC Program 4 in Appendix I to implement the approximation used in parts (i) and (ii) for various values of n.

n	Approximation
10	18.2400
20	19.7600
50	20.6976
100	21.0144
200	21.1736
500	21.2694

Table 4.1. Approximations to area of R in Example 1 using Program 4 in Appendix I.

(The actual value is $\dfrac{64}{3} \approx 21.3333$.)

In Section 5.5 we shall learn a method for calculating the exact value of the area of R, which is $\dfrac{64}{3} = 21.333.\ldots$. Note that the approximations in Table 4.1 increase toward this exact value as n increases. ∎

☐ **EXAMPLE 2**

Let R be the region bounded by the x-axis and the graph of $f(x) = \dfrac{1}{x}$ between $a = 1$ and $b = 3$. Figure 4.7 shows the result of approximating the area of R using $n = 4$ subintervals of width $\Delta x = \dfrac{3-1}{4} = \dfrac{1}{2}$ and again using the left endpoint of each interval as the "test point" t_j. Approximation (1) becomes

$$\text{Area of } R \approx \left\{ f(1) + f\left(\frac{3}{2}\right) + f(2) + f\left(\frac{5}{2}\right) \right\}\left(\frac{1}{2}\right)$$

$$= \left\{ 1 + \frac{2}{3} + \frac{1}{2} + \frac{2}{5} \right\}\left(\frac{1}{2}\right)$$

$$= \left(\frac{30 + 20 + 15 + 12}{30} \right)\left(\frac{1}{2}\right)$$

$$= \frac{77}{60}$$

$$\approx 1.2833.\ldots$$

The value of this approximation is *larger* than the actual area (which we shall later show is $\ln 3 \approx 1.0986$) since each of the approximating rectangles contains

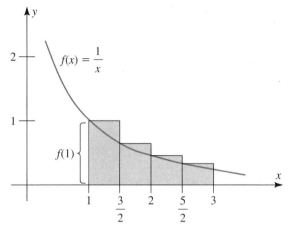

Figure 4.7 Approximating the area of the region bounded by the graph of $f(x) = \dfrac{1}{x}$ and the x-axis for $1 \le x \le 3$ using $n = 4$ subintervals.

more than just the part of R over the corresponding subinterval. Table 4.2 shows the result of using BASIC Program 4 in Appendix I to approximate the area of R. Note that the approximations decrease toward the exact value $\ln 3 \approx 1.0986$ as n increases. ■

n	Approximation
10	1.1682
20	1.1327
50	1.1121
100	1.1053
200	1.1019
500	1.0999

Table 4.2. Approximations to the area of the region bounded by the graph of the function $f(x) = \dfrac{1}{x}$ and the x-axis for $1 \le x \le 3$ using BASIC Program 4 in Appendix I. (The actual value, approximated to four decimal places, is 1.0986.)

Limits of Approximating Sums

The idea of approximating regions in the plane by rectangles leads to more than just a method for making ''good'' estimates for the areas of these regions. The following theorem guarantees that for a continuous function f and a closed finite interval $[a, b]$ all approximations by rectangles *will approach the same limit* as n increases without bound. The proof of this theorem is beyond the scope of this text.

Theorem 2

Let f be a continuous function on the interval $[a, b]$. Let the n numbers $t_1, t_2, \ldots, t_n$ be chosen arbitrarily, one from each of the n subintervals of $[a, b]$ of equal length $\Delta x = \dfrac{b - a}{n}$ as previously described. Then the limit as n increases without bound of

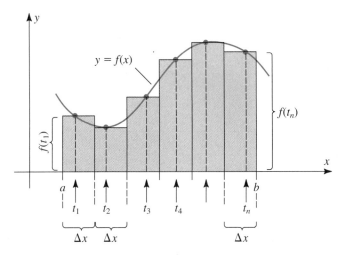

Figure 4.8 Approximating sum S_n in Theorem 2.

the approximating sum

$$S_n = \{ f(t_1) + f(t_2) + \cdots + f(t_n) \} \, \Delta x$$

exists and is unique, regardless of how the numbers $t_1, t_2, \ldots, t_n$ are selected. When $f(x) \geq 0$ for all x in $[a, b]$, this limit is the area of the region bounded by the graph of $y = f(x)$ and the x-axis between $x = a$ and $x = b$. (See Figure 4.8.)

$$S_n = \sum_{j=1}^{n} f(t_j) \, \Delta x = [f(t_1) + \cdots + f(t_n)] \, \Delta x.$$

Here is some insight into why Theorem 2 is true. Figure 4.9 shows the same function as in Figure 4.8, except that two different approximating sums, $\underline{S}_n$ and $\overline{S}_n$, have been superimposed on the region bounded by the graph of f:

a. The *lower* approximating sum $\underline{S}_n$ has been formed by choosing the test number $t_j = c_j$ in each subinterval that produces the *minimum* value of f on that interval. That is,

$$\underline{S}_n = \{ f(c_1) + f(c_2) + \cdots + f(c_n) \} \, \Delta x$$

where $f(c_j) = \{ \min f(x) | x_{j-1} \leq x \leq x_j \}$ for all $j = 1, 2, \ldots, n$.

b. Similarly, the *upper* approximating sum $\overline{S}_n$ has been formed using $t_j = d_j$, where $f(d_j)$ is the maximum value of f on the jth subinterval. That is,

$$\overline{S}_n = \{ f(d_1) + f(d_2) + \cdots + f(d_n) \} \, \Delta x$$

with $f(d_j) = \{ \max f(x) | x_{j-1} \leq x \leq x_j \}$ for all $j = 1, 2, \ldots, n$.

Figure 4.10 shows the point of thinking about lower approximating sums and upper approximating sums: For a given integer n, *any* approximating sum

$$S_n = \{ f(t_1) + f(t_2) + \cdots + f(t_n) \} \, \Delta x$$

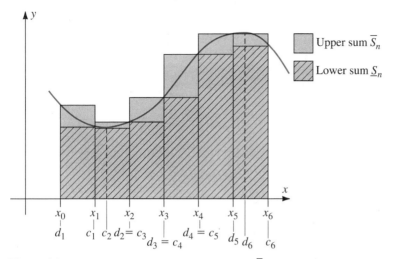

Figure 4.9 Upper and lower approximating sums, $\overline{S}_n$ and $\underline{S}_n$, for f on $[a, b]$.

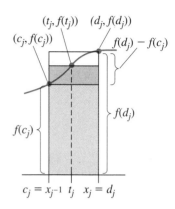

Figure 4.10 On each subinterval, $f(c_j) \leq f(t_j) \leq f(d_j)$ no matter how t_j is chosen.

for f on $[a, b]$ must have the property that

$$f(c_j) \leq f(t_j) \leq f(d_j), \qquad 1 \leq j \leq n.$$

That is, in every interval, no matter how t_j is chosen, the height of the approximating rectangle in the *arbitrary* approximating sum must be (a) at least as high as the corresponding rectangle in the lower sum $\underline{S}_n$, and (b) no higher than the corresponding rectangle in the upper sum $\overline{S}_n$.

Since this is true for *every* rectangle, we must have

$$\underline{S}_n \leq S_n \leq \overline{S}_n. \qquad (2)$$

That is, *every* approximating sum for f on $[a, b]$, with n subintervals, lies between the lower sum and the upper sum.

The clincher is the fact that the difference between $\underline{S}_n$ and $\overline{S}_n$ must shrink to zero as $n \to \infty$. To see this, note that

$$\begin{aligned}
\overline{S}_n - \underline{S}_n &= \{f(d_1) + f(d_2) + \cdots + f(d_n)\} \Delta x - \{f(c_1) + f(c_2) + \cdots + f(c_n)\} \Delta x \\
&= \{[f(d_1) - f(c_1)] + [f(d_2) - f(c_2)] + \cdots + [f(d_n) - f(c_n)]\} \Delta x.
\end{aligned}$$

As n becomes large, the width $\Delta x = \dfrac{b - a}{n}$ of each of the subintervals approaches zero. This means that the differences $[f(d_j) - f(c_j)]$ also approach zero. These observations, plus a result from advanced calculus about "uniform continuity," establish the fact that $\lim\limits_{n \to \infty} \overline{S}_n = \lim\limits_{n \to \infty} \underline{S}_n$. Thus, the lower and upper sums have a common limit as $n \to \infty$, which must also be the limit for *every* approximating sum because of the inequality.

☐ **EXAMPLE 3**

To illustrate the idea behind this proof, we return to Example 1 and note that the approximating sums S_4 and S_8 for $f(x) = x^2$ on the interval $[0, 4]$ were really *lower* sums, because we used the left endpoint of each subinterval as the "test number" t_j.

We can obtain the corresponding *upper* sums by using the *right* endpoints:

(a) With $n = 4$ subintervals of equal length $\Delta x = \dfrac{4 - 0}{4} = 1$, we have the upper sum

$$\overline{S}_4 = \{f(1) + f(2) + f(3) + f(4)\}(1)$$
$$= (1^2 + 2^2 + 3^2 + 4^2)(1)$$
$$= 30$$

whereas the lower sum $\underline{S}_4$ in Example 1 had been found to be $\underline{S}_4 = 14$.

(b) Similarly, with $n = 8$ subintervals of equal length, $\Delta x = \dfrac{4 - 0}{8} = \dfrac{1}{2}$, we obtain the upper sum

$$\overline{S}_8 = \left\{ f\left(\frac{1}{2}\right) + f(1) + f\left(\frac{3}{2}\right) + \cdots + f(4) \right\}\left(\frac{1}{2}\right)$$
$$= \left\{ \left(\frac{1}{2}\right)^2 + 1^2 + \left(\frac{3}{2}\right)^2 + \cdots + 4^2 \right\}\frac{1}{2}$$
$$= \frac{204}{4} \cdot \frac{1}{2} = 25.5.$$

In Example 1 we had found $\underline{S}_8 = 17.5$.

From these calculations you can see that

$$\underline{S}_4 < \underline{S}_8 < \overline{S}_8 < \overline{S}_4$$

as predicted.

Table 4.3 shows the values of the upper and lower approximating sums for $f(x) = x^2$ on $[0, 4]$ for larger integers n. Note how the values $\overline{S}_n$ and $\underline{S}_n$ approach a common limit as n increases.

Table 4.3 Lower and Upper Approximating Sums for $f(x) = x^2$ on $[0, 4]$.

n	Lower Sums $\underline{S}_n$	Upper Sums $\overline{S}_n$
10	18.2400	24.6400
20	19.7600	22.9600
50	20.6976	21.9776
100	21.0144	21.6544
200	21.1736	21.4936
500	21.2694	21.3974

As was stated at the end of Example 1, these approximations are approaching the exact value $\dfrac{64}{3} = 21.333$ as n increases. Notice that $\underline{S}_n < \dfrac{64}{3} < \overline{S}_n$ for each entry in Table 4.3.

■

Sigma Notation

The symbol $\sum$, capital sigma, is often used as shorthand notation to indicate the sum of a number of similar terms. For example

$$\sum_{j=1}^{5} x_j \qquad \text{means} \qquad x_1 + x_2 + x_3 + x_4 + x_5$$

$$\sum_{j=1}^{4} j^2 \qquad \text{means} \qquad 1^2 + 2^2 + 3^2 + 4^2 = 30$$

and

$$\sum_{j=1}^{4} x^j \qquad \text{means} \qquad x + x^2 + x^3 + x^4.$$

In other words, $\sum_{j=1}^{n} f(x_j)$ means, "sum all expressions of the form $f(x_j)$ for j beginning at $j = 1$ and proceeding through all positive integers up to and including n."

□ **EXAMPLE 4**

(a) $\displaystyle\sum_{j=1}^{5} j^2 = 1^2 + 2^2 + 3^2 + 4^2 + 5^2 = 55.$

(b) $\displaystyle\sum_{j=3}^{6} (2j + 1) = (2 \cdot 3 + 1) + (2 \cdot 4 + 1) + (2 \cdot 5 + 1) + (2 \cdot 6 + 1)$

$$= 7 + 9 + 11 + 13$$
$$= 40.$$

■

Using sigma notation, we can write the approximating sum in Theorem 2 as

$$S_n = \{f(t_1) + f(t_2) + \cdots + f(t_n)\} \Delta x$$
$$= f(t_1) \Delta x + f(t_2) \Delta x + \cdots + f(t_n) \Delta x$$
$$= \sum_{j=1}^{n} f(t_j) \Delta x$$

since each term in the sum is the product of $f(t_j)$ (a height of a rectangle, when $f(t_j) \geq 0$) and Δx (the width of the rectangle).

When $f(x) \geq 0$ for all x in the interval $[a, b]$, we can summarize the conclusions of Theorem 2 by writing that

$$\text{Area of } R = \lim_{n\to\infty} S_n = \lim_{n\to\infty} \sum_{j=1}^{n} f(t_j)\,\Delta x \tag{3}$$

where Δx and t_j are as defined above.

Of course, the question remains of how to find the limit of the approximating sums in equation (3). This is the topic of Section 5.5.

The Definite Integral

A special symbol denotes the limit of the approximating sum in equation (3) for the continuous function f. It is

$$\int_a^b f(x)\,dx$$

which is called the **definite integral** of the function f on the interval $[a, b]$. That is, we *define*

$$\int_a^b f(x)\,dx = \lim_{n\to\infty} \sum_{j=1}^{n} f(t_j)\,\Delta x. \tag{4}$$

(Remember that the widths Δx and the numbers t_j change as n increases.) As with the indefinite integral, the elongated s, $\int$, is referred to as the **integral sign**. But the **lower limit** a and **upper limit** b identify the fact that the definite integral is not a function (as is an antiderivative). Rather, $\int_a^b f(x)\,dx$ is a *number* associated with the integrand f and the *interval* $[a, b]$. The symbol $\int_a^b f(x)\,dx$ is read, "the integral from a to b of f with respect to x."

When $f(x) \geq 0$ for all x in $[a, b]$, we may combine equations (3) and (4) by writing

$$\text{Area of } R = \int_a^b f(x)\,dx \tag{5}$$

if $f(x) \geq 0 \qquad$ for all x in $[a, b]$.

(See Figure 4.11.)

□ **EXAMPLE 5**

As stated in part (iii) of Example 1, we shall show in Section 5.5 that

$$\int_0^4 x^2\,dx = \frac{64}{3}.$$

(See Figure 4.12.) ■

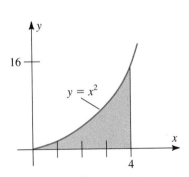

Figure 4.11 Area of $R = \int_a^b f(x)\,dx$ when $f(x) \geq 0$.

Figure 4.12 $\int_0^4 x^2\,dx = \dfrac{64}{3}$.

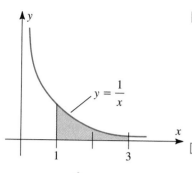

Figure 4.13 $\int_1^3 \frac{1}{x} \, dx = \ln 3.$

☐ **EXAMPLE 6**

According to Example 2, we have

$$\int_1^3 \frac{1}{x} \, dx = \ln 3 \approx 1.0986.$$

(See Figure 4.13.)   ■

☐ **EXAMPLE 7**

Figure 4.14 shows the region R bounded above by the graph of $f(x) = 2x + 1$ and below by the x-axis for $1 \leq x \leq 3$. Since R is a trapezoid with bases of length $b = 3$ and $B = 7$, and height $h = 2$, the area of R is

$$A = \frac{1}{2}(B + b)h = \frac{1}{2}(3 + 7)(2) = 10.$$

Thus using equation (5), we can write that

$$\int_1^3 (2x + 1) \, dx = 10.$$

                                                             ■

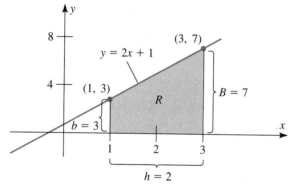

Figure 4.14 Since area of $R = \frac{1}{2}(3 + 7)(2) = 10$,
$\int_1^3 (2x + 1) \, dx = 10.$

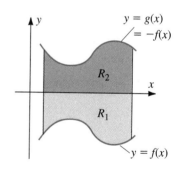

Figure 4.15 Region bounded by graph of $-f$ is congruent to region bounded by f.

Area and Negative Functions

The definite integral can also be used to define the area of a region bounded by the graph of a negative function, and even of a function that changes sign on the interval $[a, b]$. We present a careful treatment of this issue in Section 5.6, but we note the basic ideas here for completion.

If $f(x) \leq 0$ for all x in $[a, b]$, then the function $g(x) = -f(x)$ is nonnegative on $[a, b]$. Also, the region bounded by the graph of g is congruent to the region bounded by the graph of f, because it is just its reflection in the x-axis. (See Figure 4.15.) We therefore define the area of the region bounded by the graph of f to be the same as the area of the region bounded by the graph of $g = -f$. Thus,

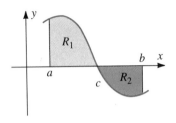

Figure 4.16 Region $(R_1 + R_2)$ bounded by the graph of a function that is both positive and negative on $[a, b]$.

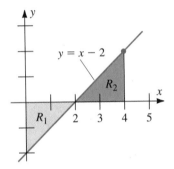

Figure 4.17 Area of region bounded by $f(x) = x - 2$ on $[0, 4]$ is $2 + 2 = 4$.

$$\text{Area of } R = \int_a^b [-f(x)]\, dx \qquad (6)$$

$$\text{if } f(x) \leq 0 \qquad \text{for all } x \text{ in } [a, b].$$

Finally, if the function f is both positive and negative on $[a, b]$, we define this area of the region bounded by the graph of f on $[a, b]$ by dividing $[a, b]$ into subintervals on which f is either nonnegative or nonpositive. On each subinterval we calculate the area of the corresponding part of the region using either equation (5) or equation (6) as appropriate. The area of the entire region is then defined to be the sum of the areas of the regions associated with these subintervals. (See Figure 4.16.)

□ **EXAMPLE 8**

Find the area of the region bounded by the graph of $f(x) = -x^2$ for $0 \leq x \leq 4$.

Solution: Since $f(x) = -x^2 \leq 0$ for all x in $[0, 4]$, we use equation (6) to write

$$\text{Area of } R = \int_0^4 -[f(x)]\, dx = \int_0^4 -(-x^2)\, dx$$

$$= \int_0^4 x^2\, dx.$$

In Example 5 we have already seen the value of this integral to be $\dfrac{64}{3}$. ■

□ **EXAMPLE 9**

Find the area of the region bounded by the graph of $f(x) = x - 2$ for $0 \leq x \leq 4$.

Solution: As illustrated in Figure 4.17, we have

$$f(x) = x - 2 \begin{cases} \leq 0 & \text{for} & 0 \leq x \leq 2 \\ \geq 0 & \text{for} & 2 \leq x \leq 4. \end{cases}$$

We therefore calculate the areas separately on the intervals $[0, 2]$ and $[2, 4]$.

(a) On $[0, 2]$, we use Equation (6) to write

$$\text{Area of } R_1 = \int_0^2 -(x - 2)\, dx = \int_0^2 (2 - x)\, dx.$$

The region bounded by $g(x) = -f(x) = 2 - x$ on $[0, 2]$ is a triangle with base $b = 2$ and height $h = 2$, so its area is $\dfrac{1}{2} bh = \dfrac{1}{2} \cdot 2 \cdot 2 = 2$.

(b) On $[2, 4]$, we use Equation (5) to write

$$\text{Area of } R_2 = \int_2^4 (x - 2)\, dx = 2$$

by the same reasoning as in part (a).

The area of the entire region R is then

$$\text{Area of } R = \text{area of } R_1 + \text{area of } R_2$$

$$= \int_0^2 -(x - 2) \, dx + \int_2^4 (x - 2) \, dx$$

$$= 2 + 2$$

$$= 4. \qquad \blacksquare$$

☑ **PRACTICE PROBLEMS 5.4**

1. By geometry, find the value of the definite integral $\int_{-2}^{2} (6 + \sqrt{4 - x^2}) \, dx$.

2. Evaluate the sum: $\sum_{j=3}^{6} (4j^2 + 3j - 2)$.

3. Express the area of the region bounded by the graph of $f(x) = (x + 1)^3$ and the x-axis for $-2 \le x \le 2$, using the definite integral.

Exercise Set 5.4

In each of Exercises 1–5, find the approximating sum, equation (1), for f on the interval $[a, b]$ using n subintervals of equal length and the left endpoint of each subinterval as the "test number" t.

1. $f(x) = 2x + 5$, $a = 0$, $b = 4$, $n = 4$

2. $f(x) = x^2 + 3$, $a = 0$, $b = 2$, $n = 4$

3. $f(x) = 4 - x^2$, $a = -2$, $b = 2$, $n = 8$

4. $f(x) = \dfrac{1}{x + 2}$, $a = 0$, $b = 3$, $n = 6$

5. $f(x) = \dfrac{1}{1 + x^2}$, $a = -1$, $b = 1$, $n = 4$

In each of Exercises 6–10, apply the instructions for Exercises 1–5 except that the right endpoint of each subinterval should be used as the "test number."

6. $f(x) = 2x + 5$, $a = 0$, $b = 4$, $n = 4$

7. $f(x) = x^2 + 3$, $a = 0$, $b = 2$, $n = 4$

8. $f(x) = 9 - x^2$, $a = -3$, $b = 3$, $n = 6$

9. $f(x) = \dfrac{1}{4 - x}$, $a = 0$, $b = 2$, $n = 4$

10. $f(x) = \dfrac{1}{2 + x^2}$, $a = -2$, $b = 2$, $n = 4$

11. Which of the approximating sums in Exercises 1–5 are lower sums?

12. Which of the approximating sums in Exercises 1–5 are upper sums?

13. Which of the approximating sums in Exercises 6–10 are lower sums?

14. Which of the approximating sums in Exercises 6–10 are upper sums?

In Exercises 15–22, find the value of the indicated sum.

15. $\sum_{j=1}^{6} (3j + 2)$

16. $\sum_{j=1}^{5} (2j^2 - 5)$

17. $\sum_{j=1}^{5} (2j - 5)^2$

18. $\sum_{j=3}^{6} (j^2 - 4j + 1)$

19. $\sum_{j=4}^{7} (j - 5)$

20. $\sum_{j=1}^{10} j^3$

21. $\displaystyle\sum_{j=4}^{10} (j^3 - 10)$ **22.** $\displaystyle\sum_{j=2}^{6} (j + 1)(j - 1)$

In each of Exercises 23–32, use geometry to find the value of the definite integral.

23. $\displaystyle\int_0^2 x\,dx$ **24.** $\displaystyle\int_1^3 (x + 4)\,dx$

25. $\displaystyle\int_{-1}^3 4\,dx$ **26.** $\displaystyle\int_{-1}^2 (x + 1)\,dx$

27. $\displaystyle\int_0^9 (9 - x)\,dx$ **28.** $\displaystyle\int_3^6 3\,dx$

29. $\displaystyle\int_{-1}^2 |x|\,dx$ **30.** $\displaystyle\int_2^4 (3x - 6)\,dx$

31. $\displaystyle\int_0^4 |x - 2|\,dx$ **32.** $\displaystyle\int_0^5 |2x - 4|\,dx$

In Exercises 33–38, express the area of the region bounded by the graph of the given function and the x axis, for $a \le x \le b$, as one or more definite integrals.

33. $f(x) = x$, $-2 \le x \le 2$

34. $f(x) = 2x - 2$, $0 \le x \le 6$

35. $f(x) = 3x - 6$, $0 \le x \le 4$

36. $f(x) = x + 1$, $-2 \le x \le 2$

37. $f(x) = 1 - x^2$, $-2 \le x \le 2$

38. $f(x) = x^3 + 1$, $-2 \le x \le 3$

(Computer). In each of Exercises 39–44, use Program 4 in Appendix I to approximate the area of the region R.

39. R is the region bounded above by the graph of $f(x) = \sqrt{x + 2}$ and below by the x-axis for $0 \le x \le 2$.

40. R is the region bounded above by the graph of $f(x) = \dfrac{10}{1 + x^2}$ and below by the x-axis for $0 \le x \le 3$.

41. R is the region bounded above by the graph of $f(x) = \ln(x + 3)$ and below by the x-axis for $0 \le x \le 4$.

42. R is the region whose area is $\displaystyle\int_0^2 \sqrt{4 - x^2}\,dx$.

43. R is the region whose area is $\displaystyle\int_0^4 \sqrt{5 + x^2}\,dx$.

44. R is the region whose area is $\displaystyle\int_{-2}^2 \sqrt{9 - x^2}\,dx$.

☑ **SOLUTIONS TO PRACTICE PROBLEMS 5.4**

1. The integral is the same as the area of the region in Figure 4.18. Consisting of a semicircle of radius $r = 2$ and a rectangle with area $6 \cdot 4 = 24$, the area of the entire region is

$$A = \frac{\pi \cdot 2^2}{2} + 24 = 2\pi + 24.$$

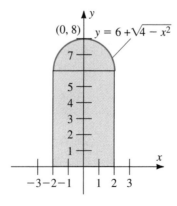

Figure 4.18

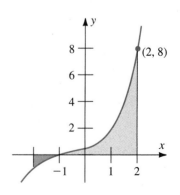

Figure 4.19

2. $\displaystyle\sum_{j=3}^{6} (4j^2 + 3j - 2) = (4 \cdot 3^2 + 3 \cdot 3 - 2) + (4 \cdot 4^2 + 3 \cdot 4 - 2) +$

$$(4 \cdot 5^2 + 3 \cdot 5 - 2) + (4 \cdot 6^2 + 3 \cdot 6 - 2)$$

$$= 390.$$

3. Area $= \displaystyle\int_{-2}^{-1} -(x + 1)^3 \, dx + \int_{-1}^{2} (x + 1)^3 \, dx.$

(See Figure 4.19.)

5.5 The Fundamental Theorem of Calculus

In Section 5.4 we have defined the definite integral of the continuous function f on the interval $[a, b]$ as

$$\int_{a}^{b} f(x) \, dx = \lim_{n \to \infty} \sum_{j=1}^{n} f(t_j) \, \Delta x \tag{1}$$

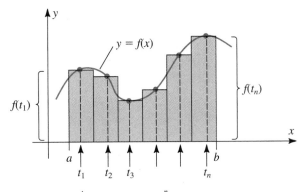

Figure 5.1 $\displaystyle\int_{a}^{b} f(x) \, dx = \lim_{n \to \infty} \sum_{j=1}^{n} f(t_j) \, \Delta x.$

where $\Delta x = \dfrac{b - a}{n}$ and $t_1, t_2, \ldots, t_n$ are as in Figure 5.1. When $f(x) \geq 0$ for $a \leq x \leq b$, the definite integral gives the area of the region bounded by the graph of f and the x-axis for $a \leq x \leq b$.

Although the definite integral $\displaystyle\int_{a}^{b} f(x) \, dx$ gives useful information about the graph of $y = f(x)$, the procedure outlined in Section 5.4 for approximating its value is tedious, at best, and we do not yet have a method for determining the precise value for the limit in equation (1).

However, the following theorem shows that the exact value of the definite integral $\displaystyle\int_{a}^{b} f(x) \, dx$ can be computed very easily if we can find an *antiderivative* for the function f. This result is so central to our theory that it is called the **Fundamental Theorem of Calculus.**

Theorem 3
Fundamental Theorem

Let f be continuous on $[a, b]$ and let F be any antiderivative for f. That is, let $F'(x) = f(x)$. Then

$$\int_a^b f(x)\, dx = F(b) - F(a). \tag{2}$$

That is, the value of the definite integral $\int_a^b f(x)\, dx$ is found by

(i) Finding an antiderivative F for f, and

(ii) Finding the difference $F(b) - F(a)$ between its values at the endpoints of $[a, b]$.

In applying the Fundamental Theorem, we will make use of the notation

$$[F(x)]_a^b = F(b) - F(a). \tag{3}$$

We shall defer the proof of the Fundamental Theorem to the end of this section.

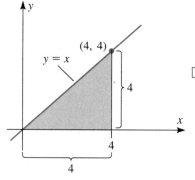

Figure 5.2 $\int_0^4 x\, dx = 8.$

☐ **EXAMPLE 1**

An antiderivative for $f(x) = x$ is $F(x) = \dfrac{x^2}{2}$. Thus,

$$\int_0^4 x\, dx = \left[\frac{x^2}{2}\right]_0^4 = \frac{4^2}{2} - \frac{0^2}{2} = 8.$$

This result is easy to verify geometrically since the value of the definite integral is the area of the triangle in Figure 5.2. ∎

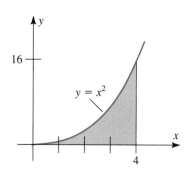

Figure 5.3 Area $= \int_0^4 x^2\, dx = \dfrac{64}{3}.$

☐ **EXAMPLE 2**

In Example 1, Section 5.4, we claimed that, for the region bounded by the graph of $y = x^2$ and the x-axis for $0 \le x \le 4$, the exact value of the area is $\dfrac{64}{3}$. We can verify this claim using the Fundamental Theorem and the antiderivative $F(x) = \dfrac{x^3}{3}$ for $f(x) = x^2$:

$$\text{Area} = \int_0^4 x^2\, dx = \left[\frac{x^3}{3}\right]_0^4 = \frac{4^3}{3} - \frac{0^3}{3} = \frac{64}{3}.$$

(See Figure 5.3.) ∎

☐ **EXAMPLE 3**

$$\int_1^3 \frac{1}{x}\, dx = \left[\ln x \right]_1^3 = \ln 3 - \ln 1 = \ln 3$$

since

$$\frac{d}{dx} \ln x = \frac{1}{x}.$$

☐ **EXAMPLE 4**

$$\int_{-1}^2 (x^3 - 3x^2 - 2x + 2)\, dx$$

$$= \left[\frac{x^4}{4} - x^3 - x^2 + 2x \right]_{-1}^2$$

$$= \left[\frac{2^4}{4} - 2^3 - 2^2 + 2(2) \right] - \left[\frac{(-1)^4}{4} - (-1)^3 - (-1)^2 + 2(-1) \right]$$

$$= (4 - 8 - 4 + 4) - \left(\frac{1}{4} + 1 - 1 - 2 \right)$$

$$= -\frac{9}{4}.$$

☐ **EXAMPLE 5**

$$\int_1^2 \left(e^{-x} + \frac{1}{x^2} \right) dx = \left[-e^{-x} - \frac{1}{x} \right]_1^2$$

$$= \left[-e^{-2} - \frac{1}{2} \right] - \left[-e^{-1} - \frac{1}{(1)} \right]$$

$$= \frac{1}{e} - \frac{1}{e^2} + \frac{1}{2}.$$

REMARK: Note that we do not include a constant of integration in writing an antiderivative for f when using the Fundamental Theorem to evaluate $\int_a^b f(x)\, dx$. That is because the Fundamental Theorem calls for *any* particular antiderivative of f, not the most general form of the antiderivative. Including an arbitrary constant would be inconsequential since

$$[F(x) + C]_a^b = [F(b) + C] - [F(a) + C]$$
$$= F(b) + C - F(a) - C$$
$$= F(b) - F(a)$$
$$= [F(x)]_a^b.$$

□ **EXAMPLE 6**

$$\int_1^4 \frac{x+1}{\sqrt{x}}\, dx = \int_1^4 \left(\sqrt{x} + \frac{1}{\sqrt{x}}\right) dx$$

$$= \int_1^4 (x^{1/2} + x^{-1/2})\, dx$$

$$= \left[\frac{2}{3} x^{3/2} + 2x^{1/2}\right]_1^4$$

$$= \left(\frac{2}{3}\cdot 4^{3/2} + 2\cdot 4^{1/2}\right) - \left(\frac{2}{3}\cdot 1^{3/2} + 2\cdot 1^{1/2}\right)$$

$$= \frac{20}{3}.$$

Substitutions in Definite Integrals

Often the method of substitution is required to find an antiderivative in evaluating a definite integral. The following example is one such situation. Note that we substitute *back* from u's to x's before the antiderivative is evaluated.

□ **EXAMPLE 7**

Find $\int_{-1}^3 \dfrac{x}{\sqrt{7+x^2}}\, dx.$

Solution: To find an antiderivative $\int \dfrac{x\,dx}{\sqrt{7+x^2}}$, we use the substitution

$$u = 7 + x^2, \qquad du = 2x\,dx.$$

Then $x\,dx = \dfrac{1}{2}\,du$, and we obtain

$$\int \frac{x\,dx}{\sqrt{7+x^2}} = \int \frac{\frac{1}{2}\,du}{\sqrt{u}} = \frac{1}{2}\int u^{-1/2}\,du = u^{1/2} + C$$

$$= \sqrt{7+x^2} + C.$$

We therefore use $F(x) = \sqrt{7+x^2}$ in the Fundamental Theorem to find that

$$\int_{-1}^3 \frac{x\,dx}{\sqrt{7+x^2}}\, dx = \left[\sqrt{7+x^2}\right]_{-1}^3 = \sqrt{7+3^2} - \sqrt{7+(-1)^2}$$

$$= \sqrt{16} - \sqrt{8}$$

$$= 4 - 2\sqrt{2}.$$

☐ **EXAMPLE 8**

Find $\int_1^2 \dfrac{3x^2 + 6}{x^3 + 6x - 6} \, dx$.

Solution: This time we notice that the numerator of the integrand is the derivative of the denominator. This suggests that we find the antiderivative by using the substitution

$$u = x^3 + 6x - 6 \quad \text{and} \quad du = (3x^2 + 6) \, dx.$$

We obtain the antiderivative

$$\int \frac{3x^2 + 6}{x^3 + 6x - 6} \, dx = \int \frac{du}{u} = \ln|u| + C = \ln|x^3 + 6x - 6| + C.$$

Thus

$$\int_1^2 \frac{3x^2 + 6}{x^3 + 6x - 6} \, dx = \left[\ln|x^3 + 6x - 6| \right]_1^2$$

$$= \ln(2^3 + 6(2) - 6) - \ln(1^3 + 6(1) - 6)$$

$$= \ln 14 - \ln 1$$

$$= \ln 14. \qquad\blacksquare$$

Properties of the Definite Integral

There are several properties of the definite integral that are useful in calculations. If f and g are continuous functions on the interval $[a, b]$

(I1) $\displaystyle\int_a^b [f(x) + g(x)] \, dx = \int_a^b f(x) \, dx + \int_a^b g(x) \, dx$

(I2) $\displaystyle\int_a^b c(x) \, dx = c \cdot \int_a^b f(x) \, dx \qquad$ (c is any constant)

(I3) $\displaystyle\int_a^a f(x) \, dx = 0$

(I4) $\displaystyle\int_a^b f(x) \, dx = \int_a^c f(x) \, dx + \int_c^b f(x) \, dx$ (c is any number between a and b)

Although each of these properties follows from the basic definition of the definite integral, it is particularly simple to demonstrate their validity using the Fundamental Theorem of Calculus when antiderivatives for f and g can be found. For example, if $F'(x) = f(x)$ and $G'(x) = g(x)$ for all x in $[a, b]$, then $F + G$ is an antiderivative for $f + g$, so

$$\int_a^b [f(x) + g(x)] \, dx = [F(x) + G(x)]_a^b$$

$$= [F(b) + G(b)] - [F(a) + G(a)]$$

$$= [F(b) - F(a)] + [G(b) - G(a)]$$

$$= \int_a^b f(x) \, dx + \int_a^b g(x) \, dx$$

which demonstrates property (I1). We leave it for you as an exercise to verify properties (I2)–(I4) in the same way.

Properties (I3) and (I4) have particularly simple geometric interpretations. Property (I3) means that the definite integral over an interval of length zero (i.e., a single point) must equal zero. This corresponds to the fact that a rectangle of height $f(a) \geq 0$ and width zero has area equal to $(0) f(a) = 0$.

Figure 5.4 gives the geometric interpretation of property (I4) when $f(x) \geq 0$ for all x in $[a, b]$. The area of the region bounded by the graph of $y = f(x)$ and the x-axis for $a \leq x \leq b$ equals the sum of the areas of the regions bounded by the graph of $y = f(x)$ and the x-axis for $a \leq x \leq c$ (region R_1) and for $c \leq x \leq b$ (region R_2).

Proof of the Fundamental Theorem of Calculus

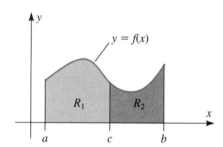

Figure 5.4 $\displaystyle\int_a^b f(x)\, dx =$
$\displaystyle\int_a^c f(x)\, dx + \int_c^b f(x)\, dx.$

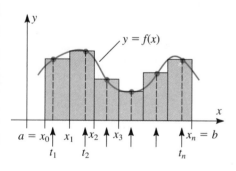

Figure 5.5 Approximating sum for $\displaystyle\int_a^b f(x)\, dx.$

Proof: Since the definite integral is the limit

$$\int_a^b f(x)\, dx = \lim_{n \to \infty} \sum_{j=1}^{n} f(t_j)\, \Delta x \qquad (4)$$

of an approximating sum, we begin by letting $x_0, x_1, x_2, \ldots, x_n$ denote the successive endpoints of the subintervals of $[a, b]$ of length $\Delta x = \dfrac{b - a}{n}$. (See Figure 5.5.) Also, since F is an antiderivative for f, the function F is differentiable and continuous on the interval $[a, b]$. Thus F satisfies the hypotheses of the Mean Value Theorem, which guarantees that in each subinterval $[x_{j-1}, x_j]$ there is a number t_j so that

$$\frac{F(x_j) - F(x_{j-1})}{x_j - x_{j-1}} = F'(t_j) = f(t_j). \qquad (5)$$

This is the test number t_j that we shall use in each interval to form the approximating sum in equation (4). Using equation (5) and the fact that $\Delta x = x_j - x_{j-1}$ for each $j = 1, 2, \ldots, n$ gives

$$\int_a^b f(x)\, dx = \lim_{n \to \infty} \sum_{j=1}^{n} f(t_j)\, \Delta x$$

$$= \lim_{n \to \infty} \sum_{j=1}^{n} \left[\frac{F(x_j) - F(x_{j-1})}{x_j - x_{j-1}} \right] (x_j - x_{j-1})$$

$$= \lim_{n \to \infty} \sum_{j=1}^{n} [F(x_j) - F(x_{j-1})].$$

Now the last line above contains a telescoping sum in which every term cancels except the first and the last:

$$\sum_{j=1}^{n} [F(x_j) - F(x_{j-1})] = \{[F(x_1) - F(x_0)] + [F(x_2) - F(x_1)]$$

$$+ [F(x_3) - F(x_2)] + [F(x_4) - F(x_3)]$$
$$+ \cdots$$
$$+ [F(x_{n-1}) - F(x_{n-2})] + [F(x_n) - F(x_{n-1})]\}$$
$$= F(x_n) - F(x_0)$$
$$= F(b) - F(a)$$

since $x_0 = a$ and $x_n = b$. (See Figure 5.5.) Thus

$$\int_a^b f(x)\,dx = \lim_{n\to\infty} \sum_{j=1}^n [F(x_j) - F(x_{j-1})]$$

$$= \lim_{n\to\infty} [F(b) - F(a)]$$

$$= F(b) - F(a)$$

as stated.   ∎

☑ PRACTICE PROBLEMS 5.5

1. Use the Fundamental Theorem to evaluate

$$\int_0^2 (2xe^{x^2} + 6x + 2)\,dx.$$

2. Find the area of the region bounded by the graph of $f(x) = e^{-x} - 1$ and the x-axis for $1 \le x \le \ln 6$.

Exercise Set 5.5

In Exercises 1–24, use the Fundamental Theorem of Calculus to evaluate the definite integral.

1. $\displaystyle\int_0^2 (x + 3)\,dx$

2. $\displaystyle\int_1^3 (4 - 2x)\,dx$

3. $\displaystyle\int_1^5 (x^2 - 6)\,dx$

4. $\displaystyle\int_2^7 3\,dx$

5. $\displaystyle\int_{-3}^2 (9 + x^2)\,dx$

6. $\displaystyle\int_2^3 \left(6 + \frac{1}{x^2}\right) dx$

7. $\displaystyle\int_0^1 e^{4x}\,dx$

8. $\displaystyle\int_1^5 \frac{1}{x + 3}\,dx$

9. $\displaystyle\int_1^4 \left(\sqrt{x} - \frac{3}{\sqrt{x}}\right) dx$

10. $\displaystyle\int_0^2 xe^{x^2}\,dx$

11. $\displaystyle\int_0^1 (x^4 - 6x^3 + x)\,dx$

12. $\displaystyle\int_0^2 \left(\frac{x - 1}{x + 1}\right) dx$

13. $\displaystyle\int_1^4 \left(\frac{x + 3}{\sqrt{x}}\right) dx$

14. $\displaystyle\int_0^2 (\sqrt{x} - 2)(x + 1)\,dx$

15. $\displaystyle\int_0^2 (x^3 - 6x^2 + 3x + 3)\,dx$

16. $\displaystyle\int_{-1}^1 (4x^3 - 3x^4)\,dx$

17. $\displaystyle\int_1^2 \frac{x + 6}{x^2 + 12x}\,dx$

18. $\displaystyle\int_0^1 xe^{3x^2}\,dx$

19. $\displaystyle\int_2^4 \frac{x - 1}{\sqrt{x} - 1}\,dx$

20. $\displaystyle\int_0^3 x(\sqrt[3]{x} - 2)\,dx$

21. $\displaystyle\int_0^1 (x^{3/5} - x^{5/3})\,dx$

22. $\displaystyle\int_1^2 \frac{1 - x}{x^3}\,dx$

23. $\displaystyle\int_0^4 \frac{dx}{\sqrt{2x + 1}}$

24. $\displaystyle\int_1^4 \frac{e^{\sqrt{x}}}{\sqrt{x}}\,dx$

In Exercises 25–30, use the method of substitution to evaluate the definite integral.

25. $\displaystyle\int_0^2 \frac{x}{\sqrt{16 + x^2}}\, dx$

26. $\displaystyle\int_0^1 \frac{x^2 + 1}{x^3 + 3x + 7}\, dx$

27. $\displaystyle\int_0^3 x\sqrt{9 - x^2}\, dx$

28. $\displaystyle\int_1^2 \frac{x}{(2x^2 - 1)^3}\, dx$

29. $\displaystyle\int_1^2 x(x^2 - 1)^{1/3}\, dx$

30. $\displaystyle\int_1^4 \left(1 - \frac{1}{2\sqrt{x}}\right) e^{x - \sqrt{x}}\, dx$

In Exercises 31–38, use the Fundamental Theorem and the definition of area to find the area of the region bounded by the graph of $y = f(x)$ and the x-axis for $a \le x \le b$.

31. $f(x) = \sqrt{x}, \qquad 0 \le x \le 8$

32. $f(x) = \dfrac{1}{x + 2}, \qquad -1 \le x \le 3$

33. $f(x) = e^{-x}, \qquad 0 \le x \le \ln 5$

34. $f(x) = \dfrac{e^x}{1 + e^x}, \qquad 0 \le x \le \ln 2$

35. $f(x) = x^2 - 4, \qquad -2 \le x \le 2$

36. $f(x) = 1 - e^x, \qquad 0 \le x \le \ln 4$

37. $f(x) = x^3 - x^2, \qquad 0 \le x \le 1$

38. $f(x) = \dfrac{x}{\sqrt{9 + x^2}}, \qquad -4 \le x \le 0$

☑ **SOLUTIONS TO PRACTICE PROBLEMS 5.5**

1. An antiderivative for $f(x) = 2xe^{x^2} + 6x + 2$ is $F(x) = e^{x^2} + 3x^2 + 2x$. Thus,

$$\int_0^2 (2xe^{x^2} + 6x + 2)\, dx = [e^{x^2} + 3x^2 + 2x]_0^2$$

$$= (e^4 + 3 \cdot 2^2 + 4) - (e^0 + 0)$$

$$= e^4 + 15.$$

2. The function $f(x) = e^{-x} - 1$ is nonpositive for $1 \le x \le \ln 6$. Thus,

$$\text{Area} = \int_1^{\ln 6} -(e^{-x} - 1)\, dx$$

$$= \int_1^{\ln 6} (1 - e^{-x})\, dx$$

$$= [x + e^{-x}]_1^{\ln 6}$$

$$= (\ln 6 + e^{-\ln 6}) - (1 + e^{-1})$$

$$= \ln 6 + \frac{1}{6} - 1 - \frac{1}{e}$$

$$\approx 0.5905.$$

5.6 Finding Areas by Integration

Figure 6.1 summarizes the fact that when $f(x) \ge 0$ for all x in $[a, b]$, the area of the region R bounded by the graph of the continuous function f and the x-axis between $x = a$ and $x = b$ is given by the definite integral $\displaystyle\int_a^b f(x)\, dx$:

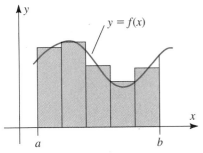

Figure 6.1 Area of $R =$
$$\int_a^b f(x)\,dx = \lim_{n \to \infty} \sum_{j=1}^{n} f(t_j)\,\Delta x.$$

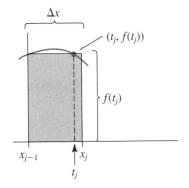

Figure 6.2 Area of jth approximating rectangle is $f(t_j)\,\Delta x$.

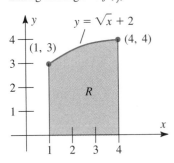

Figure 6.3 Region R in Example 1.

Strategy · · · · · · · ·
Sketch the graph to locate the region R.

Determine the interval $[a, b]$ defining the region by finding the zeros of f.

$$\boxed{\text{Area of } R = \int_a^b f(x)\,dx \qquad (1)}$$
$$\text{if} \quad f(x) \geq 0 \qquad \text{for all } x \text{ in } [a, b].$$

That is because the area of R is approximated by the areas of rectangles whose heights are $f(t_j)$ and whose widths are Δx, as illustrated in Figure 6.2.

□ **EXAMPLE 1**

Find the area of the region R bounded by the graph of $f(x) = \sqrt{x} + 2$ and the x-axis between $x = 1$ and $x = 4$. (See Figure 6.3.)

Solution: Here $f(x) > 0$ for all x in $[1, 4]$, so we apply equation (1) with $a = 1$ and $b = 4$:

$$\text{Area of } R = \int_1^4 (\sqrt{x} + 2)\,dx$$
$$= \int_1^4 (x^{1/2} + 2)\,dx$$
$$= \left[\frac{2}{3}x^{3/2} + 2x\right]_1^4$$
$$= \left(\frac{2}{3} \cdot 4^{3/2} + 2 \cdot 4\right) - \left(\frac{2}{3} \cdot 1^{3/2} + 2 \cdot 1\right)$$
$$= \frac{2}{3}(8) + 8 - \frac{2}{3} - 2$$
$$= \frac{32}{3}. \qquad \blacksquare$$

In the next example the endpoints a and b defining the region R are not explicitly stated. They must be found by finding the *zeros* of the function f.

□ **EXAMPLE 2**

Find the area of the region bounded by the graph of $f(x) = 2 + x - x^2$ and the x-axis.

Solution
The region bounded by the graph of $f(x) = 2 + x - x^2$ and the x-axis lies above the x-axis, as shown in Figure 6.4. To find the largest and smallest values of x associated with this region, we locate the zeros of f by factoring:

$$f(x) = 2 + x - x^2$$
$$= (2 - x)(1 + x).$$

Use equation (1) to find the area of R.

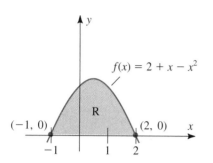

Figure 6.4 Region R in Example 2.

Thus $x = a = -1$ and $x = b = 2$ are the zeros of f. The area of R therefore is

$$\text{Area} = \int_{-1}^{2} (2 + x - x^2)\, dx$$

$$= \left[2x + \frac{1}{2}x^2 - \frac{1}{3}x^3 \right]_{-1}^{2}$$

$$= \left[2 \cdot 2 + \frac{1}{2} \cdot 2^2 - \frac{1}{3} \cdot 2^3 \right]$$

$$- \left[2(-1) + \frac{1}{2}(-1)^2 - \frac{1}{3}(-1)^3 \right]$$

$$= \frac{9}{2}.$$ ∎

☐ **EXAMPLE 3**

Find the area of the region R bounded above by the graph of $y = |x - 3|$ and below by the x-axis for $1 \le x \le 6$.

Strategy   ·   ·   ·   ·   ·   ·   ·

Use definition of absolute value to rewrite $f(x) = |x - 3|$.

Solution

Since we do not have an antiderivative for $f(x) = |x - 3|$, we cannot proceed directly to apply equation (1). However, using the definition of absolute value, we may rewrite f as

$$f(x) = |x - 3| = \begin{cases} x - 3 & \text{if } x \ge 3 \\ 3 - x & \text{if } x < 3. \end{cases}$$

Calculate areas of regions over $[1, 3]$ and $[3, 6]$ separately, writing $f(x)$ as a simple linear function in each interval.

This suggests that we calculate separately the areas of regions R_1 and R_2 as illustrated in Figure 6.5. We obtain

$$\text{Area of } R = \text{area of } R_1 + \text{area of } R_2$$

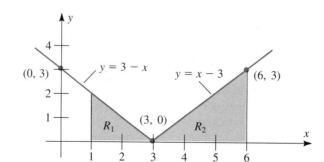

Figure 6.5 Region bounded by the graph of $f(x) = |x - 3|$ and the x-axis for $1 \le x \le 6$.

$$= \int_1^3 (3 - x)\, dx + \int_3^6 (x - 3)\, dx$$

$$= \left[3x - \frac{1}{2}x^2 \right]_1^3 + \left[\frac{1}{2}x^2 - 3x \right]_3^6$$

$$= \left\{ \left(3 \cdot 3 - \frac{1}{2} \cdot 3^2 \right) - \left(3 \cdot 1 - \frac{1}{2} \cdot 1^2 \right) \right\}$$

$$+ \left\{ \left(\frac{1}{2} \cdot 6^2 - 3 \cdot 6 \right) - \left(\frac{1}{2} \cdot 3^2 - 3 \cdot 3 \right) \right\}$$

$$= \frac{13}{2}.$$

The Area of a Region Bounded by Two Curves

Figure 6.6 shows a region R bounded by the graphs of two continuous functions—above by the graph of f, and below by the graph of g—for values of x between a and b.

We can use the definite integral to compute the area of such regions as follows. If we divide the interval $[a, b]$ into n equal subintervals of length $\Delta x = \dfrac{b - a}{n}$ and select one "test number" t_j in each subinterval, we can approximate the part of the region corresponding to that subinterval by the rectangle with width Δx and height $[f(t_j) - g(t_j)]$. (See Figures 6.7 and 6.8.) Summing the individual approximations then gives the approximation to the area of R:

$$\text{Area of } R \approx \sum_{j=1}^{n} [f(t_j) - g(t_j)]\, \Delta x \tag{2}$$

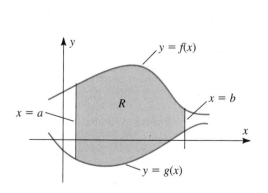

Figure 6.6 Region bounded by two graphs.

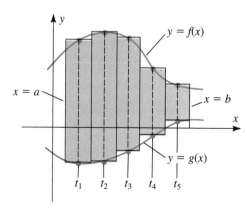

Figure 6.7 Approximating R by rectangles.

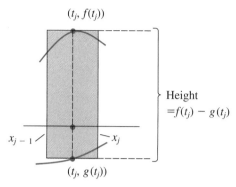

Figure 6.8 Area of jth rectangle is $[f(t_j) - g(t_j)] \Delta x$.

Now in the limit as n becomes infinitely large the approximating sum on the right-hand side of equation (2) becomes the definite integral

$$\int_a^b [f(x) - g(x)] \, dx = \lim_{n \to \infty} \sum_{j=1}^n [f(t_j) - g(t_j)] \Delta x \tag{3}$$

which we define to be the area of R:

> The area of the region R bounded above by the graph of the continuous function f and below by the graph of the continuous function g, between $x = a$ and $x = b$, is
>
> $$\text{Area of } R = \int_a^b [f(x) - g(x)] \, dx. \tag{4}$$
>
> (Note that this requires $f(x) \geq g(x)$ for all x. See Figure 6.6.)

Note that equation (4) generalizes equation (1), since $g(x) = 0$ when the region R is bounded below by the x-axis. Notice also that there are no restrictions on the sign of $f(x)$ or $g(x)$ in equation (4)—either may be positive or negative. *It is essential that $f(x) \geq g(x)$*, however, so that the integrand $[f(x) - g(x)]$ is nonnegative.

□ **EXAMPLE 4**

Find the area of the region R bounded above by the graph of $f(x) = e^x$ and below by the graph of $g(x) = \dfrac{1}{x}$ for $1 \leq x \leq 2$. (See Figure 6.9.)

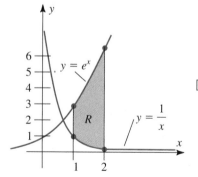

Figure 6.9 Region R in Example 4.

Solution: Since $f(x) = e^x > \dfrac{1}{x} = g(x)$ for all x with $1 \leq x \leq 2$, the top curve is indeed $f(x) = e^x$ for all such x. According to equation (4), the area of R is

$$\text{Area of } R = \int_1^2 \left[e^x - \frac{1}{x} \right] dx$$
$$= [e^x - \ln x]_1^2$$
$$= (e^2 - \ln 2) - (e^1 - \ln 1)$$
$$= e^2 - e - \ln 2. \quad (\ln 1 = 0)$$ ∎

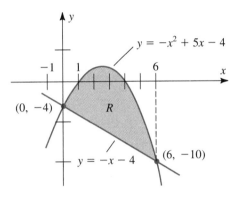

Figure 6.10 Region R in Example 5.

☐ EXAMPLE 5

Find the area of the region R bounded by the graphs of the equations $y = -x^2 + 5x - 4$ and $y = -x - 4$ and the lines $x = 0$ and $x = 6$. (See Figure 6.10.)

Strategy · · · · · · ·
Determine which graph is on top.

(To find area, we must integrate top minus bottom.)

Apply equation (4).

Solution
By graphing the two equations (or by checking individual values), we find that the graph of $f(x) = -x^2 + 5x - 4$ forms the top boundary while the graph of $g(x) = -x - 4$ is the bottom boundary of the region R. Applying equation (4) gives

$$\text{Area of } R = \int_0^6 [(-x^2 + 5x - 4) - (-x - 4)] \, dx$$
$$= \int_0^6 (-x^2 + 6x) \, dx$$
$$= \left[-\frac{1}{3}x^3 + 3x^2 \right]_0^6$$
$$= \left(-\frac{1}{3} \right) 6^3 + 3 \cdot 6^2$$
$$= 36. $$ ∎

In Example 5 the region R was completely determined by the graphs of the two functions f and g, even though the numbers $x = 0$ and $x = 6$ were provided in the statement of the problem. If these numbers are not provided in such problems, it is necessary to first solve the equation $f(x) = g(x)$ in order to determine the horizontal extremities of the region R.

☐ **EXAMPLE 6**

Find the area of the region R bounded by the graphs of the functions $y = x^4 + 1$ and $y = 2x^2$.

Strategy · · · · · · · ·

Sketch the region.

Find the points of intersection by equating the two functions and factoring.

Solution

A rough sketch of the region shows that the graphs intersect at two points. To find these points, we equate the two functions, obtaining

$$x^4 + 1 = 2x^2$$

or

$$x^4 - 2x^2 + 1 = (x^2 - 1)^2 = 0.$$

Thus $x^2 - 1 = 0$, so $x = \pm 1$. The points of intersection are therefore $(-1, 2)$ and $(1, 2)$.

Determine which curve is on top.

Checking function values for any x in $(-1, 1)$ shows that the graph of $f(x) = x^4 + 1$ is the upper boundary, while the graph of $g(x) = 2x^2$ is the lower boundary. Thus by equation (4)

Apply equation (4).

$$\text{Area of } R = \int_{-1}^{1} [(x^4 + 1) - (2x^2)] \, dx$$

$$= \left[\frac{1}{5}x^5 - \frac{2}{3}x^3 + x \right]_{-1}^{1}$$

$$= \left[\frac{1}{5}(1)^5 - \frac{2}{3}(1)^3 + 1 \right]$$

$$\quad - \left[\frac{1}{5}(-1)^5 - \frac{2}{3}(-1)^3 + (-1) \right]$$

$$= \frac{16}{15}.$$

(See Figure 6.11.)   ∎

Sometimes a region bounded by two curves will actually consist of several parts with different "top" and "bottom" graphs in each part. In such cases you should calculate the area of each part separately, being careful to identify properly the upper and lower boundary for each part.

☐ **EXAMPLE 7**

Find the area of the region R bounded by the graphs of the functions $f(x) = x^3 - 4x$ and $g(x) = 5x$.

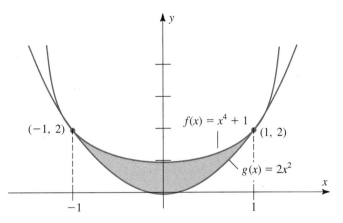

Figure 6.11 Region R in Example 6.

Solution: Equating the two functions, we find that

$$x^3 - 4x = 5x$$

gives

$$x^3 - 9x = 0, \quad \text{or} \quad x(x^2 - 9) = 0.$$

Thus the two graphs intersect when $x = -3, 0,$ and 3. The region therefore consists of two subregions: R_1, corresponding to the interval $[-3, 0]$, and R_2, corresponding to the interval $[0, 3]$.

On the interval $[-3, 0]$ we have $x^3 - 4x \geq 5x$ for all x, so the area of R_1 is

$$\text{Area of } R_1 = \int_{-3}^{0} [(x^3 - 4x) - (5x)]\, dx$$

$$= \left[\frac{1}{4}x^4 - \frac{9}{2}x^2 \right]_{-3}^{0}$$

$$= 0 - \left[\frac{1}{4}(-3)^4 - \frac{9}{2}(-3)^2 \right]$$

$$= \frac{81}{4}.$$

On the interval $[0, 3]$ we have $5x \geq x^3 - 4x$ for all x, so the area is

$$\text{Area of } R_2 = \int_{0}^{3} [5x - (x^3 - 4x)]\, dx$$

$$= \left[\frac{9}{2}x^2 - \frac{1}{4}x^4 \right]_{0}^{3}$$

$$= \left[\frac{9}{2}3^2 - \frac{1}{4}3^4 \right] - 0$$

$$= \frac{81}{4}.$$

Thus

$$\text{Area of } R = \text{area of } R_1 + \text{area of } R_2$$

$$= \frac{81}{4} + \frac{81}{4}$$

$$= \frac{81}{2}.$$

(See Figure 6.12.)

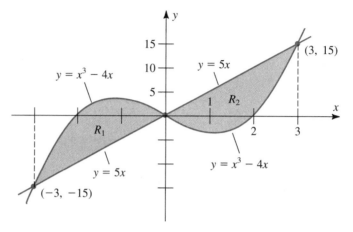

Figure 6.12 Area of R is sum of area of R_1 and area of R_2.

(Note that if we had mistakenly calculated only the integral $\displaystyle\int_{-3}^{3} (f(x) - g(x))\, dx$, we would have obtained a number that is *not* the total area of the region R. In fact, we would have obtained

$$\int_{-3}^{3} (f(x) - g(x))\, dx = \int_{-3}^{3} [(x^3 - 4x) - (5x)]\, dx$$

$$= \int_{-3}^{3} (x^3 - 9x)\, dx$$

$$= \left[\frac{1}{4}x^4 - \frac{9}{2}x^2 \right]_{-3}^{3}$$

$$= \left(\frac{81}{4} - \frac{81}{2} \right) - \left(\frac{81}{4} - \frac{81}{2} \right)$$

$$= 0.$$

The reason for this result is that the integrand $f(x) - g(x)$ is positive on $[-3, 0)$ and negative on $(0, 3]$, so the integrals corresponding to the two intervals "cancel.")

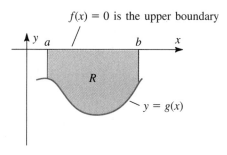

f(x) = 0 is the upper boundary

Figure 6.13 Area of $R = -\int_a^b g(x)\, dx$ when $g(x) \leq 0$ for $a \leq x \leq b$.

Regions Bounded by Graphs of Negative Functions

The area formula

$$\text{Area of } R = \int_a^b [\, f(x) - g(x)]\, dx \tag{5}$$

allows us to resolve the problem of finding the area of a region R bounded by the graph of the function g and the x-axis when $g(x) \leq 0$ for $a \leq x \leq b$ as in Figure 6.13. In this case the curve defining the upper boundary of R is simply the x-axis, which has equation $f(x) = 0$ for all x. Equation (5) then gives

$$\text{Area of } R = \int_a^b [0 - g(x)]\, dx$$

$$= \int_a^b [-g(x)]\, dx$$

$$= -\int_a^b g(x)\, dx \qquad \text{(by Property (I2), Section 5.5)}.$$

That is, when $g(x) \leq 0$ for all x in $[a, b]$, the definite integral $\int_a^b g(x)\, dx$ gives the *negative* of the area of the region R. This is why we must be so careful in ensuring that the integrand $f(x) - g(x)$ is nonnegative for all values of x when calculating the area of a region using equation (5).

□ **EXAMPLE 8**

What is the error in attempting to calculate the area of the region bounded by the graph of the function $f(x) = x^2 - 2x$ between $x = 0$ and $x = 6$ as the integral

$$\int_0^6 (x^2 - 2x)\, dx = \left[\frac{x^3}{3} - x^2 \right]_0^6 = 72 - 36 = 36?$$

Solution: The *definite integral* above has been calculated correctly, but its value is not the *area* of the stated region. This is because the integrand $f(x) = x^2 - 2x = x(x - 2)$ is *negative* on the interval $[0, 2]$. (See Figure 6.14.) To calculate the area of

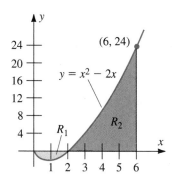

Figure 6.14 Region bounded by graph of $f(x) = x^2 - 2x$ for $0 \leq x \leq 6$.

the stated region we must use two integrals, recognizing that the integrand in the first is a negative function for $0 \le x \le 2$:

$$\text{Area} = -\int_0^2 (x^2 - 2x)\, dx + \int_2^6 (x^2 - 2x)\, dx$$

$$= -\left[\frac{x^3}{3} - x^2\right]_0^2 + \left[\frac{x^3}{3} - x^2\right]_2^6$$

$$= -\left[\left(\frac{8}{3} - 4\right) - \left(\frac{0}{3} - 0\right)\right] + \left[\left(\frac{216}{3} - 36\right) - \left(\frac{8}{3} - 4\right)\right]$$

$$= -\left(-\frac{4}{3}\right) + \left[36 - \left(-\frac{4}{3}\right)\right]$$

$$= 36 + \frac{8}{3} = \frac{116}{3} \approx 38.6\overline{6}. \qquad \blacksquare$$

☑ PRACTICE PROBLEMS 5.6

1. Find the area of the region bounded by the graphs of $f(x) = \sqrt{x}$ and $g(x) = x^2$.

2. Find the area of the region bounded by the graphs of $f(x) = x^3$ and $g(x) = x^{1/3}$.

Exercise Set 5.6

In each of Exercises 1–12, find the area of the region bounded above by the graph of $y = f(x)$ and below by the x-axis for $a \le x \le b$.

1. $f(x) = 2x + 5$, $\quad a = 0$, $\quad b = 2$

2. $f(x) = 9 - x^2$, $\quad a = -3$, $\quad b = 3$

3. $f(x) = \dfrac{1}{x - 2}$, $\quad a = 3$, $\quad b = 5$

4. $f(x) = e^{2x}$, $\quad a = 0$, $\quad b = \ln 2$

5. $f(x) = \dfrac{x + 1}{x^2 + 2x}$, $\quad a = 1$, $\quad b = 2$

6. $f(x) = xe^{1 - x^2}$, $\quad a = 0$, $\quad b = 1$

7. $f(x) = \sqrt{5 + x}$, $\quad a = -4$, $\quad b = 4$

8. $f(x) = \dfrac{x}{\sqrt{9 + x^2}}$, $\quad a = 0$, $\quad b = 4$

9. $f(x) = \dfrac{e^x}{1 + e^x}$, $\quad a = 0$, $\quad b = \ln 5$

10. $f(x) = \dfrac{1}{\sqrt{x}(1 + \sqrt{x})}$, $\quad a = 1$, $\quad b = 4$

11. $f(x) = \dfrac{\sqrt{1 + \ln x}}{x}$, $\quad a = 1$, $\quad b = e$

12. $f(x) = 3x^{2/3} + \sqrt[3]{x}$, $\quad a = 0$, $\quad b = 8$

In each of Exercises 13–20, find the area of the region bounded by the graphs of the given functions for $a \le x \le b$.

13. $f(x) = 9 - x^2$, $\quad g(x) = -2$, $\quad a = -2$, $\quad b = 2$

14. $f(x) = -x - 1$, $\quad g(x) = \sqrt{x}$, $\quad a = 1$, $\quad b = 4$

15. $f(x) = x + 1$, $\quad g(x) = -2x + 1$, $\quad a = 0$, $\quad b = 2$

16. $f(x) = 2x + 3$, $\quad g(x) = x^2 - 4$, $\quad a = -1$, $\quad b = 1$

17. $f(x) = \sqrt{x}$, $\quad g(x) = -x^2$, $\quad a = 0$, $\quad b = 4$

18. $f(x) = \dfrac{1}{x^2}$, $\quad g(x) = x^{2/3}$, $\quad a = 1$, $\quad b = 8$

19. $f(x) = x\sqrt{9 - x^2}$, $\quad g(x) = -x$, $\quad a = -3$, $\quad b = 3$

20. $f(x) = |4 - x^2|$, $\quad g(x) = 5$, $\quad a = -3$, $\quad b = 3$

In each of Exercises 21–28, find the area of the region bounded by the graphs of the given functions.

21. $y = 4 - x^2, \qquad y = x - 2$

22. $y = x^2, \qquad y = x^3$

23. $y = x^3, \qquad y = x$

24. $y = 9 - x^2, \qquad 9y - x^2 + 9 = 0$

25. $y = x^2 - 4, \qquad y = 2 - x$

26. $y = \sqrt{x}, \qquad y = \sqrt[3]{x}$

27. $y = x^{2/3}, \qquad y = x^2$

28. $y = x^{2/3}, \qquad y = 2 - x^2$

In Exercises 29–32, set up (but do not evaluate) the integral(s) for the areas of the regions bounded by the graphs of the given functions and the x-axis.

29. $f(x) = x^3 e^x, \qquad x = -2 \quad \text{and} \quad x = 2$

30. $f(x) = \ln\left(\sqrt{\dfrac{x}{2}} - 1\right), \qquad 1 \leq x \leq 16$

31. $f(x) = e^{x^2} - e, \quad -1 \leq x \leq 1$

32. $f(x) = \sqrt{16 - x^4}$

33. Find the area of the region bounded by the graphs of $y = x^3$, $y = -x^3$, $y = 1$, and $y = -1$.

34. Find the area of the region bounded *below* by the graph of $y = x^2 - 9$ and above by the x-axis.

35. Find the number a so that the line with equation $x = a$ divides into two parts of equal area the region bounded by the graph of the equation $y = \sqrt{x}$ and the x-axis between $x = 0$ and $x = 4$.

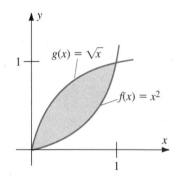

Figure 6.15 Region in Practice Problem 1.

☑ **SOLUTIONS TO PRACTICE PROBLEMS 5.6**

1. The graphs f and g cross where $x^2 = \sqrt{x}$, which is where $x = 0$ or $x = 1$. For $0 \leq x \leq 1$, $x^2 < \sqrt{x}$. (See Figure 6.15.) Thus, the desired area is

$$A = \int_0^1 (\sqrt{x} - x^2)\, dx = \left[\frac{2}{3}x^{3/2} - \frac{1}{3}x^3\right]_0^1$$

$$= \frac{2}{3} - \frac{1}{3}$$

$$= \frac{1}{3}.$$

2. The graphs of f and g cross where $x^3 = \sqrt[3]{x}$, which is where $x = -1$, 0, or 1. Then,
a. for $-1 \leq x \leq 0$, $\sqrt[3]{x} < x^3$, and
b. for $0 \leq x \leq 1$, $x^3 < \sqrt[3]{x}$. (See Figure 6.16.)
The area is

$$A = \int_{-1}^0 (x^3 - \sqrt[3]{x})\, dx + \int_0^1 (\sqrt[3]{x} - x^3)\, dx$$

$$= \left[\frac{1}{4}x^4 - \frac{3}{4}x^{4/3}\right]_{-1}^0 + \left[\frac{3}{4}x^{4/3} - \frac{1}{4}x^4\right]_0^1$$

$$= \left[0 - \left(\frac{1}{4} - \frac{3}{4}\right)\right] + \left[\left(\frac{3}{4} - \frac{1}{4}\right) - 0\right]$$

$$= 1.$$

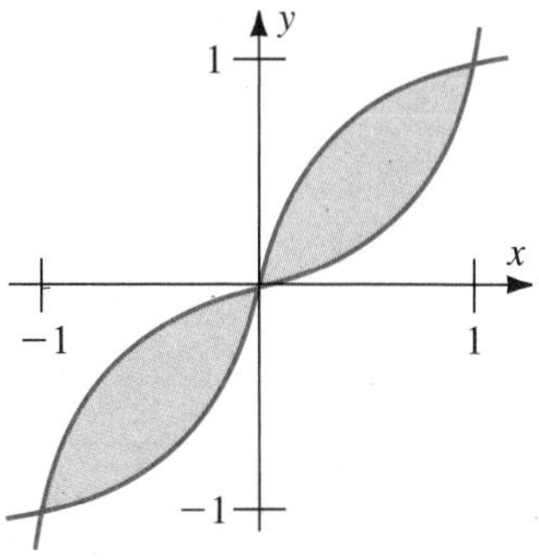

Figure 6.16 Region in Practice Problem 2.

5.7 Applications of the Definite Integral to Economics and Business

The definite integral has wide application in business and economics because of its ability to "sum up" the results of processes that unfold over time.

The most practical of these applications have to do with calculating total value and present value for financial payment plans: deposits into retirement plans, returns on capital investments, comparisons between purchase options, and so forth. We begin with these, and then we consider some slightly more theoretical applications of the definite integral to other business concepts.

Revenue Streams

Certain types of assets, such as rental properties, timber stands, or annuities, produce income for their owners over time. If such a "revenue stream" is assumed to be a continuous function of time, the definite integral can be used to calculate the value of the revenue stream.

Suppose that revenue flows continuously from an asset at a rate of $R(t)$ dollars per year after t years. As Figure 7.1 illustrates, in any interval of time of length Δt the amount of revenue that flows from the asset is approximated by a product of the form $R(t_j)\,\Delta t$, the rate per unit time (at a "test" point) multiplied by the length of time. The total revenue flowing between times $t = a$ and $t = b$ is approximated by a sum of the form $\sum_{j=1}^{n} R(t_j)\,\Delta t$, which in the limit as $n \to \infty$ gives the following integral.

$$TV = \int_a^b R(t)\,dt \tag{1}$$

is the (nominal) **total value** of a revenue stream flowing at the rate of $R(t)$ dollars per year from time $t = a$ to time $t = b$. (See Figure 7.2.)

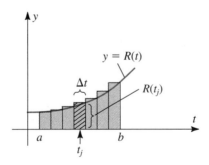

Figure 7.1 Revenue flowing in any time interval is approximated as $R(t_j)\,\Delta t$.

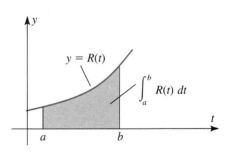

Figure 7.2 Total value of revenue stream from time a to time b is $\int_a^b R(t)\,dt$.

□ **EXAMPLE 1**

An **annuity** is a financial instrument created to make specified payments to the beneficiary (or beneficiaries) of the annuity over a specified period of time. (Many retirement plans are of this type.) The revenue produced by a particular annuity is expected to be $R(t) = 1000\sqrt{t + 4}$ dollars per year for five years. Find the total revenue to be produced by the annuity during that time.

Solution: Using expression (1), we find the total value of the revenue stream to be

$$\int_0^5 1000\sqrt{t + 4}\, dt = \left[\frac{2(1000)}{3}(t + 4)^{3/2}\right]_0^5$$

$$= \frac{2000}{3}(9^{3/2} - 4^{3/2})$$

$$= \$12,666.67. \qquad ■$$

Present Value of a Revenue Stream

The concept of **present value** allows us to analyze payments scheduled for future dates in terms of their worth today. In working with payment or revenue streams, like annuities, it is useful (and common practice) to convert nominal values to *present values.*

Recall that the present value of the amount $R(t_j)\, \Delta t$ of a revenue stream that will become available after t_j years is, according to equation (10) of Section 4.5, $P_0(t_j) = e^{-rt_j}R(t_j)\, \Delta t$, assuming a nominal interest rate of r percent compounded continuously. The limit as $n \to \infty$ of the approximating sum $\sum_{j=1}^{n} R(t_j)e^{-rt_j}\, \Delta t$ is therefore the present value of the revenue stream.

$$PV = \int_a^b R(t)e^{-rt}\, dt \qquad (2)$$

is the **present value** of the revenue stream flowing at the rate $R(t)$ dollars per year from time $t = a$ to time $t = b$.

For most functions R more advanced techniques will be required in order for the integral in expression (11) to be evaluated. However, our next example shows how to calculate the present value of a constant revenue stream.

□ **EXAMPLE 2**

Find the present value of a constant revenue stream of $R(t) = R$ dollars per year flowing between $t = a$ and $t = b$ years assuming a nominal interest rate of r percent.

Solution: Using expression (11), we find the value of the revenue stream to be

$$\int_a^b Re^{-rt}\, dt = \left[-\frac{R}{r} e^{-rt} \right]_a^b$$

$$= -\frac{R}{r}(e^{-rb} - e^{-ra})$$

$$= \frac{R}{r}(e^{-ra} - e^{-rb}).$$ ∎

□ **EXAMPLE 3**

Ms. Smith is now age 40. She wishes to fund an annuity, making a single payment now, that will pay her $20,000 per year for 10 years, beginning at age 60. Assuming a prevailing interest rate of 8% for the entire 30-year period (age 40 to age 70), what should Ms. Smith expect to pay as the single premium?

Strategy · · · · · · · ·

First, find the present value, at age 60, of the payment stream.

Solution

When the payment stream begins, on Ms. Smith's 60th birthday, its present value will then be

$$PV_{60} = \int_0^{10} (20{,}000)e^{-.08t}\, dt$$

$$= 20{,}000 \left[\frac{-1}{0.08} e^{-0.08t} \right]_{t=0}^{t=10}$$

$$\approx (20{,}000)(6.8834)$$

$$= 137{,}667 \text{ dollars.}$$

Convert PV_{60} to its present value at age 40 (present) by

$$P_{40} = e^{-r(20)}P_{60}.$$

Since this starting date is 20 years in the future, the actual present value (now) of this amount is

$$PV_{40} = (137{,}667)e^{(-0.08)(20)}$$

$$= \approx\$27{,}795.$$

This is her expected premium. ∎

Net Present Value and Business Decisions

Businesses often make use of the concept of **net present value** to compare investment options or business strategy. The term ''net'' refers to the fact that one must subtract the present value of the *cost* of an investment from its (gross) returns in analyzing the *net* return (or *margin*) from the investment.

□ **EXAMPLE 4**

The Rightanswer Scientific Instrument Company wishes to expand its manufacturing facility in order to increase production, hence, revenue. Two proposals have been developed, and it has been decided that the choice between them is to be made on the basis of the net present value of the return on the investment over the five-year period following completion of the new facility.

(a) Plan A calls for a $10 million facility that will increase net revenues by $3 million per year for five years.

(b) Plan B calls for a $6 million facility that will increase net revenues by $2 million per year for five years.

Assuming a prevailing interest rate of 10%, which plan should be chosen?

Solution: We calculate the net present value for both plans for the 5-year period, using $r = 0.10$.

(a) For Plan A, it is

$$PV_A = \int_0^5 (\$3 \text{ million}) e^{(-0.10t)} \, dt - \$10 \text{ million}$$

$$= \left\{ 3 \left[\frac{-1}{0.10} (e^{-0.10t}) \right]_0^5 - 10 \right\} \text{ million dollars}$$

$$= \{ 3[10(1 - e^{-0.5})] - 10 \} \text{ million dollars}$$
$$= 1.804080 \text{ million dollars}$$
$$= \$1,804,080.$$

(b) For Plan B the present value is

$$PV_B = \int_0^5 (\$2 \text{ million}) e^{(-0.10t)} \, dt - \$6 \text{ million}$$

$$= \left\{ 2 \left[\frac{-1}{0.10} (e^{-0.10t}) \right]_0^5 - 6 \right\} \text{ million dollars}$$

$$= \{ 2[10(1 - e^{-0.5})] - 6 \} \text{ million dollars}$$
$$= 1.869,387 \text{ million dollars}$$
$$= \$1,869,387.$$

Thus, Plan B should be chosen on the basis of the net present value criteria stated. ■

REMARK ON MODELLING: Example 4 is a good illustration of our earlier remarks (Section 4.6) about the limitations of mathematical models. Even though the mathematical formulation of present value in equation (2) is precise, the use of the present value *model* to represent actual business situations is, at best, only approximate. In this example, the results were affected by the assumptions about the revenue streams, the interest rate, and the relevant length of time. Changes in any one can affect the calculations significantly. (And no doubt would, in "real life." Take interest rates, for example, which hardly ever remain constant for a single year, let alone for five. But, as a logical device for *comparing* options, the mathematical model of net present value provides an objective assessment of obvious utility.)

Social Utility of Consumption

Figure 7.3 shows the graph of a typical demand function giving the selling price p of an item as a function $D(x)$ of the number x of items that the public is willing to consume (that is, purchase) in a given period of time. The shaded region lying

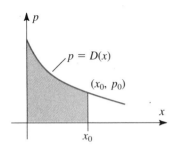

Figure 7.3 Utility of consumption $= \int_0^{x_0} D(x) \, dx$.

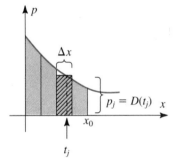

Figure 7.4 Area of rectangle is $p_j \, \Delta x =$ total cost for that interval.

between the graph of the demand function and the x-axis for x between 0 and x_0 is called the **social utility of consumption** at level x_0. Since utility refers to the value that we attach to an item, this phrase may be interpreted as the aggregate value placed by the public on its consumption of x_0 items per unit time.

This interpretation is illustrated in Figure 7.4. If we subdivide the interval $[0, x_0]$ into small subintervals of length Δx, the area of the rectangle that approximates the shaded part of the region over any subinterval has the form $p_j \, \Delta x = D(t_j) \, \Delta x$, the price per item at consumption level $x = t_j$ multiplied by Δx, the number of items associated with that subinterval. Since

$$\text{(price per item) times (number of items)} = \text{total cost}$$

the area of the approximating rectangle is the total cost to the public of the purchases corresponding to that subinterval. Summing these individual approximations and taking the limit as the number of subintervals becomes infinitely large gives

$$\text{Utility of consumption} = \int_0^{x_0} D(x) \, dx. \qquad (3)$$

$$\text{(Total value)}$$

□ **EXAMPLE 5**

The price that a producer of a particular software package must charge in order to sell x packages per month is determined to be $p = D(x) = \dfrac{500}{1 + 0.02x}$ dollars. Find the utility of consumption associated with the purchase and sale of 200 packages per month.

Solution: According to equation (3), the total value to the public of these 200 packages is

$$\int_0^{200} \frac{500}{1 + 0.02x} \, dx = \left[\frac{500}{0.02} \ln(1 + 0.02x) \right]_0^{200}$$

$$= 25{,}000 \ln 5$$

$$\approx 40{,}236 \text{ dollars.}$$

(See Figure 7.5.) ∎

Consumers' Surplus

Of course, not every software package in Example 5 will be sold for the highest price its purchaser is willing to pay. As is the case in "open" economies, the software packages will all be sold at the same price, $p = D(200) = 100$ dollars. Thus the producer will receive not the total value held by the public, $40,236, but the actual total revenues $(200)(100) = \$20{,}000$ from the sale of 200 packages at $100 each. This difference is explained by the fact that of the 200 buyers willing to

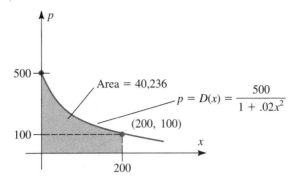

Figure 7.5 Utility of consumption in Example 5.

purchase the package at the price of $100, some (fewer) would have been willing to pay $150 for it, and some (even fewer) would have been willing to pay $250, and so on.

The difference between the total value of a number of items (utility of consumption) and the actual total price that consumers have to pay for these items is called the **consumers' surplus.** (See Figure 7.6.) Since the total paid by consumers for x_0 items, each priced at p_0 dollars, is $x_0 p_0$, consumers' surplus is given by the following equation:

$$\left.\begin{array}{l}\text{Consumers' surplus at}\\ \text{consumption level } x_0\end{array}\right\} = \int_0^{x_0} D(x)\, dx - x_0 p_0, \qquad p_0 = D(x_0). \qquad (4)$$

(See Figure 7.7.)

Suppliers' Surplus

The notion of **suppliers' surplus** is similar to that of consumers' surplus. Let $p = S(x)$ be a supply function giving the price p that must be offered in order that

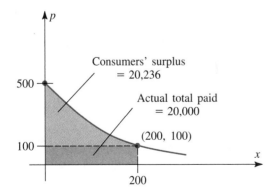

Figure 7.6 Consumers' surplus. (Refer to Example 5.)

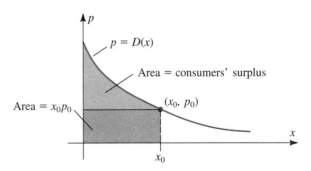

Figure 7.7 Consumers' surplus at consumption level x_0 is $\int_0^{x_0} D(x)\, dx - x_0 p_0$.

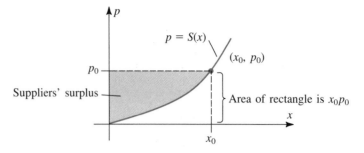

Figure 7.8 Supplier's surplus at supply level x_0 is $x_0 p_0 - \int_0^{x_0} S(x)\, dx$.

suppliers will provide x units of a particular item in a given period of time. (See Figure 7.8.) If the point (x_0, p_0) is on the graph of this function, suppliers will together provide a total of x_0 items to sell at price p_0. But if the price had been less, some (but not all) of these suppliers would still have been willing to produce items for sale. These suppliers benefit from the higher price received by all sellers. Figure 7.8 illustrates that the magnitude of this benefit is the following:

$$\left.\begin{array}{l} \text{Suppliers' surplus at} \\ \text{supply level } x_0 \end{array}\right\} = x_0 p_0 - \int_0^{x_0} S(x)\, dx, \qquad p_0 = S(x_0). \qquad (5)$$

□ **EXAMPLE 6**

Figure 7.9 shows a demand curve $D(x) = \dfrac{2500}{x + 50}$ and a supply curve $S(x) = 0.01x^2$ for a single product. With respect to the equilibrium point $(x_0, p_0) = (50, 25)$, we have from equation (4)

$$\text{Consumers' surplus} = \int_0^{50} \frac{2500}{x + 50}\, dx - (50)(25)$$

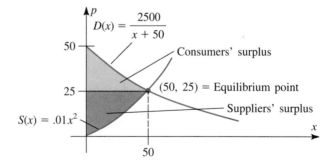

Figure 7.9 Demand and supply curves in Example 6.

$$= 2500[\ln(x + 50)]_0^{50} - 1250$$

$$= 2500 \ln 2 - 1250$$

$$\approx 483 \text{ dollars}$$

while from equation (5) we have

$$\text{Suppliers' surplus} = (50)(25) - \int_0^{50} 0.01x^2 \, dx$$

$$= 1250 - \left[\frac{x^3}{300}\right]_0^{50}$$

$$= 1250 - \frac{1250}{3}$$

$$\approx 833 \text{ dollars.} \qquad \blacksquare$$

Total Functions from Marginal Functions

We have already seen that the derivative of the total cost function $y = C(x)$ is the marginal cost function $MC(x) = C'(x)$. Thus one antiderivative of marginal cost is $C(x)$ and, in general

$$\int MC(x) \, dx = C(x) + K \tag{6}$$

where K is an arbitrary constant. Because of equation (6) we can evaluate the definite integral of the marginal cost function MC between any two production levels a and b as

$$\int_a^b MC(x) \, dx = [C(x)]_a^b = C(b) - C(a). \tag{7}$$

That is, the definite integral of the marginal cost function from $x = a$ to $x = b$ is the change in total cost resulting from a change in production from $x = a$ to $x = b$ units per unit time.

Rewritten in the following form, equation (7) shows how total cost at production level b can be determined from total cost at production level a and knowledge of the marginal cost function:

$$C(b) = C(a) + \int_a^b MC(x) \, dx. \tag{8}$$

Figure 7.10 shows that the area of the region between the graph of the marginal cost function and the x-axis may be interpreted as change in total cost. Figure 7.11 shows that this region can be approximated by rectangles with area $MC(t_j) \, \Delta x$. The corresponding approximating sum with these terms leads to the integral in equation (7).

Equations similar to (6)–(8) hold for marginal revenue functions. That is, if $R(x)$ is the revenue received from the sale of x items, and if $MR(x) = R'(x)$ is the

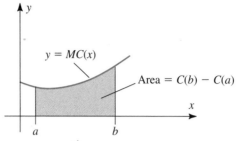

Figure 7.10 $\int_a^b MC(x)\,dx = C(b) - C(a) =$ change in total cost.

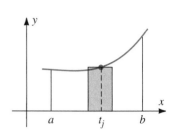

Figure 7.11 Approximation of $\int_a^b MC(x)\,dx$ by rectangles of area $MC(t_j)\,\Delta x$.

corresponding marginal revenue function, then since

$$\int MR(x)\,dx = R(x) + K \tag{9}$$

we have

$$\int_a^b MR(x)\,dx = [R(x)]_a^b = R(b) - R(a) \tag{10}$$

and

$$R(b) = R(a) + \int_a^b MR(x)\,dx. \tag{11}$$

☐ **EXAMPLE 7**

A manufacturer of pocket cameras finds that its total cost in producing 100 cameras per week is $C(100) = \$2150$ and that its marginal cost is $MC(x) = 10 + 0.2x$ dollars per camera at production level x cameras per week.

(a) Find the amount by which total cost will increase if production is increased from $a = 100$ to $b = 120$ cameras per week.
(b) Find the total cost in producing 120 cameras per week.

Solution:

(a) Using equation (7), we find that the change in total cost is

$$C(120) - C(100) = \int_{100}^{120} (10 + 0.2x)\,dx$$

$$= [10x + 0.1x^2]_{100}^{120}$$
$$= [10(120) + (0.1)(120)^2] - [10(100) + 0.1(100)^2]$$
$$= 640 \text{ dollars.}$$

(b) Equation (8) now gives the total cost in producing $b = 120$ cameras as

$$C(120) = C(100) + \int_{100}^{120} (10 + 0.2x)\, dx$$

$$= 2150 + 640$$

$$= 2790 \text{ dollars.} \qquad \blacksquare$$

☐ **EXAMPLE 8**

The camera manufacturer in Example 7 received total revenues of $R(100) = 3000$ dollars from the sale of 100 cameras per week. Also, it has determined that its marginal revenue function is $MR(x) = 50 - 0.4x$ at sales level x cameras per week.

(a) Find the change in total revenues if sales are increased from 100 to 120 cameras per week.
(b) Find $R(120)$.
(c) What is the change in profit as production and sales levels are increased from $x = 100$ to $x = 120$ cameras per week?

Solution:

(a) Using equation (10), we find that

$$R(120) - R(100) = \int_{100}^{120} (50 - 0.4x)\, dx$$

$$= \left[50x - 0.2x^2 \right]_{100}^{120}$$

$$= [50(120) - 0.2(120)^2] - [50(100) - 0.2(100)^2]$$

$$= 120 \text{ dollars.}$$

(b) Equation (11) gives $R(120)$ as

$$R(120) = R(100) + \int_{100}^{120} (50 - 0.4x)\, dx$$

$$= 3000 + 120$$

$$= 3120 \text{ dollars.}$$

(c) Since profit is defined by the equation $P(x) = R(x) - C(x)$, we have

$$P(100) = R(100) - C(100) = 3000 - 2150 = 850 \text{ dollars}$$

while

$$P(120) = R(120) - C(120) = 3120 - 2790 = 330 \text{ dollars.}$$

Thus profits decline by $520 on an increase in production from 100 to 120 cameras per week. $\blacksquare$

☑ **PRACTICE PROBLEMS 5.7**

1. A student can purchase a "whole life" insurance policy for annual premiums of $200 per year for 40 years. What is the present value of this payment stream? (Assume a prevailing rate of interest of 8%.)

2. The demand x for a new model of camera is related to its retail price p by the equation

$$p = D(x) = \frac{4000}{x + 5}.$$

Find the consumer's surplus associated with a decision to sell the camera at price $p_0 = \$80$.

Exercise Set 5.7

In Exercises 1–5, a demand function $p = D(x)$ is given. Find the consumers' surplus at consumption level x_0.

1. $D(x) = 20 - 0.5x$, $x_0 = 10$

2. $D(x) = 40 - 0.02x^2$, $x_0 = 10$

3. $D(x) = 100(40 - x^2)$, $x_0 = 5$

4. $D(x) = \dfrac{500}{x + 10}$, $x_0 = 15$

5. $D(x) = \dfrac{40}{\sqrt{2x + 1}}$, $x_0 = 12$

In Exercises 6–10, a supply function $p = S(x)$ is given. Find the suppliers' surplus at supply level x_0.

6. $S(x) = 5 + \sqrt{x}$, $x_0 = 16$

7. $S(x) = \dfrac{1}{100}x^2$, $x_0 = 6$

8. $S(x) = x\sqrt{9 + x^2}$, $x_0 = 4$

9. $S(x) = e^{0.2x} - 1$, $x_0 = 20$

10. $S(x) = xe^{0.01x^2}$, $x_0 = 10$

11. Sarah works at her father's company for the summer. The company manufactures ball-point pens, and Sarah does a study that determines the company's marginal cost at production level x pens per day to be $MC(x) = 200 + 0.4x$ dollars per pen.
    a. Write a definite integral representing the increase in total costs resulting from an increase in production from 400 to 500 pens per day.
    b. Find the value of this integral.

12. Sarah's company (see Exercise 11) is considering the purchase of another firm that manufacturers vacuum cleaners. She analyzes this company and determines that its marginal cost per vacuum cleaner is $MC = 60 + \dfrac{40}{x + 10}$ dollars per day per vacuum cleaner at production level x per day.
    a. Write a definite integral giving the increase in total cost resulting from an increase in production from $x = 20$ to $x = 40$ vacuum cleaners per day.
    b. Find the value of this integral.

13. The total cost of producing 30 items per day for the manufacturer in Exercise 11 is $C(30) = 7000$ dollars. Find its total cost in producing 40 items per day.

14. The manufacturer in Exercise 12 experiences fixed costs of production of $C(0) = 5000$ dollars per day. Find $C(20)$, its total cost of producing $x = 20$ items per day.

15. The manufacturer in Exercise 11 finds that it has a marginal revenue function $MR(x) = 400 - 0.5x$ dollars at sales level x items per day. Find the increase in revenue resulting from an increase in sales level from $x = 30$ to $x = 50$ pens per day.

16. The manufacturer in Exercise 12 has a marginal revenue function $MR(x) = \dfrac{100}{1 + 0.02x}$ at production level x vacuum cleaners per day. Find its total weekly revenues at sales level $x = 30$ cleaners per day.

17. What is the capital formation (total nominal value) of a revenue flow of $A(t) = 3000t + 2000$ dollars per year for three years?

18. Carol inherits an oil well from her uncle's estate. The well is

under contract at the rate of $A(t) = 100\sqrt{t+1}$ dollars per year for the next eight years. What is the nominal value of this contract?

19. Find the total nominal value of a revenue stream flowing at a rate of $A(t) = 1000e^{-0.2t}$ between years $t_1 = 5$ and $t_2 = 10$.

20. What is the present value of a revenue stream flowing at the constant rate of $A(t) = 2000$ dollars per year for five years if the discount rate is assumed to be $r = 0.08$?

21. What is the present value of a cash flow of 5000 dollars per year for ten years if the discount rate is assumed to be $r = 0.10$?

22. Jerry's grandfather has established an annuity to support Jerry's undergraduate and medical school education. The annuity will provide $5000\sqrt{t+1}$ dollars per year for eight years. What is the total nominal value of the annuity?

23. Robert deposits $2000 per year into an IRA account for 20 years. Assuming an interest rate of 8%, find
   a. the present value of this payment stream.
   b. the nominal value of this account after 20 years.

24. Answer Exercise 23 assuming an interest rate of 10% per year.

25. Mrs. Brown wins ''one million dollars'' in the state lottery. If she is to be paid her winnings continually, at a constant rate over 20 years, what rate of payment should she expect, assuming a prevailing rate of interest of 8%?

26. Answer Exercise 25 under the assumption of a prevailing rate of interest of 4%.

27. A recent college graduate is considering the purchase of a new automobile. The dealer's payment plan will require monthly payments of $600 for five years. What is the present value of this payment stream, assuming an interest rate of 10%? (Assume the payments to be made continuously at a uniform rate for five years.)

28. The same automobile as in Exercise 27 can be leased for five years at $400 per month and purchased at the end of the lease for $4000. Assuming the car is purchased at the end of the lease, what is the present value of all payments under this plan?

29. In Example 4, what would be the net present values of the two options for capital investment under an assumption of a prevailing rate of interest of 8%? Which plan would be chosen?

30. In Example 4, what would be the net present values of the two options for capital investment assuming a period of ten years, rather than five, and a prevailing interest rate of 10%? Which plan would be chosen?

31. An investor wishes to find an annuity capable of producing a revenue stream of $30,000 per year for ten years, beginning in 30 years. What is the present value of this revenue stream, assuming an interest rate of 6%?

☑ SOLUTIONS TO PRACTICE PROBLEMS 5.7

1. $PV = \displaystyle\int_0^{40} 200e^{-0.08t}\, dt$

$$= 200\left[\frac{-1}{0.08}e^{-0.08t}\right]_0^{40}$$

$$\approx \$2398.$$

2. The equilibrium point associated with $p_0 = 80$ is (x_0, p_0) with x_0 obtained from the equation $p = \dfrac{4000}{x+5}$. This gives $x = \dfrac{4000}{p} - 5$, so $x_0 = \dfrac{4000}{80} - 5 = 45$. Then, using equation (4), we obtain

$$\text{Consumer's surplus} = \int_0^{45} \frac{4000}{x+5}\, dx - (45)(80)$$

$$= 4000[\ln(x+5)]_0^{45} - 3600$$

$$= 4000\ln(10) - 3600$$

$$\approx \$5610.$$

5.8   Other Applications of the Definite Integral

Many manufactured objects are produced by shaping a rotating piece of stock. For example, in using a lathe to produce a wooden table leg, a craftsman presses a chisel against a rapidly rotating block of wood (Figure 8.1). Similarly, a potter works a ball of clay into a vase by using a potter's wheel, which allows the clay to be rotated at a uniform speed about a central axis (Figure 8.2).

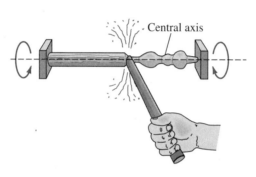

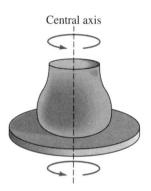

Figure 8.1 Table leg produced on a lathe by pressing a chisel against a rotating piece of wood stock.

Figure 8.2 Pottery produced by shaping clay rotating on a wheel.

Such objects are called *solids of revolution*. Although they are actually three-dimensional objects in space, their volumes can often be calculated as the definite integral of a function of just one variable.

The problem of calculating the volume of such solids is idealized mathematically as follows. Let f be a continuous nonnegative function for $a \le x \le b$. Let R denote the region bounded by the graph of f, the x-axis, and the lines $x = a$ and $x = b$ (Figure 8.3). As the region R rotates about the x-axis (Figure 8.4), it sweeps out a **solid of revolution,** S. Just as for the lathe and pottery wheel illustrations, the cross-sections for S taken perpendicular to the x-axis will be circles of radius $r = f(x)$. This is because the cross-section taken at location x is described by rotating about the x-axis the line segment from $(x, 0)$ to $(x, f(x))$.

To find a formula for the volume of S, we begin by developing an approximation to the solid S. We do this by dividing the interval $[a, b]$ into n equal subintervals of length $\Delta x = \dfrac{b - a}{n}$, and with endpoints $a = x_0, x_1, \ldots, x_n = b$. We arbitrarily select one "test number" t_j in each interval $[x_{j-1}, x_j]$ and approximate the value of the function f throughout the interval $[x_{j-1}, x_j]$ by the constant value $f(t_j)$.

In our approximation, corresponding to each interval $[x_{j-1}, x_j]$, we shall be rotating a rectangle of height $y = f(t_j)$ and width Δx about the x-axis. This will

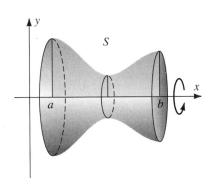

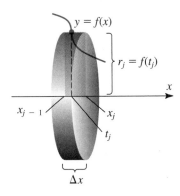

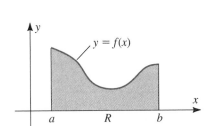

Figure 8.3 Region to be rotated.

Figure 8.4 Solid obtained by rotating R about the x-axis.

Figure 8.5 Rectangle of radius $r_j = f(t_j)$ generates disc of volume $V_j = \pi f^2(t_j)\,\Delta x$.

generate a disc of radius $r_j = f(t_j)$ and thickness Δx. The volume of this disc is therefore

$$\Delta V_j = \pi r_j^2 \Delta x = \pi[\,f(t_j)]^2 \Delta x$$

(See Figure 8.5.)

Summing the volumes of these individual discs from 1 to n gives the volume of our approximating solid as

$$\sum_{j=1}^{n} \Delta V_j = \sum_{j=1}^{n} \pi f^2(t_j)\,\Delta x.$$

(See Figure 8.6.) Next, we argue that as $n \to \infty$ and the size Δx of each individual disc becomes small, the volume of our approximating solid should approach the volume of S. That is, we want to *define* the volume V of S by the equation

$$V = \lim_{n\to\infty} \sum_{j=1}^{n} \Delta V_j = \lim_{n\to\infty} \sum_{j=1}^{n} \pi[\,f(t_j)]^2 \Delta x.$$

Since the sum on the right is an approximating sum for the integral of the function $\pi[\,f(x)]^2$, we have arrived at the following definition:

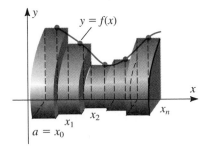

Figure 8.6 One quarter of the approximation to the volume of revolution S obtained by assuming f constant on subintervals.

Let f be continuous for $a \le x \le b$ and let R denote the region bounded by the graph of f, the x-axis, and the lines $x = a$ and $x = b$. The **volume of the solid** obtained by rotating R about the x-axis is

$$V = \int_a^b \pi[\,f(x)]^2\,dx. \tag{1}$$

☐ **EXAMPLE 1**

Verify that equation (1) produces the formula $V = \dfrac{1}{3}\pi r^2 h$ for the volume of a right circular cone.

Strategy   ·   ·   ·   ·   ·   ·   ·

Label variables.

Use a coordinate system to view cone as solid of revolution.

Find an equation for the line bounding the cross-section from above.

Apply (1).

Solution

Let S be the cone with radius r and height h. We impose a coordinate system on S as illustrated in Figure 8.7. We can then view the cone as the solid obtained by rotating the triangle with vertices $(0, 0)$, $(h, 0)$, and (h, r) about the x-axis. Since the equation for the hypotenuse is $f(x) = \dfrac{r}{h}x$, we apply equation (1) to find that

$$V = \int_0^h \pi \left[\frac{r}{h}x\right]^2 dx = \left[\frac{\pi r^2}{3h^2}x^3\right]_0^h = \frac{1}{3}\pi r^2 h$$

which is the desired formula.   ■

☐ **EXAMPLE 2**

Find the volume of the solid obtained by rotating the region bounded by the graphs of $f(x) = \sqrt{x}$ and $g(x) = x^2$ about the x-axis.

Strategy   ·   ·   ·   ·   ·   ·   ·

Find points where the graphs cross.

Draw solid as difference of two solids of revolution.

Apply (1) to each.

Solution

The two graphs cross at $(0, 0)$ and $(1, 1)$ since the equation $\sqrt{x} = x^2$ implies $x = x^4$ or $x(1 - x^3) = 0$. Since $\sqrt{x} > x^2$ for $0 < x < 1$, the region is bounded above by the graph of $f(x) = \sqrt{x}$ and below by the graph of $g(x) = x^2$. (See Figure 8.8.) As Figure 8.9 indicates, we may view the resulting solid as the solid obtained by rotation of $f(x) = \sqrt{x}$ from which the solid obtained by rotation of $g(x) = x^2$ is removed. The calculation for volume, by equation (1), is therefore

$$V = \int_0^1 \pi(\sqrt{x})^2\, dx - \int_0^1 \pi(x^2)^2\, dx$$

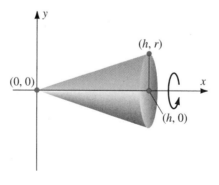

Figure 8.7 Cone as a solid of revolution.

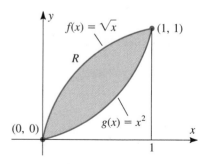

Figure 8.8 Region to be rotated about x-axis.

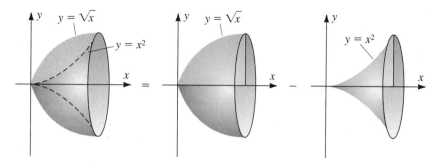

Figure 8.9 Volume obtained by expressing area between curves $\sqrt{x}$ and x^2 as the difference of volumes corresponding to upper curve $\sqrt{x}$ and lower curve x^2.

$$= \left[\frac{\pi}{2}x^2\right]_0^1 - \left[\frac{\pi}{5}x^5\right]_0^1$$

$$= \frac{3\pi}{10}.$$

NOTE: It is important to notice that the answer we obtained, the difference between the two volumes, is given by

$$\int_a^b \pi([f(x)]^2 - [g(x)]^2)\, dx$$

but *not* by

$$\int_a^b \pi(f(x) - g(x))^2\, dx.$$

The Average Value of a Function

Often a single number is sought that describes the "typical" or "average" value of a function f on an interval $[a, b]$. For example, consider the problem of determining average daily temperature, for the purpose of calculating energy consumption in an office building. By noting the two daily temperature functions g and h in Figures 8.10 and 8.11, we can see that such an average should not be computed simply from the difference between the maximum and minimum temperatures for the day in question. Indeed, intuition suggests that heating costs would be greater on the day whose temperature function h is given in Figure 8.11 since the temperatures $h(t)$ are lower than the temperatures $g(t)$, except at times $t = 0$, $t = 12$, and $t = 24$ hours. Notice, however, that on both days the maximum temperatures (6°C) and minimum temperatures (-6°C) are the same.

These remarks suggest that a measurement of average temperature for a temperature function f, for $a \le t \le b$, should reflect not only the difference between maximum and minimum temperatures but also some measurement of how long the temperature function remained at various temperature levels in between. One way to do this is to divide the interval $[a, b]$ into n subintervals of equal length $\Delta t = \dfrac{b - a}{n}$ at

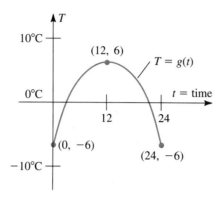

Figure 8.10 Temperature

$$g(t) = 6 - \frac{1}{12}(t - 12)^2.$$

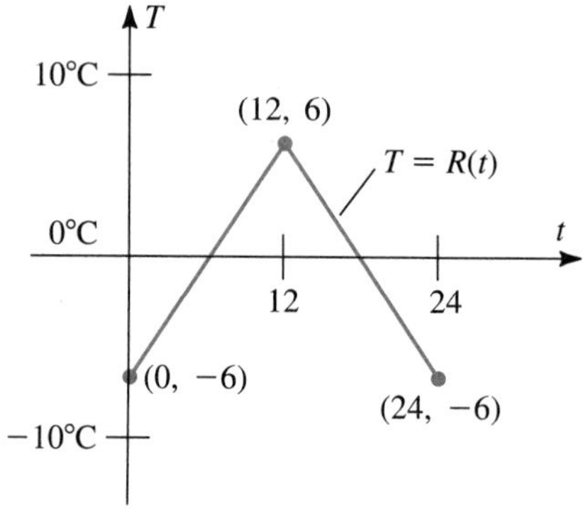

Figure 8.11 Temperature

$$h(t) = \begin{cases} t - 6, & 0 \le t \le 12 \\ 18 - t, & 12 \le t \le 24. \end{cases}$$

points $a = t_0 < t_1 < t_2 < \cdots < t_n = b$. If we select one "test" time s_j in each of the subintervals $[t_{j-1}, t_j]$, the n numbers $f(s_1), f(s_2), \ldots, f(s_n)$ represent temperature readings taken from among equally spaced time intervals. By averaging these values, we arrive at a number

$$\overline{f}_n = \frac{f(s_1) + f(s_2) + \cdots + f(s_n)}{n}$$

reflecting an approximate value for f in each subinterval $[t_{j-1}, t_j]$ of the time interval $[a, b]$. We therefore argue that by letting $n \to \infty$, we should obtain an average f, reflecting *each* individual function value $f(t)$, t in $[a, b]$. That is, we take

$$\overline{f} = \lim_{n \to \infty} \overline{f}_n = \lim_{n \to \infty} \frac{1}{n} \sum_{j=1}^{n} f(s_j). \qquad (2)$$

Since $\Delta t = \dfrac{b - a}{n}$, we can write the sum in equation (2) as an approximating sum as follows:

$$\frac{1}{n} \sum_{j=1}^{n} f(s_j) = \sum_{j=1}^{n} f(s_j) \cdot \frac{1}{n}$$

$$= \left(\frac{b - a}{b - a}\right) \sum_{j=1}^{n} f(s_j) \cdot \frac{1}{n}$$

$$= \frac{1}{b - a} \sum_{j=1}^{n} f(s_j)\left(\frac{b - a}{n}\right)$$

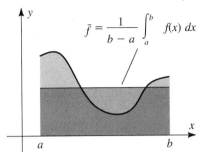

$$\bar{f} = \frac{1}{b-a} \int_a^b f(x)\, dx$$

Figure 8.12 When $f(x) \geq 0$ for all x in $[a, b]$, $\bar{f}$ is the height of the rectangle with base $(b - a)$ and area $\int_a^b f(x)\, dx$.

$$= \frac{1}{b-a} \sum_{j=1}^{n} f(s_j)\, \Delta t.$$

If f is continuous for t in $[a, b]$, the limit as $n \to \infty$ of this approximating sum is a definite integral:

$$\bar{f} = \lim_{n\to\infty} \frac{1}{b-a} \sum_{j=1}^{n} f(s_j)\, \Delta t = \frac{1}{b-a} \int_a^b f(t)\, dt.$$

Thus if $f(x)$ is a continuous function for x in $[a, b]$, we define the **average value** A of $f(x)$ on $[a, b]$ by

$$A = \bar{f} = \frac{1}{b-a} \int_a^b f(x)\, dx. \tag{3}$$

When $f(x)$ is nonnegative, we may interpret $\bar{f}$ as the height of a rectangle whose base has length $b - a$ and whose area is $\int_a^b f(x)\, dx$. (See Figure 8.12.)

□ **EXAMPLE 3**

Find the average temperature for the temperature functions g and h in Figures 8.10 and 8.11.

Solution: Applying equation (3) to $g(t) = 6 - \frac{1}{12}(t - 12)^2$, we obtain

$$\bar{g} = \frac{1}{24 - 0} \int_0^{24} \left[6 - \frac{1}{12}(t - 12)^2 \right] dt$$

$$= \frac{1}{24} \left[6t - \frac{1}{36}(t - 12)^3 \right]_0^{24}$$

$$= \frac{1}{24} \{144 - 2(48)\}$$

$$= 2°C.$$

(Figure 8.13.)

For the temperature function $h(t) = \begin{cases} t - 6, & 0 \leq t \leq 12 \\ 18 - t, & 12 \leq t \leq 24 \end{cases}$, we obtain

$$\bar{h} = \frac{1}{24 - 0} \left\{ \int_0^{12}(t - 6)\, dt + \int_{12}^{24}(18 - t)\, dt \right\}$$

$$= \frac{1}{24} \left\{ \left[\frac{1}{2}t^2 - 6t \right]_0^{12} + \left[18t - \frac{1}{2}t^2 \right]_{12}^{24} \right\}$$

$$= \frac{1}{24} \{(72 - 72) + (144 - 144)\}$$

$$= 0°C.$$

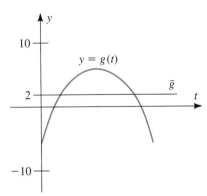

Figure 8.13 $\bar{g} = 2°C.$

☐ **EXAMPLE 4**

Suppose that the amount of heating oil required to heat a house for one day during the winter months is the product of the difference between 20°C and the average daily temperature multiplied by 0.6 gallon. Find the levels of oil consumption associated with each of the temperature functions in Figures 8.10 and 8.11.

Solution: For temperature function g the oil consumption is

$$C_g = (20°C - \bar{g}) \cdot (0.6 \text{ gal per } °C)$$
$$= (20 - 2)(0.6) = 10.8 \text{ gal.}$$

For the temperature function h the oil consumption is

$$C_h = (20°C - \bar{h}) \cdot (0.6 \text{ gal per } °C)$$
$$= (20 - 0)(0.6) = 12 \text{ gal.}$$

Thus our remark about the cost of heating was correct: The function h does lead to a greater heating cost than does g. ■

☑ **PRACTICE PROBLEMS 5.8**

1. Find the volume of the solid obtained by revolving about the x-axis the region bounded by the graph of $f(x) = 4x - x^2$ and the x-axis.

2. An amount of radioactive isotope decays according to the formula $A(t) = 10e^{-3t}$, where t is the time in hours, beginning with an initial amount of 10 grams. What is the *average* amount present during the first five hours?

Exercise Set 5.8

In Exercises 1–5, find the volume of the solid obtained by revolving the region bounded by the graph of the given function and the x-axis, for $a \leq x \leq b$, about the x-axis.

1. $f(x) = 2x + 1$, $1 \leq x \leq 4$

2. $f(x) = \sqrt{4x - 1}$, $1 \leq x \leq 5$

3. $f(x) = |x - 1|$, $0 \leq x \leq 3$

4. $f(x) = \sqrt{4 - x^2}$, $0 \leq x \leq 2$

5. $f(x) = \dfrac{\sqrt{x + 1}}{x}$, $1 \leq x \leq 2$

In Exercises 6–10, find the volume of the solid obtained by revolving about the x-axis the region bounded by the given curves.

6. $f(x) = x^2$, $g(x) = x^3$

7. $f(x) = \dfrac{1}{4}x^3$, $g(x) = x$

8. $f(x) = \dfrac{1}{x}$, $g(x) = \sqrt{x}$, $1 \leq x \leq 4$

9. $x + y = 4$, $y = 0$, $0 \leq x \leq 4$

10. $x = y^2$, $x = 4$

In each of Exercises 11–15, find the average value of the given function on the given interval.

11. $f(x) = \sqrt{2x - 1}$, x in $[1, 5]$

12. $f(x) = x^2 - 7$, x in $[-1, 3]$

13. $f(x) = \sqrt{x + 2}$, x in $[-2, 2]$

14. $f(x) = \dfrac{1 - x}{1 + x}$, x in $[0, 1]$

15. $f(x) = \dfrac{x^3 + 1}{x + 1}$, x in $[0, 2]$

16. Find the average value of the function $f(x) = 3x + 1$ on the interval $[1, 3]$ by geometry.

17. Find the average value of the function $f(x) = \sqrt{9 - x^2}$ on the interval $[-3, 3]$ by geometry. (*Hint:* The graph of $f(x) = \sqrt{9 - x^2}$ is a semicircle.)

18. Find the average value of the total cost function $C(x) = 10 + 40x + 0.3x^2$ for $0 \le x \le 20$.

19. Find the average value of the total revenue function $R(x) = 120x - 4x^2$ for $0 \le x \le 10$.

20. Find the average value of the traffic flow function

$$q(p) = \frac{p}{1 + p^2} \quad \text{for } 0 \le p \le 4.$$

21. For the total cost function $C(x)$ we have defined average cost to be the quotient $c(x) = \dfrac{C(x)}{x}$.

Explain why average cost is the average value of the marginal cost function on the interval $[0, x]$ when $C(0) = 0$.

22. Find the average value of the electric power consumption function

$$E(t) = 4 - 2\left(\frac{t - 13}{7}\right)^4$$

for $6 \le t \le 20$.

23. Let r be a positive constant. Find the volume of the solid obtained by revolving the region bounded by the graph of $f(x) = \sqrt{r^2 - x^2}$ and the x-axis about the x-axis. Do you recognize the formula for the volume that you have obtained? (See endpapers.)

24. A deposit of $1000 is made in a savings account paying 8% interest, compounded continuously, and left on deposit for ten years. What was the *average* amount on deposit?

25. The population of the earth is presently approximately 5 billion people. This number is expected to grown exponentially to 10 billion in 50 years. What will the *average* population of the earth be during this 50-year period?

☑ **SOLUTIONS TO PRACTICE PROBLEMS 5.8**

1. The function $f(x) = 4x - x^2 = x(4 - x)$ has zeros at $a = 0$ and at $x = 4$. The region bounded by its graph and the x-axis lies between these limits. The volume of the resulting solid is

$$V = \int_0^4 \pi(4x - x^2)^2 \, dx$$

$$= \pi \int_0^4 (16x^2 - 8x^3 + x^4) \, dx$$

$$= \pi \left[\frac{16}{3}x^3 - 2x^4 + \frac{1}{5}x^5\right]_0^4$$

$$= \frac{512\pi}{15} \approx 107.23.$$

2. The average value of the function A over the time interval $[0, 5]$ is

$$\bar{A} = \frac{1}{5}\int_0^5 10e^{-3t} \, dt$$

$$= \left(\frac{1}{5}\right)(10)\left(-\frac{1}{3}\right)[e^{-3t}]_0^5$$

$$= -\frac{2}{3}(e^{-15} - 1)$$

$$= 0.66\overline{6} \text{ gram.}$$

Summary Outline of Chapter 5

■ The function F is an **antiderivative** for the function f if F is differentiable and $F'(x) = f(x)$. The most general form of the antiderivative of f is then (Page 362)

$$\int f(x)\,dx = F(x) + C.$$

■ *Power Rule:* $\displaystyle \int x^n\,dx = \frac{1}{n+1}x^{n+1} + C, \qquad n \neq -1.$ (Page 365)

■ *Other Integration (Antidifferentiation) Rules* (Page 366)

$$\int cf(x)\,dx = c\int f(x)\,dx$$

$$\int [\,f(x) + g(x)]\,dx = \int f(x)\,dx + \int g(x)\,dx$$

$$\int \frac{1}{x}\,dx = \ln|x| + C, \qquad x \neq 0$$

$$\int e^x\,dx = e^x + C$$

■ *Economic Applications of the Integral* (Page 373)

$$\text{Total cost} = \int MC(x)\,dx = C(x) + A \qquad (A \text{ constant})$$

$$\text{Total revenue} = \int MC(x)\,dx = R(x) + B \qquad (B \text{ constant})$$

■ The **differential** for the function u is (Page 382)

$$du = u'(x)\,dx.$$

■ Integration by substitution: If $F' = f$, (Page 383)

$$\int f(u(x))u'(x)\,dx = \int f(u)\,du = F(u) + C$$

$$= F(u(x)) + C.$$

■ The **area** of the region R bounded by the graph of the continuous positive function f and the x-axis between $x = a$ and $x = b$ is the limit of the approximating sum (Page 398)

$$\text{Area of } R = \lim_{n \to \infty} \sum_{j=1}^{n} f(t_j)\,\Delta x.$$

■ The **definite integral** of the continuous function f from $x = a$ to $x = b$ is the limit (Page 398)

$$\int_a^b f(x)\, dx = \lim_{n\to\infty} \sum_{j=1}^{n} f(t_j)\, \Delta x.$$

- When $f(x) \ge 0$ for all x in $[a, b]$, the area of the region R described above is given by the definite integral   (Page 398)

$$\text{Area of } R = \int_a^b f(x)\, dx.$$

- ***Theorem (Fundamental Theorem of Calculus):*** If f is continuous on $[a, b]$, then   (Page 404)

$$\int_a^b f(x)\, dx = F(b) - F(a)$$

where $F' = f$ on $[a, b]$.

- The **area** of the region R bounded above by the graph of the continuous function f and below by the graph of the continuous function g between $x = a$ and $x = b$ is   (Page 414)

$$\text{Area of } R = \int_a^b [\, f(x) - g(x)]\, dx.$$

- The **(nominal) total value** of a revenue stream flowing at the rate of $R(t)$ dollars per year from time $t = a$ to $t = b$ is   (Page 422)

$$TV = \int_a^b R(t)\, dt.$$

- The **present value** of the above revenue stream subject to a discount factor of r percent per annum is   (Page 423)

$$PV = \int_a^b R(t)e^{-rt}\, dt.$$

- The **consumers' surplus** associated with the demand function $p = D(x)$ at consumption level x_0 is   (Page 427)

$$\text{Consumers' surplus} = \int_0^{x_0} D(x)\, dx - x_0 p_0, \qquad p_0 = D(x_0).$$

- The **suppliers' surplus** associated with the supply function $p = S(x)$ at supply level x_0 is   (Page 428)

$$\text{Suppliers' surplus} = x_0 p_0 - \int_0^{x_0} S(x)\, dx, \qquad p_0 = S(x_0).$$

- The **volume** of the solid obtained by revolving about the x-axis the region bounded by the graph of the continuous function f and the x-axis between $x = a$ and $x = b$ is   (Page 435)

$$V = \int_a^b \pi[\, f(x)]^2\, dx.$$

> ▌ The **average value** of the continuous function f on the interval $[a, b]$ is
>
> $$A = \frac{1}{b - a} \int_a^b f(x) \, dx.$$

(Page 437)

Review Exercises—Chapter 5

In Exercises 1–20, find the antiderivative. (integral)

1. $\displaystyle\int (6x^2 - 2x + 1) \, dx$

2. $\displaystyle\int (x^2 - 6x)^2 \, dx$

3. $\displaystyle\int x\sqrt{3x^2 + 5} \, dx$

4. $\displaystyle\int (3\sqrt{x} + 3/\sqrt{x}) \, dx$

5. $\displaystyle\int (t + \sqrt[3]{t})^2 \, dt$

6. $\displaystyle\int t\sqrt{9 - t^2} \, dt$

7. $\displaystyle\int \frac{x^3 - 7x^2 + 6}{x} \, dx$

8. $\displaystyle\int \frac{x^3 + x^2 - x + 2}{x + 2} \, dx$

9. $\displaystyle\int (2x - 1)(2x + 3) \, dx$

10. $\displaystyle\int \frac{x}{4x^4 + 4x^2 + 1} \, dx$

11. $\displaystyle\int \frac{x}{1 - x^2} \, dx$

12. $\displaystyle\int \frac{3x + 3}{4x + 2x^2} \, dx$

13. $\displaystyle\int \sqrt{e^x} \, dx$

14. $\displaystyle\int (e^x + 1)^3 \, dx$

15. $\displaystyle\int \frac{1}{x\sqrt{\ln x}} \, dx$

16. $\displaystyle\int \frac{e^x - e^{-x}}{e^x + e^{-x}} \, dx$

17. $\displaystyle\int \frac{x^3 - 1}{x + 1} \, dx$

18. $\displaystyle\int \frac{e^{\sqrt{x}}}{\sqrt{x}} \, dx$

19. $\displaystyle\int e^{2x}(1 - e^{2x})^2 \, dx$

20. $\displaystyle\int \frac{2x + 3x^2}{x^3 + x^2 - 7} \, dx$

21. A particle moves along a line with a velocity $v(t) = 2t - (t + 1)^{-2}$.
   a. Find $s(t)$, its position at time t, if $s(0) = 0$. (Recall, $v(t) = s'(t)$.)
   b. Find $a(t)$, its acceleration at time t.

22. The population of a town is growing according to the population function $P(t) = \dfrac{200,000}{20 + 40e^{-0.2t}}$. Find the horizontal asymptote.

23. A company's marginal cost of production at production level x units per day is $MC(x) = 120 + 6x$. Its fixed costs are $500 per day.
   a. Find total daily costs, $C(x)$.
   b. Find $C(20)$.

24. Refer to Exercise 23. The company's marginal revenue at sales level x units per day is $MR(x) = 250$ dollars.
   a. Find total daily revenue, $R(x)$.
   b. Find $R(20)$.

25. Find the daily profit function P for the company in Exercises 23 and 24. Is it profitable at production and sales level $x = 20$ units per day?

26. A population of rabbits is growing at a rate $\dfrac{dP}{dt} = 8e^{0.5t}$ rabbits per month t months after time $t = t_0$. If $P(t_0) = 16$, find the population function P.

27. A company purchases a computer for $100,000 and estimates that the value $V(t)$ of the computer will decrease over time at the rate $\dfrac{dV}{dt} = -\dfrac{80,000}{(t + 1)^2}$ dollars per year. Find
   a. $V(t)$, the value of the computer after t years.
   b. $V(3)$.
   c. $\displaystyle\lim_{t \to \infty} V(t)$.

28. An investment is growing at a rate of $\dfrac{500 \cdot e^{\sqrt{t}}}{\sqrt{t}}$ dollars per year. Find the value of the investment after four years if its initial value was $1000.

29. The marginal cost of producing a certain item is $MC(x) = 70 + 2x$ at production level x items per month. If the total cost of producing ten items per month is $C(10) = 1000$ dollars
   a. Find the total monthly cost function C.
   b. Find the fixed monthly costs, $C(0)$.

30. A manufacturer experiences a marginal cost of $MC(x) = 40 + 2x$ and a marginal revenue of $MR(x) = 120$ in the production and sale of x radios per week. If the manufacturer's profit from the production and sale of $x = 20$ items per week is $P(20) = 1050$, find $C(0)$, the manufacturer's fixed weekly costs.

In Exercises 31–50, use the Fundamental Theorem of Calculus to find the value of the definite integral.

31. $\displaystyle\int_0^3 (2x - 3)\, dx$

32. $\displaystyle\int_0^2 \frac{1}{x + 5}\, dx$

33. $\displaystyle\int_0^1 (x^2 - 6)^2\, dx$

34. $\displaystyle\int_{-3}^7 6\, dx$

35. $\displaystyle\int_2^9 \sqrt{x + 7}\, dx$

36. $\displaystyle\int_0^1 3e^{2x}\, dx$

37. $\displaystyle\int_0^3 \frac{x}{x + 3}\, dx$

38. $\displaystyle\int_{-1}^1 (x^2 - 3x + 9)\, dx$

39. $\displaystyle\int_3^4 \frac{x + 2}{x - 3}\, dx$

40. $\displaystyle\int_0^2 3x^2 e^{x^3}\, dx$

41. $\displaystyle\int_{-1}^3 (x - 1)(x + 5)\, dx$

42. $\displaystyle\int_4^9 (\sqrt{x} - 1)(\sqrt{x} + 1)\, dx$

43. $\displaystyle\int_1^3 |x - 4|\, dx$

44. $\displaystyle\int_0^4 x(\sqrt{x} + x^{2/3})\, dx$

45. $\displaystyle\int_{-8}^{-1} (x^{1/3} - x^{5/3})\, dx$

46. $\displaystyle\int_0^4 \frac{x}{\sqrt{x^2 + 9}}\, dx$

47. $\displaystyle\int_1^8 \frac{\sqrt[3]{x}}{5 + x^{4/3}}\, dx$

48. $\displaystyle\int_0^1 (\sqrt{x} + 5)(x^{1/3} + x)\, dx$

49. $\displaystyle\int_1^8 \frac{x^{2/3} + 3x^{5/2}}{x}\, dx$

50. $\displaystyle\int_0^{\ln 2} (e^x + e^{-x})^2\, dx$

51. Use geometry to find $\displaystyle\int_{-4}^4 \sqrt{16 - x^2}\, dx$.

52. Use geometry to find $\displaystyle\int_{-2}^0 \sqrt{4 - x^2}\, dx$.

53. Find the area of the region bounded by the graph of $f(x) = 9 - \sqrt{x}$ and the x-axis between $x = 0$ and $x = 9$.

54. Find the area of the region bounded by the graph of $f(x) = 10 - 2x$ and the coordinate axes.

55. Find the area of the region bounded by the graphs of $f(x) = 3 + x^{2/3}$ and $g(x) = 3x^2 + 1$.

56. Find the area of the region bounded by the graphs of $f(x) = e^{-x}$ and $g(x) = e^x$ for $0 \le x \le 1$.

57. Find the area of the region bounded by the graphs of $f(x) = \sqrt[3]{x}$, $g(x) = -x$, and $h(x) = \frac{2}{3}x - \frac{10}{3}$.

58. A manufacturer of microwave ovens has a total cost of $C(40) = 6000$ dollars in producing 40 units per week. If the manufacturer's marginal cost function is $MC(x) = 120$ dollars per unit,
  a. Find the total cost of producing $x = 50$ units per week.
  b. Find the manufacturer's total cost function $C(x)$.

59. A company that manufactures lawnmowers has a marginal cost of $MC(x) = 110 + \dfrac{50}{x + 10}$ dollars per lawnmower at production level x lawnmowers per week. Find the increase in total costs resulting from an increase in production from $x = 40$ to $x = 50$ lawnmowers per week.

60. A company that manufactures refrigerators finds that it has a marginal revenue function of $MR(x) = 600 - 2\sqrt{x}$ dollars at sales level x refrigerators per week. Find the increase in revenues resulting from an increase in sales from $x = 36$ to $x = 49$ refrigerators per week.

61. Find the consumers' surplus for the demand function $D(x) = 40(50 - x^2)$ at consumption level $x_0 = 6$.

62. Find the consumers' surplus for the demand function $D(x) = \dfrac{40\sqrt{x}}{1 + x^{3/2}}$ at consumption level $x_0 = 16$.

63. Find the suppliers' surplus for the supply function $S(x) = \dfrac{1}{\sqrt{x + 1}} e^{\sqrt{x+1}}$ at supply level $x_0 = 15$.

64. What is the total nominal value of a revenue flow of $A(t) = 6\sqrt{t} + 3000$ dollars per year for four years?

65. Find the nominal value of a revenue stream flowing at a rate of $A(t) = 100e^{0.2t}$ dollars per year for ten years.

66. Find the present value of a revenue stream flowing at the constant rate of $A(t) = 5000$ dollars per year for ten years if the discount rate is assumed to be $r = 0.08$.

67. An annuity pays $10,000\, t\sqrt{1 + t^2}$ dollars per year for five years. What is the total nominal value of the annuity?

68. Find the volume of the solid obtained by revolving the region bounded by the graphs of $f(x) = x^{2/3}$ and $g(x) = x$ about the x-axis.

69. Find the average value of the function $f(x) = \dfrac{x}{x^2 + 7}$ on the interval $[0, 3]$.

70. Find the average value of the function $g(x) = (1 + \sqrt{x})(1 - \sqrt{x})$ on the interval $[1, 4]$.

71. Previously, we saw that the functions $f(x) = \ln kx$ and $g(x) = \ln x$ have the same derivatives for all k. Thus, $\ln kx = \ln x + C$ for some constant C, according to Theorem 1. Find C.

72. Is it necessary for total cost to increase on an interval if marginal cost is increasing throughout the interval? Why or why not?

73. Give an example of a profit function $P(x)$, its marginal profit function $MP(x) = P'(x)$ and an interval I such that $MP(x)$ is positive on I but $P'(x)$ decreases throughout I. How can this be possible? What is the geometric interpretation for the associated graphs?

6

Demand for sporting goods is seasonal—higher at some times during the year than at others. Such "periodic" behavior is often modelled by the trigonometric functions, which are discussed in this chapter. *(Tom Stack/Tom Stack & Associates)*

Trigonometric Functions

Many phenomena in nature, economics, and business occur repeatedly and in regular cycles. Examples include the rise and fall of ocean tides, the annual fluctuation of daily temperature, body functions (such as respiration and circulation), the vibration of a tuning fork or of a violin string, and the seasonal demand for different types of sporting goods.

The trigonometric functions, especially the sine and cosine functions, provide useful mathematical models for describing this kind of oscillatory behavior. Unlike any other functions that we have studied up to this point, the trigonometric functions repeat their values infinitely often.

The trigonometric functions arise from the measurement of angles, which is where we begin.

6.1   Radian Measure

Until now you have probably used degrees as the only unit of measurement for angles. We say that a right angle measures 90 degrees (90°), that an about-face is a 180° turn, and that a complete circle (rather than just an arc) has 360°.

However, the degree is not the unit of choice for angles in the calculus. In defining the **trigonometric functions,** which involve angle measurement, we need to exploit the basic relationship between the circumference and radius of a circle, $C = 2\pi r$, which leads to the definition of the **radian** as a unit for measuring angles.

Figure 1.1 shows that in studying an angle θ associated with a right triangle, we can always position the triangle so that the vertex corresponding to θ lies at the origin, one of the legs adjacent to the right angle lies along the x-axis, and the other such leg is parallel to the y-axis. We now draw a unit circle (a circle of radius $r = 1$) centered at the origin. The hypotenuse of the triangle then determines a line that intersects the unit circle at P.

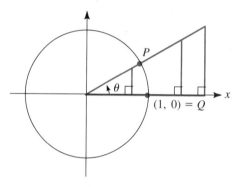

Figure 1.1 Various right triangles with angle θ, each of which is identified with the point P.

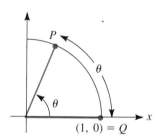

Figure 1.2 An angle of size θ radians determines an arc of length θ between P and $Q = (1, 0)$ on the unit circle.

The point of Figure 1.1 is that the angle θ is identified by the point P and the fixed point $Q = (1, 0)$ on the unit circle; the size of the triangle doesn't matter.

Figure 1.2 shows how we use the unit circle to define the size of the angle θ. The size of the angle θ in *radians* is equal to the length of the arc of the unit circle that is traversed by a point moving counterclockwise along the circle from point $Q = (1, 0)$ to point P. When the length of the arc from P to Q is one unit (equal to the radius of the circle), then $\theta = 1$ radian. Since the circumference of the unit circle is $2\pi(1) = 2\pi$ units, we say that **2π radians equal 360 degrees.** Thus

(a) The radian measure of an angle of size 90° is

$$\frac{1}{4}(2\pi) = \frac{\pi}{2} \text{ radians}$$

since 90° is one fourth of 360° (Figure 1.3).

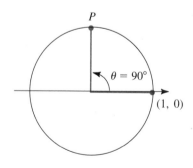

Figure 1.3 $90° = \dfrac{\pi}{2}$ radians.

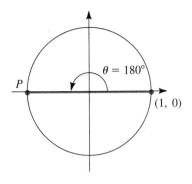

Figure 1.4 $180° = \pi$ radians.

(b) The radian measure of an angle of size 180° is

$$\frac{1}{2}(2\pi) = \pi \text{ radians}$$

since 180° is one half of 360° (Figure 1.4).

(c) The radian measure of an angle of size 30° is

$$\frac{1}{12}(2\pi) = \frac{\pi}{6} \text{ radians}$$

since 30° is $\dfrac{30}{360} = \dfrac{1}{12}$ of 360° (Figure 1.5).

Each of statements (a)–(c) follows from the more general relationship between an angle whose measurement is θ_d in degrees and θ_r in radians:

$$\frac{\theta_d}{360} = \frac{\theta_r}{2\pi}. \tag{1}$$

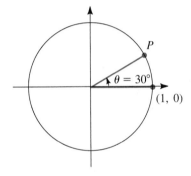

Figure 1.5 $30° = \dfrac{\pi}{6}$ radians.

Equation (1) gives the formulas for converting from degree to radian measure, and vice versa:

$$\theta_r = \frac{2\pi}{360}\theta_d = \frac{\pi}{180}\theta_d \tag{2}$$

$$\theta_d = \frac{180}{\pi}\theta_r. \tag{3}$$

Henceforth, unless an angle measurement is explicitly stated to be in units of degrees, we shall assume that it is in radians.

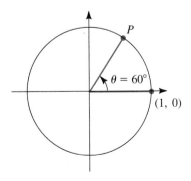

Figure 1.6 $60° = \dfrac{\pi}{3}$ radians.

☐ **EXAMPLE 1**

(a) An angle of size 60° has radian measure

$$\theta_r = \frac{\pi}{180}(60) = \frac{\pi}{3} \qquad \text{(Figure 1.6)}.$$

(b) An angle of size 135° has radian measure

$$\theta_r = \frac{\pi}{180}(135) = \frac{3\pi}{4}. \qquad \text{(Figure 1.7)}$$

(c) An angle of size $\dfrac{4\pi}{3}$ radians has degree measure

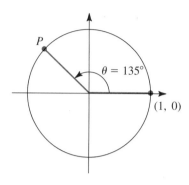

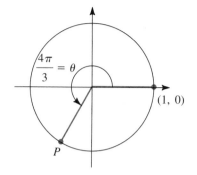

Figure 1.7 $135° = \dfrac{3\pi}{4}$ radians.

Figure 1.8 $\dfrac{4\pi}{3}$ radians $= 240°$.

$$\theta_d = \frac{180}{\pi}\left(\frac{4\pi}{3}\right) = 240°. \qquad \text{(Figure 1.8)}$$

Table 1.1 shows degree and radian measures for various angles θ with $0 \le \theta \le 2\pi$.

Table 1.1

Angle in Degrees	0	30	45	60	90	120	135	150	180
Angle in Radians	0	$\dfrac{\pi}{6}$	$\dfrac{\pi}{4}$	$\dfrac{\pi}{3}$	$\dfrac{\pi}{2}$	$\dfrac{2\pi}{3}$	$\dfrac{3\pi}{4}$	$\dfrac{5\pi}{6}$	π

Angle in Degrees	210	225	240	270	300	315	330	360
Angle in Radians	$\dfrac{7\pi}{6}$	$\dfrac{5\pi}{4}$	$\dfrac{4\pi}{3}$	$\dfrac{3\pi}{2}$	$\dfrac{5\pi}{3}$	$\dfrac{7\pi}{4}$	$\dfrac{11\pi}{6}$	2π

Extending Radian Measure

In many applications the angle measure θ is used to measure how far a lever or other device has turned, and measurements greater than 360° or 2π radians are required. For example, the instruction, "turn the set screw three complete turns outward" tells an auto mechanic to turn a carburetor adjustment screw through $3 \times 360° = 1080°$, or $3 \times 2\pi = 6\pi$ radians.

For $t > 2\pi$ the meaning of the radian measure t is the distance traveled counterclockwise around the unit circle by the point P, from the fixed point $Q = (1, 0)$, as the radius OP turns through $\dfrac{t}{2\pi}$ revolutions. (See Figure 1.9.) Thus

$$t = 4\pi \quad \text{corresponds to} \quad \frac{4\pi}{2\pi} = 2 \text{ revolutions counterclockwise}$$

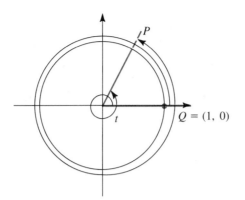

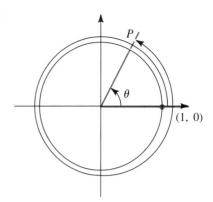

Figure 1.9 t radians corresponds to $\dfrac{t}{2\pi}$ revolutions.

Figure 1.10 The principal angle θ associated with t radians satisfies $t = \theta + 2n\pi$ with $0 \le \theta < 2\pi$.

and

$$t = \frac{5\pi}{2} \quad \text{corresponds to} \quad \frac{5\pi/2}{2\pi} = \frac{5}{4} \text{ revolutions counterclockwise.}$$

With this interpretation we can identify any positive number t with an angle θ that satisfies the equation

$$t = \theta + 2n\pi \qquad \text{for} \quad 0 \le \theta < 2\pi \quad \text{and} \quad n = 0, 1, 2, \ldots . \tag{4}$$

In this case the number θ is called the **principal angle** associated with the number t. (See Figure 1.10.)

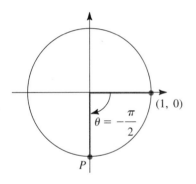

Figure 1.11 $\theta = -\dfrac{\pi}{2}$.

□ **EXAMPLE 2**

(a) $t = 7\pi$ radians corresponds to $\dfrac{7\pi}{2\pi} = \dfrac{7}{2}$ revolutions counterclockwise. The principal angle θ associated with $t = 7\pi$ radians is $\theta = \pi$, since equation (4) takes the form

$$7\pi = \pi + 3(2\pi) \qquad (n = 3).$$

(b) $t = \dfrac{9\pi}{2}$ radians corresponds to the principal angle $\theta = \dfrac{\pi}{2}$ since we can write

$$\frac{9\pi}{2} = \frac{\pi}{2} + 2(2\pi) \qquad (n = 2).$$

Finally, we can extend radian measure to negative numbers simply by letting the point P move in the *clockwise* direction along the unit circle, beginning at $Q = (1, 0)$. Figures 1.11–1.13 show several locations for P corresponding to negative radian measures.

Figure 1.12 $\theta = -\dfrac{3\pi}{4}$.

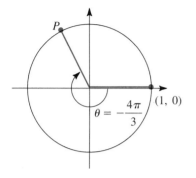

Figure 1.13 $\theta = -\dfrac{4\pi}{3}$.

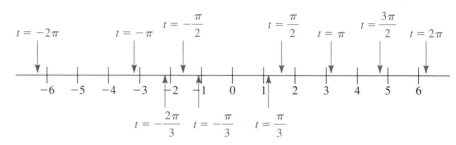

Figure 1.14 Association between radian measure and real numbers determined by constant $\pi = 3.14159.\ \ldots$

Negative Angles

Negative values of radian measure are important in simple applications having to do with the motion of revolving parts, where clockwise motion needs to be distinguished from counterclockwise motion. However, the most important application of (signed) radian measure is that it allows us to associate each real number with a radian measure t, as illustrated by the number line in Figure 1.14.

In the remaining sections of this chapter we shall define and work with the *trigonometric* functions. While you may have worked previously with trigonometric functions of *angles,* this association between radian measure and real numbers will allow us to define the trigonometric functions for numbers other than just those in the interval $[0, 2\pi]$.

□ **EXAMPLE 3**

Using equation (1), we find that

(a) A revolution of $480°$ counterclockwise corresponds to a radian measure of $t = \dfrac{8\pi}{3}$, since

$$\frac{480}{360} = \frac{t}{2\pi} \quad \text{gives} \quad t = 2\pi\left(\frac{480}{360}\right) = \frac{8\pi}{3}.$$

(The sign of t is positive since the motion is counterclockwise.)

(b) A revolution of $270°$ clockwise corresponds to a radian measure of $t = -\dfrac{3\pi}{2}$ since

$$\frac{-270}{360} = \frac{t}{2\pi} \quad \text{gives} \quad t = 2\pi\left(\frac{-270}{360}\right) = -\frac{3\pi}{2}.$$

(The sign of t is negative since the motion is clockwise.)

(c) A revolution of $810°$ clockwise corresponds to a radian measure of $t = -\dfrac{9\pi}{2}$

since

$$-\frac{810}{360} = \frac{t}{2\pi} \quad \text{gives} \quad t = 2\pi\left(\frac{-810}{360}\right) = -\frac{9\pi}{2}.$$

(The sign of t is negative since the motion is clockwise.)   ∎

☑ PRACTICE PROBLEMS 6.1

1. Convert the following angle measurements from degrees to radians.
    a. $210°$ **b.** $765°$ **c.** $-570°$

2. Convert the following angle measurements from radians to degrees.
    a. $\dfrac{7\pi}{3}$ **b.** $-\dfrac{5\pi}{12}$ **c.** $\dfrac{19\pi}{4}$

Exercise Set 6.1

1. Find a radian measure equivalent to the degree measure.
    a. $90°$ **b.** $45°$ **c.** $-135°$
    d. $30°$ **e.** $60°$ **f.** $-150°$
    g. $180°$ **h.** $210°$

2. Find a radian measure equivalent to the degree measure.
    a. $240°$ **b.** $225°$ **c.** $-270°$
    d. $300°$ **e.** $330°$ **f.** $-315°$
    g. $115°$ **h.** $235°$

3. Find a degree measure equivalent to the radian measure.
    a. $\dfrac{\pi}{4}$ **b.** $\dfrac{3\pi}{2}$ **c.** $-\dfrac{\pi}{12}$
    d. $\dfrac{7\pi}{6}$ **e.** $\dfrac{7\pi}{8}$ **f.** $-\dfrac{5\pi}{6}$
    g. $\dfrac{11\pi}{6}$ **h.** $-\dfrac{3\pi}{4}$

4. Find a radian measure equivalent to a counterclockwise rotation through the given number of degrees.
    a. $720°$ **b.** $480°$ **c.** $750°$
    d. $1440°$ **e.** $450°$ **f.** $390°$
    g. $540°$ **h.** $690°$

5. Find a radian measure equivalent to a clockwise rotation through the given number of degrees.
    a. $45°$ **b.** $270°$ **c.** $30°$
    d. $150°$ **e.** $390°$ **f.** $135°$
    g. $330°$ **h.** $540°$

6. Turning a screw three and one-third complete turns counterclockwise corresponds to what radian measure?

7. Determine the radian measure corresponding to the advance of the hour hand on a clock from midnight to each of the following times.
    a. 6 a.m.   **b.** noon
    c. 3 p.m.   **d.** 8 p.m.

In Exercises 8–13, determine the radian measure for the angle described by the figure.

8.

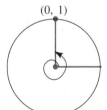

9.

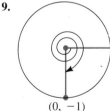

10.

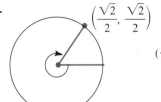

11.

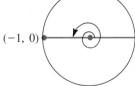

12.

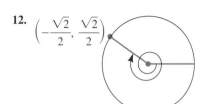

$$\left(-\frac{\sqrt{2}}{2}, \frac{\sqrt{2}}{2}\right)$$

13.

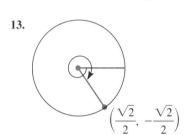

$$\left(\frac{\sqrt{2}}{2}, -\frac{\sqrt{2}}{2}\right)$$

In Exercises 14–24, sketch a figure similar to those in Exercises 8–13, describing the given angle.

14. $-\dfrac{5\pi}{4}$ **15.** 10π **16.** $-\dfrac{7\pi}{3}$

17. $\dfrac{15\pi}{4}$ **18.** $\dfrac{7\pi}{4}$ **19.** $-\dfrac{5\pi}{2}$

20. $\dfrac{10\pi}{3}$ **21.** $-\dfrac{7\pi}{4}$ **22.** $\dfrac{14\pi}{3}$

23. -7π **24.** $-\dfrac{17\pi}{6}$

25. A child turns the adjustment wheel on his mother's desk chair three and one-quarter complete revolutions in the clockwise direction. What is the radian measure?

26. Your astronomy instructor tells you that a certain star lies 15° above the horizon. What is the radian measure?

27. Give an example corresponding to a radian measure of each of the following:
  a. −180 degrees
  b. −540 degrees
  c. −270 degrees

☑ **SOLUTIONS TO PRACTICE PROBLEMS 6.1**

1. Using $\theta_r = \dfrac{2\pi}{360}\,\theta_d$, we have the following conversions to radians.

  a. $\theta_r = \dfrac{2\pi}{360}(210) = \dfrac{420\pi}{360} = \dfrac{7\pi}{6}$

  b. $\theta_r = \dfrac{2\pi}{360}(765) = \dfrac{1530}{360}\pi = \dfrac{17\pi}{4}$

  c. $\theta_r = \dfrac{2\pi}{360}(-570) = -\dfrac{1140}{360}\pi = -\dfrac{19\pi}{6}$

2. Using $\theta_r = \dfrac{180}{\pi}\,\theta_r$ gives the following conversions to degrees.

  a. $\theta_d = \dfrac{180}{\pi}\left(\dfrac{7\pi}{3}\right) = 420°$

  b. $\theta_d = \dfrac{180}{\pi}\left(-\dfrac{5\pi}{12}\right) = -75°$

  c. $\theta_d = \dfrac{180}{\pi}\left(\dfrac{19\pi}{4}\right) = 855°$

6.2 The Sine and Cosine Functions

In attempting to model economic or scientific phenomena, we sometimes encounter the need for functions whose values repeat themselves at regular intervals. For example, Figure 2.1 shows a typical graph of the average daily temperature for a

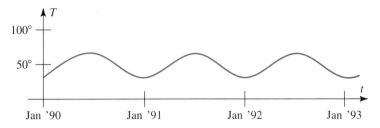

Figure 2.1 Average daily temperature over a 3-year period.

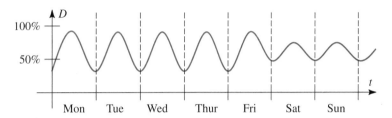

Figure 2.2 Demand for electric power as a percentage of power plant capacity over a 1-week period.

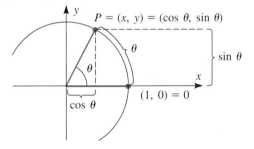

Figure 2.3 If P is a point on the unit circle with coordinates $P = (x, y)$, then

$$x = \cos \theta$$
$$y = \sin \theta.$$

New England city over a period of three years, which consists of three arcs that are nearly congruent. Similarly, Figure 2.2 shows a typical "weekly load curve," representing the electric power supplied by an urban power plant. Note that the first five arcs, corresponding to the weekdays Monday through Friday, are nearly identical.

Figures 2.1 and 2.2 suggest the need to develop **periodic** functions, that is, functions that repeat their values at regularly spaced intervals. None of the functions we have studied up to this point has this property, except the constant functions. However, by using the notion of radian measure, we may define two such functions, the **sine** and **cosine** functions.

Figure 2.3 shows how these functions are defined for angles θ with $0 \leq \theta < 2\pi$. If P is the point on the unit circle lying θ units along the circle from the point $Q = (1, 0)$ in the counterclockwise direction, we define the numbers $\sin \theta$ and $\cos \theta$

(read "sine of θ" and "cosine of θ") by

$$\sin \theta = y\text{-coordinate of } P \qquad (1)$$

and

$$\cos \theta = x\text{-coordinate of } P. \qquad (2)$$

(See Figure 2.3.)

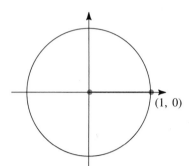

Figure 2.4 $\sin(0) = 0$
$\cos(0) = 1.$

☐ **EXAMPLE 1**

According to equations (1) and (2), we have

$$\sin(0) = 0 \quad \text{and} \quad \cos(0) = 1 \qquad \text{(Figure 2.4)}$$

$$\sin \frac{\pi}{2} = 1 \quad \text{and} \quad \cos \frac{\pi}{2} = 0 \qquad \text{(Figure 2.5)}$$

$$\sin \pi = 0 \quad \text{and} \quad \cos \pi = -1 \qquad \text{(Figure 2.6)}$$

$$\sin \frac{3\pi}{2} = -1 \quad \text{and} \quad \cos \frac{3\pi}{2} = 0 \qquad \text{(Figure 2.7)}.$$

In general, values of $\sin \theta$ and $\cos \theta$ are difficult to compute. Because, however, we know the ratios of the lengths of the sides of 30°–60°–90° and 45°–45°–90° triangles, we can calculate sines and cosines of these angles easily. Figure 2.8 shows the lengths of the legs of these triangles when the hypotenuse has length 1. ■

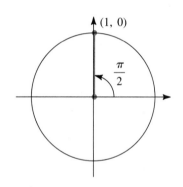

Figure 2.5 $\sin \dfrac{\pi}{2} = 1$

$\cos \dfrac{\pi}{2} = 0.$

☐ **EXAMPLE 2**

From equations (1) and (2) and the information in Figure 2.8 we may conclude that

(a) $\sin\left(\dfrac{\pi}{6}\right) = \dfrac{1}{2}$ and $\cos\left(\dfrac{\pi}{6}\right) = \dfrac{\sqrt{3}}{2}$ (Figure 2.9)

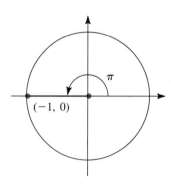

Figure 2.6 $\sin \pi = 0$
$\cos \pi = -1.$

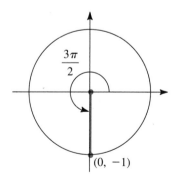

Figure 2.7 $\sin\left(\dfrac{3\pi}{2}\right) = -1$

$\cos\left(\dfrac{3\pi}{2}\right) = 0.$

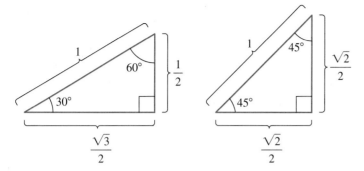

Figure 2.8 Length of sides in 30°–60°–90° and 45°–45°–90° triangles.

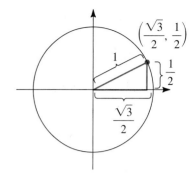

Figure 2.9 $\sin\left(\dfrac{\pi}{6}\right) = \dfrac{1}{2}$

$\cos\left(\dfrac{\pi}{6}\right) = \dfrac{\sqrt{3}}{2}$.

(b) $\sin\left(\dfrac{3\pi}{4}\right) = \dfrac{\sqrt{2}}{2}$ and $\cos\left(\dfrac{3\pi}{4}\right) = -\dfrac{\sqrt{2}}{2}$ (Figure 2.10)

(c) $\sin\left(\dfrac{4\pi}{3}\right) = -\dfrac{\sqrt{3}}{2}$ and $\cos\left(\dfrac{4\pi}{3}\right) = -\dfrac{1}{2}$ (Figure 2.11). ∎

Table 2.1 gives values of $\sin\theta$ and $\cos\theta$ for angles θ that are multiples of $\dfrac{\pi}{6}$ and $\dfrac{\pi}{4}$ in the interval $[0, 2\pi)$. Each may be calculated from equations (1) and (2) and the information in Figure 2.8. Values of the sine and cosine functions for angles other than those in Table 2.1 may be found in Table 3 in Appendix II or may be found using most calculators. In either case it is important to note whether the table or calculator is set up to accept angles measured in degrees or in radians.

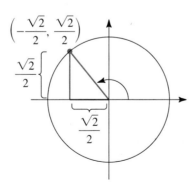

Figure 2.10 $\sin\left(\dfrac{3\pi}{4}\right) = \dfrac{\sqrt{2}}{2}$

$\cos\left(\dfrac{3\pi}{4}\right) = -\dfrac{\sqrt{2}}{2}$.

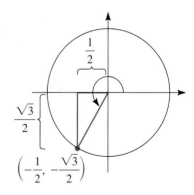

Figure 2.11 $\sin\left(\dfrac{4\pi}{3}\right) = -\dfrac{\sqrt{3}}{2}$

$\cos\left(\dfrac{4\pi}{3}\right) = -\dfrac{1}{2}$.

REMARK: Although tables and calculators are useful in providing values of trigonometric functions, you should try to reason these values yourself, without recourse to tables or to a calculator, whenever possible, so as to develop confidence in your understanding of these functions (and of radian measure).

Table 2.1

θ	0	$\dfrac{\pi}{6}$	$\dfrac{\pi}{4}$	$\dfrac{\pi}{3}$	$\dfrac{\pi}{2}$	$\dfrac{2\pi}{3}$	$\dfrac{3\pi}{4}$	$\dfrac{5\pi}{6}$
$\sin\theta$	0	$\dfrac{1}{2}$	$\dfrac{\sqrt{2}}{2}$	$\dfrac{\sqrt{3}}{2}$	1	$\dfrac{\sqrt{3}}{2}$	$\dfrac{\sqrt{2}}{2}$	$\dfrac{1}{2}$
$\cos\theta$	1	$\dfrac{\sqrt{3}}{2}$	$\dfrac{\sqrt{2}}{2}$	$\dfrac{1}{2}$	0	$-\dfrac{1}{2}$	$-\dfrac{\sqrt{2}}{2}$	$-\dfrac{\sqrt{3}}{2}$

θ	π	$\dfrac{7\pi}{6}$	$\dfrac{5\pi}{4}$	$\dfrac{4\pi}{3}$	$\dfrac{3\pi}{2}$	$\dfrac{5\pi}{3}$	$\dfrac{7\pi}{4}$	$\dfrac{11\pi}{6}$
$\sin\theta$	0	$-\dfrac{1}{2}$	$-\dfrac{\sqrt{2}}{2}$	$-\dfrac{\sqrt{3}}{2}$	-1	$-\dfrac{\sqrt{3}}{2}$	$-\dfrac{\sqrt{2}}{2}$	$-\dfrac{1}{2}$
$\cos\theta$	-1	$-\dfrac{\sqrt{3}}{2}$	$-\dfrac{\sqrt{2}}{2}$	$-\dfrac{1}{2}$	0	$\dfrac{1}{2}$	$\dfrac{\sqrt{2}}{2}$	$\dfrac{\sqrt{3}}{2}$

Equations (1) and (2) define the values $\sin\theta$ and $\cos\theta$ for angles θ with $0 \le \theta < 2\pi$. We may therefore refer to the *functions* $f(\theta) = \sin\theta$ and $g(\theta) = \cos\theta$ with domains $[0, 2\pi)$. Each is referred to as a *trigonometric* function. (Four additional trigonometric functions will be defined in Section 7.5.)

Extending the Domains of sin θ, cos θ

Just as radian measure can be defined for all real numbers t, we may extend the domains of the functions $\sin\theta$ and $\cos\theta$ to the interval $(-\infty, \infty)$ by use of the notion of the principal angle θ associated with the number t. Recall that this is the angle θ for which

$$t = \theta + 2n\pi, \qquad 0 \le \theta < 2\pi \tag{3}$$

for some integer n.

Using equation (3), we define the functions $\sin t$ and $\cos t$ for all t in $(-\infty, \infty)$ by

$$\sin t = \sin\theta, \quad \text{whenever} \quad t = \theta + 2n\pi, \qquad 0 \le \theta < 2\pi$$
$$\cos t = \cos\theta, \quad \text{whenever} \quad t = \theta + 2n\pi, \qquad 0 \le \theta < 2\pi.$$

That is, $\sin t$ is defined to be equal to $\sin\theta$ where θ is the principal angle associated with the number t, and similarly for $\cos t$. In other words, we have the identities

$$\sin\theta = \sin(\theta + 2n\pi), \qquad n = \pm 1, \pm 2, \ldots \tag{4a}$$
$$\cos\theta = \cos(\theta + 2n\pi), \qquad n = \pm 1, \pm 2, \ldots. \tag{4b}$$

☐ **EXAMPLE 3**

The entries in Table 2.1, together with identities (4a) and (4b), give

$$\sin(3\pi) = \sin(\pi + 2\pi) = \sin \pi = 0$$

$$\cos(7\pi) = \cos(\pi + 3 \cdot 2\pi) = \cos \pi = -1$$

$$\sin\left(\frac{9\pi}{2}\right) = \sin\left(\frac{\pi}{2} + 2 \cdot 2\pi\right) = \sin\left(\frac{\pi}{2}\right) = 1$$

and

$$\cos\left(-\frac{11\pi}{4}\right) = \cos\left(\frac{5\pi}{4} - 2 \cdot 2\pi\right) = \cos\left(\frac{5\pi}{4}\right) = -\frac{\sqrt{2}}{2}.$$ ∎

Identities (4a) and (4b) say that the values of the sine and cosine functions are the same at any number located a multiple of 2π radians away from the number θ as they are at the number θ. For this reason we say that these functions are *periodic* with *period* $T = 2\pi$. This periodicity appears in the graphs of $\sin t$ and $\cos t$ in Figures 2.12 and 2.13. Notice that, for both functions, the maximum value is 1 and the minimum value is -1. That is, $|\sin t| \leq 1$ and $|\cos t| \leq 1$ for all numbers t, or, in other words, the ranges of the extended sine and cosine functions are $[-1, 1]$.

Notice also that the cosine function is an *even* function. That is

$$\cos(-t) = \cos t$$

for all t. This is because the x-coordinate of a point t radians along the unit circle from $(1, 0)$ is the same regardless of whether the direction of motion is clockwise or counterclockwise. Recall, from Chapter 1, that this means the graph of $f(t) = \cos t$ is symmetric with respect to the y-axis, as you can observe in Figure 2.13.

Similarly, the sine function is an *odd* function. This means that

$$\sin(-t) = -\sin t$$

for all t. This is because $\sin t$ is the y-coordinate of a point lying t radians along the unit circle from $(1, 0)$, and the y-coordinate of such a point *does* depend on which way the motion occurs from $(1, 0)$. Reversing the direction reverses the sign of the y-coordinate of the terminal point. As with all odd functions, the graph of $f(t) = \sin t$ is symmetric with respect to the origin, as you can observe in Figure 2.12.

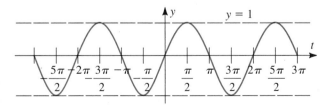

Figure 2.12 Graph of $y = \sin t$.

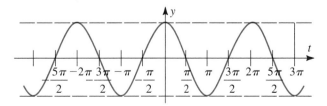

Figure 2.13 Graph of $y = \cos t$.

REMARK: We have used the letters t and θ to represent the independent variable of the trigonometric functions. As in all function notation, though, there is nothing special about the letters used. In fact, in the next section we shall most often use x instead of t.

□ **EXAMPLE 4**

Sketch the graphs of the functions

(a) $f(t) = 3 \cos t$
(b) $g(t) = \sin 4t$.

Solution: Although we must wait to apply most of the graphing techniques of Chapter 3 until the derivatives of $\sin t$ and $\cos t$ are determined in Section 7.3, we can obtain graphs for these two functions by comparing them directly with $\sin t$ and $\cos t$.

(a) The graph of $f(t) = 3 \cos t$ is the same as the graph of $\cos t$ except that the y-coordinate of every point on the graph of $f(t) = 3 \cos t$ is three times the y-coordinate of the corresponding point on the graph of $y = \cos t$. We say that the graph of $f(t) = 3 \cos t$ has *amplitude* 3 since $|f(t)| \leq 3$ for all t. The graph of $y = \cos t$ has amplitude 1 as we have already noted. See Figure 2.14. Like $\cos t$, $3 \cos t$ is an even function.

(b) The graph of $g(t) = \sin 4t$ has amplitude 1, since $|\sin 4t| \leq 1$ for all t. But the zeros of $g(t) = \sin 4t$ are spaced closer together than those of $\sin t$. Indeed, since

$$\sin t = 0 \qquad \text{for } t = 0, \pm \pi, \pm 2\pi, \ldots, \pm n\pi, \ldots$$

we have

$$\sin 4t = 0 \qquad \text{for } 4t = 0, \pm \pi, \pm 2\pi, \ldots, \pm n\pi, \ldots.$$

That is, $\sin 4t = 0$ when

$$t = 0, \pm \frac{\pi}{4}, \pm \frac{2\pi}{4}, \ldots, \pm \frac{n\pi}{4}, \ldots.$$

Thus while the function $\sin t$ has period $T = 2\pi$, the graph of $g(t) = \sin 4t$ has period

$$T = \frac{2\pi}{4} = \frac{\pi}{2}.$$

Like $\sin t$, $\sin 4t$ is an odd function. (See Figure 2.15.)   ■

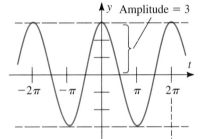

Figure 2.14 Graph of $f(t) = 3 \cos t$.

Predator–Prey Models

In certain ecological situations of interest, one species preys on another for food. Examples are foxes and rabbits, owls and mice, and so forth. These are called *predator–prey* situations, and ecologists have developed **predator–prey models** to study the long-term effect of the relationship on the two species.

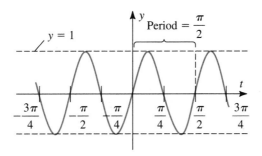

Figure 2.15 Graph of $g(t) = \sin 4t$.

Often, the fact that one species depends on the other for part of its food supply causes both populations to oscillate in size. Taking foxes and rabbits, for example, you can imagine that

a. a large rabbit population would cause an increase in foxes, because food is plentiful.
b. However, more foxes will eventually mean fewer rabbits, as they are killed off by the plentiful foxes,
c. which will eventually lead to a decrease in the fox population due to a scarcity of food,
d. which will allow the rabbit population again to increase.

Not surprisingly, we shall see here, and later in the book, that the sine and cosine functions are used in predator–prey models.

□ **EXAMPLE 5**

Rabbits and foxes occupy the same ecological niche. Foxes prey on the rabbits for food. Rabbits, in turn, feed on the (plentiful) vegetation.

As a result, the size of the fox population as a function of time is given by the function

$$F(t) = 200 - 40 \sin 2t$$

and the size of the rabbit population by

$$R(t) = 500 + 100 \cos 2t$$

where t is time in years.

Graph the two population functions on the same axes for $t \geq 0$.

Solution: The populations are graphed in Figure 2.16. Notice that

(a) the fox population oscillates between 160 and 240; and
(b) the rabbit population oscillates between 400 and 600. ■

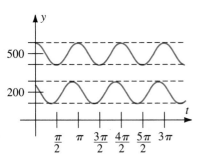

Figure 2.16 Graphs of fox and rabbit population sizes in predator–prey model.

Right Triangle Interpretation of $\sin \theta$, $\cos \theta$

For angles θ with $0 < \theta < \dfrac{\pi}{2}$ the trigonometric functions $\sin \theta$ and $\cos \theta$ may be defined as ratios of sides of a right triangle with base angle θ. If the legs of the

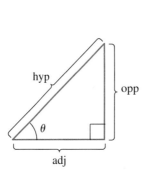

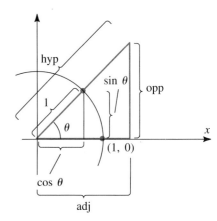

Figure 2.17 $\sin \theta = \dfrac{\text{opp}}{\text{hyp}}$

$\cos \theta = \dfrac{\text{adj}}{\text{hyp}}.$

Figure 2.18 $\sin \theta = \dfrac{\sin \theta}{1} = \dfrac{\text{opp}}{\text{hyp}}$

$\cos \theta = \dfrac{\cos \theta}{1} = \dfrac{\text{adj}}{\text{hyp}}.$

triangle are labeled as in Figure 2.17, then

$$\sin \theta = \frac{\text{opp}}{\text{hyp}} \qquad \text{and} \qquad \cos \theta = \frac{\text{adj}}{\text{hyp}} \tag{5}$$

where adj, opp, and hyp are the lengths of the legs adjacent to and opposite the angle θ, and the hypotenuse, respectively. Figure 2.18 illustrates why the definitions in line (4) give the same values for $\sin \theta$ and $\cos \theta$ as our original definitions in equations (1) and (2): The triangle in Figure 2.17 is similar to a triangle inscribed in the unit circle, and the ratios of corresponding sides give

$$\frac{\sin \theta}{1} = \frac{\text{opp}}{\text{hyp}} = \sin \theta, \qquad \frac{\cos \theta}{1} = \frac{\text{adj}}{\text{hyp}} = \cos \theta.$$

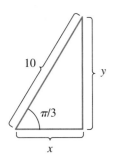

Figure 2.19

Strategy · · · · · · ·

We know that hyp = 10 and we need to find opp, so use

$$\frac{\text{opp}}{\text{hyp}} = \sin \theta.$$

Solve for y.

□ **EXAMPLE 6**

Find the lengths of the legs of the right triangle in Figure 2.19.

Solution

The length of the leg opposite the angle of size $\dfrac{\pi}{3}$ is labeled y. Since the length of the hypotenuse is $h = 10$, we have from equation (5) that

$$\frac{y}{10} = \sin\left(\frac{\pi}{3}\right) = \frac{\sqrt{3}}{2}.$$

Thus

$$y = 10\left(\frac{\sqrt{3}}{2}\right) = \frac{10\sqrt{3}}{2} \approx 8.66$$

Here we use

$$\frac{\text{adj}}{\text{hyp}} = \cos\theta.$$

Similarly, we have

$$\frac{x}{10} = \cos\left(\frac{\pi}{3}\right) = \frac{1}{2}$$

so

$$x = 10\left(\frac{1}{2}\right) = 5.$$ ∎

☐ **EXAMPLE 7**

A person walks 2 miles on a treadmill that is inclined 15° from the horizontal. Through what equivalent vertical distance has the person risen? (See Figure 2.20.)

Solution: Walking 2 miles on this treadmill is equivalent to climbing a hypotenuse of length 2 miles on a triangle whose base angle is $15° = \dfrac{\pi}{12}$. If the vertical side of this triangle has length y, we have

$$\frac{y}{2} = \sin\frac{\pi}{12}$$

so the desired vertical distance is

$$y = 2\sin\frac{\pi}{12}$$
$$= 2(0.2588)$$
$$= 0.5176 \text{ mile.}$$

(The value of $\sin\dfrac{\pi}{12}$ may be obtained from Table 3 in Appendix II or from a calculator.) ∎

Identities Involving sin θ, cos θ

Various identities involving $\sin\theta$ and $\cos\theta$ are established in courses on trigonometry. For example, the Pythagorean theorem applied to the smaller of the right triangles in Figure 2.18 gives the identity

$$\sin^2\theta + \cos^2\theta = 1$$

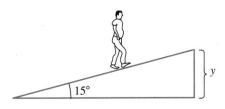

Figure 2.20

which holds for all numbers θ. Other such identities include the following:

$$\sin(\theta \pm \phi) = \sin \theta \cos \phi \pm \cos \theta \sin \phi \qquad \cos 2\theta = \cos^2 \theta - \sin^2 \theta$$

$$\cos(\theta \pm \phi) = \cos \theta \cos \phi \mp \sin \theta \sin \phi \qquad \sin \theta = \cos\left(\frac{\pi}{2} - \theta\right)$$

$$\sin^2 \theta = \frac{1}{2}(1 - \cos 2\theta) \qquad \cos \theta = \sin\left(\frac{\pi}{2} - \theta\right)$$

$$\cos^2 \theta = \frac{1}{2}(1 + \cos 2\theta) \qquad \sin(-\theta) = -\sin \theta$$

$$\sin 2\theta = 2 \sin \theta \cos \theta \qquad \cos(-\theta) = \cos \theta.$$

☑ **PRACTICE PROBLEMS 6.2**

1. Find the following values.
   a. $\sin \dfrac{10\pi}{3}$

   b. $\cos\left(-\dfrac{16\pi}{3}\right)$

2. Sketch the graph of $f(x) = 10 \cos\left(x - \dfrac{\pi}{2}\right)$.

Exercise Set 6.2

In Exercises 1–6, state the (a) sine and (b) cosine of the angle θ contained in the given triangle.

1.

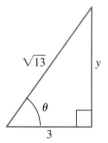

2.

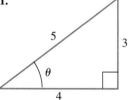

3.

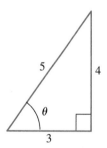

4.

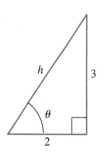

5.

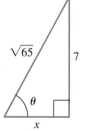

6.

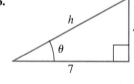

In Exercises 7–10, find $\sin t$ and $\cos t$ for the angle t described by the figure.

7. $(-2, 2)$ **8.**

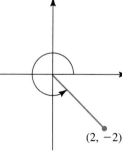

9.

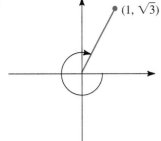

10.

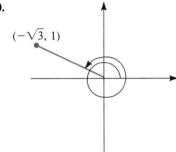

In Exercises 11–18, find the value of the sine or cosine by first finding the principal angle associated with the given angle.

11. $\sin\left(-\dfrac{\pi}{4}\right)$

12. $\cos(5\pi)$

13. $\cos\left(\dfrac{9\pi}{2}\right)$

14. $\sin\left(\dfrac{11\pi}{3}\right)$

15. $\sin\left(-\dfrac{5\pi}{3}\right)$

16. $\cos\left(-\dfrac{5\pi}{2}\right)$

17. $\cos\left(\dfrac{11\pi}{4}\right)$

18. $\sin\left(-\dfrac{9\pi}{4}\right)$

In Exercises 19–24, sketch the graph of the given function.

19. $f(t) = 2 \sin t$

20. $f(t) = -\sin t$

21. $f(t) = \sin 2t$

22. $f(t) = 3 \sin 2t$

23. $f(t) = 4 \cos(-t)$

24. $f(t) = -\cos 2t$

In Exercises 25–28, find the lengths x and y of the legs of the given triangles.

25.

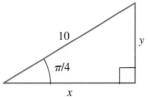

26.

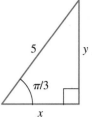

27.

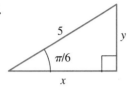

28.

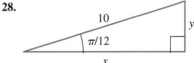

In Exercises 29–34, find the stated value of $\sin t$ or $\cos t$ from Table 3 in Appendix II or by use of a calculator.

29. $\sin 15°$

30. $\cos 68°$

31. $\cos \dfrac{\pi}{7}$

32. $\sin 140°$

33. $\sin \dfrac{2\pi}{9}$

34. $\cos \dfrac{13\pi}{5}$

35. A person walks 1 mile on a treadmill that is inclined $\dfrac{\pi}{12}$ radians from the horizontal. Through what equivalent distance will this person have risen?

36. The temperature on a particular day in St. Louis was determined to be $T(t) = 60 - 15 \cos\left(\dfrac{\pi t}{12}\right)$ degrees Fahrenheit at a time t hours after midnight. Find the temperature at
a. 6 a.m. **b.** noon **c.** 4 p.m.

37. The number of hours of daylight in a particular North American city is $D(t) = 12 + 3 \sin\left(\dfrac{\pi t}{6} - \dfrac{5\pi}{12}\right)$ hours where t represents the number of months after January 1. Find the number of hours of daylight on
a. March 15 $\left(t = \dfrac{5}{2}\right)$ **b.** June 15 $\left(t = \dfrac{11}{2}\right)$
c. December 15 $\left(t = \dfrac{23}{2}\right)$

38. The height of a particular seat on a Ferris wheel is

$$h = 15 + 15 \sin \theta \text{ meters}$$

where θ is the angle illustrated in Figures 2.21 and 2.22. Find the height of the seat above ground level when θ equals

a. 0 radians

b. $\dfrac{2\pi}{3}$ radians

c. $\dfrac{3\pi}{2}$ radians

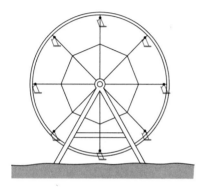

Figure 2.21 Ferris wheel.

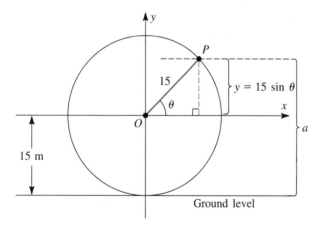

Figure 2.22 Idealized Ferris wheel.

39. Researchers interested in modelling the rate at which animals (including humans) grow know that growth is not uniform. Periods of rapid growth often occur between periods of very slow growth. One model for such types of growth is given by the function

$$h(t) = t + \sin\left(\frac{\pi t}{4}\right) + B$$

where B is a constant, t is years since birth, and $h(t)$ is human height. (See Figure 2.23.) According to this model, find

a. $h(0)$ **b.** $h(4)$ **c.** $h(6)$

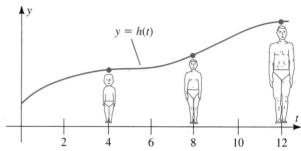

Figure 2.23 The model $h(t) = t + \sin\left(\dfrac{\pi t}{4}\right) + B$ for human growth.

40. During a certain period of time closing prices on a particular stock exchange were approximately

$$P(t) = 10t + 4 \sin\left(\frac{\pi t}{2}\right) + 500$$

where P is price in dollars and t is time in months. Find

a. $P(0)$ **b.** $P(12)$ **c.** $P(15)$

41. Explain why the following formula for the area of the triangle in Figure 2.24 is valid:

$$A = \frac{1}{2}xh \sin \theta.$$

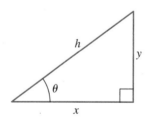

Figure 2.24

42. An individual's blood pressure is given by the function

$$P(t) = 105 + 12 \sin 5t$$

where t is time in seconds.

a. Find the individual's maximum (systolic) blood pressure.

b. Find the individual's minimum (diastolic) blood pressure.

43. What is the heart rate for the individual in Exercise 42?

44. The predator–prey model is

$$F(t) = 200 + 60 \cos t$$
$$R(t) = 100 + 80 \sin t.$$

a. What is the minimum size, F_0, of the fox population, $F(t)$?

b. What is the minimum size, R_0, of the rabbit population?

c. Does it matter if $F_0 < R_0$?

45. The height of the ocean tide as measured at the ferry landing at Adam's Island is given by the function

$$H(t) = 15 + 4 \sin \pi\left(\frac{t - 4}{6}\right).$$

where t is in hours after midnight.

a. When does high tide occur?

b. When does the low tide occur?

c. Graph the function $y = H(t)$ for $0 \le t \le 24$.

☑ **SOLUTIONS TO PRACTICE PROBLEMS 6.2**

1. a. $\sin\left(\dfrac{10\pi}{3}\right) = \sin\left(\dfrac{4\pi}{3}\right) = -\dfrac{\sqrt{3}}{2}$

   b. $\cos\left(-\dfrac{16\pi}{3}\right) = \cos\left(-\dfrac{4\pi}{3}\right) = \cos\left(\dfrac{2\pi}{3}\right) = -\dfrac{1}{2}$

2.

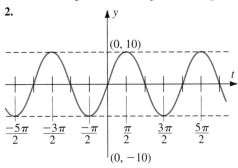

Figure 2.25

6.3 Derivatives of sin x and cos x

At the end of this section we shall show that the derivatives of the functions $\sin x$ and $\cos x$ are the following:

$$\frac{d}{dx} \sin x = \cos x \tag{1}$$

$$\frac{d}{dx} \cos x = -\sin x. \tag{2}$$

If u is a differentiable function of x, we may apply the Chain Rule together with equations (1) and (2) to conclude that

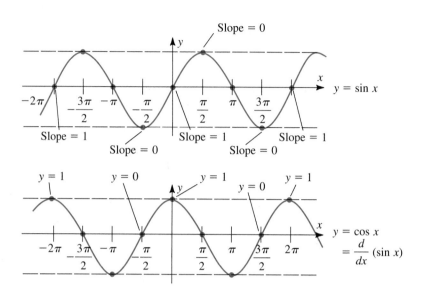

Figure 3.1 Slope of tangent to the graph of $f(x) = \sin x$ at $x = x_0$ is $f'(x_0) = \cos x_0$.

$$\frac{d}{dx} \sin u = \cos u \cdot \frac{du}{dx} \tag{3}$$

$$\frac{d}{dx} \cos u = -\sin u \cdot \frac{du}{dx}. \tag{4}$$

Figure 3.1 illustrates the geometric significance of equation (1). The derivative $f'(x_0)$ can be interpreted as the slope of the line tangent to the graph of f at the point where $x = x_0$. As the figure shows, the tangent to the graph of $f(x) = \sin x$ has

$$\text{slope } m = \cos(0) = 1 \qquad \text{when } x = 0$$

$$\text{slope } m = \cos\left(\frac{\pi}{2}\right) = 0 \qquad \text{when } x = \frac{\pi}{2}$$

$$\text{slope } m = \cos \pi = -1 \qquad \text{when } x = \pi$$

and so forth. Also, since the function $f(x) = \sin x$ is periodic with period 2π, the "slope function" $f'(x)$ should also be periodic, with period $T = 2\pi$. This is precisely the behavior of its derivative, $f'(x) = \cos x$. You can verify by a similar analysis that properties of the derivative $g'(x) = -\sin x$ are those of the slope function for the function $g(x) = \cos x$.

□ **EXAMPLE 1**

For $f(x) = \sin 4x$, find $f'(x)$.

Solution: Here $f(x) = \sin u$ with $u = 4x$. According to equation (3), we have

$$f'(x) = (\cos 4x) \cdot \frac{d}{dx}(4x)$$

$$= (\cos 4x)(4)$$

$$= 4\cos 4x. \qquad\blacksquare$$

☐ **EXAMPLE 2**

Find $\dfrac{d}{dx}\sin x^3$.

Solution: Again applying equation (3), with $u = x^3$, we have

$$\frac{d}{dx}\sin x^3 = (\cos x^3) \cdot \frac{d}{dx}(x^3)$$

$$= (\cos x^3)(3x^2)$$

$$= 3x^2\cos x^3. \qquad\blacksquare$$

☐ **EXAMPLE 3**

For $f(x) = x\cos\sqrt{x}$, find $f'(x)$.

Solution: Since f is a product, with factors x and $\cos\sqrt{x}$, we apply the Product Rule together with equation (4):

$$f'(x) = \left[\frac{d}{dx}(x)\right]\cos\sqrt{x} + x\left[\frac{d}{dx}\cos\sqrt{x}\right]$$

$$= (1)\cos\sqrt{x} + x\left[\left(-\sin\sqrt{x}\right)\left(\frac{d}{dx}\sqrt{x}\right)\right] \qquad \text{(Apply Chain Rule)}$$

$$= \cos\sqrt{x} + x(-\sin\sqrt{x})\left(\frac{1}{2\sqrt{x}}\right)$$

$$= \cos\sqrt{x} - \frac{1}{2}\sqrt{x}\sin\sqrt{x}. \qquad\blacksquare$$

☐ **EXAMPLE 4**

Find $\dfrac{d}{dx}(x + \sin x)^4$.

Solution: The function to be differentiated has the form $f(x) = [u(x)]^4$ with $u(x) = x + \sin x$. Since the derivative of such a function is $f'(x) = 4[u(x)]^3 \cdot u'(x)$, we first apply the Chain Rule to obtain $u'(x) = 1 + \cos x$ and then evaluate $f'(x)$:

$$\frac{d}{dx}(x + \sin x)^4 = 4(x + \sin x)^3(1 + \cos x).$$ ∎

☐ **EXAMPLE 5**

Find $f'(x)$ if $f(x) = \dfrac{x + \sin x}{x^2}$, $x \neq 0$.

Solution: Applying the Quotient Rule, we obtain

$$f'(x) = \frac{x^2\left[\dfrac{d}{dx}(x + \sin x)\right] - (x + \sin x)\left[\dfrac{d}{dx}x^2\right]}{(x^2)^2}$$

$$= \frac{x^2(1 + \cos x) - (x + \sin x)(2x)}{x^4}$$

$$= \frac{x^2(\cos x - 1) - 2x \sin x}{x^4}$$

$$= \frac{x(\cos x - 1) - 2 \sin x}{x^3}.$$ ∎

☐ **EXAMPLE 6**

Find the maximum and minimum values of the function $f(x) = \sqrt{2 + \sin x}$ for x in the interval $[0, 2\pi]$.

Strategy · · · · · · · **Solution**
This problem is worked in the same way as the optimization problems in Chapter 3. The only difference is that the function involves the sine, which we can now differentiate.

Find f'.

For $f(x) = \sqrt{2 + \sin x} = (2 + \sin x)^{1/2}$, we have

$$f'(x) = \frac{1}{2}(2 + \sin x)^{-1/2} \cdot \cos x$$

$$= \frac{\cos x}{2\sqrt{2 + \sin x}}.$$

Set $f'(x) = 0$ to find critical numbers. Thus $f'(x)$ equals zero when $\cos x = 0$, which occurs at the numbers

$$x = \frac{\pi}{2} \quad \text{and} \quad x = \frac{3\pi}{2}$$

in $[0, 2\pi]$. Since $f'(x)$ is defined for all x in $[0, 2\pi]$, the only critical numbers for f are $x = \dfrac{\pi}{2}$ and $\dfrac{3\pi}{2}$. Checking the value $f(x)$ at each critical number and endpoint

Calculate $f(x)$ for each critical number and endpoint.

gives

$$f(0) = \sqrt{2 + \sin(0)} = \sqrt{2 + 0}$$

$$= \sqrt{2} \quad \text{(endpoint)}$$

$$f\left(\frac{\pi}{2}\right) = \sqrt{2 + \sin\frac{\pi}{2}} = \sqrt{2 + 1}$$

$$= \sqrt{3} \quad \text{(critical number)}$$

$$f\left(\frac{3\pi}{2}\right) = \sqrt{2 + \sin\frac{3\pi}{2}} = \sqrt{2 + (-1)}$$

$$= 1 \quad \text{(critical number)}$$

$$f(2\pi) = \sqrt{2 + \sin 2\pi} = \sqrt{2 + 0}$$

$$= \sqrt{2} \quad \text{(endpoint)}.$$

Select maximum and minimum from among these values.

The maximum value of f on $[0, 2\pi]$ is therefore $f\left(\frac{\pi}{2}\right) = \sqrt{3}$, and the minimum is $f\left(\frac{3\pi}{2}\right) = 1$. The graph of f appears in Figure 3.2. ∎

□ **EXAMPLE 7**

A Ferris wheel 30 meters high turns at the rate of 3 revolutions per minute. (See Figure 3.3.) Find

(a) a function describing the rate at which the altitude of a passenger changes, and
(b) the positions at which this rate is the greatest.

Solution: Figure 3.4 represents the passenger's location as a point P on the idealized Ferris wheel. If we superimpose an xy-coordinate system with its origin O at the center of the Ferris wheel, then P is a point on a circle of radius $r = 15$ meters. If

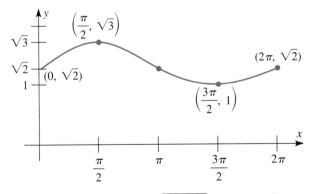

Figure 3.2 Graph of $f(x) = \sqrt{2 + \sin x}$ in Example 6.

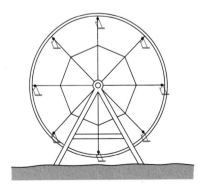

Figure 3.3 Ferris wheel.

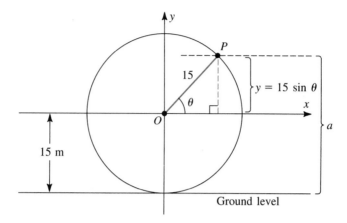

Figure 3.4 Idealized Ferris wheel.

P has coordinates $P = (x, y)$ and if θ is the angle between the ray OP and the positive x-axis, then the definition of the sine function tells us that

$$\sin \theta = \frac{y}{15}$$

so

$$y = 15 \sin \theta.$$

Now since the x-axis lies 15 meters above ground level, the *altitude h* of the point P is

$$h = 15 + y$$
$$= 15 + 15 \sin \theta \text{ meters.} \tag{5}$$

Since the angle θ is a function of t (time), equation (5) allows us to express the altitude of P as a function of t:

$$h = 15 + 15 \sin \theta(t) \text{ meters.}$$

Thus the *rate* at which altitude changes with respect to time is the derivative $h'(t)$:

$$\frac{dh}{dt} = \frac{d}{dt}[15 + 15 \sin \theta(t)]$$

$$= 15 \cos \theta(t) \cdot \frac{d\theta}{dt} \text{ meters per minute} \tag{6}$$

according to equation (3). Since we are given that $\dfrac{d\theta}{dt} = 3$ revolutions per minute, and θ in line (5) is measured in *radians,* we must convert revolutions to radians (1 revolution $= 2\pi$ radians). We obtain

$$\frac{d\theta}{dt} = \left(3\frac{\text{rev}}{\text{min}}\right)\left(2\pi\frac{\text{rad}}{\text{rev}}\right) = 6\pi \text{ rad/min.}$$

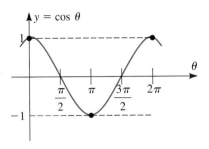

Figure 3.5 cos θ achieves its maximum value at $\theta = 0$ and its minimum value at $\theta = \pi$.

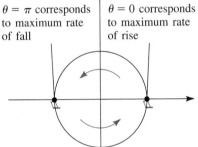

$\theta = \pi$ corresponds to maximum rate of fall | $\theta = 0$ corresponds to maximum rate of rise

Figure 3.6 Maximum rates of rise and fall occur at the halfway points.

Substituting this number for $\dfrac{d\theta}{dt}$ in equation (6) gives the desired rate as

$$\frac{dh}{dt} = 15 \cos \theta(t) \cdot 6\pi$$

$$= 90\pi \cos \theta(t) \text{ meters per minute.} \tag{7}$$

To find the positions at which this rate is the greatest, we set the derivative of $\dfrac{dh}{dt}$ (which is the *second* derivative of h) equal to zero and solve for θ. Since

$$\frac{d^2h}{dt^2} = \frac{d}{dt}[90\pi \cos \theta(t)]$$

$$= -90\pi \sin \theta(t) \cdot \frac{d\theta}{dt}$$

$$= -90\pi \sin \theta(t)(6\pi)$$

$$= -540\pi^2 \sin \theta(t)$$

we will have $\dfrac{d^2h}{dt^2} = 0$ when $\sin \theta = 0$, which occurs when $\theta = 0$ and when $\theta = \pi$.

These critical numbers correspond to what you may have already experienced from riding a Ferris wheel. The point at which you are rising most rapidly corresponds to $\theta = 0$ (that is, halfway up), and the point at which you are falling most rapidly corresponds to $\theta = \pi$ (halfway down). (See Figures 3.5 and 3.6.)   ∎

☐ **EXAMPLE 8**

The solutions of a predator–prey model for two species are

$$R(t) = 500 - 100 \sin 2t + 100 \cos 2t$$
$$F(t) = 200 + 20 \cos 2t + 20 \sin 2t.$$

Here $R(t)$ and $F(t)$ represent the sizes of the rabbit and fox population, respectively, and t is time in years. Graph these functions on the same set of axes.

Solution: Beginning with the rabbit population, we note that $R(t)$ is always positive because the constant 500 is clearly larger than the values of the other two terms, regardless of t.

The derivative for R is

$$R'(t) = -200 \cos 2t - 200 \sin 2t.$$

Setting $R'(t) = 0$ and solving gives

$$200 \sin 2t = -200 \cos 2t$$

or

$$\sin 2t = -\cos 2t. \tag{8}$$

By inspection from the graphs of $\sin \theta$ and $\cos \theta$, or by checking a table of values, we can observe that $\sin \theta = -\cos \theta$ only at the angles $\theta = \dfrac{3\pi}{4}$ and $\theta = \dfrac{7\pi}{4}$. Thus, equation (8) is satisfied for

$$2t = \frac{3\pi}{4} \qquad \text{and} \qquad 2t = \frac{7\pi}{4}$$

which gives $t_1 = \dfrac{3\pi}{8}$ or $t_2 = \dfrac{7\pi}{8}$. These are critical numbers for R.

The second derivative of R is

$$R''(t) = 400 \sin 2t - 400 \cos 2t.$$

Checking the critical numbers by the Second Derivative Test gives

$$R''(t_1) = R''\left(\frac{3\pi}{8}\right) = 400 \sin\left(\frac{3\pi}{4}\right) - 400 \cos\left(\frac{3\pi}{4}\right)$$

$$= 400\left(\frac{\sqrt{2}}{2}\right) - 400\left(-\frac{\sqrt{2}}{2}\right)$$

$$= 400\sqrt{2} > 0.$$

and

$$R''(t_2) = R''\left(\frac{7\pi}{8}\right) = 400 \sin\left(\frac{7\pi}{4}\right) - 400 \cos\left(\frac{7\pi}{4}\right)$$

$$= 400\left(-\frac{\sqrt{2}}{2}\right) - 400\left(\frac{\sqrt{2}}{2}\right)$$

$$= -400\sqrt{2} < 0.$$

Thus, $\left(\dfrac{3\pi}{8}, R\left(\dfrac{3\pi}{8}\right)\right) = \left(\dfrac{3\pi}{8}, 500 - 50\sqrt{2}\right)$ is a relative minimum, and $\left(\dfrac{7\pi}{8}, R\left(\dfrac{7\pi}{8}\right)\right) = \left(\dfrac{7\pi}{8}, 500 + 50\sqrt{2}\right)$ is a relative maximum.

Proceeding in a similar fashion, we leave it to you to verify the following:

(a) Because $R(t)$ is periodic, with period $T = \pi$, R also has relative minima at

$$t = \frac{3\pi}{8} + n\pi = \frac{11\pi}{8}, \frac{19\pi}{8}, \ldots \quad \text{and relative maxima at } t = \frac{7\pi}{8} + n\pi =$$

$$\frac{15\pi}{8}, \frac{23\pi}{8}, \ldots$$

(b) The function $F(t)$ has relative minima at $t = \dfrac{5\pi}{8} + n\pi = \dfrac{5\pi}{8}, \dfrac{13\pi}{8}, \dfrac{21\pi}{8}, \ldots$ and relative maxima

$$t = \frac{\pi}{8} + n\pi = \frac{\pi}{8}, \frac{9\pi}{8}, \frac{17\pi}{8}, \ldots$$

The graphs of R and F appear in Figure 3.7. ∎

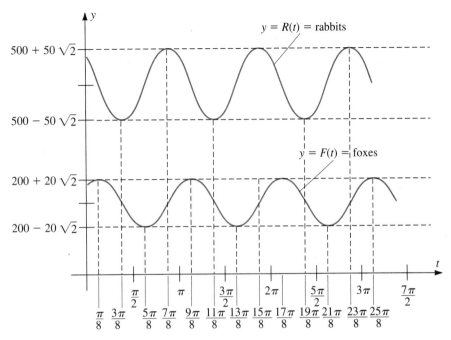

Figure 3.7 Graphs of rabbit and fox populations in predator–prey model of Example 8.

Deriving Formulas (1) and (2)

To establish formula (1) for the derivative of the function $f(x) = \sin x$, we need to make use of the following limit:

$$\lim_{\theta \to 0} \frac{\sin \theta}{\theta} = 1. \tag{8}$$

A geometric argument for this limit can be given. However, you may observe this limit experimentally quite easily. Just select a sequence of numbers θ that approach zero (from either direction) and calculate the ratio $\dfrac{\sin \theta}{\theta}$ for each, using a calculator or a computer. You will obtain results similar to those in Table 3.1.

Table 3.1 Values of $\dfrac{\sin \theta}{\theta}$ as $\theta \to 0$ (θ is in radians)

θ	$\sin \theta$	$\dfrac{\sin \theta}{\theta}$	θ	$\sin \theta$	$\dfrac{\sin \theta}{\theta}$
.5	.479426	.958851	$-.5$	$-.479426$	.958851
.1	.099833	.998334	$-.1$	$-.099833$	.998334
.05	.049979	.999583	$-.05$	$-.049979$	.999583
.01	.010000	.999983	$-.01$	$-.010000$	.999983
.005	.005000	.999996	$-.005$	$-.005000$	.999996
.001	.001000	.999999	$-.001$	$-.001000$	.999999

In addition to the limit in line (8) we need to make use of the limit

$$\lim_{\theta \to 0} \left(\frac{\cos \theta - 1}{\theta} \right) = 0 \tag{9}$$

which is explained in Exercise 46. Finally, we need to use the formula from trigonometry for the sine of the sum of two angles:

$$\sin(\theta + \phi) = \sin \theta \cos \phi + \cos \theta \sin \phi. \tag{10}$$

We are now ready to use the basic definition of the derivative to find $f'(x)$ for $f(x) = \sin x$:

$$f'(x) = \lim_{h \to 0} \frac{f(x + h) - f(x)}{h} \qquad \text{(definition of } f'(x)\text{)}$$

$$= \lim_{h \to 0} \frac{\sin(x + h) - \sin x}{h} \qquad (f(x) = \sin x)$$

$$= \lim_{h \to 0} \frac{[\sin x \cos h + \cos x \sin h] - \sin x}{h} \qquad \text{(formula (10))}$$

$$= \lim_{h \to 0} \left\{ \sin x \left(\frac{\cos h - 1}{h} \right) + \cos x \left(\frac{\sin h}{h} \right) \right\}$$

$$= \sin x \left[\lim_{h \to 0} \left(\frac{\cos h - 1}{h} \right) \right] + \cos x \left[\lim_{h \to 0} \left(\frac{\sin h}{h} \right) \right]$$

$$= \sin x \cdot (0) + \cos x \cdot (1) \qquad \text{(equations (8), (9))}$$

$$= \cos x.$$

This establishes formula (1), that $\dfrac{d}{dx} \sin x = \cos x$.

To establish formula (2), that $\dfrac{d}{dx} \cos x = -\sin x$, we use formula (3) and the identities

$$\sin\left(\frac{\pi}{2} - x \right) = \cos x; \qquad \cos\left(\frac{\pi}{2} - x \right) = \sin x. \tag{11}$$

We obtain

$$\frac{d}{dx} \cos x = \frac{d}{dx} \sin\left(\frac{\pi}{2} - x \right) \qquad \text{(equations (11))}$$

$$= \cos\left(\frac{\pi}{2} - x \right) \cdot \frac{d}{dx}\left(\frac{\pi}{2} - x \right) \qquad \text{(formula (3))}$$

$$= (-1)\cos\left(\frac{\pi}{2} - x \right)$$

$$= -\sin x. \qquad \text{(equations (11))}.$$

☑ **PRACTICE PROBLEMS 6.3**

1. Find $f'(x)$.
   a. $f(x) = x^3 \cos(3x - \pi)$
   b. $f(x) = \dfrac{x + \cos x}{2 + \sin^2 x}$

2. Find $\dfrac{dy}{dx}$ if $\sin(x + y) = \cos(x - y)$.

Exercise Set 6.3

In Exercises 1–20, find the derivative of the given function.

1. $f(x) = \sin 3x$

2. $f(x) = \cos 2x$

3. $y = x \sin(x + \pi)$

4. $f(x) = \sin\left(\dfrac{\pi}{2} - x\right)$

5. $f(x) = x^3 \cos 2x$

6. $f(\theta) = e^{\sin^2 \theta}$

7. $y = \sin^3 x \cos^2 x$

8. $f(x) = \sqrt{x + \cos x}$

9. $f(x) = \sin\sqrt{1 + x^2}$

10. $f(x) = \dfrac{\sin x}{x^2 + 1}$

11. $y = \cos^2(\ln t)$

12. $y = \dfrac{1 - \sin x}{1 + \cos x}$

13. $f(x) = \sin^2 x + \cos^2 x$

14. $f(x) = x^3 \cos\sqrt{1 - x^2}$

15. $f(t) = \ln(t^4 + \sin t)$

16. $y = (\cos \theta)e^{\cos \theta}$

17. $y = \dfrac{1 + \sin x}{3 + x^2}$

18. $f(x) = \sin^2(x^3 + \sqrt{x})$

19. $f(x) = \cos x \sin\dfrac{1}{x}$

20. $y = \sin^3 x \cos^5 x$

21. Find an equation for the line tangent to the graph of $y = \sin 2x$ at the point $\left(\dfrac{\pi}{6}, \dfrac{\sqrt{3}}{2}\right)$.

22. Find an equation for the line tangent to the graph of $y = e^{\cos t}$ at the point where $t = \dfrac{\pi}{2}$.

23. A particle moves along a line so that after t seconds its position is $s(t) = \dfrac{\sin 2t}{3 + \cos^2 t}$. Find its velocity at time $t = \dfrac{\pi}{4}$. (Units for distance are feet.)

24. A particle moves along a line so that at time t its position is $s(t) = 6 \sin 3t$. (Units are meters for distance, seconds for time.)

a. At which times does it change direction?
b. What is its maximum velocity?

25. Why do the functions $f(x) = \sin^2 x$ and $g(x) = 1 - \cos^2 x$ have the same derivatives?

26. Find $f''(x)$ for $f(x) = \sqrt{x} \sin x$.

27. Find $f''(t)$ for $f(t) = \sin \ln t$.

In Exercises 28–31, use implicit differentiation to find $\dfrac{dy}{dx}$.

28. $x = \sin(x + y)$

29. $\cos xy = x + y$

30. $\sin(x + y) + \cos y = 1$

31. $\sin y = x \cos y$

In Exercises 32–35, find the maximum and minimum values of the given function on the given interval.

32. $f(x) = \sin 2x, \quad x$ in $\left[0, \dfrac{\pi}{2}\right]$

33. $f(x) = \sin x + \cos x, \quad x$ in $[0, 2\pi]$

34. $f(x) = \sin x - \cos x, \quad x$ in $\left[-\dfrac{\pi}{2}, \dfrac{\pi}{2}\right]$

35. $f(x) = x - \sin x, \quad x$ in $\left[\dfrac{\pi}{2}, \dfrac{3\pi}{2}\right]$

In Exercises 36–41, use information provided by the first and second derivatives of the given function to sketch its graph.

36. $f(x) = \sin 3x$

37. $f(x) = \cos\left(x - \dfrac{\pi}{2}\right)$

38. $f(x) = x \sin x$

39. $f(x) = x + \sin x$

40. $f(x) = \sin x + \cos x$

41. $f(x) = \dfrac{\sin x}{2 + \cos x}, \quad -\pi \le x \le \pi$

42. A water trough is to be constructed from three metal sheets each 1 meter wide and 6 meters long plus end panels in the

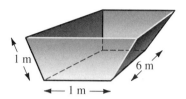

Figure 3.8

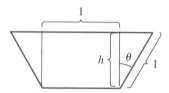

Figure 3.9

shape of trapezoids. (See Figure 3.8.) Find the angle θ at which the long panels should be joined so as to provide a trough of maximum volume. (See Figure 3.9.)

43. Researchers interested in modelling the rate at which animals grow have used the model

$$y = t + \sin\left(\frac{\pi t}{4}\right) + B$$

where y is height in centimeters, B is birth height, and t is in units of months from birth. Find the maximum and minimum values of the rate of growth, $\dfrac{dy}{dt}$, and the times during the first year at which they occur.

44. The temperature on a particular day in St. Louis was determined to be $T(t) = 60 - 15 \cos\left(\dfrac{\pi t}{12}\right)$ degrees Fahrenheit t hours after midnight.
   a. What was the maximum temperature, and when did it occur?
   b. What was the minimum temperature, and when did it occur?
   c. When was the temperature increasing most rapidly?

45. The number of hours of daylight in a particular North American city is $D(t) = 12 + 3 \sin\left(\dfrac{\pi t}{6} - \dfrac{5\pi}{12}\right)$, where t represents months after January 1. Find the time t at which
   a. the days are the longest.
   b. the days are the shortest.

46. Explain the steps in the following demonstration that

$$\lim_{\theta \to 0} \frac{\cos \theta - 1}{\theta} = 0:$$

$$
\begin{aligned}
\lim_{\theta \to 0} \frac{\cos \theta - 1}{\theta} &= \lim_{\theta \to 0}\left[\left(\frac{\cos \theta - 1}{\theta}\right)\left(\frac{\cos \theta + 1}{\cos \theta + 1}\right)\right] \\
&= \lim_{\theta \to 0} \frac{\cos^2 \theta - 1}{\theta(1 + \cos \theta)} \\
&= \lim_{\theta \to 0} \frac{-\sin^2 \theta}{\theta(1 + \cos \theta)} \\
&= \lim_{\theta \to 0}\left(\frac{\sin \theta}{\theta}\right)\left(\frac{-\sin \theta}{1 + \cos \theta}\right) \\
&= (1)\left(\frac{0}{1 + 1}\right) \\
&= 0.
\end{aligned}
$$

47. Show that the function $F(t)$ in Example 8 has relative maxima at $t = \dfrac{\pi}{8} + n\pi$ and relative minima at $t = \dfrac{5\pi}{8} + n\pi$.

48. The predator–prey model is

$$R(t) = 1000 + 200 \sin t + 200 \cos t$$
$$F(t) = 500 - 50 \cos t + 50 \sin t.$$

   a. Find the numbers t for which R has relative maxima.
   b. Find the numbers t for which R has relative minima.
   c. Find the values of these extrema.

49. For the function F in Exercise 48, answer the questions asked for R.

50. Graph the functions F and R in Exercise 48.

51. The average daily temperature in a particular North American city is modelled by the trigonometric function

$$f(t) = 55 + 35 \sin 2\pi\left(\frac{t - 90}{365}\right)$$

where t represents the number of days into the calendar year and $f(t)$ is in degrees Fahrenheit.
   a. After how many days does the maximum temperature occur?
   b. When is it the coldest in this city?

52. A biology student specializing in animal ecology decides to model the size of a population of voles by the trigonometric function

$$f(t) = 100 + 40 \cos \frac{\pi t}{2}$$

where t is time in years. According to this model, and for $0 \le t \le 6$,
   a. When is the population the largest?
   b. When is the population the smallest?
   c. What is the length of time between the two maxima?

✓ **SOLUTIONS TO PRACTICE PROBLEMS 6.3**

1. a. $f'(x) = 3x^2 \cos(3x - \pi) - 3x^2 \sin(3x - \pi)$

b. $f'(x) = \dfrac{(2 + \sin^2 x)(1 - \sin x) - (x + \cos x)(2 \sin x \cos x)}{(2 + \sin^2 x)^2}$

2. $[\cos(x + y)]\left(1 + \dfrac{dy}{dx}\right) = [-\sin(x - y)]\left(1 - \dfrac{dy}{dx}\right)$

gives

$$[\cos(x + y) - \sin(x - y)]\frac{dy}{dx} = -\sin(x - y) - \cos(x + y)$$

so

$$\frac{dy}{dx} = \frac{\sin(x - y) + \cos(x + y)}{\sin(x - y) - \cos(x + y)}.$$

6.4 Integrals of Sine and Cosine

The differentiation formulas $\dfrac{d}{dx} \sin x = \cos x$ and $\dfrac{d}{dx} \cos x = -\sin x$ lead immediately to the following antiderivatives of the sine and cosine functions.

$$\int \cos x \, dx = \sin x + C \tag{1}$$

$$\int \sin x \, dx = -\cos x + C. \tag{2}$$

These formulas, together with the method of substitutions, allow us to evaluate a variety of integrals involving the sine and cosine functions.

☐ **EXAMPLE 1**

Find $\displaystyle\int 3 \cos 3x \, dx$.

Solution: If we let $u = 3x$, then $du = 3 \, dx$, and we obtain

$$\int 3 \cos 3x \, dx = \int \underbrace{\cos 3x}_{\cos u} \cdot \underbrace{3 \, dx}_{du} = \int \cos u \, du$$

$$= \sin u + C \quad \text{(by equation (1))}$$

$$= \sin 3x + C.$$

This result is easy to verify: $\dfrac{d}{dx}(\sin 3x + C) = \cos 3x \cdot \dfrac{d}{dx}(3x) = 3 \cos 3x.$ ∎

□ **EXAMPLE 2**

Find $\int \sin 5x \, dx$.

Solution: This integral is similar to that of Example 1. If we let

$$u = 5x, \quad \text{then} \quad du = 5 \, dx.$$

Thus $dx = \dfrac{1}{5} \, du$. Using these substitutions and equation (2), we obtain

$$\int \sin 5x \, dx = \int \sin u \cdot \frac{1}{5} \, du = \frac{1}{5} \int \sin u \, du$$

$$= \frac{1}{5}(-\cos u) + C$$

$$= -\frac{1}{5} \cos 5x + C. \qquad \blacksquare$$

□ **EXAMPLE 3**

Find $\displaystyle\int_0^{\pi/4} \cos 2x \, dx$.

Solution: By the method of Example 1 we find that the antiderivative for $\cos 2x$ is

$$\int \cos 2x \, dx = \frac{1}{2} \sin 2x + C.$$

The definite integral may therefore be evaluated using this antiderivative and the Fundamental Theorem:

$$\int_0^{\pi/4} \cos 2x \, dx = \left[\frac{1}{2} \sin 2x \right]_0^{\pi/4}$$

$$= \frac{1}{2} \sin \frac{\pi}{2} - \frac{1}{2} \sin(0)$$

$$= \frac{1}{2}(1) - \frac{1}{2}(0)$$

$$= \frac{1}{2}. \qquad \blacksquare$$

□ **EXAMPLE 4**

Find $\int x^2 \sin x^3 \, dx$.

Strategy · · · · · · · ·

Make the substitution

$u = x^3$.

Determine du and then solve for the remaining factors of the integrand.

Make the substitution.

Apply equation (2).

Substitute back in terms of x.

Solution

If we let

$$u = x^3, \quad \text{then} \quad du = 3x^2 \, dx.$$

Solving the second equation for the factor $x^2 \, dx$ that appears in the integrand gives $x^2 \, dx = \dfrac{1}{3} \, du$. Making these substitutions, we then obtain

$$\int x^2 \sin x^3 \, dx = \int (\sin x^3) x^2 \, dx$$

$$= \int \sin u \cdot \frac{1}{3} \, du$$

$$= \frac{1}{3} \int \sin u \, du$$

$$= -\frac{1}{3} \cos u + C$$

$$= -\frac{1}{3} \cos x^3 + C.$$ ∎

☐ **EXAMPLE 5**

Find $\displaystyle\int_0^{\pi/2} \frac{\sin x \cos x}{\sqrt{1 + \sin^2 x}} \, dx.$

Strategy · · · · · · ·

Begin by finding antiderivative for $\dfrac{\sin x \cos x}{\sqrt{1 + \sin^2 x}}$.

Try the substitution

$$u = 1 + \sin^2 x$$

since this expression is underneath the radical sign.

Determine du.

Solution

Since this is a definite integral, we first find the antiderivative

$$\int \frac{\sin x \cos x}{\sqrt{1 + \sin^2 x}}.$$

To do so, we begin by making a substitution for the expression under the radical sign. We let

$$u = 1 + \sin^2 x.$$

Then

$$du = \left[\frac{d}{dx} (1 + \sin^2 x) \right] dx = 2 \sin x \cos x \, dx.$$

Thus the factor $\sin x \cos x \, dx$ in the integrand is just $\dfrac{1}{2} \, du$, and we obtain

Make the substitution.

$$\int \frac{\sin x \cos x \, dx}{\sqrt{1 + \sin^2 x}} = \int \frac{\frac{1}{2} du}{\sqrt{u}}$$

Find the antiderivative using the Power Rule. Substitute back in terms of x.

$$= \int \frac{1}{2} u^{-1/2} \, du$$

$$= u^{1/2} + C$$

$$= \sqrt{1 + \sin^2 x} + C.$$

The definite integral may therefore be evaluated as follows:

Evaluate definite integral using the Fundamental Theorem of Calculus.

$$\int_0^{\pi/2} \frac{\sin x \cos x \, dx}{\sqrt{1 + \sin^2 x}} = \left[\sqrt{1 + \sin^2 x} \right]_0^{\pi/2}$$

$$= \sqrt{1 + 1^2} - \sqrt{1 + 0^2}$$

$$= \sqrt{2} - 1. \qquad \blacksquare$$

Applications of Integrals Involving sin x, cos x

Applications involving integrals of the sine and cosine functions are handled just as the applications of the definite integral that were discussed in Chapter 5. The following two examples are typical. Others appear in the exercise set.

☐ **EXAMPLE 6**

A revenue stream (interest from a bond, or rent from a building, for example) flows to the owner of an asset at a rate of

$$R(t) = 1000 + 500 \sin \pi t \qquad \text{(See Figure 4.1.)}$$

dollars per year t years after the asset is purchased. Find the total amount produced by the revenue stream during the first 6 years after the asset is purchased.

Solution: The total T produced by the revenue stream is given by the formula $T = \int_0^6 R(t) \, dt.$ (See equation (10), Section 5.7.)

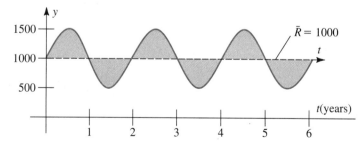

Figure 4.1 Revenue function $R(t) = 1000 + 500 \sin \pi t$ showing deviations above and below average value $\bar{R} = 1000$ on interval $[0, 6]$.

Thus

$$T = \int_0^6 (1000 + 500 \sin \pi t)\, dt$$

$$= \left[1000t - \frac{500}{\pi} \cos \pi t \right]_0^6$$

$$= \left(6000 - \frac{500}{\pi} \cos 6\pi \right) - \left(0 - \frac{500}{\pi} \cos(0) \right)$$

$$= \left(6000 - \frac{500}{\pi} \right) - \left(-\frac{500}{\pi} \right)$$

$$= 6000 \text{ dollars.}$$

REMARK: In this case the total revenue is the same as that produced by the *constant* revenue stream $R(t) \equiv 1000$ over the period $t = 0$ to $t = 6$. That is because the additional revenue flowing during the intervals $(0, 1)$, $(2, 3)$, and $(4, 5)$ is exactly offset by the shortfall that occurs in the intervals $(1, 2)$, $(3, 4)$, and $(5, 6)$. This is another way of saying that the *average value* of the revenue function $R(t) = 1000 + 500 \sin \pi t$ over the interval $[0, 6]$ is $\overline{R} = 1000$. (See Exercise 30.)

☐ **EXAMPLE 7**

Find the area of the region bounded by the graphs of $f(x) = \sin x$ and $g(x) = \cos x$ for $0 \le x \le \pi$. (See Figure 4.2.)

Strategy · · · · · · · ·
Determine where the two graphs intersect.

Solution

In calculating the area of a region bounded by two curves, we must know which curve is on top. To determine this we first determine where the curves intersect by solving the equation $f(x) = g(x)$. That is, we must find the numbers x for which

$$\sin x = \cos x, \qquad 0 \le x \le \pi.$$

Checking the values of $\sin x$ and $\cos x$ in Table 2.1, Section 7.2, we find that $x = \pi/4$ is the only such number. Since

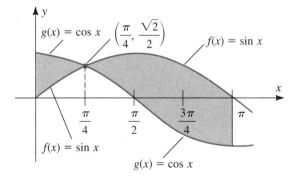

Figure 4.2 Region in Example 7.

Determine which curve is on top in each interval.

$$\cos x \geq \sin x \quad \text{for } x \text{ in } \left[0, \frac{\pi}{4}\right] \text{ and}$$

$$\sin x \geq \cos x \quad \text{for } x \text{ in } \left[\frac{\pi}{4}, \pi\right]$$

the area of the region is (see equation (4), Section 5.6)

Calculate area using formula

$$A = \int_a^b [f(x) - g(x)]\, dx$$

when $f(x) \geq g(x)$ for all x in $[a, b]$.

$$A = \int_0^{\pi/4} (\cos x - \sin x)\, dx + \int_{\pi/4}^{\pi} (\sin x - \cos x)\, dx$$

$$= \Big[\sin x + \cos x\Big]_0^{\pi/4} + \Big[-\cos x - \sin x\Big]_{\pi/4}^{\pi}$$

$$= \left[\left(\frac{\sqrt{2}}{2} + \frac{\sqrt{2}}{2}\right) - (0 + 1)\right] + \left[(-(-1) - 0) - \left(-\frac{\sqrt{2}}{2} - \frac{\sqrt{2}}{2}\right)\right]$$

$$= 2\sqrt{2}.$$

■

☑ PRACTICE PROBLEMS 6.4

1. Evaluate the definite integral $\displaystyle\int_0^{\pi/2} \frac{\sin x \cos x}{1 + \sin^2 x}\, dx$.

2. Find the area of the region bounded by the graph of $f(x) = \cos x$ and the x-axis for $0 \leq x \leq 2\pi$.

Exercise Set 6.4

In Exercises 1–22, evaluate the given integral.

1. $\displaystyle\int \cos 6x\, dx$

2. $\displaystyle\int \sin 3x\, dx$

3. $\displaystyle\int_0^{\pi} 3\sin(\pi - x)\, dx$

4. $\displaystyle\int_0^{\sqrt{\pi/2}} x \cos x^2\, dx$

5. $\displaystyle\int x^2 \sin(1 + x^3)\, dx$

6. $\displaystyle\int_0^{\pi/4} \sin^2 x \cos x\, dx$

7. $\displaystyle\int_0^{\sqrt{\pi}} t \cos(\pi - t^2)\, dt$

8. $\displaystyle\int \frac{\cos \sqrt{t}}{\sqrt{t}}\, dt$

9. $\displaystyle\int_0^{\pi} \cos^3 t \sin t\, dt$

10. $\displaystyle\int \frac{\sin x}{\cos^2 x}\, dx$

11. $\displaystyle\int \cos x \sqrt{1 - \sin x}\, dx$

12. $\displaystyle\int_0^1 \frac{\sin x}{\cos x}\, dx$

13. $\displaystyle\int \frac{\sin(3 + \ln x)}{x}\, dx$

14. $\displaystyle\int_0^1 e^x \sin(e^x)\, dx$

15. $\displaystyle\int \frac{\cos(\ln x)}{x}\, dx$

16. $\displaystyle\int \frac{\cos x}{\sin x}\, dx$

17. $\displaystyle\int_0^{\pi/2} (\sin t) e^{\cos t}\, dt$

18. $\displaystyle\int \sin t\, (\cos t) e^{\sin^2 t}\, dt$

19. $\displaystyle\int \sin^2 x\, dx \left(\textit{Hint:} \text{ Use the identity } \sin^2 x = \frac{1}{2} - \frac{1}{2}\cos 2x.\right)$

20. $\displaystyle\int \cos^2 x\, dx \left(\textit{Hint:} \text{ Use the identity } \cos^2 x = \frac{1}{2} + \frac{1}{2}\cos 2x.\right)$

21. $\displaystyle\int_0^{\sqrt{\pi/2}} x \sin^2 x^2 \cos x^2\, dx$

22. $\displaystyle\int \frac{\sin \sqrt{x} \cos \sqrt{x}}{\sqrt{x}}\, dx$

23. Find the area of the region bounded by the graph of $f(x) = \sin \pi x$ and the x-axis between $x = 0$ and $x = 1$.

24. Find the total amount of money produced by a revenue stream yielding $R(t) = 1000 + 400\cos 2\pi t$ dollars per year between $t = 0$ and $t = 4$ years.

25. Find the average value of the function $f(t) = \cos \pi t$ on the interval $[0, 1]$.

26. Find the area of the region bounded by the graphs of $f(x) = x$ and $g(x) = \sin x$ for $0 \le x \le \pi$.

27. Find the area of the region bounded by the graphs of $f(x) = \cos\left(\dfrac{1}{2}x\right)$ and $g(x) = \dfrac{1}{2}x - \dfrac{\pi}{2}$ for $0 \le x \le \pi$.

28. Find the volume of the solid obtained by revolving about the x-axis the region bounded above by the graph of $y = \sin x$ and below by the x-axis for $0 \le x \le \pi$. (See Exercise 19.)

29. Find the volume of the solid obtained by revolving about the x-axis the region bounded above by the graph of $y = \cos x$ and below by the x-axis for $0 \le x \le \pi/2$. (See Exercise 20.)

30. Find the average value of the revenue function $R(x) = 1000 + 500 \sin \pi t$ on the interval $[0, 6]$.

31. An envelope company predicts that its annual profits will follow the model

$$P(t) = 40 + 60 \sin \pi t$$

for $0 \le t \le 10$ where P is in thousands of dollars and t is in years.

a. What is the total profit expected over the ten-year period?
b. What is the average profit per year for the ten-year period, as predicted by this model?

32. What is the average profit per year for the first five years, $0 \le t \le 5$, for the company in Exercise 31? Explain why this is different than the average profit over ten years.

33. A growth company's annual earnings are projected to follow the model

$$P(t) = 100 + 5t + 200 \cos \pi\left(\frac{t-5}{5}\right)$$

for the next decade, $0 \le t \le 10$, where P is in thousands. According to this model,

a. What is the rate of profit at time $t = 0$? What does this mean?
b. What total earnings are projected for the decade, $0 \le t \le 10$?

34. Find the number c so that the region bounded by the graph of the function

$$f(x) = x \sin cx^2$$

for $0 < x < \dfrac{\sqrt{\pi}}{c}$ has area equal to 10.

☑ **SOLUTIONS TO PRACTICE PROBLEMS 6.4**

1. In $\displaystyle\int_0^{\pi/2} \frac{\sin x \cos x}{1 + \sin^2 x}\, dx,$ we let $u = 1 + \sin^2 x.$ Then $du = 2 \sin x \cos x\, dx$ so $\sin x \cos x\, dx = \dfrac{1}{2} du.$ Thus,

$$\int \frac{\sin x \cos x}{1 + \sin^2 x}\, dx = \int \frac{1}{u}\left(\frac{1}{2}\right) du = \frac{1}{2}\int \frac{1}{u}\, du$$

$$= \frac{1}{2} \ln |u| + C.$$

Returning to the definite integral, we have

$$\int_0^{\pi/2} \frac{\sin x \cos x}{1 + \sin^2 x}\, dx = \left[\frac{1}{2}\ln(1 + \sin^2 x)\right]_0^{\pi/2}$$

$$= \frac{1}{2} \ln(1 + 1) - \frac{1}{2} \ln(1 + 0)$$

$$= \frac{1}{2} \ln 2.$$

2. Since $\cos x \ge 0$ for $0 \le x \le \dfrac{\pi}{2}$ and for $\dfrac{3\pi}{2} \le x \le 2\pi,$ we have

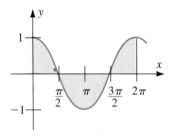

$$\text{Area} = \int_0^{\pi/2} \cos x \, dx - \int_{\pi/2}^{3\pi/2} \cos x \, dx + \int_{3\pi/2}^{2\pi} \cos x \, dx$$

$$= [\sin x]_0^{\pi/2} - [\sin x]_{\pi/2}^{3\pi/2} + [\sin x]_{3\pi/2}^{2\pi}$$

$$= (1 - 0) - ((-1) - 1) + (0 - (-1))$$

$$= 4.$$

(See Figure 4.3.)

Figure 4.3 Region bounded by $f(x) = \cos x$ and x-axis for $0 \le x \le 2\pi$.

6.5 Other Trigonometric Functions

For a given right triangle containing the angle θ the numbers $\sin \theta$ and $\cos \theta$ are only two of six possible ratios of lengths of sides. In this section we describe how each of the remaining four ratios defines a trigonometric function, and how these functions are related to the sine and cosine functions.

Figure 5.1 shows a rocket that has been launched vertically x yards from a camera that is inclined at an angle θ from the horizontal. If we let y represent the altitude at which the rocket will be sighted by the camera, we have described a right triangle with angle θ for which the side opposite the angle θ has length y and the side adjacent to θ has length x. The **tangent** of this angle θ, denoted by $\tan \theta$, is the ratio

$$\tan \theta = \frac{y}{x}. \qquad \left(\frac{\text{opposite}}{\text{adjacent}}\right) \tag{1}$$

Figures 5.2–5.4 show familiar $30°$–$60°$–$90°$ and $45°$–$45°$–$90°$ right triangles and the facts that

$$\tan \frac{\pi}{6} = \frac{1}{\sqrt{3}}, \qquad \tan \frac{\pi}{3} = \sqrt{3}, \qquad \text{and} \qquad \tan \frac{\pi}{4} = 1$$

each of which follows from equation (1).

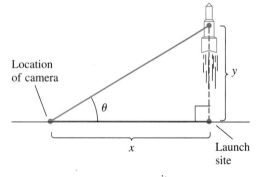

Location of camera

θ

x

Launch site

Figure 5.1 $\tan \theta = \dfrac{y}{x} = \dfrac{\text{opposite}}{\text{adjacent}}$.

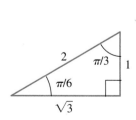

Figure 5.2 $\tan \dfrac{\pi}{6} = \dfrac{1}{\sqrt{3}}$.

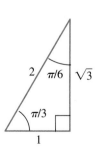

Figure 5.3 $\tan \dfrac{\pi}{3} = \sqrt{3}$.

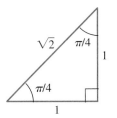

Figure 5.4 $\tan \dfrac{\pi}{4} = 1$.

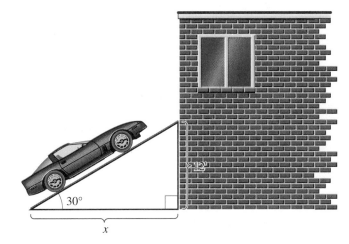

Figure 5.5 $\tan \dfrac{\pi}{6} = \dfrac{12}{x}$.

Values of tan θ for other angles appear in the table of trigonometric functions in Table 3 of Appendix II. The tangent function is useful when two of the numbers x, y, and tan θ in equation (1) are known and we desire to calculate the third.

□ **EXAMPLE 1**

An architect wishes to design a ramp inclined at 30° leading from the ground level to a second-story door in a parking garage. How far from the building must the ramp begin if the bottom of the door is 12 feet above ground level? (See Figure 5.5.)

Solution: From Figure 5.5 we can see that the ramp, the ground level, and the building wall form a right triangle with base angle = $30° = \dfrac{\pi}{6}$, with opposite side of length 12 feet, and with adjacent side of length x feet. From equation (1) we have

$$\tan \frac{\pi}{6} = \frac{12}{x}. \tag{2}$$

Since $\tan \dfrac{\pi}{6} = \dfrac{1}{\sqrt{3}}$ (Figure 5.2) equation (2) becomes

$$\frac{1}{\sqrt{3}} = \frac{12}{x}.$$

Thus $x = 12\sqrt{3}$ feet ≈ 20.8 feet. ∎

Other Trigonometric Functions

When θ is an angle of a right triangle with opposite side of length y, adjacent side of length x, and hypotenuse of length h, three other trigonometric functions of θ may be defined: the **cotangent** of θ, written cot θ, the **secant** of θ, written sec θ, and the

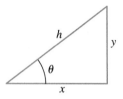

Figure 5.6

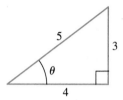

Figure 5.7

cosecant of θ, written csc θ, as follows:

$$\cot \theta = \frac{x}{y} \left(\frac{\text{adjacent}}{\text{opposite}} \right)$$

$$\sec \theta = \frac{h}{x} \left(\frac{\text{hypotenuse}}{\text{adjacent}} \right)$$

$$\csc \theta = \frac{h}{y} \left(\frac{\text{hypotenuse}}{\text{opposite}} \right)$$

(See Figure 5.6.)

□ **EXAMPLE 2**

For the right triangle in Figure 5.7, we have

$$\tan \theta = \frac{3}{4} \qquad \sec \theta = \frac{5}{4}$$

$$\cot \theta = \frac{4}{3} \qquad \csc \theta = \frac{5}{3}. \qquad ■$$

Since the sine and cosine of the angle θ in Figure 5.6 may be expressed as $\sin \theta = \dfrac{y}{h}$ and $\cos \theta = \dfrac{x}{h}$, we may express the other four trigonometric functions in terms of $\sin \theta$ and $\cos \theta$ as follows:

$$\tan \theta = \frac{\sin \theta}{\cos \theta} \qquad \left(\text{since } \frac{y/h}{x/h} = \frac{y}{x} \right) \qquad (3)$$

$$\cot \theta = \frac{\cos \theta}{\sin \theta} \qquad \left(\text{since } \frac{x/h}{y/h} = \frac{x}{y} \right) \qquad (4)$$

$$\sec \theta = \frac{1}{\cos \theta} \qquad \left(\text{since } \frac{1}{x/h} = \frac{h}{x} \right) \qquad (5)$$

and

$$\csc \theta = \frac{1}{\sin \theta} \qquad \left(\text{since } \frac{1}{y/h} = \frac{h}{y} \right). \qquad (6)$$

The advantage of using equations (3)–(6) to define these four trigonometric functions is that the right-hand sides of these equations are defined for all numbers θ for which the denominators are not zero. This allows us to use periodicity to define the function $f(x) = \tan x$ for all numbers x in $(-\infty, \infty)$ for which $\cos x \neq 0$ $\left(\text{that is, for all } x \text{ except } x = \pm \dfrac{\pi}{2}, \pm \dfrac{3\pi}{2}, \ldots \right)$, and similarly for the functions $\cot x$, $\sec x$, and $\csc x$.

Graphs of these four functions appear in Figures 5.8–5.11.

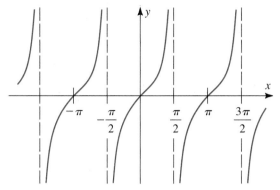

Figure 5.8 Graph of $y = \tan x$.

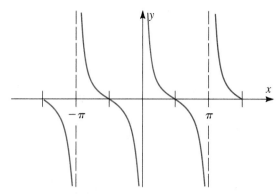

Figure 5.9 Graph of $y = \cot x$.

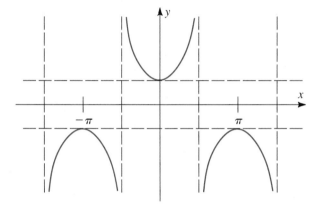

Figure 5.10 Graph of $y = \sec x$.

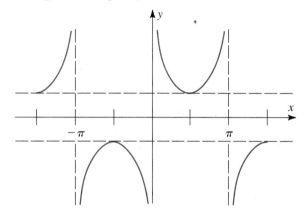

Figure 5.11 Graph of $y = \csc x$.

□ **EXAMPLE 3**

According to equations (3)–(6), we have

(a) $\tan\left(\dfrac{7\pi}{4}\right) = \dfrac{\sin\left(\dfrac{7\pi}{4}\right)}{\cos\left(\dfrac{7\pi}{4}\right)} = \dfrac{\left(-\dfrac{\sqrt{2}}{2}\right)}{\left(\dfrac{\sqrt{2}}{2}\right)} = -1$

(b) $\cot\left(-\dfrac{\pi}{2}\right) = \dfrac{\cos\left(-\dfrac{\pi}{2}\right)}{\sin\left(-\dfrac{\pi}{2}\right)} = \dfrac{0}{-1} = 0$

(c) $\sec(5\pi) = \dfrac{1}{\cos(5\pi)} = \dfrac{1}{-1} = -1$

(d) $\csc\left(-\dfrac{3\pi}{4}\right) = \dfrac{1}{\sin\left(-\dfrac{3\pi}{4}\right)} = \dfrac{1}{\left(-\dfrac{\sqrt{2}}{2}\right)} = -\dfrac{2}{\sqrt{2}}.$ ■

Since the four functions $\tan x$, $\cot x$, $\sec x$, and $\csc x$ are defined as quotients involving $\sin x$ and $\cos x$, their derivatives can be found by using the quotient rule. For example, the derivative of the function $y = \tan x$ is

$$\frac{d}{dx}\tan x = \frac{d}{dx}\left(\frac{\sin x}{\cos x}\right)$$

$$= \frac{\cos x\left(\dfrac{d}{dx}\sin x\right) - \sin x\left(\dfrac{d}{dx}\cos x\right)}{\cos^2 x}$$

$$= \frac{\cos x(\cos x) - \sin x(-\sin x)}{\cos^2 x}$$

$$= \frac{\cos^2 x + \sin^2 x}{\cos^2 x}$$

$$= \frac{1}{\cos^2 x} \qquad (\text{since } \cos^2 x + \sin^2 x = 1)$$

$$= \sec^2 x \qquad \left(\text{since } \frac{1}{\cos x} = \sec x, \ \cos x \neq 0\right).$$

That is

$$\frac{d}{dx}\tan x = \sec^2 x \tag{7}$$

In Exercise 45 you are asked to use the same technique to establish the following additional differentiation formulas.

$$\frac{d}{dx}\cot x = -\csc^2 x \tag{8}$$

$$\frac{d}{dx}\sec x = \sec x \tan x \tag{9}$$

$$\frac{d}{dx}\csc x = -\csc x \cot x. \tag{10}$$

☐ **EXAMPLE 4**

Find $f'(x)$ for $f(x) = x \sec x$.

Strategy · · · · · · ·
Recognize f as a product $g(x)h(x)$ with $g(x) = x$ and $h(x) = \sec x$. Apply Product Rule and formula (9).

Solution

By the Product Rule and formula (9) we have

$$f'(x) = \left(\frac{d}{dx}x\right)\sec x + x\left(\frac{d}{dx}\sec x\right)$$

$$= (1)\sec x + x(\sec x \tan x)$$

$$= \sec x(1 + x \tan x). \qquad \blacksquare$$

□ **EXAMPLE 5**

Find $f'(x)$ for $f(x) = \ln \tan x$.

Strategy · · · · · · ·
Recognize f as $f(x) = \ln u$ with $u = \tan x$.
Apply Chain Rule

and formula (7).

Simplify result by expressing $\tan x$ and $\sec x$ in terms of $\sin x$ and $\cos x$.

Solution

Since $f(x) = \ln \tan x$ is a composite function, the Chain Rule and equation (7) give

$$f'(x) = \frac{1}{\tan x} \cdot \frac{d}{dx}\tan x$$

$$= \left(\frac{1}{\tan x}\right)\sec^2 x$$

$$= \left(\frac{\cos x}{\sin x}\right)\left(\frac{1}{\cos x}\right)^2$$

$$= \left(\frac{1}{\sin x}\right)\left(\frac{1}{\cos x}\right)$$

$$= \sec x \cdot \csc x. \qquad \blacksquare$$

REMARK: It is often easiest to simplify a complicated product of trigonometric functions by first expressing all of them in terms of the sine and cosine, as was done in Example 5.

Integrals

Differentiation formulas (7)–(10) immediately give the following integration formulas.

$$\int \sec^2 x\, dx = \tan x + C \qquad (11)$$

$$\int \csc^2 x\, dx = -\cot x + C \qquad (12)$$

$$\int \sec x \tan x\, dx = \sec x + C \qquad (13)$$

$$\int \csc x \cot x\, dx = -\csc x + C. \qquad (14)$$

In addition, the following integration formulas can be verified by differentiation.

$$\int \tan x \, dx = \ln |\sec x| + C \tag{15}$$

$$\int \cot x \, dx = \ln |\sin x| + C \tag{16}$$

$$\int \sec x \, dx = \ln |\sec x + \tan x| + C \tag{17}$$

$$\int \csc x \, dx = \ln |\csc x - \cot x| + C. \tag{18}$$

☐ **EXAMPLE 6**

Verify integration formula (15):

$$\int \tan x \, dx = \ln |\sec x| + C.$$

Solution: Because of the absolute value sign, we must examine the two cases $\sec x > 0$ and $\sec x < 0$ separately.

(a) If $\sec x > 0$, then $|\sec x| = \sec x$, and

$$\frac{d}{dx} \ln \sec x = \frac{1}{\sec x} \cdot \frac{d}{dx} \sec x$$

$$= \frac{1}{\sec x} (\sec x \tan x)$$

$$= \tan x.$$

(b) If $\sec x < 0$, then $|\sec x| = -\sec x > 0$, and

$$\frac{d}{dx} \ln |\sec x| = \frac{d}{dx} \ln(-\sec x)$$

$$= \frac{1}{(-\sec x)} \frac{d}{dx} (-\sec x)$$

$$= \frac{1}{(-\sec x)} (-\sec x \tan x)$$

$$= \tan x.$$

Thus in either case formula (15) holds. ■

□ **EXAMPLE 7**

Find $\displaystyle\int_0^{\pi/4} \sec x \, dx.$

Solution: Using formula (17), we find that

$$\int_0^{\pi/4} \sec x \, dx = \ln |\sec x + \tan x|\Big|_0^{\pi/4}$$

$$= \ln \left|\sec\left(\frac{\pi}{4}\right) + \tan\left(\frac{\pi}{4}\right)\right| - \ln |\sec(0) + \tan(0)|$$

$$= \ln|\sqrt{2} + 1| - \ln |1 + 0|$$

$$= \ln(\sqrt{2} + 1).$$

REMARK: When working with the four trigonometric functions $\tan x$, $\cot x$, $\sec x$, and $\csc x$, we should note that these functions are not defined for all x, as are the functions $\sin x$ and $\cos x$. It is particularly important in calculations involving definite integrals of these functions to ensure that the integrands are defined for all x involved in the integration. For example, $\displaystyle\int_0^{\pi} \tan x \, dx$ is not defined, since $\tan x$ is undefined for $x = \dfrac{\pi}{2}$, which lies in the interval $[0, \pi]$.

☑ **PRACTICE PROBLEMS 6.5**

1. Find the values.

   a. $\tan\left(\dfrac{5\pi}{4}\right)$ **b.** $\sec\left(\dfrac{5\pi}{3}\right)$ **c.** $\csc\left(\dfrac{3\pi}{2}\right)$

2. Find the derivatives.

   a. $f(x) = \tan \sqrt{x}$ **b.** $f(x) = e^{\sec x}$

3. Find the integrals.

   a. $\displaystyle\int x \sec^2 x^2 \tan x^2 \, dx$ **b.** $\displaystyle\int \frac{\cot \sqrt{x} \csc \sqrt{x}}{\sqrt{x}} \, dx$

Exercise Set 6.5

In Exercises 1–4, find (a) $\tan \theta$, (b) $\cot \theta$, (c) $\sec \theta$, and (d) $\csc \theta$ for the given triangle and angle.

1.

2.

3.

4.

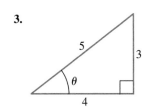

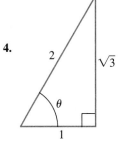

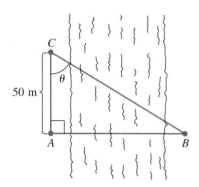

C

θ

50 m

A

B

Figure 5.12

5. Figure 5.12 shows two points A and B on opposite sides of a straight river bed. A third point C is located 50 meters from point A as indicated in Figure 5.12. A is directly opposite point B. What is the distance between points A and B if $\theta = \dfrac{\pi}{6}$?

6. What is the answer to the question in Exercise 5 if $\theta = \dfrac{\pi}{3}$?

7. A child stands 30 meters from a point directly below the location of an airplane. If the angle between ground level and the child's line of sight to the airplane is $30°$, what is the altitude of the airplane? (Neglect the child's height.)

In Exercises 8–23, find the derivative of the given function.

8. $y = \tan 2\pi x$

9. $f(x) = x^2 \sec x$

10. $f(x) = \sec(x + \pi/6)$

11. $y = \cot^3 6x$

12. $y = e^x \sec^3 x$

13. $f(x) = \sec x \cdot \tan x$

14. $f(x) = \ln \sec x$

15. $y = \dfrac{x}{\sec x}$

16. $f(x) = \sqrt{1 + \sec^2 x}$

17. $f(x) = \cot^2 3x$

18. $y = x^3 \csc(1 - x)$

19. $y = \tan x^3$

20. $f(x) = \dfrac{\tan(x + \pi)}{x}$

21. $f(x) = \sec \sqrt{1 + x^2}$

22. $y = e^{\sec^2 \pi x}$

23. $f(x) = \cot \ln \sqrt{x}$

In Exercises 24–35, find the integral.

24. $\displaystyle\int \cot 2x \, dx$

25. $\displaystyle\int_0^{\pi/16} \sec^2 4x \, dx$

26. $\displaystyle\int_0^{\pi/4} 3 \sec^3 x \tan x \, dx$

27. $\displaystyle\int x \sec^2 x^2 \, dx$

28. $\displaystyle\int \tan \pi x \, dx$

29. $\displaystyle\int_0^{\pi/4} \sec^2(\pi + x) \, dx$

30. $\displaystyle\int \dfrac{\sec^2 \sqrt{x}}{\sqrt{x}} \, dx$

31. $\displaystyle\int (x - \csc^2 x) \, dx$

32. $\displaystyle\int_0^{\pi/\sqrt{2}} x \tan(\pi - x^2) \, dx$

33. $\displaystyle\int \csc^3(\pi x)\cot(\pi x) \, dx$

34. $\displaystyle\int \dfrac{\sec \sqrt{2x + 1}}{\sqrt{2x + 1}} \, dx$

35. $\displaystyle\int (\csc^2 \pi x - \cot \pi x) \, dx$

36. Find the area of the region bounded by the graph of $y = \tan x$ and the x-axis for $0 \le x \le \dfrac{\pi}{4}$.

37. Find the average value of the function $f(x) = \sec^2 x$ for $-\dfrac{\pi}{4} < x < \dfrac{\pi}{4}$.

38. Does the graph of the tangent function, $y = \tan x$, have a relative maximum or minimum on the interval $\left(-\dfrac{\pi}{2}, \dfrac{\pi}{2}\right)$? Where, or why not?

39. Determine the concavity of the graph of $y = \tan x \sin x$ for $-\dfrac{\pi}{2} < x < \dfrac{\pi}{2}$.

40. Find the area of the region bounded by the graphs of $y = \tan x$ and $y = \dfrac{4}{\pi} x$. $\left(\textit{Hint:}\ \text{Superimpose the graph of } y = \dfrac{4}{\pi} x \text{ on the graph of } y = \tan x \text{ to identify the region.}\right)$

41. Find the volume of the solid obtained by revolving about the x-axis the region bounded above by the graph of $y = \sec x$ and below by the x-axis for $-\dfrac{\pi}{4} \le x \le \dfrac{\pi}{4}$.

42. Find the volume of the solid obtained by revolving about the x-axis the region bounded above by the graph of $y = \csc x$ and below by the x-axis for $\dfrac{\pi}{4} \le x \le \dfrac{3\pi}{4}$.

43. Find the average value of the function $y = \sec x$ on the interval $\left[0, \dfrac{\pi}{4}\right]$.

44. What are the vertical asymptotes for the graph of $y = \tan x$? Why?

45. Verify differentiation formulas (8)–(10).

46. Verify integration formulas (16)–(18).

☑ SOLUTIONS TO PRACTICE PROBLEMS 6.5

1. a. $\tan\left(\dfrac{5\pi}{4}\right) = 1$

   b. $\sec\dfrac{5\pi}{3} = 2$

   c. $\csc\left(\dfrac{3\pi}{2}\right) = -1$

2. a. $f'(x) = (\sec^2\sqrt{x})\left(\dfrac{1}{2\sqrt{x}}\right)$

   b. $f'(x) = e^{\sec x}(\sec x \cdot \tan x)$

3. a. Let $u = \tan x^2$. Then $du = \sec^2 x^2 \cdot 2x\,dx$ and $x\sec^2 x^2 = \dfrac{1}{2}\,du$. Then,

$$\int x\sec^2 x^2 \cdot \tan x^2\,dx = \int u\left(\frac{1}{2}\,du\right) = \frac{1}{2}\int u\,du$$

$$= \frac{1}{4}u^2 + C$$

$$= \frac{1}{4}\tan^2 x^2 + C.$$

   b. Let $u = \sqrt{x}$; then $du = \dfrac{1}{2\sqrt{x}}\,dx$ and $\dfrac{1}{\sqrt{x}}\,dx = 2\,du$. Then,

$$\int \frac{\cot\sqrt{x}\,\csc\sqrt{x}}{\sqrt{x}}\,dx = 2\int \cot u \cdot \csc u \cdot du$$

$$= -2\csc u + C$$

$$= -2\csc\sqrt{x} + C.$$

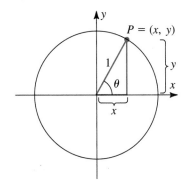

Figure 6.1

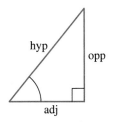

Figure 6.2

Summary Outline of Chapter 6

■ Angles are measured in **radians** and **degrees:**   (Page 448)

$$2\pi \text{ radians} = 360°.$$

■ If $P = (x, y)$ is a point on the unit circle corresponding to an angle θ (Page 455) (see Figure 6.1), then

$$\sin\theta = y \quad \text{and} \quad \cos\theta = x.$$

■ If opp, adj, and hyp are the lengths of the sides of a right triangle   (Page 462) containing the angle θ, as in Figure 6.2, then

$$\sin\theta = \frac{\text{opp}}{\text{hyp}} \quad \text{and} \quad \cos\theta = \frac{\text{adj}}{\text{hyp}}.$$

■ Identities involving $\sin\theta$ and $\cos\theta$:   (Page 464)

$$\left.\begin{cases}\sin(\theta + 2n\pi) = \sin\theta \\ \cos(\theta + 2n\pi) = \cos\theta\end{cases}\right\}$$ Extending definitions of $\sin\theta$, $\cos\theta$ to all numbers θ.

$$\sin^2 \theta + \cos^2 \theta = 1$$

$$\sin^2 \theta = \frac{1}{2}(1 - \cos 2\theta)$$

$$\cos^2 \theta = \frac{1}{2}(1 + \cos 2\theta).$$

▌ Derivatives of sine and cosine functions: (Page 468)

$$\frac{d}{dx} \sin u = \cos u \cdot \frac{du}{dx}$$

$$\frac{d}{dx} \cos u = -\sin u \cdot \frac{du}{dx}.$$

▌ Integrals of sine and cosine functions: (Page 479)

$$\int \sin u \, du = -\cos u + C$$

$$\int \cos u \, du = \sin u + C.$$

▌ Four additional trigonometric functions are defined as follows: (Page 486)

$$\tan \theta = \frac{\sin \theta}{\cos \theta} = \frac{\text{opp}}{\text{adj}} \qquad \sec \theta = \frac{1}{\cos \theta} = \frac{\text{hyp}}{\text{adj}}$$

$$\cot \theta = \frac{\cos \theta}{\sin \theta} = \frac{\text{adj}}{\text{opp}} \qquad \csc \theta = \frac{1}{\sin \theta} = \frac{\text{hyp}}{\text{opp}}.$$

(See Figure 6.2.)

▌ Derivatives of these four functions are (Page 490)

$$\frac{d}{dx} \tan x = \sec^2 x \qquad \frac{d}{dx} \sec x = \sec x \tan x$$

$$\frac{d}{dx} \cot x = -\csc^2 x \qquad \frac{d}{dx} \csc x = -\csc x \cot x.$$

▌ Integrals involving these four functions are (Page 491)

$$\int \sec^2 x \, dx = \tan x + C$$

$$\int \sec x \tan x \, dx = \sec x + C$$

$$\int \csc^2 x \, dx = -\cot x + C$$

$$\int \csc x \cot x \, dx = -\csc x + C$$

$$\int \tan x \, dx = \ln |\sec x| + C$$

$$\int \cot x \, dx = \ln |\sin x| + C$$

$$\int \sec x \, dx = \ln |\sec x + \tan x| + C$$

$$\int \csc x \, dx = \ln |\csc x - \cot x| + C.$$

Review Exercises—Chapter 6

1. Convert the following degree measures to radian measures.
   a. $60°$ **b.** $35°$ **c.** $120°$
   d. $210°$ **e.** $10°$ **f.** $75°$

2. Convert the following radian measures to degree measures.
   a. $\dfrac{\pi}{4}$ **b.** $\dfrac{3\pi}{4}$ **c.** $\dfrac{5\pi}{4}$
   d. $\dfrac{3\pi}{2}$ **e.** $\dfrac{7\pi}{6}$ **f.** $\dfrac{17\pi}{12}$

3. Find the principal angle equivalent, in radians, for each of the following.
   a. $-\dfrac{\pi}{2}$ **b.** $\dfrac{7\pi}{2}$ **c.** $\dfrac{11\pi}{4}$
   d. $-\dfrac{5\pi}{3}$ **e.** -7π **f.** 9π

4. Find the following values of the sine and cosine functions.
   a. $\sin \dfrac{5\pi}{6}$ **b.** $\cos\left(-\dfrac{3\pi}{2}\right)$ **c.** $\sin \dfrac{9\pi}{2}$
   d. $\cos \dfrac{11\pi}{3}$ **e.** $\sin\left(-\dfrac{5\pi}{3}\right)$ **f.** $\sin(8\pi)$
   g. $\cos \dfrac{7\pi}{2}$ **h.** $\cos 3\pi$ **i.** $\sin\left(-\dfrac{11\pi}{6}\right)$

In Exercises 5–20, find the derivative.

5. $y = \sin(\pi - x)$

6. $f(x) = \pi x \cos 3x$

7. $f(x) = \tan 3x$

8. $y = \sin \sqrt{x}$

9. $y = \cos(\pi \sin x)$

10. $f(x) = \dfrac{x}{\cos x}$

11. $y = \ln \tan^2 x$

12. $y = \sqrt{1 + \cos^2 x}$

13. $f(x) = e^{\sec \pi x}$

14. $f(x) = \dfrac{\cos x}{\tan x}$

$y = (x + \sec x)^3$

16. $y = (\cos x - \cot x)^2$

17. $f(x) = \dfrac{e^{\cos x}}{1 + \sin^2 x}$

18. $f(x) = \tan e^x$

19. $y = \ln \sqrt{4 + \cos x}$

20. $f(x) = \sec x - \tan 2x$

In Exercises 21–36, find the integral.

21. $\displaystyle\int \sin 4x \, dx$

22. $\displaystyle\int x \cos \pi x^2 \, dx$

23. $\displaystyle\int \sec \pi x \tan \pi x \, dx$

24. $\displaystyle\int \sec^2 x \tan x \, dx$

25. $\displaystyle\int \sqrt{\tan x} \sec^2 x \, dx$

26. $\displaystyle\int \dfrac{dx}{\tan x \cos^2 x}$

27. $\displaystyle\int \sec^2(3x) e^{\tan 3x} \, dx$

28. $\displaystyle\int \dfrac{\sec^2 \sqrt{x}}{\sqrt{x}} \, dx$

29. $\displaystyle\int x \cos^{10}(x^2) \sin x^2 \, dx$

30. $\displaystyle\int \sin x \sqrt{1 + \cos x} \, dx$

31. $\displaystyle\int_0^{\pi/4} \cos\left(x + \dfrac{\pi}{2}\right) dx$

32. $\displaystyle\int_{-\pi/4}^{\pi/4} \sec^2 x \, dx$

33. $\displaystyle\int_0^{\pi/4} \sec x \tan x e^{\sec x} \, dx$

34. $\displaystyle\int_{\pi/4}^{\pi/2} x \csc^2 x^2 \, dx$

35. $\displaystyle\int_0^1 \sin \pi x \cos \pi x \, dx$

36. $\displaystyle\int_0^{\pi/4} \dfrac{\sec^2 x}{1 + \tan x} \, dx$

37. A predator–prey model is one consisting of two species, say, x's and y's (foxes and rabbits, for example), where the x's prey on the y's for food. A typical solution to a predator–prey model involves functions $x(t)$ and $y(t)$, representing the size of the two populations as functions of time, of the form

$$x(t) = 10 + 2 \sin\left(t + \dfrac{\pi}{2}\right)$$

$$y(t) = 20 + 5 \cos\left(t + \dfrac{\pi}{2}\right).$$

a. Graph these two functions on the same pair of axes.
b. Find the maximum and minimum values of $x(t)$.
c. Find the maximum and minimum values of $y(t)$.

38. A mass connected to a spring oscillates back and forth according to the function

$$x(t) = 10 \cos\left(\pi t - \frac{\pi}{4}\right)$$

where $x(t)$ is the location of the mass at time t relative to its rest position.
a. What is the location of the mass at time $t = 0$?
b. What is the velocity of the mass at time t? (*Hint:* Recall $v(t) = x'(t)$.)
c. What is the farthest the mass travels from its rest position?

39. Find the slope of the line tangent to the graph of $y = \tan x$ at the point $\left(\frac{\pi}{4}, 1\right)$.

40. Find an equation for the line tangent to the graph of $y = \sec x$ at the point $\left(\frac{\pi}{3}, 2\right)$.

41. Find the area of the region bounded by the graph of $y = x \sec x^2$ and the x-axis for $0 \le x \le \sqrt{\frac{\pi}{3}}$.

42. Find the area of the region bounded by the graph of $y = \sec x \cdot \tan x$ and the x-axis for $-\frac{\pi}{3} \le x \le \frac{\pi}{3}$.

43. Find the average value of the function $f(x) = \csc x$ for $\frac{\pi}{6} \le x \le \frac{\pi}{3}$.

44. Find the volume of the solid obtained by revolving about the x-axis the region bounded by the graph of $y = \sqrt{1 + \sin x}$ and the x-axis for $0 \le x \le \pi$.

45. Where on the interval $[0, \pi]$ is the graph of $f(x) = \sin x + \cos x$
a. concave up?
b. concave down?

46. The height of the ocean tide at Sagmore Beach is modelled by the trigonometric function

$$h(t) = 8 + 3 \cos \pi\left(\frac{t - 2}{6}\right)$$

where t is in hours after midnight and $f(t)$ is in feet.
a. What is the height of the tide at midnight?
b. What are the times of high tide?
c. What are the times of low tide?

47. A small island is inhabited by a population of hares of size

$$P(t) = 300 + 120 \sin \pi\left(\frac{2 + t}{5}\right)$$

where $P(t)$ is the number of hares and t is time in years.
a. Does the population size oscillate? Why?
b. What is the time between population maxima?
c. For $0 < t < 10$, when does the minimum population size occur?

Timber is a perpetually productive asset—properly cared for, a forest can yield timber on a continuing basis. Proceeds from the sale of such timber represents one kind of ''revenue stream''; its value can be calculated using the methods discussed in this chapter. *(Larry Lefever/Grant Heilman Photography, Inc.)*

Techniques of Integration

7.1   Review of Method of Substitutions

Much of the calculus that we have discussed involves evaluating definite integrals using the Fundamental Theorem of Calculus

$$\int_a^b f(x)\, dx = F(b) - F(a) \tag{1}$$

where $F' = f$. Both the process of evaluating the definite integral in equation (1) and finding an antiderivative (or indefinite integral) F for f are referred to as **integration.**

Up until this point all antiderivatives F have been found by recognizing the integrand f as the derivative of some known function or by using a simple substitution. The purpose of this chapter is to develop additional techniques for evaluating more general types of integrals. Before presenting these additional techniques, we

499

summarize those integration rules we have already developed and review briefly the method of substitutions.

Constants and Powers

1. $\int a \, dx = ax + C$

2. $\int x^n \, dx = \dfrac{x^{n+1}}{n+1} + C, \qquad n \neq -1$

3. $\int \dfrac{1}{x} \, dx = \ln |x| + C, \qquad x \neq 0$

Exponential Functions

4. $\int e^x \, dx = e^x + C$

5. $\int a^x \, dx = \dfrac{1}{\ln a} a^x + C, \qquad a \neq 1, \, a > 0$

Trigonometric Functions

6. $\int \sin x \, dx = -\cos x + C$

7. $\int \cos x \, dx = \sin x + C$

8. $\int \sec^2 x \, dx = \tan x + C$

9. $\int \csc^2 x \, dx = -\cot x + C$

10. $\int \sec x \cdot \tan x \, dx = \sec x + C$

11. $\int \csc x \cdot \cot x \, dx = -\csc x + C$

12. $\int \tan x \, dx = \ln |\sec x| + C$

13. $\int \cot x \, dx = \ln |\sin x| + C$

14. $\int \sec x \, dx = \ln |\sec x + \tan x| + C$

15. $\int \csc x \, dx = \ln |\csc x - \cot x| + C$

The exercise set of this section offers additional practice in the use of these integration formulas together with the technique of **substitutions.** Recall that an integral of the form

$$\int f(g(x)) \cdot g'(x) \, dx \qquad (2)$$

may be evaluated by means of the substitution

$$u = g(x); \qquad du = g'(x) \, dx.$$

We obtain

$$\int f(g(x)) \, g'(x) \, dx = \int f(u) \, du.$$

Thus the integral in line (2) can be evaluated if an antiderivative F for f can be found.

☐ **EXAMPLE 1**

Find $\displaystyle\int \cos x \cdot e^{\sin x} \, dx$.

Strategy · · · · · · ·
The key is to notice that $\cos x$ is the derivative of the exponent $\sin x$. Thus try the substitution

$$u = \sin x.$$

Solution
We make the substitution

$$u = \sin x; \qquad du = \cos x \, dx.$$

We obtain

$$\int \cos x \cdot e^{\sin x} \, dx = \int \underbrace{e^{\sin x}}_{e^u} \underbrace{\cos x \, dx}_{du}$$

Apply formula 4 from the list of integration formulas.

$$= \int e^u \, du$$

$$= e^u + C$$

Substitute back in terms of x.

$$= e^{\sin x} + C. \qquad \blacksquare$$

☐ **EXAMPLE 2**

Find $\displaystyle\int_0^1 \frac{x}{\sqrt{x^2 + 4}} \, dx$.

Strategy · · · · · · ·
To use the Fundamental Theorem, first find an antiderivative of the integrand.

Solution
First, we find $\displaystyle\int \frac{x}{\sqrt{x^2 + 4}} \, dx$.

Since the derivative of $x^2 + 4$ is $2x$, we try the substitution

$$u = x^2 + 4$$
$$du = 2x \, dx.$$

Apply formula 2 with $n = -\dfrac{1}{2}$.

We let $u = x^2 + 4$. Then $du = 2x \, dx$, so $x \, dx = \dfrac{1}{2} \, du$. We obtain

$$\int \frac{x}{\sqrt{x^2 + 4}} \, dx = \int \underbrace{(x^2 + 4)^{-1/2}}_{u^{-1/2}} \cdot \underbrace{x \, dx}_{\frac{1}{2} \, du}$$

$$= \int u^{-1/2} \cdot \frac{1}{2} \, du$$

$$= \frac{1}{2} \int u^{-1/2} \, du$$

$$= \frac{1}{2} (2u^{1/2}) + C$$

Substitute back in terms of x.

$$= \sqrt{x^2 + 4} + C.$$

Then the definite integral is

Use this antiderivative to compute the definite integral from (1).

$$\int_0^1 \frac{x}{\sqrt{x^2 + 4}} \, dx = \left[\sqrt{x^2 + 4} \right]_0^1$$

$$= \sqrt{5} - 2.$$

■

□ **EXAMPLE 3**

Find $\displaystyle\int \frac{x^2 - 3}{x^3 - 9x} \, dx$.

Solution: We try the substitution

$$u = x^3 - 9x; \qquad du = (3x^2 - 9) \, dx.$$

Then $(x^2 - 3) \, dx = \dfrac{1}{3}(3x^2 - 9) \, dx = \dfrac{1}{3} \, du$, and we obtain

$$\int \frac{x^2 - 3}{x^3 - 9x} \, dx = \int \frac{\frac{1}{3} \, du}{u}$$

$$= \frac{1}{3} \int \frac{du}{u}$$

$$= \frac{1}{3} \ln |u| + C \qquad \text{(by formula 3)}$$

$$= \frac{1}{3} \ln |x^3 - 9x| + C.$$

■

Substitution in Definite Integrals   Up to this point, when using the method of substitution in definite integrals we have used the substitution to find an antiderivative for the integrand, and then we converted this antiderivative back into the terms of the original variable before evaluating at the upper and lower limits of integration. (See, for example, Example 2.)

There is a more direct approach, which involves using the substitution to change the limits of integration, as well as the integrand, and evaluating the antiderivative directly as a function of u.

CHANGE OF LIMITS RULE: Let g' be continuous on $[a, b]$ and let f be continuous on an interval containing the values $g(x)$ for all $x \in [a, b]$. If f has an antiderivative on this interval, then

$$\int_a^b f(g(x))\, g'(x)\, dx = \int_{g(a)}^{g(b)} f(u)\, du. \qquad (3)$$

That is, if the substitution $u = g(x)$ is used to change the integrand, the same equation can be used to change the limits of integration.

Before explaining why equation (3) is true, we use it to rework Example 2.

☐ **EXAMPLE 4**

Evaluate $\displaystyle\int_0^1 \frac{x}{\sqrt{x^2 + 4}}\, dx$ using the Change of Limits Rule.

Strategy   · · · · · · · ·
Make substitution

$$u = x^2 + 4$$

in integrand.

Solve du equation for term $x\, dx$.

Change limits of integration also by the substitution

$$u = x^2 + 4.$$

Make all substitutions.

Evaluate definite integral over new limits.

Solution
As before, we change the integrand by the substitution

$$u = x^2 + 4; \qquad du = 2x\, dx.$$

Thus,

$$x\, dx = \frac{1}{2}\, du.$$

Now we also change the limits of integration:
(a) If $x = 0$, $\quad u = 0^2 + 4 = 4$.
(b) If $x = 1$, $\quad u = 1^2 + 4 = 5$.
With these substitutions, the integral becomes

$$\int_0^1 \frac{x}{\sqrt{x^2 + 4}}\, dx = \int_4^5 \frac{1}{\sqrt{u}} \left(\frac{1}{2}\right) du$$

$$= \frac{1}{2} \int_4^5 u^{-1/2}\, du$$

$$= \left[u^{1/2} \right]_4^5$$

$$= \sqrt{5} - \sqrt{4}$$

$$= \sqrt{5} - 2.$$

■

☐ **EXAMPLE 5**

Find $\int_0^{\pi/4} \tan^2 x \sec^2 x \, dx$.

Solution: Since $\sec^2 x = \dfrac{d}{dx} \tan x$, we try the substitution

$$u = \tan x; \qquad du = \sec^2 x \, dx.$$

We also change the limits of integration:

(a) If $x = 0$, $u = \tan(0) = 0$.
(b) If $x = \pi/4$, $u = \tan(\pi/4) = 1$.

Then

$$\int_0^{\pi/4} \tan^2 x \sec^2 dx = \int_0^1 u^2 \, du = \left[\frac{1}{3} u^3 \right]_0^1 = \frac{1}{3}. \qquad ■$$

Justification for Change of Limits Rule

If F is an antiderivative for f, then the composite function $F \circ g$ is an antiderivative for $(f \circ g)g'$. (Verify this using the Chain Rule.) Thus, by the Fundamental Theorem,

$$\int_a^b f(g(x)) \, g'(x) \, dx = \left[F(g(x)) \right]_a^b$$

$$= F(g(b)) - F(g(a))$$

$$= \left[F(u) \right]_{g(a)}^{g(b)}$$

$$= \int_{g(a)}^{g(b)} f(u) \, du.$$

☑ **PRACTICE PROBLEMS 7.1**

1. Find $\int \sin x \sqrt{1 + \cos x} \, dx$.

2. Find $\int_1^4 x^{1/2} \sqrt{1 + x^{3/2}} \, dx$.

Exercise Set 7.1

In Exercises 1–42, evaluate the integral using a substitution where necessary.

1. $\int \cos x \sqrt{4 + \sin x} \, dx$

2. $\int_0^2 x \sqrt{1 + x^2} \, dx$

3. $\int_3^4 (x^2 - 3) \sqrt{x^3 - 9x} \, dx$

4. $\int \dfrac{x}{1 + x} \, dx$

5. $\int_0^1 x e^{x^2} \, dx$

6. $\int_0^1 \sin \pi x \, dx$

7. $\displaystyle\int \frac{x^4}{1+x^5}\,dx$

8. $\displaystyle\int \frac{x^3}{\sqrt{1-x^4}}\,dx$

9. $\displaystyle\int \frac{e^x}{1+e^x}\,dx$

10. $\displaystyle\int \tan x \cdot \sec^2 x\,dx$

11. $\displaystyle\int_0^{\pi/4} \tan^3 x \cdot \sec^2 x\,dx$

12. $\displaystyle\int \frac{x+2}{x^2+4x+7}\,dx$

13. $\displaystyle\int (x+3)(x^2+6x+4)^3\,dx$

14. $\displaystyle\int_0^1 \frac{\cos \pi x}{4+\sin \pi x}\,dx$

15. $\displaystyle\int \sec x \tan x \cdot e^{\sec x}\,dx$

16. $\displaystyle\int x^{1/3}\sqrt{1+x^{4/3}}\,dx$

17. $\displaystyle\int_1^4 \frac{e^{\sqrt{x}}}{\sqrt{x}}\,dx$

18. $\displaystyle\int \frac{\sin x \cos x}{1+\sin^2 x}\,dx$

19. $\displaystyle\int \sin^3 x \cos x\,dx$

20. $\displaystyle\int_0^{\sqrt{\pi/2}} x \tan x^2\,dx$

21. $\displaystyle\int \frac{dx}{\cos^2 x}$

22. $\displaystyle\int \frac{\sec^2 x\,dx}{\sqrt{1+2\tan x}}$

23. $\displaystyle\int_1^2 \frac{dx}{x^2+2x+1}$

24. $\displaystyle\int_0^3 \frac{2^{\sqrt{x+1}}}{\sqrt{x+1}}\,dx$

25. $\displaystyle\int e^x \tan(1+e^x)\,dx$

26. $\displaystyle\int x \sec(\pi + x^2)\,dx$

27. $\displaystyle\int \frac{\cos x\,dx}{\sqrt{1-\sin^2 x}}$

28. $\displaystyle\int (e^x+7)^2\,dx$

29. $\displaystyle\int_e^{e^2} \frac{1}{x \ln x}\,dx$

30. $\displaystyle\int \frac{(1+2\sqrt{x})^3}{\sqrt{x}}\,dx$

31. $\displaystyle\int \frac{1}{\sqrt{x}(1+\sqrt{x})}\,dx$

32. $\displaystyle\int_1^2 \frac{x^2-3x-4}{x-4}\,dx$

33. $\displaystyle\int_3^5 x\sqrt{x^2-9}\,dx$

34. $\displaystyle\int_0^1 x(x^2+1)^4\,dx$

35. $\displaystyle\int_0^2 x\sqrt{1+x^2}\,dx$

36. $\displaystyle\int_0^2 xe^{2x^2}\,dx$

37. $\displaystyle\int_0^{\sqrt{\pi/2}} t \sin(\pi - t^2)\,dt$

38. $\displaystyle\int_0^1 x^{1/2}(1-x^{3/2})\,dx$

39. $\displaystyle\int_0^{\pi/4} \tan^3 x \sec^2 x\,dx$

40. $\displaystyle\int_0^1 \frac{2x}{3x^2+1}\,dx$

41. $\displaystyle\int_1^4 \frac{(4+\sqrt{x})^2}{\sqrt{x}}\,dx$

42. $\displaystyle\int_0^{\ln 2} e^x \sin(\pi e^x)\cos(\pi e^x)\,dx$

43. Find the area of the region bounded above by the graph of $f(x) = x \sin x^2$ and below by the x-axis between $x = 0$ and $x = \dfrac{\sqrt{\pi}}{2}$.

44. Find the volume of the solid obtained by revolving about the x-axis the region bounded by the graph of $y = \sin x$ and the x-axis between $x = 0$ and $x = \pi$. (*Hint:* Use the identity $\sin^2 x = \dfrac{1}{2} - \dfrac{1}{2}\cos 2x$.)

45. A supplier of microwave ovens determines that the selling price p at which consumers will purchase x ovens per week is given by the demand function $p = D(x) = \dfrac{20{,}000}{20+5x}$. If the supplier wishes to sell ovens at a rate of $x = 16$ per week, the corresponding selling price must, therefore, be
$$p_0 = D(x_0) = \frac{20{,}000}{20+5\cdot 16} = 200 \text{ dollars per oven. Find}$$
the consumers' surplus $\displaystyle\int_0^{16} D(x)\,dx - (16)(200)$, corresponding to this equilibrium point $(x_0, p_0) = (16, 200)$.

46. Sue operates a manufacturing company that produces plumbing fixtures. She determines that the marginal revenue corresponding to the production and sale of x faucets per day is given by the function $MR(x) = \dfrac{x}{\sqrt{9+x^2}}$. Find the increase in total daily revenues, $\displaystyle\int_4^6 MR(x)\,dx$, resulting from an increase from $x = 4$ to $x = 6$ faucets per day.

47. Terry inherits a small gas well located on his grandfather's farm. The family accountant tells Terry that he may expect a royalty (revenue) stream paying
$$R(t) = 4000 + 2000 \sin \pi t \cos \pi t$$
dollars per year for the next several years. Find the total capital formation, $\displaystyle\int_0^4 R(t)\,dt$, expected over the next four years.

48. Paula's grandmother owns an annuity that will pay her
$$A(t) = 5000 + 200t\sqrt{4+t^2}$$
dollars per year, where t is time in years. Find the integral $\displaystyle\int_0^4 A(t)\,dt$ giving the total expected amount over the first four years of the annuity.

49. Find the average value of the function $f(x) = \dfrac{x^3}{2 + x^4}$ on the interval $[0, 2]$.

50. Find the average value of the traffic flow function $q(p) = \dfrac{p}{1 + p^2}$ for $0 < p < 3$.

✓ **SOLUTIONS TO PRACTICE PROBLEMS 7.1**

1. In $\displaystyle\int \sin x \sqrt{1 + \cos x}\, dx$, let $u = \cos x$; then $du = -\sin x\, dx$ and

$$\int \sin x \sqrt{1 + \cos x}\, dx = \int (-1)\sqrt{1 + u}\, du$$

$$= -\frac{2}{3}(1 + u)^{3/2} + C$$

$$= -\frac{2}{3}(1 + \cos x)^{3/2} + C.$$

2. In $\displaystyle\int_1^4 x^{1/2}\sqrt{1 + x^{3/2}}\, dx$, let $u = x^{3/2}$; then $du = \dfrac{3}{2}x^{1/2}\, dx$, and $x^{1/2}\, dx = \dfrac{2}{3}\, du$. Also,

(a) If $x = 1$, then $u = 1^{3/2} = 1$.
(b) If $x = 4$, then $u = 4^{3/2} = 8$.

Then

$$\int_1^4 x^{1/2}(1 + x^{3/2})^{1/2}\, dx = \int_1^8 \frac{2}{3}(1 + u)^{1/2}\, du$$

$$= \left[\frac{4}{9}(1 + u)^{3/2}\right]_1^8$$

$$= \frac{4}{9}(9)^{3/2} - \frac{4}{9}(2)^{3/2}$$

$$= 12 - \frac{8\sqrt{2}}{9} \approx 10.7429.$$

7.2 Integration by Parts

The Product Rule tells us how to differentiate a product of two functions. **Integration by parts** is a method that is sometimes helpful in finding an antiderivative for the product of two functions. It says

$$\int f(x)g'(x)\, dx = f(x)g(x) - \int f'(x)g(x)\, dx. \tag{1}$$

Equation (1) is called the *integration by parts formula*. It allows us to replace the integral of a product of two functions, f and $g' = \dfrac{dg}{dx}$, by the *difference* of

(a) the product fg (involving an *integral* of the original function g'), and

(b) the integral $\displaystyle\int f'g\,dx$ (involving the *derivative* of the original function f, and an *integral* of the original function g').

The advantage in using the integration by parts formula is that the integral on the right-hand side of equation (1) is often easier to evaluate than the integral on the left. To use equation (1), we must be able to envision an integrand as the product of two functions, one called f, the other g'.

☐ **EXAMPLE 1**

Find $\displaystyle\int xe^x\,dx$.

Solution: If we choose to let

$$f(x) = x \quad \text{and} \quad g'(x) = e^x$$

it follows that

$$f'(x) = 1 \quad \text{and} \quad g(x) = e^x$$

since $g(x) = e^x$ is an antiderivative (integral) for $g'(x) = e^x$. The integration by parts formula then gives

$$\int \underbrace{x}_{f(x)}\ \underbrace{e^x}_{g'(x)}\ dx = \underbrace{x}_{f(x)}\ \underbrace{e^x}_{g(x)} - \int \underbrace{(1)}_{f'(x)}\ \underbrace{e^x}_{g(x)}\ dx$$

$$= xe^x - \int e^x\,dx$$

$$= xe^x - e^x + C.$$

Thus

$$\int xe^x\,dx = xe^x - e^x + C.$$

☐ **EXAMPLE 2**

Find $\displaystyle\int x\sqrt{x+5}\,dx$.

Strategy · · · · · · · ·

Use integration by parts. Choose

$$f(x) = x$$

since $f'(x) = 1$ is simpler than $f(x)$.

Solution

We choose

$$f(x) = x \quad \text{and} \quad g'(x) = \sqrt{x + 5} = (x + 5)^{1/2}.$$

Then

$$f'(x) = 1 \quad \text{and} \quad g(x) = \frac{2}{3}(x + 5)^{3/2}.$$

By the integration by parts formula

Apply equation (1).

$$\int \underbrace{x}_{f} \underbrace{(x + 5)^{1/2}}_{g'} dx = \underbrace{x}_{f} \cdot \underbrace{\frac{2}{3}(x + 5)^{3/2}}_{g} - \int \underbrace{1}_{f'} \cdot \underbrace{\frac{2}{3}(x + 5)^{3/2}}_{g} dx$$

$$= \frac{2}{3}x(x + 5)^{3/2} - \frac{4}{15}(x + 5)^{5/2} + C.$$

∎

REMARK 1: In applying the integration by parts formula, we often find more than one choice for which function to take as f and which for g'. In general, we try to choose these functions in such a way that the integral on the right-hand side of equation (1) is "simpler" than the one on the left. For example, in Example 1 we did not make the choice

$$f(x) = e^x, \qquad g'(x) = x$$

since we would have then had

$$f'(x) = e^x, \qquad g(x) = \frac{1}{2}x^2$$

and equation (1) would have given

$$\int xe^x dx = \frac{1}{2}x^2 e^x - \int \frac{1}{2}x^2 e^x dx. \tag{2}$$

Although equation (2) is not incorrect, it is not helpful since we have no hint as to how to evaluate the integral on its right-hand side.

REMARK 2: There is no need to include an arbitrary constant C when finding an antiderivative g for g' when using equation (1) since this equation holds for *any* antiderivative of g'. The simplest choice is therefore to let the arbitrary constant C equal zero.

We can use the notation of differentials to write equation (1) in a simpler form. Recall, if we let $u = f(x)$, we define the differential du by the equation $du = f'(x)\, dx$. Thus if we let

$$u = f(x) \quad \text{and} \quad dv = g'(x)\, dx$$

then

$$du = f'(x)\, dx \quad \text{and} \quad v = g(x)$$

and equation (1) becomes

$$\int u\, dv = uv - \int v\, du. \tag{3}$$

☐ **EXAMPLE 3**

Find $\int x \cos x\, dx$.

Strategy · · · · · · ·
Choose $u = x$, since the differential du is simply $du = dx$.

Then $dv = \cos x\, dx$, so $v = \sin x$.

Apply equation (3).

Solution
We let

$$u = x \quad \text{and} \quad dv = \cos x\, dx.$$

Then

$$du = dx \quad \text{and} \quad v = \sin x.$$

Equation (3) then gives

$$\int \underbrace{x}_{u}\ \underbrace{\cos x\, dx}_{dv} = \underbrace{x}_{u}\ \underbrace{\sin x}_{v} - \int \underbrace{\sin x}_{v}\ \underbrace{dx}_{du}$$

$$= x \sin x - (-\cos x) + C$$

$$= x \sin x + \cos x + C.$$

Often more than one application of integration by parts is required, as the following example shows.

☐ **EXAMPLE 4**

Find $\int x^2 e^{x+3}\, dx$.

Strategy · · · · · · ·
Take $u = x^2$ since differentiation reduces the exponent by one.

Find du and v.

Solution
We take

$$u = x^2, \qquad dv = e^{x+3}\, dx.$$

Then

$$du = 2x\, dx, \qquad v = e^{x+3}$$

and integration by parts gives

Apply equation (3).

$$\int x^2 e^{x+3}\, dx = x^2 e^{x+3} - \int 2x e^{x+3}\, dx$$

$$= x^2 e^{x+3} - 2 \int x e^{x+3}\, dx. \tag{4}$$

The integral on the right requires a second application of integration by parts. In

$$\int x e^{x+3}\, dx$$

In $\int x e^{x+3}\, dx$ again take $u = x$ since differentiation will give $du = dx$.

we take

$$u = x, \qquad dv = e^{x+3}\, dx.$$

Then

Find du and v.

$$du = dx, \qquad v = e^{x+3}$$

and integration by parts gives

Apply equation (3) again.

$$\int x e^{x+3}\, dx = x e^{x+3} - \int e^{x+3}\, dx$$

$$= x e^{x+3} - e^{x+3} + C_1. \tag{5}$$

Combine equations (4) and (5).

Combining equations (4) and (5), we obtain

$$\int x^2 e^{x+3}\, dx = x^2 e^{x+3} - 2[x e^{x+3} - e^{x+3} + C_1]$$

$$= (x^2 - 2x + 2)e^{x+3} + C$$

where $C = -2C_1$. (Since C_1 is an arbitrary constant, so is $C = -2C_1$, but in a simpler form.) ∎

Sometimes integration by parts can be used to evaluate an integral of the form $\int f(x)\, dx$ by taking $u = f(x)$ and $dv = dx$, as in the following example.

□ **EXAMPLE 5**

Use integration by parts to show that

$$\int \ln x\, dx = x \ln x - x + C, \qquad x > 0.$$

Solution: Since the only factor of the integrand is $f(x) = \ln x$, we take

$$u = \ln x, \qquad dv = dx.$$

Then

$$du = \frac{1}{x}\,dx, \qquad v = x$$

and equation (3) gives

$$\int \ln x \, dx = x \ln x - \int x\left(\frac{1}{x}\right) dx$$

$$= x \ln x - \int 1 \, dx$$

$$= x \ln x - x + C$$

as claimed.   ■

□ **EXAMPLE 6**

Find $\int e^x \cos x \, dx$.

Solution: This time there is no clue as to which function to take as u. We arbitrarily choose

$$u = e^x, \qquad dv = \cos x \, dx.$$

Then

$$du = e^x \, dx, \qquad v = \sin x$$

and the integration by parts formula gives

$$\int e^x \cos x \, dx = e^x \sin x - \int e^x \sin x \, dx. \tag{6}$$

Now the integral on the right-hand side of equation (6) seems no simpler than the integral on the left. However, let's try another application of the integration by parts formula in the integral $\int e^x \sin x \, dx$. Again taking $u = e^x$, we have

$$u = e^x, \qquad dv = \sin x \, dx$$

and

$$du = e^x \, dx, \qquad v = -\cos x.$$

Thus

$$\int e^x \sin x \, dx = -e^x \cos x - \int (-\cos x)e^x \, dx$$

$$= -e^x \cos x + \int e^x \cos x \, dx. \tag{7}$$

Now note that the desired integral has reappeared on the right-hand side of equation (7)! Combining equations (6) and (7) gives

$$\int e^x \cos x \, dx = e^x \sin x - \left\{ -e^x \cos x + \int e^x \cos x \, dx \right\}$$

$$= e^x(\sin x + \cos x) - \int e^x \cos x \, dx.$$

We may now add $\int e^x \cos x \, dx$ to both sides to obtain

$$2 \int e^x \cos x \, dx = e^x(\sin x + \cos x)$$

so

$$\int e^x \cos x \, dx = \frac{1}{2} e^x(\sin x + \cos x) + C. \qquad \blacksquare$$

The next example illustrates how the integration by parts formula can be applied to definite integrals.

□ **EXAMPLE 7**

Find $\displaystyle\int_1^e \sqrt{x} \ln x \, dx$.

Solution: We first find $\displaystyle\int \sqrt{x} \ln x \, dx$ by taking

$$u = \ln x, \qquad dv = \sqrt{x} \, dx = x^{1/2} \, dx.$$

Then

$$du = \frac{1}{x} \, dx, \qquad v = \frac{2}{3} x^{3/2}$$

so integration by parts gives

$$\int \sqrt{x} \ln x \, dx = \frac{2}{3} x^{3/2} \ln x - \int \frac{2}{3} x^{3/2} \left(\frac{1}{x} \right) dx$$

$$= \frac{2}{3} x^{3/2} \ln x - \frac{2}{3} \int x^{1/2} \, dx$$

$$= \frac{2}{3} x^{3/2} \ln x - \frac{4}{9} x^{3/2} + C.$$

Then by the Fundamental Theorem we have

$$\int_1^e \sqrt{x} \ln x \, dx = \left[\frac{2}{3} x^{3/2} \ln x - \frac{4}{9} x^{3/2} \right]_1^e$$

$$= \left(\frac{2}{3} e^{3/2} \ln e - \frac{4}{9} e^{3/2} \right) - \left(\frac{2}{3} \cdot 1^{3/2} \ln (1) - \frac{4}{9} \cdot 1^{3/2} \right)$$

$$= \frac{2}{3} e^{3/2} - \frac{4}{9} e^{3/2} + \frac{4}{9}$$

$$= \frac{2}{9} e^{3/2} + \frac{4}{9}.$$

☐ **EXAMPLE 8**

A parent intends to create a college education fund by depositing $1000t$ dollars per year into a savings account over the next ten years, where t represents time in years. Assuming a prevailing rate of interest of 8%, find the present value of this stream of payments, assuming that payments are made continuously at the rate of $1000t$ dollars per year.

Solution: Recall that the formula for the present value of a revenue (payment) stream producing $R(t)$ dollars at time t is

$$PV = \int_0^T R(t) e^{-rt} \, dt$$

where T is the length of the time period and r is the prevailing rate of interest. In this case $T = 10$ and $r = 0.08$, so we obtain

$$PV = \int_0^{10} (1000t) e^{-0.08t} \, dt$$

$$= (1000) \int_0^{10} t e^{-0.08t} \, dt.$$

We use integration by parts to evaluate the integral

$$\int t e^{-0.08t} \, dt$$

by taking

$$u = t; \qquad dv = e^{-0.08t dt}.$$

Then

$$du = dt; \qquad v = -12.5 e^{-0.08t}$$

and the integration by parts formula gives

$$\int te^{-0.08t}\, dt = (-12.5)te^{-0.08t} - \int (-12.5)e^{-0.08t}\, dt$$

$$= (-12.5)te^{-0.08t} - (12.5)^2 e^{-0.08t} + C$$

$$= -12.5e^{-0.08t}(t + 12.5) + C.$$

Returning to the definite integral, we now have

$$PV = (1000)[-12.5e^{-0.08t}(t + 12.5)]_0^{10}$$

$$= (1000)[(12.5)^2 - (12.5)(22.5)e^{-0.8}]$$

$$= \$29,876.00.$$

By comparison:

(a) The (nominal) sum of all payments into the account will be

$$S = \int_0^{10} 1000t\, dt = [500t^2]_0^{10} = \$50,000.00.$$

(b) The (nominal) total in the account, assuming 8% interest compounded continuously, will be

$$(\$29,876)e^{(+0.08)(10)} = \$66,490.00. \qquad \blacksquare$$

Justifying the Integration by Parts Formula

The Product Rule, applied to the product fg, gives

$$\frac{d}{dx}[f(x)g(x)] = f'(x)g(x) + f(x)g'(x).$$

Solving for the last term on the right, we obtain

$$f(x)g'(x) = \frac{d}{dx}[f(x)g(x)] - f'(x)g(x). \qquad (8)$$

Now the meaning of equation (8) is that the functions on either side of the equation are the same. Thus they must have the same indefinite integrals. That is

$$\int f(x)g'(x)\, dx = \int \left\{ \frac{d}{dx}[f(x)g(x)] \right\} dx - \int f'(x)g(x)\, dx.$$

Since

$$\int \left\{ \frac{d}{dx}[f(x)g(x)] \right\} dx = f(x)g(x) + C \qquad (9)$$

we can write*

$$\int f(x)g'(x)\,dx = f(x)g(x) - \int f'(x)g(x)\,dx$$

as claimed, since the constant C in equation (9) may be combined with the constant of integration in $\int f'(x)g(x)\,dx$.

☑ **PRACTICE PROBLEMS 7.2**

1. Find $\int x^2 \cos \pi x\,dx$.

2. A student plans to deposit $100t$ dollars into a savings account continuously, for the next five years. Find the present value of this deposit stream, assuming a prevailing rate of interest of 6%. What will be the account total in five years under these assumptions?

Exercise Set 7.2

In Exercises 1–22, evaluate the given integral.

1. $\int xe^{-x}\,dx$

2. $\int (x-4)e^x\,dx$

3. $\int x \ln x\,dx$.

4. $\int_1^e x^2 \ln x\,dx$

5. $\int_0^3 x\sqrt{x+1}\,dx$

6. $\int \dfrac{x}{\sqrt{x+4}}\,dx$

7. $\int x \sin x\,dx$

8. $\int x^2 \cos x\,dx$

9. $\int x(2x+1)^5\,dx$

10. $\int x \ln x^2\,dx$

11. $\int x^2 e^x\,dx$

12. $\int x^3 \ln x\,dx$

13. $\int_0^{\pi/4} x \sec^2 x\,dx$

14. $\int_0^{\pi/4} x \sec x \tan x\,dx$

15. $\int_0^1 x^2 e^{-x}\,dx$

16. $\int_1^e (\ln x)^2\,dx$

17. $\int_0^1 \dfrac{x^3}{\sqrt{1+x^2}}\,dx$

18. $\int x^3\sqrt{1+x^2}\,dx$

19. $\int e^{2x} \cos x\,dx$

20. $\int \sin (\ln x)\,dx$

21. $\int x^3 e^{-x^2}\,dx$

22. $\int_0^4 e^{\sqrt{x}}\,dx$

23. Find the area of the region bounded by the graphs of $y = \ln(1+x)$, $y = x$, and $x = 1$.

24. Find the volume of the solid obtained by revolving about the x-axis the region bounded by the graph of $y = \ln x$ and the x-axis for $1 \le x \le e$.

25. A high technology company agrees to support a public service project of students at a local college by contributing amounts equivalent to $1000t$ dollars per year, contributed continuously over the next five years. Assume a nominal rate of interest of $r = 10\%$ compounded continuously.
    a. Find the present value of this stream of contributions.
    b. Find the value of the total contributions after five years.

---

*Here we use the fact that one antiderivative of the derivative of u is the function u itself. That is,

$$\int u'(x)\,dx = u(x) + C. \quad \cdot$$

26. Sarah proposes to save for a post-college vacation by depositing amounts into a savings account equivalent to $100t$ dollars deposited continuously over the next four years. Her aunt, as a high-school graduation gift, decides to sponsor this vacation by giving Sarah a cash gift equal to the present value of this payment stream. Assuming a rate of interest of 5%, what is the amount of the gift?

27. Find the average value of the function $f(x) = \ln x$ for x in the interval $[1, e]$.

28. Find the average value of the function $f(x) = xe^{-2x}$ on the interval $[0, \ln 5]$.

29. A start-up business is projected to earn $R(t) = 10,000te^{-0.2t}$ dollars per year for the first five years. Find the (nominal) total earnings for the five-year period.

30. Find the present value of the revenue stream in Exercise 29, assuming a prevailing rate of interest of $r = 5\%$ during the five-year period.

31. A particle moves along a line with velocity $v(t) = 2te^{0.5t}$ during the first ten seconds of its motion. How far does it travel if v is in terms of feet per second? (Recall, $v(t) = s'(t)$ where $s(t)$ is position at time t.)

32. A manufacturing company predicts that the total sales resulting from a new product over the next five years will be

$$R(t) = 100,000 - 100t$$

dollars per year. Find the present value of this revenue stream, assuming a prevailing interest rate of 8%.

☑ **SOLUTIONS TO PRACTICE PROBLEMS 7.2**

1. In $\int x^2 \cos \pi x \, dx$, we use integration by parts: Let $u = x^2$; $dv = \cos(\pi x) \, dx$. Then, $du = 2x \, dx$; $v = \dfrac{1}{\pi} \sin(\pi x)$. We obtain

$$\int x^2 \cos \pi x \, dx = \frac{x^2}{\pi} \sin(\pi x) - \frac{2}{\pi} \int x \sin(\pi x) \, dx.$$

In $\int x \sin(\pi x) \, dx$, let $u = x$; $dv = \sin \pi x \, dx$. Then, $du = dx$; $v = -\dfrac{1}{\pi} \cos \pi x$. We obtain

$$\int x \sin(\pi x) \, dx = -\frac{x}{\pi} \cos \pi x + \frac{1}{\pi} \int \cos \pi x \, dx$$

$$= -\frac{x}{\pi} \cos \pi x + \frac{1}{\pi^2} \sin \pi x + C.$$

Combining these results gives

$$\int x^2 \cos \pi x \, dx = \frac{x^2}{\pi} \sin \pi x - \frac{2}{\pi} \left(-\frac{x}{\pi} \cos \pi x + \frac{1}{\pi^2} \sin \pi x \right) + C$$

$$= \frac{1}{\pi} \left(x^2 - \frac{1}{\pi} \right) \sin \pi x + \frac{2x}{\pi^2} \cos \pi x + C.$$

2. Using $PV = \displaystyle\int_0^T R(t)e^{-rt} \, dt$ with $T = 5$, $R(t) = 100t$, and $r = 0.06$ gives

$$PV = \int_0^5 100te^{-0.06t} \, dt$$

$$= 100 \int_0^5 te^{-0.06t} \, dt.$$

To evaluate $\int te^{-0.06t}\,dt$, we use integration by parts: Let $u = t$; $dv = e^{-0.06t}$. Then, $du = dt$; $v = -\dfrac{1}{0.06}e^{-0.06t}$. We obtain

$$\int te^{-0.06t}\,dt = -\frac{t}{0.06}e^{-0.06t} - \int \left(-\frac{1}{0.06}\right)e^{-0.06t}\,dt$$

$$= -\frac{te^{-0.06t}}{0.06} - \frac{1}{(0.06)^2}e^{-0.06t} + C.$$

With this result the definite integral is

$$PV = 100\left[-\frac{te^{-0.06t}}{(0.06)} - \frac{1}{(0.06)^2}e^{-0.06t}\right]_0^5$$

$$= 100\left[\frac{1}{(0.06)^2} - \frac{5e^{-0.3}}{(0.06)} - \frac{e^{-0.3}}{(0.06)^2}\right]$$

$$\approx \$1026.$$

In five years, this amount would have nominal value $(\$1026)e^{(0.06)(5)} \approx \$1385$.

7.3 The Use of Integral Tables

For many functions the techniques of this chapter will not succeed in finding an antiderivative. For some of these functions the reason for this failure is that more sophisticated techniques are required. For others, antiderivatives simply do not exist, at least in the form we have come to expect in this text.

Fortunately, a great many antiderivatives have been discovered and tabulated. Hundreds appear in various standard books of mathematical tables. A sample of 34 of these formulas appears on the endpapers of this book. Our purpose here is to demonstrate how these formulas are used.

The integral formulas 1–34 are written in terms of the variable u. The key to using them is to remember the notation of a *substitution:*

$$\int f'(g(x))g'(x)\,dx = \int f'(u)\,du = f(u) + C$$

under the substitution $u = g(x)$, $du = g'(x)\,dx$.

☐ **EXAMPLE 1**

Integral formula 24 states that

$$\int \ln u\,du = u \ln u - u + C.$$

This answers the question, ''What is the antiderivative of the natural logarithm function?'' With $u = x$ we have $du = dx$, and the formula simply states that

$$\int \ln x \, dx = x \ln x - x + C.$$

∎

☐ **EXAMPLE 2**

To evaluate the integral $\displaystyle \int \frac{dx}{x(3 + 5x)}$, we use formula 10:

$$\int \frac{du}{u(a + bu)} = -\frac{1}{a} \ln \left| \frac{a + bu}{u} \right| + C$$

with $u = x$, $a = 3$, and $b = 5$. We obtain

$$\int \frac{dx}{x(3 + 5x)} = -\frac{1}{3} \ln \left| \frac{3 + 5x}{x} \right| + C.$$

∎

☐ **EXAMPLE 3**

To evaluate the integral $\displaystyle \int \ln (4x) \, dx$, we again use formula 24:

$$\int \ln u \, du = u \ln u - u + C.$$

However, since our integral is not quite of this form, we need first to make the substitution

$$u = 4x, \qquad du = 4 \, dx.$$

Thus $dx = \dfrac{1}{4} \, du$, and using formula 24, we obtain

$$\int \ln(4x) \, dx = \int (\ln u) \left(\frac{1}{4} \right) du$$

$$= \frac{1}{4} \int \ln u \, du$$

$$= \frac{1}{4} [u \ln u - u + C]$$

$$= \frac{1}{4} (4x) \ln (4x) - \frac{1}{4} (4x) + \frac{1}{4} C$$

$$= x \ln (4x) - x + C.$$

(We write C rather than $\dfrac{C}{4}$ in the last line since C represents only an unknown constant. If a specific value of C were known we would have written $\dfrac{C}{4}$ rather than C.) ∎

Example 3 illustrates how we must often execute a substitution before a given integral matches one in our list of formulas. Our final example requires this step also.

□ **EXAMPLE 4**

Evaluate the integral $\displaystyle\int x^3\sqrt{9+4x^2}\,dx$.

Strategy · · · · · · · ·

Choose a candidate from the list of integral formulas.

Determine what substitution is required.

Find du and dx.

Apply substitution.

Apply formula 11.

"Substitute back" x^2 in place of u, and write C rather than $\dfrac{C}{2}$.

Solution

Inspecting our list of formulas suggests that formula 11 might prove to be a match for our integral:

$$\int u\sqrt{a+bu}\,du = -\frac{2(2a-3bu)(a+bu)^{3/2}}{15b^2}+C.$$

If this were the case, we would need to apply the substitution

$$u=x^2, \qquad du=2x\,dx.$$

Thus $x\,dx=\dfrac{1}{2}\,du$ and, using formula 11 with $a=9$ and $b=4$, we obtain

$$\int x^3\sqrt{9+4x^2}\,dx = \int x^2\sqrt{9+4x^2}\,x\,dx$$

$$= \int u\sqrt{9+4u}\left(\frac{1}{2}\right)du$$

$$= \frac{1}{2}\int u\sqrt{9+4u}\,du$$

$$= \frac{1}{2}\left[-\frac{2(2\cdot9-3\cdot4\cdot u)(9+4u)^{3/2}}{15\cdot4^2}+C\right]$$

$$= -\frac{2(18-12x^2)(9+4x^2)^{3/2}}{2\cdot15\cdot16}+C$$

$$= -\frac{(3-2x^2)(9+4x^2)^{3/2}}{40}+C. \qquad ∎$$

☑ **PRACTICE PROBLEMS 7.3**

Use the table of integrals in the front endpapers to evaluate the following integrals.

1. $\int \dfrac{dx}{x\sqrt{x^4 + 16}}$

2. $\int \dfrac{\sin x \cos x}{\sqrt{9 - \sin x}}\, dx$

Exercise Set 7.3

In each of Exercises 1–28, use the integral tables on the endpapers to evaluate the given integral.

1. $\int (4 + 3x)^5\, dx$

2. $\int \dfrac{dx}{(3 - 2x)^2}$

3. $\int \dfrac{x\, dx}{(5 + x)^2}$

4. $\int \dfrac{dx}{x(6 + 3x)}$

5. $\int x\sqrt{7 + 2x}\, dx$

6. $\int x\sqrt{1 + x}\, dx$

7. $\int \dfrac{x\, dx}{\sqrt{3 + 2x}}$

8. $\int \dfrac{dx}{9 - x^2}$

9. $\int \dfrac{dx}{\sqrt{16 + x^2}}$

10. $\int xe^{6x}\, dx$

11. $\int \dfrac{x\, dx}{(5 + x^2)^2}$

12. $\int \dfrac{x\, dx}{x^2(3 + 5x^2)}$

13. $\int \dfrac{dx}{9 - 16x^2}$

14. $\int x\sqrt{x^4 + 1}\, dx$

15. $\int \dfrac{dx}{x\sqrt{x^4 + 9}}$

16. $\int x^3 e^{x^2}\, dx$

17. $\int \dfrac{4x}{1 + e^{x^2}}\, dx$

18. $\int \dfrac{x\, dx}{7 - 2e^{x^2}}$

19. $\int \dfrac{dx}{\sqrt{x}(1 + e^{\sqrt{x}})}$

20. $\int \dfrac{dx}{x \ln x^2}$

21. $\int x \sin^3(x^2)\, dx$

22. $\int e^x \cos^3(e^x)\, dx$

23. $\int \dfrac{\sin x}{\cos x(5 - 2 \cos x)}\, dx$

24. $\int \dfrac{1}{\sqrt{x}(4 - x)}\, dx$

25. $\int \sqrt{\sec^2 x + 9}\, \sec x \tan x\, dx$ **26.** $\int \sqrt{\sec^2 x + 25}\, \tan x\, dx$

27. $\int \dfrac{1}{4\sqrt{x}(1 + e^{\sqrt{x}})}\, dx$

28. $\int \dfrac{1}{\sec x(1 + e^{\sin x})}\, dx$

29. The consumer's surplus at consumption level x_0 for an item with demand function $D(x) = \dfrac{100}{1 + e^{2x}}$ is

$$\int_0^{x_0} \dfrac{100}{1 + e^{2x}}\, dx - p_0 x_0$$

where $p_0 = D(x_0)$. Find the consumer's surplus at price $p_0 = 20$.

30. Find the average value of the function $f(x) = 4 \sin^3 \pi x$ on the interval $\left[0, \dfrac{\pi}{2}\right]$.

31. Find the area of the region bounded by the graphs of

$$f(x) = \dfrac{1}{9 - x^2} \quad \text{and} \quad g(x) = \dfrac{1}{x^2 - 9}$$

for $-1 < x < 1$.

☑ **SOLUTIONS TO PRACTICE PROBLEMS 7.3**

1. If we try the substitution

$$u = x^2; \qquad du = 2x\, dx$$

we can write this integral as

$$\int \frac{dx}{x\sqrt{x^4 + 16}} = \int \frac{x \, dx}{x^2\sqrt{(x^2)^2 + 16}}$$

$$= \frac{1}{2} \int \frac{2x \, dx}{x^2\sqrt{(x^2)^2 + 16}}$$

$$= \frac{1}{2} \int \frac{du}{u\sqrt{u^2 + 4^2}}.$$

Using integral formula 17, which states

$$\int \frac{du}{u\sqrt{u^2 + a^2}} = -\frac{1}{a} \ln\left(\frac{a + \sqrt{u^2 + a^2}}{u}\right) + C$$

with $u = x^2$ and $a = 4$, we obtain

$$\int \frac{dx}{x\sqrt{x^4 + 16}} = \frac{1}{2}\left\{-\frac{1}{4} \ln \frac{4 + \sqrt{(x^2)^2 + 4^2}}{x^2}\right\} + C$$

$$= -\frac{1}{8} \ln\left(\frac{4 + \sqrt{x^4 + 16}}{x^2}\right) + C.$$

2. If we let $u = \sin x$, then $du = \cos x \, dx$ and the integral becomes

$$\int \frac{\sin x \cos x}{\sqrt{9 - \sin x}} \, dx = \int \frac{u}{\sqrt{9 - u}} \, du$$

which is in the form of integral formula 12 with $u = \sin x$, $a = 9$, and $b = -1$. We obtain

$$\int \frac{\sin x \cos x}{\sqrt{9 - \sin x}} \, dx = -\frac{2[2 \cdot 9 - (-1)u]}{3(-1)^2}\sqrt{9 - u} + C$$

$$= -\left(\frac{36 + 2 \sin x}{3}\right)\sqrt{9 - \sin x} + C.$$

7.4 Improper Integrals

Up to this point the definite integral $\int_a^b f(x) \, dx$ has been defined only when the function f is continuous on the closed bounded interval $[a, b]$. There are certain situations in which we wish to extend this definition to the cases (i) where one or both of the limits of integration is infinite, or (ii) where the integrand f has a vertical asymptote (hence, a discontinuity) at some number in $[a, b]$. These are the types of situations in which we define **improper integrals.**

Here is a typical example of how an improper integral of type (i) occurs.

☐ **EXAMPLE 1**

(Revenue streams) A large stand of timber may be harvested annually to produce $10,000 worth of hardwood per year. Thus over a 10-year period the woodlot will yield a total of $10 \times (\$10,000) = \$100,000$ worth of timber.

We may think of the value of this timber as a *revenue stream* that produces $10,000 per year. Although this revenue stream produces a nominal value of $100,000 over a 10-year period, the *present value* of this 10-year stream is considerably less than $100,000, since the revenue is received over time, and the opportunity to invest it at current interest rates is lost until the money is actually received. Formula (2) in Section 5.7 gives the *present value* of such a revenue stream as

$$P_0 = \int_0^{10} 10,000 e^{-rt}\, dt$$

where r is the nominal interest rate, under continuous compounding, that is available to investors (bank depositors, for example). If, for example, we expect a nominal rate of $r = 0.10 = 10\%$ to prevail over this period, then the present value of this revenue stream is

$$P_0 = \int_0^{10} 10,000 e^{-0.10t}\, dt$$

$$= \left[-\frac{10,000}{0.10} e^{-0.10t} \right]_0^{10}$$

$$= 100,000 \left(1 - \frac{1}{e} \right)$$

$$\approx 63,212 \text{ dollars.}$$

Figure 4.1 illustrates this notion. The nominal value of the revenue stream ($100,000) is represented by the area enclosed by the rectangles, and the present value, discounted by the factor e^{-rt}, is represented by the area of the shaded region.

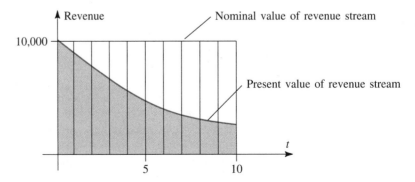

Figure 4.1 Nominal value versus present value.

Now suppose we ask for the value of this revenue stream "in perpetuity." That is, assuming that the timber stand will continue to produce revenue of $10,000 per year forever, what is the present value of the revenue stream it represents? (That is, what is a fair price at which to sell the woodlot from the standpoint of revenue?) This is sometimes called the *capital value* of a revenue-producing asset.

Although the time period over which the woodlot will produce revenue is infinite, the present value of this revenue stream is not infinite. To see this, note that the present value of this revenue stream up to time T years is

$$P_0 = \int_0^T 10,000e^{-0.10t}\, dt \qquad \text{(formula (2), Section 5.7)}$$

$$= \left[-\frac{10,000}{0.10} e^{-0.10t} \right]_0^T$$

$$= 100,000\left(1 - \frac{1}{e^{0.10T}} \right).$$

Thus in the limit as T approaches infinity, we obtain the present value

$$P_0 = \lim_{T \to \infty} \left[100,000\left(1 - \frac{1}{e^{0.10T}} \right) \right]$$

$$= 100,000 \text{ dollars.}$$

This is the present value of a revenue stream paying $10,000 per year forever, assuming the availability of continuous compounding of interest at a nominal rate of 10%.

Figure 4.2 gives the geometric interpretation of this result. As T approaches infinity, (that is, as the right-hand boundary of the shaded region moves to the right without bound), the **area** of the region lying under the present-value curve approaches 100,000. ∎

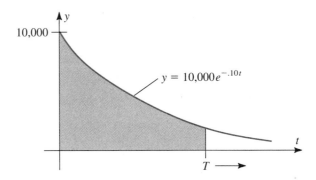

Figure 4.2 Present value of perpetual revenue stream is

$$\lim_{T \to \infty} \int_0^T 10,000e^{-0.10T}\, dt.$$

Type I Improper Integrals

The preceding example gives one reason why we define the improper integral of the type $\int_a^\infty f(x)\, dx$ as the limit as $t \to \infty$ of the definite integral $\int_a^t f(x)\, dx$.

Definition 1

If f is continuous on the interval $[a, \infty)$, we define the **improper integral** $\int_a^\infty f(x)\, dx$ as the limit

$$\int_a^\infty f(x)\, dx = \lim_{t \to \infty} \int_a^t f(x)\, dx. \tag{1}$$

When the limit in equation (1) exists, we say that the improper integral $\int_a^\infty f(x)\, dx$ **converges.** When this limit does not exist, we say that the improper integral **diverges.**

Figure 4.3 shows the geometric interpretation of the improper integral $\int_a^\infty f(x)\, dx$ for the case in which $f(x) \geq 0$ for $x \geq a$. If the function f can take negative values for some numbers x, then the improper integral is still defined by (1), but it cannot be interpreted easily as an area.

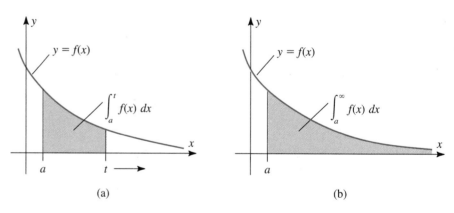

(a)   (b)

Figure 4.3 The improper integral $\int_a^\infty f(x)\, dx$, **(b)**, is the limit $\lim_{t \to \infty} \int_a^t f(x)\, dx$, **(a)**.

□ **EXAMPLE 2**

Evaluate the improper integral $\int_1^\infty e^{-x}\, dx$.

Strategy · · · · · · ·

Evaluate the integral

$$\int_1^t e^{-x}\, dx.$$

Find the limit as $t \to \infty$ of this result.

Solution

Since an antiderivative for e^{-x} is $-e^{-x}$, we have

$$\int_1^t e^{-x}\, dx = \left[-e^{-x}\right]_1^t = -e^{-t} - (-e^{-1})$$

$$= \frac{1}{e} - e^{-t}.$$

Thus

$$\int_1^\infty e^{-x}\, dx = \lim_{t \to \infty} \int_1^t e^{-x}\, dx$$

$$= \lim_{t \to \infty}\left(\frac{1}{e} - e^{-t}\right)$$

$$= \frac{1}{e}$$

since $\displaystyle\lim_{t \to \infty} e^{-t} = \lim_{t \to \infty}\left(\frac{1}{e^t}\right) = 0.$ ∎

☐ **EXAMPLE 3**

The improper integral

$$\int_2^\infty \frac{1}{\sqrt{x}}\, dx$$

diverges. To see this, note that

$$\int_2^\infty \frac{1}{\sqrt{x}}\, dx = \lim_{t \to \infty} \int_2^t x^{-1/2}\, dx$$

$$= \lim_{t \to \infty} \left[2\sqrt{x}\right]_2^t$$

$$= \lim_{t \to \infty}[2\sqrt{t} - 2\sqrt{2}]$$

$$= +\infty. \quad ∎$$

Improper integrals of Type I may also involve an infinite *lower* limit of integration. Figure 4.4 illustrates the definition of an improper integral of the form $\int_{-\infty}^b f(x)\, dx$:

$$\int_{-\infty}^b f(x)\, dx = \lim_{t \to -\infty} \int_t^b f(x)\, dx. \qquad (2)$$

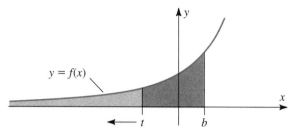

Figure 4.4 $\displaystyle\int_{-\infty}^{b} f(x)\, dx = \lim_{t \to -\infty} \int_{t}^{b} f(x)\, dx.$

As before, when the limit on the right-hand side of equation (2) exists, we say that the improper integral converges. Otherwise it is said to diverge.

□ **EXAMPLE 4**

Evaluate the improper integral $\displaystyle\int_{-\infty}^{1} e^{2x}\, dx.$

Solution: Using equation (2), we have

$$\int_{-\infty}^{1} e^{2x}\, dx = \lim_{t \to -\infty} \int_{t}^{1} e^{2x}\, dx$$

$$= \lim_{t \to -\infty} \left[\frac{1}{2} e^{2x} \right]_{t}^{1}$$

$$= \lim_{t \to -\infty} \left(\frac{1}{2} e^{2} - \frac{1}{2} e^{2t} \right)$$

$$= \frac{1}{2} e^{2} - \lim_{t \to -\infty} \frac{1}{2} e^{2t}$$

$$= \frac{1}{2} e^{2}$$

since $\displaystyle\lim_{t \to -\infty} \frac{1}{2} e^{2t} = 0.$ ■

REMARK: Improper integrals of the form $\displaystyle\int_{-\infty}^{\infty} f(x)\, dx$ may also be defined. We say that the improper integral $\displaystyle\int_{-\infty}^{\infty} f(x)\, dx$ converges if, for any constant a, *both* the improper integrals $\displaystyle\int_{-\infty}^{a} f(x)\, dx$ and $\displaystyle\int_{a}^{\infty} f(x)\, dx$ converge. In this case the value of the integral is

$$\int_{-\infty}^{\infty} f(x)\,dx = \int_{-\infty}^{a} f(x)\,dx + \int_{a}^{\infty} f(x)\,dx.$$

Type II Improper Integrals

A second type of improper integral occurs when the integrand in a definite integral becomes infinite at one or both limits of integration. For example, suppose that the function f is defined and continuous on the interval $[a, b)$, but that $\lim_{x \to b^-} f(x)$ fails to exist (see Figure 4.5). In this case the definite integral $\int_{a}^{b} f(x)\,dx$ as defined in Chapter 5 does not exist. However, we define the associated *improper integral* by using a left-hand limit as follows.

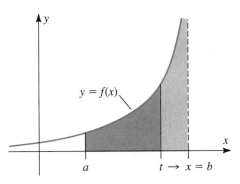

Figure 4.5 $\displaystyle\int_{a}^{b} f(x)\,dx = \lim_{t \to b^-} \int_{a}^{t} f(x)\,dx.$

Definition 2

If f is continuous on $[a, b)$ but $\lim_{x \to b^-} f(x)$ fails to exist, we define the **improper integral** $\int_{a}^{b} f(x)\,dx$ as the limit

$$\int_{a}^{b} f(x)\,dx = \lim_{t \to b^-} \int_{a}^{t} f(x)\,dx \tag{3}$$

provided that this limit exists.

As with improper integrals of Type I, we say that the improper integral in equation (3) converges if the limit on the right-hand side of equation (3) exists. Figure 4.5 illustrates that when $f(x) \geq 0$ for $a < x < b$, we may interpret the value of the improper integral in equation (3) as the area of the region bounded by the graph of f and the x-axis for $a \leq x < b$, which may be finite even though this region has infinite extent in the y-direction.

☐ **EXAMPLE 5**

Determine whether the improper integral

$$\int_0^1 \frac{x}{\sqrt{1-x^2}}\, dx$$

converges or diverges.

Strategy · · · · · · · · ·

Determine where the integrand fails
to exist.

Apply Definition 2.
Use a substitution $u = 1 - x^2$, $du = -2x\, dx$ to obtain

$$\int \frac{x}{\sqrt{1-x^2}}\, dx = \int \frac{-(1/2)\, du}{\sqrt{u}}$$
$$= -\sqrt{u} + C.$$

Solution

The integrand becomes infinite at $x = 1$ since $\sqrt{1 - (1)^2} = 0$. Thus

$$\int_0^1 \frac{x}{\sqrt{1-x^2}} = \lim_{t \to 1^-} \int_0^t \frac{x}{\sqrt{1-x^2}}\, dx$$

$$= \lim_{t \to 1^-} \left[-\sqrt{1-x^2} \right]_0^t$$

$$= \lim_{t \to 1^-} (1 - \sqrt{1 - t^2})$$

$$= 1.$$

The integral converges to 1. (See Figure 4.6.)   ■

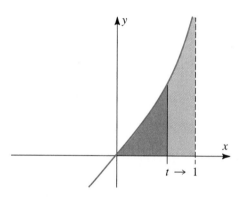

Figure 4.6 Graph of $y = \dfrac{x}{\sqrt{1-x^2}}$.

When an integrand f becomes infinite at the *left* endpoint of an interval $[a, b]$,
the improper integral is defined by analogy with equation (3) using the right-hand
limit at a. That is

$$\int_a^b f(x)\, dx = \lim_{t \to a^+} \int_t^b f(x)\, dx \tag{4}$$

if f is continuous on $(a, b]$ but $\lim_{x \to a^+} f(x)$ fails to exist.

□ **EXAMPLE 6**

The improper integral $\int_{-2}^{2} (x + 2)^{-3/2}\, dx$ fails to exist. To see this, use equation (4) to find that

$$\int_{-2}^{2} (x + 2)^{-3/2}\, dx = \lim_{t \to -2^+} \int_{t}^{2} (x + 2)^{-3/2}\, dx$$

$$= \lim_{t \to -2^+} \left[-2(x + 2)^{-1/2} \right]_{t}^{2}$$

$$= \lim_{t \to -2^+} \left(\frac{-2}{\sqrt{4}} - \frac{-2}{\sqrt{t + 2}} \right)$$

$$= +\infty$$

since $\displaystyle \lim_{t \to -2^+} \frac{2}{\sqrt{t + 2}} = +\infty$. (See Figure 4.7.)   ■

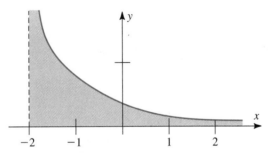

Figure 4.7 Graph of $y = (x + 2)^{-3/2}$. Area of shaded region is infinite.

☑ **PRACTICE PROBLEMS 7.4**

Evaluate the following improper integrals.

1. $\displaystyle \int_{1}^{\infty} \frac{x}{(4 + x^2)^{2/3}}\, dx$

2. $\displaystyle \int_{2}^{5} \frac{3}{\sqrt{x - 2}}\, dx$

Exercise Set 7.4

In Exercises 1–14, determine whether the improper integral of Type I converges. Evaluate those that converge.

1. $\displaystyle \int_{2}^{\infty} \frac{1}{x^2}\, dx$

2. $\displaystyle \int_{1}^{\infty} \frac{1}{x^3}\, dx$

3. $\displaystyle \int_{0}^{\infty} e^{-x}\, dx$

4. $\displaystyle \int_{1}^{\infty} x e^{x^2}\, dx$

5. $\displaystyle \int_{1}^{\infty} \frac{1}{\sqrt{x}}\, dx$

6. $\displaystyle \int_{0}^{\infty} e^{\pi x}\, dx$

7. $\displaystyle\int_0^\infty \frac{x}{\sqrt{4+x^2}}\, dx$

8. $\displaystyle\int_1^\infty \frac{e^{-\sqrt{x}}}{\sqrt{x}}\, dx$

9. $\displaystyle\int_0^\infty \frac{1}{x+2}\, dx$

10. $\displaystyle\int_0^\infty x\sqrt{1+x^2}\, dx$

11. $\displaystyle\int_{-\infty}^{-2} \frac{1}{x^2}\, dx$

12. $\displaystyle\int_{-\infty}^0 e^x\, dx$

13. $\displaystyle\int_{-\infty}^0 \frac{1}{\sqrt{1-x}}\, dx$

14. $\displaystyle\int_0^\infty \frac{x}{1+x^2}\, dx$

In Exercises 15–22, determine whether the integral of Type II converges. Evaluate those that converge.

15. $\displaystyle\int_0^1 \frac{1}{\sqrt{1-x}}\, dx$

16. $\displaystyle\int_0^1 \frac{1}{x}\, dx$

17. $\displaystyle\int_0^1 \frac{1}{x^2}\, dx$

18. $\displaystyle\int_1^3 \frac{x}{\sqrt{9-x^2}}\, dx$

19. $\displaystyle\int_1^e \frac{1}{x\ln x}\, dx$

20. $\displaystyle\int_0^1 (1-x)^{-2/3}\, dx$

21. $\displaystyle\int_1^3 \frac{1}{x^2-2x+1}\, dx$

22. $\displaystyle\int_0^2 \frac{1}{(x-2)^2}\, dx$

23. Find the present value of a perpetual revenue stream paying $100 per year. Assume that the prevailing rate of interest, compounded continuously, will remain constant at the nominal rate $r = 10\%$.

24. Find the present value of the revenue stream in Exercise 23 if the prevailing rate of interest is assumed to remain constant at $r = 5\%$.

25. A business expects to generate profits at a rate of 1 million dollars per year indefinitely. Assume a constant prevailing rate of interest of $r = 10\%$.
   (a) Find the present value of its anticipated profits over the next 10 years.
   (b) Find the present value of all anticipated future profits.

26. What is a fair price to pay today for a stand of timber that will yield $1000 worth of lumber per year indefinitely, assuming that operating costs are negligible and that prevailing interest rates remain constant at $r = 0.05$?

27. Find the volume of the solid obtained by revolving about the x-axis the region bounded by the graph of $y = e^{-x}$ and the y-axis for $0 \le x < \infty$.

28. For what set of numbers p does the improper integral $\displaystyle\int_1^\infty x^p\, dx$ converge?

29. For what set of numbers p does the integral $\displaystyle\int_0^1 \frac{1}{x^p}\, dx$ converge?

30. The Ajax Corporation wishes to raise money by selling perpetual bonds that would pay the owners of the bonds $1000 per year per bond indefinitely. What is the value of one of these bonds to a potential investor who believes that the prevailing rate of interest will remain constant at
   a. 5% per year?
   b. 10% per year?
   c. 15% per year?

31. Find the present value of a capital asset producing a revenue stream of $R(t) = \$5000$ per year in perpetuity, if interest rates remain at 10%.

32. A business producing a profit of 1 million dollars per year is destroyed by a negligent act of another company. What is a fair amount of compensation, assuming that the damaged business would have remained healthy in perpetuity and would have experienced a continuous growth in profits of 5% per year? (Assume a prevailing interest rate of $r = 10\%$.)

Using the ideas of this section we may define improper integrals for integrands that have a discontinuity, or that are undefined, at a number c that is not an endpoint by saying that

$$\int_a^b f(x)\, dx = \int_a^c f(x)\, dx + \int_c^b f(x)\, dx$$

where $a < c < b$ and *both* of the improper integrals on the right exist. (They will both be of Type II.) Using this definition, determine whether the integrals in Exercises 33–38 exist and, if so, the value of the integral.

33. $\displaystyle\int_0^6 \frac{1}{x-2}\, dx$

34. $\displaystyle\int_0^6 \frac{1}{(x-2)^2}\, dx$

35. $\displaystyle\int_0^4 \frac{1}{(x-2)^{2/3}}\, dx$

36. $\displaystyle\int_0^\pi \tan x\, dx$

37. $\displaystyle\int_0^2 \frac{1}{x^2-2x+1}\, dx$

38. $\displaystyle\int_{-5}^0 \frac{1}{\sqrt[3]{x+3}}\, dx$

☑ **SOLUTIONS TO PRACTICE PROBLEMS 7.4**

1. $\displaystyle\int_1^\infty \frac{x}{(4+x^2)^{3/2}} = \lim_{t\to\infty} \int_1^t \frac{x}{(4+x^2)^{3/2}}\,dx$

$\displaystyle = \lim_{t\to\infty} \left[-(4+x^2)^{-1/2} \right]_1^t$

$\displaystyle = \left[\lim_{t\to\infty} \frac{-1}{\sqrt{4+t^2}} \right] - \left[\frac{-1}{\sqrt{4+1^2}} \right]$

$\displaystyle = \frac{1}{\sqrt{5}}$

2. $\displaystyle\int_2^5 \frac{3}{\sqrt{x-2}}\,dx = \lim_{t\to2^+} \int_t^5 3(x-2)^{-1/2}\,dx$

$\displaystyle = \lim_{t\to2^+} \left[6(x-2)^{1/2} \right]_t^5$

$\displaystyle = 6(5-2)^{1/2} - \lim_{t\to2^+} 6(t-2)^{1/2}$

$\displaystyle = 6\sqrt{3}$

7.5 Rules for Approximating Integrals

Many functions, such as $\sqrt{x^2+1}$ or e^{x^2}, do not have antiderivatives that are easily found. For such functions the Fundamental Theorem of Calculus is not usable, and we can only *approximate* definite integrals involving these functions.

One way to approximate the definite integral

$$\int_a^b f(x)\,dx$$

is by using approximating sums of the form

$$\int_a^b f(x)\,dx \approx \sum_{j=1}^n f(t_j)\,\Delta x, \quad \text{where} \quad \Delta x = \frac{b-a}{n} \tag{1}$$

and where t_j is an arbitrary number in $[x_{j-1}, x_j]$ as described in Chapter 5 (and as implemented in Program 4 in Appendix I). In this section we present two additional methods for approximating $\displaystyle\int_a^b f(x)\,dx$.

The Trapezoidal Rule

The sum in (1) involves approximating "slices" of the region R bounded by the graph of f with rectangles. Figure 5.1 illustrates the fact that an approximating rectangle often does not fit this graph very well. There may be large regions under the graph of f that are not included in the rectangle, and vice versa.

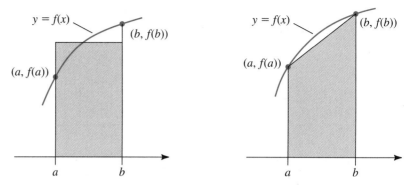

Figure 5.1 Approximations of trapezoids often provide a "better fit" than do approximations by rectangles.

We can try to improve on these "rectangular" estimates by drawing a line from $(a, f(a))$ to $(b, f(b))$ in Figure 5.1 and using the area of the resulting trapezoid in the same way that we previously used approximating rectangles. In doing so, we will make use of the formula from geometry for the area A of the trapezoid with altitude* h and bases of length b and B:

$$A = \frac{1}{2}(B + b)h. \tag{2}$$

To use this idea in approximating the area of the region R bounded by the graph of f and the x-axis for $a \le x \le b$, we divide the interval $[a, b]$ into n subintervals of equal length $\Delta x = \dfrac{b - a}{n}$, and we denote the endpoints of these subintervals by the numbers

$$a = x_0 < x_1 < x_2 < \cdots < x_n = b.$$

But instead of using the area of an approximating rectangle in each subinterval, we use the approximation

$$\int_{x_{j-1}}^{x_j} f(x)\, dx \approx \frac{1}{2}[f(x_{j-1}) + f(x_j)]\, \Delta x \tag{3}$$

which, according to equation (2), is the area of the trapezoid with bases $B = f(x_{j-1})$ and $b = f(x_j)$, and altitude $h = \Delta x$. (See Figures 5.2 and 5.3.)

---

*Here we use "altitude" to mean the distance between the parallel sides of the trapezoid; don't confuse it with "height." See Figure 5.3.

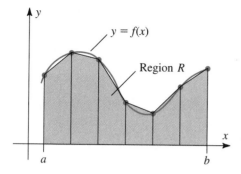

Figure 5.2 Approximating the region R by trapezoids.

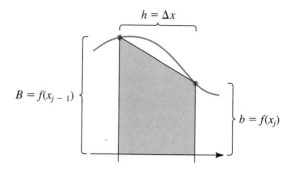

Figure 5.3 The area of the jth trapezoid is $\dfrac{1}{2}(f(x_{j-1}) + f(x_j))\,\Delta x$.

Summing the approximations in line (3), one for each of the n subintervals, gives the following approximation:

$$\int_a^b f(x)\, dx \approx \frac{\Delta x}{2}\{[f(x_0) + f(x_1)] + [f(x_1) + f(x_2)] + [f(x_2) + f(x_3)]$$

$$+ \cdots + [f(x_{n-2}) + f(x_{n-1})] + [f(x_{n-1}) + f(x_n)]\}.$$

Since each function value $f(x_j)$, except $f(x_0)$ and $f(x_n)$, appears *twice* in the above sum (why?), we can restate this approximation as follows.

Trapezoidal Rule: Let f be continuous on $[a, b]$, let $\Delta x = \dfrac{b-a}{n}$, and let

$$x_0 = a, \quad x_1 = a + \Delta x, \quad x_2 = a + 2\,\Delta x, \ldots, \quad x_n = a + n\,\Delta x = b.$$

Then

$$\int_a^b f(x)\, dx \approx \frac{b-a}{2n}\{f(x_0) + 2f(x_1) + 2f(x_2) + \cdots + 2f(x_{n-1}) + f(x_n)\}.$$

$$\tag{4}$$

Note that while the motivation for stating the Trapezoidal Rule was based on area considerations, the statement of the Trapezoidal Rule does not require that $f(x) \geq 0$ for all x in $[a, b]$. That is, the Trapezoidal Rule may be used to approximate the definite integral of a continuous function f whether or not that integral corresponds to the area of a region bounded by the graph of f and the x-axis.

☐ **EXAMPLE 1**

Approximate $\int_1^4 \dfrac{1}{x}\, dx$ using the Trapezoidal Rule with $n = 6$.

Solution: With $a = 1$, $b = 4$, and $n = 6$ we have $\Delta x = \dfrac{4 - 1}{6} = \dfrac{1}{2}$, so

$$x_0 = 1, \quad x_1 = \frac{3}{2}, \quad x_2 = 2, \quad x_3 = \frac{5}{2}, \quad x_4 = 3, \quad x_5 = \frac{7}{2}, \quad x_6 = 4.$$

(See Figure 5.4.)

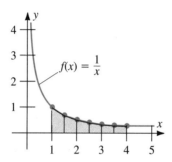

Figure 5.4 Approximations in Example 1.

The Trapezoidal Rule thus gives the approximation

$$\int_1^4 \frac{1}{x}\, dx \approx \frac{3}{12}\left\{1 + \frac{4}{3} + 1 + \frac{4}{5} + \frac{2}{3} + \frac{4}{7} + \frac{1}{4}\right\} = \frac{2361}{1680} = 1.4054.$$

REMARK 1: From the geometry of Figure 5.4 we can see that the approximation in Example 1 is actually *larger* than the actual value of the integral. This is because the graph of f is concave up on $[1, 4]$.

REMARK 2: Notice that if we evaluate the definite integral in Example 1 using the Fundamental Theorem, we find that

$$\int_1^4 \frac{1}{x}\, dx = \Big[\ln x\Big]_1^4 = \ln 4 - \ln 1$$

$$= \ln 4 \qquad (\ln 1 = 0).$$

Combining this with the result of Example 1 gives the approximation

$$\ln 4 \approx 1.4054.$$

More generally, this shows how we can use the Trapezoidal Rule to approximate values of the natural logarithm function as

$$\ln x = \int_1^x \frac{1}{t}\,dt, \qquad x > 0.$$

This is an important observation because it shows one way in which values of a transcendental function can be approximated without resorting to a table of values or a calculating device.

ERROR IN TRAPEZOIDAL APPROXIMATIONS: In more advanced courses it is proved that the error in using the Trapezoidal Rule to approximate the integral $\int_a^b f(x)\,dx$ with n subdivisions has the following bound:

$$|\text{Error}| \leq \frac{(b-a)^3 M}{12n^2} \tag{5}$$

where M is the maximum value of $|f''(x)|$ on the interval $[a, b]$.

☐ **EXAMPLE 2**

Find a bound on the error for the approximation in Example 1.

Solution: For $f(x) = \dfrac{1}{x}$, $f''(x) = \dfrac{2}{x^3}$, which has a maximum value of $M = 2$ on the interval $[1, 4]$. Thus by inequality (5) we have

$$|\text{Error}| \leq \frac{3^3}{12(6^2)}(2) = \frac{1}{8} = 0.125. \qquad ■$$

Program 5 in Appendix I is a BASIC program implementing the Trapezoidal Rule to approximate the integral $\int_a^b \dfrac{1}{x}\,dx$. Running this program on a computer, we obtained the results in Table 5.1. The student with access to a computer is encour-

Table 5-1

$[A, B]$	n	S
$[1, 4]$	5	1.41348
$[1, 4]$	20	1.38805
$[1, 4]$	100	1.38636
$[1, 4]$	250	1.38631
$[1, 20]$	5	3.76955
$[1, 20]$	20	3.06566
$[1, 20]$	100	2.99872
$[1, 20]$	250	2.99621

aged to experiment with modifications of this program and to compare its results with integrals previously calculated using the Fundamental Theorem.

Simpson's Rule

This approximation procedure uses parabolic arcs, rather than line segments, to approximate portions of the graph of $y = f(x)$. It uses the fact that if x_0, x_1, and x_2 are three values of x with

$$x_1 - x_0 = x_2 - x_1 = \Delta x$$

then the definite integral of the quadratic function passing through the three points (x_0, y_0), (x_1, y_1), and (x_2, y_2) equals

$$\frac{\Delta x}{3}[y_0 + 4y_1 + y_2]. \tag{6}$$

(You're asked to complete the proof of this in Exercise 37.) We apply this result to obtain Simpson's Rule. As before, we divide $[a, b]$ into n subintervals, but now we must require that n be an *even* integer. We then approximate the integral

$$\int_{x_{2j-2}}^{x_{2j}} f(x)\, dx$$

over each *pair* of subintervals by expression (6). Thus we are approximating the actual value of the integral of $f(x)$ over $[x_{2j-2}, x_{2j}]$ by the integral of the approximating quadratic function. We obtain the approximation

$$\int_a^b f(x)\, dx \approx \frac{\Delta x}{3}\{[f(x_0) + 4f(x_1) + f(x_2)] + [f(x_2) + 4f(x_3) + f(x_4)]$$
$$+ [f(x_4) + 4f(x_5) + f(x_6)] + \cdots$$
$$+ [f(x_{n-4}) + 4f(x_{n-3}) + f(x_{n-2})]$$
$$+ [f(x_{n-2}) + 4f(x_{n-1}) + f(x_n)]\}.$$

Again, notice that each $f(x_{2j})$ is counted twice, except for $f(x_0)$ and $f(x_n)$, for the same reason as in the Trapezoidal Rule. We can state this approximation rule as follows.

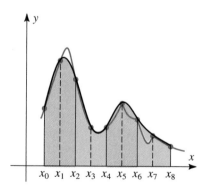

Figure 5.5 Approximation by Simpson's Rule.

Simpson's Rule: Let n be an even integer and let $\Delta x = \dfrac{b - a}{n}$. Let

$$x_0 = a, \quad x_1 = a + \Delta x, \quad x_2 = a + 2\,\Delta x, \quad \dots, \quad x_n = a + n\,\Delta x = b.$$

Then

$$\int_a^b f(x)\, dx \approx \frac{b - a}{3n}\{f(x_0) + 4f(x_1) + 2f(x_2) + 4f(x_3)$$
$$+ 2f(x_4) + \cdots + 2f(x_{n-2}) + 4f(x_{n-1}) + f(x_n)\}.$$

(See Figure 5.5.)

□ **EXAMPLE 3**

Use Simpson's Rule with $n = 6$ to approximate $\int_1^4 \frac{1}{x} dx$ (that is, ln 4).

Solution: With $x_0, x_1, \ldots, x_6$ as in Example 1 we obtain from the statement of Simpson's Rule the approximation

$$\int_1^4 \frac{1}{x} dx = \frac{4-1}{3 \cdot 6} \left\{ 1 + 4\left(\frac{2}{3}\right) + 2\left(\frac{1}{2}\right) + 4\left(\frac{2}{5}\right) + 2\left(\frac{1}{3}\right) + 4\left(\frac{2}{7}\right) + \frac{1}{4} \right\}$$

$$= \frac{3497}{2520} = 1.3877.$$

∎

ERROR IN SIMPSON'S RULE APPROXIMATIONS: For the approximation provided by Simpson's Rule it is proved in more advanced courses that

$$|\text{Error}| \le \frac{(b-a)^5 M}{180n^4} \tag{7}$$

where M is the maximum value of $|f^{(4)}(x)|$, the fourth derivative, on the interval $[a, b]$.

□ **EXAMPLE 4**

Find how large n must be in order that the approximation of the integral in Example 3 by Simpson's Rule will be accurate to within 0.005.

Solution: For $f(x) = \frac{1}{x}$, $f^{(4)}(x) = 24x^{-5}$. The maximum value of this fourth derivative on $[1, 4]$ is $M = 24$. According to inequality (7), we must find n sufficiently large that

$$\frac{(4-1)^5}{180n^4}(24) \le 0.005.$$

Solving this inequality for n, we find that

$$n^4 \ge \frac{(24)(243)}{(0.005)(180)} = 6480.$$

Here $n = 10$ will suffice since $10^4 = 10,000 > 6480$.

∎

Program 6 in Appendix I is a BASIC program that implements Simpson's Rule to approximate the integral $\int_a^b \frac{1}{x} dx$. Table 5.2 was obtained by use of this program.

Table 5-2

$[A, B]$	n	S
$[1, 4]$	6	1.38770
$[1, 4]$	20	1.38631
$[1, 4]$	100	1.38629
$[1, 4]$	250	1.38629
$[1, 20]$	6	3.21696
$[1, 20]$	20	3.00677
$[1, 20]$	100	2.99577
$[1, 20]$	250	2.99573

In conclusion, several observations should be made about the two approximation procedures presented in this section.

(1) While the Trapezoidal Rule approximates curves by line segments, Simpson's Rule fits second-degree curves to the given curve. Thus we would expect Simpson's Rule to be more accurate for the same value of n.

(2) Since the error formula for the Trapezoidal Rule involves f'', the Trapezoidal Rule gives exact information for first-degree polynomials, for which $f''(x) \equiv 0$.

(3) Since, however, the error formula for Simpson's Rule involves the fourth derivative of f, Simpson's Rule gives exact results for polynomials of degree three or less, for which $f^{(4)}(x) \equiv 0$.

☑ **PRACTICE PROBLEMS 7.5**

1. Approximate the integral $\displaystyle\int_1^2 \frac{1}{x + 1}\, dx$:

  a. Use the Trapezoidal Rule with $n = 10$.
  b. Use Simpson's Rule with $n = 10$.

2. Determine the number of subintervals required to approximate the integral in Problem 1 to accuracy 0.0001:
  a. Use the Trapezoidal Rule.
  b. Use Simpson's Rule.

3. Use a calculator to find the exact value, correct to six decimal places, for the integral in Problem 1.

Exercise Set 7.5

In Exercises 1–10, use the Trapezoidal Rule with the given value of n to approximate the integral.

1. $\displaystyle\int_0^4 (x^3 - 7x + 4)\, dx, \quad n = 4$

2. $\displaystyle\int_0^2 \frac{4}{1 + x^2}\, dx, \quad n = 4$

3. $\displaystyle\int_0^\pi \sin x\, dx, \quad n = 4$

4. $\displaystyle\int_0^{\pi} \sin x \, dx, \quad n = 6$

5. $\displaystyle\int_0^4 \frac{4}{1 + x^2} \, dx, \quad n = 8$

6. $\displaystyle\int_0^2 \sqrt{1 + x^2} \, dx, \quad n = 4$

7. $\displaystyle\int_0^4 \cos\left(\frac{\pi x}{4}\right) dx, \quad n = 4$

8. $\displaystyle\int_0^2 \frac{x}{1 + x^3} \, dx, \quad n = 4$

9. $\displaystyle\int_2^4 \frac{1}{1 - x^2} \, dx, \quad n = 8$

10. $\displaystyle\int_{-4}^4 x \sin\left(\frac{\pi x}{4}\right) dx, \quad n = 8$

In Exercises 11–20, use Simpson's Rule to approximate the integral.

11. In Exercise 1   **12.** In Exercise 2

13. In Exercise 3   **14.** In Exercise 4

15. In Exercise 5   **16.** In Exercise 6

17. In Exercise 7   **18.** In Exercise 8

19. In Exercise 9   **20.** In Exercise 10

(Calculator) In Exercises 21–26, use the Trapezoidal Rule with $n = 6$ to approximate the given integral.

21. $\displaystyle\int_0^{\pi/4} \frac{2}{1 + x^2} \, dx$ **22.** $\displaystyle\int_0^3 \sqrt{1 + x^2} \, dx$

23. $\displaystyle\int_1^3 \sqrt{x^2 + 2} \, dx$ **24.** $\displaystyle\int_0^1 \sin x^2 \, dx$

25. $\displaystyle\int_0^2 x \sin\left(\frac{\pi x}{2}\right) dx$ **26.** $\displaystyle\int_0^{\pi/4} \tan \sqrt{x} \, dx$

(Calculator) In Exercises 27–32, use Simpson's Rule with $n = 6$ to approximate the integral.

27. In Exercise 21   **28.** In Exercise 22

29. In Exercise 23   **30.** In Exercise 24

31. In Exercise 25   **32.** In Exercise 26

33. (Computer) Modify Program 5 in Appendix I to approximate the integral in Exercise 21 with $n = 5$, 20, 100, and 250.

34. (Computer) Modify Program 6 in Appendix I to approximate the integral in Exercise 21 with $n = 6$, 20, 100, and 250.

35. (Calculator) Use the Trapezoidal Rule with $n = 6$ to approximate

   a. $\displaystyle\int_0^3 \sin \sqrt{x} \, dx.$ **b.** $\displaystyle\int_0^{\pi/3} \frac{1}{\sqrt{\cos x}} \, dx.$

36. (Calculator) Repeat Exercise 21 using Simpson's Rule.

37. Verify equation (6) by completing the following steps. (Refer to Figure 5.6.)

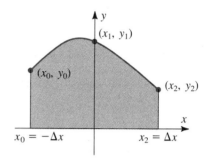

Figure 5.6

   a. Let $x_0 = -\Delta x$, $x_1 = 0$, and $x_2 = \Delta x$ as in Figure 5.6.
   b. Let the parabola through (x_0, y_0), (x_1, y_1), and (x_2, y_2) be denoted as $y = ax^2 + bx + c$.
   c. Use the resulting values

$$y_0 = a(\Delta x)^2 - b(\Delta x) + c$$
$$y_1 = c, \quad \text{and}$$
$$y_2 = a(\Delta x)^2 + b(\Delta x) + c$$

   to show that

$$\int_{-\Delta x}^{\Delta x} (ax^2 + bx + c) \, dx = \frac{\Delta x}{3}[y_0 + 4y_1 + y_2].$$

38. **a.** Use the Trapezoidal Rule with $n = 8$ to approximate ln 3. (See Example 1.)
   b. What is the bound on the error in the approximation in part (a) according to equation (5)?
   c. Use a calculator or Table 2 in Appendix II to compare the actual value of ln 3 with your approximation from part (a). What is the difference? How does this compare with the estimate of the errors in part (b)?

39. **a.** Use Simpson's Rule with $n = 8$ to approximate ln 5.
   b. What is the bound on the error in the approximation in part (a) according to equation (7)?
   c. Find the actual value of ln 5 from Table 2 in Appendix II or by using a calculator. What is the difference between this actual value and your approximation in part (a)? How does this compare with the estimate of the error in part (b)?

☑ **SOLUTIONS TO PRACTICE PROBLEMS 7.5**

1. With $n = 10$ and $[a, b] = [1, 2]$, $\Delta x = \dfrac{1}{10}$ and $x_0 = 1$, $x_1 = 1.1$, $x_2 = 1.2, \ldots, x_{10} = 2$.

a. Using the Trapezoidal Rule, we have

$$\int_1^2 \frac{1}{x + 1}\, dx \approx \frac{0.1}{2}\left(\frac{1}{2} + \frac{2}{2.1} + \frac{2}{2.2} + \frac{2}{2.3} + \frac{2}{2.4} + \frac{2}{2.5}\right.$$

$$\left. + \frac{2}{2.6} + \frac{2}{2.7} + \frac{2}{2.8} + \frac{2}{2.9} + \frac{1}{3}\right)$$

$$= 0.4056.$$

b. Using Simpson's Rule, we obtain

$$\int_1^2 \frac{1}{x + 1}\, dx \approx \frac{0.1}{3}\left(\frac{1}{2} + \frac{4}{2.1} + \frac{2}{2.2} + \frac{4}{2.3} + \frac{2}{2.4} + \frac{4}{2.5} + \frac{2}{2.6}\right.$$

$$\left. + \frac{4}{2.7} + \frac{2}{2.8} + \frac{4}{2.9} + \frac{1}{3}\right)$$

$$= 0.4055.$$

2. a. For trapezoidal approximations, the error estimate (5) and the required accuracy imply that we must have

$$\frac{(2 - 1)^3}{12n^3} M < 0.0001$$

where M is the maximum value of $\dfrac{d^2}{dx^2}\left(\dfrac{1}{1 + x}\right)$ on $[1, 2]$. Since $\dfrac{d}{dx}\left(\dfrac{1}{x + 1}\right) = \dfrac{-1}{(x + 1)^2}$, we have $\dfrac{d^2}{dx^2}\left(\dfrac{1}{x + 1}\right) = \dfrac{d}{dx}\left(\dfrac{-1}{(1 + x)^2}\right) = \dfrac{2}{(1 + x)^3}$. The largest value of this function on $[1, 2]$ occurs at $x = 1$; $\dfrac{2}{(1 + 1)^3} = \dfrac{1}{4}$. Thus, we must have

$$\frac{1}{12n^3}\left(\frac{1}{4}\right) < 0.0001$$

or

$$48n^3 > \frac{1}{0.0001} = 10,000$$

or

$$n^3 > \frac{10,000}{48} = 208.33.$$

Thus, we must have $n > \sqrt[3]{208.33} \approx 5.928$, so $n \geq 7$ will suffice.

b. For Simpson's Rule, we need to use the maximum value of

$$\frac{d^4}{dx^4}\left(\frac{1}{x + 1}\right) = \frac{d^2}{dx^2}\left(\frac{2}{(x + 1)^2}\right) = \frac{d}{dx}\left(\frac{-4}{(x + 1)^3}\right) = \frac{12}{(x + 1)^4}$$

which occurs when $x = 1$, and equals $M = \dfrac{3}{4}$.

Inequality (7) and the requirement that the error be less than 0.0001 give

$$\frac{(2 - 1)^5\left(\dfrac{3}{4}\right)}{180n^4} < 0.0001$$

so

$$180n^4 > \left(\frac{3}{4}\right)\left(\frac{1}{0.0001}\right) = 7500$$

and

$$n^4 > \frac{7500}{180} = 41.667$$

so

$$n > (41.667)^{1/4} \approx 2.54$$

Thus, $n > 4$ will suffice. (Remember, n must be even.)

3. The exact value of the integral is

$$\int_1^2 \frac{1}{x + 1}\, dx = \left[\ln(x + 1)\right]_1^2 = \ln 3 - \ln 2$$

$$= 0.405465$$

to six decimal place accuracy.

Summary Outline of Chapter 7

▌ *Method of Substitutions*   (Page 501)

$$\int f(g(x))g'(x)\, dx = \int f(u)\, du = F(u) + C$$
$$= F(u(x)) + C$$

where $f = f'$ and $u = g(x)$.

▌ *Integration by Parts*   (Page 509)

$$\int u\, dv = uv - \int v\, du$$

or

$$\int f(x)g'(x)\, dx = f(x)g(x) - \int f'(x)g(x)\, dx.$$

▌ *Improper Integrals*   (Page 524)

$$\int_a^\infty f(x)\, dx = \lim_{t \to \infty} \int_a^t f(x)\, dx \qquad \text{(Type I)}$$

$$\int_{-\infty}^b f(x)\, dx = \lim_{t \to -\infty} \int_t^b f(x)\, dx \qquad \text{(Type I)}$$

$$\int_a^b f(x)\, dx = \lim_{t \to b^-} \int_a^t f(x)\, dx \qquad \text{(Type II)}$$

$$\int_a^b f(x)\, dx = \lim_{t \to a^+} \int_t^b f(x)\, dx \qquad \text{(Type II)}$$

■ **Trapezoidal Rule**   (Page 533)

$$\int_a^b f(x)\, dx \approx \frac{b-a}{2n}\{f(x_0) + 2f(x_1) + 2f(x_2) + \cdots + \qquad (1)$$
$$2f(x_{n-1}) + f(x_n)\}$$

■ **Simpson's Rule**   (Page 536)

$$\int_a^b f(x)\, dx \approx \frac{b-a}{3n}\{f(x_0) + 4f(x_1) + 2f(x_2) + 4f(x_3) + \cdots + \quad (2)$$
$$2f(x_{n-2}) + 4f(x_{n-1}) + f(x_n)\}$$

In (1) and (2), $a = x_0 < x_1 < x_2 < \cdots < x_n = b$ with $x_j = a + j\,\Delta x =$
$a + j\left(\dfrac{b-a}{n}\right)$, $\quad j = 1, 2, \ldots, n$.

In (2), n must be even.

Review Exercises—Chapter 7

In Exercises 1–30, evaluate the integral.

1. $\displaystyle\int \sqrt{x+5}\, dx$

2. $\displaystyle\int x \cos x^2\, dx$

3. $\displaystyle\int \frac{x}{1+x^2}\, dx$

4. $\displaystyle\int \frac{e^{\sqrt{x+1}}}{\sqrt{x+1}}\, dx$

5. $\displaystyle\int_0^1 (x-2)(x^2+3)\, dx$

6. $\displaystyle\int \frac{x}{\sqrt{1-x^2}}\, dx$

7. $\displaystyle\int_0^{\pi/6} \sin^3 x \cos x\, dx$

8. $\displaystyle\int e^{2x} \ln e^{2x}\, dx$

9. $\displaystyle\int x\sqrt{x^2+2}\, dx$

10. $\displaystyle\int_0^1 xe^{3x}\, dx$

11. $\displaystyle\int_0^2 \frac{dx}{(x-3)^2}$

12. $\displaystyle\int xe^{-3x}\, dx$

13. $\displaystyle\int x^2 \ln x\, dx$

14. $\displaystyle\int x^2 \sin x\, dx$

15. $\displaystyle\int_0^3 \frac{1}{\sqrt[3]{x+1}}\, dx$

16. $\displaystyle\int_{-2}^{-1} x(x+3)^6\, dx$

17. $\displaystyle\int_0^{1/4} \sec^2 \pi x\, dx$

18. $\displaystyle\int xe^{-x}\, dx$

19. $\displaystyle\int x^3 \ln x\, dx$

20. $\displaystyle\int_1^\infty \frac{dx}{\sqrt[3]{x+2}}$

21. $\displaystyle\int x \csc^2 x\, dx$

22. $\displaystyle\int \sin(\ln x)\, dx$

23. $\displaystyle\int_{-\infty}^0 e^x\, dx$

24. $\displaystyle\int \frac{x\, dx}{\sqrt{9+x^2}}$

25. $\displaystyle\int_{e^2}^\infty \frac{dx}{x \ln x}$

26. $\displaystyle\int_2^\infty \frac{x}{5+x^2}\, dx$

27. $\displaystyle\int_1^4 \frac{x}{\sqrt{16-x^2}}\, dx$

28. $\displaystyle\int (x+2) \ln x\, dx$

29. $\displaystyle\int \frac{2x+4}{x^2+4x+3}\, dx$

30. $\displaystyle\int \tan 3x\, dx$

31. Carol owns a greeting-card company. The marginal cost of producing its most popular card is

$$MC(x) = \frac{40x^2}{\sqrt{4+x^3}}$$

cents per dozen cards. Find the increase in total costs resulting from an increase in production from two dozen to four dozen cards per day.

32. Terry (see Exercise 47, Section 7.1) inherits a second gas well, this one from his father's uncle. His accountant predicts that this well will produce royalties in the amounts

$$R(t) = 500 + 300 \sin^2 \pi t \cos \pi t$$

dollars per year. Find the total anticipated royalties in the first five years, $\int_0^5 R(t)\, dt$.

33. An ecologist estimates the amount of a certain toxic trace element deposited in a small ecological niche to be

$$A(t) = 400\, te^{2 - t^2}$$

ounces per year t years after a new plant is opened nearby. Find the total amount deposited in the niche during the first four years, $\int_0^4 A(t)\, dt$.

34. Find the consumer's surplus $\int_0^{x_0} D(x)\, dx - p_0 x_0$ for the demand function

$$D(x) = \frac{100}{x\sqrt{x^2 + 9}}$$

at the demand and price levels $x_0 = 4$, $p_0 = D(x_0) = 5$.

35. Find the average value of the function $f(x) = 4 \cos^3 \pi x$ on the interval $\left[0, \dfrac{1}{2}\right]$.

36. Find the area of the region bounded by the graphs of the functions

$$f(x) = \frac{1}{x^2 - 4} \qquad \text{and} \qquad g(x) = \frac{1}{4 - x^2}$$

for $-1 < x < 1$.

CHAPTER 8

Raincoats and umbrellas are "complementary" products—sales of each tend to rise and fall together. Multivariable calculus can be used to analyze relations between complementary and other types of paired products.
(Michael Pasdzior/The Image Bank)

Multivariable Calculus

8.1 Functions of Several Variables

Up to this point, all functions that we have encountered have shared the property of having only a single independent variable. That is, they all have had the form $y = f(x)$. But a function may have more than one independent variable. Here are two examples of functions of the form $z = f(x, y)$. That is, functions with *two* independent variables.

(i) A manufacturing company produces two products, bicycles and roller skates. Its fixed costs of production are $1200 per week. Its variable costs of production are $40 for each bicycle produced and $15 for each pair of roller skates. Its total weekly costs in producing x bicycles and y pairs of roller skates are therefore

$$C(x, y) = 1200 + 40x + 15y.$$

For example, in producing $x = 20$ bicycles and $y = 30$ pairs of roller skates per week the manufacturer experiences total costs of

$$C(20, 30) = 1200 + 40(20) + 15(30)$$

$$= 2450 \text{ dollars.}$$

(ii) The Cobb–Douglas production function

$$f(K, L) = \lambda K^{\alpha} L^{1-\alpha}$$

is a model used by economists to study the relationship between levels of labor, L, and capital goods, K, supplied in a manufacturing process and the resulting level of production, f. Here λ and α are constants, with $0 < \alpha < 1$, and L and K are the two independent variables. For example, in the Cobb–Douglas model

$$f(K, L) = 100 K^{1/4} L^{3/4}$$

the inputs of $K = 256$ units of capital and $L = 16$ units of labor result in

$$f(256, 16) = 100(256)^{1/4}(16)^{3/4}$$
$$= 100(4)(8)$$
$$= 3200$$

units of production.

Functions can be specified with more than two independent variables. For example, the amount of interest I that accrues in a savings account from a single initial deposit of P dollars for t years under continuous compounding of interest at rate r is actually a function of the three independent variables P, r, and t:

$$I(P, r, t) = P(e^{rt} - 1).$$

More generally, we would write a function of the n independent variables $x_1, x_2, \ldots, x_n$ in the form

$$y = f(x_1, x_2, \ldots, x_n).$$

You will encounter many examples of functions of several variables in this chapter. While the number of independent variables may change from example to example, what will not change is the essential property that a *unique* value of the function will be determined for each choice of the independent variables.

□ **EXAMPLE 1**

For the function $f(x, y) = x^2 + 4xy - 2y^3$, we have

$$f(2, 3) = 2^2 + 4(2)(3) - 2(3)^3 = 4 + 24 - 54 = -26$$
$$f(4, 0) = 4^2 + 4(4)(0) - 2(0)^3 = 16 + 0 - 0 = 16$$

and

$$f(-3, 1) = (-3)^2 + 4(-3)(1) - 2(1)^3 = 9 - 12 - 2 = -5. \qquad \blacksquare$$

□ **EXAMPLE 2**

A manufacturer of automobile tires produces three different types—regular, snow, and racing tires. If the regular tires sell for \$60 each, the snow tires for \$50 each, and the racing tires for \$100 each, find a function giving the manufacturer's total receipts from the sale of x regular tires, y snow tires, and z racing tires.

Solution: Since the receipts from the sale of any tire type is the price per tire times the number of tires sold, the total receipts are

$$R(x, y, z) = 60x + 50y + 100z.$$

For example, receipts from the sale of ten tires of each type would be

$$R(10, 10, 10) = 60(10) + 50(10) + 100(10)$$

$$= 2100 \text{ dollars.} \qquad \blacksquare$$

Three-Dimensional Coordinate Systems

Graphing a function of two variables of the form $z = f(x, y)$ requires a **three-dimensional coordinate system** in which to plot the three variables x, y, and z. Figure 1.1 illustrates the convention for coordinatizing three-dimensional space. The usual xy-plane is positioned horizontally, with the z-axis intersecting the xy-plane at the common location of the zeros of each of the three axes. (This point is called the **origin**.) Points of the form (x_0, y_0) in the xy-plane are assigned the coordinates $(x_0, y_0, 0)$ in space, and the point (x_0, y_0, z_0) is located $|z_0|$ units above or below the point $(x_0, y_0, 0)$, depending on the sign of z_0. Several particular points are labeled in Figure 1.2.

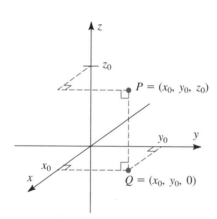

Figure 1.1 Coordinatizing xyz space.

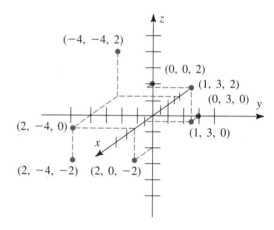

Figure 1.2 Coordinates of several points in space.

☐ **EXAMPLE 3**

Plot the points $P = (2, 1, -3)$ and $Q = (-2, -2, 3)$.

Solution: These points are plotted in Figure 1.3. $\qquad \blacksquare$

Graphs of Functions of Two Variables

We may use a three-dimensional coordinate system to sketch the graph of a function of two variables. Figure 1.4 shows the usual convention for sketching the graph of a function of the form $z = f(x, y)$. For each pair of numbers (x_0, y_0) for which $f(x_0, y_0)$ is defined, the point (x_0, y_0, z_0) is plotted, with $z_0 = f(x_0, y_0)$. Thus the

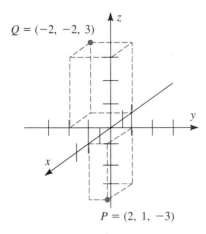

Figure 1.3 Plotting the points P and Q in Example 3.

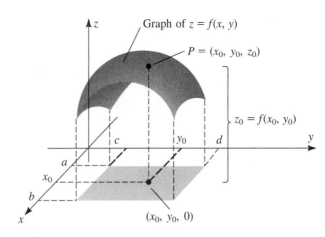

Figure 1.4 The graph of a continuous function $z = f(x, y)$ is a surface in space.

value $z_0 = f(x_0, y_0)$ is represented as the distance of the point (x_0, y_0, z_0) above or below the point $(x_0, y_0, 0)$, depending on the sign of $f(x_0, y_0)$.

For example, Figure 1.5 shows the graph of the function $f(x, y) = x^2 + y^2$, including several particular points, while Figure 1.6 shows the graph of the "hemisphere" $z = \sqrt{4 - x^2 - y^2}$.

Level Curves

Another way to describe the graph of a function of two variables is by the use of *level curves.* Figures 1.7 and 1.8 show the basic idea: For various numbers c we plot the points (x, y) whose coordinates satisfy the equation $c = f(x, y)$. For a given number c the set of all points so obtained constitutes a **level curve.** This level curve

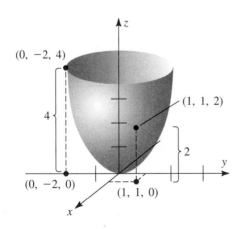

Figure 1.5 Graph of the function $f(x, y) = x^2 + y^2$.

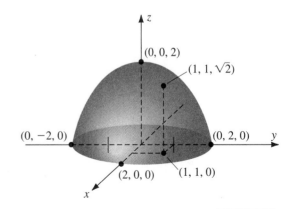

Figure 1.6 Graph of the function $z = \sqrt{4 - x^2 - y^2}$.

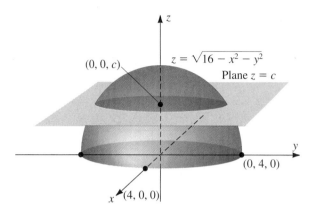

Figure 1.7 Level curves lie at intersection of horizontal plane with graph of $z = f(x, y)$.

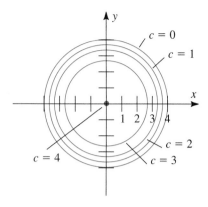

Figure 1.8 Level curves for the function $f(x, y) = \sqrt{16 - x^2 - y^2}$.

may be interpreted as the intersection of the horizontal plane $z = c$ with the graph of the equation $z = f(x, y)$. Although the graph of the function $z = f(x, y)$ is sketched in a three-dimensional coordinate system, its level curves are sketched in the coordinate plane.

One common application of level curves is in contour maps (see Figures 1.9 and 1.10). Other applications are in the construction of maps showing regions of equal temperature (isothermal maps) or maps of equal atmospheric pressure (isobaric maps).

Domains

Unless specified otherwise, the **domain** of a function $z = f(x, y)$ of two variables is the set of all pairs (x, y) for which $f(x, y)$ is defined. Similarly, the domain of a function $y = f(x_1, x_2, \ldots, x_n)$ of n variables is the set of all n-tuples $(x_1, x_2, \ldots, x_n)$ for which $f(x_1, x_2, \ldots, x_n)$ is defined. The following example shows two typical situations in which the domain of a function $z = f(x, y)$ fails to include all points in the plane.

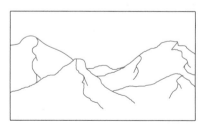

Figure 1.9 A sketch of a mountainous region.

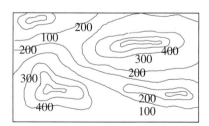

Figure 1.10 A topographical map of the region.

□ **EXAMPLE 4**

Find the domain of each function.

(a) $f(x, y) = \dfrac{6}{2 - x - y}$ (b) $g(x, y) = \sqrt{4 - x^2 - y^2}$

Solution:

(a) The function f is defined for all pairs (x, y) for which the denominator $2 - x - y$ is not zero. Thus we must exclude all pairs (x, y) for which

$$2 - x - y = 0 \quad \text{or} \quad y = 2 - x.$$

Thus the domain of f includes all points (x, y) except those points lying on the line $y = 2 - x$.

(b) The function g is defined only when the quantity $4 - x^2 - y^2$ underneath the radical sign is nonnegative. That is, when $4 - x^2 - y^2 \geq 0$, or $x^2 + y^2 \leq 4$. Thus the domain is the set of all (x, y) for which $\sqrt{x^2 + y^2} \leq 2$. These are the points on and inside the circle with center at the origin and radius $r = 2$ as illustrated in Figure 1.6.   ∎

Continuity

The graph of a *continuous* function of two variables will be a surface in space without any "holes" or "tears," just as the graph of a continuous function $y = f(x)$ of one variable is a curve with the same property. A more precise characterization of continuity is beyond our needs here since almost all functions that we shall encounter in this chapter will be continuous.

☑ **PRACTICE PROBLEMS 8.1**

1. For the function $f(x, y) = 6xy^2 + e^{xy}$, find the following values:
   a. $f(2, 1)$
   b. $f(1, \ln 2)$

2. Find the domain of the function $f(x, y) = \dfrac{xy}{9 - x^2 - y^2}$.

3. The Cobb–Douglas production function is $f(K, L) = 400\, K^{3/4} L^{1/4}$.
   a. Find the production level $f(16, 81)$ resulting from inputs of 16 units of capital and 81 units of labor.
   b. Find $f(81, 16)$.

Exercise Set 8.1

In each of Exercises 1–8, find the indicated values of the given function.

1. $f(x, y) = 3x + 7y$
  a. $f(2, 3)$ **b.** $f(0, -6)$ **c.** $f(-1, 5)$

2. $f(x, y) = 4xy^2 - 3x^2y + 6$
  a. $f(0, 0)$ **b.** $f(1, -2)$ **c.** $f(3, 5)$

3. $f(x, y) = \sqrt{xy} - \dfrac{1}{xy}$
  a. $f(1, 1)$ **b.** $f(-2, -2)$ **c.** $f(1, 9)$

4. $f(x, y) = xe^y - ye^x + e^{xy}$
  a. $f(0, 2)$ **b.** $f(-2, \ln 2)$ **c.** $f(4, 1)$

5. $f(x, y, z) = x^2 - 2xy + xz^3$
  a. $f(1, 2, -1)$ **b.** $f(3, -3, 0)$ **c.** $f(-1, 1, 4)$

6. $f(x, y, z) = xye^z + \ln(x + y) + 3$
  a. $f(2, 1, 0)$ **b.** $f(2, 2, -1)$ **c.** $f(0, 1, 3)$

7. $f(x, y, z) = \sqrt{x^2 + y^2 + z^2}$
  a. $f(0, 1, 0)$ **b.** $f(-2, 1, 2)$ **c.** $f(3, -3, \sqrt{7})$

8. $f(x, y, z) = x\sqrt{y} + \sqrt[3]{xz} - y^{2/3}z^{-1/3}$
  a. $f(1, 1, 0)$ **b.** $f(2, 1, 4)$ **c.** $f(0, 1, -8)$

9. Plot the following points on a three-dimensional coordinate system.
  a. $(1, 1, 2)$ **b.** $(0, 0, 3)$
  c. $(-2, 2, 4)$ **d.** $(1, -3, -2)$

10. Plot the following points on a three-dimensional coordinate system.
  a. $(2, -3, -2)$ **b.** $(-2, -2, 4)$
  c. $(-3, 3, -2)$ **d.** $(2, -1, -3)$

In each of Exercises 11–16, state the domain of the given function.

11. $f(x, y) = 3xy^2 - 5x^3y + 7$

12. $f(x, y) = \sqrt{x^2 + y^2}$

13. $f(x, y) = \dfrac{10x^2}{y^2 - x^2}$

14. $f(x, y) = \ln xy$

15. $f(x, y) = 4x^{2/3}y^{1/4}$

16. $f(x, y, z) = \sqrt{16 - (x^2 + y^2 + z^2)}$

17. Peter runs a hardware store that sells two types of brooms, plastic and fiber. The plastic brooms sell for $10 each, while the fiber brooms sell for $15. Write a function $z = R(x, y)$ giving Peter's weekly revenues from the sale of x plastic and y fiber brooms.

18. Peter, in Exercise 17, assigns $20 per week of his fixed costs to the sale of brooms. If the plastic brooms cost Peter $4 each and the fiber brooms cost Peter $6 each, find the function $z = C(x, y)$ giving Peter's total weekly cost from the sale of x plastic and y fiber brooms.

19. Find the weekly profit function $z = P(x, y)$ for Peter's store in Exercises 17 and 18.

20. Carol runs a bakery that sells muffins and bagels. The muf-

fins cost 35¢ each to make, and the bagels cost 20¢ each. The fixed costs of operating the bakery (light, heat, payroll, etc.) are $75 per day.
  a. Write a function $C(x, y)$ giving the total daily cost of producing x muffins and y bagels.
  b. Find $C(200, 150)$.

21. In Exercise 20, Carol sells the muffins for 75¢ each and the bagels sell for 60¢ each.
  a. Write a function $R(x, y)$ giving the total daily revenues from the sale of x muffins and y bagels.
  b. Find $R(200, 150)$.

22. a. Find the profit function $P(x, y) = R(x, y) - C(x, y)$ for the functions in Exercises 20 and 21.
  b. Find $P(200, 150)$.

23. The amount of $500 is invested in a savings account paying r percent interest compounded continuously.
  a. Find the function $z = P(r, t)$ giving the amount on deposit after t years.
  b. Find $P(0.03, 5)$.
  c. Find $P(0.10, 7)$.

24. Write a function of two variables $z = P_0(r, T)$ giving the *present* value, discounted under the assumption of continuous compounding of interest at the nominal rate of r percent per year, of an investment worth $10,000 in T years.

25. The Cobb–Douglas production function is

$$f(K, L) = 100K^{1/4}L^{3/4}.$$

  a. Find the production level $f(81, 16)$ resulting from $K = 81$ units of capital and $L = 16$ units of labor.
  b. Find the production level $f(16, 81)$.

26. Paul's father runs a business that sells its products in two distinct markets, one domestic and one foreign. In the domestic market, the demand function giving the relationship between selling price p and the number x of items the company can expect to sell per month is given by the equation

$$p = 200 - 2x$$

while in the foreign market the relationship between price, q, and sales level, y, is

$$q = 150 - 3y.$$

The company's monthly cost of producing x items for the domestic market and y items for the foreign market is

$$C(x, y) = 500 + 4x + 5y.$$

a. Find the monthly revenue function

$$R(x, y) = xp + yq$$

in terms of x and y.

b. Find the monthly profit function

$$z = P(x, y) = R(x, y) - C(x, y).$$

27. A medical researcher determines that the effect $E(x, t)$ of a dosage of x units of a certain hypertension drug on a patient t hours after it is administered is given by the function

$$E(x, t) = 20x^{3/2}e^{-0.05t}.$$

a. Find $E(16, 20)$. **b.** Find $E(64, 10)$.

28. Show that in the Cobb–Douglas production function $f(K, L) = \lambda K^{\alpha}L^{1-\alpha}$, with $0 < \alpha < 1$ and λ a constant, doubling the size of both inputs K and L will result in a doubling of the output, $f(K, L)$. Economists refer to this property by saying that such models exhibit *constant returns to scale*.

☑ **SOLUTIONS TO PRACTICE PROBLEMS 8.1**

1. a. $f(2, 1) = 6 \cdot 2 \cdot 1^2 + e^{2 \cdot 1} = 12 + e^2$
  b. $f(1, \ln 2) = 6 \cdot 1(\ln 2)^2 + e^{\ln 2} = 6(\ln 2)^2 + 2.$
2. We require that $9 - x^2 - y^2 \neq 0$, or

$$x^2 + y^2 \neq 3^2.$$

Thus, the domain consists of all points (x, y) not on the circle with center $(0, 0)$ and radius $r = 3$.

3. a. $f(16, 81) = 400 \cdot (16)^{3/4}(81)^{1/4}$
$= 400(2^4)^{3/4}(3^4)^{1/4}$
$= 400 \cdot 2^3 \cdot 3$
$= 9600$

b. $f(81, 16) = 400 \cdot (81)^{3/4}(16)^{1/4}$
$= 400 \cdot (3^4)^{3/4}(2^4)^{1/4}$
$= 400 \cdot 3^3 \cdot 2$
$= 21,600.$

8.2 Partial Differentiation

For a function f of a single variable, the derivative f' measures the rate at which the values $f(x)$ change as the independent variable x changes. For functions $y = f(x_1, x_2, \ldots, x_n)$ of more than one variable we may also ask for the rate at which $f(x_1, x_2, \ldots, x_n)$ changes as the independent variables change, but the question is much more complex. Which of the independent variables are to change, and how? And just what does the answer mean?

Fortunately, a great deal can be learned in such situations from the **partial derivatives** of the function $y = f(x_1, x_2, \ldots, x_n)$. A partial derivative of a function of several variables is just the rate at which the values of the function change as *one* of the independent variables changes and all others are held constant. Thus one partial derivative is obtained for each independent variable.

Definition 1

For the function $z = f(x, y)$ and the point (x_0, y_0) in the domain of f

(a) the partial derivative with respect to x at (x_0, y_0) is the limit

$$\frac{\partial f}{\partial x}(x_0, y_0) = \lim_{h \to 0} \frac{f(x_0 + h, y_0) - f(x_0, y_0)}{h} \qquad (1)$$

(b) the partial derivative with respect to y at (x_0, y_0) is the limit

$$\frac{\partial f}{\partial y}(x_0, y_0) = \lim_{h \to 0} \frac{f(x_0, y_0 + h) - f(x_0, y_0)}{h}. \tag{2}$$

The partial derivative $\frac{\partial f}{\partial x}(x, y)$ is defined whenever the point (x, y) is in the domain of the function f and the limit in equation (1) exists. Its value at (x, y) is the *rate* at which the values $f(x, y)$ change *as x varies but y is held constant*. Thus the partial derivative $\frac{\partial f}{\partial x}(x, y)$ may be calculated by applying appropriate differentiation rules for functions of x alone, treating x as the independent variable and y as a constant.

Similarly, the partial derivative $\frac{\partial f}{\partial y}(x, y)$ may be found by treating y as the single independent variable and x as a constant.

□ EXAMPLE 1

For the function $f(x, y) = x^3 + 4x^2y^3 + y^2$

(a) $\frac{\partial f}{\partial x}(x, y) = 3x^2 + 8xy^3$

since when we treat y as a constant, we have

$$\frac{d}{dx}(x^3) = 3x^2; \qquad \frac{d}{dx}(4x^2y^3) = 8xy^3; \qquad \frac{d}{dx}(y^2) = 0.$$

(b) $\frac{\partial f}{\partial y}(x, y) = 12x^2y^2 + 2y$

since when we treat x as a constant, we have

$$\frac{d}{dy}(x^3) = 0; \qquad \frac{d}{dy}(4x^2y^3) = 12x^2y^2; \qquad \frac{d}{dy}(y^2) = 2y.$$

(c) $\frac{\partial f}{\partial x}(1, 3) = 3(1)^2 + 8(1)(3)^3 = 3 + 8(27) = 219.$

(d) $\frac{\partial f}{\partial y}(2, -4) = 12(2)^2(-4)^2 + 2(-4) = 12(4)(16) - 8 = 760.$ ■

□ EXAMPLE 2

A small factory produces two types of machine parts, bearings and grease seals. The plant manager determines that the total daily cost of production of x hundred bearings and y hundred seals is

$$C(x, y) = 400 + 20x + 8y - 4\sqrt{xy}.$$

For the daily production schedule $x = 10$ and $y = 40$ total daily cost is

$$C(10, 40) = 400 + 20(10) + 8(40) - 4\sqrt{(10)(40)}$$
$$= 840 \text{ dollars.}$$

The partial derivative

$$\frac{\partial C}{\partial x}(x, y) = 20 - \frac{2y}{\sqrt{xy}}$$

gives the rate at which total cost changes with respect to change in x, the number of (hundred) bearings produced. The *rate*

$$\frac{\partial C}{\partial x}(10, 40) = 20 - \frac{2(40)}{\sqrt{(10)(40)}} = 16$$

means that an increase in bearing production from $x = 10$ to $x = 11$, while seal production remains fixed at $y = 40$, will result in an increase in total cost of approximately \$16. Similarly, since

$$\frac{\partial C}{\partial y} = 8 - \frac{2x}{\sqrt{xy}}$$

we have

$$\frac{\partial C}{\partial y}(10, 40) = 8 - \frac{2(10)}{\sqrt{(10)(40)}} = 7$$

which means that an increase in seal production from $y = 40$ to $y = 41$ hundred units, while bearing production remains fixed at $x = 10$, will result in an increase in total cost of approximately \$7.   ■

Notation for Partial Derivatives

There are several commonly used symbols for partial derivatives. For the function $z = f(x, y)$ of two variables

(i) the symbols z_x, $\dfrac{\partial z}{\partial x}$, f_x, and $\dfrac{\partial f}{\partial x}$ all mean $\dfrac{\partial f}{\partial x}(x, y)$;

(ii) the symbols z_y, $\dfrac{\partial z}{\partial y}$, f_y, and $\dfrac{\partial f}{\partial y}$ all mean $\dfrac{\partial f}{\partial y}(x, y)$;

(iii) the expression "$\dfrac{\partial}{\partial x}$" means, "the partial derivative with respect to x of."

Thus,

$$\frac{\partial}{\partial x}f(x, y) \qquad \text{means} \qquad \frac{\partial f}{\partial x}(x, y)$$

$$\frac{\partial}{\partial x}(x^2y^2) = 2xy^2 \qquad \text{and}$$

$$\frac{\partial}{\partial x}(y \ln x + x^3 - \sqrt{y}) = y\left(\frac{1}{x}\right) + 3x^2.$$

(iv) the expression $``\dfrac{\partial}{\partial y}"$ means, "the partial derivative with respect to y of."

Thus,

$$\frac{\partial}{\partial y}f(x, y) \qquad \text{means} \qquad \frac{\partial f}{\partial y}(x, y)$$

$$\frac{\partial}{\partial y}(x^2 y^2) = 2x^2 y \qquad \text{and}$$

$$\frac{\partial}{\partial y}(y \ln x + x^3 - \sqrt{y}) = \ln x - \frac{1}{2\sqrt{y}}.$$

□ **EXAMPLE 3**

For the function $f(x, y) = x^2 e^{y^3} + \sqrt{2x + 3y}$ find (a) $\dfrac{\partial f}{\partial x}$ and (b) $\dfrac{\partial f}{\partial y}$.

Strategy · · · · · · · ·

(a) Treat y, and any terms involving y alone, as constants.

First term has form

$$\frac{d}{dx}(x^2 C) = 2xC$$

with $C = e^{y^3}$.

Second term has form

$$\frac{d}{dx}(2x + C)^{1/2}$$

$$= \frac{1}{2}(2x + C)^{-1/2}(2)$$

with $C = 3y$.

(b) Treat x, and any terms involving x alone, as constants.

First term has form

$$\frac{d}{dy}(Ce^{y^3}) = 3y^2 Ce^{y^3}$$

with $C = x^2$.

Second term has form

$$\frac{d}{dy}(C + 3y)^{1/2}$$

$$= \frac{1}{2}(C + 3y)^{-1/2}(3)$$

with $C = 2x$.

Solution

(a) Differentiating with respect to x, we find

$$\frac{\partial f}{\partial x} = \frac{\partial}{\partial x}(x^2 e^{y^3} + \sqrt{2x + 3y})$$

$$= \frac{\partial}{\partial x}(x^2 e^{y^3}) + \frac{\partial}{\partial x}[(2x + 3y)^{1/2}]$$

$$= \left[\frac{d}{dx}(x^2)\right]e^{y^3} + \frac{1}{2}(2x + 3y)^{-1/2}\left[\frac{\partial}{\partial x}(2x + 3y)\right]$$

$$= [2x]e^{y^3} + \frac{1}{2}(2x + 3y)^{-1/2}(2)$$

$$= 2xe^{y^3} + (2x + 3y)^{-1/2}.$$

(b) Differentiating with respect to y, we find

$$\frac{\partial f}{\partial y} = \frac{\partial}{\partial y}(x^2 e^{y^3} + \sqrt{2x + 3y})$$

$$= \frac{\partial}{\partial y}(x^2 e^{y^3}) + \frac{\partial}{\partial y}[(2x + 3y)^{1/2}]$$

$$= x^2\left[\frac{d}{dy}(e^{y^3})\right] + \frac{1}{2}(2x + 3y)^{-1/2}\left[\frac{\partial}{\partial y}(2x + 3y)\right]$$

$$= x^2[e^{y^3}(3y^2)] + \frac{1}{2}(2x + 3y)^{-1/2}(3)$$

$$= 3x^2 y^2 e^{y^3} + \frac{3}{2}(2x + 3y)^{-1/2}.$$

■

□ **EXAMPLE 4**

For the Cobb–Douglas production function

$$f(K, L) = 20K^{1/4}L^{3/4}$$

(a) Find the rate at which production changes with respect to capital K, called the *marginal productivity of capital,* when $K = 16$ units and $L = 81$ units.
(b) Find the rate at which production changes with respect to labor L, called the *marginal productivity of labor,* when $K = 16$ units and $L = 81$ units.

Solution

(a) The marginal productivity of capital is the partial derivative

$$\frac{\partial f}{\partial K} = \frac{\partial}{\partial K}(20K^{1/4}L^{3/4})$$

$$= 20\left[\frac{d}{dK}(K^{1/4})\right]L^{3/4}$$

$$= 20\left[\frac{1}{4}K^{-3/4}\right]L^{3/4}$$

$$= 5K^{-3/4}L^{3/4}.$$

The desired rate is therefore

$$\frac{\partial f}{\partial K}(16, 81) = 5(16^{-3/4})(81)^{3/4}$$

$$= \frac{5(81)^{3/4}}{16^{3/4}}$$

$$= \frac{5 \cdot 27}{8}$$

$$= \frac{135}{8}.$$

This means that an increase in capital from level $K = 16$ to level $K = 17$ units will result in an increase of approximately $\dfrac{135}{8}$ units of production.

(b) The marginal productivity of labor is

$$\frac{\partial f}{\partial L} = \frac{\partial}{\partial L}(20K^{1/4}L^{3/4})$$

$$= 20K^{1/4}\left[\frac{d}{dL}(L^{3/4})\right]$$

$$= 20K^{1/4}\left[\frac{3}{4}L^{-1/4}\right]$$

$$= 15K^{1/4}L^{-1/4}$$

The desired rate is therefore

$$\frac{\partial f}{\partial L}(16, 81) = 15(16^{1/4})(81^{-1/4})$$

$$= \frac{15(16^{1/4})}{81^{1/4}}$$

$$= \frac{15(2)}{3}$$

$$= 10 \text{ units.}$$

This means that an increase in labor from $L = 81$ to $L = 82$ units will result in an increase of approximately 10 units of production. ∎

Competitive and Complementary Products

An important application of partial derivatives occurs in economic theory where one considers *pairs* of products that either (a) compete with each other or (b) complement each other.

Two products are said to be *competitive* with each other if an increase in demand for one results in a decrease in demand for the other. Coffee and tea are classic examples of competitive products. Others are domestic versus foreign automobiles, commuting by automobile versus commuting by public transportation, and consuming beef versus consuming fish and poultry.

Complementary products have just the opposite relation to each other. An increase in the demand for one results in increased demand for the other as well. Examples of complementary products are golf clubs and golf shoes, razors and shaving creams, and raincoats and umbrellas.

Suppose that the two products, A and B, are competitive. Let p represent the unit price of product A, and let q represent the unit price of product B. Also, let the function $f(p, q)$ represent the *demand* for product A, and let $g(p, q)$ represent the demand for product B, both at price levels p for A and q for B. We can use the partial derivatives $\dfrac{\partial f}{\partial p}, \dfrac{\partial f}{\partial q}, \dfrac{\partial g}{\partial p}$, and $\dfrac{\partial g}{\partial q}$ to distinguish between competitive and complementary products as follows.

(a) First, we observe that we must have both

$$\frac{\partial f}{\partial p} < 0 \quad \text{and} \quad \frac{\partial g}{\partial q} < 0.$$

This is because an increase in the price p for product A must result (at least in theory) in a decrease in demand for that product. Thus, $\dfrac{\partial f}{\partial p} < 0$. Similarly, $\dfrac{\partial g}{\partial q} < 0$ because an increase in the price q for product B will result in a decrease in demand for that product.

(b) Now if $\dfrac{\partial f}{\partial q} > 0$, this would mean that demand for product A increases when the price of product B increases (and the price of product A is held fixed). Similarly, $\dfrac{\partial g}{\partial p} > 0$ would mean that an increase in the price for product A causes an increase in demand for product B. These are the conditions that describe *competitive* products.

(c) If, however, we have $\dfrac{\partial f}{\partial q} < 0$ and $\dfrac{\partial g}{\partial q} < 0$, then an increase in the price of either product results in a decreased demand for the other (and, hence, for both). This is the condition of complementary products.

We summarize our findings as follows.

> If the functions $f(p, q)$ and $g(p, q)$ give the demand for two products, A and B, at respective price levels p and q, then we have the following relationships:
>
> (a) We will always have $\dfrac{\partial f}{\partial p}(p, q) < 0$ and $\dfrac{\partial g}{\partial q}(p, q) < 0.$
>
> (b) If $\dfrac{\partial f}{\partial q}(p, q) > 0$ and $\dfrac{\partial g}{\partial q}(p, q) > 0$, then the products A and B are *competitive* at price levels (p, q).
>
> (c) If $\dfrac{\partial f}{\partial q}(p, q) < 0$ and $\dfrac{\partial g}{\partial q}(p, q) < 0$, then the products A and B are *complementary* at price levels (p, q).

□ **EXAMPLE 5**

Demand for two products, A and B, at respective price levels p and q, is given by the functions

$$f(p, q) = 400 - 5p^2 + 16q \qquad \text{(demand for } A\text{)}$$

and

$$g(p, q) = 600 + 12p - 4q^2 \qquad \text{(demand for } B\text{)}.$$

Are these products competitive or complementary?

Solution: The relevant partial derivatives are

$$\frac{\partial f}{\partial q}(p, q) = \frac{\partial}{\partial q}[400 - 5p^2 + 16q] = 16 > 0$$

and

$$\frac{\partial g}{\partial p}(p, q) = \frac{\partial}{\partial p}[600 + 12p - 4q^2] = 12 > 0.$$

Thus, the products are competitive by statement (b) above. ∎

☐ **EXAMPLE 6**

Demand for raincoats at price p and for umbrellas at price q is given by the functions

$$f(p, q) = \frac{20p}{2p + q}$$

and

$$g(p, q) = \frac{50q}{p + 5q}$$

respectively. Verify that these are complementary products.

Solution: The relevant partial derivatives are

$$\frac{\partial f}{\partial q}(p, q) = \frac{\partial}{\partial q}\left[\frac{20p}{2p + q}\right] = \frac{-20p}{(2p + q)^2} < 0$$

and

$$\frac{\partial g}{\partial p} = \frac{\partial}{\partial p}\left[\frac{50q}{p + 5q}\right] = \frac{-50q}{(p + 5q)^2} < 0.$$

These partial derivatives are both negative because the variables p and q, which represent prices, must be positive. Thus, by statement (c) above, the products are complementary. ∎

A Geometric Interpretation of Partial Derivatives

Figures 2.1 and 2.2 illustrate the geometric interpretations of the partial derivatives in Definition 1. To interpret $\frac{\partial f}{\partial x}(x_0, y_0)$, we note that the set of all points (x, y, z) in space, with $y = y_0$ fixed, is a plane. The intersection of this plane with the graph of $z = f(x, y)$ is a curve in the plane $y = y_0$, which is called the **trace** of $z = f(x, y)$ in the plane $y = y_0$. This curve may be viewed as the graph of the function of one variable

$$h(x) = f(x, y_0) \qquad (y_0 \text{ fixed}).$$

Since

$$h'(x_0) = \frac{\partial f}{\partial x}(x_0, y_0)$$

the partial derivative $\frac{\partial f}{\partial x}(x_0, y_0)$ gives the slope of the line tangent to this trace at the point $P_0 = (x_0, y_0, z_0)$ with $z_0 = f(x_0, y_0)$. That is, $\frac{\partial f}{\partial x}(x_0, y_0)$ *is the slope of the graph of* $z = f(x, y)$ *in the direction of the x-axis at the point* P_0. Similarly, the partial derivative $\frac{\partial f}{\partial y}(x_0, y_0)$ gives the slope of the graph of $z = f(x, y)$ in the direction of the y-axis at the point P_0.

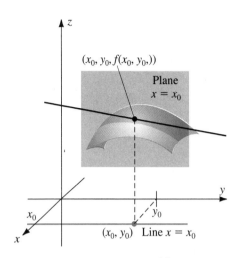

Figure 2.1 Partial derivative $\dfrac{\partial f}{\partial x}(x_0, y_0)$ is the slope of the line tangent to the trace of $z = f(x, y)$ in the plane $y = y_0$.

Figure 2.2 Partial derivative $\dfrac{\partial f}{\partial y}(x_0, y_0)$ is the slope of the line tangent to the trace of $z = f(x, y)$ in the plane $x = x_0$.

☐ **EXAMPLE 7**

A company produces two types of tools, hammers and screwdrivers. The company's profit from the sale of x hundred hammers and y hundred screwdrivers per week is

$$P(x, y) = 20x - x^2 + 40y - y^2.$$

Find the slopes of the graph of $z = P(x, y)$ in the directions of the x- and y-axes at the point $(10, 20, P(10, 20)) = (10, 20, 500)$.

Solution: The partial derivative of P with respect to x is

$$\frac{\partial P}{\partial x} = \frac{\partial}{\partial x}(20x - x^2 + 40y - y^2)$$

$$= 20 - 2x$$

so the slope of the graph of $z = P(x, y)$ at the point $(10, 20, 500)$ in the direction of the x-axis is

$$\frac{\partial P}{\partial x}(10, 20) = 20 - 2(10) = 0.$$

Similarly, since

$$\frac{\partial P}{\partial y} = \frac{\partial}{\partial y}(20x - x^2 + 40y - y^2)$$

$$= 40 - 2y$$

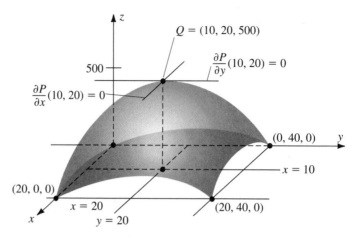

Figure 2.3 Graph of profit function $z = P(x, y)$ in Example 7. At high point, both partial derivatives are zero.

the slope of the graph of $z = P(x, y)$ at the point $(10, 20, 500)$ in the direction of the y-axis is

$$\frac{\partial P}{\partial y}(10, 20) = 40 - 2(20) = 0.$$

Figure 2.3 shows the significance of the fact that both of these slopes are zero at the point $Q = (10, 20, 500)$. In fact, Q is the high point on the graph of $z = P(x, y)$. We shall exploit this idea further to find maximum and minimum values of functions of two variables in Section 6.3. ∎

Functions of More Than Two Variables

Partial derivatives are defined for functions of more than two variables by the same idea used in Definition 1: Hold all variables constant except one, and differentiate the resulting function of a single variable as before. For example, if $w = f(x, y, z)$ is a function of the three independent variables x, y, and z, the three partial derivatives are defined as follows:

$$\frac{\partial f}{\partial x}(x, y, z) = \lim_{h \to 0} \frac{f(x + h, y, z) - f(x, y, z)}{h} \tag{3}$$

$$\frac{\partial f}{\partial y}(x, y, z) = \lim_{h \to 0} \frac{f(x, y + h, z) - f(x, y, z)}{h} \tag{4}$$

$$\frac{\partial f}{\partial z}(x, y, z) = \lim_{h \to 0} \frac{f(x, y, z + h) - f(x, y, z)}{h} \tag{5}$$

Unfortunately, we lose our geometric interpretation in the presence of more than two independent variables. However, we do have the basic interpretation of the derivative as a rate of change. For example, the partial derivative $\dfrac{\partial f}{\partial x}$ in equation (3) is the rate at which the values $f(x, y, z)$ change with respect to change in x. Also, we make use of subscript notation for partial derivatives for functions of more than two variables just as in the two-variable case. That is, if $w = f(x, y, z)$

$$\frac{\partial f}{\partial z}(x, y, z) = \frac{\partial}{\partial z}f(x, y, z) = f_z(x, y, z) = w_z.$$

☐ **EXAMPLE 8**

Let $f(x, y, z) = \sqrt{x}\,e^{y/z}$, $z \neq 0$, $x \geq 0$. Then,

$$\frac{\partial f}{\partial x}(x, y, z) = \left\{\frac{d}{dx}\sqrt{x}\right\}e^{y/z} = \frac{1}{2\sqrt{x}} \cdot e^{y/z}$$

$$\frac{\partial f}{\partial y}(x, y, z) = \sqrt{x}\left\{\frac{\partial}{\partial y}(e^{y/z})\right\} = \sqrt{x}\,e^{y/z} \cdot \frac{1}{z} = \frac{\sqrt{x}}{z}e^{y/z}$$

$$\frac{\partial f}{\partial z}(x, y, z) = \sqrt{x}\left\{\frac{\partial}{\partial z}(e^{y/z})\right\} = \sqrt{x}\,e^{y/z}\left(\frac{-y}{z^2}\right) = \frac{-y\sqrt{x}}{z^2}e^{y/z}. \qquad ■$$

Higher Order Partial Derivatives

Repeated applications of partial differentiation lead to **higher order partial derivatives.** There is nothing terribly complicated about this concept, except that we must be very careful about notation since we encounter **mixed partial derivatives,** in which one differentiation is performed with respect to a particular variable, followed by another differentiation with respect to a different variable.

We shall use the following notation:

$$\frac{\partial^2 f}{\partial x^2}(x, y) = \frac{\partial^2}{\partial x^2}f(x, y) \qquad \text{means} \qquad \frac{\partial}{\partial x}\left(\frac{\partial f}{\partial x}(x, y)\right).$$

$$\frac{\partial^2 f}{\partial y \partial x}(x, y) = \frac{\partial^2}{\partial y \partial x}f(x, y) \qquad \text{means} \qquad \frac{\partial}{\partial y}\left(\frac{\partial f}{\partial x}(x, y)\right).$$

$$\frac{\partial^2 f}{\partial x \partial y}(x, y) = \frac{\partial^2}{\partial x \partial y}f(x, y) \qquad \text{means} \qquad \frac{\partial}{\partial x}\left(\frac{\partial f}{\partial y}(x, y)\right).$$

$$\frac{\partial^2 f}{\partial y^2}(x, y) = \frac{\partial^2}{\partial y^2}f(x, y) \qquad \text{means} \qquad \frac{\partial}{\partial y}\left(\frac{\partial f}{\partial y}(x, y)\right).$$

Note that the order in which the differentiations are performed is indicated by reading the "denominator" of the derivative notation from *right* to *left*. Similar definitions hold for third and higher order partial derivatives.

☐ **EXAMPLE 9**

For the function $f(x, y) = x^2y^3 + e^{4x}\ln y$

$$\frac{\partial^2 f}{\partial x^2}(x, y) = \frac{\partial}{\partial x}\left(\frac{\partial f}{\partial x}(x, y)\right) = \frac{\partial}{\partial x}(2xy^3 + 4e^{4x}\ln y) = 2y^3 + 16e^{4x}\ln y$$

$$\frac{\partial^2 f}{\partial y \partial x}(x, y) = \frac{\partial}{\partial y}\left(\frac{\partial f}{\partial x}(x, y)\right) = \frac{\partial}{\partial y}(2xy^3 + 4e^{4x}\ln y) = 6xy^2 + \frac{4}{y}e^{4x}$$

$$\frac{\partial^2 f}{\partial x \partial y}(x, y) = \frac{\partial}{\partial x}\left(\frac{\partial f}{\partial y}(x, y)\right) = \frac{\partial}{\partial x}\left(3x^2 y^2 + \frac{1}{y}e^{4x}\right) = 6xy^2 + \frac{4}{y}e^{4x}$$

$$\frac{\partial^2 f}{\partial y^2}(x, y) = \frac{\partial}{\partial y}\left(\frac{\partial f}{\partial y}(x, y)\right) = \frac{\partial}{\partial y}\left(3x^2 y^2 + \frac{1}{y}e^{4x}\right) = 6x^2 y - \frac{1}{y^2}e^{4x}$$

$$\frac{\partial^3 f}{\partial y^3}(x, y) = \frac{\partial}{\partial y}\left(\frac{\partial^2 f}{\partial y^2}(x, y)\right) = \frac{\partial}{\partial y}\left(\frac{\partial^2 f}{\partial y^2}\right) = \frac{\partial}{\partial y}\left(6x^2 y - \frac{1}{y^2}e^{4x}\right)$$

$$= 6x^2 + \frac{2}{y^3}e^{4x}.$$

∎

□ **EXAMPLE 10**

For the function $f(x, y) = 4x^2 y - 6xy^3$ show that

$$\frac{\partial^2 f}{\partial x \partial y}(x, y) = \frac{\partial^2 f}{\partial y \partial x}(x, y).$$

Solution: We have

$$\frac{\partial f}{\partial y}(x, y) = \frac{\partial}{\partial y}(4x^2 y - 6xy^3) = 4x^2 - 18xy^2$$

so

$$\frac{\partial^2 f}{\partial x \partial y}(x, y) = \frac{\partial}{\partial x}(4x^2 - 18xy^2) = 8x - 18y^2.$$

Also, since

$$\frac{\partial f}{\partial x}(x, y) = \frac{\partial}{\partial x}(4x^2 y - 6xy^3) = 8xy - 6y^3$$

we have

$$\frac{\partial^2 f}{\partial y \partial x} = \frac{\partial}{\partial y}(8xy - 6y^3) = 8x - 18y^2.$$

Thus

$$\frac{\partial^2 f}{\partial x \partial y}(x, y) = 8x - 18y^2 = \frac{\partial^2 f}{\partial y \partial x}(x, y)$$

as claimed.

∎

Equality of Mixed Partials

The fact that the mixed partial derivatives $\frac{\partial^2 f}{\partial x \partial y}$ and $\frac{\partial^2 f}{\partial y \partial x}$ are the same for the functions in both Example 9 and Example 10 is not a coincidence. Although this is not the case for all functions of two variables, it is true when the function $z = f(x, y)$ and various of its partial derivatives are continuous, as the following theorem states. Its proof is beyond the scope of this text.

Theorem 1	If the function $z = f(x, y)$ and the partial derivatives

$$\frac{\partial f}{\partial x}, \quad \frac{\partial f}{\partial y}, \quad \frac{\partial^2 f}{\partial x \partial y}, \quad \text{and} \quad \frac{\partial^2 f}{\partial y \partial x}$$

are all continuous near the point (x_0, y_0), then

$$\frac{\partial^2 f}{\partial x \partial y}(x_0, y_0) = \frac{\partial^2 f}{\partial y \partial x}(x_0, y_0).$$

☑ **PRACTICE PROBLEMS 8.2**

1. For $f(x, y) = x^3 y^2 + e^{\sqrt{xy}}$ find

   a. $\dfrac{\partial f}{\partial x}(x, y)$

   b. $\dfrac{\partial f}{\partial y}(x, y)$

2. Determine whether the demand functions

$$f(p, q) = 40 + \sqrt{pq} - 10p^{3/2}$$

$$g(p, q) = 10 + 8p^{3/2} - 6q^2$$

represent complementary or competitive products, where f is the demand for the product with price p and g is the demand for the product with price q.

Exercise Set 8.2

In Exercises 1–14, find (a) $\dfrac{\partial f}{\partial x}(x, y)$ and (b) $\dfrac{\partial f}{\partial y}(x, y)$.

1. $f(x, y) = 3x - 6y + 5$

2. $f(x, y) = x^2 - 2xy + y^3$

3. $f(x, y) = 4xy^2 - 3x^3 y + y^5$

4. $f(x, y) = (x + y)^3$

5. $f(x, y) = \sqrt{x + y}$

6. $f(x, y) = x\sqrt{y} - y\sqrt{x}$

7. $f(x, y) = \dfrac{x + y}{x - y}$

8. $f(x, y) = e^{x^2 - 2y}$

9. $f(x, y) = \ln \sqrt{x^2 + y^2}$

10. $f(x, y) = xe^{\sqrt{y}}$

11. $f(x, y) = x^{2/3} y^{-1/3} + \sqrt{\dfrac{y}{x}}$

12. $f(x, y) = \dfrac{x - e^y}{y + e^x}$

13. $f(x, y) = \dfrac{\sqrt{x}}{y} - \dfrac{y}{\sqrt{x}}$

14. $f(x, y) = x^2 2^y + 2^{x - y}$

In Exercises 15–20, find z_x and z_y.

15. $z = \dfrac{x}{y^2} - \dfrac{y}{x^2}$

16. $z = 4 - x^{2/3}\sqrt{y + 1}$

17. $z = ye^{\sqrt{x - 1}}$

18. $z = \ln(x + ye^x)$

19. $z = \sqrt{3^{xy} + e^{x - y}}$

20. $z = \dfrac{x^{5/2} + y^{2/3}}{y - x}$

In Exercises 21–28, find the indicated partial derivative at the given point.

21. For $f(x, y) = 2x(y - 7)$, find $\dfrac{\partial f}{\partial x}(3, 5)$.

22. For $f(x, y) = \dfrac{x}{y + x}$, find $\dfrac{\partial f}{\partial y}(2, -3)$.

23. For $f(x, y) = \sqrt{y^2 + 2x}$, find $\dfrac{\partial f}{\partial y}(4, 1)$.

24. For $f(x, y) = ye^{-2x} + x \ln y$, find $\dfrac{\partial f}{\partial y}(1, 4)$.

25. For $f(x, y, z) = xyz + \dfrac{x}{y + z}$ find $\dfrac{\partial f}{\partial z}(1, -2, 3)$.

26. For $f(x, y, z) = xe^{yz}$, find $\dfrac{\partial f}{\partial y}(2, 0, 3)$.

27. For $f(x, y, z) = xe^{yz}$, find $\dfrac{\partial f}{\partial z}(2, 0, 3)$.

28. For $f(x, y, z) = \sqrt{xyz}$, find $\dfrac{\partial f}{\partial y}(2, 3, 6)$.

29. For $f(x, y) = x^2 - 2xy + y^2$, find

   a. $\dfrac{\partial^2 f}{\partial x^2}$ **b.** $\dfrac{\partial^2 f}{\partial x \partial y}$ **c.** $\dfrac{\partial^2 f}{\partial y \partial x}$ **d.** $\dfrac{\partial^2 f}{\partial y^2}$

30. For $f(x, y) = xe^{y-x}$, find

   a. $\dfrac{\partial^2 f}{\partial x^2}$ **b.** $\dfrac{\partial^2 f}{\partial y \partial x}$ **c.** $\dfrac{\partial^2 f}{\partial x \partial y}$ **d.** $\dfrac{\partial^2 f}{\partial y^2}$

31. For $f(x, y) = \ln(x^2 + y^2)$, find

   a. $\dfrac{\partial^2 f}{\partial x^2}$ **b.** $\dfrac{\partial^2 f}{\partial y \partial x}$ **c.** $\dfrac{\partial^2 f}{\partial x \partial y}$ **d.** $\dfrac{\partial^2 f}{\partial y^2}$

32. For the Cobb–Douglas production function

$$f(K, L) = 40K^{1/3}L^{2/3}$$

   a. Find the marginal productivity of capital, $\dfrac{\partial f}{\partial K}$, at capital level $K = 27$ units and labor level $L = 8$ units.

   b. Find the marginal productivity of labor, $\dfrac{\partial f}{\partial L}$, at capital level $K = 27$ units and labor level $L = 8$ units.

33. Recalling that the partial derivative $\dfrac{\partial f}{\partial K}$ is the *rate* at which the value of the function $z = f(K, L)$ will change with respect to change in K, use the result of Exercise 32a to esti-

mate the change in production resulting from an increase in capital level from $K = 27$ units to $K = 28$ units if the labor level remains constant at $L = 8$ units.

34. A manufacturer of two different types of drugs determines that its monthly revenues from the sale of x units of drug A and y units of drug B is

$$R(x, y) = 40x^2 + 80y^2 - 100x - 200y - 20\sqrt{xy} \text{ dollars.}$$

   a. Find $\dfrac{\partial R}{\partial x}(4, 9)$, the rate at which revenues will increase with respect to increase in sales of drug A, at sales level $x = 4$ units and $y = 9$ units.

   b. $\dfrac{\partial R}{\partial y}(4, 9)$, the rate at which revenues will increase with respect to increase in sales of drug B at sales level $x = 4$ units and $y = 9$ units.

35. Suppose that a person's level of satisfaction resulting from the consumption of x slices of pizza and y glasses of soda in a certain period of time is given by the *utility function* $u(x, y) = 4x^{2/3} + 6y^{3/2} - xy^2$.

   a. Find the marginal utility $\dfrac{\partial u}{\partial x}(8, 4)$.

   b. Find the marginal utility $\dfrac{\partial u}{\partial y}(2, 4)$.

   How would you interpret these results?

36. The amount of interest earned by a deposit of $P_0 = 100$ dollars in a savings account paying a nominal interest rate of r percent per year compounded continuously for t years is given by the function of two variables $P(r, t) = 100(e^{rt} - 1)$.

   a. Find $\dfrac{\partial P}{\partial t}(0.10, 5)$

   b. Use the answer to part (a) to estimate the increase in earned interest if the time period is increased from $t = 5$ to $t = 6$ years and the interest rate remains fixed at $r = 10\%$.

37. For the production function $f(K, L) = 100\sqrt{KL}$

   a. Find $\dfrac{\partial f}{\partial K}(3, 27)$, the marginal productivity of capital when $K = 3$ and $L = 27$.

   b. Find $\dfrac{\partial f}{\partial L}(3, 27)$, the corresponding marginal productivity of labor.

38. An automobile manufacturer determines that the demand for a certain model of automobile is given by a function $z =$

$f(x, y)$ where x is the list price of the automobile and y is the amount of money spent on advertising the automobile per unit time.

a. What would you expect the *sign* of the quantity $\dfrac{\partial f}{\partial x}(x, y)$ to be? Why?

b. What would you expect the sign of $\dfrac{\partial f}{\partial y}(x, y)$ to be? Why?

39. A grocer sells two types of eggs, white and brown. The grocer determines that when the white eggs sell for x dollars per dozen and the brown eggs sell for y dollars per dozen the weekly demand for white eggs is

$$W(x, y) = 150 - 30x^2 + 20y$$

and the weekly demand for brown eggs is

$$B(x, y) = 200 + 40x - 30y^2.$$

a. Show that $\dfrac{\partial W}{\partial x}(1, 1) < 0$ but $\dfrac{\partial W}{\partial y}(1, 1) > 0$, and explain these results.

b. Show that $\dfrac{\partial B}{\partial x}(1, 1) > 0$ but $\dfrac{\partial B}{\partial y}(1, 1) < 0$, and explain these results.

40. A grocery wholesaler determines that demand for coffee is related to the current prices p for coffee and q for tea, by the function

$$f(p, q) = 500 - 30p^2 + hq$$

while the demand for tea is given by the function

$$g(p, q) = 200 - 4q^2 + kp.$$

What can you say about h and k, assuming these products to be competitive?

In each of Exercises 41–45, determine whether the products with the given demand functions would be competitive or complementary.

41. $f(p, q) = 30 - 4p^2 + 16q$
   $g(p, q) = 80 - 12q^2 + 10p$

42. $f(p, q) = 16 - 12p^2 - 4q$
   $g(p, q) = 40 - 6p^2 - 8q^3$

43. $f(p, q) = 25 - 2p^{3/2} + 4 \ln q$
   $g(p, q) = 40 + e^{p/100} - q^{7/3}$

44. $f(p, q) = \dfrac{10p}{4p + 2q}$

   $f(p, q) = \dfrac{30q}{2p + 5q}$

45. $f(p, q) = \dfrac{10q}{q - p}$

   $g(p, q) = \dfrac{5p}{p - 2q}$

☑ **SOLUTIONS TO PRACTICE PROBLEMS 8.2**

1. a. $\dfrac{\partial}{\partial x}(x^3 y^2 + e^{\sqrt{xy}}) = 3x^3 y + \dfrac{ye^{\sqrt{xy}}}{2\sqrt{xy}}$

$$= 3x^2 y^2 + \dfrac{\sqrt{y}e^{\sqrt{xy}}}{2\sqrt{x}}$$

b. $\dfrac{\partial}{\partial y}(x^3 y^2 + e^{\sqrt{xy}}) = 2x^3 y + \dfrac{xe^{\sqrt{xy}}}{2\sqrt{xy}}$

$$= 2x^3 y + \dfrac{\sqrt{x}e^{\sqrt{xy}}}{2\sqrt{y}}$$

2. The relevant partial derivatives are

$$\frac{\partial}{\partial q}f(p, q) = \frac{\partial}{\partial q}[40 + \sqrt{pq} - 10p^{3/2}]$$

$$= \frac{p}{2\sqrt{pq}} > 0$$

and

$$\frac{\partial}{\partial p} g(p, q) = \frac{\partial}{\partial p}[10 + 8p^{3/2} - 6q^2]$$

$$= 12p^{1/2} > 0.$$

Thus, since both of these partial derivatives are positive, the products are competitive.

8.3 Relative Maxima and Minima

Just as for functions of a single variable, we wish to know how to find maximum and minimum values of functions of several variables. Our discussion of how to do so will be largely confined to finding *relative extrema* for functions of two variables.

Definition 2

The number $z_0 = f(x_0, y_0)$ is called a **relative maximum** for the function $z = f(x, y)$ if there exists a circle C with center (x_0, y_0) and radius $r \neq 0$ so that, for all points inside C, $f(x, y)$ is defined and

$$f(x_0, y_0) \geq f(x, y).$$

The number $f(x_0, y_0)$ is a **relative minimum** for $z = f(x, y)$ if, for all points (x, y) inside such a circle C, $f(x, y)$ is defined and

$$f(x_0, y_0) \leq f(x, y).$$

A **relative extremum** refers to either a relative maximum or a relative minimum.

In other words, a relative maximum $f(x_0, y_0)$ is the largest value of the function $z = f(x, y)$ for all points (x, y) ''near'' (x_0, y_0), and similarly for relative minima.

☐ **EXAMPLE 1**

Figure 3.1 shows a portion of the graph of the function $f(x, y) = 2x + 4y - x^2 - y^2 - 1$. This function has a relative maximum value at the point $(1, 2)$ of $z = f(1, 2) = 4$, as you can observe by calculating values of $f(x, y)$ near this point. Note also that both partial derivatives $\dfrac{\partial f}{\partial x}$ and $\dfrac{\partial f}{\partial y}$ are zero at this point. Indeed, since

$$\frac{\partial f}{\partial x}(x, y) = 2 - 2x; \qquad \frac{\partial f}{\partial y}(x, y) = 4 - 2y$$

we have $\dfrac{\partial f}{\partial x}(1, 2) = 2 - 2(1) = 0$ and $\dfrac{\partial f}{\partial y}(1, 2) = 4 - 2(2) = 0.$ ∎

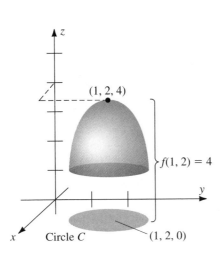

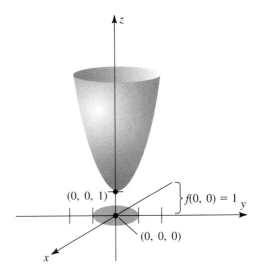

Figure 3.1 $f(1, 2) = 4$ is relative maximum for the function $f(x, y) = 2x + 4y - x^2 - y^2 - 1$.

Figure 3.2 $f(0, 0) = 1$ is relative minimum for $f(x, y) = e^{x^2+y^2}$.

□ **EXAMPLE 2**

Figure 3.2 shows a portion of the graph of $f(x, y) = e^{x^2+y^2}$. This function has a relative minimum value at $(0, 0)$ of $f(0, 0) = e^0 = 1$, where the exponent $x^2 + y^2$ has its minimum value. Again, note that both partial derivatives are zero at this point:

$$\frac{\partial f}{\partial x}(x, y) = 2xe^{x^2+y^2} \qquad \text{so} \qquad \frac{\partial f}{\partial x}(0, 0) = 0$$

$$\frac{\partial f}{\partial y}(x, y) = 2ye^{x^2+y^2} \qquad \text{so} \qquad \frac{\partial f}{\partial y}(0, 0) = 0.$$

Figure 3.3 illustrates why both partial derivatives, if they exist, must equal zero at a point (x_0, y_0) corresponding to a relative extremum:

(i) If $f(x_0, y_0)$ is a relative maximum and $\frac{\partial f}{\partial x}(x, y)$ exists for all (x, y) near (x_0, y_0), then by holding y fixed at $y = y_0$ we obtain a differentiable function of the single variable x, $g(x) = f(x, y_0)$. Since $f(x_0, y_0)$ is a relative maximum for f, $g(x_0)$ must be a relative maximum for g. Thus we must have

$$g'(x_0) = \frac{\partial f}{\partial x}(x_0, y_0) = 0.$$

(ii) Similarly, if $f(x_0, y_0)$ is a relative maximum, we may fix x at $x = x_0$ and obtain

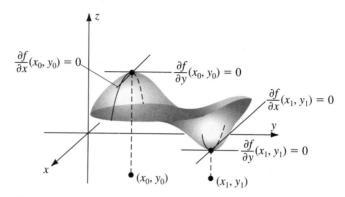

Figure 3.3 At a relative maximum or minimum of f both partial derivatives, if they exist, must equal zero.

the function $h(y) = f(x_0, y)$, which has a maximum at $y = y_0$. Thus,

$$h'(y_0) = \frac{\partial f}{\partial y}(x_0, y_0) = 0.$$

Statements (i) and (ii) apply to relative minima as well. Geometrically, these conclusions simply state that if $f(x_0, y_0)$ is a relative extremum, the slopes of the tangents to the graph of $z = f(x, y)$ parallel to the x- and y-axes at the point $(x_0, y_0, f(x_0, y_0))$, if they exist, must equal zero. ∎

The following theorem summarizes these observations.

Theorem 2

If the number $z = f(x_0, y_0)$ is a relative maximum or minimum for the function $z = f(x, y)$, and if both partial derivatives $\frac{\partial f}{\partial x}(x_0, y_0)$ and $\frac{\partial f}{\partial y}(x_0, y_0)$ exist, then we must have

$$\frac{\partial f}{\partial x}(x_0, y_0) = \frac{\partial f}{\partial y}(x_0, y_0) = 0.$$

Theorem 2 suggests a very straightforward procedure for finding points where extrema may occur: Find those points at which both partial derivatives simultaneously equal zero. As for functions of a single variable, we shall refer to such points as **critical points.** (Extrema can also occur at points where one or both partial derivatives fail to exist, but we shall not consider such functions here. See Exercise 26 for one such example.)

Before stating how to determine whether a critical point corresponds to a relative maximum or relative minimum, if either, we should note that a critical point need not correspond to an extremum at all. Figure 3.4 shows the graph of the function $f(x, y) = y^2 - x^2$. Since

$$\frac{\partial f}{\partial x}(x, y) = \frac{\partial}{\partial x}(y^2 - x^2) = -2x$$

and

$$\frac{\partial f}{\partial y}(x, y) = \frac{\partial}{\partial y}(y^2 - x^2) = 2y$$

it is easy to see that $\frac{\partial f}{\partial x}(0, 0) = \frac{\partial f}{\partial y}(0, 0) = 0$, so the point $(0, 0)$ is a critical point. But it is just as easy to see that the value $f(0, 0) = 0$ is neither a relative maximum nor a relative minimum. With y fixed at $y = 0$ the point $(0, 0, 0)$ corresponds to a relative maximum for the function $g(x) = f(x, 0) = -x^2$, but with x fixed at $x = 0$ the point $(0, 0, 0)$ corresponds to a relative minimum for the function $h(y) = f(0, y) = y^2$. (See Figure 3.4.) Such points are called **saddle points.**

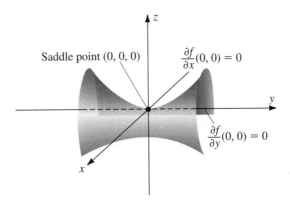

Figure 3.4 The point $(0, 0, 0)$ on the graph of $z = y^2 - x^2$ is a *saddle point*—neither a relative maximum or minimum, even though $\frac{\partial f}{\partial x}(0, 0) = \frac{\partial f}{\partial y}(0, 0) = 0$.

The following theorem is a sort of "Second Derivative Test" for functions of two variables. We shall use it to classify critical points as relative maxima, relative minima, or saddle points. Its proof is omitted.

Theorem 3
Second Derivative Test

Suppose that all second order partial derivatives of $z = f(x, y)$ are continuous in a circle with center (x_0, y_0) and that $\frac{\partial f}{\partial x}(x_0, y_0) = \frac{\partial f}{\partial y}(x_0, y_0) = 0$. Let

$$A = \frac{\partial^2 f}{\partial x^2}(x_0, y_0), \qquad B = \frac{\partial^2 f}{\partial y \partial x}(x_0, y_0), \qquad C = \frac{\partial^2 f}{\partial y^2}(x_0, y_0)$$

and

$$D = B^2 - AC.$$

Then

(i) If $D < 0$ and $A < 0$, $f(x_0, y_0)$ is a relative maximum.
(ii) If $D < 0$ and $A > 0$, $f(x_0, y_0)$ is a relative minimum.
(iii) If $D > 0$, $(x_0, y_0, f(x_0, y_0))$ is a saddle point.
(iv) If $D = 0$, no conclusions may be drawn.

□ **EXAMPLE 3**

We can use the Second Derivative Test to verify that the critical point $(1, 2)$ for the function

$$f(x, y) = 2x + 4y - x^2 - y^2 - 1$$

of Example 1 indeed corresponds to a relative maximum. Since

$$\frac{\partial f}{\partial x}(x, y) = 2 - 2x \quad \text{and} \quad \frac{\partial f}{\partial y}(x, y) = 4 - 2y$$

we have

$$\frac{\partial^2 f}{\partial x^2} = -2; \quad \frac{\partial^2 f}{\partial y \partial x} = 0; \quad \frac{\partial^2 f}{\partial y^2} = -2.$$

Thus $A = -2$, $B = 0$, $C = -2$, and $D = 0^2 - (-2)(-2) = -4$. Since $D < 0$ and $A < 0$, the critical point $(1, 2)$ corresponds to a relative maximum by part (i) of Theorem 3. ∎

□ **EXAMPLE 4**

Find and classify all extreme points for the function $f(x, y) = 4x - 2y - x^2 - 2y^2 + 2xy - 10$.

Strategy

Set $\dfrac{\partial f}{\partial x} = 0$.

Solution

We begin by finding the critical point(s). Setting

$$\frac{\partial f}{\partial x} = 4 - 2x + 2y = 0$$

gives the equation

$$-2x + 2y = -4. \tag{1}$$

Similarly, setting

Set $\dfrac{\partial f}{\partial y} = 0$.

$$\frac{\partial f}{\partial y} = -2 - 4y + 2x = 0$$

gives the equation

$$2x - 4y = 2. \tag{2}$$

Solve the resulting pair of equations by substitution (or by addition) to find the critical point(s).

We must therefore find the simultaneous solution of the pair of equations (1) and (2):

$$-2x + 2y = -4 \tag{3}$$

$$2x - 4y = 2. \tag{4}$$

Solving the first equation for x gives

$$-2x = -4 - 2y$$

or

$$x = 2 + y. \tag{5}$$

Substituting this expression for x into equation (4) gives

$$2(2 + y) - 4y = 2$$

or

$$4 - 2y = 2.$$

Thus

$$-2y = -2$$

so

$$y = 1.$$

Substituting this value of y back into equation (5) then gives

$$x = 2 + (1) = 3.$$

Calculate the second order partials and determine A, B, C, and D for each critical point.

The single critical point is therefore $(3, 1)$. To test this critical point, we calculate

$$A = \frac{\partial^2 f}{\partial x^2}(3, 1) = -2$$

$$B = \frac{\partial^2 f}{\partial y \partial x}(3, 1) = 2$$

$$C = \frac{\partial^2 f}{\partial y^2}(3, 1) = -4$$

and

$$D = B^2 - AC = (2)^2 - (-2)(-4) = -4.$$

Apply the Second Derivative Test.

Since $D < 0$ and $A < 0$ the critical point $(3, 1)$ corresponds to the *relative maximum* value

$$f(3, 1) = 4(3) - 2(1) - 3^2 - 2(1^2) + 2(3)(1) - 10$$
$$= -5.$$

☐ **EXAMPLE 5**

Find and classify all relative extrema for the function

$$f(x, y) = x^4 + y^4 - 4xy.$$

Strategy · · · · · · · ·

Set $\dfrac{\partial f}{\partial x} = 0$ and solve.

Solution

To find the critical points we begin by setting

$$\frac{\partial f}{\partial x} = 4x^3 - 4y = 0$$

which gives the equation

$$y = x^3. \tag{6}$$

Set $\dfrac{\partial f}{\partial y} = 0$ and solve.

Similarly, setting $\dfrac{\partial f}{\partial y}$ equal to zero gives

$$\frac{\partial f}{\partial y} = 4y^3 - 4x = 0$$

or

$$x = y^3. \tag{7}$$

Solve the two resulting equations by substitution, obtaining a single equation for y and then finding the corresponding values for x.

Since both equations (6) and (7) must hold at a critical point, we substitute $x = y^3$ from equation (7) into equation (6) to obtain

$$y = x^3 = (y^3)^3 = y^9$$

or

$$y = y^9. \tag{8}$$

Each pair (x_0, y_0) gives a critical point for $f(x, y)$.

Thus either $y = 0$ or, after dividing both sides of equation (8) by y, $y^8 = 1$. This last equation has solutions $y = -1$ and $y = 1$. Using equation (7), we then find that

$$\text{if} \quad y = 0, \qquad x = 0^3 = 0$$
$$\text{if} \quad y = -1, \qquad x = (-1)^3 = -1$$
$$\text{if} \quad y = 1, \qquad x = (1)^3 = 1.$$

We therefore have three critical points to check: $(0, 0)$, $(-1, -1)$, and $(1, 1)$.

Calculate all second order partials.

The second partials of $f(x, y)$ are

$$\frac{\partial^2 f}{\partial x^2} = \frac{\partial}{\partial x}(4x^3 - 4y) = 12x^2$$

$$\frac{\partial^2 f}{\partial y \partial x} = \frac{\partial}{\partial y}(4x^3 - 4y) = -4$$

$$\frac{\partial^2 f}{\partial y^2} = \frac{\partial}{\partial y}(4y^3 - 4x) = 12y^2.$$

At each critical point substitute the coordinates to obtain A, B, C, and D and apply Theorem 3.

Thus at the critical point $(0, 0)$ we have

$$A = 12(0)^2 = 0, \qquad B = -4, \qquad C = 12(0)^2 = 0$$

and

$$D = (-4)^2 - (0)(0) = 16 > 0.$$

Thus $(0, 0, 0)$ is a saddle point.

At the critical point $(-1, -1)$, we have

$$A = 12(-1)^2 = 12, \qquad B = -4, \qquad C = 12(-1)^2 = 12$$

and

$$D = (-4)^2 - (12)(12) = -128 < 0.$$

Thus since $A > 0$, $f(-1, -1) = -2$ is a relative minimum.

Finally, at the critical point $(1, 1)$, we have

$$A = 12(1)^2, \qquad B = -4, \qquad C = 12(1)^2 = 12$$

and

$$D = (-4)^2 - (12)(12) = -128 < 0.$$

Since, again, $A > 0$, $f(1, 1) = -2$ is a relative minimum. ■

Applications of Relative Extrema

The following examples are typical of applied problems in which the desired maximum or minimum value of a function occurs at a relative extremum. Although there are other ways in which absolute extrema can occur (such as at points where partial derivatives fail to exist, or at "boundary points" of the domain of the function), we shall not consider such problems in this text.

☐ **EXAMPLE 6**

A company produces electronic typewriters and word processors. It sells the electronic typewriters for $100 each and the word processors for $300 each. The company has determined that its weekly total cost in producing x electronic typewriters and y word processors is given by the joint cost function

$$C(x, y) = 2000 + 50x + 80y + x^2 + 2y^2.$$

Find the numbers x and y of machines that the company should manufacture and sell weekly in order to maximize profits.

Solution: Since the typewriters sell for $100 each and the word processors for $300 each, the weekly revenue from the sale of x typewriters and y word processors is

$$R(x, y) = 100x + 300y.$$

The weekly profit function to be maximized is therefore

$$P(x, y) = R(x, y) - C(x, y)$$

$$= (100x + 300y) - (2000 + 50x + 80y + x^2 + 2y^2)$$

$$= 50x + 220y - x^2 - 2y^2 - 2000.$$

Setting the two partial derivatives equal to zero gives

$$\frac{\partial P}{\partial x} = 50 - 2x = 0$$

so

$$x = 25$$

and

$$\frac{\partial P}{\partial y} = 220 - 4y = 0$$

so

$$y = 55.$$

To test the single critical point $(25, 55)$, we note that

$$A = \frac{\partial^2 P}{\partial x^2} = -2; \qquad B = \frac{\partial^2 P}{\partial y \partial x} = 0; \qquad C = \frac{\partial^2 P}{\partial y^2} = -4$$

and $D = B^2 - AC = 0 - (-2)(-4) = -8$. Since $D < 0$ and $A < 0$, the critical point $(25, 55)$ corresponds to a relative maximum. The production schedule for maximum profit is therefore $x = 25$ typewriters and $y = 55$ word processors, which yields a profit of

$$P = (25, 55) = 50(25) + 220(55) - 25^2 - 2(55)^2 - 2000$$

$$= 4675 \text{ dollars.} \qquad \blacksquare$$

☐ **EXAMPLE 7**

A grocer sells two types of eggs, white and brown, which compete with each other for sales depending on how they are priced. The grocer has determined that when the white eggs sell for x dollars per dozen and the brown eggs for y dollars per dozen, the daily sales of the white eggs will be

$$W(x, y) = 30 - 15x + 3y$$

dozen, while the daily sales of the brown eggs will be

$$B(x, y) = 20 - 12y + 2x$$

dozen. Find the prices x and y for which the grocer's daily revenue from the sale of eggs will be a maximum.

Solution: The grocer's daily revenue from selling white eggs at price x and brown eggs at price y will be

$$R(x, y) = xW(x, y) + yB(x, y)$$

$$= x(30 - 15x + 3y) + y(20 - 12y + 2x)$$

$$= 30x - 15x^2 + 5xy + 20y - 12y^2.$$

To find the critical point(s), we set the partial derivatives equal to zero:

$$\frac{\partial R}{\partial x} = 30 - 30x + 5y = 0$$

gives

$$30x - 5y = 30$$

or

$$6x - y = 6 \tag{9}$$

and

$$\frac{\partial R}{\partial y} = 5x + 20 - 24y = 0$$

gives

$$5x - 24y = -20. \tag{10}$$

To find the simultaneous solution of equations (9) and (10), we first solve (9) for y, obtaining

$$y = 6x - 6 \tag{11}$$

which we use to substitute for y in equation (10) to obtain

$$5x - 24(6x - 6) = -20$$

which gives

$$-139x + 144 = -20$$

or

$$x = \frac{164}{139} \approx 1.18.$$

From equation (11) we then obtain

$$y = 6\left(\frac{164}{139}\right) - 6 = \frac{150}{139} \approx 1.08.$$

To test the critical point $\left(\dfrac{164}{139}, \dfrac{150}{139}\right)$, we calculate

$$A = \frac{\partial^2 R}{\partial x^2} = -30, \qquad B = \frac{\partial^2 R}{\partial y \partial x} = 5, \qquad C = \frac{\partial^2 R}{\partial y^2} = -24$$

and $D = B^2 - AC = 25 - (-30)(-24) = -695$. Since $D < 0$ and $A < 0$, the critical point corresponds to a relative maximum by Theorem 3. The grocer will therefore maximize egg revenues by pricing the white eggs at $1.18 per dozen and the brown eggs at $1.08 per dozen. ∎

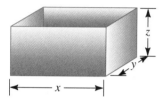

Figure 3.5 Container in Example 8.

□ **EXAMPLE 8**

A container company wishes to design an open rectangular container with a capacity of 144 cubic feet. If the material for the bottom costs $4 per square foot and the material for the sides costs $3 per square foot, find the dimensions for which the cost of materials will be a minimum.

Solution: Let the container have length x feet, width y feet, and height z feet, as in Figure 3.5. Since the area of the bottom is xy square feet, the cost of the bottom will be $4xy$. Similarly, the cost of the front and back panels will be $3xz$ each, and the cost of the end panels will be $3yz$ each. The total cost function to be minimized is therefore

$$\begin{aligned} C(x, y, z) &= 4xy + 2(3xz) + 2(3yz) \\ &= 4xy + 6xz + 6yz. \end{aligned}$$

Although this is a function of three variables, there is an *auxiliary* equation that we can use to substitute for one of the variables in terms of the other two. It is simply the statement that volume equals 144 cubic feet. That is

$$xyz = 144 \qquad \text{or} \qquad z = \frac{144}{xy}.$$

Substituting this expression for z into the cost function gives the function of two variables:

$$C(x, y) = 4xy + 6x\left(\frac{144}{xy}\right) + 6y\left(\frac{144}{xy}\right)$$

$$= 4xy + \frac{864}{y} + \frac{864}{x}.$$

We now proceed to minimize C as before. The equation

$$\frac{\partial C}{\partial x}(x, y) = 4y - \frac{864}{x^2} = 0$$

gives

$$y = \frac{216}{x^2} \tag{12}$$

and the equation

$$\frac{\partial C}{\partial y}(x, y) = 4x - \frac{864}{y^2} = 0$$

gives, using equation (12)

$$x = \frac{216}{y^2} = \frac{216}{\left(\dfrac{216}{x^2}\right)^2} = \frac{x^4}{216}.$$

Thus, either $x = 0$ or else

$$x^3 = 216 \qquad \text{so} \qquad x = \sqrt[3]{216} = 6.$$

With $x = 6$, equation (12) gives $y = \dfrac{216}{6^2} = 6$. We leave it to you to verify that the single critical point $(6, 6)$ actually yields a relative minimum. The dimensions for minimum cost are therefore $x = 6$ feet, $y = 6$ feet, and $z = \dfrac{144}{6^2} = 4$ feet. ∎

Functions of More Than Two Variables

The discussion of this section has focused on finding relative extrema for functions of two variables. For functions of more than two variables Theorem 2 generalizes directly. For example, if the function $w = f(x, y, z)$ of three variables has a relative extremum at the point (x_0, y_0, z_0) and each of its three partial derivatives exists at this point, then we must have

$$\frac{\partial f}{\partial x}(x_0, y_0, z_0) = \frac{\partial f}{\partial y}(x_0, y_0, z_0) = \frac{\partial f}{\partial z}(x_0, y_0, z_0) = 0.$$

However, the Second Derivative Test does not generalize quite so easily. For functions of more than two variables the classification of critical points is considerably more difficult and will not be pursued here.

☑ PRACTICE PROBLEMS 8.3

1. For the following function, find all critical points and determine whether each corresponds to a relative maximum, a relative minimum, or a saddle point.

$$f(x, y) = x^2 - y^3 - 10x + 12y + 6$$

2. A company produces two products, called product A and product B. The total cost of producing x units of product A and y units of product B per week is determined to be

$$C(x, y) = 100 + 40x + 2x^2 + 60y + \frac{5}{2}y^2 + 2xy \text{ dollars.}$$

If product A sells for $80 per unit and product B sells for $160 per unit, what amounts of product A and product B should the company manufacture and sell per week in order to maximize profits?

Exercise Set 8.3

In each of Exercises 1–16, find all critical points for f and determine whether each corresponds to a relative maximum, a relative minimum, or a saddle point.

1. $f(x, y) = x^2 + y^2 + 4y + 4$

2. $f(x, y) = x^2 - 3y^2 + 4x + 6y + 10$

3. $f(x, y) = x^2 + 2y^2 - 6x + 4y - 8$

4. $f(x, y) = 2x - 6y - x^2 - 2y^2 + 10$

5. $f(x, y) = x^2 - y^2 + 6x + 4y + 5$

6. $f(x, y) = x^2 - 5xy + 6y^2 + 3x - 2y - 3$

7. $f(x, y) = xy + 9$

8. $f(x, y) = 3x^2 - 7xy + 4y^2 - x - y + 5$

9. $f(x, y) = 5x^2 + y^2 - 10x - 6y + 15$

10. $f(x, y) = x^2 + y^3 - 3y$

11. $f(x, y) = x^3 - y^3$

12. $f(x, y) = e^{x^2 - 2x + y^2 + 4}$

13. $f(x, y) = x^3 + y^3 + 4xy$

14. $f(x, y) = y^3 - x^2 - 5x - 12y + 5$

15. $f(x, y) = x^2 + y^2 + x - 2y + xy + 5$

16. $f(x, y) = x^2 + 3y^2 - 2x + 3y + 2xy - 6$

17. A sewing machine manufacturer sells its machines in two markets, foreign and domestic. It determines that the profit resulting from the sale of x machines in the domestic market and y machines in the foreign market per week is

$$P(x, y) = 30x + 90y - 0.5x^2 - 2y^2 - xy.$$

Find the number of machines that should be sold in the domestic and foreign markets per week in order to maximize profits.

18. For the tool company in Example 5, Section 8.2, with profit equation

$$P(x, y) = 20x - x^2 + 40y - y^2$$

find the point (x, y) for which profit is a maximum.

19. A company determines that the productivity of its manufacturing plant resulting from weekly expenditures of x thousand dollars in labor and y thousand dollars in equipment is

$$P(x, y) = 40x + 80y - 2x^2 - 10y^2 - 4xy.$$

Find the point (x, y) for which productivity is a maximum.

20. A company determines that if x units of labor and y units of capital equipment are used to meet its weekly production schedule, the total cost of operating the factory is

$$C(x, y) = 10,000 + 10x^2 + 15y^2 - 100x - 200y + 10xy.$$

Find the mix (x, y) of labor and equipment that minimizes costs.

21. The prices p and q of two items are related to the number of items, x and y, that will be sold during a fixed period of time by the demand equations

$$p = 20 - x; \qquad q = 46 - \frac{5}{2}y.$$

The total cost of producing x items of the first kind and y items of the second kind during this period is

$$C(x, y) = 100 + 4x + 2y + xy.$$

Find the number of items, x and y, for which profit will be a maximum.

22. A grocer sells two brands of coffee, A and B. Brand A is a premium coffee that costs the grocer $2 per pound. Brand B, a generic brand, costs only $1 per pound. The grocer determines that if he charges x dollars per pound for Brand A and y dollars per pound for Brand B, he can sell

$$D_A(x, y) = 30 - 5x + y$$

pounds of brand A and

$$D_B(x, y) = 40 - 4y + x$$

pounds of brand B per week.
a. Find the grocer's weekly revenue function $R(x, y) = xD_A(x, y) + yD_B(x, y)$ from the sale of coffee.
b. Assuming the grocer's only cost in selling coffee is the price paid per pound, find the grocer's weekly profit function $P = R - C$.
c. Find the values of x and y for which P is a maximum.

23. A rectangular box, with a top, is to hold 64 cubic meters. Find the dimensions that produce the least expensive box if the material for the side walls is half as expensive as the material for the top and bottom.

24. Find the dimensions of the closed rectangular box of volume $V = 64$ cubic meters and of minimum surface area.

25. Find the dimensions of the rectangular package of largest volume that can be mailed under the restrictions that length plus girth cannot exceed 84 inches. (Girth is the perimeter of the cross-section taken perpendicular to the length.)

26. Figure 3.6 shows the graph of the function $f(x, y) = \sqrt{x^2 + y^2}$.

   a. Explain why the function $f(x, y)$ has a relative minimum value of $f(0, 0) = 0$ at $(0, 0)$.

   b. Show that neither $\dfrac{\partial f}{\partial x}(0, 0)$ nor $\dfrac{\partial f}{\partial y}(0, 0)$ is defined.

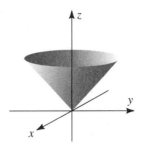

Figure 3.6 Graph of $f(x, y) = \sqrt{x^2 + y^2}$.

☑ **SOLUTIONS TO PRACTICE PROBLEMS 8.3**

1. To find the critical points, we set

$$\frac{\partial f}{\partial x}(x, y) = \frac{\partial}{\partial x}[x^2 - y^3 - 10x + 12y + 6] = 2x - 10 = 0$$

to obtain $x = 5$, and

$$\frac{\partial f}{\partial y}(x, y) = \frac{\partial}{\partial y}[x^2 - y^3 - 10x + 12y + 6] = -3y^2 + 12 = 0$$

to obtain $y = \pm\sqrt{\dfrac{12}{3}} = \pm 2$.

The critical points are therefore $(5, -2)$ and $(5, 2)$.
   At $(5, -2)$, we have

$$A = \frac{\partial^2 f}{\partial x^2}(5, -2) = 2; \quad B = \frac{\partial^2 f}{\partial x \partial y}(5, -2) = 0; \quad C = \frac{\partial^2 f}{\partial y^2}(5, -2) = 12.$$

Thus,

$$B^2 - AC = 0 - 2(12) = -24 < 0, \quad \text{and} \quad A = 2 > 0.$$

Thus,

$$f(5, -2) = 5^2 - (-2)^3 - (10)(5) + (12)(-2) + 6 = -35$$

is a relative minimum.
   At $(5, 2)$ we have

$$A = \frac{\partial^2 f}{\partial x^2}(5, 2) = 2; \quad B = \frac{\partial^2 f}{\partial x \partial y}(5, 2) = 0; \quad \text{and} \quad C = \frac{\partial^2 f}{\partial y^2}(5, 2) = -12$$

so

$$B^2 - AC = 0 - 2(-12) = 24 > 0$$

which shows that $f(5, 2) = -3$ corresponds to a saddle point.

2. The revenue resulting from the sale of x units of product A and y units of product B is

$$R(x, y) = 80x + 160y$$

so the profit function is

$$P(x, y) = R(x, y) - C(x, y)$$

$$= (80x + 160y) - \left(100 + 40x + 2x^2 + 60y + \frac{5}{2}y^2 + 2xy\right)$$

$$= 40x + 100y - 100 - 2x^2 - \frac{5}{2}y^2 - 2xy.$$

Then

$$\frac{\partial P}{\partial x}(x, y) = 40 - 4x - 2y = 0$$

gives

$$2x + y = 20$$

and

$$\frac{\partial P}{\partial y}(x, y) = 100 - 5y - 2x = 0$$

gives

$$2x + 5y = 100.$$

The system of equations

$$2x + y = 20$$

$$2x + 5y = 100$$

has simultaneous solution $x = 0$, $y = 20$. At the critical point $(0, 20)$, we have

$$\frac{\partial^2 P}{\partial x^2}(0, 20) = -4 \qquad \text{(equals } A\text{)}$$

$$\frac{\partial^2 P}{\partial x \partial y}(0, 20) = -2 \qquad \text{(equals } B\text{)}$$

$$\frac{\partial^2 P}{\partial y^2}(0, 20) = -5 \qquad \text{(equals } C\text{)}$$

Thus $B^2 - AC = 4 - (-4)(-5) = -16 < 0$ and $A = -4 < 0$. Thus, the maximum value of the profit function is

$$P(0, 20) = 100(20) - 100 - \frac{5}{2}(20)^2$$

$$= 900$$

which occurs at production level $x = 0$, $y = 20$.

8.4 Optimization Problems with Constraints

Frequently, especially in business applications, it is necessary to find the maximum or minimum value of a function of two variables subject to a **constraint,** which is an additional condition that must be satisfied by the independent variables. The presence of such a constraint can change both the optimum (maximum or minimum) value of the function as well as the points at which the optimum occurs.

For example, suppose that a company determines that the profit resulting from the production and sale of x standard and y deluxe dishwashers per day is given by the profit function

$$P(x, y) = 40x + 20y - x^2 - y^2 \text{ dollars.} \tag{1}$$

In order to find the production schedule (x, y) for which profit is a maximum, we would apply the technique of Section 6.3. Setting the partial derivative $\dfrac{\partial P}{\partial x}$ equal to zero, we obtain

$$\frac{\partial P}{\partial x}(x, y) = 40 - 2x = 0$$

which gives $2x = 40$, or $x = 20$. Setting $\dfrac{\partial P}{\partial y} = 0$, we obtain

$$\frac{\partial P}{\partial y} = 20 - 2y = 0$$

which gives $2y = 20$, or $y = 10$. Thus the only critical point is $(x, y) = (20, 10)$. You can verify, using the Second Derivative Test, that this critical point corresponds to a relative maximum. Thus profit will be a maximum when the company manufactures 20 standard and 10 deluxe dishwashers per day. The maximum profit is $P(20, 10) = 500$ dollars per day.

But now suppose that the production capacity of the company's manufacturing plant is limited to a total of 20 dishwashers per day. This is an example of a *constraint,* which we can represent by the equation

$$x + y = 20. \tag{2}$$

Equation (2) simply states that the number of standard and deluxe dishwashers produced per day must equal 20. Clearly, this constraint prohibits the production schedule $(x, y) = (20, 10)$.

Finding the production schedule (x, y) for which the profit function P is a maximum subject to the constraint given by equation (2) is an example of an *optimization problem with a constraint,* which we can show as follows.

☐ **EXAMPLE 1**

Find the maximum value of the profit function

$$P(x, y) = 40x + 20y - x^2 - y^2 \tag{3}$$

subject to the constraint

$$x + y = 20. \tag{4}$$

Solution: Solving equation (4) for y gives

$$y = 20 - x. \tag{5}$$

Substituting this expression for y in equation (3) then gives the profit function P as a function of the single variable x:

$$P(x) = 40x + 20(20 - x) - x^2 - (20 - x)^2$$
$$= 40x + 400 - 20x - x^2 - (400 - 40x + x^2)$$
$$= 60x - 2x^2.$$

To find the maximum value of P, we set

$$P'(x) = 60 - 4x = 0$$

and conclude that $4x = 60$, or $x = 15$. Since $P''(15) = -4 < 0$, the Second Derivative Test verifies that this critical number corresponds to a relative maximum value for P. Equation (5) then gives $y = 20 - 15 = 5$. The maximum profit therefore occurs when $x = 15$ standard and $y = 5$ deluxe dishwashers are manufactured per day. It is

$$P(15, 5) = 40(15) + 20(5) - (15)^2 - 5^2$$
$$= 450 \text{ dollars.} \qquad \blacksquare$$

The Geometry of Constraints

Figure 4.1 illustrates the effect of a constraint on the problem of finding the maximum or minimum value of a function. In this case the problem is to find the maximum value of the function

$$f(x, y) = 16 - x^2 - y^2 \tag{6}$$

subject to the constraint

$$x + y = 2. \tag{7}$$

If the constraint were not present, the maximum value of f would be $f(0, 0) = 16$ since the highest point on the graph of $z = f(x, y)$ is $(0, 0, 16)$, which lies directly above the point $(0, 0, 0)$ in the xy-plane.

However, since the constraint restricts the domain of f to the points (x, y) lying on the line $x + y = 2$, the constrained maximum corresponds to the highest point lying on the curve C, which is the part of the graph of f lying above the line $x + y = 2$.

To find this maximum, we proceed as before to solve the constraint equation (7) for y, obtaining $y = 2 - x$, and substitute this expression for y into equation (6). This gives the function whose graph corresponds to the curve C:

$$f(x) = 16 - x^2 - (2 - x)^2$$
$$= 16 - x^2 - (x^2 - 4x + 4)$$
$$= 12 + 4x - 2x^2.$$

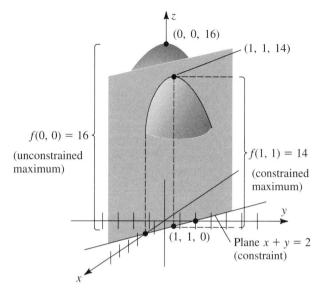

Figure 4.1 Maximum value of $f(x, y) = 16 - x^2 - y^2$, subject to the constraint $x + y = 2$, is $f(1, 1) = 14$.

The maximum value of this function is found by setting $f'(x) = 0$. Since

$$f'(x) = 4 - 4x$$

the equation $f'(x) = 0$ gives $4x - 4 = 0$, or $x = 1$. Equation (7) then gives $y = 1$. Thus the constrained maximum is $f(1, 1) = 16 - 1^2 - 1^2 = 14$, which corresponds to the "high" point on the curve C, namely, $(1, 1, 14)$.

The Method of Lagrange Multipliers

Up to this point we have approached the problem of finding the maximum or minimum value of $z = f(x, y)$ subject to a constraint by solving the constraint equation for one of the independent variables and substituting this result into the expression for $f(x, y)$. This reduces f to a function of a single variable to which the techniques of Chapter 3 can be applied.

However, this method is not always ideal, since the constraint equation may be difficult to solve, or the resulting function of a single variable may be difficult to work with.

The mathematician Joseph L. Lagrange (1736–1813) discovered a different method for solving such problems, which is often superior to the substitution method. In order to describe Lagrange's method, we need to think of the constraint equation in the form

$$g(x, y) = 0. \qquad \text{(constraint)}$$

This can always be done by simply moving all nonzero terms to one side of the equation. For example, the constraint equation $x + y = 20$ in Example 1 can be written

$$x + y - 20 = 0$$

by subtracting 20 from both sides. Thus $g(x, y) = x + y - 20$ in this example. The following theorem, whose proof is beyond the scope of this text, is the basis for Lagrange's method.

Theorem 4

Method of Lagrange

Let f and g have continuous partial derivatives. If a relative maximum or minimum value of the function f subject to the constraint

$$g(x, y) = 0$$

occurs at the point (x, y), then there is a number λ for which the point (x, y, λ) is a critical point for the function $L = f + \lambda g$.

The variable λ that appears in Theorem 4 is called the **Lagrange multiplier.** Since the critical points of the function $L = f + \lambda g$ are found by setting all partial derivatives equal to zero, the **method of Lagrange multipliers** is:

(i) Form the function $L = f + \lambda g$, with values

$$L(x, y, \lambda) = f(x, y) + \lambda g(x, y).$$

(ii) Set all partial derivatives of L equal to zero, obtaining the equations

$$\frac{\partial L}{\partial x} = 0, \quad \text{or} \quad \frac{\partial f}{\partial x} + \lambda \frac{\partial g}{\partial x} = 0 \tag{L1}$$

$$\frac{\partial L}{\partial y} = 0, \quad \text{or} \quad \frac{\partial f}{\partial y} + \lambda \frac{\partial g}{\partial y} = 0 \tag{L2}$$

$$\frac{\partial L}{\partial \lambda} = 0, \quad \text{or} \quad g(x, y) = 0. \tag{L3}$$

(iii) For the simultaneous solutions (x, y, λ) of equations (L1)–(L3), inspect the values $f(x, y)$ to obtain the desired maximum or minimum.

□ **EXAMPLE 2**

Find the maximum value of the utility function

$$u(x, y) = xy$$

subject to the constraint that

$$5x + 2y = 20.$$

(This problem would arise, for example, if the utility of consumption of x pizzas and y sodas is xy, the cost of pizzas is $5 each, the cost of sodas is $2 each, and the total amount available for snacks is $20.)

Strategy · · · · · · · ·
Identify the constraint function $g(x, y)$.

Solution

Here we can write the constraint as $g(x, y) = 0$ with

$$g(x, y) = 5x + 2y - 20.$$

Form the function $L(x, y, \lambda) = f(x, y) + \lambda g(x, y)$.

The Lagrange function is therefore

$$L(x, y, \lambda) = xy + \lambda(5x + 2y - 20).$$

Set the partials equal to zero.

Setting the partial derivatives equal to zero gives the equations

$$\frac{\partial L}{\partial x} = 0$$

$$y + 5\lambda = 0 \qquad (8)$$

$$\frac{\partial L}{\partial y} = 0$$

$$x + 2\lambda = 0 \qquad (9)$$

$$\frac{\partial L}{\partial \lambda} = 0$$

$$5x + 2y - 20 = 0. \qquad (10)$$

Solve the first equation for y, the second for x, and insert the results in the third equation.

Solve the resulting equation for λ. Then find x, y.

Substituting the values $y = -5\lambda$ and $x = -2\lambda$ from equations (8) and (9) into equation (10) gives

$$5(-2\lambda) + 2(-5\lambda) - 20 = 0$$

or

$$-20\lambda = 20.$$

Thus $\lambda = -1$, so $x = -2(-1) = 2$ and $y = -5(-1) = 5$. We leave it to you to verify that the value

$$u(2, 5) = 2 \cdot 5 = 10$$

is the maximum value of utility rather than the minimum. ∎

☐ **EXAMPLE 3**

Use the method of Lagrange multipliers to find the maximum and minimum values of the function

$$f(x, y) = xy$$

subject to the constraint that $x^2 + y^2 = 8$.

Solution: The constraint is $g(x, y) = 0$ with $g(x, y) = x^2 + y^2 - 8$, so the Lagrange function is

$$L(x, y, \lambda) = xy + \lambda(x^2 + y^2 - 8).$$

Setting the three partial derivatives equal to zero gives

$$\left(\frac{\partial L}{\partial x} = 0\right) \qquad y + 2\lambda x = 0, \qquad \text{or} \qquad y = -2\lambda x \qquad (11)$$

$$\left(\frac{\partial L}{\partial y} = 0\right) \qquad x + 2\lambda y = 0, \qquad \text{or} \qquad x = -2\lambda y \qquad (12)$$

$$\left(\frac{\partial L}{\partial \lambda} = 0\right) \qquad x^2 + y^2 - 8 = 0. \qquad (13)$$

Multiplying both sides of equation (11) by y gives

$$y^2 = -2\lambda xy$$

and multiplying both sides of equation (12) by x gives

$$x^2 = -2\lambda xy.$$

It then follows that $y^2 = x^2$, so equation (13) becomes

$$2x^2 - 8 = 0, \quad \text{or} \quad x^2 = 4.$$

Thus $x = \pm 2$, and since $y^2 = x^2$, $y = \pm x$. The four critical points to be checked are therefore $(-2, -2)$, $(-2, 2)$, $(2, -2)$, and $(2, 2)$. We find that

$$f(-2, -2) = (-2)(-2) = 4 \quad \text{(constrained maximum)}$$

$$f(-2, 2) = (-2)(2) = -4 \quad \text{(constrained minimum)}$$

$$f(2, -2) = (2)(-2) = -4 \quad \text{(constrained minimum)}$$

$$f(2, 2) = (2)(2) = 4. \quad \text{(constrained maximum)}$$

The maximum value of f subject to the constraint is therefore 4, and the minimum is -4.

Figure 4.2 illustrates the geometry of this example. The constraint describes the circle with center at the origin and radius $\sqrt{8}$, which intersects the level curves for the graph of $f(x, y) = xy$ at the critical points. ∎

Constraints often arise in business and economics applications due to limitations on budget, manufacturing capacity, or other economic factors. The following is one such example.

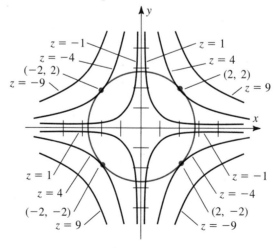

Figure 4.2 Level curves for $f(x, y) = xy$ intersect constraint curve $x^2 + y^2 = 8$ at critical points for Lagrange function $L(x, y, \lambda) = f(x, y) + \lambda g(x, y)$.

□ **EXAMPLE 4**

A manufacturing company determines that the level of production resulting from the use of x units of labor and y units of capital per hour to produce a certain product is given by the Cobb–Douglas production function

$$P(x, y) = 100x^{1/4}y^{3/4}.$$

Each unit of labor costs \$200 and each unit of capital costs \$100. If a total of \$800 worth of labor and capital is to be used per hour, find the amounts of labor and capital for which production will be a maximum.

Solution: Since labor costs \$200 per unit, the cost of x units of labor is $200x$. Similarly, the cost of y units of capital is $100y$. The *budget* constraint is therefore

$$200x + 100y = 800.$$

The problem is thus to maximize

$$P(x, y) = 100x^{1/4}y^{3/4}$$

subject to the constraint

$$g(x, y) = 200x + 100y - 800 = 0.$$

The Lagrange function is

$$L(x, y, \lambda) = 100x^{1/4}y^{3/4} + \lambda(200x + 100y - 800).$$

Setting the three partial derivatives equal to zero gives the equations

$$\left(\frac{\partial L}{\partial x} = 0\right) \qquad 25x^{-3/4}y^{3/4} + 200\lambda = 0 \tag{14}$$

$$\left(\frac{\partial L}{\partial y} = 0\right) \qquad 75x^{1/4}y^{-1/4} + 100\lambda = 0 \tag{15}$$

$$\left(\frac{\partial L}{\partial \lambda} = 0\right) \qquad 200x + 100y - 800 = 0. \tag{16}$$

Equation (14) gives

$$\lambda = \frac{-25}{200}x^{-3/4}y^{3/4} = -\frac{1}{8}x^{-3/4}y^{3/4}$$

and equation (15) gives

$$\lambda = \frac{-75}{100}x^{1/4}y^{-1/4} = -\frac{3}{4}x^{1/4}y^{-1/4}.$$

Thus,

$$-\frac{1}{8}x^{-3/4}y^{3/4} = -\frac{3}{4}x^{1/4}y^{-1/4}. \tag{17}$$

Multiplying both sides of equation (17) by $-8x^{3/4}y^{1/4}$ gives

$$y = 6x. \tag{18}$$

Substituting this expression for y into equation (16) then gives

$$200x + 100(6x) - 800 = 0$$

or

$$800x = 800.$$

Thus $x = 1$ and, by equation (18), $y = 6$.

Since it is clear that smaller values of production can be obtained (say, $P(4, 0) = 0$ with $x = 4$ and $y = 0$), the value $P(1, 6) = 100(1)^{1/4}(6)^{3/4} = 100(6)^{3/4}$ must be the maximum production level attainable within this budget constraint.

■

Functions of Three Variables

The method of Lagrange multipliers also applies to the problem of finding the maximum or minimum value of a function of three variables $w = f(x, y, z)$ subject to a constraint of the form $g(x, y, z) = 0$. The Lagrange function is again $L = f + \lambda g$. That is

$$L(x, y, z, \lambda) = f(x, y, z) + \lambda g(x, y, z)$$

and the method is again to set all partial derivatives of L equal to zero and solve the resulting set of (four) equations. To illustrate this technique, we shall rework Example 8 from Section 6.3.

☐ **EXAMPLE 5**

A container company wishes to design an open rectangular container with capacity 144 cubic feet. If the material for the bottom costs \$4 per square foot and the material for the sides costs \$3 per square foot, find the dimensions for which the cost of materials will be a minimum.

Solution: If we label the dimensions of the container x, y, and z as in Figure 4.3, the area of the front and back panels is xz each, so their total cost is $2(3)xz = 6xz$ dollars. Similarly, the cost of the two end panels is $2(3)yz = 6yz$ dollars, and the cost of the bottom is $4xy$ dollars. The total cost of the material is therefore

$$C(x, y, z) = 4xy + 6xz + 6yz$$

which we must minimize subject to the volume constraint

$$V(x, y, z) = xyz - 144 = 0.$$

The Lagrange function is therefore

$$L(x, y, z, \lambda) = 4xy + 6xz + 6yz + \lambda(xyz - 144).$$

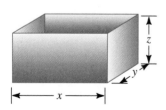

Figure 4.3 Container in Example 5.

Setting the four partial derivatives equal to zero gives the equations

$$\left(\frac{\partial L}{\partial x} = 0\right) \qquad 4y + 6z + \lambda yz = 0 \tag{19}$$

$$\left(\frac{\partial L}{\partial y} = 0\right) \qquad 4x + 6z + \lambda xz = 0 \tag{20}$$

$$\left(\frac{\partial L}{\partial z} = 0\right) \qquad 6x + 6y + \lambda xy = 0 \tag{21}$$

$$\left(\frac{\partial L}{\partial \lambda} = 0\right) \qquad xyz - 144 = 0. \tag{22}$$

This time it is helpful to begin by multiplying both sides of equation (19) by x, both sides of equation (20) by y, and both sides of equation (21) by z and then solving each for the form λxyz. We obtain

$$4xy + 6xz = -\lambda xyz \tag{23}$$

$$4xy + 6yz = -\lambda xyz \tag{24}$$

$$6xz + 6yz = -\lambda xyz. \tag{25}$$

Equating the left-hand sides of equations (23) and (24) then gives

$$4xy + 6xz = 4xy + 6yz$$

so

$$6xz = 6yz.$$

Dividing both sides by $6z$ (which cannot be zero since z is a dimension of a box) then gives

$$x = y. \tag{26}$$

Similarly, equating the left-hand sides of equations (24) and (25) gives

$$4xy + 6yz = 6xz + 6yz$$

so

$$4xy = 6xz$$

and

$$z = \frac{4xy}{6x} = \frac{2}{3}y. \tag{27}$$

From equations (26) and (27) we now have $y = x$ and $z = \frac{2}{3}y = \frac{2}{3}x$. Returning to equation (22), we find that

$$x(x)\left(\frac{2}{3}x\right) - 144 = 0$$

or

$$\frac{2}{3}x^3 = 144.$$

Thus

$$x^3 = \frac{3}{2}(144) = 216$$

so

$$x = \sqrt[3]{216} = 6$$
$$y = 6$$

and

$$z = \frac{2}{3}(6) = 4$$

as found in Section 8.3. ∎

☑ **PRACTICE PROBLEMS 8.4**

1. Find the minimum value of the function

$$f(x, y, z) = x^2 + y^2 + z^2$$

   subject to the constraint $x + y + z = 25$.
2. A manufacturer wishes to construct a rectangular box, with a top, of volume 8 cubic feet. If the material for the sides costs $2 per square foot, the material for the bottom costs $3 per square foot, and the material for the top costs $1 per square foot, find the dimensions that give the box of minimum cost.

Exercise Set 8.4

In Exercises 1–12, find the minimum and maximum values of the function f subject to the given constraint.

1. $f(x, y) = xy$ subject to $x + 4y = 8$.

2. $f(x, y) = 2x^2 + 4y^2$ subject to $2x - 4y + 3 = 0$.

3. $f(x, y) = x^2 - 8x + y^2 + 4y - 6$ subject to $2x = y - 5$.

4. $f(x, y) = 4y - 2x$ subject to $x^2 + y^2 = 2$.

5. $f(x, y) = xy$ subject to $x^2 + y^2 = 32$.

6. $f(x, y) = x^2 + y$ subject to $x^2 + y^2 = 9$.

7. $f(x, y) = x^3 - y^3$ subject to $x - y = 2$.

8. $f(x, y, z) = x + 2y - z$ subject to $x^2 + y^2 + z^2 = 24$.

9. $f(x, y, z) = xyz$ subject to $x^2 + y^2 + z^2 = 12$.

10. $f(x, y, z) = x + y + z$ subject to $x^2 + y^2 + z^2 = 12$.

11. $f(x, y, z) = x^2 + y^2 + z^2$ subject to $x - y + z = 1$.

12. $f(x, y, z) = x + 2y + z$ subject to $x^2 + y^2 + z^2 = 4$.

13. Find the production levels x and y for which the production function

$$P(x, y) = 60x^{1/4}y^{3/4}$$

   is a maximum when subjected to the constraint $20x + 10y = 80$.

14. Find the critical point for the Lagrange function

$$L(x, y, \lambda) = 8x^2 + 2y^2 - 4xy + \lambda(4x + 2y - 20).$$

Does this point correspond to a maximum or a minimum for the function $f(x, y) = 8x^2 + 2y^2 - 4xy$ subject to the constraint $4x + 2y = 20$?

15. A manufacturer of television sets produces both color and black and white sets. The weekly profit from the production and sale of x color and y black and white sets is

$$P(x, y) = 200x + 100y - 4x^2 - 2y^2.$$

In order to produce one color set 20 units of labor are required, while only 10 units of labor are required to produce a black and white set. If 600 units of labor are available per week, how many of each type of set should the manufacturer produce in order to maximize profit?

16. Find the maximum value of the production function

$$P(x, y) = 10x + 25y - 5xy$$

subject to the budget constraint $4x + 2y = 40$.

17. Find the maximum value of the profit function

$$P(x, y) = 20x + 40y - x^2 - y^2$$

subject to the capacity constraint that $x + y = 40$.

18. A rectangular box, with a top, is to hold 16 cubic meters. Find the dimensions that produce the least expensive box if the material for the side walls is half as expensive as the material for the top and the bottom.

19. Find the dimensions of the rectangular package of largest volume that can be mailed under the restrictions that length plus girth cannot exceed 84 inches. (Girth is the perimeter of the cross-section taken perpendicular to the length.)

20. A shipper wishes to design an open rectangular container. The material for the sides costs $4 per square foot and the material for the bottom costs $5 per square foot. If the total cost of materials is not to exceed $960, find the dimensions of the container of maximum volume.

21. A cylindrical can, with a top and a bottom, is to be manufactured using 100 square centimeters of tin, ignoring waste. What dimensions produce the can of maximum volume? (See Figure 4.4.)

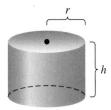

Figure 4.4

22. A builder wishes to design a rectangular house containing V cubic meters of heated space, so as to minimize heating costs. One wall of the building is to face south. The annual heating costs are estimated to be $4 per square meter of floor space, $3 per square meter for all exterior walls not facing south, and $2 per square meter for exterior wall space facing south. What dimensions will produce the most energy-efficient building? (See Figure 4.5.)

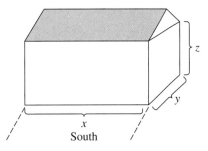

Figure 4.5

23. Find the dimensions for the cylindrical jar with a volume of 2 liters, which has minimum exterior surface area. Assume that the jar has a lid.

24. Recall that for the production function $z = P(x, y)$, where x represents units of labor and y represents units of capital used in production per unit time, the partial derivative $\dfrac{\partial P}{\partial x}$ is called the *marginal productivity of labor* and the partial derivative $\dfrac{\partial P}{\partial y}$ is called the *marginal productivity of capital*. For the production function $P(x, y) = 100x^{1/4}y^{3/4}$ in Example 4

a. Find $\dfrac{\partial P}{\partial x}(1, 6)$, the marginal productivity of labor at the optimum production level.

b. Find $\dfrac{\partial P}{\partial y}(1, 6)$, the marginal productivity of capital at the optimum production level.

c. Recall that the unit cost of labor in this example is 200, while the unit cost of capital is 100. Show that the ratio

$$\frac{200}{100} = 2 \text{ also equals the ratio } \frac{\dfrac{\partial P}{\partial x}(1, 6)}{\dfrac{\partial P}{\partial y}(1, 6)} \text{ of the marginal}$$

productivities of labor and capital.

d. Show that the same conclusion holds for the production function in Exercise 13.

✓ **SOLUTIONS TO PRACTICE PROBLEMS 8.4**

1. The constraint is $g(x, y, z) = x + y + z - 25 = 0$, so the Lagrange function is

$$L(x, y, z, \lambda) = x^2 + y^2 + z^2 + \lambda(x + y + z - 25).$$

Setting the four partial derivatives equal to zero gives

$$\left(\frac{\partial L}{\partial x} = 0\right) \qquad 2x + \lambda = 0 \tag{28}$$

$$\left(\frac{\partial L}{\partial y} = 0\right) \qquad 2y + \lambda = 0 \tag{29}$$

$$\left(\frac{\partial L}{\partial z} = 0\right) \qquad 2z + \lambda = 0 \tag{30}$$

$$\left(\frac{\partial L}{\partial \lambda} = 0\right) \qquad x + y + z = 25. \tag{31}$$

Solving equations (28)–(30) for x, y, and z, respectively, gives the equations

$$x = -\frac{\lambda}{2}; \qquad y = -\frac{\lambda}{2}; \qquad z = -\frac{\lambda}{2}.$$

Substituting this value for x, y, and z in equation (31) then gives

$$3\left(-\frac{\lambda}{2}\right) = 25$$

so

$$\lambda = -\frac{50}{3}.$$

Thus,

$$x = y = z = \left(-\frac{\lambda}{2}\right) = \frac{25}{3}$$

and the minimum value of the function f subject to the given constraint is

$$f\left(\frac{25}{3}, \frac{25}{3}, \frac{25}{3}\right) = \frac{625}{3}.$$

The verification that this is the *minimum* value of f subject to the constraint, rather than the maximum value, is left to you.

2. Let the variables x, y, and z represent the length, width, and height of the box, respectively. Then the costs associated with the various panels are as follows:

Top: $(xy)(\$1) = xy$ dollars;
Sides: $2(xz)(\$2) + 2(yz)(\$2) = 4xz + 4yz$ dollars;
Bottom: $xy(\$3) = 3xy$ dollars.

The volume of such a box will be $V(x, y, z) = xyz$, so the constraint is that $xyz = 8$. We may therefore state the problem as follows:

Find the minimum value of the total cost function

$$C(x, y, z) = 4xy + 4xz + 4yz$$

subject to the constraint

$$xyz - 8 = 0.$$

To solve this problem, we form the Lagrange function

$$L(x, y, z, \lambda) = 4xy + 4xz + 4yz + \lambda(xyz - 8)$$

and set the partial derivatives equal to zero:

$$(L_x = 0): \qquad 4y + 4z + \lambda yz = 0 \qquad\qquad (32)$$

$$(L_y = 0): \qquad 4x + 4z + \lambda xz = 0 \qquad\qquad (33)$$

$$(L_z = 0): \qquad 4x + 4y + \lambda xy = 0 \qquad\qquad (34)$$

$$(L_\lambda = 0): \qquad xyz - 8 = 0. \qquad\qquad (35)$$

Multiplying all terms of equation (32) by x gives

$$4xy + 4xz + \lambda xyz = 0.$$

Multiplying all terms of equation (33) by y gives

$$4xy + 4yz + \lambda xyz = 0.$$

Subtracting the second of these equations from the first gives

$$4xz - 4yz = 0, \qquad \text{so} \qquad x = y.$$

Similarly, equations (33) and (34) give

$$4z - 4y = 0, \qquad \text{or} \qquad z = y.$$

Thus, $x = y = z$, and equation (35) gives

$$x^3 = 8, \qquad \text{or} \qquad x = 2.$$

Thus, the cube $x = y = z = 2$ feet gives the box of minimum cost, as you can verify.

8.5 Linear Approximation and Total Differentials

In Chapter 3 we saw that values of a differentiable function f could be approximated by the linear approximation

$$f(x) \approx f(x_0) + f'(x_0)(x - x_0) \qquad\qquad (1)$$

for x near x_0. Equation (1) was used in applications where $x_0, f(x_0),$ and $f'(x_0)$ were known from given information.

Equation (1) generalizes directly to a linear approximation for a function of two variables when both partial derivatives exist:

$$f(x, y) \approx f(x_0, y_0) + \frac{\partial f}{\partial x}(x_0, y_0)(x - x_0) + \frac{\partial f}{\partial y}(x_0, y_0)(y - y_0) \qquad\qquad (2)$$

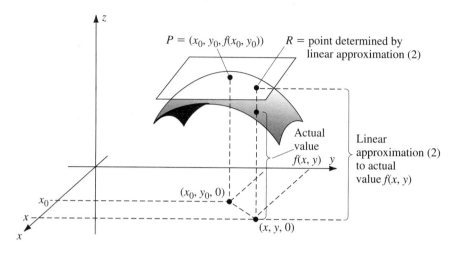

Figure 5.1 Linear approximation to values $f(x, y)$ for (x, y) near (x_0, y_0).

Figure 5.1 shows a geometric interpretation of approximation (2). As with linear approximations for functions of a single variable, we shall use approximation (2) to approximate values of functions and to estimate errors in such approximations.

☐ **EXAMPLE 1**

Find a linear approximation for values of the function $f(x, y) = 2x^2 + 4y^2$ near the points $(1, 2)$.

Solution: Here $x_0 = 1$, $y_0 = 2$,

$$\frac{\partial f}{\partial x}(x_0, y_0) = 4x\big|_{x=1} = 4$$

and

$$\frac{\partial f}{\partial y}(x_0, y_0) = 8y\big|_{y=2} = 16.$$

Linear approximation (2) becomes

$$f(x, y) \approx f(1, 2) + \frac{\partial f}{\partial x}(1, 2)(x - 1) + \frac{\partial f}{\partial y}(1, 2)(y - 2)$$

$$= (2 \cdot 1^2 + 4 \cdot 2^2) + 4(x - 1) + 16(y - 2)$$

$$= 18 + 4(x - 1) + 16(y - 2).$$

Thus, for $(x, y) = (2, 3)$, we have

$$f(2, 3) \approx 18 + 4(2 - 1) + 16(3 - 2)$$

$$= 38$$

while the actual value is

$$f(2, 3) = 2 \cdot 2^2 + 4 \cdot 3^2 = 44.$$

Similarly, for $(x, y) = (1.2, 2.1)$, we have

$$f(1.2, 2.1) \approx 18 + 4(1.2 - 1) + 16(2.1 - 2)$$

$$= 20.4$$

while the actual value is

$$f(1.2, 2.1) = 2(1.2)^2 + 4(2.1)^2 = 20.52.$$

As with linear approximations for functions of a single variable, the linear approximation (2) is more accurate for points (x, y) nearer (x_0, y_0), in general. ■

☐ **EXAMPLE 2**

Use the linear approximation (2) to approximate the value of the expression $\sqrt{(3.04)^2 + (3.95)^2}$.

Solution: If we let $f(x, y) = \sqrt{x^2 + y^2}$, the problem is then to approximate $f(3.04, 3.95)$. To do so we note that for $x_0 = 3$ and $y_0 = 4$ it is easy to compute

$$f(x_0, y_0) = \sqrt{3^2 + 4^2} = \sqrt{25} = 5.$$

Also, we can see that

$$\frac{\partial f}{\partial x}(x_0, y_0) = \frac{\partial}{\partial x}(\sqrt{x^2 + y^2})\big|_{(3, 4)} = \frac{x}{\sqrt{x^2 + y^2}}\big|_{(3, 4)} = \frac{3}{\sqrt{3^2 + 4^2}} = 0.6$$

and

$$\frac{\partial f}{\partial y}(x_0, y_0) = \frac{\partial}{\partial y}(\sqrt{x^2 + y^2})\big|_{(3, 4)} = \frac{y}{\sqrt{x^2 + y^2}}\big|_{(3, 4)} = \frac{4}{\sqrt{3^2 + 4^2}} = 0.8$$

Then, with $x = 3.04$ and $y = 3.95$, approximation (2) and the above observations give

$$\sqrt{(3.04)^2 + (3.95)^2} \approx 5 + (0.6)(3.04 - 3) + (0.8)(3.95 - 4)$$

$$= 5 + (0.6)(0.04) + (0.8)(-0.05)$$

$$= 4.984.$$

The actual value is $\sqrt{(3.04)^2 + (3.95)^2} = 4.98439$ to five decimal places. ■

☐ **EXAMPLE 3**

In the Cobb–Douglas production model

$$f(K, L) = 400K^{1/4}L^{3/4}$$

giving output f as a function of the inputs K (capital) and L (labor), approximate the change in output resulting from a change in capital from $K_0 = 16$ to $K = 18$ units, and a change in labor from $L_0 = 81$ units to $L = 78$ units.

Solution: In this example we have

$$f(K_0, L_0) = 400(16)^{1/4}(81)^{3/4}$$

$$= 400(2)(3)^3$$

$$= 21{,}600.$$

Also,

$$\frac{\partial f}{\partial K}(K_0, L_0) = \frac{\partial}{\partial K}[400K^{1/4}L^{3/4}]\big|_{(16, 81)}$$

$$= 400\left(\frac{1}{4}\right)K^{-3/4}L^{3/4}\big|_{(16, 81)}$$

$$= \frac{100 \cdot 81^{3/4}}{16^{3/4}}$$

$$= \frac{100 \cdot 27}{8} = \frac{675}{2}$$

and

$$\frac{\partial f}{\partial L}(K_0, L_0) = \frac{\partial}{\partial L}[400K^{1/4}L^{3/4}]\big|_{(16, 81)}$$

$$= 400\left(\frac{3}{4}\right)K^{1/4}L^{-1/4}\big|_{(16, 81)}$$

$$= \frac{300 \cdot 16^{1/4}}{81^{1/4}}$$

$$= 200.$$

Then, using the above and approximation (2), we find that

$$f(18, 78) = f(K, L) \approx f(K_0, L_0) + \frac{\partial f}{\partial K}(K_0, L_0)(K - K_0) + \frac{\partial f}{\partial L}(K_0, L_0)(L - L_0)$$

$$= 21{,}600 + \frac{675}{2}(18 - 16) + 200(78 - 81)$$

$$= 21{,}675.$$

Thus, the resulting change in output is approximately

$$f(18, 78) - f(16, 81) \approx 21{,}675 - 21{,}600$$

$$= 75 \text{ units.}$$

■

Approximating Changes in Function Values

Example 3 illustrates how an equivalent form of approximation (2) can be used to approximate the *change* in the value of a function $f(x, y)$ resulting from changes in the independent variables, from x_0 to x and y_0 to y. Subtracting $f(x_0, y_0)$ from both sides of approximation (2) gives

$$f(x, y) - f(x_0, y_0) \approx \frac{\partial f}{\partial x}(x_0, y_0)(x - x_0) + \frac{\partial f}{\partial y}(x_0, y_0)(y - y_0). \qquad (3)$$

☐ **EXAMPLE 4**

The ideal gas law in chemistry states that $PV = nRT$ where P is pressure, V is volume, n is the number of moles of gas present, R is a constant, and T is temperature. Suppose that a certain amount of gas has volume $V_0 = 1000$ cc at temperature $T_0 = 300°K$ and pressure $P_0 = 780$ mm of mercury. Approximate the change in volume resulting from an increase in temperature of $10°K$ and a decrease in pressure of 5 mm of mercury.

Strategy · · · · · · ·
First, express volume as a function of temperature and pressure.

Solution
In the equation

$$PV = nRT$$

we divide both sides by P to obtain

$$V = \frac{nRT}{P}.$$

Determine the constant(s) nR by substituting given values for the variables.

To determine the constant nR, we substitute the given data $V_0 = 1000$, $T = 300$, and $P = 780$ to obtain

$$1000 = \frac{(nR)300}{780}$$

so

$$nR = \frac{1000 \cdot 780}{300} = 2600.$$

Write V as a function $V(T, P)$ of temperature T and pressure P.

We may now express V clearly as a function of T and P alone:

$$V(T, P) = \frac{2600T}{P}.$$

Identify T_0, T, P_0, and P; apply approximation (3).

With $T = 310$, $T_0 = 300$, $P = 775$, and $P_0 = 780$ we have, from approximation (3), that the change in volume is approximately

$$V(310, 775) - V(300, 780)$$

$$\approx \frac{\partial}{\partial T}\left(\frac{2600T}{P}\right)\Big|_{(300,\,780)}(10) + \frac{\partial}{\partial P}\left(\frac{2600T}{P}\right)\Big|_{(300,\,780)}(-5)$$

$$= (10)\frac{2600}{P}\Big|_{(300,\,780)} + (-5)\left(\frac{-2600T}{P^2}\right)\Big|_{(300,\,780)}$$

$$= (10)\left(\frac{2600}{780}\right) + (5)\left(\frac{2600 \cdot 300}{780^2}\right)$$

$$\approx 39.74 \text{ cubic centimeters.} \qquad ■$$

Relative and Percent Errors

Just as for functions of a single variable, we may calculate relative and percent errors for approximations (2) and (3). If one of these produces an approximation $\overline{f}(x, y)$ to an actual value $f(x, y)$, then

(a) the *relative error* in the approximation is

$$\text{Relative error} = \left|\frac{\overline{f}(x, y) - f(x, y)}{f(x, y)}\right|$$

(b) the *percent error* in the approximation is

$$\text{Percent error} = \left|\frac{\overline{f}(x, y) - f(x, y)}{f(x, y)}\right| \times 100\%$$

This is the same use made of these terms in Chapter 3 for functions of a single variable.

□ **EXAMPLE 5**

In Example 3 we used a linear approximation to the Cobb–Douglas production function

$$f(K, L) = 400K^{1/4}L^{3/4}$$

to obtain the approximation

$$f(18, 78) \approx \overline{f}(18, 78) = 21{,}675.$$

The actual value, to the nearest integer, is

$$f(18, 78) = 21{,}625 \qquad (4)$$

which you can obtain using a calculator. Thus,

(a) the *relative* error in approximation (4) is

$$\frac{21{,}675 - 21{,}625}{21{,}625} = 0.00231, \qquad \text{and}$$

(b) the *percent* error is

$$(0.00231) \times 100\% = 0.231\%. \qquad ■$$

The Total Differential

As we did for functions of a single variable, we may use the notation of differentials to express the preceding ideas about linear approximations more compactly. Recall, for a function of a single variable, $y = f(x)$, the differential df is defined by the equation

$$df = f'(x) \, dx. \tag{5}$$

The differential in equation (5) results from the linear approximation

$$f(x) - f(x_0) \approx f'(x_0)(x - x_0)$$

where we have written $dx = x - x_0$.

For the function $f(x, y)$ of two variables, we define the *total differential* to be

$$df = \frac{\partial f}{\partial x}(x, y) \, dx + \frac{\partial f}{\partial y}(x, y) \, dy. \tag{6}$$

The total differential results from the linear approximation

$$f(x, y) - f(x_0, y_0) \approx \frac{\partial f}{\partial x}(x_0, y_0)(x - x_0) + \frac{\partial f}{\partial y}(x_0, y_0)(y - y_0) \tag{7}$$

where we have written $dx = x - x_0$ and $dy = y - y_0$.

By comparing equation (6) and approximation (7), you can see that the *total differential* is useful in remembering the (linear) approximation to the change in f resulting in changes from x_0 to x in x, and from y_0 to y in y.

☐ **EXAMPLE 6**

For the general Cobb–Douglas production function

$$f(K, L) = CK^{\alpha}L^{1-\alpha}$$

the total differential is

$$
\begin{aligned}
df &= \frac{\partial}{\partial K}(CK^{\alpha}L^{1-\alpha}) \, dK + \frac{\partial}{\partial L}(CK^{\alpha}L^{1-\alpha}) \, dL \\
&= \alpha CK^{\alpha-1}L^{1-\alpha} \, dK + (1 - \alpha)CK^{\alpha}L^{-\alpha} \, dL.
\end{aligned}
$$ ∎

Functions of Three Variables

The approximations and equations of the section generalize directly to functions of three (or more) variables. For example, in the case of a function $f(x, y, z)$ of the three independent variables x, y, and z, we have the linear approximation

$$f(x, y, z) \approx f(x_0, y_0, z_0) + \frac{\partial f}{\partial x}(x_0, y_0, z_0)(x - x_0)$$

$$+ \frac{\partial f}{\partial y}(x_0, y_0, z_0)(y - y_0) + \frac{\partial f}{\partial z}(x_0, y_0, z_0)(z - z_0) \tag{8}$$

and the total differential

$$df = \frac{\partial f}{\partial x}(x, y, z) \, dx + \frac{\partial f}{\partial y}(x, y, z) \, dy + \frac{\partial f}{\partial z}(x, y, z) \, dx.$$

☑ **PRACTICE PROBLEMS 8.5**

1. Let $f(x, y) = x^2 e^{-3y}$. Find a linear approximation to $f(2.1, -0.2)$ based on the value $f(2, 0)$.

2. A rectangle is measured and found to have length $x_0 = 36.4$ centimeters and width $y_0 = 18.6$ centimeters where the measurements are accurate only to within 0.2 centimeter. Estimate the accuracy of the calculation for area based on these measurements.

Exercise Set 8.5

In Exercises 1–10, use approximation (2) or (8) to approximate the given function and function value.

1. $f(x, y) = 6x^2 + 4y^3$; $f(1.2, 3.9)$

2. $f(x, y) = 4x^3 y^6$; $f(0.2, 1.9)$

3. $f(x, y) = 3x^2 e^{-y}$; $f(4.1, -2)$

4. $f(x, y) = 4e^{xy^2}$; $f(11, 0.9)$

5. $f(x, y) = \sqrt{x} \ln y$; $f(4.15, 1.2)$

6. $f(x, y) = x^{4/3} y^{2/3}$; $f(8.1, 26.5)$

7. $f(x, y) = \dfrac{x}{x + y}$; $f(6.1, 2.05)$

8. $f(x, y) = x 2^{y^2}$; $f(7.15, -0.1)$

9. $f(x, y, z) = xy + yz + xz$; $f(0.95, 3.10, 7.05)$

10. $f(x, y, z) = e^{xyz}$; $f(0.9, 1.10, 1.05)$

In Exercises 11–18, find the total differential df at the given point.

11. $f(x, y) = 3xy^2 + 4x^3 y$; $(1, -1)$

12. $f(x, y) = \sqrt{x^2 + y^2}$; $(1, 2)$

13. $f(x, y) = 3^{xy}$; $(1, 2)$

14. $f(x, y) = \dfrac{x}{x - y}$; $(2, 1)$

15. $f(x, y) = \ln(x^2 + y^2)$; $(0, e)$

16. $f(x, y) = x^3 y - ye^{-2x}$; $(0, 2)$

17. $f(x, y, z) = xyz + xe^{-z}$; $(1, 1, 0)$

18. $f(x, y, z) = x^2 \cdot 3^y - e^{xz}$; $(1, 3, 0)$

19. The money supply in the economy is defined by the equation $M = C + D$ where C is the currency outstanding in banks and D is the amount of money in demand and term deposits. Approximate the percent change in the money supply caused by a 10% increase in the outstanding currency and a 5% decrease in total deposits.

20. A cylindrical bearing is measured and found to be have diameter $d = 4$ centimeters and length $\ell = 12$ centimeters. Approximate the relative and percent errors in the calculation of the volume if both of these measurements are in error by no more than 0.2 centimeter.

21. The productivity of a certain company is given by the Cobb–Douglas model as

$$f(x, y) = 400x^{3/4} y^{1/4}$$

where x units of labor and y units of capital are utilized. Find the approximate change in output if the input of labor is decreased from 16 to 14 units, and the input of capital is increased from 256 units to 280 units.

22. When three electronic resistors are connected in parallel, the resistance of the resulting circuit is

$$\frac{1}{R} = \frac{1}{R_1} + \frac{1}{R_2} + \frac{1}{R_3}$$

where R_1, R_2, and R_3 are the corresponding resistances. What is the approximate percent change in R resulting from an increase of 10% in each of R_1, R_2, and R_3?

23. Find the *actual* change in volume resulting from the changes in temperature and pressure described in Example 4.

24. What is the *relative* error in the approximation to the *change* in volume calculated in Example 4. (*Hint:* You will be comparing this approximation to the *actual* change calculated in Exercise 23.)

25. Student interns in a manufacturing company learn from the planning department that the sales anticipated from an investment of K units of capital and L units of labor are given by the function

$$S(K, L) = 4KL - L^2.$$

a. Find the sales corresponding to inputs of $K = 16$ and $L = 20$.

b. Use the total differential to approximate the change in sales resulting from an increase in capital from 16 to 18 units.

26. For the company in Exercise 25, use the total differential to approximate the change in labor input required to keep sales at the level $S(20, 16)$ despite a decrease in capital from 20 to 17.

✓ **SOLUTIONS TO PRACTICE PROBLEMS 8.5**

1. With $x_0 = 2$, $y_0 = 0$, and $f(x, y) = x^2 e^{-3y}$ we use approximation (2) to obtain the linear approximation to $f(2.1, -0.2)$ as

$$f(2.1, -0.2) \approx 2^2 e^{-3(0)} + \left\{ \frac{\partial}{\partial x} [x^2 e^{-3y}]_{\substack{x=2 \\ y=0}} \right\}(0.1) + \left\{ \frac{\partial}{\partial y} [x^2 e^{-3y}]_{\substack{x=2 \\ y=0}} \right\}(-0.2)$$

$$= 4 + \{[2xe^{-3y}]_{\substack{x=2 \\ y=0}}\}(0.1) + \{[-3x^2 e^{-3y}]_{\substack{x=2 \\ y=0}}\}(-0.2)$$

$$= 4 + (2 \cdot 2 \cdot e^0)(0.1) + (-3)(4 \cdot e^0)(-0.2)$$

$$= 6.8.$$

2. The given measurements $x_0 = 36.4$ and $y_0 = 18.6$ centimeters are approximations to the *actual* dimensions, x and y. We are given that $|x - x_0| \leq 0.2$ centimeter and $|y - y_0| \leq 0.2$ centimeter. Since the area $A = xy$ is a function $A(x, y)$ of two variables, we may use approximation (3) to approximate the difference between the actual area $A(x, y) = xy$ and the calculated area $A(x_0, y_0) = x_0 y_0$:

$$A(x, y) - A(x_0, y_0) \approx \frac{\partial A}{\partial x}(x_0, y_0)(x - x_0) + \frac{\partial A}{\partial y}(x_0, y_0)(y - y_0)$$

$$= y_0(x - x_0) + x_0(y - y_0)$$

$$= 18.6(x - x_0) + 36.4(y - y_0).$$

The expression on the right-hand side is no greater than

$$(18.6)|x - x_0| + (36.4)|y - y_0| \leq (18.6)(0.2) + (36.4)(0.2)$$

$$= 11 \text{ square centimeters}$$

while the calculated area is

$$A(x_0, y_0) = (36.4 \text{ centimeters})(18.6 \text{ centimeters}) = 677.04 \text{ square centimeters.}$$

Thus, the relative error is approximately

$$\frac{11}{677.04} \approx 0.0162$$

and the percent error is

$$(0.0162) \times 100\% = 1.62\%.$$

8.6 The Method of Least Squares

Students often ask where the functions of the calculus come from. For example, when a text states that, "the profit resulting from the sale of x toasters will be $P(x) = 30x - x^2$," how was the function P determined? Obviously, many (indeed, most) textbook functions are simply made up. But in real applications researchers often spend a great deal of time collecting data about how two or more variables are related before actually deciding what function gives the desired relationship. And often the resulting function is not a perfect match to the data, but rather, a "best fit," according to some agreed-upon meaning of this term.

One of the simplest functions that can describe the relationship between two variables is the linear function $y = mx + b$. The purpose of this section is to describe how we can determine from a set of data $(x_1, y_1), (x_2, y_2), \ldots, (x_n, y_n)$ the "best" straight line "fitting" this set of data. The technique we shall describe is called the **Method of Least Squares.**

For example, suppose that a calculus teacher wishes to know the relationship, if any, between students' scores on a mathematics achievement test given at the beginning of the course and their scores on the final examination. The teacher administers the achievement test to six students at the beginning of the course, records the scores, $x_1, x_2, \ldots, x_6$, and then waits until the end of the course and records the scores of the same students' final exams $y_1, y_2, \ldots, y_6$. The data are given in Table 6.1.

Table 6.1 Scores for Six Students on an Achievement Test (x_j) and a Final Examination in Calculus (y_j)

j	1	2	3	4	5	6
x_j	6	4	8	7	3	9
y_j	7	4	9	5	5	8

The meaning of the entries in Table 6.1 is that the first student scored $x_1 = 6$ on the achievement test and $y_1 = 7$ on the final examination, the second student scored $x_2 = y_2 = 4$ on each, and so on.

Figure 6.1 shows the result of plotting the six data points $(x_1, y_1), (x_2, y_2), \ldots, (x_6, y_6)$ in the xy-plane. While it is clear that these six points do not all lie on a common line, it does seem that the points lie generally grouped about some line, so we might ask, "What straight line best describes the relationship between x and y, that is, 'best fits' these data?"

Figure 6.2 shows the line ℓ that we wish to determine—the line that strikes the "happy medium" in a sense that we now make precise.

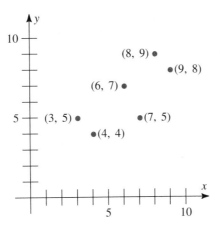

Figure 6.1 The data of Table 6.1.

Figure 6.2 What line ℓ ''best fits'' these data?

The Principle of Least Squares

Figure 6.3 shows a line ℓ with equation $y = mx + b$ and several data points (x_1, y_1), $(x_2, y_2), \ldots, (x_n, y_n)$. For each data point (x_j, y_j) we define the **error** E_j to be the (vertical) distance between the data point (x_j, y_j) and the point on ℓ with the same x-coordinate. Since the y-coordinate of the point on ℓ with x-coordinate x_j is $(mx_j + b)$, the error associated with the data point (x_j, y_j) is

$$E_j = y_j - (mx_j + b)$$
$$= y_j - mx_j - b.$$

One approach to defining the ''best-fitting'' line ℓ would be to find the line for which the sum of these errors, $E_1 + E_2 + \ldots + E_n$, is a minimum. The difficulty in this is that since, in general, some data points lie above ℓ and some lie below ℓ, the errors $E_1, E_2, \ldots, E_n$ are of differing sign, and some of the error will therefore ''cancel out.'' To prevent this, we work instead with the sum of the *squares* of the errors.

Principle of Least Squares

The line ℓ with equation $y = mx + b$ that best fits the data points (x_1, y_1), (x_2, y_2), $\ldots, (x_n, y_n)$ is the line for which the sum of the squares of the errors

$$E_1^2 + E_2^2 + \ldots + E_n^2 = \sum_{j=1}^{n} E_j^2 = \sum_{j=1}^{n} (y_j - mx_j - b)^2$$

is a minimum.

Since all of the numbers $x_1, x_2, \ldots, x_n$ and $y_1, y_2, \ldots, y_n$ are known, the Principle of Least Squares simply requires that we find the minimum value of the function of two variables

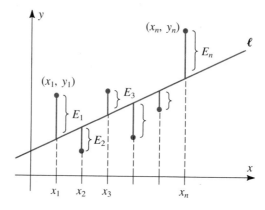

Figure 6.3 Errors E_j for the data points $(x_1, y_1), (x_2, y_2), \ldots, (x_n, y_n)$ and the line ℓ.

$$f(m, b) = \sum_{j=1}^{n} [y_j - mx_j - b]^2$$

$$= (y_1 - mx_1 - b)^2 + (y_2 - mx_2 - b)^2 + \ldots + (y_n - mx_n - b)^2.$$

Once we have found the numbers m and b for which this function is a minimum, we shall know the equation $y = mx + b$ for the best-fitting straight line ℓ, called the *regression line*.

At the end of this section we shall show how partial differentiation can be used to find m and b. The result is the following.

Theorem 5

Method of Least Squares

The equation of the straight line ℓ that best fits the data points $(x_1, y_1), (x_2, y_2), \ldots, (x_n, y_n)$ according to the Principle of Least Squares has equation

$$y = mx + b$$

where

$$m = \frac{n \sum_{j=1}^{n} x_j y_j - \left(\sum_{j=1}^{n} x_j\right)\left(\sum_{j=1}^{n} y_j\right)}{n \sum_{j=1}^{n} x_j^2 - \left(\sum_{j=1}^{n} x_j\right)^2} \tag{1}$$

and

$$b = \frac{\left(\sum_{j=1}^{n} x_j^2\right)\left(\sum_{j=1}^{n} y_j\right) - \left(\sum_{j=1}^{n} x_j\right)\left(\sum_{j=1}^{n} x_j y_j\right)}{n \sum_{j=1}^{n} x_j^2 - \left(\sum_{j=1}^{n} x_j\right)^2}. \tag{2}$$

In the statement of Theorem 5

$$\sum_{j=1}^{n} x_j \qquad \text{means} \qquad x_1 + x_2 + \ldots + x_n,$$

$$\sum_{j=1}^{n} x_j^2 \qquad \text{means} \qquad x_1^2 + x_2^2 + \ldots + x_n^2,$$

$$\left(\sum_{j=1}^{n} x_j\right)^2 \qquad \text{means} \qquad (x_1 + x_2 + \ldots + x_n)^2,$$

and so on.

Although the equations for m and b may seem a bit overwhelming, they are really only tedious at worst, although you must be very careful in calculating the various expressions. The advantage of stating them in this general form is that they can be used for any number of data points.

☐ **EXAMPLE 1**

Find the equation for the least squares regression line for the data in the example given at the beginning of this section.

Solution: In order to apply formulas (1) and (2), we complete the following table for the data in Table 6.1.

Table 6.2 Entries in Formulas (1) and (2) for the Data in Table 6.1

j	x_j	y_j	x_j^2	$x_j y_j$
1	6	7	36	42
2	4	4	16	16
3	8	9	64	72
4	7	5	49	35
5	3	5	9	15
6	9	8	81	72
Σ	37	38	255	252

From the bottom row of Table 6.2, we have the totals

$$\sum_{j=1}^{6} x_j = 37; \qquad \sum_{j=1}^{6} y_j = 38; \qquad \sum_{j=1}^{6} x_j^2 = 255; \qquad \sum_{j=1}^{6} x_j y_j = 252.$$

Using these totals in formulas (1) and (2), with $n = 6$, gives

$$m = \frac{6(252) - (37)(38)}{6(255) - (37)^2} = \frac{106}{161} \approx 0.66$$

and

$$b = \frac{(255)(38) - (37)(252)}{6(255) - (37)^2} = \frac{366}{161} \approx 2.27.$$

The least squares regression line therefore has equation $y = \left(\frac{106}{161}\right)x + \left(\frac{366}{161}\right)$, which can be approximated by

$$y = 0.66x + 2.27.$$ ∎

Regression Lines as Predictors

One of the most important uses of regression lines is as predictors. Once we have determined the least squares line $y = mx + b$ from a set of data, we can use this equation to predict the value of y that will result from the selection of an additional value of x. Of course, the result is only a prediction, since the regression line does not fit the data precisely.

□ **EXAMPLE 2**

Use the regression line obtained in Example 1 to predict the final exam score for a calculus student who scores a 5 on the achievement test.

Solution: With $x = 5$, the least squares regression line $y = 0.66x + 2.27$ predicts a final exam score of

$$y = 0.66(5) + 2.27$$
$$= 5.57.$$ ∎

□ **EXAMPLE 3**

Table 6.3 shows the United States' Federal Funds discount rate for 5 months beginning in June of a given year.

(a) Find a least squares regression line for these data.
(b) Use this line to predict from the data what the discount rate would have been in December of that year.

Table 6.3. United States' Federal Funds Discount Rate for Five Months

Month	June	July	August	September	October
Rate	14%	13%	10%	10%	9%

Solution: When data correspond to time, it is often convenient to let the independent variable represent time after some starting date. We therefore let x represent the number of months after June, and we let y denote the discount rate. We may then restate the data in Table 6.3 as follows for the $n = 5$ months in question:

Table 6.4

n	x_j	y_j	x_j^2	$x_j y_j$
1	0	14	0	0
2	1	13	1	13
3	2	10	4	20
4	3	10	9	30
5	4	9	16	36
Σ	10	56	30	99

From the bottom row of the table we can see that

$$\sum_{j=1}^{5} x_j = 10; \quad \sum_{j=1}^{5} y_j = 56; \quad \sum_{j=1}^{5} x_j^2 = 30; \quad \sum_{j=1}^{5} x_j y_j = 99.$$

Using these sums and $n = 5$ in formulas (1) and (2) gives

$$m = \frac{5(99) - (10)(56)}{5(30) - (10)^2} = \frac{-65}{50} = -\frac{13}{10}$$

and

$$b = \frac{(30)(56) - (10)(99)}{5(30) - (10)^2} = \frac{690}{50} = \frac{69}{5}.$$

Thus

(a) The least squares regression line is

$$y = -\frac{13}{10}x + \frac{69}{5}.$$

(b) Since December is $x = 6$ months after June, the predicted discount rate for December is

$$y = -\frac{13}{10}(6) + \frac{69}{5}$$

$$= 6\%.$$

(In fact, the actual rate for the year in question was just under 9%, which illustrates the difficulty in using straight lines to predict something as volatile as interest rates.) ∎

Proof of Theorem 5: To find the relative minimum value of the sum of squares function

$$f(m, b) = \sum_{j=1}^{n} (y_j - mx_j - b)^2$$

we first set $\dfrac{\partial f}{\partial m}$ equal to zero, obtaining

$$0 = \frac{\partial f}{\partial m} = \sum_{j=1}^{n} 2(y_j - mx_j - b)(-x_j)$$

$$= -2 \sum_{j=1}^{n} x_j y_j + 2m \sum_{j=1}^{n} x_j^2 + 2b \sum_{j=1}^{n} x_j.$$

Thus,

$$m \sum_{j=1}^{n} x_j^2 + b \sum_{j=1}^{n} x_j = \sum_{j=1}^{n} x_j y_j. \tag{3}$$

We next set $\dfrac{\partial f}{\partial b}$ equal to zero, obtaining

$$0 = \frac{\partial f}{\partial b} = \sum_{j=1}^{n} 2(y_j - mx_j - b)(-1)$$

$$= -2 \sum_{j=1}^{n} y_j + 2m \sum_{j=1}^{n} x_j + 2nb. \qquad \left(\sum_{j=1}^{n} b = nb \right).$$

Thus,

$$b = \frac{1}{n} \left(\sum_{j=1}^{n} y_j - m \sum_{j=1}^{n} x_j \right). \tag{4}$$

Substituting the expression for b in equation (4) into equation (3) then gives

$$m \sum_{j=1}^{n} x_j^2 + \frac{1}{n} \sum_{j=1}^{n} x_j \left(\sum_{j=1}^{n} y_j - m \sum_{j=1}^{n} x_j \right) = \sum_{j=1}^{n} x_j y_j$$

so

$$m \left[\sum_{j=1}^{n} x_j^2 - \frac{1}{n} \left(\sum x_j \right)^2 \right] = \sum_{j=1}^{n} x_j y_j - \frac{1}{n} \left(\sum_{j=1}^{n} x_j \right) \left(\sum_{j=1}^{n} y_j \right)$$

or

$$m = \frac{n \sum_{j=1}^{n} x_j y_j - \left(\sum_{j=1}^{n} x_j \right) \left(\sum_{j=1}^{n} y_j \right)}{n \sum_{j=1}^{n} x_j^2 - \left(\sum_{j=1}^{n} x_j \right)^2}.$$

We leave it to you to verify that substituting the expression for m into equation (4) gives

$$b = \frac{\left(\sum\limits_{j=1}^{n} x_j^2\right)\left(\sum\limits_{j=1}^{n} y_j\right) - \left(\sum\limits_{j=1}^{n} x_j\right)\left(\sum\limits_{j=1}^{n} x_j y_j\right)}{n \sum\limits_{j=1}^{n} x_j^2 - \left(\sum\limits_{j=1}^{n} x_j\right)^2}.$$

Verifying that this critical point actually yields the relative minimum is beyond the scope of this text. □

☑ PRACTICE PROBLEMS 8.6

1. Find the straight line that best fits the following data, according to the principle of least squares:

$$(1, 7), \qquad (2, 5), \qquad (3, 11), \qquad (4, 10)$$

2. A company's personnel department reports that the percentage of its employees enrolling in the company's health-care plan for the past five years has been as follows:

Year	1989	1990	1991	1992	1993
Percent Enrolled	50	55	58	57	62

   a. Find the straight line that best fits these data according to the principle of least squares.
   b. Use this linear model to predict the percentage enrollment in the years 1995 and 1997.

Exercise Set 8.6

In each of Exercises 1–5, find the equation for the least squares regression line $y = mx + b$ corresponding to the given data.

1.

x	4	3	5	5
y	9	6	7	8

2.

x	12	6	10	18	3	5
y	4	14	9	2	16	16

3.

x	52	46	69	54	61	48
y	74	66	94	91	84	80

4.

x	6	8	9	10	12	6	11
y	2	5	5	7	9	4	8

5.

x	0	1	1	2	2	3	3	3	4	4
y	1	0	2	1	2	2	1	3	2	3

6. A tax accountant observed that his clients' personal savings, as a percent of disposable income, was shown for three years, 1991–1993, in Table 6.5.

a. Find the least squares regression line for these data.

b. Use this line to predict the personal savings rate for 1995.

Table 6.5

Year	1991	1992	1993
Rate	5.6	6.2	5.3

7. A manufacturer of railroad cars received orders for new cars according to Table 6.6 for the years 1988–1993. (Orders are in thousands.)

a. Find the least squares regression line.

b. Use this line to predict the number of orders the company would have received in 1994.

Table 6.6

Year	1988	1989	1990	1991	1992	1993
Orders	10	14	8	4	2	3

8. A study produced the data of Table 6.7 showing the number of deaths per 100,000 male automobile drivers versus the age of these drivers.

a. Find the least squares regression line giving the number of deaths as a function of age.

b. How many deaths does this model predict for males age 65?

Table 6.7

Age	25	35	45	55
Deaths per 100,000	52	30	26	21

9. A college dean, worried about grade inflation, noted the overall grade point averages for undergraduates over a five-year period to be as shown in Table 6.8:

Table 6.8

Year	1989	1990	1991	1992	1993
Student GPA	3.21	3.29	3.08	3.15	3.23

a. Find the least-squares line best approximating this data.
b. What GPA does this line predict for the year 1995?
c. Do the data suggest grade inflation over the five-year period? Why or why not?

10. The percent of United States adults aged 25–29 who had graduated from college is shown for each of five years in Table 6.9.
a. Find the least squares regression line giving this percentage as a function of time.
b. What percent does this model predict for 2000?

Table 6.9

Year	1950	1960	1970	1980	1990
Percent	7	11	16	23	25

11. A life insurance company finds that the percentage of policyholders electing to purchase an "inflation adjustment" option on their policies has been as given in Table 6.10.

Table 6.10

Year	1984	1986	1988	1990	1992
Percent	20	24	25	32	34

What do these data predict the percentage participation in this option for
a. 1994?
b. 2000?

12. A group of men was examined every five years and found to have average weights as shown in Table 6.11.

Table 6.11

Year	1970	1975	1980	1985	1990
Weight	160	164	168	171	175

What do these data predict the average weight to be in
a. 1995?
b. 1998?

In Exercises 13–16, find the least squares regression line. Then plot the points and sketch the graph of the least squares line on the same set of axes.

13. (2, 5), (0, 7), (4, 2), (6, 4), and (8, 3)

14. (0, 3), (4, 4), (3, 2), and (6, 9)

15. (4, −2), (2, 6), (0, 3), and (−2, 8)

16. (0, 0), (1, 4), (2, 3), (4, −1), and (5, 5).

17. Mrs. Brown breeds Cocker Spaniels. She records the sizes of the litters produced by two of her dogs at various ages as shown in Table 6.12:

Table 6.12

Age of Dog	2	3	3.5	4.2	5
Size of litter	4	5	3	4	6

a. Find the least squares regression line for this data.

b. Does the size of the litter increase or decrease with age on average? Why?

18. Paul drives an ice cream truck in the summers, and notes the relationship between the price of ice cream cones, in cents, and the number sold per day as shown in Table 6.13.

Table 6.13

Price	40	50	60	70	80
Sales	65	70	55	52	46

a. Find the least squares regression line for sales as a function of price.

b. Do sales increase or decrease as price increases, according to this regression model?

c. What daily sales are predicted by this model if the price is increased to $1.00 per ice cream cone?

19. Consider the relationship between the price charged for the ice cream cones in Exercise 18, and the revenue received.
a. Find a least squares regression line for revenue as a function of price.
b. Does revenue increase or decrease with increases in price according to this model?

☑ **SOLUTIONS TO PRACTICE PROBLEMS 8.6**

1. We organize the given data into the following table

j	x_j	y_j	x_j^2	$x_j y_j$
1	1	7	1	7
2	2	5	4	10
3	3	11	9	33
4	4	10	16	40
Σ	10	33	30	90

Thus,

$$\sum_{j=1}^{4} x_j = 10; \quad \sum_{j=1}^{4} y_j = 33; \quad \sum_{j=1}^{4} x_j^2 = 30; \quad \sum_{j=1}^{4} x_j y_j = 90.$$

Using these totals in formulas (1) and (2) gives

$$m = \frac{4(90) - (10)(33)}{4(30) - (10)^2} = \frac{30}{20} = 1.5$$

and

$$b = \frac{(30)(33) - (10)(90)}{4(30) - (10)^2} = \frac{90}{20} = 4.5.$$

Thus, the least squares line has equation

$$y = 1.5x + 4.5.$$

2. We code the data, using 1989 as time $t = 1$, according to the following table (where we also use t_j as the independent variable, rather than x_j).

n	Year	t_j	y_j	t_j^2	$t_j y_j$
1	1989	1	50	1	50
2	1990	2	55	4	110
3	1991	3	58	9	174
4	1992	4	57	16	228
5	1993	5	62	25	310
Σ		15	282	55	872

Thus,

$$\sum_{j=1}^{5} t_j = 15; \quad \sum_{j=1}^{5} y_j = 282; \quad \sum_{j=1}^{5} t_j^2 = 55; \quad \sum_{j=1}^{5} t_j y_j = 872.$$

Using these totals in formulas (1) and (2) we obtain

$$m = \frac{5(872) - (15)(282)}{5(55) - (15)^2} = \frac{4360 - 4230}{275 - 225} = \frac{130}{50} = 2.6$$

and

$$b = \frac{(55)(282) - (15)(872)}{5(55) - (15)^2} = \frac{15,510 - 13,080}{275 - 225} = \frac{2430}{50} = 48.6.$$

Thus,
a. the least squares line has equation

$$y = 2.6t + 48.6.$$

b. Since the year 1995 corresponds to the year numbered $n = 7$, to obtain the percent participation predicted for the year 1995, we substitute $t = 7$ in the least squares model to obtain

$$y = (2.6)(7) + 48.6$$

$$= 66.8\%$$

Similarly, in 1997 ($n = t = 9$) the model predicts a percentage participation of

$$y = (2.6)(9) + 48.6$$

$$= 72\%.$$

8.7 Double Integrals

Figure 7.1 recalls the definition of the definite integral of a continuous function of a single variable as the limit of an approximating sum. When $f(x) \geq 0$ the terms in the approximating sum can be interpreted as areas of rectangles that approximate a region in the xy-plane bounded by the graph of $y = f(x)$.

Figure 7.2 illustrates how the notion of a definite integral is generalized for continuous functions of two variables. The integral is defined over a region R, rather than an interval, which is "partitioned" by a rectangular grid into small rectangles of area $\Delta A = \Delta x\, \Delta y$. In each such rectangle lying within R a "test point" (s_j, t_j) is chosen. The products $f(s_j, t_j)\,\Delta x\, \Delta y$, one for each rectangle lying in R, are then summed, giving an approximating sum $\sum_{j=1}^{n} f(s_j, t_j)\,\Delta x\, \Delta y$. The limit of this approximating sum, as n becomes infinitely large (and the dimensions Δx and Δy of the small rectangles approach zero), is called the **double integral** of the function $z = f(x, y)$ over the region R:

$$\iint_R f(x, y)\, dA = \lim_{n \to \infty} \sum_{j=1}^{n} f(s_j, t_j)\,\Delta x\, \Delta y. \tag{1}$$

Rather than concern ourselves with the technical description of just what the limit in equation (1) means, we shall rely on your intuitive understanding of approximating sums from the single variable case and simply state how several types of

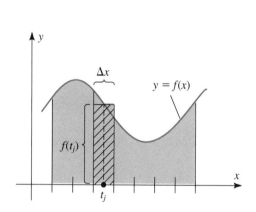

Figure 7.1 The integral is the limit

$$\int_a^b f(x)\, dx = \lim_{n \to \infty} \sum_{j=1}^{n} f(t_j)\,\Delta x.$$

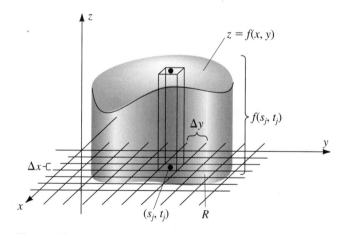

Figure 7.2 The *double integral* is the limit

$$\iint_R f(x, y)\, dA = \lim_{n \to \infty} \sum_{j=1}^{n} f(s_j, t_j)\,\Delta x\, \Delta y.$$

double integrals can be evaluated. Before doing so, however, we note the relationship between double integrals and volumes of certain solids, the analog of the relationship between definite integrals and areas of certain regions.

The Double Integral as Volume

When $f(x, y) \geq 0$ for all (x, y) in R, each of the terms $f(s_j, t_j) \, \Delta x \, \Delta y$ in the approximating sum in equation (1) may be interpreted as the volume of a rectangular prism whose base has area $\Delta x \, \Delta y$ and whose height is $f(s_j, t_j)$. As $n \to \infty$ these prisms more nearly fill the volume of the solid lying between the graph of $z = f(x, y)$ and the xy-plane. We therefore define the volume of this solid to be the double integral in equation (1).

> If $z = f(x, y)$ is continuous and $f(x, y) \geq 0$ for all (x, y) in R, the volume of the solid bounded above by the graph of $z = f(x, y)$ and below by the region R is
>
> $$V = \iint_R f(x, y) \, dA. \tag{2}$$
>
> (See Figure 7.3.)

□ **EXAMPLE 1**

Figure 7.4 shows the portion of the graph of the constant function $f(x, y) = 4$ above the rectangle $R = \{(x, y) \,|\, 1 \leq x \leq 3, \, 1 \leq y \leq 4\}$. Since the area of R is $2 \cdot 3 = 6$,

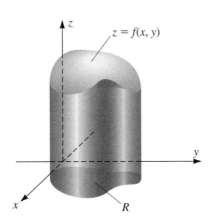

Figure 7.3 Volume of solid is
$$\iint_R f(x, y) \, dA.$$

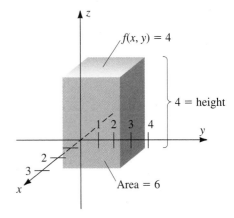

Figure 7.4 $\iint_R 4 \, dA = 24$ where $R = \{(x, y) \,|\, 1 \leq x \leq 3, 1 \leq y \leq 4\}$.

the volume of the rectangular prism lying between the graph of $z = f(x, y)$ and R is $4 \cdot 6 = 24$. Thus by equation (2),

$$\iint_R f(x, y) \, dA = 24.$$ ∎

Evaluating Double Integrals

The following theorem, which we state without proof, shows how double integrals over certain types of regions may be evaluated.

Theorem 6

Let $z = f(x, y)$ be a continuous function on the region R.

(i) If there exist continuous functions $x = g_1(y)$ and $x = g_2(y)$ for which

$$R = \{(x, y) \mid g_1(y) \leq x \leq g_2(y), \, c \leq y \leq d\}$$

then

$$\iint_R f(x, y) \, dA = \int_c^d \left\{ \int_{g_1(y)}^{g_2(y)} f(x, y) \, dx \right\} dy. \tag{3}$$

(See Figure 7.5.)

(ii) If there exist continuous functions $y = h_1(x)$ and $y = h_2(x)$ for which

$$R = \{(x, y) \mid a \leq x \leq b, \, h_1(x) \leq y \leq h_2(x)\}$$

then

$$\iint_R f(x, y) \, dA = \int_a^b \left\{ \int_{h_1(x)}^{h_2(x)} f(x, y) \, dy \right\} dx. \tag{4}$$

(See Figure 7.6.)

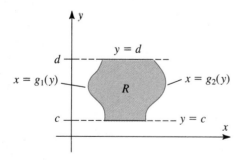

Figure 7.5 A region of the form $R = \{(x, y) \mid g_1(y) \leq x \leq g_2(y), c \leq y \leq d\}$.

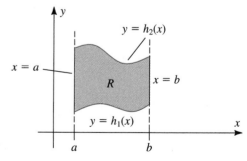

Figure 7.6 A region of the form $R = \{(x, y) \mid a \leq x \leq b, h_1(x) \leq y \leq h_2(x)\}$.

The integrals on the right-hand sides of equations (3) and (4) are called **iterated** integrals because they are evaluated in two steps, "inside out":

Step 1: The inside integral is evaluated by treating one independent variable as a constant. The result is a function of the other independent variable.

Step 2: The resulting function is then integrated over the limits indicated by the "outside integral sign."

The order of the differentials dx and dy indicates which type of integration is performed first.

☐ **EXAMPLE 2**

Evaluate the iterated integral

$$\int_0^4 \left\{ \int_1^{\sqrt{y}} (x + y) \, dx \right\} dy.$$

Solution: We begin by evaluating the integral $\int_1^{\sqrt{y}} (x + y) \, dx$ inside the braces as a function of x alone, treating y as a constant. Since the antiderivative of the function $f(x, y) = x + y$ *with respect to x alone* is

$$\int (x + y) \, dx = \frac{1}{2} x^2 + xy + C$$

the "inside" integral is

$$\int_1^{\sqrt{y}} (x + y) \, dx = \left[\frac{1}{2} x^2 + xy \right]_1^{\sqrt{y}}$$

$$= \left[\frac{1}{2} (\sqrt{y})^2 + (\sqrt{y})y \right] - \left[\frac{1}{2} (1)^2 + (1)y \right]$$

$$= y^{3/2} - \frac{1}{2} y - \frac{1}{2}.$$

This is the function of y alone that we must then integrate from $y = 0$ to $y = 4$. The complete solution is

$$\int_0^4 \left\{ \int_1^{\sqrt{y}} (x + y) \, dx \right\} dy$$

$$= \int_0^4 \left[\frac{1}{2} x^2 + xy \right]_1^{\sqrt{y}} dy$$

$$= \int_0^4 \left\{ \left[\frac{1}{2} (\sqrt{y})^2 + (\sqrt{y})y \right] - \left[\frac{1}{2} (1)^2 + (1)y \right] \right\} dy$$

$$= \int_0^4 \left(y^{3/2} - \frac{1}{2} y - \frac{1}{2} \right) dy$$

$$= \left[\frac{2}{5} y^{5/2} - \frac{1}{4} y^2 - \frac{1}{2} y \right]_0^4$$

$$= \left[\frac{2}{5} (4)^{5/2} - \frac{1}{4} (4)^2 - \frac{1}{2} (4) \right] - \left[\frac{2}{5} (0) - \frac{1}{4} (0) - \frac{1}{2} (0) \right]$$

$$= \frac{2}{5} (32) - \frac{1}{4} (16) - \frac{1}{2} (4)$$

$$= \frac{34}{5}.$$

□ **EXAMPLE 3**

Evaluate $\displaystyle\int_2^4 \left\{ \int_1^3 (2x + y) \, dy \right\} dx$.

Strategy · · · · · · · ·   **Solution**

First, find an antiderivative for $(2x + y)$ *with respect to* y, and evaluate between $y = 1$ and $y = 3$, carrying x along as a constant.

$$\int_2^4 \left\{ \int_1^3 (2x + y) \, dy \right\} dx$$

$$= \int_2^4 \left[2xy + \frac{1}{2} y^2 \right]_1^3 dx$$

Then integrate the resulting function of x over the outside limits from $x = 2$ to $x = 4$.

$$= \int_2^4 \left\{ \left[2x(3) + \frac{1}{2} (3)^2 \right] - \left[2x(1) + \frac{1}{2} (1)^2 \right] \right\} dx$$

$$= \int_2^4 (4x + 4) \, dx$$

$$= \left[2x^2 + 4x \right]_2^4$$

$$= (2 \cdot 4^2 + 4 \cdot 4) - (2 \cdot 2^2 + 4 \cdot 2)$$

$$= 32. \qquad \blacksquare$$

It is important to compare the solutions to Examples 2 and 3. In Example 2 the "inside" differential was dx, so the first integration was with respect to x. In Example 3 the inside differential was dy, so the first integration was with respect to y.

Notation for Iterated Integrals

We usually omit the braces in writing iterated integrals. Thus

$$\int_c^d \int_{g_1(y)}^{g_2(y)} f(x, y) \, dx \, dy \qquad \text{means} \qquad \int_c^d \left\{ \int_{g_1(y)}^{g_2(y)} f(x, y) \, dx \right\} dy$$

and

$$\int_a^b \int_{h_1(x)}^{h_2(x)} f(x, y) \, dy \, dx \qquad \text{means} \qquad \int_a^b \left\{ \int_{h_1(x)}^{h_2(x)} f(x, y) \, dy \right\} dx$$

In using this notation, however, it is important to follow the order of the differentials and integrate "inside out." Using this notation, we can write the results of Examples 2 and 3 as

$$\int_0^4 \int_1^{\sqrt{y}} (x + y)\, dx\, dy = \frac{34}{5}$$

and

$$\int_2^4 \int_1^3 (2x + y)\, dy\, dx = 32.$$

From Double Integrals to Iterated Integrals

In using Theorem 6 to evaluate a double integral of the form $\iint\limits_R f(x, y)\, dA$, we must first express the region R using inequalities. The type of description obtained then determines how $\iint\limits_R f(x, y)\, dA$ may be expressed as an iterated integral.

□ **EXAMPLE 4**

Evaluate $\iint\limits_R \dfrac{y}{x}\, dA$ where R is the region in Figure 7.7.

Solution: The region R is a rectangle described by the inequalities

$$R: \quad 1 \le x \le e, \qquad 2 \le y \le 4.$$

Since both variables are bounded by constants, we could begin by integrating with respect to either one. If we choose to integrate first with respect to x, using equation (3), we have

$$\iint\limits_R \frac{y}{x}\, dA = \int_2^4 \int_1^e \frac{y}{x}\, dx\, dy$$

$$= \int_2^4 \left[y \ln x \right]_1^e dy$$

$$= \int_2^4 (y \ln e - y \ln 1)\, dy$$

$$= \int_2^4 y\, dy \qquad (\ln e = 1; \ln 1 = 0)$$

$$= \left[\frac{1}{2} y^2 \right]_2^4$$

$$= 6.$$

If we had chosen to integrate first with respect to y, using equation (4), we would

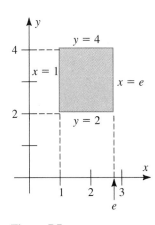

Figure 7.7 The region R in Example 4.

have obtained

$$\iint\limits_{R} \frac{y}{x}\,dA = \int_{1}^{e}\int_{2}^{4} \frac{y}{x}\,dy\,dx$$

$$= \int_{1}^{e}\left[\frac{y^2}{2x}\right]_{2}^{4}\,dx$$

$$= \int_{1}^{e}\left\{\frac{4^2}{2x} - \frac{2^2}{2x}\right\}\,dx$$

$$= \int_{1}^{e} \frac{6}{x}\,dx$$

$$= [6\ln x]_{1}^{e}$$

$$= 6.$$

For double integrals taken over rectangles either order of integration is possible, and both yield the same result. ∎

□ **EXAMPLE 5**

Evaluate $\displaystyle\iint\limits_{R} 2xy\,dA$ where R is the region in Figure 7.8.

Solution: Here R is described by the inequalities

$$R:\quad -2 \le x \le 2, \qquad 0 \le y \le \sqrt{4 - x^2}.$$

Since the inequality for y involves the function $h(x) = \sqrt{4 - x^2}$, which is not constant, we must use equation (4), integrating first with respect to y. We obtain

$$\iint\limits_{R} 2xy\,dA = \int_{-2}^{2}\int_{0}^{\sqrt{4-x^2}} 2xy\,dy\,dx$$

$$= \int_{-2}^{2}\left[xy^2\right]_{0}^{\sqrt{4-x^2}}\,dx$$

$$= \int_{-2}^{2} x(\sqrt{4 - x^2})^2\,dx$$

$$= \int_{-2}^{2} (4x - x^3)\,dx$$

$$= \left[2x^2 - \frac{1}{4}x^4\right]_{-2}^{2}$$

$$= (8 - 4) - (8 - 4)$$

$$= 0. \qquad ∎$$

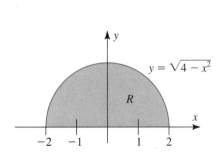

$y = \sqrt{4 - x^2}$

R

Figure 7.8 The region R in Example 5.

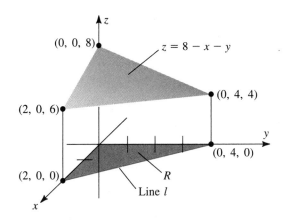

Figure 7.9 Solid in Example 6.

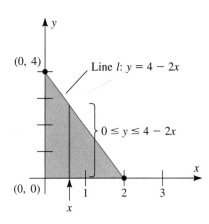

Figure 7.10 For any point (x, y) in R with $0 \le x \le 2$, we have $0 \le y \le 4 - 2x$.

REMARK: It is not unusual for the value of a double integral to be zero, or even a negative number. It is only in the case $f(x, y) \ge 0$ that the double integral corresponds to a volume. In Example 5 the function $f(x, y) = 2xy$ is positive in the first quadrant but negative in the second quadrant. Thus "canceling" occurs, and the answer is not the volume of a solid, but simply the value of the double integral.

◻ **EXAMPLE 6**

Find the volume of the solid lying below the graph of $f(x, y) = 8 - x - y$ and above the triangular region R in the xy-plane with vertices $(0, 0, 0)$, $(2, 0, 0)$, and $(0, 4, 0)$. (See Figure 7.9.)

Strategy · · · · · · ·
Find an equation for the hypotenuse of R.

Solution
The region R is shown in Figure 7.10. The slope of the line ℓ through the points $(2, 0)$ and $(0, 4)$ is

$$m = \frac{4 - 0}{0 - 2} = -2$$

so the line ℓ has equation

$$y - 4 = -2(x - 0), \quad \text{or}$$
$$y = -2x + 4.$$

Using this equation, write the inequalities in x and y describing the region R.

Thus the region R is described by the inequalities

$$0 \le x \le 2, \quad \text{and} \quad 0 \le y \le 4 - 2x.$$

Use the definition of volume and equation (4) to write volume as an iterated integral.

Using equations (2) and (4), we find that

$$\text{Volume} = \iint_R (8 - x - y) \, dA$$

Integrate first with respect to y.

$$= \int_0^2 \int_0^{4-2x} (8 - x - y)\, dy\, dx$$

$$= \int_0^2 \left[8y - xy - \frac{1}{2}y^2 \right]_0^{(4-2x)} dx$$

$$= \int_0^2 \left[8(4 - 2x) - x(4 - 2x) - \frac{1}{2}(4 - 2x)^2 \right] dx$$

Then integrate with respect to x.

$$= \int_0^2 (24 - 12x)\, dx$$

$$= \left[24x - 6x^2 \right]_0^2$$

$$= (48 - 24)$$

Result is volume.

$$= 24.$$

We leave it as an exercise for you to show that this volume could also have been calculated as

$$\text{Volume} = \int_0^4 \int_0^{2-1/2\,y} (8 - x - y)\, dx\, dy. \qquad\blacksquare$$

Interchanging the Order of Integration

There are occasions on which we need to interchange the order of integration in a given double integral. This usually occurs when an antiderivative cannot be found with respect to the "inside" variable. For example, in the iterated integral

$$\int_0^1 \int_{y^2}^1 ye^{x^2}\, dx\, dy \qquad (5)$$

we are in deep trouble, since we cannot find a (formal) antiderivative for the integrand ye^{x^2} with respect to x.

However, such integrals can often be evaluated by reversing the order of integration. In particular, the antiderivative of ye^{x^2} with respect to y is easily seen to be the function $\frac{1}{2}y^2 e^{x^2}$. But if we are going to reverse the order in which the antidifferentiations are performed, we must also determine correct limits of integration corresponding to this new order of integration. We do so as follows:

To reverse the order of integration in the iterated integral

$$\int_c^d \int_{h_1(y)}^{h_2(y)} f(x, y)\, dx\, dy$$

(i) Identify the region Q for which the iterated integral can be written as the double integral

$$\int_c^d \int_{h_1(y)}^{h_2(y)} f(x, y) \, dx \, dy = \int\int_Q f(x, y) \, dA.$$

(ii) Find constants a and b and continuous functions g_1 and g_2, so that the region Q can be expressed as

$$Q = \{(x, y) | a \le x \le b, \, g_1(x) \le y \le g_2(x)\}.$$

(iii) Rewrite the iterated integral as

$$\int_c^d \int_{h_1(y)}^{h_2(y)} f(x, y) \, dx \, dy = \int\int_Q f(x, y) \, dA$$

$$= \int_a^b \int_{g_1(x)}^{g_2(x)} f(x, y) \, dy \, dx.$$

Although the procedure is stated for reversing the order of integration from $dx \, dy$ to $dy \, dx$, the procedure for changing from order $dy \, dx$ to order $dx \, dy$ is analogous. Also, there is no guarantee that the resulting integral can be more easily evaluated than the original one.

□ **EXAMPLE 7**

Use the procedure for reversing order of integration to evaluate the iterated integral

$$\int_0^1 \int_{y^2}^1 y e^{x^2} \, dx \, dy.$$

Solution: From the given limits of integration the region Q is described by the inequalities

$$y^2 \le x \le 1, \qquad 0 \le y \le 1.$$

That is, Q is the region bounded between the graphs of $x = y^2$ and $x = 1$ for $0 \le y \le 1$. From Figure 7.11 (which must always be sketched when applying this method), we can see that Q is regular and can also be described by the inequalities

$$0 \le x \le 1, \qquad 0 \le y \le \sqrt{x}.$$

(See Figure 7.12.)

Beginning with the given integral, we therefore reverse the order of integration as follows:

$$\int_0^1 \int_{y^2}^1 y e^{x^2} \, dx \, dy = \int\int_Q y e^{x^2} \, dA = \int_0^1 \int_0^{\sqrt{x}} y e^{x^2} \, dy \, dx$$

$$= \int_0^1 \left[\frac{1}{2} y^2 e^{x^2} \right]_{y=0}^{y=\sqrt{x}} dx$$

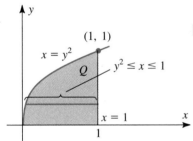

Figure 7.11 $Q = \{(x, y) | y^2 \le x \le 1, 0 \le y \le 1\}$.

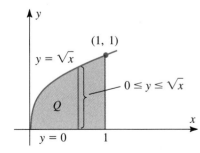

Figure 7.12 $Q = \{(x, y) | 0 \le x \le 1, 0 \le y \le \sqrt{x}\}$.

$$= \int_0^1 \frac{1}{2} xe^{x^2} dx$$

$$= \left[\frac{1}{4} e^{x^2} \right]_0^1$$

$$= \frac{1}{4}(e - 1)$$

$$\approx 0.43 \qquad \blacksquare$$

REMARK: It is important to note that we cannot simply interchange limits of integration when we interchange the order of integration. There is no alternative to sketching the region Q and working out the new limits of integration from knowledge of the boundary of Q.

☐ **EXAMPLE 8**

Evaluate the iterated integral

$$\int_0^1 \int_0^{\sqrt{1-x}} xy^2 \, dy \, dx$$

by first reversing the order of integration.

Solution: The given limits of integration are

$$0 \le x \le 1, \qquad 0 \le y \le \sqrt{1-x}$$

which describe the region Q bounded above by the graph of $y = \sqrt{1-x}$ and below by the x-axis for $0 \le x \le 1$ (see Figure 7.13). By solving the equation $y = \sqrt{1-x}$ for x, we find that this region may also be described by the inequalities

$$0 \le x \le 1 - y^2, \qquad 0 \le y \le 1.$$

(See Figure 7.14.) We may therefore evaluate the iterated integral as

$$\int_0^1 \int_0^{\sqrt{1-x}} xy^2 \, dy \, dx = \int_Q xy^2 \, dA = \int_0^1 \int_0^{1-y^2} xy^2 \, dx \, dy$$

$$= \int_0^1 \left[\frac{1}{2} x^2 y^2 \right]_{x=0}^{x=1-y^2} dy$$

$$= \int_0^1 \frac{1}{2}(1 - y^2)^2 y^2 \, dy$$

$$= \int_0^1 \left(\frac{1}{2} y^2 - y^4 + \frac{1}{2} y^6 \right) dy$$

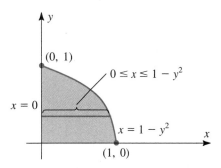

Figure 7.13 $Q = \{(x, y) \mid 0 \le x \le 1, 0 \le y \le \sqrt{1-x}\}$.

Figure 7.14 $Q = \{(x, y) \mid 0 \le x \le 1 - y^2, 0 \le y \le 1\}$.

$$= \left[\frac{1}{6} y^3 - \frac{1}{5} y^5 + \frac{1}{14} y^7 \right]_0^1$$

$$= \frac{4}{105}. \qquad \blacksquare$$

REMARK: If we attempt to evaluate the integral of Example 8 without first inter-changing the order of integration, the following intermediate step will appear:

$$\int_0^1 \frac{1}{3} x (1 - x)^{3/2} \, dx.$$

Evaluation of this integral requires the technique of integration by parts, which involves somewhat more work than does the method of the example. As you work more problems, you will learn to recognize which order of integration is likely to be easier.

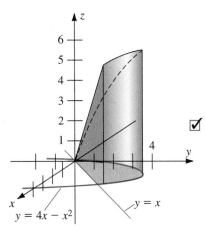

Figure 7.15

☑ **PRACTICE PROBLEMS 8.7**

1. Evaluate the following iterated integral:

$$\int_0^1 \int_0^x (2x + e^{-y}) \, dy \, dx.$$

2. Find the volume of the solid bounded above by the graph of $f(x, y) = x + y$ and below by the region in the xy-plane lying between the graphs of $g(x) = 4x - x^2$ and $h(x) = x$. (See Figure 7.15.)

Exercise Set 8.7

In Exercises 1–12, evaluate the iterated integral.

1. $\displaystyle\int_0^2 \int_0^1 (x - y) \, dx \, dy$

2. $\displaystyle\int_0^1 \int_1^3 (2x + 4y) \, dy \, dx$

3. $\displaystyle\int_{-1}^1 \int_0^2 x^2 y \, dy \, dx$

4. $\displaystyle\int_{-2}^1 \int_0^1 x\sqrt[3]{y} \, dy \, dx$

5. $\displaystyle\int_0^2 \int_0^{x^2} (x - 2y) \, dy \, dx$

6. $\displaystyle\int_{-1}^2 \int_0^x y\sqrt{x^3 + 1} \, dy \, dx$

7. $\displaystyle\int_0^1 \int_0^1 y e^{x - y^2} \, dy \, dx$

8. $\displaystyle\int_{-1}^0 \int_{-1}^{y+1} (xy - x) \, dx \, dy$

9. $\displaystyle\int_0^1 \int_{-x}^{\sqrt{x}} \frac{y}{1+x}\, dy\, dx$

10. $\displaystyle\int_1^2 \int_0^{y^3} e^{x/y}\, dx\, dy$

11. $\displaystyle\int_1^e \int_1^2 \frac{\ln^2 y}{x^2 y}\, dx\, dy$

12. $\displaystyle\int_0^2 \int_0^1 x^3 y 2^{y^2}\, dy\, dx$

In Exercises 13–18, evaluate $\displaystyle\iint_R f(x, y)\, dA$.

13. $\displaystyle\iint_R (x + y^2)\, dA, \qquad R = \{(x, y) \mid 0 \le x \le 1,\ 0 \le y \le 2\}$

14. $\displaystyle\iint_R (x^2 + y^2)\, dA, \qquad R = \{(x, y) \mid 0 \le x \le a,\ 0 \le y \le b\}$

15. $\displaystyle\iint_R \frac{xy}{\sqrt{x^2 + y^2}}\, dA, \qquad R = \{(x, y) \mid 1 \le x \le 2,\ 1 \le y \le 2\}$

16. $\displaystyle\iint_R \frac{x^2}{1 + y}\, dA, \qquad R = \{(x, y) \mid 0 \le x \le 1,\ 0 \le y \le e^x - 1\}$

17. $\displaystyle\iint_R xy\, dA, \qquad R = \{(x, y) \mid y \le x \le \sqrt{y},\ 0 \le y \le 1\}$

18. $\displaystyle\iint_R (2x + y)\, dA, \qquad R = \{(x, y) \mid 0 \le x \le \sqrt{1 - y^2},\ 0 \le y \le 1\}$

In Exercises 19–22, sketch the region Q determined by the limits of integration, interchange the order of integration, and evaluate the given integral, where possible.

19. $\displaystyle\int_{-1}^1 \int_0^{x+1} (x + y)\, dy\, dx$

20. $\displaystyle\int_0^1 \int_{x^2}^1 xe^{y^2}\, dy\, dx$

21. $\displaystyle\int_0^1 \int_0^y xy^2\, dx\, dy$

22. $\displaystyle\int_{-2}^0 \int_{x^2}^4 xe^{y^2}\, dy\, dx$

In each of Exercises 23–26, use a double integral to find the volume of the solid indicated by the figure.

23.

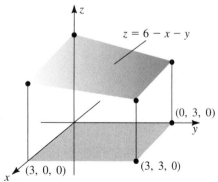

24.

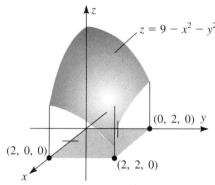

25.

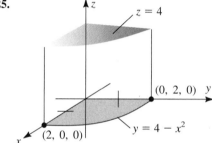

26.

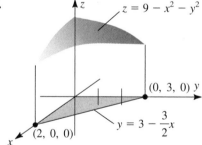

27. Find the volume of the solid bounded above by the graph of $f(x) = 12 - 4x - 2y$ and below by the rectangle $R = \{(x, y) \mid 0 \le x \le 2,\ 0 \le y \le 1\}$.

28. Find the volume of the solid bounded above by the graph of $f(x, y) = \dfrac{e^{\sqrt{x}}}{\sqrt{xy}}$ and below by the rectangle $R = \{(x, y) \mid 1 \le x \le 4,\ 1 \le y \le 9\}$.

29. Find the volume of the solid bounded above by the graph of $f(x, y) = 4 + x + y$ and below by the region enclosed by the triangle with vertices $(0, 0, 0)$, $(2, 0, 0)$, and $(0, 3, 0)$.

30. Find the area of the region R bounded by the graphs of $y = 4 - x^2$ and $y = x + 2$ by finding the volume of the solid bounded above by the graph of $f(x, y) \equiv 1$ and below by the region R.

31. Use the method of Exercise 30 to find the area of the region bounded by the graphs of $y = x^2$ and $y = x^3$.

32. For a function $f(x, y)$ of two variables, the *average value* of the function f over a region R is defined to be:

$$\text{Average value of } f \text{ over } R = \frac{1}{\text{Area of } R} \iint_R f(x, y) \, dA.$$

Use this definition to find the average value of the function $f(x, y) = xy$ over the square defined by the inequalities $0 \le x \le 2$, $0 \le y \le 2$.

33. Show that the average value of $f(x, y)$ on the region R can be written

$$\text{Average value of } f \text{ over } R = \frac{\iint_R f(x, y) \, dA}{\iint_R 1 \cdot dA}.$$

(See Exercise 32.)

34. Find the average value of the function $f(x, y) = 6x + e^y$ on the rectangle with vertices $(0, 0)$, $(0, \ln 2)$, $(\ln 3, \ln 2)$, and $(\ln 3, 0)$.

35. Find the average value of the function $f(x, y) = 12x$ over the triangle with vertices $(0, 0)$, $(0, 3)$, and $(4, 0)$.

☑ **SOLUTIONS TO PRACTICE PROBLEMS 8.7**

1.
$$\int_0^1 \int_0^x (2x + e^{-y}) \, dy \, dx = \int_0^1 [2xy - e^{-y}]_{y=0}^{y=x} \, dx$$
$$= \int_0^1 (2x^2 - e^{-x} + 1) \, dx$$
$$= \left[\frac{2}{3}x^3 + e^{-x} + x \right]_0^1$$
$$= \left(\frac{2}{3} + \frac{1}{e} + 1 \right) - (0 + 1 + 0)$$
$$= \frac{2}{3} + \frac{1}{e}.$$

2. The region in the xy-plane that bounds the solid form below may be described by the inequalities

$$x \le y \le 4x - x^2; \qquad 0 \le x \le 3.$$

(See Figure 7.16.) The volume is therefore given by the integral

$$V = \int_0^3 \int_x^{4x-x^2} (x + y) \, dy \, dx$$
$$= \int_0^3 \left[xy + \frac{1}{2}y^2 \right]_{y=x}^{y=4x-x^2} dx$$
$$= \int_0^3 \left[x(4x - x^2) + \frac{1}{2}(4x - x^2)^2 - \left(x^2 + \frac{1}{2}x^2 \right) \right] dx$$
$$= \int_0^3 \left(\frac{1}{2}x^4 - 5x^3 + \frac{21}{2}x^2 \right) dx$$
$$= \left[\frac{1}{10}x^5 - \frac{5}{4}x^4 + \frac{7}{2}x^3 \right]_0^3$$

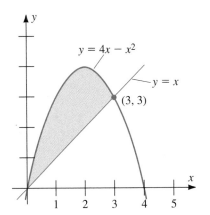

Figure 7.16

$$= \frac{243}{10} - \frac{405}{4} + \frac{189}{2}$$

$$\approx 56.03.$$

Summary Outline of Chapter 8

■ The **partial derivatives**, $\dfrac{\partial f}{\partial x}$ and $\dfrac{\partial f}{\partial y}$, for the function $z = f(x, y)$ of (Page 551)
two variables are

$$\frac{\partial f}{\partial x}(x, y) = \lim_{h \to 0} \frac{f(x + h, y) - f(x, y)}{h}$$

$$\frac{\partial f}{\partial y}(x, y) = \lim_{h \to 0} \frac{f(x, y + h) - f(x, y)}{h}.$$

■ Other **notation** for partial derivatives of $z = f(x, y)$ is (Page 553)

$$\frac{\partial f}{\partial x}(x, y) = \frac{\partial f}{\partial x} = f_x = z_x, \text{ etc.}$$

■ The **second order** partial derivatives for $z = f(x, y)$ are (Page 561)

$$\frac{\partial^2 f}{\partial x^2}(x, y) = \frac{\partial}{\partial x}\left(\frac{\partial f}{\partial x}(x, y)\right); \qquad \frac{\partial^2 f}{\partial y \partial x}(x, y) = \frac{\partial}{\partial y}\left(\frac{\partial f}{\partial x}(x, y)\right)$$

$$\frac{\partial^2 f}{\partial x \partial y}(x, y) = \frac{\partial}{\partial x}\left(\frac{\partial f}{\partial y}(x, y)\right); \qquad \frac{\partial^2 f}{\partial y^2}(x, y) = \frac{\partial}{\partial y}\left(\frac{\partial f}{\partial y}(x, y)\right).$$

■ *Theorem:* If $f(x_0, y_0)$ is a relative extremum for $z = f(x, y)$, and if (Page 568)
$\dfrac{\partial f}{\partial x}(x_0, y_0)$ and $\dfrac{\partial f}{\partial y}(x_0, y_0)$ exist, then $\dfrac{\partial f}{\partial x}(x_0, y_0) = \dfrac{\partial f}{\partial y}(x_0, y_0) = 0.$

■ *Theorem:* If all second order partial derivatives of $z = f(x, y)$ are (Page 569)
continuous, if $\dfrac{\partial f}{\partial x}(x_0, y_0) = \dfrac{\partial f}{\partial y}(x_0, y_0) = 0$, and if

$$A = \frac{\partial^2 f}{\partial x^2}(x_0, y_0), \quad B = \frac{\partial^2 f}{\partial y \partial x}(x_0, y_0), \quad C = \frac{\partial^2 f}{\partial y^2}(x_0, y_0)$$

and $D = B^2 - AC$, then

  (i) $D < 0$ and $A < 0$ imply $f(x_0, y_0)$ is a relative maximum.
  (ii) $D < 0$ and $A > 0$ imply $f(x_0, y_0)$ is a relative minimum.
  (iii) $D > 0$ implies $(x_0, y_0, f(x_0, y_0))$ is a saddle point.
  (iv) $D = 0$ yields no conclusion.

■ *Theorem:* If f and g have continuous partials, the relative maxima (Page 584)
and minima of f subject to the **constraint**

$$g(x, y) = 0$$

occur at critical points for the **Lagrange** function $L = f + \lambda g$.

▌ The **linear approximation** for a function of two variables is   (Page 593)

$$f(x, y) \approx f(x_0, y_0) + \frac{\partial f}{\partial x}(x_0, y_0)(x - x_0) + \frac{\partial f}{\partial y}(x_0, y_0)(y - y_0).$$

▌ The **relative error** of the function value $f(x, y)$ by the approximation   (Page 598)
$\overline{f}(x, y)$ is

$$\text{Relative error} = \left| \frac{\overline{f}(x, y) - f(x, y)}{f(x, y)} \right|.$$

▌ The **total differential** for a function $f(x, y)$ of two variables is   (Page 599)

$$df = \frac{\partial f}{\partial x}(x, y) \, dx + \frac{\partial f}{\partial y}(x, y) \, dy.$$

▌ *Theorem:* The straight line that best fits the data points   (Page 604)
$(x_1, y_1), (x_2, y_2), \ldots, (x_n, y_n)$ in the sense of "least squares" has
equation $y = mx + b$ where

$$m = \frac{n \sum_{j=1}^{n} x_j y_j - \left(\sum_{j=1}^{n} x_j \right) \left(\sum_{j=1}^{n} y_j \right)}{n \sum_{j=1}^{n} x_j^2 - \left(\sum_{j=1}^{n} x_j \right)^2}$$

and

$$b = \frac{\left(\sum_{j=1}^{n} x_j^2 \right) \left(\sum_{j=1}^{n} y_j \right) - \left(\sum_{j=1}^{n} x_j \right) \left(\sum_{j=1}^{n} x_j y_j \right)}{n \sum_{j=1}^{n} x_j^2 - \left(\sum_{j=1}^{n} x_j \right)^2}.$$

▌ The **double integral** of the continuous function $z = f(x, y)$ over the   (Page 614)
region R is

$$\iint_R f(x, y) \, dA = \lim_{n \to \infty} \sum_{j=1}^{n} f(s_j, t_j) \, \Delta x \, \Delta y$$

where one test point (s_j, t_j) lies in each of the rectangles of area
$\Delta x \, \Delta y$, which together approximate the region R.

▌ If $f(x, y) \geq 0$, the **volume** of the solid bounded above by the graph of   (Page 615)
$z = f(x, y)$ and below by the region R in the xy-plane is

$$V = \iint_R f(x, y) \, dA.$$

▌ *Theorem:* If $z = f(x, y)$ is continuous on R, then   (Page 616)

(i) $\displaystyle \iint_R f(x, y) \, dA = \int_c^d \int_{g_1(y)}^{g_2(y)} f(x, y) \, dx \, dy$

if $R = \{(x, y) \mid g_1(y) \leq x \leq g_2(y), \ c \leq y \leq d\}$

(ii) $\displaystyle\iint_R f(x, y)\, dA = \int_a^b \int_{h_1(x)}^{h_2(x)} f(x, y)\, dy\, dx$

if $R = \{(x, y)\,|\,a \le x \le b,\ h_1(x) \le y \le h_2(x)\}$

where the functions g_1, g_2, h_1, and h_2 are assumed continuous.

Review Exercises—Chapter 8

1. State the domain of the function $f(x, y) = \sqrt{25 - x^2 - y^2}$.

2. For the function $f(x, y) = x^3 - y \ln(3 + x)$, find
   a. $f(0, 2)$ b. $f(1, -2)$

3. For the function $f(x, y) = \dfrac{y - x}{y + x}$, find
   a. $f(2, -1)$ b. $f(1, -2)$

4. Plot the following points in a three-dimensional coordinate space.
   a. $(2, 3, 1)$ b. $(1, -3, -2)$ c. $(-2, -2, 3)$

5. State the points (x, y) at which the function $f(x, y) = \dfrac{1 + x^2}{1 - xy}$ is discontinuous.

In each of Exercises 6–15, find $\dfrac{\partial f}{\partial x}$ and $\dfrac{\partial f}{\partial y}$.

6. $f(x, y) = x^4 + 2xy - 3y^3$ 7. $f(x, y) = (x - y)^3 + \ln xy$

8. $f(x, y) = (4 - xy)^5 + \sqrt{xy}$ 9. $f(x, y) = \dfrac{xy}{x + y}$

10. $f(x, y) = xye^{xy}$

11. $f(x, y) = x^{2/3}y^{1/3} - \dfrac{x^{3/4}}{y^{1/4}}$

12. $f(x, y) = \ln\sqrt{x^2 + y^2}$

13. $f(x, y) = xy\sqrt{y^2 - x^2}$

14. $f(x, y) = \dfrac{e^{x+y}}{1 + xy}$

15. $f(x, y) = (xy^2 - x^2y)^{2/3}$

In Exercises 16 and 17, find all three first order partial derivatives

16. $f(x, y, z) = \dfrac{xyz^2}{x + y + z}$

17. $f(x, y, z) = \ln\sqrt{x^2 + 4y^2 + 2z}$

In Exercises 18 and 19, find the second order partial derivatives $\dfrac{\partial^2 f}{\partial x^2}$, $\dfrac{\partial^2 f}{\partial x \partial y}$, and $\dfrac{\partial^2 f}{\partial y^2}$.

18. $f(x, y) = ye^{x+y}$

19. $f(x, y) = \sqrt{y^2 - x^2}$

In Exercises 20–26, find and classify all relative extrema.

20. $f(x, y) = 4y^2 - 2x^2$

21. $f(x, y) = 3x^2 + xy - 6y^2$

22. $f(x, y) = x^2y + xy^2 + 4x + 4y$

23. $f(x, y) = e^{x^2 - 4xy}$

24. $f(x, y) = \ln(1 + x^2 + y^2)$

25. $f(x, y) = e^{1 + x^2 - y^2}$

26. $f(x, y) = 6x^2 - 2x - 3xy + y^2 + 5y + 5$

In Exercises 27–32, evaluate the iterated integral.

27. $\displaystyle\int_{-1}^{1} \int_0^2 (2x + 3y)\, dx\, dy$

28. $\displaystyle\int_0^3 \int_0^1 \dfrac{xy}{\sqrt{x^2 + y^2}}\, dx\, dy$

29. $\displaystyle\int_0^1 \int_0^x xy\sqrt{x^2 + y^2}\, dy\, dx$

30. $\displaystyle\int_0^1 \int_0^y y^4 e^{xy^2}\, dx\, dy$

31. $\displaystyle\int_0^1 \int_0^x xy(7 + y^2)\, dy\, dx$

32. $\displaystyle\int_{-1}^1 \int_{-y}^y (xy^3 + x^3y)\, dx\, dy$

33. A monopolist can sell x items per week in its domestic market at price p where

$$p = 80 - 2x$$

and it can sell y items per week in its foreign market at price q where

$$q = 120 - 4y.$$

The monopolist's total weekly cost in producing x items for the domestic market and y items for the foreign market is

$$C(x, y) = 1000 + 20x + 20y.$$

a. Find the weekly revenue function $R(x, y) = xp + yq$.
b. Find the weekly profit function $P = R - C$.
c. Find the weekly production level (x, y) for which revenue is a maximum.

d. Find the weekly production level (x, y) for which profit is a maximum.

34. For the monopolist in Exercise 33 find the production schedule (x, y) for which profit is a maximum subject to the constraint that a maximum of 20 items per week can be produced for sale.

35. A company determines that the productivity of a manufacturing plant is given by the function

$$P(x, y) = 200\sqrt{xy}$$

where x is units of capital and y is units of labor scheduled per unit time.
a. Find the production level corresponding to $x = 4$ units of capital and $y = 16$ units of labor.
b. Using $\dfrac{\partial P}{\partial x}$, approximate the increase in production resulting from an increase from $x = 4$ to $x = 5$ units of capital, if labor is held constant at $y = 16$ units.

36. An equipment-leasing firm uses the depreciation formula $V(r, t) = 10,000e^{-(0.05+r)t}$ to find the value of a \$10,000 tractor after t years when r is the prevailing rate of interest.
a. Find $V(0.10, 2)$, the value of the tractor after 2 years if interest rates remain at 10%.
b. Estimate, using your answer to part (a), the amount by which the value of the tractor will decrease between year 2 and year 3 if interest rates remain constant at 10%.

37. A house cleaning firm determines that its weekly profit from cleaning x houses and y apartments is

$$P(x, y) = 24x + 8y - x^2 - y^2 \text{ dollars.}$$

What weekly schedule (x, y) should it follow in order to maximize profits?

38. A closed rectangular box is to contain 1000 cm³. If the material for the top and bottom costs 2 cents/cm² and the material for the sides costs 3 cents/cm², what are the dimensions for which cost is a minimum?

39. Find the maximum value of the function $f(x, y, z) = x + 2y - 3z + 1$ subject to the constraint that $x^2 + y^2 + z^2 = 14$.

40. Find the rectangular solid of maximum volume that can be inscribed in the ellipsoid $\dfrac{x^2}{4} + \dfrac{y^2}{9} + \dfrac{z^2}{4} = 1$. That is, find the maximum value for the function $V(x, y, z) =$

$(2x)(2y)(2z) = 8xyz$ subject to the constraint that $\dfrac{x^2}{4} + \dfrac{y^2}{9} + \dfrac{z^2}{4} = 1$. (See the figure below.)

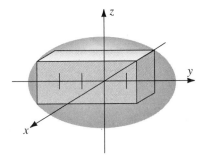

41. A group of calculus students believe that their success rate S resulting from reading their textbook for x hours and working homework problems for y hours will be $S(x, y) = 10xy + 2x + 4y$.

Assuming the validity of this model, how should their time be allocated between reading the textbook and working homework problems if ten hours of study time are available?

42. A new company records its sales revenues for its first five years as follows:

Year	1	2	3	4	5
Sales in thousands	34	72	220	290	345

a. Find the least squares model for these data.
b. What sales total does this model predict for year 7?

43. Use the double integral to find the area of the region bounded by the graphs of the functions $f(x) = \sqrt{x}$ and $g(x) = x^2$.

44. In the flow of blood through an artery, the equation $A_1v_1 = A_2v_2$ expresses the relationship between the respective cross-sectional areas and velocities at two points in the artery.
a. Express v_2 as a function of A_1, A_2, and v_1.
b. Find $\dfrac{\partial v_2}{\partial A_2}$, the rate at which v_2 changes with respect to change in A_2 alone.

c. Suppose $A_1 = 5$ mm, $A_2 = 3$ mm, and $v_1 = 20$ cm/second. Find the rate of change of v_2 with respect to A_2 if A_1 and v_1 are held constant.

45. A company manufactures two models of a portable stereo ("boom box")—the standard model and the deluxe model. Manufacturing costs are $65 for the standard model and $80 for the deluxe model. Market research indicates that, if the standard model is priced at x dollars and the deluxe model is priced at y dollars, then the company will sell $1200 - 40x + 20y$ standard models and $2650 + 10x - 30y$ deluxe models. What prices x and y maximize profits?

CHAPTER

9

Harvesting fish is an example of receiving a perpetual asset—under proper conditions, a fishery should produce fish on a continuing basis. Determining the value of such perpetual assets often involves infinite series. *(Grant Heilman/Grant Heilman Photography, Inc.)*

Infinite Series

9.1 Infinite Sequences

Up to this point we have worked almost exclusively with continuous functions, even though many of the functions that arise in business and economic applications are defined only for nonnegative integers. In doing so, we have taken the view that such discontinuous functions can be approximated by continuous functions to which the techniques of the differential and integral calculus can be applied.

For example, in saying that the selling price p and the daily demand x for bicycles are related by the equation $p = 100 - 2x$, we referred to the differentiable function

$$p(x) = 100 - 2x, \qquad x \geq 0$$

defined for all real numbers $x \geq 0$, although this relationship really involves the function

$$p(n) = 100 - 2n, \qquad n = 0, 1, 2, 3, \ldots$$

whose domain is the nonnegative integers, because demand refers to the number of whole bicycles that will be purchased per day.

In some instances it is more appropriate to use techniques that are designed specifically for functions whose domains are subsets of the integers, rather than assuming these functions to be defined for all real numbers. The purpose of this chapter is to develop these techniques, primarily the theory of *infinite sequences* and *infinite series*. Although the initial motivation for these topics will come from functions defined only for integers, we shall see later in the chapter that the theory we develop for infinite series (in particular, *Taylor series*) can be used to analyze certain types of continuous functions.

Infinite Sequences

An **infinite sequence** is simply an infinite list of numbers, such as

$$\{1, 2, 3, 4, \ldots\} \tag{1}$$

or

$$\left\{1, \frac{1}{2}, \frac{1}{3}, \frac{1}{4}, \frac{1}{5}, \ldots\right\} \tag{2}$$

or

$$\{1, e, e^2, e^3, e^4, \ldots\}. \tag{3}$$

The order in which the numbers are listed is important, and we must always indicate which is the first number in a sequence, which is the second, etc. We often make this ordering explicit by using the positive integers, as subscripts, to **index** the terms of a sequence by writing

$$\{a_1, a_2, a_3, \ldots\} \quad \text{or} \quad \{a_n\}, \quad \text{where } n = 1, 2, 3, \ldots. \tag{4}$$

We say that equation (4) is the **general form** of an infinite sequence, and that a_n (without the braces) is the **general term.**

□ **EXAMPLE 1**

(a) The general term $a_n = n$ generates the sequence $\{1, 2, 3, 4, \ldots\}$ where $a_1 = 1$, $a_2 = 2$, $a_3 = 3$, $a_4 = 4, \ldots$, etc.

(b) The general term $a_n = \dfrac{1}{n}$ gives the sequence $\left\{1, \dfrac{1}{2}, \dfrac{1}{3}, \dfrac{1}{4}, \dfrac{1}{5}, \ldots\right\}$ where $a_1 = 1$, $a_2 = \dfrac{1}{2}$, $a_3 = \dfrac{1}{3}$, $a_4 = \dfrac{1}{4}, \ldots$.

(c) The general term $a_n = e^{n-1}$ gives the sequence $\{1, e, e^2, e^3, e^4, \ldots\}$ where $a_1 = e^0$, $a_2 = e^1$, $a_3 = e^2$, $a_4 = e^3, \ldots$.

(d) Using the general terms identified above, we can abbreviate each of these sequences using equation (4) as follows:

$$\{1, 2, 3, 4, \ldots\} = \{n\}, \qquad n = 1, 2, \ldots$$

$$\left\{1, \frac{1}{2}, \frac{1}{3}, \frac{1}{4}, \ldots\right\} = \left\{\frac{1}{n}\right\}, \qquad n = 1, 2, \ldots$$

$$\{1, e, e^2, e^3, \ldots\} = \{e^{n-1}\}, \qquad n = 1, 2, \ldots. \quad ■$$

☐ **EXAMPLE 2**

Write out the first few terms of the sequence $\{a_n\}$ whose general term is

(a) $a_n = \dfrac{n}{n+1}$

(b) $a_n = \sin\left(\dfrac{n\pi}{2}\right)$.

Solution

(a) Since the terms of a sequence are obtained from the general term a_n by setting $n = 1, 2, 3, \ldots$, we find that

$$a_1 = \frac{1}{1+1} = \frac{1}{2} \qquad a_3 = \frac{3}{3+1} = \frac{3}{4}$$

$$a_2 = \frac{2}{2+1} = \frac{2}{3} \qquad a_4 = \frac{4}{4+1} = \frac{4}{5}$$

etc., so

$$\left\{\frac{n}{n+1}\right\} = \left\{\frac{1}{2}, \frac{2}{3}, \frac{3}{4}, \frac{4}{5}, \ldots\right\}.$$

(b) Substituting $n = 1, 2, 3, \ldots$ in $a_n = \sin\left(\dfrac{n\pi}{2}\right)$ gives

$$a_1 = \sin\left(\frac{1 \cdot \pi}{2}\right) = \sin\left(\frac{\pi}{2}\right) = 1$$

$$a_2 = \sin\left(\frac{2\pi}{2}\right) = \sin(\pi) = 0$$

$$a_3 = \sin\left(\frac{3\pi}{2}\right) = -1$$

$$a_4 = \sin\left(\frac{4\pi}{2}\right) = \sin(2\pi) = 0$$

$$a_5 = \sin\left(\frac{5\pi}{2}\right) = 1$$

etc. Thus,

$$\left\{\sin\frac{n\pi}{2}\right\} = \{1, 0, -1, 0, 1, 0, -1, 0, \ldots\}. \qquad ■$$

REMARK: Note in part (b) of Example 2 that we include those terms of the sequence that are zeros, and that the terms of a sequence can be negative numbers as well as positive numbers.

☐ **EXAMPLE 3**

If $100 is deposited in a savings account paying 10% interest compounded annually, the amounts $P(n)$ on deposit at the end of $n = 1, 2, 3, \ldots$ years can be thought of as the terms of the sequence whose general term is $a_n = P(n)$:

$$\{a_n\} = \{P(n)\} = \{\$100(1.10)^n\}, \qquad n = 1, 2, \ldots$$
$$= \{\$100(1.1), \$100(1.1)^2, \$100(1.1)^3, \ldots\}$$
$$= \{\$110, \$121, \$133.10, \ldots\}. \qquad \blacksquare$$

The following formal definition captures our notion that a sequence is a list of numbers indexed by the positive integers.

Definition 1

An **infinite sequence** is a function whose domain is the positive integers. That is, the sequence $\{a_n\}$ is the set of values of a function f for which

$$f(n) = a_n, \qquad n = 1, 2, 3, \ldots.$$

Thinking of sequences as functions allows us to apply the techniques previously used with functions to sequences. For example, we can add two sequences to form a new sequence by adding the corresponding terms:

$$\{a_n\} + \{b_n\} = \{a_n + b_n\}, \qquad n = 1, 2, \ldots.$$

And we can multiply a sequence by a constant by multiplying each term by that constant:

$$c\{a_n\} = \{ca_n\}, \qquad n = 1, 2, \ldots.$$

Finally, we can graph the sequence $\{a_n\}$ by plotting the points $(n, f(n)) = (n, a_n)$ for $n = 1, 2, 3, \ldots$ (but *not* connecting these points). See Figure 1.1.

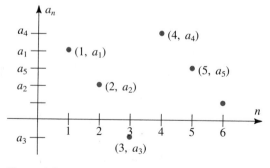

Figure 1.1 Graphing a sequence $\{a_n\}$.

☐ **EXAMPLE 4**

For the sequences

$$\{a_n\} = \{2n\} = \{2, 4, 6, 8, \ldots\} \quad \text{and}$$
$$\{b_n\} = \{n + 5\} = \{6, 7, 8, 9, \ldots\}$$

(a) the sequence $\{c_n\} = \{a_n + b_n\}$ is

$$\{c_n\} = \{2 + 6, 4 + 7, 6 + 8, 8 + 9, \ldots\}$$
$$= \{8, 11, 14, 17, \ldots\}$$

for which the general term is

$$c_n = a_n + b_n = (2n) + (n + 5) = 3n + 5.$$

(b) The sequence $\{d_n\} = 6\{a_n\} = \{6a_n\}$ is

$$\{d_n\} = \{6 \cdot 2, 6 \cdot 4, 6 \cdot 6, 6 \cdot 8, \ldots\}$$
$$= \{12, 24, 36, 48, \ldots\}$$

with general term

$$d_n = 6 \cdot a_n = 6(2n) = 12n.$$

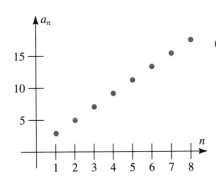

Figure 1.2 Graph of sequence
$$\{a_n\} = \{2_n + 1\}.$$

☐ **EXAMPLE 5**

Graph the sequences whose general terms are

(a) $a_n = 2n + 1$

(b) $a_n = 2 + \dfrac{(-1)^n}{n}.$

Solution: The sequences are

(a) $\{a_n\} = \{2n + 1\} = \{3, 5, 7, 9, \ldots\}$
(See Figure 1.2.)

(b) $\{a_n\} = \left\{2 + \dfrac{(-1)^n}{n}\right\} = \left\{2 - 1, 2 + \dfrac{1}{2}, 2 - \dfrac{1}{3}, 2 + \dfrac{1}{4}, \ldots\right\}$

$$= \left\{1, \dfrac{5}{2}, \dfrac{5}{3}, \dfrac{9}{4}, \ldots\right\}.$$

(See Figure 1.3.)

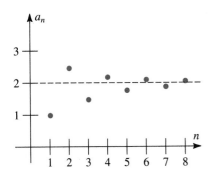

Figure 1.3 Graph of sequence
$$\{a_n\} = \left\{2 + \dfrac{(-1)^n}{n}\right\}.$$

REMARK: Recall that $(-1)^n = 1$ when n is even and $(-1)^n = -1$ when n is odd. This is how we signify a term whose sign *alternates* with increasing n.

Limits of Sequences

There is an important difference between the sequence $\{2n + 1\}$ in Figure 1.2 and the sequence $\left\{2 + \dfrac{(-1)^n}{n}\right\}$ in Figure 1.3. In the first sequence the terms increase at a constant rate, not approaching any particular number. In the language of Chapter 2 we would say that

$$\lim_{n \to \infty}\{2n + 1\} = +\infty$$

since the terms of this sequence increase without bound as $n \to \infty$.

However, the terms of the sequence $2 + \dfrac{(-1)^n}{n}$ "approach" the number $L = 2$ as $n \to \infty$ since the term $\dfrac{(-1)^n}{n}$ approaches zero as $n \to \infty$. Thus we write

$$\lim_{n \to \infty}\left\{2 + \frac{(-1)^n}{n}\right\} = 2$$

and we say that "the limit of the sequence $\left\{2 + \dfrac{(-1)^n}{n}\right\}$ is the number 2." Thus the limit of an infinite sequence is just the infinite limit "$\lim\limits_{x \to \infty} f(x)$," which we discussed in Chapter 2, except that the general term (function) $f(n) = a_n$ is defined only for positive integers.

Definition 2

$L = \lim\limits_{n \to \infty} a_n$ means that the terms of the sequence $\{a_n\}$ approach the unique number L as n increases without bound.

☐ **EXAMPLE 6**

$\lim\limits_{n \to \infty}\left(\dfrac{3n + 5}{n}\right) = \lim\limits_{n \to \infty}\left(3 + \dfrac{5}{n}\right) = 3$ since $\dfrac{5}{n}$ approaches zero as $n \to \infty$. ∎

☐ **EXAMPLE 7**

$\lim\limits_{n \to \infty} \sin \dfrac{\pi}{n} = \sin(0) = 0$ since $\dfrac{\pi}{n}$ approaches zero as $n \to \infty$. ∎

☐ **EXAMPLE 8**

$\lim\limits_{n \to \infty} \sin\left(\dfrac{n\pi}{2}\right)$ does not exist since

$$\left\{\sin\left(\frac{n\pi}{2}\right)\right\} = \left\{\sin\frac{\pi}{2}, \sin\pi, \sin\frac{3\pi}{2}, \sin 2\pi, \ldots\right\}$$

$$= \{1, 0, -1, 0, 1, 0, -1, \ldots\}$$

and these terms do not approach any *single* (that is, *unique*) number as $n \to \infty$. Rather, they oscillate back and forth among the three numbers 1, 0, and -1. ■

Since sequences are functions, we may use the same algebra in evaluating limits of sequences that we use in evaluating infinite limits of the form $\lim_{x \to \infty} f(x)$, including the following **properties of limits of sequences:**

$$\lim_{n \to \infty}\{a_n + b_n\} = \lim_{n \to \infty}\{a_n\} + \lim_{n \to \infty}\{b_n\} \tag{5}$$

$$\lim_{n \to \infty}\{ca_n\} = c \lim_{n \to \infty}\{a_n\} \tag{6}$$

$$\lim_{n \to \infty}\{a_n b_n\} = \left(\lim_{n \to \infty}\{a_n\}\right)\left(\lim_{n \to \infty}\{b_n\}\right) \tag{7}$$

$$\lim_{n \to \infty}\left\{\frac{a_n}{b_n}\right\} = \frac{\lim\limits_{n \to \infty}\{a_n\}}{\lim\limits_{n \to \infty}\{b_n\}}, \qquad \text{provided } \lim_{n \to \infty}\{b_n\} \neq 0. \tag{8}$$

In writing equations (5)–(8), we assume that each of the limits on the right-hand sides of the equations exists.

□ **EXAMPLE 9**

Find $\lim\limits_{n \to \infty} \dfrac{6n^3 + 5n^2 + 7}{4n^3 - 2n + 2}$.

Strategy · · · · · · · ·
Divide all terms by n^3 (the highest power of n present).

Solution

$$\lim_{n \to \infty} \frac{6n^3 + 5n^2 + 7}{4n^3 - 2n + 2} = \lim_{n \to \infty}\left(\frac{6n^3 + 5n^2 + 7}{4n^3 - 2n + 2}\right)\left(\frac{\dfrac{1}{n^3}}{\dfrac{1}{n^3}}\right)$$

$$= \lim_{n \to \infty} \frac{6 + \dfrac{5}{n} + \dfrac{7}{n^3}}{4 - \dfrac{2}{n^2} + \dfrac{2}{n^3}}$$

Use properties (5)–(7) to take the limit of each individual term, using the facts that

$$\lim_{n \to \infty} \frac{1}{n} = 0, \quad \lim_{n \to \infty} \frac{1}{n^2} = 0$$

$$\text{and} \quad \lim_{n \to \infty} \frac{1}{n^3} = 0.$$

$$= \frac{6 + 0 + 0}{4 - 0 + 0}$$

$$= \frac{3}{2}. \qquad ■$$

☐ **EXAMPLE 10**

Find $\lim\limits_{n\to\infty}[\ln(n+4) - \dfrac{1}{2}\ln(n)]$.

Strategy · · · · · · ·

Use properties of natural logarithms that

$$r\ln a = \ln a^r \quad \text{and}$$

$$\ln a - \ln b = \ln\dfrac{a}{b}.$$

Divide each term in numerator by $\sqrt{n}$.

Solution

$$\lim_{n\to\infty}\left[\ln(n+4) - \frac{1}{2}\ln n\right] = \lim_{n\to\infty}[\ln(n+4) - \ln(n^{1/2})]$$

$$= \lim_{n\to\infty}\ln\frac{n+4}{\sqrt{n}}$$

$$= \lim_{n\to\infty}\ln\left(\sqrt{n} + \frac{4}{\sqrt{n}}\right)$$

$$= +\infty. \qquad \blacksquare$$

When $\lim\limits_{n\to\infty} a_n = L$ exists, we say that the sequence $\{a_n\}$ **converges** to L. When the number $L = \lim\limits_{n\to\infty} a_n$ does not exist, we say that the sequence $\{a_n\}$ **diverges**. Thus the sequence in Example 9 converges to the number $L = \dfrac{3}{2}$, while the sequence in Example 10 diverges.

☐ **EXAMPLE 11**

Find $\lim\limits_{n\to\infty}(-1)^n\left(\dfrac{n+1}{n}\right)$.

Strategy · · · · · · ·

Because of the factor of $(-1)^n$, examine even and odd terms separately.

Divide through by n.

Determine whether odd terms approach the same limit as even terms.

Solution

For even integers n we have $(-1)^n = 1$, so

$$\lim_{n\to\infty}(-1)^n\left(\frac{n+1}{n}\right) = \lim_{n\to\infty}(1)\left(1 + \frac{1}{n}\right)$$

$$= 1$$

(even integers only).
However, for odd integers n

$$(-1)^n = -1$$

so

$$\lim_{n\to\infty}(-1)^n\left(\frac{n+1}{n}\right) = \lim_{n\to\infty}(-1)\left(1 + \frac{1}{n}\right)$$

$$= -1$$

(odd integers only).

This shows that the terms do not approach a *single* number L as $n \to \infty$, so the limit $\lim_{n \to \infty} (-1)^n \left(\dfrac{n+1}{n} \right)$ does not exist. Thus the sequence $\left\{ (-1)^n \left(\dfrac{n+1}{n} \right) \right\}$ diverges. (See Figure 1.4.) ∎

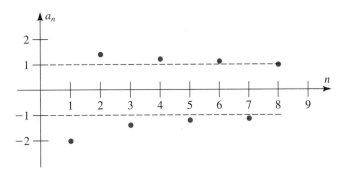

Figure 1.4 The sequence $\left\{ a_n = \left\{ (-1)^n \left(\dfrac{n+1}{n} \right) \right\} \right.$.

The last two examples concern limits of two important sequences that we have studied previously, those for compound interest and approximating sums.

☐ **EXAMPLE 12**

(Continuous compounding of interest). In Chapter 4 we developed the following formula for the amount of money $P_n(1)$ on deposit one year after placing an initial amount P_0 in a savings account paying fractional interest rate r compounded n times per year:

$$P_n(1) = \left(1 + \frac{r}{n} \right)^n P_0.$$

This expression may be viewed as the general term of the sequence $\{a_n\} = \{P_n(1)\}$. Letting $n \to \infty$, we obtain the limit

$$P(1) = \lim_{n \to \infty} \left(1 + \frac{r}{n} \right)^n P_0$$
$$= e^r P_0 \tag{9}$$

where we have used the fact that $\lim_{n \to \infty} \left(1 + \dfrac{r}{n} \right)^n = e^r$ as developed in Chapter 4.

Equation (9) is the formula for *continuous* compounding of interest for the period of one year. For continuous compounding of interest over a period of t years we use the limit

$$P(t) = \lim_{n \to \infty} \left(1 + \frac{r}{n}\right)^{nt} P_0$$

$$= \left[\lim_{n \to \infty} \left(1 + \frac{r}{n}\right)^{n}\right]^{t} P_0$$

$$= [e^r]^t P_0$$

$$= e^{rt} P_0$$

also developed in Chapter 4. ∎

□ **EXAMPLE 13**

(Lot sampling for defectives). A manufacturer of spark plugs wishes to inspect its products for defects by examining a *sample* of size n drawn randomly from an entire lot of spark plugs. It can be shown that, if $\alpha\%$ of the entire lot is defective, then the probability of finding *no* defective spark plugs in a sample of size n is $\left(\dfrac{100 - \alpha}{100}\right)^n$, and the probability of finding *at least one* defective spark plug is $P(n) = 1 - \left(\dfrac{100 - \alpha}{100}\right)^n$.

(a) If the percentage of defective spark plugs in the entire lot is $\alpha = 2\%$, find the numbers $P(1)$, $P(2)$, and $P(3)$, giving the probabilities of finding at least one defective spark plug in samples of size 1, 2, and 3, respectively.
(b) Find $\lim_{n \to \infty} P_n$ and explain this limit.

Solution: With $\alpha = 2$, we have $P_n = 1 - \left(\dfrac{100 - 2}{100}\right)^n = 1 - \left(\dfrac{98}{100}\right)^n$ so the probabilities of finding at least one defective plug are

$$P(1) = 1 - \frac{98}{100} = \frac{2}{100} = 0.02 = 2\%$$

$$P(2) = 1 - \left(\frac{98}{100}\right)^2 = 0.0396 = 3.96\%$$

$$P(3) = 1 - \left(\frac{98}{100}\right)^3 = 0.058 = 5.8\%.$$

Using a hand calculator, you can verify the limit

$$\lim_{n \to \infty} \left(\frac{98}{100}\right)^n = 0$$

by calculating $\left(\dfrac{98}{100}\right)^n$ for large n. Thus,

$$\lim_{n\to\infty} P(n) = \lim_{n\to\infty}\left[1 - \left(\frac{98}{100}\right)^n\right] = 1 = 100\%$$

which says that as the samples get increasingly large, the probability of finding at least one defective spark plug approaches 100%. ■

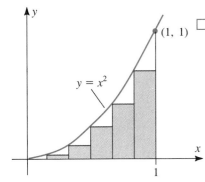

Figure 1.5 The definite integral $\displaystyle\int_0^1 x^2\,dx$ is the limit of a sequence of approximating sums

$$\int_0^1 x^2\,dx = \lim_{n\to\infty} \underline{S}_n = \lim_{n\to\infty} -\sum_{j=1}^{n} t_j^2 \Delta x.$$

□ **EXAMPLE 14**

(Approximating sums.) Each of the procedures for approximating the definite integral $\displaystyle\int_a^b f(x)\,dx$ that we have described (approximating sums, Trapezoidal Rule, Simpson's Rule) is really a procedure for generating the nth term in a sequence of approximations, where n is the number of subintervals into which the interval $[a, b]$ is divided. Figure 1.5 shows one term of the sequence $\{S_n\}$ of approximating sums for the function $f(x) = x^2$ on the interval $[0,1]$, using the minimum value of $f(x) = x^2$ in each subinterval. In this case we know that

$$\int_0^1 x^2\,dx = \lim_{n\to\infty} \sum_{j=1}^{n}\left(\frac{j-1}{n}\right)^2\left(\frac{1}{n}\right)$$

$$= \frac{1}{3}$$

as demonstrated in Chapter 5. ■

☑ **PRACTICE PROBLEMS 9.1**

1. Write out the first six terms of the following sequences.

   a. $\left\{\dfrac{n+2}{1+n^2}\right\}$

   b. $\left\{n\cos\dfrac{n\pi}{4}\right\}$

2. Find the limits of the following sequences.

   a. $\displaystyle\lim_{n\to\infty}\left\{\dfrac{\sqrt{n}+3n^2-7}{2n^{3/2}+5n^2}\right\}$

   b. $\displaystyle\lim_{n\to\infty}\left\{\dfrac{\sqrt{n}}{n^{3/2}+5}\right\}$

3. A savings account pays 12% interest, compounded monthly. Find the amount, a_n, on deposit after n months, if a person deposits $100 monthly on the first day of each of the first three months.

Exercise Set 9.1

In each of Exercises 1–10, write out the first five terms of the sequence whose general term is given.

1. $\{2n + 3\}$

2. $\left\{\dfrac{n}{2n + 1}\right\}$

3. $\left\{\dfrac{2n + 1}{n + 5}\right\}$

4. $\left\{\dfrac{(-1)^n}{1 + n^2}\right\}$

5. $\left\{\dfrac{(-1)^n}{e^n}\right\}$

6. $\left\{\dfrac{20n}{1 + n^3}\right\}$

7. $\left\{\dfrac{(n - 1)(n + 1)}{2n^2 + 2n + 2}\right\}$

8. $\{\ln(n + 2)\}$

9. $\left\{(-1)^{n+1} \sin\left(\dfrac{n\pi}{4}\right)\right\}$

10. $\left\{\dfrac{1 + n^2}{5 + n^3}\right\}$

In each of Exercises 11–32, determine whether the sequence converges or diverges. For those that converge find the limits.

11. $\left\{\dfrac{n}{3n + 6}\right\}$

12. $\left\{\dfrac{2n - \sqrt{n}}{n + 3}\right\}$

13. $\{\sqrt{5 + n}\}$

14. $\left\{\dfrac{n - 1}{n^3 + 3}\right\}$

15. $\left\{\dfrac{e^n + 3}{e^n}\right\}$

16. $\left\{\dfrac{2n - n^2}{2n^2 + 1}\right\}$

17. $\left\{\dfrac{n^2 - 2n + 1}{3 + n^2}\right\}$

18. $\left\{\dfrac{n^2 + 3n + 5}{n^5 + 2}\right\}$

19. $\{\ln(n + 1) - \ln(n)\}$

20. $\{e^{(n-1)/n}\}$

21. $\{\sin n\pi\}$

22. $\left\{\dfrac{(-1)^n n^2}{9 - n^2}\right\}$

23. $\left\{\cos \dfrac{n - 1}{n^2}\right\}$

24. $\left\{\dfrac{e^n - e^{-n}}{e^n + e^{-n}}\right\}$

25. $\left\{\dfrac{1}{n} - \dfrac{1}{n + 1}\right\}$

26. $\left\{\dfrac{2^n}{3^n + 4^n}\right\}$

27. $\left\{\left(1 + \dfrac{1}{n}\right)^n\right\}$

28. $\left\{\left(1 - \dfrac{1}{n}\right)^n\right\}$

29. $\left\{\dfrac{\sqrt{n}}{1 + \sqrt{n}}\right\}$

30. $\left\{\ln\left(\dfrac{n^2 + 6}{9 + n^2}\right)\right\}$

31. $\left\{\cos\left(\dfrac{n\pi}{4}\right)\right\}$

32. $\left\{\sin \dfrac{(n + 1)\pi}{n^2}\right\}$

33. A biological population grows in number so that after n years it has $N(n) = \dfrac{A}{B + Ce^{-n}}$ members. Find $\lim\limits_{n \to \infty} N(n)$, its long-term size.

34. Find $\lim\limits_{n \to \infty} N(n)$ for the growth model $N(n) = \dfrac{A}{B + Ce^n}$.

35. Carol deposits $1000 in a savings account paying 8% interest compounded annually. Let a_n be the amount on deposit after n years and assume no additional deposits are made.
   a. Find a_1.
   b. Find a_2.
   c. Find a_5.

36. For his 21st birthday Paul is given a savings bond that will be worth $1000 in seven years. Let a_n represent the present value of this bond after n years. Assume continuous compounding of interest at the nominal rate of $r = 5\%$.
   a. Find a_0, the present value at the time of the gift.
   b. Find a_1, the present value after one year.
   c. Find a_5, the present value after five years.

37. A certain make and model of automobile has a fleet average fuel consumption of 22 miles per gallon. It is claimed that average will increase annually by 10% per year. Let a_n be the fleet average after n years.
   a. Find a_1.
   b. Find a_2.
   c. Find a formula for the fleet average a_n after n years.
   d. Does this sequence have a limit? If so, what is it? If not, why not?

38. The population of Megacity is currently 3 million and it is said to be growing in population by 6% per year. Let P_n be the population of Megacity after n years.
   a. Find P_1.
   b. Find P_2.
   c. Find a formula for the size of Megacity's population after n years. (See Exercise 37.)
   d. What is the limit of this sequence?

39. A patient receives 50 milligrams of a drug daily. Each day, the body eliminates 50% of the drug present. Write a sequence $\{a_n\}$ in which a_n is the amount of the drug present in the body on the nth day, just after the dosage is administered.

40. A child deposits $10 on the first day of each month in a savings account. The bank pays 12% interest, compounded monthly, on this account. Find the sequence $\{a_n\}$ in which a_n is the amount in the account at the end of the nth month.

41. A manufacturer of costume jewelry wishes to test its bracelets for defects by examining samples of size n drawn from entire lots at random. If 10% of all bracelets are defective, find the probabilities $P(1)$, $P(2)$, $P(3)$, and $P(n)$, given the probability of finding at least one defective bracelet in a sample size 1, 2, 3, or n, respectively. (See Example 13.)

42. The *Fibonacci numbers* are the sequence

$$\{1, 1, 2, 3, 5, 8, 13, 21, 34, \ldots \}$$

which is defined by the following rules:

(a) $a_1 = 1$

(b) $a_2 = 1$

(c) $a_{n+2} = a_n + a_{n+1}, \qquad n = 1, 2, 3, \ldots$

This sequence is sometimes described as the solution to the following problem: Assume that we begin with a single pair of rabbits (male and female), that this pair and each resulting pair of rabbits become fertile one month after birth, that each pair of fertile rabbits gives birth to one new pair of rabbits each month, and that no rabbit dies. Let a_n be the number of pairs of rabbits present n months after this experiment begins. Explain why the Fibonacci sequence describes the sequence $\{a_n\}$.

☑ **SOLUTIONS TO PRACTICE PROBLEMS 9.1**

1. a. For $a_n = \dfrac{n+2}{1+n^2}$: $a_1 = \dfrac{3}{2}$; $a_2 = \dfrac{4}{5}$; $a_3 = \dfrac{1}{2}$; $a_4 = \dfrac{6}{17}$; $a_5 = \dfrac{7}{26}$; $a_6 = \dfrac{8}{37}$.

b. For $a_n = n \cos \dfrac{n\pi}{4}$: $a_1 = \dfrac{\sqrt{2}}{2}$; $a_2 = 0$; $a_3 = -\dfrac{3\sqrt{2}}{2}$; $a_4 = -4$; $a_5 = -\dfrac{5\sqrt{2}}{2}$; $a_6 = 0$.

2. a. $\displaystyle\lim_{n \to \infty} \dfrac{\sqrt{n} + 3n^2 - 7}{2n^{3/2} + 5n^2} = \lim_{n \to \infty} \dfrac{\dfrac{1}{n^{3/2}} + 3 - \dfrac{7}{n^2}}{\dfrac{2}{\sqrt{n}} + 5} = \dfrac{3}{5}$

b. $\displaystyle\lim_{n \to \infty} \left(\dfrac{\sqrt{n}}{n^{3/2} + 5} \right) = \lim_{n \to \infty} \left(\dfrac{\dfrac{1}{n}}{1 + \dfrac{5}{n^{3/2}}} \right) = 0$

3. $a_1 = (1.01)(\$100) = \$101$

$a_2 = (1.01)[\$100 + (1.01)(\$100)] = \$100(1.01 + (1.01)^2)$
$$= \$203.01$$

$a_3 = (1.01)[\$100 + 100(1.01) + 100(1.01)^2]$
$$= \$100[1.01 + (1.01)^2 + (1.01)^3] = \$306.04$$

9.2 Infinite Series

In Chapter 8 we introduced the concept of an improper integral of the form $\displaystyle\int_a^\infty f(x)\, dx$. One reason for doing this was to extend certain applications of the definite integral (such as the calculation of area) to intervals extending infinitely far to the right. For these same reasons we sometimes need to use a similar concept that applies to functions that are defined only for integers. This is the concept of *infinite series*. The following example shows one situation to which this concept applies.

□ **EXAMPLE 1**

An investor has the opportunity to place $100,000 in an investment account that pays 20% interest compounded annually. The investor plans to withdraw one half of the total amount on deposit annually, just after the interest is credited to the account.

(a) Find $S(1)$, the sum that the investor will receive at the end of the first year.
(b) Find $S(n)$, the sum that the investor will receive *(total)* over the first n years.
(c) Find $\lim_{n \to \infty} S(n)$, the sum of all payments due to the investor and his heirs in

    perpetuity.

(Work in nominal dollars, rather than convert to present values.)

Solution

(a) After the first annual payment the total in the account will be

$$T(1) = (1.2)(\$100,000) = \$120,000.$$

The investor will withdraw half this amount

$$W(1) = (0.5)(1.2)(\$100,000) = \$60,000$$

leaving the amount

$$R(1) = (0.5)(1.2)(\$100,000) = \$60,000$$

remaining in the account. Thus $S(1) = W(1) = \$60,000$.
(b) After the second annual interest payment the account will contain

$$T(2) = (1.2)R(1) = (0.5)(1.2)^2(\$100,000) = \$72,000$$

of which the amount withdrawn will be

$$W(2) = (0.5)T(2) = (0.5)^2(1.2)^2(\$100,000) = \$36,000.$$

The sum of the withdrawals during the first 2 years will therefore be

$$S(2) = W(1) + W(2)$$

$$= (0.5)(1.2)(\$100,000) + (0.5)^2(1.2)^2(\$100,000)$$

$$= \left[\frac{3}{5} + \left(\frac{3}{5} \right)^2 \right](\$100,000)$$

$$= \$96,000.$$

Continuing in this way, we find that the total of all withdrawals during the first n years will be

$$S(n) = \left[\frac{3}{5} + \left(\frac{3}{5} \right)^2 + \left(\frac{3}{5} \right)^3 + \ldots + \left(\frac{3}{5} \right)^n \right](\$100,000)$$

$$= \frac{3}{5} \left[1 + \frac{3}{5} + \left(\frac{3}{5} \right)^2 + \ldots + \left(\frac{3}{5} \right)^{n-1} \right](\$100,000). \qquad (1)$$

To simplify this expression, we use the formula

$$1 + x + x^2 + \ldots + x^k = \frac{1 - x^{k+1}}{1 - x} \tag{2}$$

which we shall verify later in this section. With $k = n - 1$ and $x = \dfrac{3}{5}$, we find that

$$1 + \frac{3}{5} + \left(\frac{3}{5}\right)^2 + \ldots + \left(\frac{3}{5}\right)^{n-1} = \frac{1 - \left(\dfrac{3}{5}\right)^n}{1 - \dfrac{3}{5}}$$

$$= \frac{5}{2}\left[1 - \left(\frac{3}{5}\right)^n\right]. \tag{3}$$

Substituting the right-hand side of equation (3) into equation (1) in place of the expression in brackets gives

$$S(n) = \frac{3}{5}\left(\frac{5}{2}\right)\left[1 - \left(\frac{3}{5}\right)^n\right](\$100{,}000)$$

$$= \$150{,}000\left[1 - \left(\frac{3}{5}\right)^n\right] \tag{4}$$

as the total of all withdrawals over the first n years. (See Figure 2.1.)

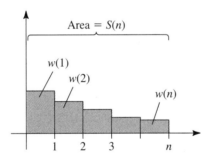

Figure 2.1 $S(n)$ is the sum of the annual withdrawals

$$S(n) = W(1) + W(2) + \ldots + W(n).$$

(c) The sum of all annual withdrawals, in perpetuity (meaning forever), is just the limit as $n \to \infty$ of the expression for $S(n)$ in equation (4):

$$S = \lim_{n \to \infty} S(n) = \lim_{n \to \infty} \$150{,}000\left[1 - \left(\frac{3}{5}\right)^n\right]$$

$$= \$150{,}000[1 - 0]$$

$$= \$150{,}000$$

since $\lim\limits_{n\to\infty}\left(\dfrac{3}{5}\right)^n = 0$ (a fact that you can observe experimentally by using a calculator, for example).

Figure 2.2 shows that this limit S corresponds to the area associated with the infinitely many rectangles with widths one and heights $W(1)$, $W(2)$, $W(3)$, ... ∎

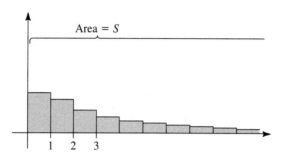

Figure 2.2 $S = \lim\limits_{n\to\infty} S(n)$ is the sum of all annual withdrawals in perpetuity.

The point of Example 1 is that we can think of summing infinitely many function values $f(1)$, $f(2)$, $f(3)$, . . . in the same way that we evaluate the improper integral $\displaystyle\int_a^\infty f(x)\,dx$ of a continuous function: by first summing finitely many terms, and then evaluating the limit at infinity of the resulting expression. (See Figures 2.3 and 2.4.) This is the concept of *infinite series,* which we define as follows.

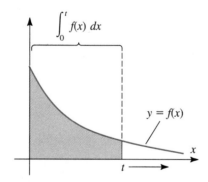

Figure 2.3 The improper integral
$$\int_0^\infty f(x)\,dx$$
is the *limit* of the partial integrals
$$\int_0^t f(x)\,dx:$$
$$\int_0^\infty f(x)\,dx = \lim_{t\to\infty}\int_0^t f(x)\,dx.$$

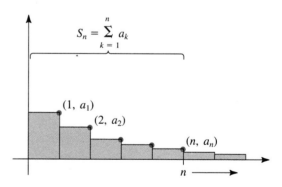

Figure 2.4 The sum of the infinite series
$$\sum_{k=1}^\infty a_k = a_1 + a_2 + a_3 + \ldots$$
is the *limit* of the sequence of partial sums
$$\sum_{k=1}^\infty a_k = \lim_{n\to\infty} S_n = \lim_{n\to\infty}\sum_{k=1}^n a_k.$$

Definition 3

An **infinite series** is an expression of the form

$$\sum_{k=1}^{\infty} a_k = a_1 + a_2 + a_3 + \ldots .$$

For such infinite series the **partial sums** $S_1, S_2, S_3, \ldots$ are defined by

$$S_1 = a_1$$
$$S_2 = a_1 + a_2$$
$$S_3 = a_1 + a_2 + a_3$$
$$\vdots$$

$$S_n = a_1 + a_2 + a_3 + \ldots + a_n = \sum_{k=1}^{n} a_k, \text{ etc.}$$

The infinite series $\sum_{k=1}^{\infty} a_k$ is said to **converge** to the *sum S* if

$$S = \lim_{n \to \infty} S_n = \lim_{n \to \infty} \sum_{k=1}^{n} a_k \tag{5}$$

exists. (That is, the sum of an infinite series is the limit at infinity of the sequence of its partial sums.) If the limit in equation (5) does not exist, the infinite series is said to **diverge**.

□ **EXAMPLE 2**

The total of the annual withdrawals in Example 1 is an infinite series:

$$W(1) + W(2) + W(3) + \ldots$$

$$= \left(\frac{3}{5}\right)(100,000) + \left(\frac{3}{5}\right)^2 (100,000) + \left(\frac{3}{5}\right)^3 (100,000) + \ldots$$

$$= \sum_{k=1}^{\infty} \left(\frac{3}{5}\right)^k (100,000).$$

In that example the partial sums for the series were found to be

$$S_n = S(n) = \left[\frac{3}{5} + \left(\frac{3}{5}\right)^2 + \ldots + \left(\frac{3}{5}\right)^n\right](100,000)$$

$$= 150,000\left[1 - \left(\frac{3}{5}\right)^n\right]$$

and the sum of the series is

$$S = \lim_{n \to \infty} S_n = 150,000.$$

That is

$$\sum_{k=1}^{\infty} \left(\frac{3}{5}\right)^k (100{,}000) = 150{,}000.$$

Thus this series *converges*. (This is an example of a *geometric* series, which we shall discuss later in this chapter.) ∎

□ **EXAMPLE 3**

The infinite series

$$\sum_{k=1}^{\infty} (-1)^k = -1 + 1 + (-1) + 1 + (-1) + \ldots$$

is an example of a divergent series. To see this, simply note the sequence of partial sums:

$$S_1 = -1$$
$$S_2 = -1 + 1 = S_1 + 1 = 0$$
$$S_3 = -1 + 1 + (-1) = S_2 - 1 = -1$$
$$S_4 = -1 + 1 + (-1) + 1 = S_3 + 1 = 0$$
$$\vdots$$
$$S_{2n} = S_{2n-1} + 1 = -1 + 1 = 0$$
$$S_{2n+1} = S_{2n} - 1 = 0 - 1 = -1$$
$$\vdots$$

Thus the sequence of partial sums is

$$\{S_n\} = \{-1, 0, -1, 0, -1, 0, -1, \ldots\}$$

which oscillates between -1 and 0, so $\lim_{n \to \infty} S_n$ does not exist. This series, therefore, diverges. ∎

Geometric Series

A **geometric series** is an infinite series of the form

$$1 + x + x^2 + \ldots + x^n + \ldots = \sum_{k=0}^{\infty} x^k. \tag{6}$$

That is, a geometric series is one involving positive integral powers of some number x. Note that the first term of this series is $1 = x^0$, which is why the index k begins at $k = 0$. The partial sums of a geometric series may be found using formula (2) given earlier:

$$1 + x + x^2 + \ldots + x^n = \frac{1 - x^{n+1}}{1 - x}, \qquad x \neq 1. \tag{7}$$

To verify equation (7), we note that

$$(1 - x)(1 + x + x^2 + \ldots + x^n)$$
$$= 1(1 + x + x^2 + \ldots + x^n) - x(1 + x + x^2 + \ldots + x^n)$$
$$= (1 + x + x^2 + \ldots + x^n) - (x + x^2 + x^3 + \ldots + x^{n+1})$$
$$= 1 - x^{n+1}$$

since all of the powers of x between x and x^n are added in the first parentheses and subtracted in the second parentheses. Dividing the left-hand and right-hand sides of this equation by $(1 - x)$ then gives formula (7).

Using formula (7), we find that the partial sums S_n of the geometric series in equation (6) can be written

$$S_n = 1 + x + x^2 + \ldots + x^n$$

$$= \frac{1 - x^{n+1}}{1 - x}, \qquad x \neq 1. \tag{8}$$

To determine whether the sequence $\{S_n\}$ converges, we need to know something about $\lim\limits_{n \to \infty} x^{n+1}$. This limit depends on the number x. A fact that we shall not prove, but that you can observe using a calculator, is that $\lim\limits_{n \to \infty} x^{n+1}$ (a) equals zero if $|x| < 1$, (b) equals 1 if $x = 1$, and (c) fails to exist if $x = -1$ (by Example 3) or if $|x| > 1$.

Since the case $x = 1$ is already ruled out in equation (8), the limit $\lim\limits_{n \to \infty} S_n$ exists only when $|x| < 1$. In this case we have

$$\lim_{n \to \infty} S_n = \lim_{n \to \infty} \frac{1 - x^{n+1}}{1 - x} = \frac{1 - 0}{1 - x} = \frac{1}{1 - x}$$

since $\lim\limits_{n \to \infty} x^{n+1} = 0$. The behavior of geometric series is therefore the following.

Theorem 1

The geometric series

$$\sum_{k=0}^{\infty} x^k = 1 + x + x^2 + x^3 + \ldots$$

(a) converges to $\dfrac{1}{1 - x}$ if $|x| < 1$

(b) diverges if $|x| \geq 1$.

We may summarize Theorem 1 by saying that

$$\sum_{k=0}^{\infty} x^k = \frac{1}{1-x} \qquad \text{if } |x| < 1.\tag{9}$$

The following examples illustrate how equation (9) may be used.

☐ **EXAMPLE 4**

The series

$$1 + \frac{1}{2} + \frac{1}{4} + \frac{1}{8} + \ldots + \frac{1}{2^k} + \ldots$$

is a geometric series whose general term is $a_k = \dfrac{1}{2^k} = \left(\dfrac{1}{2}\right)^k$. It therefore has the form of the geometric series in equation (9) with $x = \dfrac{1}{2}$. Thus since $|x| = \left|\dfrac{1}{2}\right| = \dfrac{1}{2} < 1$, the series converges, with sum

$$\sum_{k=0}^{\infty}\left(\frac{1}{2}\right)^k = \frac{1}{1-\dfrac{1}{2}} = \frac{1}{\dfrac{1}{2}} = 2.$$

■

☐ **EXAMPLE 5**

The series

$$1 + \frac{2}{3} + \frac{4}{9} + \frac{8}{27} + \ldots + \frac{2^k}{3^k} + \ldots$$

has the form of equation (9) with $x = \dfrac{2}{3}$, since $x^k = \dfrac{2^k}{3^k} = \left(\dfrac{2}{3}\right)^k$. Thus since $|x| = \left|\dfrac{2}{3}\right| = \dfrac{2}{3} < 1$, the series converges, with sum

$$\sum_{k=0}^{\infty}\frac{2^k}{3^k} = \sum_{k=0}^{\infty}\left(\frac{2}{3}\right)^k = \frac{1}{1-\dfrac{2}{3}} = \frac{1}{\dfrac{1}{3}} = 3.$$

■

☐ **EXAMPLE 6**

The series

$$1 + 2 + 4 + 8 + \ldots + 2^k + \ldots$$

is a geometric series with general term $a_k = x^k = 2^k$. Since $x = 2$, we have $|x| = |2| = 2 > 1$, so this geometric series diverges.   ◼

☐ **EXAMPLE 7**

The series

$$\frac{1}{2} + \frac{1}{4} + \frac{1}{8} + \ldots + \frac{1}{2^k} + \ldots$$

has the form of the geometric series in equation (9) with $x^k = \dfrac{1}{2^k} = \left(\dfrac{1}{2}\right)^k$, so $x = \dfrac{1}{2}$. *But the first term* $x^0 = \left(\dfrac{1}{2}\right)^0 = 1$ *is missing*. Since $|x| = \left|\dfrac{1}{2}\right| = \dfrac{1}{2} < 1$, the series converges, but we must subtract the missing term 1 from the formula for the sum of this series:

$$\frac{1}{2} + \frac{1}{4} + \frac{1}{8} + \ldots + \frac{1}{2^k} = \sum_{k=1}^{\infty} \left(\frac{1}{2}\right)^k$$

$$= \sum_{k=0}^{\infty} \left(\frac{1}{2}\right)^k - \left(\frac{1}{2}\right)^0$$

$$= \frac{1}{1 - \dfrac{1}{2}} - 1$$

> Note the change in the starting index.

$$= 2 - 1$$

$$= 1.$$ ◼

REMARK: Example 7 raises an important point about infinite series. If the series $\sum_{k=1}^{\infty} a_k$ converges, then adding or subtracting a *finite* number of terms will not change the fact that the series converges, *but it will change the value of the sum* (by whatever amount was added or subtracted). Thus, for example, since

$$1 + \frac{1}{3} + \left(\frac{1}{3}\right)^2 + \ldots + \left(\frac{1}{3}\right)^k + \ldots = \sum_{k=0}^{\infty} \left(\frac{1}{3}\right)^k = \frac{1}{1 - \dfrac{1}{3}} = \frac{3}{2}$$

we have

$$\frac{1}{3} + \left(\frac{1}{3}\right)^2 + \ldots + \left(\frac{1}{3}\right)^k + \ldots$$

$$= \sum_{k=1}^{\infty}\left(\frac{1}{3}\right)^k = \sum_{k=0}^{\infty}\left(\frac{1}{3}\right)^k - 1 = \frac{3}{2} - 1 = \frac{1}{2}$$

$$\left(\frac{1}{3}\right)^2 + \left(\frac{1}{3}\right)^3 + \ldots + \left(\frac{1}{3}\right)^k + \ldots$$

| Note change in starting index from $k = 2$ to $k = 0$. |

$$= \sum_{k=2}^{\infty}\left(\frac{1}{3}\right)^k = \sum_{k=0}^{\infty}\left(\frac{1}{3}\right)^k - 1 - \frac{1}{3} = \frac{3}{2} - 1 - \frac{1}{3} = \frac{1}{6}$$

etc. When working with the formula for the sum of a *geometric* series, be very careful to note the value of the index corresponding to the first term. If it is not $k = 0$, you must adjust the formula for the sum accordingly.

Properties of Infinite Series

We may perform simple algebra on convergent infinite series just as we do for finite sums. Specifically, if $\Sigma\, a_k$ and $\Sigma\, b_k$ are convergent infinite series and c is a constant

$$\sum ca_k = c \sum a_k \qquad (10)$$

and

$$\sum(a_k + b_k) = \sum a_k + \sum b_k. \qquad (11)$$

That is, multiplying each term of a convergent series by a constant c multiplies the sum by this same constant, and the sum of series formed by pairwise addition of the terms of two convergent series is found by adding the individual sums.

REMARK 1: In writing equations (10) and (11), we have not indicated initial values for the indices since these equations are true independent of whether the series begins at $k = 0$, $k = 1$, etc. (However, the series in equation (11) must all begin at the same value of the index.)

REMARK 2: This sort of algebra is valid only if all the series involved are convergent. Adding a convergent series termwise to a divergent series just gives another divergent series.

□ **EXAMPLE 8**

Find the sum of the series

$$\sum_{k=0}^{\infty} \frac{3 \cdot 2^k + 3^k}{5^k} = 4 + \frac{9}{5} + \frac{21}{25} + \frac{51}{125} + \ldots.$$

Solution: We use formula (9) together with equations (10) and (11) as follows:

$$\sum_{k=0}^{\infty} \frac{3 \cdot 2^k + 3^k}{5^k} = \sum_{k=0}^{\infty}\left(\frac{3 \cdot 2^k}{5^k} + \frac{3^k}{5^k}\right)$$

$$= 3\sum_{k=0}^{\infty} \frac{2^k}{5^k} + \sum_{k=0}^{\infty} \frac{3^k}{5^k}$$

$$= 3\sum_{k=0}^{\infty}\left(\frac{2}{5}\right)^k + \sum_{k=0}^{\infty}\left(\frac{3}{5}\right)^k$$

$$= 3\left(\frac{1}{1-\dfrac{2}{5}}\right) + \left(\frac{1}{1-\dfrac{3}{5}}\right)$$

$$= 3\left(\frac{5}{3}\right) + \frac{5}{2}$$

$$= \frac{15}{2}.$$

☑ **PRACTICE PROBLEMS 9.2**

1. Find the sum of each series, if it converges.

a. $\displaystyle\sum_{k=0}^{\infty} \frac{3 + 4^k}{6^k}$

b. $\displaystyle\sum_{k=1}^{\infty} \frac{2^k - 1}{3^k}$

2. The present value, assuming an interest rate of r percent, of a payment P to be received n years in the future is $P_0(n) = e^{-nr}P$. An annuity pays \$10,000 per year to its beneficiary.

a. Find the present value of the first four annual payments.

b. Find the present value of the annuity in perpetuity.

Assume an interest rate of $r = 10\%$.

Exercise Set 9.2

In Exercises 1–8. write out the first four terms of the infinite series.

1. $\displaystyle\sum_{k=1}^{\infty}(2k + 3)$

2. $\displaystyle\sum_{k=1}^{\infty} \sqrt{1 + k^2}$

3. $\displaystyle\sum_{k=0}^{\infty} \frac{1}{5^k}$

4. $\displaystyle\sum_{k=0}^{\infty} \frac{1 + 3^k}{5^k}$

5. $\displaystyle\sum_{k=1}^{\infty} \frac{(-1)^k}{1 + k^2}$

6. $\displaystyle\sum_{k=0}^{\infty} \frac{2^k}{7^k}$

7. $\sum_{k=1}^{\infty} \dfrac{\cos(\pi k)}{1 + k}$

8. $\sum_{k=1}^{\infty} \sqrt{k}^k$

In Exercises 9–22, determine whether the series converges. If it does, find its sum.

9. $\sum_{k=0}^{\infty} \dfrac{1}{4^k}$

10. $\sum_{k=0}^{\infty} \dfrac{3^k}{2^k}$

11. $\sum_{k=0}^{\infty} \dfrac{3^k}{7^k}$

12. $\sum_{k=0}^{\infty} \left(\dfrac{\sqrt{2}}{2}\right)^k$

13. $\sum_{k=1}^{\infty} \dfrac{1}{e^{-k}}$

14. $\sum_{k=2}^{\infty} \dfrac{1}{2^k}$

15. $\sum_{k=1}^{\infty} \dfrac{7^k}{5^k}$

16. $\sum_{k=2}^{\infty} \dfrac{9^k}{7^k}$

17. $\sum_{k=0}^{\infty} \dfrac{1 + 3^k}{8^k}$

18. $\sum_{k=0}^{\infty} \dfrac{2 \cdot 3^k}{2^k}$

19. $\sum_{k=1}^{\infty} \dfrac{2^k - 3^k}{4^k}$

20. $\sum_{k=0}^{\infty} \dfrac{2^k + 5^k}{4^k}$

21. $\sum_{k=1}^{\infty} \dfrac{5 \cdot 3^k - 3 \cdot 7^k}{5^k}$

22. $\sum_{k=0}^{\infty} \dfrac{7 \cdot 2^{k+1} - 3 \cdot 4^{k+1}}{5^{k+1}}$

23. The repeating decimal $0.33\overline{33}$ may be written as a geometric series as follows:

$$0.33\overline{33} = \frac{3}{10} + \frac{3}{100} + \frac{3}{1000} + \dots$$

$$= 3\left(\frac{1}{10}\right) + 3\left(\frac{1}{10}\right)^2 + 3\left(\frac{1}{10}\right)^3 + \dots$$

$$= 3\sum_{k=1}^{\infty} \left(\frac{1}{10}\right)^k$$

Show that the sum of this series is $\dfrac{1}{3}$.

24. Write the repeating decimal $0.22\overline{22}$ as a geometric series. (See Exercise 23.) What is the sum of this series in fraction form?

25. A life insurance agent is to be paid a commission according to the following scheme: $1000 in year 1, half the year 1 amount in year 2, half the year 2 amount in year 3, etc.

a. What is the total of all amounts received by the agent in the first 5 years?

b. What is the total of all amounts to be received by the agent in perpetuity?

26. When dropped from a height h, a ball rebounds to height $\dfrac{2}{3}h$.

a. Write an infinite series describing the total distance traveled by the ball.

b. What is the sum of this series?

27. In a certain economic model, every dollar received by an individual or corporation will result in an expenditure of 75 cents (that is, a transfer to another individual or corporation). What is the total of all expenditures including and resulting from an initial expenditure of $1 million dollars, according to this model?

28. A marketing firm determines that for every 100 high school students who are told a piece of information (positive or negative) about a particular college, 60 of these students will each pass the information on to one additional student. In total, how many students will learn about such a piece of information if 500 are told initially?

29. Assume that the present value of an amount $P(n)$ to be received after n years is $P_0 = e^{-rn}P(n)$. Consider an annuity that pays the owner $P(n) = \$1000$ per year in perpetuity.

a. Show that the present value of the sum of the first n payments is

$$S(n) = \sum_{k=1}^{n} 1000e^{-rk}.$$

b. Find an expression for $S(n)$ using equation (7).

c. Show that the present value of all payments to be received in perpetuity is

$$S = \sum_{k=1}^{\infty} 1000e^{-rk}.$$

d. Explain why the series in part (c) is a convergent geometric series.

e. Find S.

30. Explain why the geometric series $\sum_{k=0}^{\infty} x^k$ diverges for $x = 1$.

31. A paper carrier agrees to be paid $20 for the first week's delivery of a daily paper and, for each week thereafter, to be paid 75% of the previous week's pay. If this scheme continues in perpetuity, how much will the paper carrier be paid?

32. Explain why the following formulas are true:

a. $\displaystyle\sum_{k=1}^{\infty} x^k = \frac{x}{1-x}$, $\quad |x| < 1$.

b. $\displaystyle\sum_{k=2}^{\infty} x^k = \frac{x^2}{1-x}$, $\quad |x| < 1$.

33. A rumor spreads according to the television commercial's description: "They told two friends, and they told two friends, and they told two friends. . . ." Assume that one person starts the rumor by telling it to two friends on day one, and for each day thereafter each person who knows it tells it to two more people who have not yet heard it.
a. How many people will have heard the rumor by the fourth day?
b. Does the series of rumor knowers converge?

34. The rumor spread in Exercise 33 is modified so that each person who hears the rumor spreads it only twice, by telling it on the very next day to two people who had not heard it. For this scheme,
a. How many people have heard the rumor by the end of the fourth day?
b. Does this series of rumor knowers converge?

35. A new microbe is engineered that has the capability of eating and destroying a certain type of industrial pollutant. Assume the microbes can destroy 60% of the pollutant initially present in a breeding pond in each 24-hour period.
a. What percentage of the original amount of pollutant remains after three days?
b. What is the limit of this process?

☑ **SOLUTIONS TO PRACTICE PROBLEMS 9.2**

1. a. $\displaystyle\sum_{k=0}^{\infty} \frac{3+4^k}{6^k} = \sum_{k=0}^{\infty} \frac{3}{6^k} + \sum_{k=0}^{\infty} \frac{4^k}{6^k}$

$\displaystyle = 3\sum_{k=0}^{\infty} \left(\frac{1}{6}\right)^k + \sum_{k=0}^{\infty} \left(\frac{2}{3}\right)^k$

$\displaystyle = 3\left(\frac{1}{1-\dfrac{1}{6}}\right) + \frac{1}{1-\dfrac{2}{3}}$

$\displaystyle = 3\left(\frac{6}{5}\right) + 3$

$\displaystyle = \frac{33}{5}.$

b. $\displaystyle\sum_{k=1}^{\infty} \frac{2^k - 1}{3^k} = \sum_{k=1}^{\infty} \left(\frac{2}{3}\right)^k - \sum_{k=1}^{\infty} \left(\frac{1}{3}\right)^k$

$\displaystyle = \left\{\sum_{k=0}^{\infty} \left(\frac{2}{3}\right)^k - 1\right\} - \left\{\sum_{k=0}^{\infty} \left(\frac{1}{3}\right)^k - 1\right\}$

$\displaystyle = \left[\frac{1}{1-\dfrac{2}{3}} - 1\right] - \left[\frac{1}{1-\dfrac{1}{3}} - 1\right]$

$\displaystyle = \frac{3}{2}.$

2. a. $\displaystyle\sum_{n=1}^{4} P_0(n) = (e^{-(1)(0.10)} + e^{-(2)(0.10)} + e^{-(3)(0.10)} + e^{-(4)(0.10)})(10{,}000)$

$= (e^{-0.1} + e^{-0.2} + e^{-0.3} + e^{-0.4})(10{,}000) = \$31{,}347.$

b. $\displaystyle\sum_{n=1}^{\infty} P_0(n) = \sum_{n=1}^{\infty} e^{-n(0.10)}(10{,}000)$

$$= (10{,}000) \sum_{n=1}^{\infty} \left(\frac{1}{e^{1/10}}\right)^n$$

$$= 10{,}000\left[\sum_{n=0}^{\infty} \left(\frac{1}{e^{1/10}}\right)^n - 1 \right]$$

$$= 10{,}000\left[\frac{1}{1 - e^{-1/10}} - 1 \right]$$

$$= \$95{,}083.$$

9.3 Tests for Convergence

We began our discussion of infinite series with geometric series because we can actually calculate the sum of a convergent geometric series. For most other infinite series we shall only be able to determine whether or not the series converges but not be able to find its sum. However, we shall see later that even this is useful information. In this section we present three criteria for determining whether an infinite series converges.

The Integral Test

Figure 3.1 shows the (positive) terms $a_1, a_2, a_3, \ldots$ of an infinite series $\displaystyle\sum_{k=1}^{\infty} a_k$ represented as areas of rectangles. Each rectangle has width equal to one, and the heights are just the terms of the series $\displaystyle\sum_{k=1}^{\infty} a_k$. Also shown is the graph of a continuous decreasing function f that has the property that $f(k) = a_k, k = 1, 2, \ldots$. That is, the graph of f passes through the upper right-hand corner of each rectangle.

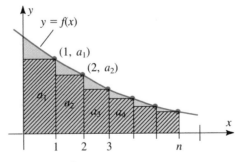

Figure 3.1 $\displaystyle\sum_{k=1}^{n} a_k < \int_{1}^{n} f(x)\, dx$ for all integers $n \geq 1$.

Figure 3.1 suggests that since the function f is decreasing, the area of the first n rectangles $(a_1 + a_2 + \ldots + a_n)$ is less than the area of the region bounded by the graph of f and the x-axis between $x = 0$ and $x = n$. That is

$$\overline{S_n} = \sum_{k=1}^{n} a_k < \int_0^n f(x)\, dx. \tag{1}$$

Now as $n \to \infty$ the integral on the right-hand side of inequality (1) becomes the improper integral $\int_0^\infty f(x)\, dx$. Since the left-hand side of inequality (1) is a partial sum for the series $\sum_{k=1}^{\infty} a_k$, it follows that *if the improper integral* $\int_0^\infty f(x)\, dx$ *converges, the infinite series* $\sum_{k=1}^{\infty} a_k$ *also converges.* That is because the partial sums for $\sum_{k=1}^{\infty} a_k$ can never exceed the number $\int_0^\infty f(x)\, dx$. (The details of a careful proof of this statement require more theory of infinite sequences than we have developed, but the essence of the argument is illustrated in Figure 3.1.)

In Figure 3.2 we represent the same terms $a_1, a_2, \ldots$ and function f, except that for each k the rectangle with area a_k extends to the right of the point (k, a_k) rather than to the left. Since f is decreasing, this means that the area of the first n rectangles is *greater* than the area of the region bounded by the graph of f and the x-axis for $1 \le x \le n + 1$. Thus

$$\int_1^{n+1} f(x)\, dx < \sum_{k=1}^{n} a_k = S_n. \tag{2}$$

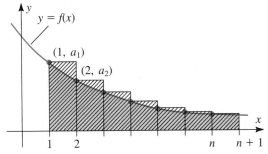

Figure 3.2 $\displaystyle\sum_{k=1}^{n} a_k > \int_1^{n+1} f(x)\, dx$ for all integers $n \ge 1$.

From inequality (2) we draw a different conclusion: Since the a_k's are positive, if the improper integral $\int_1^\infty f(x)\,dx$ diverges, the "partial integrals" on the left-hand side of inequality (2) become infinitely large as $n \to \infty$. This means that the infinite series $\sum_{k=1}^\infty a_k$ must also diverge, since the partial sums $\sum_{k=1}^n a_k$ become infinitely large as $n \to \infty$. That is, *if the improper integral $\int_1^\infty f(x)\,dx$ diverges, so must the infinite series $\sum_{k=1}^\infty a_k$.*

Combining these two statements gives us the statement of the Integral Test.

Theorem 2

Integral Test

Let each of the terms of the infinite series $\sum_{k=1}^\infty a_k$ be positive, and let f be a continuous decreasing function with $f(k) = a_k$ for $k = 1, 2, \ldots$. Then

$$\sum_{k=1}^\infty a_k \text{ converges if and only if } \int_1^\infty f(x)\,dx \text{ converges.}$$

That is, the series and the improper integral either both converge or both diverge.

To use the integral test on the series $\sum_{k=1}^\infty a_k$, we must first ensure that all terms of the series are positive. We then find the required decreasing function f (usually by simply replacing k in the general term for $\sum_{k=1}^\infty a_k$ with x) and check to see whether the improper integral $\int_1^\infty f(x)\,dx$ converges.

□ **EXAMPLE 1**

The series $\sum_{k=1}^\infty \dfrac{1}{k} = 1 + \dfrac{1}{2} + \dfrac{1}{3} + \dfrac{1}{4} + \ldots$ is called the **harmonic series.** Determine whether the harmonic series converges.

Solution: The series has general term $a_k = \dfrac{1}{k}$, so we use the function $f(x) = \dfrac{1}{x}$. Since f is continuous and decreasing on $[1, \infty)$, the Integral Test applies. The improper integral is

$$\int_1^\infty \frac{1}{x}\, dx = \lim_{t\to\infty} \int_1^t \frac{1}{x}\, dx$$

$$= \lim_{t\to\infty} \left[\ln x \right]_1^t$$

$$= \lim_{t\to\infty} (\ln t - \ln 1)$$

$$= +\infty.$$

(Here we use the fact that $\lim_{t\to\infty} \ln t = +\infty$, which we established in Chapter 4.) Thus the improper integral diverges and, according to the Integral Test, so does the harmonic series. ∎

The harmonic series

$$\sum_{k=1}^\infty \frac{1}{k} = 1 + \frac{1}{2} + \frac{1}{3} + \frac{1}{4} + \dots$$

diverges.

☐ **EXAMPLE 2**

Determine whether the series $\displaystyle\sum_{k=1}^\infty \frac{1}{(k+1)^2} = \frac{1}{4} + \frac{1}{9} + \frac{1}{16} + \dots$ converges.

Solution: The function corresponding to the general term $a_k = \dfrac{1}{(k+1)^2}$ is $f(x) = \dfrac{1}{(x+1)^2}$, which is continuous and decreasing on $[1, \infty)$. Since

$$\int_1^\infty \frac{1}{(x+1)^2}\, dx = \lim_{t\to\infty} \int_1^t (x+1)^{-2}\, dx$$

$$= \lim_{t\to\infty} \left[-(x+1)^{-1} \right]_1^t$$

$$= \lim_{t\to\infty} \left(\frac{1}{2} - \frac{1}{t+1} \right)$$

$$= \frac{1}{2}$$

the improper integral converges. Thus, by the Integral Test, the series $\displaystyle\sum_{k=1}^\infty \frac{1}{(k+1)^2}$ also converges. ∎

REMARK: Note, however, that we do not claim that the *sum* of the series is $\frac{1}{2}$. That would be incorrect. The series and the improper integral have the same convergence properties, but they do not have the same values, in general. (Can you explain why this is so, using Figures 3.1 and 3.2?)

□ **EXAMPLE 3**

A *p*-series is a series of the form

$$\sum_{k=1}^{\infty} \frac{1}{k^p} = 1 + \frac{1}{2^p} + \frac{1}{3^p} + \frac{1}{4^p} + \dots, \qquad p > 0.$$

Determine for which values of p a p-series converges.

| Strategy · · · · · · · | Solution |

Identify an appropriate function f.

We use the function $f(x) = \frac{1}{x^p} = x^{-p}$ where p is constant. Since

Verify that f satisfies the requirements of the Integral Test.

$$f'(x) = -px^{-p-1} = \frac{-p}{x^{p+1}}$$

is negative for all $x > 0$, the function f is decreasing on $[1, \infty)$. Thus the Integral Test applies.

Set up the improper integral and evaluate it, carrying p along as a constant.

Now

$$\int_1^{\infty} x^{-p} \, dx = \lim_{t \to \infty} \int_1^t x^{-p} \, dx$$

$$= \lim_{t \to \infty} \left[\frac{x^{-p+1}}{1-p} \right]_1^t, \qquad p \neq 1$$

$$= \left\{ \lim_{t \to \infty} \frac{t^{1-p}}{1-p} \right\} - \frac{1}{1-p}.$$

Determine the values of p for which the improper integral converges.

This limit will exist only if the exponent for t is negative; that is, only if $1 - p < 0$, which gives $p > 1$.

Apply the Integral Test.

Thus the improper integral (hence, the series) converges if $p > 1$ and diverges otherwise. (Note that the case $p = 1$, excluded above, yields the harmonic series, which diverges.) This result is sufficiently important that we summarize it below. ■

The *p*-series

$$\sum_{k=1}^{\infty} \frac{1}{k^p} = 1 + \frac{1}{2^p} + \frac{1}{3^p} + \frac{1}{4^p} + \dots, \qquad p > 0$$

converges only if $p > 1$.

As we remarked in Section 9.2, adding or subtracting a finite number of terms doesn't change the convergence properties of an infinite series. If the starting index is not 1, then we simply compare the series to the improper integral with the appropriate lower limit; for example

$$\sum_{k=3}^{\infty} a_k \text{ converges if and only if } \int_{3}^{\infty} f(x) \, dx \text{ converges.}$$

For this reason, when we are discussing only convergence rather than the actual value of the series, we often omit the index and write just $\Sigma \, a_k$.

The Comparison Test

Like the Integral Test, the Comparison Test is motivated by area considerations. However, instead of comparing a series with an improper integral, we compare it with another series.

Theorem 3

Comparison Test

Let $\Sigma \, a_k$ and $\Sigma \, b_k$ be two series with positive terms. If

$$0 < a_k \le b_k$$

for each $k = 1, 2, 3, \ldots$, then:

(a) If $\Sigma \, b_k$ converges, so does $\Sigma \, a_k$.
(b) If $\Sigma \, a_k$ diverges, so does $\Sigma \, b_k$.

In other words, a positive series in which each term is *smaller* than the corresponding term of a *convergent* series must also converge. And a series in which each term is *larger* than the corresponding term of a positive *divergent* series must also diverge.

Figure 3.3 conveys the idea underlying the proof of Theorem 3, which we omit. If $\Sigma \, b_k$ converges, the area of the rectangles corresponding to the terms $b_1, b_2, \ldots$ is finite. Since the rectangles corresponding to the terms $a_1, a_2, \ldots$ lie inside those corresponding to the terms $b_1, b_2, \ldots$, the area of these rectangles must also be finite, so $\Sigma \, a_k$ converges. Conversely, if $\Sigma \, a_k$ diverges, the area enclosed by the

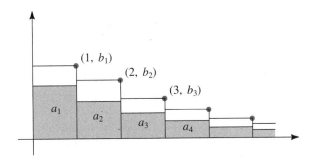

Figure 3.3 Comparison Test.

rectangles corresponding to $a_1, a_2, \ldots$ is infinite. Thus the (larger) area associated with $b_1, b_2, \ldots$, must be infinite, so $\Sigma\, b_k$ diverges.

The following examples illustrate how the Comparison Test is used.

☐ **EXAMPLE 4**

The series $\displaystyle\sum \frac{1}{1 + k^3}$ converges, by comparison with the convergent p-series $\displaystyle\sum \frac{1}{k^3}$ since

$$\frac{1}{1 + k^3} < \frac{1}{k^3}.$$

■

☐ **EXAMPLE 5**

The series $\displaystyle\sum \frac{1 + \ln k}{k}$ diverges by comparison with the (divergent) harmonic series $\displaystyle\sum \frac{1}{k}$ since

$$\frac{1 + \ln k}{k} > \frac{1}{k} \qquad \text{if } k > 1.$$

■

☐ **EXAMPLE 6**

To determine whether the series $\displaystyle\sum \frac{\sqrt{k} - 1}{k^2 + 2}$ converges we make the comparison.

$$\frac{\sqrt{k} - 1}{k^2 + 2} < \frac{\sqrt{k}}{k^2 + 2} < \frac{\sqrt{k}}{k^2} = \frac{1}{k^{3/2}}, \qquad k \geq 1.$$

Since $\displaystyle\sum \frac{1}{k^{3/2}}$ is a p-series with $p = \dfrac{3}{2} > 1$, it converges. Thus $\displaystyle\sum \frac{\sqrt{k} - 1}{k^2 + 2}$ also converges, by the Comparison Test.

■

REMARK 1: Successful application of the Comparison Test to the series $\Sigma\, a_k$ depends on finding another series $\Sigma\, b_k$ with which you can make a useful comparison. If you suspect that $\Sigma\, a_k$ converges, you should look for a *convergent series* $\Sigma\, b_k$ with $a_k \leq b_k$. But if you suspect that $\Sigma\, a_k$ diverges, look for a divergent series $\Sigma\, b_k$ with $a_k \geq b_k$.

REMARK 2: It is important to remember that the Integral Test and the Comparison Test apply only to *series with positive terms.* If a series contains negative terms, these tests do not apply.

The Limit Comparison Test

The following variation on the basic Comparison Test is often easier to apply.

Theorem 4
Limit Comparison Test

Let $\Sigma\, a_k$ and $\Sigma\, b_k$ be series with $a_k > 0$, $b_k > 0$ for all $k = 1, 2, \ldots$. If the limit

$$\rho = \lim_{k \to \infty} \frac{a_k}{b_k}$$

exists, and $\rho \neq 0$, then either both series converge or both series diverge.

The Limit Comparison Test states that if the ratio of the general terms of two series tends to a positive limit, then the two series have the same convergence property—either both converge or both diverge. This is most useful in determining the convergence of series whose general terms are rational functions or quotients of functions involving rational exponents.

Before proving this theorem, we consider several examples of its use.

☐ **EXAMPLE 7**

The series $\displaystyle\sum_{k=1}^{\infty} \frac{1}{2k+1}$ diverges, as can be shown by Theorem 4. Comparing this series with the harmonic series $\displaystyle\sum b_k = \sum_{k=1}^{\infty} \frac{1}{k}$ we find that

$$\rho = \lim_{k \to \infty} \left(\frac{\dfrac{1}{2k+1}}{\dfrac{1}{k}} \right) = \lim_{k \to \infty} \frac{k}{2k+1} = \frac{1}{2} > 0.$$

Since the limit $\rho > 0$ exists, and since the harmonic series diverges, so must the given series. ∎

☐ **EXAMPLE 8**

To apply the Limit Comparison Test to the series

$$\sum_{k=1}^{\infty} \frac{\sqrt{k} + 2}{k^2 + k + 1},$$

we observe that the general term is a quotient containing a highest exponent of $\dfrac{1}{2}$ in its numerator and a highest exponent of 2 in its denominator. This suggests a comparison with the series whose general term is $b_k = \dfrac{k^{1/2}}{k^2} = \dfrac{1}{k^{3/2}}$. We therefore take

Σb_k to be the p-series $\displaystyle\sum_{k=1}^{\infty} \frac{1}{k^{3/2}}$. We obtain

$$\rho = \lim_{k\to\infty}\left(\frac{\dfrac{\sqrt{k}+2}{k^2+k+1}}{\dfrac{1}{k^{3/2}}}\right) = \lim_{k\to\infty}\left(\frac{k^2+2k^{3/2}}{k^2+k+1}\right) = 1 > 0.$$

We may now conclude that since the p-series $\displaystyle\sum_{k=1}^{\infty} \frac{1}{k^{3/2}}$ converges, so does the series

$$\sum_{k=1}^{\infty} \frac{\sqrt{k}+2}{k^2+k+1}.$$

$\blacksquare$

□ **EXAMPLE 9**

Determine whether the series $\displaystyle\sum_{k=1}^{\infty} \sin\left(\frac{\pi}{k}\right)$ converges.

Solution: Let's systematically try each of the techniques available thus far:

(a) The Integral Test is not appropriate, since the improper integral $\displaystyle\int_1^{\infty} \sin\left(\frac{\pi}{x}\right)\,dx$
cannot easily be evaluated.

(b) The basic Comparison Test depends on our ability to choose a valid comparison series. We do have the comparison

$$0 < \sin\left(\frac{\pi}{k}\right) < \frac{\pi}{k}, \qquad k = 1, 2, 3, \ldots$$

but the Comparison Test gives no information since the series $\displaystyle\sum \frac{\pi}{k} = \pi \sum \frac{1}{k}$

diverges.

However, the Limit Comparison Test may be applied by recalling that we have previously established the limit

$$\rho = \lim_{k\to\infty} \frac{\sin\left(\dfrac{\pi}{k}\right)}{\left(\dfrac{\pi}{k}\right)} = \lim_{x\to 0^+} \frac{\sin x}{x} = 1.$$

Thus by Theorem 4, the series $\displaystyle\sum_{k=1}^{\infty} \sin\left(\frac{\pi}{k}\right)$ has the same convergence property as

does the series $\displaystyle\sum_{k=1}^{\infty} \frac{\pi}{k}$. That is, $\displaystyle\sum_{k=1}^{\infty} \sin\left(\frac{\pi}{k}\right)$ diverges.

$\blacksquare$

Proof of the Limit Comparison Test: As we did for the (basic) Comparison Test, we present only a sketch of the proof in order to focus attention on the basic idea.

If we assume that $\rho = \lim\limits_{k \to \infty} \dfrac{a_k}{b_k} > 0$, then there must exist positive numbers L and M and a positive integer K, so that

$$0 < L < \frac{a_k}{b_k} < M$$

for all $k > K$. Multiplying through by $b_k > 0$ gives the statements

$$a_k < Mb_k \tag{3}$$

and

$$a_k > Lb_k. \tag{4}$$

Since a_k, b_k, L, and M are positive numbers, we may use the basic Comparison Test to conclude from inequality (3) that $\Sigma\, a_k$ converges if $\Sigma\, b_k$ converges and, from inequality (4), that $\Sigma\, a_k$ diverges if $\Sigma\, b_k$ diverges. These two conclusions establish the statement of the Limit Comparison Test. ☐

A NECESSARY CONDITION: The following is a condition that must be satisfied by any convergent series.

Theorem 5

(Necessary Condition)

If the infinite series $\Sigma\, a_k$ converges, then $\lim\limits_{k \to \infty} a_k = 0$.

Theorem 5 says that in order for $\Sigma\, a_k$ to converge, the size of the general term a_k must approach zero as $k \to \infty$. But although necessary, this condition is not strong enough to guarantee that a series converges, as the following example shows.

☐ **EXAMPLE 10**
The harmonic series $\sum\limits_{k=1}^{\infty} \dfrac{1}{k}$ diverges. (See Example 1.) However, the harmonic series does satisfy the criterion of Theorem 5, since

$$\lim_{k \to \infty} a_k = \lim_{k \to \infty} \frac{1}{k} = 0.$$
■

What, then, is the use of Theorem 5? The answer is that Theorem 5 can identify a divergent series when $\lim\limits_{k \to \infty} a_k \neq 0$. This will save you the work of applying the Integral Test or the Comparison Test for these series.

☐ **EXAMPLE 11**
Determine whether the series $\sum\limits_{k=1}^{\infty} \dfrac{k}{5 + k}$ converges.

Solution: Checking the limit as $k \to \infty$ of the general term, we find that

$$\lim_{k \to \infty} a_k = \lim_{k \to \infty} \frac{k}{k + 5}$$

$$= \lim_{k \to \infty} \left(\frac{k}{k + 5} \right) \left(\frac{\dfrac{1}{k}}{\dfrac{1}{k}} \right)$$

$$= \lim_{k \to \infty} \frac{1}{1 + \dfrac{5}{k}}$$

$$= 1.$$

Since this limit is not zero, the series cannot converge, according to Theorem 5.

Figure 3.4 summarizes how Theorem 5 is used to detect divergent series.

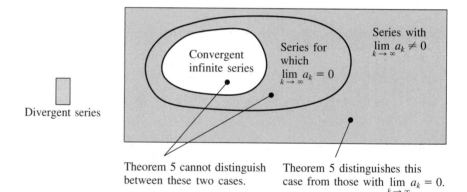

Figure 3.4 Diagram on the applicability of Theorem 5.

✓ PRACTICE PROBLEMS 9.3

Determine whether each of the following series converges:

1. $\sum \dfrac{3}{k + k^3}$

2. $\sum \dfrac{\ln^2 k}{k}$

3. $\sum \dfrac{\sqrt{k}}{(k^2 + 3)^{3/2}}$

Exercise Set 9.3

In Exercises 1–8, use the Integral Test to determine whether the series converges or diverges.

1. $\sum \dfrac{1}{k+2}$

2. $\sum \dfrac{1}{2k+5}$

3. $\sum \dfrac{k}{(k^2+1)^{3/2}}$

4. $\sum \dfrac{k}{k^2+5}$

5. $\sum \dfrac{1}{k \ln k}$

6. $\sum ke^{-k^2}$

7. $\sum k^2 e^{-k^3}$

8. $\sum ke^k$

In Exercises 9–16, use the Comparison Test to determine whether the series converges or diverges.

9. $\sum \dfrac{3}{k}$

10. $\sum \dfrac{3}{1+k^2}$

11. $\sum \dfrac{1}{2+k^{3/2}}$

12. $\sum \dfrac{\sqrt{k}}{1+k^3}$

13. $\sum \dfrac{3+k}{k^2}$

14. $\sum \dfrac{\sqrt{k}}{1+k}$

15. $\sum \dfrac{2k}{1+k^3}$

16. $\sum \dfrac{3}{\sqrt{k}+2}$

In Exercises 17–20, use the Limit Comparison Test to determine whether the given series converges or diverges.

17. $\sum \dfrac{k+3}{2k^2+1}$

18. $\sum \dfrac{k^2-4}{k^3+k+5}$

19. $\sum \dfrac{k+\sqrt{k}}{k+k^3}$

20. $\sum \dfrac{2k+3}{\sqrt{k^3+2}}$

In Exercises 21–48, determine whether the series converges or diverges and state which test applies.

21. $\sum \dfrac{k^2+5}{3k^2}$

22. $\sum \dfrac{3^k}{3k+5^k}$

23. $\sum \dfrac{k}{4+k^3}$

24. $\sum \dfrac{1}{\sqrt{k+1}}$

25. $\sum \dfrac{\cos^2 \pi k}{k^2}$

26. $\sum \dfrac{k-3}{k}$

27. $\sum \dfrac{e^{\sqrt{k}}}{\sqrt{k}}$

28. $\sum \cos\left(\dfrac{\pi k}{4}\right)$

29. $\sum \dfrac{2k^2-2k}{k^4+3k}$

30. $\sum \dfrac{k^2-2}{k^2+2}$

31. $\sum \dfrac{k}{\sqrt{1+k^2}}$

32. $\sum \dfrac{4}{1+k^3}$

33. $\sum \dfrac{1}{\sqrt{4k(k+1)}}$

34. $\sum \dfrac{2k}{\sqrt{k^3-1}}$

35. $\sum \dfrac{2^k}{5+3^{k+1}}$

36. $\sum \dfrac{2}{(k+3)^{3/2}}$

37. $\sum \dfrac{\ln k}{k}$

38. $\sum \dfrac{\sqrt{k}\ln k}{1+\ln k}$

39. $\sum \dfrac{7+k}{1+k^2}$

40. $\sum \dfrac{k^2}{k^4+2k+1}$

41. $\sum \dfrac{2^k}{k+5}$

42. $\sum \dfrac{2k^2}{\sqrt{k^3+6}}$

43. $\sum \dfrac{k}{(k+2)2^k}$

44. $\sum \dfrac{\sin(\pi k)}{\sqrt{1+k^2}}$

45. $\sum \dfrac{2k+2}{\sqrt{k^3+2}}$

46. $\sum \dfrac{\ln k}{k^3}$

47. $\sum \dfrac{k}{2+\ln k}$

48. $\sum \dfrac{k+3}{(k+2)2^k}$

☑ **SOLUTIONS TO PRACTICE PROBLEMS 9.3**

1. We note the comparison

$$\frac{3}{k+k^3} < \frac{3}{k^3}.$$

Since the series $\sum \dfrac{3}{k^3} = 3 \sum \dfrac{1}{k^3}$ is a *p*-series with $p = 3 > 1$, it converges. Thus, by the Comparison Test, the original series does also.

2. We use the Integral Test, by considering the integral

$$\int_1^\infty \frac{\ln^2 x}{x}\, dx = \lim_{t \to \infty} \int_1^t \frac{\ln^2 x}{x}\, dx$$

$$= \lim_{t \to \infty} \left[\frac{1}{3} \ln^3 x \right]_1^t$$

$$= \lim_{t \to \infty} \frac{1}{3} \ln^3 t$$

$$= +\infty.$$

Thus, both the improper integral and the infinite series diverge.

3. We note the comparison

$$\frac{\sqrt{k}}{(k^2 + 3)^{3/2}} < \frac{k}{(k^2 + 3)^{3/2}}.$$

To determine whether the series $\sum \dfrac{k}{(k^2 + 3)^{3/2}}$ converges, we use the Integral Test:

$$\int_1^\infty \frac{x}{(x^2 + 3)^{3/2}}\, dx = \lim_{t \to \infty} \int_1^t \frac{x}{(x^2 + 3)^{3/2}}\, dx$$

$$= \lim_{t \to \infty} \left[\frac{-1}{\sqrt{x^2 + 3}} \right]_1^t$$

$$= \lim_{t \to \infty} \left[\frac{1}{2} - \frac{1}{\sqrt{t^2 + 3}} \right]$$

$$= \frac{1}{2}.$$

Thus, the improper integral converges. Hence, so do both of the infinite series.

9.4 The Ratio Test and Absolute Convergence

The Ratio Test is another test for convergence of series with positive terms. Rather than comparing the series with an integral or another series, the Ratio Test uses the limit of the ratios of successive terms of the series itself.

Theorem 6

Let $\sum a_k$ be a series with positive terms. Assume that the limit

$$\rho = \lim_{k \to \infty} \frac{a_{k+1}}{a_k}$$

exists. Then:

(i) If $0 \le \rho < 1$ the series $\sum a_k$ converges.

(ii) If $\rho > 1$ the series $\sum a_k$ diverges.

(iii) If $\rho = 1$ there is no conclusion.

To use the Ratio Test on a series with positive terms we do the following:

(a) Identify the general term a_k, involving the index k.
(b) Find the expression a_{k+1} by replacing k by $k + 1$ in the general term a_k.
(c) Form the ratio $\dfrac{a_{k+1}}{a_k}$ and simplify this expression as much as possible.
(d) Find the limit $\rho = \lim\limits_{k \to \infty} \dfrac{a_{k+1}}{a_k}$.
(e) Apply the Ratio Test, according to the number ρ.

In applying the Ratio Test, we must remember that the outcome $\rho = 1$ leads to no conclusion. In this case the series may either converge or diverge, and you must try another test.

□ **EXAMPLE 1**

For the series $\displaystyle\sum_{k=1}^{\infty} \frac{k}{2^k} = \frac{1}{2} + \frac{2}{2^2} + \frac{3}{2^3} + \ldots$ the general term is

$$a_k = \frac{k}{2^k}$$

so

$$a_{k+1} = \frac{k + 1}{2^{k+1}}.$$

The limit ρ is therefore

$$\rho = \lim_{k \to \infty} \frac{a_{k+1}}{a_k} = \lim_{k \to \infty} \frac{\left(\dfrac{k + 1}{2^{k+1}}\right)}{\left(\dfrac{k}{2^k}\right)}$$

$$= \lim_{k \to \infty} \left(\frac{k + 1}{2^{k+1}}\right)\left(\frac{2^k}{k}\right) \qquad \text{(multiply by reciprocal of denominator)}$$

$$= \lim_{k \to \infty} \frac{1}{2}\left(\frac{k + 1}{k}\right) \qquad \begin{array}{l}\text{(rearrange, and cancel } 2^k \text{ from numerator}\\ \text{and denominator)}\end{array}$$

$$= \lim_{k \to \infty} \frac{1}{2}\left(1 + \frac{1}{k}\right)$$

$$= \frac{1}{2} \qquad \left(\text{since } \lim_{k \to \infty} \frac{1}{k} = 0\right).$$

Thus since $\dfrac{1}{2} < 1$, the Ratio Test guarantees that the series converges.   ■

□ **EXAMPLE 2**

For the geometric series $\Sigma \, x^k$ the general term is

$$a_k = x^k$$

so

$$a_{k+1} = x^{k+1}.$$

The ratio ρ is therefore

$$\rho = \lim_{k \to \infty} \frac{a_{k+1}}{a_k} = \lim_{k \to \infty} \frac{x^{k+1}}{x^k} = \lim_{k \to \infty} x = x.$$

Thus the Ratio Test confirms some of what we already know about the convergence of the geometric series when $x \geq 0$: $\Sigma \, x^k$ converges when $x = \rho < 1$ and diverges when $x = \rho > 1$. (In case $\rho = x = 1$ the Ratio Test is inconclusive, but we already know that the series $\Sigma \, 1^k = 1 + 1 + 1 + \ldots$ diverges.) ∎

The Ratio Test is often useful in dealing with series involving factorial expressions. Recall that $k!$ (k factorial) means the product of all integers from 1 to k inclusive:

$$k! = k(k - 1)(k - 2) \cdot \ldots \cdot 2 \cdot 1.$$

Thus $3! = 3 \cdot 2 \cdot 1 = 6$, $5! = 5 \cdot 4 \cdot 3 \cdot 2 \cdot 1 = 120$, etc.

Because of their common factors, ratios of factorials can often be simplified greatly. For example

$$\frac{(k + 1)!}{k!} = \frac{(k + 1)(k)(k - 1) \cdot \ldots \cdot 2 \cdot 1}{k(k - 1) \cdot \ldots \cdot 2 \cdot 1} = k + 1$$

$$\frac{(k + 2)!}{k!} = \frac{(k + 2)(k + 1)(k)(k - 1) \cdot \ldots \cdot 2 \cdot 1}{k(k - 1) \cdot \ldots \cdot 2 \cdot 1} = (k + 2)(k + 1)$$

etc. The next two examples involve such factorials.

□ **EXAMPLE 3**

Determine whether the series $\displaystyle\sum_{k=1}^{\infty} \frac{k + 2}{k!}$ converges.

Strategy · · · · · · · ·
Identify a_k.

Solution

For this series the general term is

$$a_k = \frac{k + 2}{k!}$$

Find a_{k+1} by replacing each k with $(k + 1)$ and simplify.

so

$$a_{k+1} = \frac{(k + 1) + 2}{(k + 1)!} = \frac{k + 3}{(k + 1)!}.$$

The ratio limit is therefore

Form ratio and simplify, using the fact that

$$\frac{k!}{(k + 1)!} = \frac{k!}{(k + 1)k!}$$
$$= \frac{1}{k + 1}.$$

Evaluate limit using fact that

$$\lim_{k \to \infty} \frac{k + 3}{k + 2} = 1.$$

$$\rho = \lim_{k \to \infty} \frac{a_{k+1}}{a_k} = \lim_{k \to \infty} \frac{\left(\dfrac{k + 3}{(k + 1)!}\right)}{\left(\dfrac{k + 2}{k!}\right)}$$

$$= \lim_{k \to \infty} \frac{k + 3}{(k + 1)!} \cdot \frac{k!}{k + 2}$$

$$= \lim_{k \to \infty} \left(\frac{k + 3}{k + 2}\right)\left[\frac{k!}{(k + 1)!}\right]$$

$$= \lim_{k \to \infty} \left(\frac{k + 3}{k + 2}\right)\left(\frac{1}{k + 1}\right)$$

$$= 1 \cdot 0$$

$$= 0.$$

Apply conclusions of Ratio Test.   Thus $\rho = 0 < 1$, so the series converges, according to the Ratio Test.   ■

□ **EXAMPLE 4**

Determine whether the series $\sum \dfrac{k^k}{k!}$ converges.

Strategy · · · · · · · ·
Identify a_k.

Solution
Here the general term is

$$a_k = \frac{k^k}{k!}$$

Find a_{k+1} by replacing each k by $(k + 1)$ in a_k.

so

$$a_{k+1} = \frac{(k + 1)^{k+1}}{(k + 1)!}$$

and the ratio limit is

Form the ratio $\dfrac{a_{k+1}}{a_k}$ and simplify.

$$\rho = \lim_{k \to \infty} \frac{\dfrac{(k + 1)^{k+1}}{(k + 1)!}}{\dfrac{k^k}{k!}}$$

$$= \lim_{k \to \infty} \frac{(k + 1)^{k+1}}{(k + 1)!} \cdot \frac{k!}{k^k}$$

$$= \lim_{k \to \infty} \frac{k!}{(k + 1)!} \cdot \frac{(k + 1)^{k+1}}{k^k}$$

Use fact that

$$\frac{k!}{(k+1)!} = \frac{1}{k+1}.$$

Use fact that

$$\lim_{k \to \infty} \left(1 + \frac{1}{k}\right)^k = e$$

from Chapter 4 to evaluate limit. Apply conclusions of Ratio Test.

$$= \lim_{k \to \infty} \frac{1}{k+1} \cdot \frac{(k+1)^{k+1}}{k^k}$$

$$= \lim_{k \to \infty} 1 \cdot \left(\frac{k+1}{k}\right)^k$$

$$= \lim_{k \to \infty} \left(1 + \frac{1}{k}\right)^k$$

$$= e \approx 2.71828 \ldots.$$

Since $\rho = e > 1$, the series diverges.   ■

☐ **EXAMPLE 5**

If we attempt to use the Ratio Test on the series $\sum \frac{k+1}{k^2}$, we find that the ratio limit is

$$\rho = \lim_{k \to \infty} \frac{a_{k+1}}{a_k} = \lim_{k \to \infty} \frac{\dfrac{[(k+1)+1]}{(k+1)^2}}{\dfrac{k+1}{k^2}}$$

$$= \lim_{k \to \infty} \frac{k+2}{(k+1)^2} \cdot \frac{k^2}{k+1}$$

$$= \lim_{k \to \infty} \frac{k^2(k+2)}{(k+1)^3}$$

$$= \lim_{k \to \infty} \frac{k^3 + 2k^2}{k^3 + 3k^2 + 3k + 1}$$

$$= 1.$$

Thus since $\rho = 1$, the Ratio Test is inconclusive. However, we can compare the general term $a_k = \dfrac{k+1}{k^2}$ with the general term $b_k = \dfrac{1}{k}$ of the harmonic series $\sum \dfrac{1}{k}$ as follows.

$$a_k = \frac{k+1}{k^2} > \frac{k}{k^2} = \frac{1}{k} = b_k.$$

Since the harmonic series diverges, the Comparison Test determines that the series $\sum \dfrac{k+1}{k^2}$ also diverges, as its general term is larger than that of the harmonic series.   ■

Series with Negative Terms

When an infinite series $\Sigma\, a_k$ contains negative terms, we cannot apply the Integral, Comparison, or Ratio Tests directly, since they are valid only for series with positive terms. There are, however, two types of series with negative terms for which there are straightforward tests for convergence.

Alternating Series

An **alternating series** is a series such as

$$\sum_{k=0}^{\infty} (-1)^k a_k = a_0 - a_1 + a_2 - a_3 + a_4 - \ldots$$

where $a_k > 0$ for all k. That is, the terms of an alternating series alternate signs. Examples of alternating series are:

(i) $\displaystyle\sum_{k=1}^{\infty} \frac{(-1)^k}{k} = -1 + \frac{1}{2} - \frac{1}{3} + \frac{1}{4} - \frac{1}{5} + \ldots$ (here k begins at 1)

(ii) $\displaystyle\sum_{k=0}^{\infty} \frac{(-1)^k}{1+k^2} = 1 - \frac{1}{2} + \frac{1}{5} - \frac{1}{10} + \ldots$ (here k begins at 0)

(iii) $\displaystyle\sum_{k=0}^{\infty} \frac{\cos k\pi}{\sqrt{k+1}} = 1 - \frac{1}{\sqrt{2}} + \frac{1}{\sqrt{3}} - \frac{1}{\sqrt{4}} + \ldots$ (here k begins at 0).

The following theorem gives a very simple criterion for identifying convergent alternating series.

Theorem 7
Alternating Series Test

Let $a_k > 0$ for all k. The alternating series $\Sigma(-1)^k a_k$ converges if both of the following hold:

(i) $a_k > a_{k+1}$ for all k larger than some fixed integer K.
(ii) $\displaystyle\lim_{k \to \infty} a_k = 0$.

Condition (i) says that the absolute values of the terms eventually must be decreasing, and condition (ii) says that, in the limit, these terms must decrease to zero. Note that each of the series in Examples (i)–(iii) above meet both criteria, so each of these is a convergent alternating series.

☐ **EXAMPLE 6**

Determine whether the alternating harmonic series

$$\sum_{k=1}^{\infty} \frac{(-1)^{k+1}}{k} = 1 - \frac{1}{2} + \frac{1}{3} - \frac{1}{4} + \ldots$$

converges.

Solution: This series is an alternating series of the form $\Sigma(-1)^{k+1}a_k$ with $a_k = \dfrac{1}{k}$.
Since

$$a_k = \frac{1}{k} > \frac{1}{k+1} = a_{k+1}$$

the terms of a_k are decreasing. Moreover

$$\lim_{k \to \infty} a_k = \lim_{k \to \infty} \frac{1}{k} = 0.$$

Thus both requirements of the alternating series test are satisfied, so the series converges. ∎

□ **EXAMPLE 7**

Does the series $\displaystyle\sum_{k=0}^{\infty} \frac{(-1)^k k^2}{4 + k^2}$ converge?

Solution: This series has the form $\Sigma(-1)^k a_k$ with $a_k = \dfrac{k^2}{1 + k^2}$. Since

$$\lim_{k \to \infty} a_k = \lim_{k \to \infty} \frac{k^2}{1 + k^2}$$

$$= \lim_{k \to \infty}\left(\frac{k^2}{1 + k^2}\right)\left(\frac{\dfrac{1}{k^2}}{\dfrac{1}{k^2}}\right)$$

$$= \lim_{k \to \infty} \frac{1}{\dfrac{1}{k^2} + 1}$$

$$= 1$$

the second condition of the alternating series test fails. This series diverges because the necessary condition of Theorem 5 fails. ∎

Figure 4.1 illustrates the reason why an infinite series that satisfies the requirements of Theorem 7 must converge. Because each term of the series is of an opposite sign from the one preceding it, the partial sums for the series oscillate back and forth on the number line. Because the absolute values of the terms decrease, the distance between successive partial sums decreases. Finally, since the size of the terms of the series approaches zero, the distance between successive partial sums

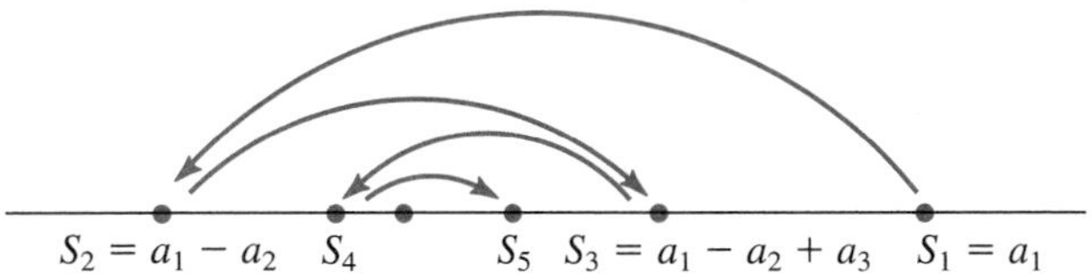

$$S_2 = a_1 - a_2 \quad S_4 \qquad S_5 \quad S_3 = a_1 - a_2 + a_3 \quad S_1 = a_1$$

Figure 4.1 For the alternating series $\Sigma(-1)^k a_k$, the partial sums oscillate back and forth on the number line.

approaches zero in the limit. This means that the sequence of partial sums converges.

Absolute Convergence

When an infinite series $\Sigma\, a_k$ contains negative terms but is not an alternating series, we may test the series for *absolute convergence,* which is defined as follows.

Definition 4

The series $\Sigma\, a_k$ is said to **converge absolutely** if the series of absolute values $\Sigma\, |a_k|$ converges.

In other words, the series $\Sigma\, a_k$ converges *absolutely* if, by changing the signs of all negative terms, we obtain a convergent series.

☐ **EXAMPLE 8**

The series $\displaystyle\sum_{k=1}^{\infty} \frac{(-1)^{k+1}}{k^2} = 1 - \frac{1}{4} + \frac{1}{9} - \frac{1}{16} + \ldots$ converges absolutely since in this case

$$\sum |a_k| = \sum \left| \frac{(-1)^{k+1}}{k^2} \right| = \sum \frac{1}{k^2}$$

which is a convergent *p*-series ($p = 2$). ∎

☐ **EXAMPLE 9**

The series $\displaystyle\sum_{k=1}^{\infty} (-1)^{k+1} = 1 - 1 + 1 - 1 + 1 - \ldots$ does *not* converge absolutely since

$$\sum |(-1)^{k+1}| = \sum 1 = 1 + 1 + 1 + \ldots$$

which is a divergent series. ∎

It is important to note the relationship between absolute convergence (that is, convergence of the series $\Sigma |a_k|$) and convergence of the series Σa_k itself. The following theorem states that the series Σa_k converges if it is absolutely convergent.

Theorem 8

If the series $\Sigma |a_k|$ converges, so does the series Σa_k. That is, every absolutely convergent series converges.

Theorem 8 is simple to apply. If the series Σa_k contains negative terms, we test the positive series $\Sigma |a_k|$ for convergence. If $\Sigma |a_k|$ converges, so does Σa_k. However, if $\Sigma |a_k|$ diverges, we can draw no conclusion about Σa_k.

□ **EXAMPLE 10**

To test the series $\sum\limits_{k=0}^{\infty} \dfrac{(-1)^k k^2}{(k+1)!}$ for convergence, we apply the Ratio Test to the series

$$\sum_{k=0}^{\infty} \left| \frac{(-1)^k k^2}{(k+1)!} \right| = \sum_{k=0}^{\infty} \frac{k^2}{(k+1)!}.$$

We obtain the ratio limit

$$\rho = \lim_{k \to \infty} \frac{|a_{k+1}|}{|a_k|} = \lim_{k \to \infty} \frac{\dfrac{(k+1)^2}{[(k+1)+1]!}}{\dfrac{k^2}{(k+1)!}}$$

$$= \lim_{k \to \infty} \frac{(k+1)^2}{(k+2)!} \cdot \frac{(k+1)!}{k^2}$$

$$= \lim_{k \to \infty} \frac{(k+1)!}{(k+2)!} \cdot \frac{(k+1)^2}{k^2}$$

$$= \lim_{k \to \infty} \frac{1}{k+2} \left(\frac{k+1}{k} \right)^2$$

$$= \lim_{k \to \infty} \frac{1}{k+2} \left(1 + \frac{1}{k} \right)^2$$

$$= 0.$$

Thus since $\rho = 0 < 1$, the series $\sum\limits_{k=0}^{\infty} \left| \dfrac{(-1)^k k^2}{(k+1)!} \right|$ converges, so the original series

$\sum\limits_{k=0}^{\infty} \dfrac{(-1)^k k^2}{(k+1)!}$ converges absolutely.   ■

☐ **EXAMPLE 11**

Determine whether the series

$$\sum_{k=0}^{\infty} \frac{\cos \pi k}{2^k} = 1 - \frac{1}{2} + \frac{1}{4} - \frac{1}{8} + \ldots$$

converges.

Solution: Testing for absolute convergence, we find that

$$\sum_{k=0}^{\infty} \left| \frac{\cos \pi k}{2^k} \right| = \sum_{k=0}^{\infty} \frac{|\cos \pi k|}{2^k} = \sum_{k=0}^{\infty} \frac{1}{2^k} = \sum_{k=0}^{\infty} \left(\frac{1}{2} \right)^k$$

which converges since it is a geometric series. The series $\displaystyle\sum_{k=0}^{\infty} \frac{\cos \pi k}{2^k}$ therefore converges absolutely. (The Alternating Series Test also can be used to show that this series converges.) ■

If a series does not converge absolutely, it still may converge. (That is, $\Sigma \, a_k$ may converge even though $\Sigma \, |a_k|$ diverges.) Such series are said to be *conditionally convergent*. Our last example is one such series.

☐ **EXAMPLE 12**

For the series $\displaystyle\sum_{k=1}^{\infty} \frac{(-1)^{k+1}}{k} = 1 - \frac{1}{2} + \frac{1}{3} - \frac{1}{4} + \frac{1}{5} - \ldots$ the series of absolute values is just the harmonic series

$$\sum_{k=1}^{\infty} \left| \frac{(-1)^{k+1}}{k} \right| = \sum_{k=1}^{\infty} \frac{1}{k} = 1 + \frac{1}{2} + \frac{1}{3} + \frac{1}{4} + \ldots$$

which we have shown to diverge. Thus the series $\displaystyle\sum_{k=1}^{\infty} \frac{(-1)^{k+1}}{k}$ does not converge absolutely. But this series does converge conditionally, as the Alternating Series Test showed in Example 6. ■

☑ **PRACTICE PROBLEMS 9.4**

1. Determine whether each of the following series converges or diverges.

a. $\displaystyle\sum_{k=1}^{\infty} = \frac{3^k}{k!}$

b. $\displaystyle\sum_{k=0}^{\infty} \frac{k!}{k + 5}$

2. Test the following series for absolute and conditional convergence.

a. $\displaystyle\sum_{k=1}^{\infty} \frac{\cos(\pi k)}{k+2}$

b. $\displaystyle\sum_{k=1}^{\infty} \frac{(-1)^k k}{1+k^2}$

Exercise Set 9.4

In Exercises 1–12, use the Ratio Test, where applicable, to determine whether the given series converges or diverges.

1. $\displaystyle\sum \frac{2^k}{k+2}$

2. $\displaystyle\sum \frac{3^k}{k!}$

3. $\displaystyle\sum k^2 e^{-k}$

4. $\displaystyle\sum \frac{k!}{5^k}$

5. $\displaystyle\sum \frac{\ln k}{ke^k}$

6. $\displaystyle\sum \frac{(3k)!}{(k!)^2}$

7. $\displaystyle\sum \frac{k+2}{1+k^3}$

8. $\displaystyle\sum \frac{\sqrt{k}}{k!}$

9. $\displaystyle\sum \frac{k!}{ke^k}$

10. $\displaystyle\sum \frac{k^2 e^k}{k!}$

11. $\displaystyle\sum \frac{e^{5k}}{k!}$

12. $\displaystyle\sum \frac{\pi k}{(k+1)!}$

In Exercises 13–18, determine whether the alternating series converges.

13. $\displaystyle\sum_{k=0}^{\infty} \frac{(-1)^k}{k+2} = \frac{1}{2} - \frac{1}{3} + \frac{1}{4} - \frac{1}{5} + \cdots$

14. $\displaystyle\sum_{k=1}^{\infty} \frac{(-1)^{k+1}}{k^2} = 1 - \frac{1}{4} + \frac{1}{9} - \frac{1}{16} + \cdots$

15. $\displaystyle\sum_{k=1}^{\infty} \frac{\cos \pi k}{k} = -1 + \frac{1}{2} - \frac{1}{3} + \frac{1}{4} - \cdots$

16. $\displaystyle\sum_{k=1}^{\infty} \frac{(-1)^k k}{k+5} = -\frac{1}{5} + \frac{2}{6} - \frac{3}{7} + \frac{4}{8} - \cdots$

17. $\displaystyle\sum_{k=1}^{\infty} \frac{(-1)^k k^2}{\sqrt{k+1}} = -\frac{1}{\sqrt{2}} + \frac{4}{\sqrt{3}} - \frac{9}{\sqrt{4}} + \frac{16}{\sqrt{5}} - \cdots$

18. $\displaystyle\sum_{k=1}^{\infty} \frac{(-1)^{k+1} k}{\sqrt{k+1}} = \frac{1}{\sqrt{2}} - \frac{2}{\sqrt{3}} + \frac{3}{\sqrt{4}} - \frac{4}{\sqrt{5}} + \cdots$

In Exercises 19–30, determine whether the series converges absolutely. If the series does not converge absolutely, determine whether it converges conditionally or diverges.

19. $\displaystyle\sum_{k=1}^{\infty} \frac{(-1)^k}{k^2}$

20. $\displaystyle\sum_{k=1}^{\infty} \frac{(-1)^k}{2k+1}$

21. $\displaystyle\sum_{k=1}^{\infty} \frac{(-1)^k \cdot k}{(k+1)!}$

22. $\displaystyle\sum_{k=1}^{\infty} \frac{(-1)^k \sqrt{k}}{k!}$

23. $\displaystyle\sum_{k=1}^{\infty} \frac{(-1)^k}{1+\sqrt{k}}$

24. $\displaystyle\sum_{k=1}^{\infty} \frac{\cos \pi k}{\sqrt{k}}$

25. $\displaystyle\sum_{k=1}^{\infty} \frac{1}{k} \sin \frac{k\pi}{2}$

26. $\displaystyle\sum_{k=1}^{\infty} \frac{(-1)^k k^3}{2^k}$

27. $\displaystyle\sum_{k=1}^{\infty} \frac{(-1)^k \sqrt{k}}{1+k^2}$

28. $\displaystyle\sum_{k=1}^{\infty} \frac{(-1)^k}{1+k^2}$

29. $\displaystyle\sum_{k=1}^{\infty} \frac{(-1)^{k+1} k!}{3^k}$

30. $\displaystyle\sum_{k=2}^{\infty} \frac{(-1)^k \cdot k}{\ln \sqrt{k}}$

31. Let $\Sigma(-1)^k a_k$ be an alternating series with $a_k > a_{k+1}$ for all k. Suppose that $\lim_{k \to \infty} a_k = L$ with $L \neq 0$ (thus violating condition (ii) of the Alternating Series Test). Explain why this series cannot converge.

32. Complete the following steps in this intuitive explanation of why the Ratio Test is true.

a. Assume that $\rho < 1$, where $\rho = \lim_{k \to \infty} \dfrac{a_{k+1}}{a_k}$.

b. Let $\alpha = \dfrac{\rho + 1}{2}$. Explain why $\alpha < 1$.

c. Since $\rho = \lim_{k \to \infty} \dfrac{a_{k+1}}{a_k}$, explain why we must have $\dfrac{a_{k+1}}{a_k} < \alpha$ for all k equal to or larger than some fixed integer, say, N.

d. Since $\dfrac{a_{N+1}}{a_N} < \alpha$ show that

$$a_{N+1} < \alpha a_N$$
$$a_{N+2} < \alpha a_{N+1} < \alpha^2 a_N$$
$$a_{N+3} < \alpha a_{N+2} < \alpha^2 a_{N+1} < \alpha^3 a_N$$

and, in general

$$a_{N+p} < \alpha^p a_N$$

e. Explain why the series $\Sigma \, \alpha^k$ is a geometric series that converges.

f. Use the results of parts (d) and (e), together with the Comparison Test, to explain why the series $\Sigma \, a_k$ must converge when $\rho < 1$.

g. Find an analogous argument to show why the series $\Sigma \, a_k$ must diverge when $\rho > 1$.

☑ **SOLUTIONS TO PRACTICE PROBLEMS 9.4**

1. a. Using the Ratio Test on $\displaystyle\sum_{k=1}^{\infty} \dfrac{3^k}{k!}$, we find that, with $a_k = \dfrac{3^k}{k!}$, the ratio limit is

$$\rho = \lim_{k \to \infty} \left(\frac{a_{k+1}}{a_k} \right) = \lim_{k \to \infty} \frac{\dfrac{3^{k+1}}{(k+1)!}}{\dfrac{3^k}{k!}} = \lim_{k \to \infty} \frac{3^{k+1}k!}{3^k(k+1)!} = \lim_{k \to \infty} \left(\frac{3}{k+1} \right) = 0.$$

Since $\rho = 0 < 1$, the series converges.

b. Using the Ratio Test on $\displaystyle\sum_{k=0}^{\infty} \dfrac{k!}{k+5}$, with $a_k = \dfrac{k!}{k+5}$, gives

$$\rho = \lim_{k \to \infty} \left(\frac{a_{k+1}}{a_k} \right) = \lim_{k \to \infty} \frac{\dfrac{(k+1)!}{k+6}}{\dfrac{k!}{k+5}} = \lim_{k \to \infty} \frac{(k+5)(k+1)!}{(k+6) \cdot k!} = \lim_{k \to \infty} \frac{(k+5)(k+1)}{k+6} = \infty.$$

Thus, the series diverges.

2. a. The series

$$\sum_{k=1}^{\infty} \frac{\cos \pi k}{k+2} = -\frac{1}{3} + \frac{1}{4} - \frac{1}{5} + \frac{1}{6} - \cdots$$

is an alternating harmonic series, minus the first two terms. By the Alternating Series Test, this series converges (see Example 6) conditionally, but not absolutely (see Example 12) because the (positive) harmonic series diverges.

b. To test the series $\displaystyle\sum_{k=1}^{\infty} \dfrac{(-1)^k k}{1+k^2}$ for absolute convergence we note that $|a_k| = \left| \dfrac{(-1)^k k}{1+k^2} \right| = \dfrac{k}{1+k^2}$, and we examine

$$\rho = \lim_{k \to \infty} \frac{|a_{k+1}|}{|a_k|} = \lim_{k \to \infty} \frac{\left(\dfrac{k+1}{1+(k+1)^2} \right)}{\left(\dfrac{k}{1+k^2} \right)} = \lim_{k \to \infty} \frac{(k+1)(1+k^2)}{k[1+(k+1)^2]} = 1$$

so the Ratio Test is inconclusive for absolute convergence.

We observe, however, that $|a_k| = \dfrac{k}{1 + k^2}$ may be compared with the series with positive terms $b_k = \dfrac{k}{k^2} = \dfrac{1}{k}$ by the Limit Comparison Test. We obtain

$$\rho = \lim_{k \to \infty} \frac{|a_k|}{b_k} = \lim_{k \to \infty} \frac{\left(\dfrac{k}{1 + k^2}\right)}{\left(\dfrac{1}{k}\right)} = \lim_{k \to \infty} \frac{k^2}{1 + k^2} = 1.$$

Thus, since the series $\sum b_k = \sum \dfrac{1}{k}$ diverges (it is the harmonic series), the series of absolute values $\displaystyle\sum_{k=1}^{\infty} |a_k|$ diverges also. Thus, the series $\displaystyle\sum_{k=1}^{\infty} \frac{(-1)^k k}{1 + k^2}$ does not converge absolutely. It *does* converge conditionally, however, because it is an alternating series for which

$$\lim_{k \to \infty} |a_k| = \lim_{k \to \infty} \frac{k}{1 + k^2} = 0$$

and $|a_{k+1}| < |a_k|$ for $k \geq 1$.

9.5 Taylor Polynomials

We have seen many applications of the transcendental functions e^x, ln x, and the trigonometric functions. As important as these functions are, however, at this point we have no clues as to how to calculate values of these functions other than resorting to a calculator, computer, or table of values. Even though such "aids" are readily available, our study of calculus would be incomplete if we did not raise the question of how the tables are constructed or how the calculator is programmed.

Taylor polynomials can be used to approximate values of transcendental functions to any desired degree of accuracy. We shall present the rudiments of Taylor polynomials here and discuss their important relationship to infinite Taylor series in the next two sections.

Approximating the Function
$f(x) = e^x$

Figure 5.1 shows the graph of the function $f(x) = e^x$. It is easy to see that the value of this function at $x = 0$ is $f(0) = e^0 = 1$. But how might we approximate values of $f(x) = e^x$ for x *near* zero?

Figure 5.2 shows one approach—simply to approximate the values $f(x) = e^x$ by the constant value $P_0(x) = f(0) = 1$. That is, we could use the value $f(0) = e^0 = 1$ to approximate values of $f(x)$ for x near 0. It is easy to see that, except for x's very close to 0, this is not a very good approximation.

Figure 5.3 suggests a better way to approximate values of $f(x) = e^x$ near $a = 0$, that is, by using the first degree polynomial

$$\begin{aligned} P_1(x) &= f(0) + f'(0)x \\ &= 1 + x. \quad \text{(For } f(x) = e^x, f'(0) = e^0 = 1.) \end{aligned} \tag{1}$$

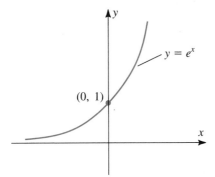

Figure 5.1 The function $f(x) = e^x$ has value $f(0) = 1$ at $x = 0$.

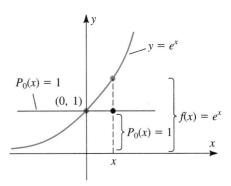

Figure 5.2 Approximating values $f(x) = e^x$ by the constant function $P_0(x) = f(0) = 1$.

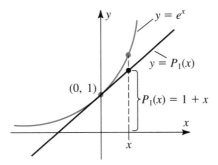

Figure 5.3 Approximating values $f(x) = e^x$ by the first degree polynomial $P_1(x) = 1 + x$.

This function has the same value as $f(x) = e^x$ at $a = 0$, but it also has the same first derivative as f at $x = 0$. To see this, simply note that

$$P_1'(x) = f'(0) = 1$$

for all x, so $P_1'(0) = f'(0)$. In a sense, the graph of P_1 is "shaped more like" the graph of f than is the graph of P_0.

Figure 5.4 shows yet a better way to approximate $f(x)$ near $x = 0$: Use the second degree polynomial

$$P_2(x) = f(0) + f'(0)x + \frac{f''(0)}{2}x^2$$

$$= 1 + x + \frac{1}{2}x^2. \qquad \text{(For } f(x) = e^x, f''(0) = e^0 = 1.\text{)} \tag{2}$$

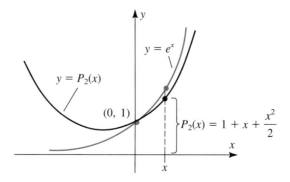

Figure 5.4 Approximating values of $f(x) = e^x$ by the second degree polynomial

$$P_2(x) = 1 + x + \frac{x^2}{2}.$$

The polynomial $P_2(x)$ has the following properties:

(i) $P_2(0) = f(0)$.

(ii) Since $P_2'(x) = f'(0) + f''(0)x$,

$$P_2'(0) = f'(0).$$

(iii) Since $P_2''(x) = f''(0)$,

$$P_2''(0) = f''(0).$$

That is, $P_2(x)$ and each of its first two derivatives have the same values as $f(x) = e^x$ and its first two derivatives at $x = 0$. The graph of P_2 is even more like the graph of f than its two predecessors.

Table 5.1 illustrates our claim that the values $P_0(x)$, $P_1(x)$, and $P_2(x)$ provide increasingly better approximations to the values $f(x) = e^x$ for x near zero. (Note that the closer x is chosen to zero, the better the approximation is.)

As you might suspect, we can provide even better approximations to $f(x) = e^x$ by using a third degree polynomial, with the requirements that it and each of its first three derivatives have the same values as $f(x) = e^x$ and its first three derivatives at $x = 0$. We leave it to you to verify that the polynomial

$$P_3(x) = f(0) + f'(0)x + \frac{f''(0)}{2}x^2 + \frac{f'''(0)}{3!}x^3$$

$$= 1 + x + \frac{1}{2}x^2 + \frac{1}{6}x^3 \tag{3}$$

satisfies these requirements and to calculate the values $P_3(x)$ for the x's listed in Table 5.1.

The advantage in using these polynomials to approximate values of the function $f(x) = e^x$ is that values of polynomials are easy to compute.

Table 5.1. Values of $f(x) = e^x$ and Approximating Polynomials $P_0(x)$, $P_1(x)$, $P_2(x)$ to Four-Decimal-Place Accuracy for Various Numbers x

x	$P_0(x)$	$P_1(x)$	$P_2(x)$	$f(x) = e^x$
-1.0	1.0	0.0	0.5000	0.3679
-0.5	1.0	0.5	0.6250	0.6065
-0.2	1.0	0.8	0.8200	0.8187
-0.1	1.0	0.9	0.9050	0.9048
0	1.0	1.0	1.0	1.0
0.1	1.0	1.1	1.1050	1.052
0.2	1.0	1.2	1.2200	1.2214
0.5	1.0	1.5	1.6250	1.6487
1.0	1.0	2.0	2.5000	2.7183

□ **EXAMPLE 1**

Use the polynomial P_3 in equation (3) to approximate the value $\sqrt[3]{e} = e^{1/3}$.

Solution: With $x = \dfrac{1}{3}$ we have, from equation (3), that

$$P_3\left(\frac{1}{3}\right) = 1 + \frac{1}{3} + \frac{1}{2}\left(\frac{1}{3}\right)^2 + \frac{1}{6}\left(\frac{1}{3}\right)^3$$

$$= 1 + \frac{1}{3} + \frac{1}{18} + \frac{1}{162}$$

$$= \frac{162 + 54 + 9 + 1}{162}$$

$$= \frac{113}{81} \approx 1.3951.$$

The value of $\sqrt[3]{e}$, to four-decimal-place accuracy, is $\sqrt[3]{e} \approx 1.3956$. ■

Taylor Polynomials

The preceding discussion on approximating values of the exponential function with polynomials can be extended to apply to a wide variety of functions. The idea, however, remains the same: To approximate values of the function f near $x = 0$ with a polynomial of degree n, use a polynomial whose value at $x = 0$ and those of its first n derivatives are the same as the value of f and those of its first n derivatives at $x = 0$.

Assuming that $f(0)$ and each of the derivatives $f'(0), f''(0), \ldots, f^{(n)}(0)$ exist, there will be only one such polynomial, which we refer to as the nth *Taylor polynomial*.

Definition 5

If the function f and each of its first n derivatives are defined for $x = 0$, the **nth Taylor polynomial** expanded about $x = 0$ is the function

$$P_n(x) = f(0) + f'(0)x + \frac{f''(0)}{2}x^2 + \frac{f'''(0)}{3!}x^3 + \ldots + \frac{f^{(n)}(0)}{n!}x^n.$$

Thus

$$P_1(x) = f(0) + f'(0)x$$

$$P_2(x) = f(0) + f'(0)x + \frac{f''(0)}{2}x^2$$

$$P_3(x) = f(0) + f'(0)x + \frac{f''(0)}{2}x^2 + \frac{f'''(0)}{6}x^3$$

etc.

□ **EXAMPLE 2**

Find the first three Taylor polynomials for the function $f(x) = \ln(1 + x)$ expanded about $x = 0$.

Solution: First, we need to know the first three derivatives of $f(x) = \ln(1 + x)$. They are

$$f'(x) = \frac{1}{1 + x} = (1 + x)^{-1}$$

$$f''(x) = -(1 + x)^{-2}$$

$$f'''(x) = 2(1 + x)^{-3}$$

Thus $f(0) = \ln(1 + 0) = 0$, $f'(0) = 1$, $f''(0) = -1$, and $f'''(0) = 2$. Using these values in Definition 5 gives

$$P_1(x) = 0 + 1 \cdot x = x$$

$$P_2(x) = 0 + 1 \cdot x + \frac{(-1)}{2}x^2 = x - \frac{1}{2}x^2$$

$$P_3(x) = 0 + 1 \cdot x + \frac{(-1)}{2}x^2 + \frac{2}{6}x^3 = x - \frac{1}{2}x^2 + \frac{1}{3}x^3.$$

We leave it to you to verify that for $f(x) = \ln(1 + x)$

$$P_4(x) = x - \frac{1}{2}x^2 + \frac{1}{3}x^3 - \frac{1}{4}x^4$$

and

$$P_5(x) = x - \frac{1}{2}x^2 + \frac{1}{3}x^3 - \frac{1}{4}x^4 + \frac{1}{5}x^5$$

as the pattern for $P_1(x)$, $P_2(x)$, and $P_3(x)$ suggests. ∎

Table 5.2 shows values of each of the Taylor polynomials $P_1(x), \ldots, P_5(x)$ for $f(x) = \ln(1 + x)$ in Example 2 for various choices of x near zero, as well as the values of $\ln(1 + x)$ correct to four-decimal-place accuracy. Again, note that the accuracy of these approximations increases as the degree of the polynomial increases, and that the approximations are better for x's nearer zero.

Table 5.2. Values of Taylor polynomials for $f(x) = \ln(1 + x)$ for x near zero, to four-decimal-place accuracy.

x	$P_1(x)$	$P_2(x)$	$P_3(x)$	$P_4(x)$	$P_5(x)$	$\ln(1 + x)$
-0.4	-0.4	-0.4800	-0.5013	-0.5077	-0.5098	-0.5108
-0.3	-0.3	-0.3450	-0.3540	-0.3560	-0.3565	-0.3567
-0.2	-0.2	-0.2200	-0.2227	-0.2231	-0.2231	-0.2231
-0.1	-0.1	-0.1050	-0.1053	-0.1054	-0.1054	-0.1054
0	0.0	0.0	0.0	0.0	0.0	0.0
0.1	1.0	0.0950	0.0953	0.0953	0.0953	0.0953
0.2	0.2	0.1800	0.1827	0.1823	0.1823	0.1823
0.3	0.3	0.2550	0.2640	0.2620	0.2625	0.2624
0.4	0.4	0.3200	0.3413	0.3349	0.3370	0.3365

The next example shows how the entries of Table 5.2 are computed.

□ **EXAMPLE 3**

Use the results of Example 2 to approximate $\ln\left(\frac{3}{2}\right)$.

Solution: With $x = \dfrac{1}{2}$ so that $\ln(1 + x) = \ln\left(1 + \dfrac{1}{2}\right) = \ln\left(\dfrac{3}{2}\right)$ we obtain the approximations

$$P_1\left(\frac{1}{2}\right) = \frac{1}{2} = 0.5000$$

$$P_2\left(\frac{1}{2}\right) = \frac{1}{2} - \frac{1}{2}\left(\frac{1}{2}\right)^2 = \frac{1}{2} - \frac{1}{8} = \frac{3}{8} = 0.3750$$

$$P_3\left(\frac{1}{2}\right) = \frac{1}{2} - \frac{1}{2}\left(\frac{1}{2}\right)^2 + \frac{1}{3}\left(\frac{1}{2}\right)^3 = \frac{1}{2} - \frac{1}{8} + \frac{1}{24} = \frac{5}{12} \approx 0.4167$$

$$P_4\left(\frac{1}{2}\right) = \frac{1}{2} - \frac{1}{2}\left(\frac{1}{2}\right)^2 + \frac{1}{3}\left(\frac{1}{2}\right)^3 - \frac{1}{4}\left(\frac{1}{2}\right)^4 = \frac{77}{192} \approx 0.4010$$

$$P_5\left(\frac{1}{2}\right) = \frac{1}{2} - \frac{1}{2}\left(\frac{1}{2}\right)^2 + \frac{1}{3}\left(\frac{1}{2}\right)^3 - \frac{1}{4}\left(\frac{1}{2}\right)^4 + \frac{1}{5}\left(\frac{1}{2}\right)^5 = \frac{391}{960} \approx 0.4073.$$

The value of $\ln\left(\dfrac{3}{2}\right)$, approximated to four-decimal-place accuracy, is $\ln\left(\dfrac{3}{2}\right) \approx 0.4055$. ∎

☐ **EXAMPLE 4**

Find the first five Taylor polynomials for the function $f(x) = \sin x$ expanded about $x = 0$.

Solution: The values of $f(x) = \sin x$ and its first five derivatives at $x = 0$ are as follows:

$$f(x) = \sin x \qquad f(0) = \sin(0) = 0$$
$$f'(x) = \cos x \qquad f'(0) = \cos(0) = 1$$
$$f''(x) = -\sin x \qquad f''(0) = -\sin(0) = 0$$
$$f'''(x) = -\cos x \qquad f'''(0) = -\cos(0) = -1$$
$$f^{(4)}(x) = \sin x \qquad f^{(4)}(0) = \sin(0) = 0$$
$$f^{(5)}(x) = \cos x \qquad f^{(5)}(0) = \cos(0) = 1.$$

Using these values in Definition 5 gives the Taylor polynomials

$$P_1(x) = 0 + 1 \cdot x = x$$

$$P_2(x) = 0 + 1 \cdot x + \frac{0}{2}x^2 = x$$

$$P_3(x) = 0 + 1 \cdot x + \frac{0}{2}x^2 + \frac{(-1)}{3!}x^3 = x - \frac{x^3}{3!}$$

$$P_4(x) = 0 + 1 \cdot x + \frac{0}{2}x^2 + \frac{(-1)}{3!}x^3 + \frac{0}{4!}x^4 = x - \frac{x^3}{3!}$$

$$P_5(x) = 0 + 1 \cdot x + \frac{0}{2}x^2 + \frac{(-1)}{3!}x^3 + \frac{0}{4!}x^4 + \frac{1}{5!}x^5 = x - \frac{x^3}{3!} + \frac{x^5}{5!}.$$

Notice that

$$P_1(x) = P_2(x) = x$$

$$P_3(x) = P_4(x) = x - \frac{x^3}{3!} \qquad \text{(See Figure 5.5.)}$$

and

$$P_5(x) = x - \frac{x^3}{3!} + \frac{x^5}{5!}.$$

■

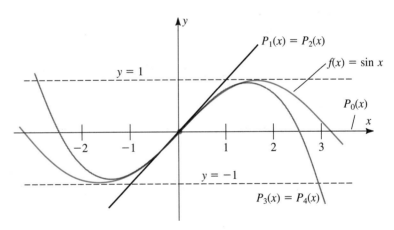

Figure 5.5 Five Taylor polynomials for $f(x) = \sin x$ expanded about $x = 0$. Note that $P_1(x)$ and $P_2(x)$ coincide, as do $P_3(x)$ and $P_4(x)$.

This example shows that an nth Taylor polynomial may actually have a degree less than n.

□ **EXAMPLE 5**

Use the Taylor polynomial P_3 found in Example 4 to approximate $\sin(0.2)$ (where 0.2 is in radian measure).

Solution: With $x = 0.2$, we have

$$\sin(0.2) \approx P_3(0.2) = 0.2 - \frac{(0.2)^3}{3!}$$

$$= 0.2 - \frac{0.008}{6}$$

$$= 0.2 - 0.0013$$

$$= 0.1987.$$

The value of $\sin(0.2)$ to four-decimal-place accuracy is $\sin(0.2) \approx 0.1987$. ■

Expanding About $x = a$

There is no reason why the values $f(x)$ should be approximated only for x near zero. We may, for example, wish to approximate values of the square root function $f(x) = \sqrt{x}$ for x near 4. Since we know the value $f(4) = \sqrt{4} = 2$, in this case it makes sense to base our approximation scheme at $x = 4$, rather than at $x = 0$. This is done as follows.

Definition 6

If the function f and each of its first n derivatives are defined at $x = a$, the **nth Taylor polynomial expanded about $x = a$** is

$$P_n(x) = f(a) + f'(a)(x - a) + \frac{f''(a)}{2}(x - a)^2 + \frac{f'''(a)}{3!}(x - a)^3$$

$$+ \ldots + \frac{f^{(n)}(a)}{n!}(x - a)^n.$$

Note that the nth Taylor polynomial expanded about $x = a$ differs from the nth Taylor polynomial expanded about $x = 0$ in that (i) f and its derivatives are evaluated at $x = a$ rather than at $x = 0$ and (ii) the polynomial involves powers of $(x - a)$ rather than powers of x.

□ **EXAMPLE 6**

Show that at $x = a$, values of the third Taylor polynomial P_3 and each of its first three derivatives are the same as the values of f and its first three derivatives.

Solution: Since

$$P_3(x) = f(a) + f'(a)(x - a) + \frac{f''(a)}{2}(x - a)^2 + \frac{f'''(a)}{3!}(x - a)^3$$

we have $P_3(a) = f(a)$. Next, note that

$$P_3'(x) = f'(a) + f''(a)(x - a) + \frac{f'''(a)}{2}(x - a)^2 \quad \left(\text{since } \frac{3}{3!} = \frac{3}{6} = \frac{1}{2}\right)$$

so

$$P_3'(a) = f'(a).$$

Continuing by differentiating P_3, we obtain

$$P_3''(x) = f''(a) + f'''(a)(x - a)$$

so

$$P_3''(a) = f''(a).$$

Finally, since $P_3'''(x) = f'''(a)$, we have $P_3'''(a) = f'''(a)$. ∎

The point of Example 6 is that the nth Taylor polynomial and its first n derivatives have the same value at $x = a$ as the function f and its first n derivatives, regardless of whether or not a is zero.

☐ **EXAMPLE 7**

Find the first three Taylor polynomials for the function $f(x) = \sqrt{x}$ expanded about $a = 4$.

Solution: The values of f and its first three derivatives at $a = 4$ are found as follows:

$$f(x) = \sqrt{x} = x^{1/2} \qquad f(4) = 4^{1/2} = 2$$

$$f'(x) = \frac{1}{2}x^{-1/2} \qquad f'(4) = \frac{1}{2} \cdot 4^{-1/2} = \frac{1}{2} \cdot \frac{1}{2} = \frac{1}{4}$$

$$f''(x) = -\frac{1}{4}x^{-3/2} \qquad f''(4) = -\frac{1}{4} \cdot 4^{-3/2} = -\frac{1}{4} \cdot \frac{1}{8} = -\frac{1}{32}$$

$$f'''(x) = \frac{3}{8}x^{-5/2} \qquad f'''(4) = \frac{3}{8} \cdot 4^{-5/2} = \frac{3}{8} \cdot \frac{1}{32} = \frac{3}{256}.$$

With these values, Definition 6 gives

$$P_1(x) = 2 + \frac{1}{4}(x - 4)$$

$$P_2(x) = 2 + \frac{1}{4}(x - 4) - \frac{1}{64}(x - 4)^2$$

$$P_3(x) = 2 + \frac{1}{4}(x - 4) - \frac{1}{64}(x - 4)^2 + \frac{1}{512}(x - 4)^3.$$ ∎

Table 5.3 shows the result of using these Taylor polynomials to approximate values of $f(x) = \sqrt{x}$ near $x = 4$.

Table 5.3

x	$P_1(x)$	$P_2(x)$	$P_3(x)$	$f(x) = \sqrt{x}$
3.5	1.875	1.8711	1.8708	1.8708
3.8	1.95	1.9494	1.9494	1.9494
3.9	1.975	1.9748	1.9748	1.9748
4.0	2.0	2.0	2.0	2.0
4.1	2.025	2.0248	2.0248	2.0248
4.2	2.05	2.0494	2.0494	2.0494
4.5	2.125	2.1211	2.1213	2.1213

Summary

In this section we have demonstrated that values of transcendental functions (or of any differentiable function, for that matter) may be approximated by Taylor polynomials, and that the accuracy of these approximations seems to increase with the degree of the polynomial. Taylor's theorem, which we discuss in Section 9.6, enables us to estimate the accuracy of these approximations. Using this theorem, and the preceding ideas about infinite series, we shall show in Section 9.7 that Taylor polynomials can be viewed, in general, as partial sums of infinite *Taylor series,* which converge to the function values of interest for appropriate choices of the independent variable x.

☑ PRACTICE PROBLEMS 9.5

1. Find the third Taylor polynomial for the function $f(x) = \dfrac{1}{x}$ at $a = 4$.

2. Find the second Taylor polynomial of $f(x) = \sqrt{x}$ at $a = 16$ and use it to approximate $\sqrt{15.4}$.

Exercise Set 9.5

In Exercises 1–8, find the nth Taylor polynomial for the given function expanded about $x = 0$.

1. $f(x) = e^{-x}, \quad n = 3$

2. $f(x) = \cos x, \quad n = 2$

3. $f(x) = \cos x, \quad n = 4$

4. $f(x) = \ln(2 + x), \quad n = 4$

5. $f(x) = \dfrac{1}{1+x}, \quad n = 2$

6. $f(x) = \tan x, \quad n = 2$

7. $f(x) = \sqrt{x+2}, \quad n = 3$

8. $f(x) = \sqrt{1+x}, \quad n = 2$

In Exercises 9–18, find the nth Taylor polynomial expanded about $x = a$.

9. $f(x) = \sin x, \quad a = \dfrac{\pi}{4}, \quad n = 4$

10. $f(x) = \cos x, \quad a = \dfrac{\pi}{3}, \quad n = 4$

11. $f(x) = e^x$, $a = 1$, $n = 4$

12. $f(x) = \ln x$, $a = 1$, $n = 5$

13. $f(x) = \sqrt{x}$, $a = 9$, $n = 3$

14. $f(x) = \sqrt{1 + x}$, $a = 3$, $n = 3$

15. $f(x) = e^{x^2}$, $a = 0$, $n = 2$

16. $f(x) = \sin x$, $a = \dfrac{\pi}{2}$, $n = 6$

17. $f(x) = x \cos x$, $a = \dfrac{\pi}{4}$, $n = 2$

18. $f(x) = \dfrac{1}{1 + x}$, $a = 1$, $n = 3$

19. Use the third Taylor polynomial for e^{-x} expanded about $x = 0$ to approximate $\dfrac{1}{e} = e^{-1}$. (See Exercise 1.)

20. Use the second Taylor polynomial for $f(x) = \cos x$ expanded about $x = 0$ to approximate $\cos \dfrac{\pi}{12}$. (See Exercise 2.)

21. Use the third Taylor polynomial for $f(x) = \sqrt{x}$ expanded about $x = 9$ to approximate $\sqrt{10}$. (See Exercise 13.)

22. Let $P_n(x)$ be the nth Taylor polynomial for $f(x) = e^x$ expanded about $x = 0$. Show that $P_n'(x) = P_{n-1}(x)$.

23. Let $P_n(x)$ be the nth Taylor polynomial for $f(x) = e^{-x}$ expanded about $x = 0$. Show that $P_n'(x) = -P_{n-1}(x)$.

24. Let $P_5(x)$ be the fifth Taylor polynomial for $f(x) = \sin x$ expanded about $x = 0$, and let $Q_5(x)$ be the fifth Taylor polynomial for $g(x) = \cos x$ expanded about $x = 0$. Show that $P_5'(x) = Q_5(x)$.

25. Let $Q_4(x)$ be the fourth Taylor polynomial for $g(x) = \cos x$, and let $P_4(x)$ be the fourth Taylor polynomial for $f(x) = \sin x$, both expanded about $x = 0$. Show that $Q_4'(x) = -P_4(x)$.

☑ **SOLUTIONS TO PRACTICE PROBLEMS 9.5**

1. For $f(x) = \dfrac{1}{x} = x^{-1}$, $\qquad f(4) = \dfrac{1}{4}$

$$f'(x) = -x^{-2}, \qquad f'(4) = -4^{-2} = -\dfrac{1}{16}$$

$$f''(x) = 2x^{-3}, \qquad f''(4) = \dfrac{2}{4^3} = \dfrac{1}{32}$$

$$f'''(x) = -6x^{-4}, \qquad f'''(4) = \dfrac{-6}{4^4} = -\dfrac{3}{128}.$$

Then, the third Taylor polynomial at $a = 4$ is

$$P_3(x) = \dfrac{1}{4} - \dfrac{1}{16}(x - 4) + \dfrac{1}{32}\left(\dfrac{1}{2}\right)(x - 4)^2 - \dfrac{3}{128}\left(\dfrac{1}{3!}\right)(x - 4)^3$$

$$= \dfrac{1}{4} - \dfrac{1}{16}(x - 4) + \dfrac{1}{64}(x - 4)^2 - \dfrac{1}{256}(x - 4)^3.$$

2. For $f(x) = \sqrt{x} = x^{1/2}$, $\qquad f(16) = \sqrt{16} = 4$

$$f'(x) = \dfrac{1}{2}x^{-1/2}, \qquad f'(16) = \dfrac{1}{2\sqrt{16}} = \dfrac{1}{8}$$

$$f''(x) = -\dfrac{1}{4}x^{-3/2}, \qquad f''(16) = \dfrac{-1}{4(16)^{3/2}} = \dfrac{-1}{256}.$$

Thus, the second Taylor polynomial at $a = 16$ is

$$P_2(x) = 4 + \frac{1}{8}(x - 16) - \frac{1}{256}\left(\frac{1}{2}\right)(x - 16)^2$$

$$= 4 + \frac{1}{8}(x - 16) - \frac{1}{512}(x - 16)^2.$$

This gives the approximation

$$\sqrt{15.4} \approx 4 + \frac{1}{8}(15.4 - 16) - \frac{1}{512}(15.4 - 16)^2$$

$$= 4 - \frac{0.6}{8} - \frac{(0.6)^2}{512}$$

$$= 3.9243.$$

The actual value of $\sqrt{15.4}$, correct to four decimal places, is also 3.9243.

9.6   Taylor's Theorem

If f is a differentiable function of x, we have seen in Section 9.5 how to approximate values $f(x)$ by values of the nth Taylor polynomial $P_n(x)$. If we write

$$f(x) = P_n(x) + R_n(x) \tag{1}$$

then the term $R_n(x) = f(x) - P_n(x)$ represents the error in this approximation. (See Figure 6.1.) The term $R_n(x)$ is referred to as the *remainder* in a Taylor approximation. Taylor's Theorem provides an estimate on the size of the remainder $R_n(x)$ in equation (1).

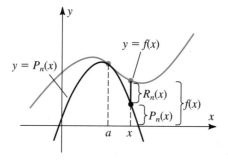

Figure 6.1 $R_n(x) = f(x) - P_n(x)$ is the *remainder* in a Taylor approximation.

Theorem 9

(Taylor's Theorem)

Let n be a positive integer. If the function f and its derivatives f', f'', . . . , $f^{(n)}$ are continuous on the interval $[c, d]$ and if the derivative $f^{(n+1)}(t)$ exists for each $t \in (c, d)$, then for any numbers x and a in $[c, d]$

$$f(x) = f(a) + f'(a)(x - a) + \frac{f''(a)}{2}(x - a)^2 \qquad (2)$$

$$+ \ldots + \frac{f^{(n)}(a)}{n!}(x - a)^n + R_n(x)$$

with

$$|R_n(x)| \le \frac{M}{(n + 1)!}|x - a|^{n+1} \qquad (3)$$

where M is any number so that

$$|f^{(n+1)}(t)| \le M \qquad (4)$$

for all t between a and x.

Since equation (2) is just the restatement of equation (1) displaying the terms of the Taylor polynomial $P_n(x)$ expanded about a, inequality (3) says that the error in approximating the function value $f(x)$ by the value $P_n(x)$ of the nth Taylor polynomial expanded about a is no greater than $\frac{M}{(n + 1)!}|x - a|^{n+1}$, where M is the maximum value of $|f^{(n+1)}(t)|$ for t between the numbers a and x. The proof of Taylor's theorem is given at the end of this section.

☐ **EXAMPLE 1**

Use Taylor's theorem to estimate the accuracy in approximating values of the function $f(x) = e^x$ for x in the interval $[0, 1]$ using the third Taylor polynomial $P_3(x)$ expanded about $a = 0$.

Solution: For the function $f(x) = e^x$ all derivatives are $f^{(n)}(x) = e^x$, so the hypotheses of Taylor's theorem are satisfied. Since $f(x) = e^x$ is an increasing function for all x, the maximum value of the derivative $f^{(4)}(x) = e^x$ on the interval $[0, 1]$ is $f^{(4)}(1) = e^1 = e$. If we allow the assumption that $e \le 3$, an upper bound M for the value of this derivative on $[0, 1]$ is $M = 3$. Thus in place of inequality (4) we have

$$|f^{(4)}(t)| \le 3 \quad \text{for} \quad 0 \le t \le 1.$$

In Section 9.5 we have already shown that the third Taylor polynomial expanded about $a = 0$ is

$$P_3(x) = 1 + x + \frac{x^2}{2} + \frac{x^3}{6}.$$

According to Taylor's theorem, the approximation

$$e^x \approx 1 + x + \frac{x^2}{2} + \frac{x^3}{6} \tag{5}$$

for x in the interval $[0, 1]$ is in error by no more than

$$|R_3(x)| \leq \frac{3}{(3+1)!}|x - 0|^{3+1} \qquad (n = 3)$$

$$= \frac{3}{4!}|x|^4$$

$$= \frac{|x|^4}{8}.$$

Thus, for example

(a) With $x = 1$ the approximation (5) is

$$e \approx 1 + 1 + \frac{1}{2} + \frac{1}{6} = \frac{8}{3}$$

which is accurate to within $|R_3(1)| \leq \frac{1}{8}$.

(b) With $x = \frac{1}{3}$ the approximation (5) is

$$\sqrt[3]{e} = e^{1/3} \approx 1 + \frac{1}{3} + \frac{(1/3)^2}{2} + \frac{(1/3)^3}{6} = \frac{113}{81}$$

which is accurate to within $\left|R_3\left(\frac{1}{3}\right)\right| \leq \frac{1}{8}\left(\frac{1}{3}\right)^4 = \frac{1}{648}.$ ■

□ **EXAMPLE 2**

Use the Taylor polynomial $P_3(x)$ expanded about $a = 1$ to approximate $\ln(1.5)$ and estimate the accuracy of this approximation.

Strategy · · · · · · · ·
Calculate the derivatives
$f', f'',$ and f''' and their values at
$a = 1$.

Solution
We have

$$f(x) = \ln x; \qquad f(1) = 0$$

$$f'(x) = \frac{1}{x}; \qquad f'(1) = 1$$

$$f''(x) = -\frac{1}{x^2}; \qquad f''(1) = -1$$

$$f'''(x) = \frac{2}{x^3}; \qquad f'''(1) = 2$$

Form the Taylor polynomial $P_3(x)$ and use its value at $x = 1.5$ to approximate $\ln(1.5)$.

The third Taylor polynomial expanded about $a = 1$ is therefore

$$P_3(x) = (x - 1) - \frac{1}{2}(x - 1)^2 + \frac{2}{3!}(x - 1)^3$$

and with $x = 1.5$ the approximation is

$$\ln(1.5) \approx P_3(1.5) = (0.5) - \frac{1}{2}(0.5)^2 + \frac{1}{3}(0.5)^3$$

$$= 0.416\overline{6}. \tag{6}$$

Find the bound M on $\left| f^{(n+1)}(t) \right|$ for t in the interval $[a, x]$.

To estimate the accuracy, we note that the absolute value of the fourth derivative is

$$\left| f^{(4)}(x) \right| = \left| \frac{-6}{x^4} \right| = \frac{6}{x^4}$$

which is a decreasing function on the interval $[a, x] = [1, 1.5]$. Its maximum value on this interval is therefore

$$M = \left| f^{(4)}(1) \right| = \frac{6}{1^4} = 6.$$

Apply Taylor's theorem to estimate the error.

Inequality (3) then gives the estimate

$$\left| R_3(1.5) \right| \leq \frac{6}{(3 + 1)!}(1.5 - 1)^{(3+1)}$$

$$= \frac{1}{64}$$

which shows that the approximation in line (6) is accurate to within $\dfrac{1}{64} = 0.015625$. ∎

☐ EXAMPLE 3

Suppose we wish to use the approximation

$$\sin x \approx x \tag{7}$$

for angles x with $|x| < \dfrac{\pi}{45}(=4°)$. What is the maximum possible error in this approximation?

Solution: The approximation in line (7) can be written

$$\sin x \approx P_2(x) \tag{8}$$

where $P_2(x)$ is the second Taylor polynomial for the function $f(x) = \sin x$ expanded about $a = 0$. (See Example 4, Section 9.5. Note that $g(x) = x$ is also the first Taylor polynomial $P_1(x)$ for sin x, but taking $n = 2$ is preferable since it allows us to verify better accuracy for the approximation.)

Thus $n = 2$ in approximation (7). Since the third derivative of $f(x) = \sin x$ is $f^{(3)}(x) = -\cos x$, and since $|\cos x| \le 1$ for all x, we have

$$|f^{(3)}(x)| = |-\cos x| \le 1$$

for all x. We may therefore use $M = 1$ in inequality (3). With $a = 0$, $n = 2$, and $|x - a| = |x - 0| = |x| < \dfrac{\pi}{45}$, Taylor's theorem gives the bound

$$|R_3(x)| \le \frac{1}{(2 + 1)!}|x - 0|^3$$

$$= \frac{1}{6}|x|^3$$

$$< \frac{1}{6}\left(\frac{\pi}{45}\right)^3$$

$$\approx 0.00006$$

for the accuracy in approximation (8).   ■

Proving Taylor's Theorem

The proof that follows uses two properties of definite integrals of continuous functions. The proofs of these properties are sketched in Exercises 13 and 14.

PROPERTY 1:   If $f(x) \le g(x)$ for $a \le x \le b$, then

$$\int_a^b f(x)\,dx \le \int_a^b g(x)\,dx.$$

PROPERTY 2: $\left|\displaystyle\int_a^b f(x)\,dx\right| \le \displaystyle\int_a^b |f(x)|\,dx.$

Proof of Taylor's Theorem: We assume in this proof that $a < x$. The case $x < a$ follows in the same way.

The Taylor polynomial

$$P_n(x) = f(a) + f'(a)(x - a) + \frac{f''(a)}{2}(x - a)^2 + \ldots + \frac{f^{(n)}(a)}{n!}(x - a)^n$$

was defined so that

$$f(a) = P_n(a); \qquad f'(a) = P_n'(a); \qquad \ldots; \qquad f^{(n)}(a) = P_n^{(n)}(a). \tag{9}$$

Also, since $P_n(x)$ is a polynomial of degree n

$$P_n^{(n+1)}(x) = 0 \qquad \text{for all } x. \tag{10}$$

Now the remainder is defined by the equation

$$R_n(x) = f(x) - P_n(x).$$

Differentiating both sides of this equation and using equations (9), we conclude that

$$R_n(a) = R'_n(a) = R''_n(a) = \ldots = R_n^{(n)}(a) = 0 \tag{11}$$

and, using equation (10), we have

$$R^{(n+1)}(t) = f^{(n+1)}(t) \quad \text{for} \quad a < t < x. \tag{12}$$

We now proceed to integrate both sides of equation (12). Using equation (11), we obtain

$$\int_a^x f^{(n+1)}(t)\, dt = \int_a^x R_n^{(n+1)}(t)\, dt = \left[R_n^{(n)}(t) \right]_a^x = R_n^{(n)}(x). \tag{13}$$

Using the bound $\left| f^{(n+1)}(t) \right| \le M$, equation (13), and properties (1) and (2), we conclude that

$$\left| R_n^{(n)}(x) \right| = \left| \int_a^x f^{(n+1)}(t)\, dt \right| \qquad \text{(by equation (13))} \tag{14}$$

$$\le \int_a^x \left| f^{(n+1)}(t) \right| dt \qquad \text{(by property 2)}$$

$$\le \int_a^x M\, dt \qquad \text{(by the bound on } \left| f^{(n+1)} \right|)$$

$$= M(x - a), \qquad a \le x \le d.$$

Then since

$$\int_a^x R_n^{(n)}(t)\, dt = \left[R_n^{(n-1)}(t) \right]_a^x = R_n^{(n-1)}(x) - R_n^{(n-1)}(a) = R_n^{n-1}(x)$$

it follows from inequality (14) and properties (1) and (2) that

$$\left| R_n^{n-1}(x) \right| = \left| \int_a^x R_n^{(n)}(t)\, dt \right|$$

$$\le \int_a^x \left| R_n^{(n)}(t) \right| dt \qquad \text{(by property 2)}$$

$$\le \int_a^x M(t - a)\, dt \qquad \text{(by equation (14))}$$

$$= \frac{M}{2}(x - a)^2, \qquad a \le x \le d.$$

Continuing by integrating in this way, we obtain the inequalities

$$\left|R_n^{(n-k)}(x)\right| \le \frac{M}{(k+1)!}(x-a)^{k+1}, \qquad k = 2, 3, \ldots, n. \qquad (15)$$

The desired inequality

$$\left|R_n(x)\right| \le \frac{M}{(n+1)!}(x-a)^{n+1}$$

is a special case of inequality (15) with $k = n$. ☐

☑ PRACTICE PROBLEMS 9.6

1. Use Taylor's theorem to approximate $\sqrt{2}$ with a Taylor polynomial of degree 3 expanded about $a = 1$. Find the accuracy of the approximation.
2. Use a second Taylor polynomial for $f(x) = \cos x$ expanded about $a = 0$ to approximate $\cos \dfrac{\pi}{12}$ and estimate the accuracy.

Exercise Set 9.6

In Exercises 1–8, use Taylor's theorem to find an approximation to the given function value using a Taylor polynomial of degree n expanded about $x = a$ and estimate the accuracy of the approximation.

1. $\ln(1.4)$, $\quad a = 1$, $\quad n = 3$

2. $\cos 36°$, $\quad a = \dfrac{\pi}{4}$, $\quad n = 2$

3. $\sqrt{3.91}$, $\quad a = 4$, $\quad n = 2$

4. $e^{0.2}$, $\quad a = 0$, $\quad n = 3$

5. $\sin 48°$, $\quad a = \dfrac{\pi}{4}$, $\quad n = 4$

6. $\sqrt[3]{10}$, $\quad a = 8$, $\quad n = 2$

7. $\tan \dfrac{\pi}{12}$, $\quad a = 0$, $\quad n = 3$

8. $\sqrt{50}$, $\quad a = 49$, $\quad n = 3$

9. Estimate the accuracy of the approximation

$$e^x \approx 1 + x + \frac{x^2}{2}$$

for x in the interval $[0, 1]$.

10. Find a bound on the error associated with the approximation

$$\sin x \approx x - \frac{x^3}{3!} \qquad \text{for } |x| < \frac{\pi}{4}.$$

11. How large must the integer n be chosen so that the approximation

$$\sin x \approx x - \frac{x^3}{3!} + \ldots \qquad \text{(with } n \text{ finite)}$$

is accurate to within 0.001 for angles x satisfying the inequality $|x| < 0.2$ (in radians)? (*Hint:* Since $\left|f^{(n)}(x)\right| \le 1$ for all derivatives of $f(x) = \sin x$, Taylor's theorem gives $\left|R_n(x)\right| \le \dfrac{1}{(n+1)!}|x|^{n+1}$. You must therefore find n sufficiently large that $\dfrac{1}{(n+1)!}(0.2)^{(n+1)} \le 0.001$.)

12. How large must n be chosen so that the approximation

$$\cos x \approx 1 - \frac{x^2}{2} + \ldots \qquad \text{(with } n \text{ finite)}$$

is accurate to within 0.0001 for angles x satisfying the inequality $|x| < 0.2$ (in radians)? (See Exercise 11.)

13. Let f and g be continuous on $[a, b]$ with $f(x) \le g(x)$ for all $a \le x \le b$. Prove that

$$\int_a^b f(x)\, dx \le \int_a^b g(x)\, dx$$

as follows.

a. Define h by $h(x) = g(x) - f(x)$.
b. Verify that $h(x) \ge 0$ for $a \le x \le b$.
c. Write $g(x) = f(x) + h(x)$ and show that

$$\int_a^b g(x)\, dx = \int_a^b f(x)\, dx + \int_a^b h(x)\, dx.$$

d. Explain why $\int_a^b h(x)\, dx \ge 0$.

e. Conclude from parts (c) and (d) that

$$\int_a^b f(x)\, dx \le \int_a^b g(x)\, dx.$$

14. Let f be continuous on $[a, b]$. Prove that

$$\left| \int_a^b f(x)\, dx \right| \le \int_a^b |f(x)\, dx|\, dx$$

as follows.

a. Explain why $-|f(x)| \le f(x) \le |f(x)|$, $a \le x \le b$.
b. Conclude from part (a) and Exercise 13 that

$$-\int_a^b |f(x)|\, dx \le \int_a^b f(x)\, dx \le \int_a^b |f(x)|\, dx$$

c. Conclude from part (b) that

$$\left| \int_a^b f(x)\, dx \right| \le \int_a^b |f(x)|\, dx.$$

☑ **SOLUTIONS TO PRACTICE PROBLEMS 9.6**

1. We use the function

$$f(x) = \sqrt{x} = x^{1/2}, \qquad \text{where} \qquad f(1) = 1$$

$$f'(x) = \frac{1}{2}x^{-1/2}, \qquad\qquad f'(1) = \frac{1}{2}$$

$$f''(x) = -\frac{1}{4}x^{-3/2}, \qquad\qquad f''(1) = -\frac{1}{4}$$

$$f'''(x) = \frac{3}{8}x^{-5/2}, \qquad\qquad f'''(1) = \frac{3}{8}.$$

The third Taylor's polynomial for f at $a = 1$ is

$$P_3(x) = 1 + \frac{1}{2}(x - 1) - \frac{1}{8}(x - 1)^2 + \frac{1}{16}(x - 1)^3.$$

The approximation is

$$\sqrt{2} \approx P_3(2) = 1 + \frac{1}{2} - \frac{1}{8} + \frac{1}{16} = \frac{16 + 8 - 2 + 1}{16} = \frac{23}{16} = 1.4375.$$

To use Taylor's theorem to estimate the error we compute

$$f^{(4)}(x) = -\frac{15}{16}x^{-7/2} = -\frac{15}{16x^{7/2}}.$$

For t between $a = 1$ and $x = 2$, the maximum value of $|f^{(4)}(x)|$ occurs at the *minimum value of* $x^{7/2}$, which occurs at $t = 1$. Thus,

$$|f^{(4)}(t)| \le \left| -\frac{15}{16(1)^{7/2}} \right| = \frac{15}{16}.$$

Thus, by Taylor's theorem, the error $R_3(2)$ in the approximation is bounded as follows:

$$|R_3(2)| \le \frac{\frac{15}{16}}{4!}(2-1)^4 = \frac{15}{16 \cdot 4!} = 0.0391.$$

The *actual* value for $\sqrt{2}$ to four decimal places is $\sqrt{2} = 1.4142$ so the above approximation is in error by $|1.4375 - 1.4142| = 0.0233$, which is less than the estimated error.

2. For $f(x) = \cos x$, $\qquad f(0) = 1$
   $\qquad f'(x) = -\sin x$, $\qquad f'(0) = 0$
   $\qquad f''(x) = -\cos x$, $\qquad f''(0) = -1$.

The second Taylor polynomial is

$$P_2(x) = 1 - \frac{x^2}{2}$$

and the approximation is

$$\cos \frac{\pi}{12} \approx P_2\left(\frac{\pi}{12}\right) = 1 - \frac{1}{2}\left(\frac{\pi}{12}\right)^2$$

$$= 1 - \frac{\pi^2}{288}$$

$$= 0.9657$$

to four decimal places.

To estimate the accuracy we note that $f'''(x) = \sin x$, so $|f'''(x)| \le 1$ for all x. Taylor's formula for the remainder $R_2\left(\frac{\pi}{12}\right)$ gives the bound

$$\left|R_2\left(\frac{\pi}{12}\right)\right| \le \frac{1}{3!}\left|\frac{\pi}{12} - 0\right|^3 = \frac{\pi^3}{10,368} \approx 0.0030.$$

The *actual* value of $\cos \frac{\pi}{12}$ is 0.9659 to four decimal places, so our approximation is in error by less than 0.0002. (Actually, because $f'''(0) = 0$, we could have claimed that $P_2(x) = P_3(x)$, and that the error is bounded by

$$R_3\left(\frac{\pi}{12}\right) = \frac{1}{4!}\left|\frac{\pi}{12} - 0\right|^4 \approx 0.0002$$

as noted.)

9.7 Taylor Series

In Sections 9.5 and 9.6 we approximated values of the function f for x near zero using the nth Taylor polynomial

$$P_n(x) = f(0) + f'(0) + \frac{f''(0)}{2}x^2 + \ldots + \frac{f^{(n)}(0)}{n!}x^n. \tag{1}$$

Using the conventions $0! = 1$, $1! = 1$, and $f^{(0)} = f$, we can express the Taylor polynomial in equation (1) in the form

$$P_n(x) = \sum_{k=0}^{n} \frac{f^{(k)}(0)}{k!} x^k. \tag{2}$$

The Taylor polynomial $P_n(x)$ in equation (2) is defined only when f and its first n derivatives are defined for $x = 0$. Several examples in Section 9.5 suggested that the values $P_n(x)$ become increasingly good approximations to $f(x)$ as n increases.

When the function f and *all* its derivatives $f^{(n)}(x)$, $n = 1, 2, 3, \ldots$ are defined for $x = 0$, we may extend the notion of Taylor polynomials to (infinite) **Taylor series** by taking the limit as $n \to \infty$ of the sum in equations (1) and (2). That is, we view the Taylor polynomial $P_n(x)$ as a partial sum of the Taylor series (expanded about $x = 0$):

$$\sum_{k=0}^{\infty} \frac{f^{(k)}}{k!} x^k = f(0) + f'(0)x + \frac{f''(0)}{2} x^2 + \ldots + \frac{f^{(k)}(0)}{k!} x^k + \ldots. \tag{3}$$

Taylor series are of interest because under certain conditions on the function f the series in equation (3) converges to the value $f(x)$. Thus we have a method for expressing values of the function f as sums of certain infinite series. Before saying more about the general situation, we look at the particular case of the function $f(x) = e^x$.

□ **EXAMPLE 1**

Find the Taylor series expanded about $x = 0$ for the function $f(x) = e^x$.

Solution: For the function $f(x) = e^x$ all derivatives are also e^x: $f'(x) = e^x, f''(x) = e^x$, etc. Thus $f(0) = e^0 = 1, f'(0) = e^0 = 1$, and $f^{(k)}(0) = e^0 = 1$ for all $k = 2, 3, \ldots$. Equation (3) becomes

$$\sum_{k=0}^{\infty} \frac{1}{k!} x^k = 1 + x + \frac{x^2}{2} + \frac{x^3}{3!} + \ldots + \frac{x^k}{k!} + \ldots. \tag{4}$$

You should recognize the sum of the first $n + 1$ terms in this series as the nth Taylor polynomial for $f(x) = e^x$ expanded about $x = 0$ as discussed in Section 9.5. ■

□ **EXAMPLE 2**

For which numbers x does the Taylor series in Example 1 converge?

Solution: For any particular number x the right-hand side of equation (4) is just an infinite series of constants, whose general term is $a_k = \dfrac{x^k}{k!}$. We may therefore test this series for absolute convergence using the Ratio Test. We find that

$$\rho = \lim_{k \to \infty} \frac{|a_{k+1}|}{|a_k|} = \lim_{k \to \infty} \frac{\left| \dfrac{x^{k+1}}{(k+1)!} \right|}{\left| \dfrac{x^k}{k!} \right|}$$

$$= \lim_{k \to \infty} \frac{|x|^{k+1}}{(k+1)!} \cdot \frac{k!}{|x|^k}$$

$$= \lim_{k \to \infty} \frac{k!}{(k+1)!} \cdot \frac{|x|^{k+1}}{|x|^k}$$

$$= \lim_{k \to \infty} \left(\frac{1}{k+1} \right) |x|$$

$$= 0 \cdot |x|$$

$$= 0.$$

(Remember, x doesn't depend on k in this calculation, which is why $\lim_{k \to \infty} \left(\dfrac{1}{k+1} \right) |x| = 0 \cdot |x| = 0$.) Thus the ratio limit is $\rho = 0$ *for any number x*, so the Taylor series $\Sigma \dfrac{x^k}{k!}$ converges absolutely *for all x*. ∎

REMARK 1: There is a stronger statement to be made about the Taylor series for e^x in Example 2. Not only does it converge for all x, but *it converges to the function value e^x for all x.* (See Exercise 21.) Thus we can write

$$e^x = \sum_{k=0}^{\infty} \frac{x^k}{k!}$$

$$= 1 + x + \frac{x^2}{2} + \ldots + \frac{x^k}{k!} + \ldots$$

for all x. In particular, setting $x = 1$ gives an infinite series that converges to the number e:

$$e = 1 + 1 + \frac{1}{2} + \frac{1}{3!} + \ldots + \frac{1}{k!} + \ldots$$

$$= \sum_{k=0}^{\infty} \frac{1}{k!}.$$

Similarly, setting $x = -1$ gives an alternating series that converges to $e^{-1} = \dfrac{1}{e}$:

$$\frac{1}{e} = 1 - 1 + \frac{1}{2} - \frac{1}{3!} + \frac{1}{4!} - \ldots + \frac{(-1)^k}{k!} + \ldots$$

$$= \sum_{k=0}^{\infty} \frac{(-1)^k}{k!}.$$

There are some exotic examples of functions for which the corresponding Taylor series converge to numbers other than the function values, but this does not occur for any of the functions considered in this text. For a function f discussed in this chapter, if the Taylor series for f converges at x, then it converges to the value $f(x)$.

REMARK 2: A Taylor series may converge only for numbers x within a certain interval. When this is the case, we have to check for convergence separately at each endpoint—the series may converge at both endpoints, only at one, or at neither, as shown in the following examples.

☐ **EXAMPLE 3**

Find a Taylor series expanded about $x = 0$ for the function $f(x) = \ln(1 + x)$ and determine the numbers x for which the series converges.

Solution: We calculate the terms of the Taylor series just as we calculated the Taylor polynomial for $f(x) = \ln(1 + x)$ in Example 2, Section 9.5. We have

$$f(x) = \ln(1 + x) \qquad\qquad f(0) = \ln(1 + 0) = 0$$

$$f'(x) = \frac{1}{1 + x} = (1 + x)^{-1} \qquad\qquad f'(0) = (1 + 0)^{-1} = 1$$

$$f''(x) = -1(1 + x)^{-2} \qquad\qquad f''(0) = -(1 + 0)^{-2} = -1$$

$$f'''(x) = 2(1 + x)^{-3} \qquad\qquad f'''(0) = 2(1 + 0)^{-3} = 2$$

$$f^{(4)}(x) = -6(1 + x)^{-4} = -3!(1 + x)^{-4} \qquad f^{(4)}(0) = -3!(1 + 0)^{-4} = -3!$$

$$\vdots \qquad\qquad\qquad \vdots$$

$$f^{(k)}(x) = (-1)^{k+1}(k - 1)!(1 + x)^{-k} \qquad f^{(k)}(0) = (-1)^{k+1}(k - 1)!(1 + 0)^{-k}$$

$$= (-1)^{k+1}(k - 1)!$$

The Taylor series for $f(x) = \ln(1 + x)$ is therefore

$$\sum_{k=1}^{\infty} \frac{(-1)^{k+1}(k - 1)!}{k!} x^k = \sum_{k=1}^{\infty} \frac{(-1)^{k+1}}{k} x^k$$

$$= x - \frac{x^2}{2} + \frac{x^3}{3} - \frac{x^4}{4} + \ldots + \frac{(-1)^{k+1}}{k} x^k + \ldots . \quad (5)$$

Using the general term $a_k = \dfrac{(-1)^{k+1}}{k} x^k$, we test the series for absolute convergence using the Ratio Test. We obtain

$$\rho = \lim_{k \to \infty} \frac{|a_{k+1}|}{|a_k|} = \lim_{k \to \infty} \frac{\left| \dfrac{(-1)^{k+2}}{k+1} x^{k+1} \right|}{\left| \dfrac{(-1)^{k+1}}{k} x^k \right|}$$

$$= \lim_{k \to \infty} \left(\frac{k}{k+1} \right) \frac{|x|^{k+1}}{|x|^k}$$

$$= \lim_{k \to \infty} \left(\frac{k}{k+1} \right) |x|$$

$$= |x|$$

since $\lim_{k \to \infty} \dfrac{k}{k+1} = 1$. Thus the Taylor series will converge absolutely when $\rho = |x| < 1$. We leave it as an exercise for you to show that this Taylor series diverges for any x with $|x| > 1$. (See Exercises 16 and 17.)

This leaves the two cases $x = 1$ and $x = -1$ (corresponding to $|x| = 1$) to be checked individually.

Case $x = 1$: When $x = 1$, the Taylor series in equation (5) becomes the series

$$\sum_{k=1}^{\infty} \frac{(-1)^{k+1}}{k} (1)^k = 1 - \frac{1}{2} + \frac{1}{3} - \frac{1}{4} + \frac{1}{5} + \dots.$$

This is an alternating series that satisfies the requirements of the Alternating Series Test. It therefore converges.

Case $x = -1$: When $x = -1$, the Taylor series becomes

$$\sum_{k=1}^{\infty} \frac{(-1)^{k+1}}{k} (-1)^k = (-1) - \frac{(-1)^2}{2} + \frac{(-1)^3}{3} - \frac{(-1)^4}{4} + \dots$$

$$= -\left(1 + \frac{1}{2} + \frac{1}{3} + \frac{1}{4} + \dots \right).$$

This is the negative of the harmonic series, which diverges.

We have therefore determined that the Taylor series for $f(x) = \ln(1 + x)$ in equation (5):

(a) converges for $|x| < 1$
(b) diverges for $|x| > 1$
(c) converges for $x = 1$
(d) diverges for $x = -1$.

That is, the Taylor series converges only for those x in the interval $(-1, 1]$.   ■

☐ **EXAMPLE 4**

We have already determined in Theorem 1 of Section 9.2 that for $|x| < 1$ the function $f(x) = \dfrac{1}{1-x}$ may be expressed as the infinite geometric series

$$\frac{1}{1-x} = \sum_{k=0}^{\infty} x^k = 1 + x + x^2 + x^3 + \ldots + x^k + \ldots. \tag{6}$$

We leave it as an exercise for you to show that the terms of this series have the form $a_k = \dfrac{f^{(k)}(0)}{k!} x^k$. (See Exercise 18.) Thus equation (6) is a Taylor series for the function $f(x) = \dfrac{1}{1-x}$, which converges for x in the interval $(-1, 1)$. ■

☐ **EXAMPLE 5**

We leave it as additional exercises for you to show that the following are the Taylor series associated with the functions $f(x) = \sin x$ and $g(x) = \cos x$, and that both series converge for all values of x:

$$\sin x = \sum_{k=0}^{\infty} \frac{(-1)^k}{(2k+1)!} x^{2k+1} = x - \frac{x^3}{3!} + \frac{x^5}{5!} - \frac{x^7}{7!} + \ldots \tag{7}$$

$$\cos x = \sum_{k=0}^{\infty} \frac{(-1)^k}{(2k)!} x^{2k} = 1 - \frac{x^2}{2!} + \frac{x^4}{4!} - \frac{x^6}{6!} + \ldots. \tag{8}$$

(See Exercises 19 and 20.) ■

More General Taylor Series

Up to this point all examples of Taylor series have been expanded about $x = 0$. (Taylor series expanded about $a = 0$ are called **Maclaurin** series.) But, just as Taylor polynomials can be expanded about an arbitrary point $x = a$, so can Taylor series, provided that $f(a)$ and all derivatives $f^{(n)}(a)$ exist. The general form for **a Taylor series expanded about $x = a$** is

$$\sum_{k=0}^{\infty} \frac{f^{(k)}(a)}{k!} (x-a)^k = f(a) + f'(a)(x-a) + \frac{f''(a)}{2}(x-a)^2$$

$$+ \frac{f'''(a)}{3!}(x-a)^3 + \ldots + \frac{f^{(k)}(a)}{k!}(x-a)^k + \ldots. \tag{9}$$

☐ **EXAMPLE 6**

The Taylor series for the function $f(x) = \sin x$ expanded about $a = \dfrac{\pi}{4}$ is found as follows:

$$f(x) = \sin x \qquad f\left(\frac{\pi}{4}\right) = \frac{\sqrt{2}}{2}$$

$$f'(x) = \cos x \qquad f'\left(\frac{\pi}{4}\right) = \frac{\sqrt{2}}{2}$$

$$f''(x) = -\sin x \qquad f''\left(\frac{\pi}{4}\right) = -\frac{\sqrt{2}}{2}$$

$$f'''(x) = -\cos x \qquad f'''\left(\frac{\pi}{4}\right) = -\frac{\sqrt{2}}{2}$$

$$f^{(4)}(x) = \sin x \qquad f^{(4)}\left(\frac{\pi}{4}\right) = \frac{\sqrt{2}}{2}$$

$$\text{etc.} \qquad\qquad \text{etc.}$$

Using equation (9), we obtain

$$\sin x = \frac{\sqrt{2}}{2} + \frac{\sqrt{2}}{2}\left(x - \frac{\pi}{4}\right) - \frac{\sqrt{2}}{2}\frac{\left(x - \frac{\pi}{4}\right)^2}{2} - \frac{\sqrt{2}}{2}\frac{\left(x - \frac{\pi}{4}\right)^3}{3!} + \frac{\sqrt{2}}{2}\frac{\left(x - \frac{\pi}{4}\right)^4}{4!} + \cdots.$$

To find the interval of convergence for this series, we note that $|a_k| = \left|\dfrac{\sqrt{2}}{2}\dfrac{\left(x - \frac{\pi}{4}\right)^k}{k!}\right|$. Applying the Ratio Test gives

$$\rho = \lim_{k \to \infty} \frac{\left|\dfrac{\sqrt{2}}{2}\dfrac{\left(x - \frac{\pi}{4}\right)^{k+1}}{(k+1)!}\right|}{\left|\dfrac{\sqrt{2}}{2}\dfrac{\left(x - \frac{\pi}{4}\right)^k}{k!}\right|} = \lim_{k \to \infty} \frac{k!}{(k+1)!}\left|x - \frac{\pi}{4}\right|$$

$$= \lim_{k \to \infty}\left(\frac{1}{k+1}\right)\left|x - \frac{\pi}{4}\right|$$

$$= 0.$$

Thus the Ratio Test shows that this Taylor series converges for all x. ∎

Power Series

Another generalization of Taylor series is to power series, which have the form

$$\sum_{k=0}^{\infty} c_k(x - a)^k \tag{10}$$

where the coefficients c_k are constants. The infinite series in line (10) is a generalization of the Taylor series in line (9) because the coefficient c_k is not *required* to equal the kth Taylor coefficient, $c_k = \dfrac{f^{(k)}(a)}{k!}$; it can be *any* real number.

Properties of Power Series

Power series, including Taylor series, have several important properties that account for their usefulness. To keep the discussion simple, we shall discuss these properties only in general terms.

INTERVAL OF CONVERGENCE: The power series in equation (10) will always converge when $x = a$, since all terms except possibly c_0 equal zero. This may be the only number x for which a power series converges. If not, the set of all x for which the series converges will be either

(a) all real numbers x, or
(b) an interval, whose midpoint is a, which may or may not include one or both of its endpoints. This interval is called the **interval of convergence.** Half its length is called the **radius of convergence.** (See Figure 7.1.)

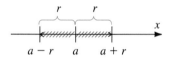

Figure 7.1 Interval and radius of convergence for a power series with radius of convergence $r > 0$.

□ **EXAMPLE 7**

Find the interval of convergence for the power series

$$\sum_{k=1}^{\infty} \frac{x^k}{3^k}.$$

Strategy · · · · · · · ·
Use Ratio Test to test for absolute convergence.

Solution

With the general term $a_k = \dfrac{x^k}{3^k}$, we find that

$$\rho = \lim_{k \to \infty} \frac{|a_{k+1}|}{|a_k|} = \lim_{k \to \infty} \frac{\left|\dfrac{x^{k+1}}{3^{k+1}}\right|}{\left|\dfrac{x^k}{3^k}\right|}$$

$$= \lim_{k \to \infty} \frac{|x|}{3} = \frac{|x|}{3}.$$

The radius of convergence is determined by the magnitude of $|x|$.

Thus, $\rho < 1$ if $|x| < 3$. Thus, the radius of convergence for this power series (centered about $a = 0$) is $r = 3$.

Check convergence at the endpoints $x = \pm 3$ by substituting into the power series.

To test for convergence at the right endpoint $r = 3$, we set $x = 3$ and obtain the series

$$\sum_{k=1}^{\infty} \frac{3^k}{3^k} = 1 + 1 + 1 + \ldots$$

which diverges. At the left endpoint, we have $x = -3$ and the series

$$\sum_{k=1}^{\infty} \frac{(-3)^k}{3^k} = 1 - 1 + 1 - 1 + \ldots$$

also diverges. The interval of convergence is therefore $(-3, 3)$. ∎

☐ **EXAMPLE 8**

Find the radius and interval of convergence for the power series

$$\sum_{k=1}^{\infty} \frac{2^k}{k}(x - 1)^k.$$

Solution: Using the Ratio Test with general term $a_k = \dfrac{2^k}{k}(x - 1)^k$ gives

$$\rho = \lim_{k \to \infty} \frac{\left| \dfrac{2^{k+1}}{k + 1}(x - 1)^{k+1} \right|}{\left| \dfrac{2^k}{k}(x - 1)^k \right|} = \lim_{k \to \infty} \left(\frac{2k}{k + 1} \right) |x - 1| = 2|x - 1|.$$

Thus $\rho = 2|x - 1| < 1$ if $|x - 1| < \dfrac{1}{2}$. This shows that the interval of convergence is centered about $a = 1$ with radius $r = \dfrac{1}{2}$.

At the right endpoint $x = a + r = 1 + \dfrac{1}{2} = \dfrac{3}{2}$, we obtain the series

$$\sum_{k=1}^{\infty} \frac{2^k}{k}\left(\frac{3}{2} - 1 \right)^k = \sum_{k=1}^{\infty} \frac{2^k}{k}\left(\frac{1}{2} \right)^k = \sum_{k=1}^{\infty} \frac{1}{k}$$

which diverges. (It is the harmonic series.)

At the left endpoint $x = a - r = 1 - \dfrac{1}{2} = \dfrac{1}{2}$, we obtain the series

$$\sum_{k=0}^{\infty} \frac{2^k}{k}\left(\frac{1}{2} - 1 \right)^k = \sum_{k=0}^{\infty} \frac{2^k}{k}\left(-\frac{1}{2} \right)^k = \sum_{k=0}^{\infty} \frac{(-1)^k}{k}$$

which converges. (It passes the alternating series test.) Thus, the interval of convergence is $\left[\dfrac{1}{2}, \dfrac{3}{2} \right)$. ∎

ALGEBRA OF SERIES: Within the interval of convergence we can multiply a power series by a constant, term by term, and the resulting series will converge. Moreover, when two power series share a common interval of convergence, they may be added term by term, and the resulting series will converge to the sum of the corresponding functions for each x in that interval. Thus within a common interval of convergence the algebra of power series is the same as that of polynomial functions.

DIFFERENTIATION AND INTEGRATION OF POWER SERIES: Within its interval of convergence (except possibly at endpoints), a power series may be differentiated term by term, just as if it were an "infinitely long polynomial," and the resulting series will have the same radius of convergence. Moreover, if a power series is a Taylor series for a function $f(x)$, then the result of differentiating the series term by term will be a Taylor series for the derivative, $f'(x)$.

☐ **EXAMPLE 9**

Using the results of Examples 1 and 5, we verify two previous differentiation results:

(a) $\dfrac{d}{dx} e^x = \dfrac{d}{dx}\left[1 + x + \dfrac{x^2}{2!} + \dfrac{x^3}{3!} + \dfrac{x^4}{4!} + \ldots \right]$

$\qquad = \dfrac{d}{dx}(1) + \dfrac{d}{dx}(x) + \dfrac{d}{dx}\left(\dfrac{x^2}{2}\right) + \dfrac{d}{dx}\left(\dfrac{x^3}{3!}\right) + \dfrac{d}{dx}\left(\dfrac{x^4}{4!}\right) + \ldots$

$\qquad = 0 + 1 + \dfrac{2x}{2} + \dfrac{3x^2}{3!} + \dfrac{4x^3}{4!} + \ldots$

$\qquad = 1 + x + \dfrac{x^2}{2} + \dfrac{x^3}{3!} + \ldots$

$\qquad = e^x.$

(b) $\dfrac{d}{dx} \sin x = \dfrac{d}{dx}\left[x - \dfrac{x^3}{3!} + \dfrac{x^5}{5!} - \dfrac{x^7}{7!} + \ldots \right]$

$\qquad = \dfrac{d}{dx}(x) - \dfrac{d}{dx}\left(\dfrac{x^3}{3!}\right) + \dfrac{d}{dx}\left(\dfrac{x^5}{5!}\right) - \dfrac{d}{dx}\left(\dfrac{x^7}{7!}\right) + \ldots$

$\qquad = 1 - \dfrac{3x^2}{3!} + \dfrac{5x^4}{5!} - \dfrac{7x^6}{7!} + \ldots$

$\qquad = 1 - \dfrac{x^2}{2} + \dfrac{x^4}{4!} - \dfrac{x^6}{6!} + \ldots$

$\qquad = \cos x.$

■

□ **EXAMPLE 10**

The Taylor series for $f(x) = \dfrac{1}{1 - x}$ is

$$\frac{1}{1 - x} = 1 + x + x^2 + x^3 + \ldots + x^k + \ldots$$

which converges for all x with $|x| < 1$. Since the derivative of f is $f'(x) = \dfrac{1}{(1 - x)^2}$, this derivative has Taylor series

$$\frac{1}{(1 - x)^2} = \frac{d}{dx}(1) + \frac{d}{dx}(x) + \frac{d}{dx}(x^2) + \frac{d}{dx}(x^3) + \ldots + \frac{d}{dx}(x^k)$$

$$= 1 + 2x + 3x^2 + \ldots + kx^{k-1} + \ldots$$

which converges for all x with $|x| < 1$. ∎

Integration of Power Series

Within its radius of convergence, we may integrate a power series term by term. When the given series is a Taylor series for a function $f(x)$, the resulting series will be a Taylor series for the antiderivative, $\displaystyle\int f(x)\, dx$.

□ **EXAMPLE 11**

In the Taylor series

$$\frac{1}{1 - x} = \sum_{k=0}^{\infty} x^k = 1 + x + x^2 + \ldots, \qquad |x| < 1$$

we may replace x by $-x$ to obtain

$$\frac{1}{1 + x} = \sum_{k=0}^{\infty} (-x)^k = 1 - x + x^2 - x^3 + \ldots, \qquad |x| < 1.$$

Now an antiderivative of $\dfrac{1}{1 + x}$ is

$$\int \frac{1}{1 + x}\, dx = \ln(1 + x), \qquad |x| < 1.$$

According to the above remark, this tells us that

$$\ln(1 + x) = \int \frac{1}{1 + x}\, dx$$

$$= \left\{ \int 1\, dx - \int x\, dx + \int x^2\, dx - \int x^3\, dx + \ldots \right\} + C$$

$$= \left\{ x - \frac{x^2}{2} + \frac{x^3}{3} - \frac{x^4}{4} + \ldots \right\} + C, \qquad |x| < 1.$$

To determine the constant C, we set $x = 0$ to obtain

$$\ln(1 + 0) = 0 = C$$

so $C = 0$. Thus,

$$\ln(1 + x) = x - \frac{x^2}{2} + \frac{x^3}{3} - \frac{x^4}{4} + \dots$$

$$= \sum_{k=1}^{\infty} \frac{(-1)^{k+1} x^k}{k}.$$

∎

CONCLUSION: We have seen that Taylor polynomials are useful in approximating values of functions that are themselves difficult to compute. The question of whether successive approximations by Taylor polynomials actually converge to the desired function value may be recast as the question of whether the corresponding power series converges to the function value at the designated number x. This may be determined by using the Ratio Test to identify the width of the interval of convergence for the given function. This leaves only the question of the convergence of the power series at the endpoints (if any) of the interval of convergence. This may be determined by using the tests for convergence of series of constants.

☑ **PRACTICE PROBLEMS 9.7**

1. Find the Taylor series for the function $f(x) = \sin x$ expanded about $a = \dfrac{\pi}{6}$.

2. Find the radius and interval of convergence for the power series.

$$\sum_{k=1}^{\infty} \frac{1}{k \cdot 2^k} x^k.$$

Exercise Set 9.7

In Exercises 1–10, find the Taylor series for the given function expanded about $x = a$.

1. $f(x) = e^{2x}, \quad a = 0$

2. $f(x) = e^{-x}, \quad a = 0$

3. $f(x) = \dfrac{1}{1 + x}, \quad a = 0$

4. $f(x) = \sqrt{1 + x}, \quad a = 0$

5. $f(x) = \ln x, \quad a = 1$

6. $f(x) = \dfrac{1}{x}, \quad a = 1$

7. $f(x) = \sin x, \quad a = \dfrac{\pi}{2}$

8. $f(x) = \cos x, \quad a = \dfrac{\pi}{4}$

9. $f(x) = \sin x, \quad a = \dfrac{\pi}{3}$

10. $f(x) = x \sin x, \quad a = 0$

11. Determine the interval of convergence for the Taylor series in Exercise 1.

12. Determine the interval of convergence for the Taylor series in Exercise 3.

13. Determine the interval of convergence for the Taylor series in Exercise 5.

14. Find a Taylor series for $f(x) = \dfrac{1}{(1 + x)^2}$ expanded about $a = 0$ by differentiating the Taylor series for $g(x) = \dfrac{1}{1 + x}$. (See Exercise 3.)

15. Find a Taylor series for $f(x) = \cos x$ expanded about $a = \dfrac{\pi}{2}$ by differentiating the Taylor series for $g(x) = \sin x$. (See Exercise 7.)

In Exercises 16–20, find a power series for a given function by integrating or differentiating a known power series.

16. $f(x) = \dfrac{2}{(1 + x)^2}$ $\left(Hint: f(x) = -2\dfrac{d}{dx}\left(\dfrac{1}{1 + x}\right)\right)$

17. $f(x) = \dfrac{2}{(1 - x)^3}$ $\left(Hint: f(x) = \dfrac{d^2}{dx^2}\left(\dfrac{1}{1 - x}\right)\right)$

18. $f(x) = x \cos x^2$

19. $f(x) = \ln(1 - x)$

20. $f(x) = \ln(4 + x)$

In Exercises 21–26, find the radius and interval of convergence for the given power series.

21. $\displaystyle\sum_{k=0}^{\infty} \dfrac{x^k}{k + 2}$

22. $\displaystyle\sum_{k=1}^{\infty} \dfrac{x^k}{2k}$

23. $\displaystyle\sum_{k=0}^{\infty} \dfrac{(-1)^{k+1}}{k!}x^k$

24. $\displaystyle\sum_{k=0}^{\infty} \dfrac{2^k x^k}{(k + 1)!}$

25. $\displaystyle\sum_{k=1}^{\infty} \dfrac{k^2 + 1}{k!}x^k$

26. $\displaystyle\sum_{k=1}^{\infty} \dfrac{(-1)^k}{k(k + 1)}x^k$

27. Explain why the Taylor series

$$\sum_{k=1}^{\infty} \dfrac{(-1)^{k+1}}{k}x^k = 1 - x + \dfrac{x^2}{2} - \dfrac{x^3}{3} + \dfrac{x^4}{4} - \ldots$$

in equation (5) diverges for $x > 1$. [*Hint:* Use the Alternating Series Test and the fact that $\displaystyle\lim_{k \to \infty} \dfrac{x^k}{k} = +\infty$ if $x > 1$.]

28. Explain why the Taylor series in Exercise 27 diverges for $x < -1$ by comparing it with the harmonic series.

29. Verify that the terms of the geometric series

$$\dfrac{1}{1 - x} = \sum_{k=0}^{\infty} x^k = 1 + x + x^2 + x^3 + \ldots + x^k + \ldots$$

have the form $a_k = \dfrac{f^{(k)}(0)}{k!}x^k$ for $f(x) = \dfrac{1}{1 - x}$.

30. Show that the Taylor series for $f(x) = \sin x$ expanded about $x = 0$ is that given by equation (7).

31. Show that the Taylor series for $f(x) = \cos x$ expanded about $x = 0$ is that given by equation (8).

32. Show that the Taylor Series for the function $f(x) = e^x$ expanded about $a = 0$ converges *to the function f* as follows:
  a. Show that for any fixed number x, the derivative $f^{(n+1)}$ satisfies the inequality

$$|f^{(n+1)}(t)| \le e^x, \qquad -\infty < t \le x.$$

  b. Let $M = e^x$. Use Taylor's theorem to show that

$$|R_n(t)| \le \dfrac{M}{(n + 1)!}|x|^{(n+1)}, \qquad t \le x$$

  where $R_n(t) = f(t) - P_n(t)$.

  c. Show that $\displaystyle\lim_{n \to \infty} \dfrac{|x|^{(n+1)}}{(n + 1)!} = 0$ by noting that if $N \ge x$, we can write

$$\dfrac{|x|^{n+1}}{(n + 1)!} = \left(|x| \cdot \dfrac{|x|}{2} \cdot \dfrac{|x|}{3} \cdot \ldots \cdot \dfrac{|x|}{N}\right)$$
$$\cdot \left(\dfrac{|x|}{N + 1} \cdot \ldots \cdot \dfrac{|x|}{(n + 1)}\right).$$

  Argue that, as $n \to \infty$, the factor in the first set of parentheses remains fixed while the factor in the second set of parentheses must approach zero.

  d. Conclude from parts (b) and (c) that

$$\lim_{n \to \infty} |R_n(t)| = 0, \qquad t \le x.$$

  e. Conclude from part (d) that

$$\lim_{n \to \infty} P_n(t) = \sum_{k=1}^{\infty} \dfrac{t^k}{k!} = e^t, \qquad t \le x.$$

  f. Since x was arbitrary in part (a), conclude from part (e) that the Taylor series for e^x converges to e^x for all x.

☑ **SOLUTIONS TO PRACTICE PROBLEMS 9.7**

1. For $a = \dfrac{\pi}{6}$, we have

$$f(a) = \sin\frac{\pi}{6} = \frac{1}{2}$$

$$f'(a) = \cos\frac{\pi}{6} = \frac{\sqrt{3}}{2}$$

$$f''(a) = -\sin\frac{\pi}{6} = -\frac{1}{2}$$

$$f'''(a) = -\cos\frac{\pi}{6} = -\frac{\sqrt{3}}{2}$$

$$f^{(4)}(a) = \sin\frac{\pi}{6} = \frac{1}{2}$$

etc.

Thus

$$\sin x = \frac{1}{2} + \frac{\sqrt{3}}{2}\left(x - \frac{\pi}{6}\right) - \left(\frac{1}{2}\right)^2\left(x - \frac{\pi}{6}\right)^2 - \left(\frac{\sqrt{3}}{2}\right)\left(\frac{1}{3!}\right)\left(x - \frac{\pi}{6}\right)^3$$
$$+ \frac{1}{2}\left(\frac{1}{4!}\right)\left(x - \frac{\pi}{6}\right)^4 + \dots$$

2. We test the series $\displaystyle\sum_{k=1}^{\infty} \frac{1}{k \cdot 2^k} x^k$ for absolute convergence using the Ratio Test:

$$\rho = \lim_{k \to \infty} \frac{\left|\dfrac{1}{(k+1)2^{k+1}} x^{k+1}\right|}{\left|\dfrac{1}{k \cdot 2^k} x^k\right|} = \lim_{k \to \infty} \frac{k}{2(k+1)}|x| = \frac{1}{2}|x|.$$

Thus, $\rho < 1$ is $|x| < 2$. The radius of convergence is therefore $r = 2$, and the interval of convergence is centered about $a = 0$.

At the endpoint $x = 2$, we obtain the series

$$\sum_{k=1}^{\infty} \frac{1}{k \cdot 2^k}(2^k) = \sum_{k=1}^{\infty} \frac{1}{k} = 1 + \frac{1}{2} + \frac{1}{3} + \dots$$

which diverges. (It is the harmonic series.) At the endpoint $x = -2$, we obtain the series

$$\sum_{k=1}^{\infty} \frac{1}{k \cdot 2^k}(-2)^k = -1 + \frac{1}{2} - \frac{1}{3} + \frac{1}{4} - \dots$$

which converges. (It passes the alternating series test.) The interval of convergence is therefore $[-2, 2)$.

9.8 Newton's Method

In solving optimization problems earlier in this book, we needed to be able to find the critical numbers that arise as solutions of the equation $f'(x) = 0$, that is, to find the *zeros* of the derivative f'. This is only one of many circumstances in mathematics in which we need to find the zeros of a particular function. While the techniques of algebra will enable us to find the zeros of certain limited classes of functions (namely, polynomials of degree 4 or less), there is no general method that succeeds in finding the zeros of all, or even most, functions.

Over three centuries ago the famous mathematician and physicist Isaac Newton (1642–1727) discovered a method for *approximating* zeros of functions that can be described in terms of Taylor polynomials. Instead of using the values of a function and its derivatives at a particular number to approximate values of the function at nearby numbers, this method uses an initial approximation for the zero of the function (a number, say, x_1) and values of the function and its derivative at this initial approximation to find a better approximation for the zero, say, x_2. The method is then repeated to generate a **sequence** of approximations $\{x_1, x_2, x_3, x_4, \ldots\}$, which under certain conditions converges to the desired zero of the function.

We may explain the method as follows. Suppose f is a differentiable function, and we wish to approximate a zero of f that is known to lie between the numbers a and b. We make an initial guess for the zero by choosing any number in the interval $[a, b]$, say, x_1. Then, using the function value $f(x_1)$ and the value $f'(x_1)$ of the derivative f' at x_1, we form the first Taylor polynomial

$$P_1(x) = f(x_1) + f'(x_1)(x - x_1) \tag{1}$$

for f at x_1. Figure 8.1 reminds you that the graph of this Taylor polynomial is the line tangent to the graph of f at the point $(x_1, f(x_1))$. Although we do not know the zero c

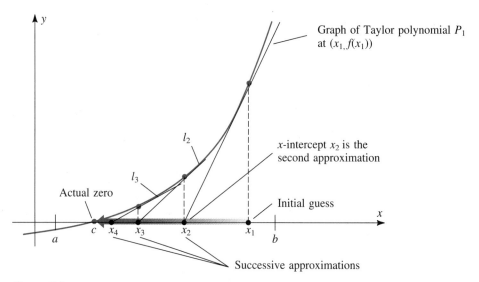

Figure 8.1 Newton's Method for approximating zero of $y = f(x)$.

of the function f, we can use equation (1) to find a zero x_2 for the Taylor polynomial P_1 by solving the equation $P_1(x_2) = 0$. That is, we set

$$P_1(x_2) = f(x_1) + f'(x_1)(x_2 - x_1) = 0$$

and solve to obtain

$$x_2 = x_1 - \frac{f(x_1)}{f'(x_1)}. \tag{2}$$

Newton's famous observation is that, for many functions, this root is a better approximation for the root c of f than is the initial approximation x_1. When this is the case, we may repeat the procedure by forming the first Taylor polynomial $P_1(x)$ for f *at* x_2 and then finding the zero x_3 of this polynomial, which yet will be a better approximation to the zero c of f. Continuing in this way, we generate a sequence of approximations $\{x_n\}$, each of which is obtained from the former via the equation

$$x_{n+1} = x_n - \frac{f(x_n)}{f'(x_n)} \tag{3}$$

Equation (3) is called **the formula for the approximation of a root of the differentiable function f by Newton's Method.**

□ **EXAMPLE 1**

Use Newton's Method to approximate the zero of the function $f(x) = x^3 - 10$ lying between $x = 0$ and $x = 4$.

Strategy · · · · · · · ·

First, verify that a zero exists in $[0, 4]$.

Make an initial guess for the first approximation.

Apply (3), using

$$f'(x) = 3x^2.$$

Solution

Before applying the method, we should verify that the given function indeed has a zero between the given numbers. Since $f(0) = -10$ and $f(4) = 54$ are of opposite sign and f is continuous, $f(x)$ must equal zero for some $x \in (0, 4)$.

We begin by making an initial guess for c, say, $x_1 = 3$. Then, from equation (3), with $n = 1$, we obtain the second approximation

$$x_2 = 3 - \frac{f(3)}{f'(3)}$$

$$= 3 - \frac{(3^3 - 10)}{3(3)^2}$$

$$= 3 - \frac{17}{27} \approx 2.37.$$

Apply (3) again, and so on.

The next approximation, x_3, is obtained from equation (3) by using $x_2 = 2.37$ and $n = 2$:

$$x_3 = 2.37 - \frac{f(2.37)}{f'(2.37)}$$

$$= 2.37 - \frac{(2.37)^3 - 10}{3(2.37)^2}$$

$$\approx 2.17$$

etc. ∎

Although the formula for Newton's Method is simple to state, the hand calculations quickly become tedious and the chance for error grows rapidly. However, this is precisely the sort of problem that is easy to implement on a hand calculator or on a computer. (A BASIC program for implementing Newton's Method is listed in Appendix I.) Table 8.1 contains the results obtained by using a computer to continue the calculations of this example through $n = 4$ iterations.

Table 8.1

n	x_n	$f(x_n)$	$f'(x_n)$	x_{n+1}
1	3.	17.	27.	2.370370
2	2.370370	3.318295	16.855967	2.173509
3	2.173509	0.267958	14.172419	2.154602
4	2.154602	0.002324	13.926924	2.154435

The advantage of listing partial calculations in a table such as this is that each approximation to the zero, x_n (column 2), can be compared directly to the function value (column 3) at each step. The results obtained in the second and fifth columns of Table 8.1 suggest that $x_4 = 2.154602$ is a good approximation to the desired zero.

The next example shows that Newton's Method can be used to approximate roots regardless of where the particular root lies.

☐ **EXAMPLE 2**

Use Newton's Method to approximate $\sqrt[3]{a}$.

Solution: Finding the number x for which $\sqrt[3]{a} = x$ is equivalent to solving the equation $a = x^3$, which in turn is equivalent to finding a zero for the function $f(x) = x^3 - a$. This is the problem treated in Example 1 with $a = 10$. ∎

☐ **EXAMPLE 3**

Use Newton's Method to find the point in the right half plane where the graphs of $f(x) = 2x^3$ and $g(x) = 5x + 1$ intersect (see Figure 8.2).

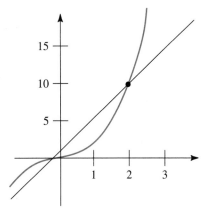

Figure 8.2

Solution: Finding a number x for which

$$2x^3 = 5x + 1$$

is equivalent to finding a zero of the function $h(x) = 2x^3 - (5x + 1)$.

For this function the approximation scheme (3) becomes

$$x_{n+1} = x_n - \frac{2x_n^3 - (5x_n + 1)}{6x_n^2 - 5}.$$

Since $h(0) = -1$ and $h(2) = 5$, we know that a zero must lie within the interval $[0, 2]$. Using a first approximation $x_1 = 2$, we obtain the information contained in Table 8.2 for four iterations of Newton's Method.

Table 8.2

n	x_n	$f(x_n)$	$f'(x_n)$	x_{n+1}
1	2.0	5.0	19.0	1.736842
2	1.736842	0.794576	13.099723	1.676186
3	1.676186	0.037894	11.857599	1.672990
4	1.672990	0.000103	11.793380	1.672982

The desired point of intersection is approximately $(1.672982, 9.364910)$. ■

When the approximations produced by Newton's Method approach the desired zero, we say that the method **converges** to that zero. Unfortunately, depending on the function and the initial approximation, Newton's Method may not converge to the desired zero. We comment on some of the reasons for this here, and pursue some of the details in the Exercise Set.

1. The function may have more than one zero. Depending on the initial approximation x_1, the method may converge to a zero other than the one desired (see Figure 8.3).
2. An approximation x_k may be obtained for which $f'(x_k) = 0$. In this case the denominator in the expression for x_{k+1} is zero, so the method fails.
3. The slope of the graph of f may be such that the approximations simply do not converge, but instead move away from the desired zero (see Figure 8.4 and Exercise 15), or simply oscillate between two or more distinct approximations.

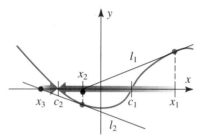

Figure 8.3 Initial approximation x_1 leads to zero c_2, where zero c_1 was desired.

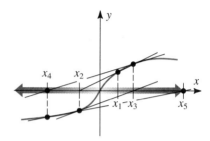

Figure 8.4 Iterates move away from zero rather than converging.

Newton's Method is not a theorem, but rather, a procedure that produces useful approximations in a large number of cases and that, unfortunately, fails in other cases. The fact that the method does not converge for all functions is not a criticism of Newton's idea, but rather, an invitation to you to pursue a deeper study of the geometric and analytic properties of functions that allow techniques such as Newton's Method to succeed. The relevant courses in which to pursue these issues are those on advanced calculus, numerical analysis, and modern analysis.

☑ PRACTICE PROBLEMS 9.8

1. Use Newton's Method to approximate $\sqrt{7}$.
2. Use Newton's Method to estimate the zeros of the function $f(x) = e^x + x - 4$.

Exercise Set 9.8

In Exercises 1–8, use Newton's Method to approximate the zero of the given function lying between the given values $x = a$ and $x = b$. In each case first verify that such a zero indeed exists. If a calculator or computer is not available to you, only two or three iterations should be performed. If a calculator or computer is available, a table such as Table 8.1 should be constructed.

1. $f(x) = x^2 - \dfrac{7}{2}x + \dfrac{3}{4}, \quad a = 0, \quad b = 2$

2. $f(x) = 1 - x - x^2, \quad a = -2, \quad b = -1$

3. $f(x) = 1 - x - x^2, \quad a = 0, \quad b = 1$

4. $f(x) = x^3 + x - 3, \quad a = 1, \quad b = 2$

5. $f(x) = \sqrt{x + 3} - x, \quad a = 1, \quad b = 3$

6. $f(x) = x^3 + x^2 + 3, \quad a = -3, \quad b = -1$

7. $f(x) = x^4 - 5, \quad a = -2, \quad b = -1$

8. $f(x) = 5 - x^4$, $a = 1$, $b = 2$

9. Use the results of Exercise 5 to find a point of intersection between the graphs of $f(x) = \sqrt{x + 3}$ and $g(x) = x$.

10. Use Newton's Method to approximate

    a. $\sqrt{40}$ **b.** $\sqrt[3]{49}$

    c. $\sqrt[5]{18}$ **d.** $\sqrt{37}$

11. What results from applying Newton's Method if the (lucky) first guess is precisely the desired zero?

12. Use a calculator or computer to find an approximation to the point where the graphs of $f(x) = 2x$ and $g(x) = \tan x$ intersect for $0 < x \le \dfrac{\pi}{2}$.

13. Attempt to use Newton's Method to find the zero of $f(x) = (x - 2)^{1/3}$ with initial guess $x_1 = 3$. What happens? Why?

14. The graphs of the functions f and g in Example 3 cross at two other points. Find them.

✓ **SOLUTIONS TO PRACTICE PROBLEMS 9.8**

1. Finding $\sqrt{7}$ is equivalent to solving the equation $x^2 = 7$ for the positive root or to finding the positive zero of the function $f(x) = x^2 - 7$.

Since $f(2) = 2^2 - 7 = -3$ and $f(3) = 3^2 - 7 = 2$, we know the desired zero lies in the interval $(2, 3)$. Taking the midpoint $x_1 = 2.5$ as our first approximation, we obtain

$$x_2 = x_1 - \frac{f(x_1)}{f'(x_1)}$$

$$= 2.5 - \frac{[(2.5)^2 - 7]}{2(2.5)}$$

$$= 2.65.$$

Similarly, we obtain the successive approximations listed in Table 8.3.

Table 8.3

n	x_n
1	2.5
2	2.65
3	2.6202
4	2.7965
5	2.6498
6	2.6457

Table 8.4

n	x_n
1	1
2	1.0758
3	1.0737
4	1.0737

The exact value, to four decimal places is 2.6457.

2. By examining the first derivative $f'(x) = e^x + 1 > 0$, we can see that f is always increasing. This, together with the observation that $f(0) = -3 < 0$ and $f(2) \approx 5.39 > 0$ tells us that the single zero of f lies between 0 and 2. Newton's formula becomes

$$x_{n+1} = x_n - \frac{f(x_n)}{f'(x_n)} = x_n - \left(\frac{e^{x_n} + x_n - 4}{e^{x_n} + 1} \right)$$

and, with initial approximation $x_1 = 1$, we obtain the information in Table 8.4.

Summary Outline of Chapter 9

▌ An **infinite sequence** is a function whose domain is the positive integers. (Page 636)

▌ L is the **limit** of the sequence $\{a_n\}$, written $L = \lim\limits_{n\to\infty} a_n$ if the terms a_n approach the unique number L as n increases without bound. (Page 638)

▌ Properties of limits of sequences: (Page 639)

$\quad$ (i) $\lim\limits_{n\to\infty} \{a_n + b_n\} = \lim\limits_{n\to\infty} \{a_n\} + \lim\limits_{n\to\infty} \{b_n\}$

$\quad$ (ii) $\lim\limits_{n\to\infty} \{ca_n\} = c \cdot \lim\limits_{n\to\infty} \{a_n\}$

$\quad$ (iii) $\lim\limits_{n\to\infty} \{a_n b_n\} = \left(\lim\limits_{n\to\infty} \{a_n\} \right) \left(\lim\limits_{n\to\infty} \{b_n\} \right)$

$\quad$ (iv) $\lim\limits_{n\to\infty} \left\{ \dfrac{a_n}{b_n} \right\} = \dfrac{\lim\limits_{n\to\infty} \{a_n\}}{\lim\limits_{n\to\infty} \{b_n\}}, \qquad$ provided $\lim\limits_{n\to\infty} \{b_n\} \neq 0,$

assuming that the limits on the right-hand sides of the equations exist.

▌ An **infinite series** is an expression of the form (Page 649)

$$\sum_{k=1}^{\infty} a_k = a_1 + a_2 + a_3 + \dots.$$

▌ The **partial sum** S_n of an infinite series $\sum\limits_{k=1}^{\infty} a_k$ is (Page 649)

$$S_n = \sum_{k=1}^{n} a_k, \qquad n = 1, 2, \dots.$$

▌ The infinite series $\Sigma\, a_k$ **converges** if the limit (Page 649)

$$S = \lim_{n\to\infty} S_n = \lim_{n\to\infty} \sum_{k=1}^{n} a_k$$

exists.

▌ *Theorem:* The **geometric series** (Page 651)

$$\sum_{k=0}^{\infty} x^k = 1 + x + x^2 + x^3 + \dots$$

$\quad$ (i) converges to the sum $\dfrac{1}{1-x} = \sum\limits_{k=0}^{\infty} x^k$ if $|x| < 1$

$\quad$ (ii) diverges if $|x| \geq 1.$

■ *Theorem (Integral Test):* Let $a_k \geq 0$ for all k and let f be a continu- (Page 660)
ous decreasing function with $f(k) = a_k$ for $k = 1, 2, \ldots$. Then,

$$\sum a_k \text{ converges if and only if } \int_1^\infty f(x)\, dx \text{ converges.}$$

■ The **harmonic** series (Page 661)

$$\sum_{k=1}^\infty \frac{1}{k} = 1 + \frac{1}{2} + \frac{1}{3} + \frac{1}{4} + \ldots$$

diverges.

■ The *p*-series $\displaystyle\sum_{k=1}^\infty \frac{1}{k^p} = 1 + \frac{1}{2^p} + \frac{1}{3^p} + \frac{1}{4^p} + \ldots, p > 0$ converges (Page 662)
only if $p > 1$.

■ *Theorem (Comparison Test):* Let $\Sigma\, a_k$ and $\Sigma\, b_k$ be series with (Page 663)

$$0 < a_k \leq b_k$$

for each $k = 1, 2, 3, \ldots$. Then,

(a) If $\Sigma\, b_k$ converges, so does $\Sigma\, a_k$.
(b) If $\Sigma\, a_k$ diverges, so does $\Sigma\, b_k$.

■ *Theorem (Limit Comparison Test):* Let $\Sigma\, a_k$ and $\Sigma\, b_k$ be series with (Page 665)
positive terms. If the limit $\rho = \displaystyle\lim_{k\to\infty} \frac{a_k}{b_k}$ exists and is nonzero, then either both series converge or both series diverge.

■ *Theorem (Necessary Condition):* If the series $\Sigma\, a_k$ converges, then (Page 667)
$\displaystyle\lim_{k\to\infty} a_k = 0$.

■ *Theorem (Ratio Test):* Let $\Sigma\, a_k$ be a series with positive terms and (Page 670)
let ρ be the limit

$$\rho = \lim_{k\to\infty} \frac{a_{k+1}}{a_k}.$$

Then

(i) If $0 \leq \rho < 1$ the series $\Sigma\, a_k$ converges.
(ii) If $\rho > 1$ the series $\Sigma\, a_k$ diverges.
(iii) If $\rho = 1$ there is no conclusion.

■ *Theorem (Alternating Series Test):* Let $a_k > 0$ for all k. The alter- (Page 675)
nating series $\displaystyle\sum (-1)^k a_k$ converges if and only if both

(i) $a_k > a_{k+1}$ for all k with $k \geq K$ (K fixed)
(ii) $\displaystyle\lim_{k\to\infty} a_k = 0$.

■ The series $\Sigma\, a_k$ is said to **converge absolutely** if $\Sigma\, |a_k|$ converges. (Page 667)

■ ***Theorem:*** If the series $\Sigma\, |a_k|$ converges, so does the series $\Sigma\, a_k$. (Page 678)

■ The ***n*th Taylor polynomial** for f expanded about $x = a$ is (Page 690)

$$P_n(x) = \sum_{k=0}^{n} \frac{f^{(k)}(a)}{k!}(x - a)^k$$

$$= f(a) + f'(a)(x - a) + \frac{f''(a)}{2}(x - a)^2$$

$$+ \ldots + \frac{f^{(n)}(a)}{n!}(x - a)^n.$$

■ **Taylor's Theorem** states that if $R_n(x) = f(x) - P_n(x)$, then under ap- (Page 695)
propriate conditions

$$|R_n(x)| \le \frac{M}{(n + 1)!}|x - a|^{n+1}$$

where the constant M is determined by the derivative $f^{(n+1)}$.

■ The **Taylor series** for f expanded about $x = a$ is (Page 703)

$$\sum_{k=0}^{\infty} \frac{f^{(k)}(a)}{k!}(x - a)^k = f(a) + f'(a)(x - a)$$

$$+ \frac{f''(a)}{2}(x - a)^2$$

$$+ \frac{f'''(a)}{3!}(x - a)^3 + \ldots.$$

■ A **power series** is a series of the form (Page 709)

$$\sum_{k=0}^{\infty} c_k(x - a)^k$$

where c_k is constant, $k = 0, 1, 2, \ldots.$

■ **Newton's Method** for approximating a zero of a differentiable func- (Page 717)
tion f uses the sequence of approximations

$$x_{n+1} = x_n - \frac{f(x_n)}{f'(x_n)}$$

Review Exercises—Chapter 9

In Exercises 1–8, determine whether the given sequence converges. If it does, find its limit.

1. $\left\{ \sin \dfrac{n\pi}{2} \right\}$

2. $\left\{ \dfrac{1}{\sqrt{n} + 5} \right\}$

3. $\{ \ln \sqrt{n} - \ln n \}$

4. $\left\{ \left(1 + \dfrac{1}{n} \right)^{2n} \right\}$

5. $\left\{ \dfrac{n^2 + n - 5}{4 + 2n^2} \right\}$

6. $\left\{ \dfrac{4 + \sqrt{n}}{n^{2/3} + 3} \right\}$

7. $\left\{ \dfrac{3^n + 4^n}{5^n} \right\}$

8. $\{\ln n - \ln(n + 1)\}$

In Exercises 9–12, find the sum of the series.

9. $\displaystyle\sum_{k=0}^{\infty} \dfrac{1}{3^k}$

10. $\displaystyle\sum_{k=0}^{\infty} \dfrac{1 + 3^k}{5^k}$

11. $\displaystyle\sum_{k=1}^{\infty} \dfrac{3^k}{2^k}$

12. $\displaystyle\sum_{k=1}^{\infty} \dfrac{7}{4^k}$

In Exercises 13–30, determine whether the series converges or diverges, and state which test you used.

13. $\displaystyle\sum_{k=1}^{\infty} \dfrac{1}{1 + k^2}$

14. $\displaystyle\sum_{k=1}^{\infty} \dfrac{1}{k(k + 1)}$

15. $\displaystyle\sum_{k=1}^{\infty} \dfrac{3^k}{k^2}$

16. $\displaystyle\sum_{k=1}^{\infty} \dfrac{3^{2k}}{k^3}$

17. $\displaystyle\sum_{k=1}^{\infty} \dfrac{k^2}{k!}$

18. $\displaystyle\sum_{k=0}^{\infty} \dfrac{k^2}{k^2 + 3}$

19. $\displaystyle\sum_{k=0}^{\infty} \dfrac{k - 1}{k + 1}$

20. $\displaystyle\sum_{k=0}^{\infty} \dfrac{3}{k + 2}$

21. $\displaystyle\sum_{k=1}^{\infty} \dfrac{1}{\sqrt{k + 1}}$

22. $\displaystyle\sum_{k=2}^{\infty} \dfrac{1}{k \ln k}$

23. $\displaystyle\sum_{k=4}^{\infty} \dfrac{1}{k^2 + 1}$

24. $\displaystyle\sum_{k=1}^{\infty} \dfrac{(-1)^k}{2k + 1}$

25. $\displaystyle\sum_{k=0}^{\infty} \dfrac{(-1)^k k}{\sqrt{k + 1}}$

26. $\displaystyle\sum_{k=0}^{\infty} \dfrac{\cos \pi k^2}{k + 1}$

27. $\displaystyle\sum_{k=1}^{\infty} \dfrac{k \cdot 2^k}{k!}$

28. $\displaystyle\sum_{k=1}^{\infty} (-1)^{k+1} \dfrac{\sqrt{k}}{k + 2}$

29. $\displaystyle\sum_{k=0}^{\infty} \dfrac{1}{(k + 2)^{3/2}}$

30. $\displaystyle\sum_{k=1}^{\infty} \dfrac{(-1)^k k}{(k + 1)!}$

In Exercises 31–38, find the nth Taylor polynomial for the function f expanded about $x = a$.

31. $f(x) = e^{-3x}, \quad a = 0, \quad n = 3$

32. $f(x) = \cos x, \quad a = \dfrac{\pi}{6}, \quad n = 3$

33. $f(x) = \tan x, \quad a = 0, \quad n = 2$

34. $f(x) = e^{x^2}, \quad a = 0, \quad n = 3$

35. $f(x) = \ln(1 + x^2), \quad a = 0, \quad n = 2$

36. $f(x) = \sin x, \quad a = \dfrac{\pi}{6}, \quad n = 3$

37. $f(x) = \sqrt{x}, \quad a = 9, \quad n = 3$

38. $f(x) = \sec x, \quad a = \dfrac{\pi}{4}, \quad n = 3$

39. Find a Taylor series for the function $f(x) = xe^x$ expanded about $x = 0$.

40. For which values of x does the Taylor series in Exercise 39 converge?

41. Find a Taylor series for the function $f(x) = \dfrac{x}{1 - x}$ expanded about $a = 0$.

42. For which numbers x does the Taylor series in Exercise 41 converge?

43. Find the Taylor series for the polynomial $f(x) = x^3 + 2x^2 - x + 3$
a. expanded about $x = 0$.
b. expanded about $x = 1$.

44. a. Express the repeating decimal $0.7\overline{777} \ldots$ as a geometric series.
b. Use the formula for the sum of a geometric series to find the rational number $\dfrac{p}{q}$ to which the series in part a converges.

45. An annuity is to pay \$500 at the end of year 1, one third of this amount at the end of year 2, and, at the end of each succeeding year, one third of the amount paid in the preceding year. What is the total amount paid by the annuity in perpetuity?

46. Use Newton's Method to approximate the solution of $x^2 - x - 1 = 0$ lying in the interval $[0, 2]$.

47. Use Newton's Method to approximate the solution of $\cot x = x$ lying in the interval $\left(0, \dfrac{\pi}{2}\right]$.

48. Use Newton's Method to approximate $\sqrt[3]{175}$.

49. Use Newton's Method to approximate the maximum value of the function $f(x) = x \sin x$ for $x \in [0, 3]$. (*Hint:* What condition holds for f' at a maximum value for f?)

50. A perpetual bond provides an interest payment of $100 per year forever. Assuming a continuing discount rate of 6%, the present value of an interest payment occurring in n years is $P(n) = 100e^{-0.06n}$ dollars. What is the present value of this entire revenue stream?

51. A ball is dropped from a height of 10 feet. Each time it strikes the ground it rebounds to $\frac{5}{6}$ of the height from which it last fell. Find the total distance traveled by the ball
  a. when it has struck the ground three times, and
  b. when it has come to rest.

CHAPTER

10

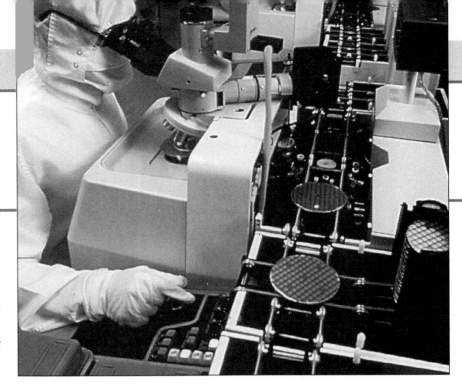

This photograph was taken in a "clean room" where computer chips are fabricated. Controlling the number of dust particles in the air in a clean room requires an understanding of "mixing" problems, an application of differential equations. *(Steve Dunwell/The Image Bank)*

Differential Equations

10.1 Introduction to Differential Equations

In Chapter 3 we introduced the notion of the derivative f' of the function f as the *rate of change* of f. Applications involving this rate of change have included the following:

(i) The derivative $MC(x) = C'(x)$ is the rate at which total cost C changes with respect to change in the quantity x.

(ii) The derivative $P'(t)$ gives the rate at which the size P of a population changes with respect to change in time t.

(iii) The derivative $v(t) = s'(t)$ gives the velocity of an object that is moving along a line and that is located at a distance $s(t)$ from the origin at time t. That is, $v(t)$ is the rate of change of position with respect to change in time.

When we attempt to develop mathematical models describing biological, economic, or physical processes, we often begin by describing the relationship between a certain function of interest (such as population size) and a growth rate (such as population growth) associated with that function. This leads to an equation such as

$$P'(t) = kP(t) \tag{1}$$

which we referred to as the *Law of Natural Growth* for the size of a population $P(t)$ in Section 4.5. That is, we obtain an equation involving one or more derivatives of a function (as well as, perhaps, the function itself and possibly even other functions). Such equations are called **differential equations.**

Thus a differential equation is an equation involving one or more derivatives of an unknown function. A **solution** of a differential equation is a function that is differentiable as many times as the equation requires and that satisfies the equation when substituted for the unknown and its derivatives.

☐ **EXAMPLE 1**

In Chapter 4 we saw that a solution of the differential equation $P'(t) = kP(t)$ in equation (1) has the form $P(t) = Ce^{kt}$ where C is an arbitrary constant. To verify that this function satisfies equation (1), we calculate

$$P'(t) = \frac{d}{dt}(Ce^{kt}) = C \cdot ke^{kt} = k(Ce^{kt}) = kP(t).$$

It can be proved that *every* function that satisfies equation (1) has the form $P(t) = Ce^{kt}$. ■

☐ **EXAMPLE 2**

The function $y = \sin x$ satisfies the differential equation $\dfrac{d^2y}{dx^2} + y = 0$. To show this, we compute the second derivative:

$$\frac{dy}{dx} = \cos x \quad \text{so} \quad \frac{d^2y}{dx^2} = -\sin x.$$

Thus substitution in the differential equation gives

$$\frac{d^2y}{dx^2} + y = (-\sin x) + \sin x$$

$$= 0$$

as required. Thus $y = \sin x$ is a solution of the differential equation. ■

Order

The **order** of a differential equation is the order of the highest derivative in the equation. Thus equation (1) is a **first order** differential equation, while the equation in Example 2 is of **second order.** We shall not consider differential equations of order higher than two in this text.

Solutions of Differential Equations

If a differential equation has any solutions at all, then it generally has infinitely many solutions, for the same reason that a given function has infinitely many antiderivatives. For example, consider the simple differential equation

$$\frac{dy}{dx} = 2x + 1. \tag{2}$$

For this differential equation it's easy to compute the antiderivative on each side, and we get

$$\int \left(\frac{dy}{dx}\right) dx = \int (2x + 1)\, dx$$

$$y = x^2 + x + C. \tag{3}$$

The constant of integration C can take any one of an infinite number of real values. For each value of C we obtain a different equation (2) called a *particular solution*. The form (3), which expresses all of the particular solutions in one compact expression, is called the *general solution* of (2). Two particular solutions of (2) are

$$y_1 = x^2 + x + 7 \quad \text{and} \quad y_2 = x^2 + x + \pi.$$

You can verify by differentiating both of these functions, and the general solution (3), that all of them indeed satisfy the differential equation (2).

In general, we expect to find one arbitrary constant in the general solution of a first order differential equation and two arbitrary constants in the general solution of a second order differential equation.

□ **EXAMPLE 3**

In Example 2 we showed that the function $y_1 = \sin x$ is a particular solution of the differential equation

$$\frac{d^2 y}{dx^2} + y = 0.$$

Another particular solution is

$$y_2 = \cos x.$$

To see this, note that $\dfrac{dy_2}{dx} = -\sin x$ and $\dfrac{d^2 y_2}{dx^2} = -\cos x$, so

$$\frac{d^2 y_2}{dx^2} + y_2 = -\cos x + \cos x = 0$$

as required.

In fact, the general solution of this differential equation is the following:

$$y = C_1 y_1 + C_2 y_2$$

$$= C_1 \sin x + C_2 \cos x \tag{4}$$

where C_1 and C_2 are arbitrary (and independent) constants. To see that this function is a solution of the differential equation, we note that

$$\frac{dy}{dx} = C_1 \cos x - C_2 \sin x$$

and

$$\frac{d^2y}{dx^2} = -C_1 \sin x - C_2 \cos x$$

so

$$\frac{d^2y}{dx^2} + y = (-C_1 \sin x - C_2 \cos x) + (C_1 \sin x + C_2 \cos x)$$

$$= 0$$

as required. It is a fact, which we shall not prove, that any particular solution of this differential equation has the form of the function y in equation (4), with specific values of C_1 and C_2. For instance, the particular solution $y_1 = \sin x$ has $C_1 = 1$ and $C_2 = 0$. ■

☐ **EXAMPLE 4**

A particular solution of the differential equation

$$\frac{d^2y}{dx^2} + 2\frac{dy}{dx} - 3y = 0$$

is $y_1 = e^{-3x}$. This is because

$$\frac{dy_1}{dx} = -3e^{-3x} \qquad \text{and} \qquad \frac{d^2y_1}{dx^2} = 9e^{-3x}$$

so

$$\frac{d^2y_1}{dx^2} + 2\frac{dy_1}{dx} - 3y_1 = 9e^{-3x} + 2(-3e^{-3x}) - 3e^{-3x}$$

$$= (9 - 6 - 3)e^{-3x}$$

$$= 0.$$

A second solution is $y_2 = e^x$. We leave this for you to verify, as well as the fact that the general solution

$$y = C_1 e^{-3x} + C_2 e^x$$

satisfies the differential equation. ■

Initial Value Problems

Once the general solution of a differential equation is known, a particular solution may be determined if information about the value of a solution, and possibly of its derivative(s), at a particular number x is given. For example, the general solution of the differential equation

$$f'(x) = 3f(x) \tag{5}$$

is $f(x) = Ce^{3x}$. If we are given the additional information that

$$f(0) = 5 \tag{6}$$

we can substitute $x = 0$ in the general solution and use equation (6) to conclude that

$$f(0) = Ce^{3 \cdot 0} = Ce^0 = C = 5$$

so the particular solution of equation (5) satisfying the *initial value* $f(0) = 5$ in equation (6) is

$$f(x) = 5e^{3x}.$$

An **initial value** is simply the value of a solution, or of one of its derivatives, at a particular number x (not necessarily zero). For a first order differential equation, one initial value (a value of the solution) is required to determine a particular solution from the general solution. For a second order differential equation, we must specify two initial values (the value of the solution and the value of its derivative, at the *same* number x) in order to determine a particular solution. A differential equation, together with enough initial values to determine a unique particular solution, is called an **initial value problem.**

□ **EXAMPLE 5**

Solve the initial value problem

$$\frac{dy}{dt} = 3t^2 + 2 \tag{7}$$

$$y(0) = 5.$$

Solution: Since the right-hand side of equation (7) is a function of the independent variable t alone, we find the general solution by integration:

$$\int \left(\frac{dy}{dt}\right) dt = \int (3t^2 + 2) \, dt$$

$$y(t) = t^3 + 2t + C.$$

We determine the constant C by setting $t = 0$ in the general solution and substituting the initial value $y(0) = 5$:

$$y(0) = 0^3 + 2 \cdot 0 + C = C = 5.$$

Thus $C = 5$, and the solution of the initial value problem is

$$y = t^3 + 2t + 5.$$ ■

☐ **EXAMPLE 6**

A manufacturer of dehumidifiers determines that its marginal cost of producing units at production level x units per week is $MC(x) = 70 + 0.2x$ dollars per unit. Find its total cost $C(x)$ in producing x units per week if its fixed cost of production is $C(0) = \$2000$ per week.

Solution: Since marginal cost is the derivative $MC(x) = C'(x)$ of total cost, we must solve the initial value problem:

$$C'(x) = 70 + 0.2x \tag{8}$$

$$C(0) = 2000. \tag{9}$$

The general solution C of equation (8) is found by integration:

$$\int C'(x)\, dx = \int (70 + 0.2x)\, dx$$

$$C(x) = 70x + 0.1x^2 + K$$

where K is a constant. To determine the constant K, we set $x = 0$ in the expression for $C(x)$ and use equation (9):

$$C(0) = 70 \cdot 0 + (0.1) \cdot 0^2 + K = 2000$$

so $K = 2000$. The solution is therefore

$$C(x) = 70x + 0.1x^2 + 2000 \text{ dollars per week.}$$ ■

Graphical Solutions

We can sometimes get a notion of the behavior of the solutions of a first order differential equation by remembering that the derivative f' gives the slope of the line tangent to the graph of f. If the form of the differential equation allows us to determine values of the derivative f' corresponding to particular points in the xy-plane, we can sketch in small tangent lines with slopes f' at various points. The resulting sketch, called a **direction field,** helps us develop an idea of how graphs of various solutions must behave.

☐ **EXAMPLE 7**

Figure 1.1 shows tangents sketched onto the plane as determined by the differential equation

$$\frac{dy}{dx} = \frac{1}{2}y. \tag{10}$$

Slopes of these tangents are obtained by selecting various numbers y and noting that the corresponding slope is always half of the selected number y. $\Big($Note that the slopes do not depend on x, since x does not appear in the expression for $\dfrac{dy}{dx}$.$\Big)$ Figure 1.2 shows several solution curves $y = Ce^{x/2}$ associated with the differential equation (10), for various values of C.   ■

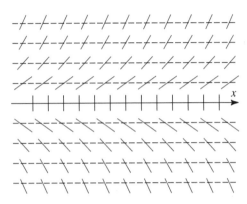

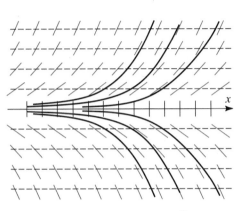

Figure 1.1 Direction field for differential equation

$$\frac{dy}{dx} = \frac{1}{2}y.$$

Figure 1.2 Solution curves $y = Ce^{x/2}$ through direction field in Figure 1.1.

☐ **EXAMPLE 8**

Figures 1.3 and 1.4 show the direction field and several corresponding solution curves for the logistic differential equation

$$\frac{dy}{dx} = y(1 - y).$$

Note that the derivative equals zero for $y = 0$ and $y = 1$, and that the sign of the derivative $\dfrac{dy}{dx}$ is

(i) negative for $y > 1$, since $1 - y < 0$.
(ii) positive for $0 < y < 1$, since $1 - y > 0$.
(iii) negative for $y < 0$, since $1 - y > 0$.

We shall show in Section 10.2 how the technique of separation of variables can be used to find explicit solutions of this differential equation.   ■

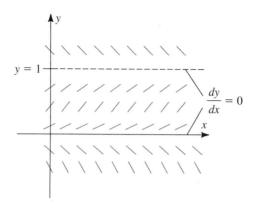

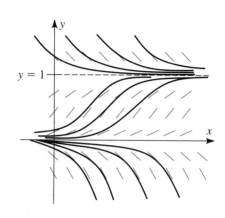

Figure 1.3 Direction field for differential equation

Figure 1.4 Solution curves associated with direction field in Figure 1.3.

$$\frac{dy}{dx} = y(1 - y).$$

□ **EXAMPLE 9**

Figures 1.5 and 1.6 show the direction field and several solution curves associated with the differential equation

$$\frac{dy}{dx} = 2xy. \tag{11}$$

Using a technique to be developed later in this chapter we can show that solutions of (11) must have the form

$$y = Ce^{x^2} \tag{12}$$

which you can verify by direction substitution.

Figure 1.6 shows several solution curves of the form in equation (12). If we specify an initial condition for equation (11), such as the condition

$$y(0) = 1 \tag{13}$$

then we obtain a particular solution to the initial value problem consisting of equations (11) and (13). (Figure 1.6 shows the corresponding solution curve as highlighted.) ■

☑ **PRACTICE PROBLEMS 10.1**

1. Find the general solution of the differential equation

$$\frac{dy}{dt} = t \cos t^2.$$

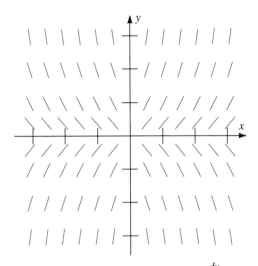

Figure 1.5 Direction field for equation $\dfrac{dy}{dx} = 2xy$.
(Note that slopes depend on both x and y coordinates.)

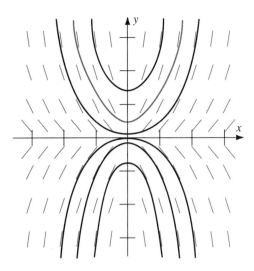

Figure 1.6 Some solution curves for equation $\dfrac{dy}{dx} = 2xy$. Solution with initial condition $y(0) = 1$ is highlighted.

2. Find the solution of the initial value problem

$$\frac{dy}{dx} = 7y$$

$$y(0) = 3.$$

Exercise Set 10.1

In Exercises 1–10, verify that the given general solution satisfies the differential equation.

1. $\dfrac{dy}{dx} = \pi y; \quad y = Ce^{\pi x}$

2. $\dfrac{dy}{dx} = \dfrac{x}{y}; \quad y = \sqrt{x^2 + C}$

3. $\dfrac{d^2y}{dx^2} + 9y = 0; \quad y = A \sin 3x + B \cos 3x$

4. $f''(t) - 16f(t) = 0; \quad f(t) = Ae^{4t} + Be^{-4t}$

5. $\dfrac{dy}{dt} = 2 - 4y; \quad y = \dfrac{1}{2} + Ce^{-4t}$

6. $f'(t) = 2 - 0.02f(t); \quad f(t) = 100 + Ce^{-0.02t}$

7. $\dfrac{dy}{dx} = 10(22 - y); \quad y = 22 - Ce^{-10x}$

8. $\dfrac{d^2y}{dx^2} - 5\dfrac{dy}{dx} - 6y = 0; \quad y = Ae^{-2x} + Be^{+3x}$

9. $f''(t) + 4f'(t) + 4f(t) = 0; \quad f(t) = Ae^{-2t} + Bte^{-2t}$

10. $\dfrac{dy}{dt} + 2ty = t; \quad y = Ce^{-t^2} + \dfrac{1}{2}$

In Exercises 11–16, find the general solution of the given differential equation by integration.

11. $\dfrac{dy}{dx} = 9 - x$

12. $f'(t) = e^{2t} + 2\sqrt{t} + 5$

13. $\dfrac{dy}{dt} = te^t$

14. $\dfrac{dy}{dx} = \sec x \tan x$

15. $\dfrac{d^2y}{dt^2} = \dfrac{t+1}{\sqrt{t}}, \quad t > 0$

16. $\dfrac{d^2y}{dt^2} = \cos t - \sin t$

In Exercises 17–20, solve the initial value problem.

17. $\dfrac{dy}{dx} = x\sqrt{x^2 + 1}$
  $y(0) = 1$

18. $\dfrac{dy}{dx} = \dfrac{x}{y}$
  $y(0) = 1$
  (See Exercise 2.)

19. $\dfrac{dy}{dt} = 2 - 4y$
  $y(0) = 3$
  (See Exercise 5.)

20. $\dfrac{dy}{dt} = \sec^2 t$
  $y(0) = \pi$

In Exercises 21–24, sketch a direction field for the differential equation and several solution curves.

21. $\dfrac{dy}{dx} = -y$

22. $\dfrac{dy}{dx} = y(4 - y)$

23. $\dfrac{dy}{dx} = y(y - 3)$

24. $f'(t) = 1 - f(t)$

25. The value of a bottle of a certain rare wine is increasing at a rate of $\sqrt{t+1}$ dollars per year when the wine is t years old. The wine sold for $5 per bottle when new.

a. Write an initial value problem that determines the value $V(t)$ of the bottle of wine after t years.

b. Find the solution of this initial value problem.

26. Catherine and Sue run a small company that produces executive calendars. They determine that their marginal cost in producing x calendars per day is $MC(x) = 2x$ dollars and that their fixed costs of operation are $400 per day.

a. Write an initial value problem that determines their total daily costs, $C(x)$.

b. Find the solution of this initial value problem.

27. Students in a psychology class are studying the concept of utility, the satisfaction derived from the consumption of a certain good. In conducting an experiment involving eating pizzas, the students conclude that an individual's utility from the consumption of x pizzas is determined by the marginal utility function $MU(x) = 6 - 2x$. Let $U(x)$ be the individual's utility function, so that $U'(x) = MU(x)$.

a. Write an initial value problem describing the individual's utility function, assuming that the utility of no pizzas is zero, that is, $U(0) = 0$.

b. Solve the initial value problem.

c. Based on your solution, would the individual who had consumed 3 pizzas be inclined to eat a fourth? A fifth? Why or why not?

28. Find a differential equation satisfied by the family of functions

a. $f(t) = Ce^{6t}$

b. $f(t) = A \sin 3t + B \cos 3t$

☑ **SOLUTIONS TO PRACTICE PROBLEMS 10.1**

1. To solve the differential equation $\dfrac{dy}{dt} = t \cos t^2$ we integrate both sides:

$$y = \int t \cos t^2 \, dt$$

$$= \frac{1}{2} \int \cos t^2 \cdot 2t \, dt$$

$$= \frac{1}{2} \sin t^2 + C.$$

This is the general solution.

2. The general solution of the differential equation $\dfrac{dy}{dx} = 7y$ is Ce^{7x}. To find the particular solution satisfying the initial condition $y(0) = 3$, we substitute $x = 0$ and $y = 3$ into the general solution:

$$3 = Ce^{7 \cdot 0} = Ce^0 = C.$$

Thus, $y = 3e^{7x}$.

10.2 Applications to Population Growth

The Law of Natural Growth (Section 4.5) describes situations in which the rate of change of a quantity is proportional to its current size. There are other possible relationships between rate of change and size. We consider two such types of growth models in this section, both of which lead to solutions involving exponential functions.

Limited Growth

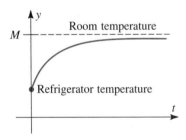

Figure 2.1 Rise of temperature $y(t)$ as a function of time for a cool drink placed in a warm room.

Figure 2.1 shows what happens to the temperature of a cool drink when it is removed from a refrigerator and placed in a warm room. Note that the temperature rises rapidly at first, but increases more slowly as it approaches room temperature. This phenomenon is an example of Newton's law of cooling, which states that the rate at which the temperature of the drink will change is proportional to the *difference* between its current temperature and that of its surrounding environment. In mathematical terms this law can be stated

$$\frac{dy}{dt} = k(M - y) \tag{1}$$

where $y(t)$ is the temperature of the drink at time t, M is the temperature in the room, and k is a constant.

A second example of such models is the "learning curve" in Figure 2.2. In this case the function y represents an individual's typing speed t days after beginning a first course on typing. Here speed increases most rapidly in the beginning, then slows as the individual's natural maximum speed is approached. Curves such as those in Figures 2.1 and 2.2 are referred to as *diffusion* curves by sociologists because they model the way certain types of information or propaganda spread throughout a population—rapidly at first, then more slowly as nearly everyone comes to know the information.

The solution of the differential equation

$$\frac{dy}{dt} = k(M - y)$$

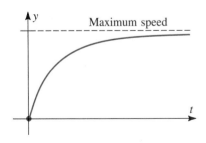

Figure 2.2 "Learning curve" for typing speed t days after beginning instruction.

has the form

$$y(t) = M(1 - Ce^{-kt}) \tag{2}$$

where C is a constant. (You are asked to verify this in Exercise 22.) When each of the constants M, C, and k is positive, the derivative

$$\frac{dy}{dt} = kMCe^{-kt}$$

is positive for all t. Thus the solution y is increasing for all t. Moreover, the second derivative

$$\frac{d^2y}{dt^2} = -k^2MCe^{-kt}$$

is negative for all t, so the graph of y is concave down for all t. Finally, since $\lim\limits_{t\to\infty} e^{-kt} = \lim\limits_{t\to\infty} \frac{1}{e^{kt}} = 0$, we have

$$\lim_{t\to\infty} y(t) = \lim_{t\to\infty} M(1 - Ce^{-kt})$$

$$= M(1 - C \cdot 0)$$

$$= M.$$

Thus the values of the solution y approach the number M as t becomes large. (See Figure 2.3.) For this reason M is sometimes called the **carrying capacity** of the system that is being modelled by equation (1), which is called the **Law of Limited Growth.**

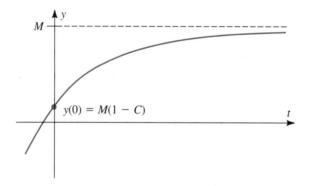

Figure 2.3 Graph of the function $y = M(1 - Ce^{-kt})$ for M, C, and k positive. This function is increasing and concave down for all t.

☐ **EXAMPLE 1**

Suppose that the percentage of the population that knows the result of an election t hours after the result is announced is

$$P(t) = 100(1 - Ce^{-kt}). \tag{3}$$

If 40% of the population knows the result 2 hours after it is announced, when will 80% of the population know it?

Strategy · · · · · · · ·

Use the initial value $P_0 = 0$ to solve for C.

Solution

Since no one knows the result until it has been announced, we have the initial value $P(0) = 0$. Inserting this data in equation (3) gives

$$0 = P(0) = 100(1 - Ce^{-k \cdot 0})$$
$$= 100(1 - C).$$

Thus $1 - C = 0$, so $C = 1$, and

$$P(t) = 100(1 - e^{-kt}). \tag{4}$$

Use data $P(2) = 40$ to obtain an equation involving the constant k.

Setting $t = 2$ in equation (4) and using the additional data $P(2) = 40$ then gives

$$40 = 100(1 - e^{-2k}).$$

Thus

$$1 - e^{-2k} = \frac{40}{100} = 0.4$$

so

$$e^{-2k} = 1 - 0.4 = 0.6$$

Take natural logs of both sides to solve for k.

and

$$-2k = \ln(0.6).$$

Thus

$$k = -\frac{\ln(0.6)}{2}$$

Write the explicit form of the function $P(t)$.

and the function $P(t)$ is

$$P(t) = 100(1 - e^{(\ln 0.6/2)t}).$$

Set up the equation $P(T) = 80$ and solve for T.

The condition that 80% of the population has heard the result after T hours is $P(T) = 80$, or

$$80 = 100(1 - e^{(\ln 0.6/2)/T})$$

which gives

$$1 - e^{(\ln 0.6/2)/T} = \frac{80}{100}$$

or

$$e^{(\ln 0.6/2)/T} = 1 - 0.8 = 0.2.$$

Take natural logs of both sides again. Thus

$$\left(\frac{\ln 0.6}{2}\right)T = \ln(0.2)$$

so

$$T = \frac{2[\ln(0.2)]}{\ln(0.6)}$$

$$\approx 6.3 \text{ hours.} \qquad \blacksquare$$

Logistic Growth

The logistic growth model resembles the model for the Law of Natural Growth in that the rate of change depends on the current size of the quantity. But it also borrows from the model for limited growth the existence of a maximum possible size M for the quantity or population. (M is called the *carrying capacity* of the system, as before.) The logistic growth model assumes that

{Rate of change} $\propto$ {Current size} $\cdot$ {Unutilized capacity for growth}.   (5)

To translate this law into a mathematical equation involving the size of a population $P(t)$ at time t, we note that for unutilized capacity for growth to exist we must have $P < M$, and that the fraction of full capacity available for additional growth will be $\left(\dfrac{M - P}{M}\right)$. We therefore express the logistic growth law in equation (5) as

$$\frac{dP}{dt} = kP\left(\frac{M - P}{M}\right)$$

where k is again called the growth constant. The solution of this differential equation is

$$P(t) = \frac{M}{1 + Ce^{-kt}}$$

where C is an arbitrary constant that is determined by an initial value for the solution.

The graph of a typical solution $y = P(t)$ is shown in Figure 2.4. Note that P is increasing for all $t > 0$, but that its graph is concave up on $(0, a)$ and concave down on (a, ∞), with an inflection point at $(a, P(a))$.

Logistic growth typically occurs when exponential growth would have resulted had the environment not been limited in size or resources. Fisheries provide a typical example, and many studies have been done that have resulted in logistic growth curves. If a pond is stocked with a small number of fish, the growth in the fish population is nearly exponential for awhile, since the limits of the pond's size are not noticeable to a small fish population. But as the size of the population increases, the competition for finite food resources and the negative effects of

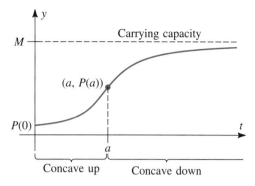

Figure 2.4 Graph of typical logistic curve

$$P(t) = \frac{M}{1 + Ce^{-kt}}.$$

crowding exert a downward pressure on the population's growth rate. As in the case of limited growth, we find that

$$\lim_{t \to \infty} P(t) = \lim_{t \to \infty} \frac{M}{1 + Ce^{-kt}} = \frac{M}{1 + 0} = M$$

which says that the population size approaches the carrying capacity M in the long run.

☐ **EXAMPLE 2**

A breeding pond is initially stocked with 10 fish. After five weeks the pond contains 30 fish. If the growth in the fish population is logistic and the maximum number of fish that the pond can support is 600, find the number of fish that will be present in the pond after 20 weeks.

Solution: Assuming logistic growth, the fish population has size

$$N(t) = \frac{M}{1 + Ce^{-kt}}$$

where t is time in weeks. We are given that the carrying capacity of the pond is $M = 600$ fish. Using this constant and the initial value $P(0) = 10$ gives

$$10 = \frac{600}{1 + Ce^{-k \cdot 0}} = \frac{600}{1 + C}.$$

We can now solve for C:

$$\frac{600}{1 + C} = 10 \quad \text{gives} \quad 1 + C = \frac{600}{10} = 60$$

so $C = 59$. We can therefore write the function P as

$$P(t) = \frac{600}{1 + 59e^{-kt}}.$$

Inserting the data $P(5) = 30$ gives an equation in k alone:

$$30 = \frac{600}{1 + 59e^{-5k}}$$

so

$$1 + 59e^{-5k} = \frac{600}{30} = 20.$$

Thus

$$59e^{-5k} = 19$$

so

$$e^{-5k} = \frac{19}{59}$$

and

$$k = -\frac{1}{5} \ln \frac{19}{59}.$$

Thus

$$P(t) = \frac{600}{1 + 59e^{[(1/5)\ln(19/59)]t}}$$

so the size of the population after 20 weeks is

$$P(20) = \frac{600}{1 + 59e^{[(1/5)\ln(19/59)]20}}$$

$$= \frac{600}{1 + 59e^{4\ln(19/59)}}$$

$$= \frac{600}{1 + 59 \cdot (19/59)^4}$$

$$\approx 367 \text{ fish.}$$

☑ PRACTICE PROBLEMS 10.2

1. Find the solution of the initial value problem

$$\frac{dy}{dt} = 8(2 - y)$$

$$y(0) = 4.$$

2. A population of rabbits is growing in an ecological niche with carrying capacity $M = 1000$ rabbits. If initially there were 20 rabbits, and after six months there were 50 rabbits, how many rabbits would we expect to find after two years?

Exercise Set 10.2

In Exercises 1–6, solve the given differential equation or initial value problem.

1. $\dfrac{dy}{dx} = 1 - y$

2. $\dfrac{dy}{dt} = 4 - 2y$

3. $\dfrac{dy}{dt} = 10 - 2y; \quad y(0) = 1$

4. $\dfrac{dy}{dt} = 10(2 - 4y); \quad y(0) = 0$

5. $\dfrac{dy}{dt} = 10y\left(\dfrac{50 - y}{50}\right)$

6. $\dfrac{dN}{dt} = 5N\left(\dfrac{100 - N}{100}\right); \quad N(0) = 10$

7. In Example 1 approximately what percentage of the population knows the result of the election 5 hours after it is announced?

8. In Example 2 how many fish will be present in the pond after ten weeks?

9. In Example 2 when will the pond contain 300 fish?

10. When word processing equipment was made available to staff in a certain corporation, it was found that t months after its introduction $W(t) = 140(1 - e^{-0.5t})$ employees used the equipment at least once per day.
  a. How many employees used word processing equipment after six months?
  b. What is the number of employees that can eventually be expected to use the equipment?

11. A marketing firm predicts that for a newly introduced personal computer the number of units that will be sold during the first month is

$$N(x) = 10,000(1 - e^{-0.002x})$$

where x is the number of dollars spent on introductory advertising. For what level of advertising x will sales increase most rapidly as a function of x?

12. An epidemiologist predicts that t days after the outbreak of winter colds

$$N(t) = \frac{500}{1 + 10e^{-kt}}$$

residents of a certain town will have caught a cold.
  a. If 100 of the residents have caught a cold after ten days, what is k?
  b. When will 200 of the residents have caught a cold?

13. The number of subscribers to cable television t months after its introduction in a certain city is expected to be

$$N(t) = \frac{80,000}{1 + 200e^{-0.2t}}.$$

  a. How many subscribers will there be after six months?
  b. How many subscribers will ultimately exist?

14. Find the inflection point for the graph of the function $f(x) = \dfrac{1}{1 + e^{-t}}$.

15. In a certain town t days after the outbreak of influenza

$$N(t) = \frac{400}{1 + 100e^{-t}}$$

individuals have the flu. When is the rate at which the influenza is spreading the greatest?

16. A rumor spreads through an office complex so that t hours after the rumor has begun

$$N(t) = \frac{50}{1 + 49e^{-t}}$$

people have heard the rumor. How many people have heard it after $t = 4$ hours?

17. The learning curve $N(t) = 30(1 - e^{-0.05t})$ models the number of vocabulary words that a student in an elementary French course can master in t minutes of study in a single study session.
  a. How many vocabulary words can a student master in 20 minutes?
  b. When will a student have mastered 20 words?

18. A bottle of soda at temperature 6°C is removed from a refrigerator and placed in a room at temperature 22°C. If, after 10 minutes, the temperature of the soda has risen to 14°C, find its temperature after 20 minutes according to Newton's law of cooling.

19. A lake is stocked with 500 fish. After two months there are 800 fish. Assume the maximum sustainable fish population for the lake is 2000 fish.
a. Find the number $N(t)$ of fish in the lake after t months.
b. Find $N(6)$.

20. Assume that the rate at which influenza spreads throughout a city is proportional and follows the logistic growth model. At the beginning of the first week of a flu epidemic, 5000 of the city's 300,000 people are infected. At the end of two weeks, an additional 10,000 have become infected. How many people will have become infected by the end of the fifth week?

21. The number of people who have heard a particular rumor t after it begins spreading is given by the function

$$N(t) = \frac{10,000}{1 + 999e^{-5t}}.$$

Find the differential equation and the initial value describing this phenomenon.

22. Verify that the function $y = M(1 - Ce^{-kt})$ satisfies the differential equation $\dfrac{dy}{dt} = k(M - y)$.

23. Verify that the function $P(t) = \dfrac{M}{1 + Ce^{-kt}}$ satisfies the logistic differential equation $\dfrac{dP}{dt} = kP\left(\dfrac{M - P}{M}\right)$.

☑ **SOLUTIONS TO PRACTICE PROBLEMS 10.2**

1. The differential equation $\dfrac{dy}{dt} = 8(2 - y)$ has the form of equation (1) with constants $k = 8$ and $M = 2$. The general solution, given by equation (2) is

$$y = 2(1 - Ce^{-8t}).$$

At $t = 0$, the initial condition $y(0) = 4$ gives

$$4 = 2(1 - Ce^0) = 2(1 - C)$$

so

$$2 = 1 - C \quad \text{or} \quad C = -1.$$

The solution to the initial value problem is therefore

$$y = 2(1 + e^{-8t}).$$

2. The rabbit population obeys the logistic growth model with carrying capacity $M = 1000$. The population function therefore has the form

$$N(t) = \frac{1000}{1 + Ce^{-kt}}.$$

The initial condition $N(0) = 20$ gives

$$20 = N(0) = \frac{1000}{1 + Ce^0} = \frac{1000}{1 + C}$$

so

$$1 + C = \frac{1000}{20} = 50$$

$$C = 49.$$

Thus,

$$N(t) = \frac{1000}{1 + 49e^{-kt}}.$$

The data $N(0.5) = 50$ then gives the equation

$$50 = \frac{1000}{1 + 49e^{-k(0.5)}}$$

so

$$1 + 49e^{-k/2} = \frac{1000}{50} = 20$$

$$e^{-k/2} = \frac{20 - 1}{49}$$

$$\frac{-k}{2} = \ln \frac{19}{49}$$

$$k = -2 \ln \frac{19}{49}.$$

Thus, the population function is

$$N(t) = \frac{1000}{1 + 49e^{2t \ln(19/49)}}$$

After two years the size of this population will be

$$N(2) = \frac{1000}{1 + 49e^{4 \ln(19/49)}} = \frac{1000}{1 + 49\left(\frac{19}{49}\right)^4} \approx 474.$$

10.3   Separation of Variables

There are several techniques, in addition to simple integration, that can be used to solve first order differential equations. Of these, **separation of variables** is the simplest. This technique applies to differential equations that have the form

$$\frac{dy}{dx} = \frac{f(x)}{g(y)}, \qquad g(y) \neq 0 \tag{1}$$

which we refer to as *separable* differential equations. The reason for this terminology is that we may multiply both sides of equation (1) by $g(y)$, thus obtaining the equation

$$g(y) \cdot \frac{dy}{dx} = f(x). \tag{2}$$

In doing so, we say that we have separated the variables in equation (1) since in equation (2) the left-hand side involves only the solution y and its derivative (assuming these exist) while the right-hand side is a function of x alone. Here is why this is helpful, in general:

(i) If we can find an antiderivative G for the function g, the left-hand side of equation (2) can be written as

$$\frac{d}{dx}G(y) = G'(y) \cdot \frac{dy}{dx} = g(y) \cdot \frac{dy}{dx}. \tag{3}$$

(ii) If we can find an antiderivative F for f, we can write the right-hand side of equation (2) as

$$\frac{d}{dx}F(x) = f(x). \tag{4}$$

(iii) Using equations (3) and (4), we can then rewrite equation (2) as

$$\frac{d}{dx}G(y) = \frac{d}{dx}F(x). \tag{5}$$

It then follows that

$$G(y) = F(x) + C \tag{6}$$

since both F and G have the same derivatives with respect to x (Theorem 1, Chapter 5).

REMARK 1: Equation (6) represents the general solution of equation (1) since the derivative $\dfrac{dy}{dx}$ has been eliminated. However, this may be an equation that involves y implicitly rather than as an explicit function of x.

REMARK 2: The differential notation $dy = \left(\dfrac{dy}{dx}\right) dx$ is often used to abbreviate the preceding discussion by saying, beginning with equation (1), that

$$\frac{dy}{dx} = \frac{f(x)}{g(y)} \quad \text{implies that} \quad g(y)\, dy = f(x)\, dx$$

so

$$\int g(y)\, dy = \int f(x)\, dx$$

and we obtain the solution by "integrating both sides."

□ **EXAMPLE 1**

Use the technique of separation of variables to find the general solution of the differential equation

$$\frac{dy}{dx} = \frac{x}{y}, \qquad y \neq 0.$$

Strategy · · · · · · · ·

Separate the variables.

Solution

Multiplying both sides by y gives

$$y \cdot \frac{dy}{dx} = x$$

so

Find antiderivatives of both sides.

$$\int y \cdot \left(\frac{dy}{dx}\right) dx = \int x \, dx.$$

Thus

$$\frac{1}{2}y^2 + C_1 = \frac{1}{2}x^2 + C_2$$

Solve for y^2, combining arbitrary constants.

so

$$y^2 + 2C_1 = x^2 + 2C_2$$

or

$$y^2 = x^2 + C$$

where $C = 2C_2 - 2C_1$. Graphs of this equation for various values of C appear in Figure 3.1.

Check result by differentiation.

To check this result, differentiate implicitly both sides of the equation $y^2 = x^2 + C$ to obtain

$$2y \cdot \frac{dy}{dx} = 2x$$

or

$$\frac{dy}{dx} = \frac{x}{y}.$$

Each solution consists of one branch above the x-axis and one branch below it. ∎

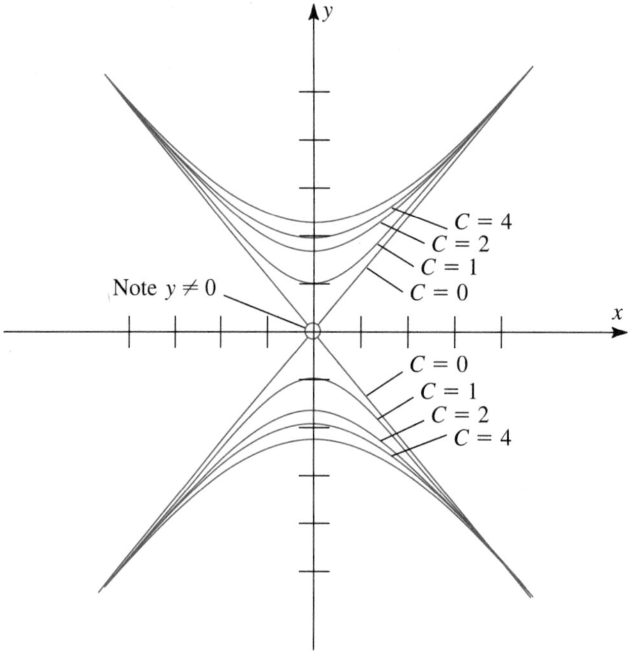

Figure 3.1 Solutions of the differential equation

$$\frac{dy}{dx} = \frac{x}{y}.$$

☐ **EXAMPLE 2**

Find the solution of the initial value problem

$$\frac{dy}{dx} = 2xy^2, \qquad y \neq 0$$

$$y(0) = \frac{1}{2}.$$

Solution: This time we separate variables by dividing both sides of the differential equation by y^2. This gives

$$y^{-2} \cdot \frac{dy}{dx} = 2x$$

so

$$\int y^{-2}\left(\frac{dy}{dx}\right) dx = \int 2x \, dx$$

and therefore

$$-y^{-1} + C_1 = x^2 + C_2.$$

Thus

$$-\frac{1}{y} = x^2 + C, \qquad \text{where } C = C_2 - C_1$$

so

$$y = \frac{-1}{x^2 + C}$$

is the general solution of the differential equation.

The initial condition $y(0) = \frac{1}{2}$ means that when $x = 0$, we must have

$$\frac{1}{2} = \frac{-1}{0^2 + C} = \frac{-1}{C}$$

so $C = -2$. The solution of the initial value problem is therefore

$$y = \frac{-1}{x^2 - 2} = \frac{1}{2 - x^2}.$$ ■

□ **EXAMPLE 3**

The equation that we have referred to as the Law of Natural Growth

$$\frac{dP}{dt} = kP$$

is a separable differential equation. Dividing both sides by the nonzero function P gives

$$\frac{1}{P} \cdot \frac{dP}{dt} = k.$$

Integrating with respect to t then gives

$$\int \frac{1}{P} \left(\frac{dP}{dt}\right) dt = \int k \, dt$$

so

$$\ln |P| + C_1 = kt + C_2$$

or

$$\ln P = kt + C_3, \qquad C_3 = C_2 - C_1, \qquad P > 0.$$

Taking exponentials of both sides then gives

$$e^{\ln P} = e^{kt + C_3} = e^{C_3} \cdot e^{kt}$$

Writing $C = e^{C_3}$ (since e to a constant power is just another constant) and noting that $e^{\ln P} = P$ gives

$$P = Ce^{kt}$$

as claimed in Chapter 4. Note that, as required, P is positive for all t. ∎

☐ **EXAMPLE 4**

In Section 10.2 we developed a logistic model for growth in a limited environment:

$$\frac{dP}{dt} = kP\left(\frac{K - P}{K}\right) \qquad (7)$$

where K is a constant representing the carrying capacity or maximum sustainable population size for the environment and the population is of size $P(t)$ at time t.

We may separate the variables in equation (7) by dividing both sides by the nonzero factor $P(K - P)$, obtaining

$$\frac{1}{P(K - P)} \cdot \frac{dP}{dt} = \frac{k}{K}$$

so

$$\int \frac{1}{P(K - P)} \cdot \left(\frac{dP}{dt}\right) dt = \int \frac{k}{K} dt. \qquad (8)$$

We leave it as an exercise for you to verify that the integrand on the left is

$$\frac{1}{P(K - P)} = \frac{1}{K} \cdot \frac{1}{P} + \frac{1}{K} \cdot \frac{1}{(K - P)}.$$

The integral on the left-hand side of equation (8) is therefore

$$\int \frac{1}{P(K - P)}\left(\frac{dP}{dt}\right) dt = \int \frac{1}{P(K - P)} dP$$

$$= \frac{1}{K}\int \left(\frac{1}{P} + \frac{1}{K - P}\right) dP$$

$$= \frac{1}{K}[\ln P - \ln(K - P)] + C_1, \qquad 0 < P < K$$

$$= \frac{1}{K}\ln\left(\frac{P}{K - P}\right) + C_1.$$

Since the integral on the right-hand side of equation (8) is $\dfrac{k}{K}t + C_2$, we have

$$\frac{1}{K} \ln\left(\frac{P}{K-P}\right) + C_1 = \frac{k}{K}t + C_2.$$

Thus

$$\ln\left(\frac{P}{K-P}\right) = kt + C, \qquad \text{where } C = K(C_2 - C_1)$$

so

$$\frac{P}{K-P} = e^{kt+C}.$$

Solving for P, we obtain

$$Pe^{-kt-C} = K - P$$

so

$$P(1 + Me^{-kt}) = K, \qquad \text{where } M = e^{-C}$$

and

$$P(t) = \frac{K}{1 + Me^{-kt}}. \tag{9}$$

The graph of this solution, for $0 < P(0) < K$, appears in Figure 3.2. Note that $\lim_{t \to \infty} P(t) = K$, so the carrying capacity of the environment is a horizontal asymptote of the population curve. ■

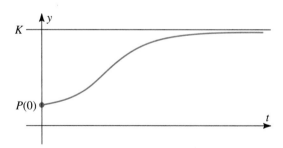

Figure 3.2 Solution of logistic growth equation in Example 4.

□ **EXAMPLE 5**

Sociologists model the movement of information (such as a rumor) through a population by assuming that the rate at which information spreads is proportional to the product of the proportion of the population that already knows the information and the proportion of the population that does not yet know the information. If we let $P(t)$ be the proportion of the population knowing the information at time t, then this model corresponds to the differential equation

$$\frac{dP}{dt} = kP(1 - P). \tag{10}$$

Now equation (10) is just the equation (7) for logistic growth with $K = 1$. The solution is therefore

$$P(t) = \frac{1}{1 + Me^{-kt}}$$

as given by equation (9) with $K = 1$.   ∎

Generalizing the Law of Natural Growth

The differential equation $\dfrac{dy}{dt} = ky$ for natural growth can be generalized in several ways. One such generalization is to differential equations of the form

$$\frac{dy}{dt} = ky - b \tag{11}$$

where b is a constant. This model applies, for example, to a fishery when the size of the fish population is small relative to the carrying capacity and fish are harvested at the constant rate of b fish per unit time.

Letting $a = \dfrac{b}{k}$, we can write equation (11) as

$$\frac{dy}{dt} = k(y - a), \qquad a \text{ constant.} \tag{12}$$

The interpretation of equation (12) is now that the rate of change of y is proportional to the *difference* between the population size y and the constant a.

The following example shows how the method of separation of variables may be applied to equation (12).

□ **EXAMPLE 6**

Find the general solution of the differential equation

$$\frac{dy}{dt} = k(y - a), \qquad y - a \neq 0. \tag{13}$$

Solution: Dividing both sides by $y - a$ gives

$$\frac{1}{y - a} \cdot \frac{dy}{dt} = k$$

so

$$\int \frac{1}{y-a}\left(\frac{dy}{dt}\right) dt = \int k\, dt.$$

Integrating both sides then gives

$$\ln|y-a| + C_1 = kt + C_2$$

so

$$\ln|y-a| = kt + C_3, \qquad C_3 = C_2 - C_1.$$

Taking exponentials of both sides gives

$$|y-a| = e^{kt+C_3}$$
$$= e^{C_3} \cdot e^{kt}$$
$$= C_4 e^{kt}, \qquad C_4 = e^{C_3}$$

so

$$y - a = \pm C_4 e^{kt}$$
$$= Ce^{kt}, \qquad C = \pm C_4.$$

Thus

$$y = a + Ce^{kt}$$

where the arbitrary constant C (which may be either positive or negative) is determined by an initial value.   ■

Since we shall use the result of Example 6 in our last three examples, we restate it as follows.

The solution of the differential equation

$$\frac{dy}{dt} = k(y - a) \tag{14}$$

is

$$y = a + Ce^{kt}. \tag{15}$$

☐ **EXAMPLE 7**

Find the solution of the initial value problem

$$\frac{dy}{dt} = 2 - y \tag{16}$$

$$y(0) = 1. \tag{17}$$

Solution: To compare equation (16) with equation (14), we rewrite it in the form

$$\frac{dy}{dt} = -(y - 2).$$

Thus equation (16) has the form of equation (14) with $k = -1$ and $a = 2$. The solution of the differential equation, according to equation (15), is

$$y = 2 + Ce^{-t}.$$

Setting $t = 0$ and applying the initial value $y(0) = 1$ from equation (17) gives

$$1 = y(0) = 2 + Ce^0 = 2 + C$$

so $C = 1 - 2 = -1$. The solution of the initial value problem is therefore

$$y = 2 - e^{-t}.$$

(See Figure 3.3.)   ∎

Mixing Problems

Differential equations of the form of equation (14) arise in problems involving the mixing of two or more liquids. The typical situation is depicted in Figure 3.4. The liquids are entering a container at a specified rate, the contents of the container are being kept well mixed, and the resulting mixture is being removed at a specified rate.

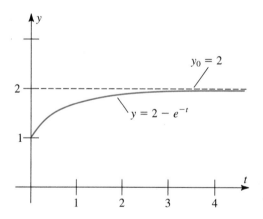

Figure 3.3 Solution of differential equation

$$\frac{dy}{dt} = 2 - y \quad \text{with} \quad y(0) = 1$$

is $y = 2 - e^{-t}$.

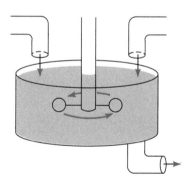

Figure 3.4 Diagram for "mixing" problems showing inputs, thorough mixing, and output.

□ **EXAMPLE 8**

A 500-liter tank in which chocolate milk is being mixed contains 460 liters of milk and 40 liters of chocolate syrup initially. Syrup and milk are then added to the tank at the rate of 2 liters per minute of syrup and 8 liters per minute of milk. Simultaneously, the mixture is withdrawn at the rate of 10 liters per minute. Assuming perfect mixing of the milk and syrup, find the function y giving the amount of syrup $y(t)$ in the tank at time t.

Solution: If y represents the amount of syrup in the tank, then $\dfrac{dy}{dt}$ is the rate of change of y, which is the rate at which syrup enters the tank (2 liters per minute) *minus* the rate at which syrup leaves the tank. The rate at which syrup leaves the tank depends on how much syrup is in the mixture; it is

$$\frac{y \text{ liters of syrup}}{500 \text{ liters of mixture}} \times (10 \text{ liters of mixture per minute withdrawn})$$

$$= \frac{y}{50} = 0.02y \text{ liters of syrup per minute.}$$

Thus

$$\frac{dy}{dt} = 2 - 0.02y$$

is the differential equation describing this process. This equation can be written in the form of equation (14) as

$$\frac{dy}{dt} = -0.02(y - 100),$$

so $k = -0.02$ and $a = 100$ in equation (14). The solution is, according to equation (15)

$$y = 100 + Ce^{-0.02t}. \tag{18}$$

Since 40 liters of syrup are present initially, we have the initial value $y(0) = 40$. Setting $t = 0$ in equation (18) and using this initial value gives

$$40 = 100 + Ce^0 = 100 + C$$

so $C = -60$. The desired solution is therefore

$$y = (100 - 60e^{-0.02t}) \text{ liters.}$$

The graph of this solution appears in Figure 3.5. Values of the solution for various times t appear in Table 3.1. ■

Table 3.1. Calculated Values $y(t)$ in Figure 3.5

t Minutes	0	10	20	30	40	50	60	100	150	200
$y = 100 - 60e^{-0.02t}$ Liters	40.0	50.9	59.8	67.1	73.1	77.9	81.9	91.9	97.0	98.9

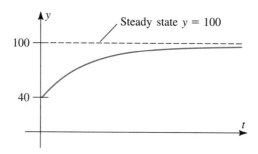

Figure 3.5 Solution of the mixing problem in Example 8.

REMARK: Figure 3.5 illustrates an important property of solutions of differential equations of the form $\dfrac{dy}{dt} = k(y - a)$, namely, when $k < 0$, the solution approaches a horizontal asymptote as $t \to \infty$. For the solution y of Example 8 we have

$$\lim_{t \to \infty} y = \lim_{t \to \infty} (100 - 60e^{-0.02t}) = 100$$

as Figure 3.5 suggests. The asymptote $y = 100$ is called the *steady state* part of the solution, while the term $60e^{-0.02t}$ is referred to as the *transient* part of the solution. The result of Example 8 is precisely what intuition suggests—regardless of the initial concentration of syrup, the steady state concentration will be $\dfrac{100}{500} = 0.2$, since 2 liters of syrup enter for every 8 liters of milk.

☐ **EXAMPLE 9**

Newton's law of cooling states that the rate at which an object gains or loses heat is proportional to the difference in temperature between the object and its surroundings. A bottle of soda at temperature 6°C is removed from a refrigerator and placed in a room at temperature 22°C. If after 10 minutes the temperature of the soda is 14°C, find its temperature $y(t)$ as a function of t.

Solution: According to Newton's law, the rate $\dfrac{dy}{dt}$ at which the temperature of the soda changes is proportional to the quantity $(y - 22)$. That is

$$\frac{dy}{dt} = k(y - 22)$$

for some constant k. This equation has the form of equation (14) with $a = 22$. The general solution is therefore

$$y = 22 + Ce^{kt} \tag{19}$$

and our task is to determine the constants C and k. Since we are given the initial value $y(0) = 6°$, we may set $t = 0$ in equation (19) and conclude that

$$6 = y(0) = 22 + Ce^0 = 22 + C$$

so $C = -16$, and the solution has the form

$$y = 22 - 16e^{kt}. \tag{20}$$

To determine k, we use the additional information that $y(10) = 14°$ by setting $t = 10$ in equation (20):

$$14 = y(10) = 22 - 16e^{10k}$$

or

$$16e^{10k} = 8.$$

Thus

$$e^{10k} = \frac{1}{2}$$

so

$$\ln(e^{10k}) = 10k = \ln\left(\frac{1}{2}\right) = -\ln 2$$

and

$$k = -\frac{\ln 2}{10}.$$

The temperature $y(t)$ of the soda at time t is therefore

$$y(t) = 22 - 16e^{(-\ln 2/10)t}.$$

The graph of this solution appears in Figure 3.6, and values $y(t)$ for various numbers t are given in Table 3.2. Again, note that the solution contains a steady state part ($y = 22°$), which $y(t)$ approaches as $t \to \infty$. ∎

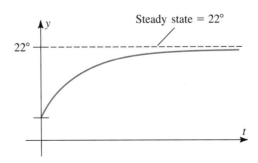

Figure 3.6 Graph of temperature function $y(t)$ in Example 9.

Table 3.2. Values of the Temperature Function y in Example 9

t	0	4	8	12	16	20	24	28	32	36
$y(t)$	6.0	9.87	12.81	15.04	16.72	18.00	18.97	19.70	20.26	20.68

☑ **PRACTICE PROBLEMS 10.3**

1. Solve the initial value problem

$$\frac{dy}{dx} = \frac{2x}{e^y}$$

$$y(0) = 1.$$

2. An individual places an initial deposit of $2000 in a savings account paying 5% interest compounded continuously. Thereafter, he deposits $1000 per year at a continuous and uniform rate.
   a. Find the differential equation satisfied by the function $y = A(t)$ giving the amount on deposit after t years.
   b. Find the amount on deposit at the end of ten years.

Exercise Set 10.3

In Exercises 1–10, use the technique of separation of variables to find the general solution of the differential equation.

1. $\dfrac{dy}{dx} = \dfrac{y}{x}, \quad x \neq 0$

2. $\dfrac{dy}{dx} = \dfrac{x}{y^2}, \quad y \neq 0$

3. $\dfrac{dy}{dx} = -4xy^2$

4. $\dfrac{dy}{dx} = \dfrac{\sqrt{x}}{\sqrt{y}}, \quad y > 0$

5. $\dfrac{dy}{dx} = e^{x-y}$

6. $\dfrac{dy}{dx} = \dfrac{y \ln^2 x}{x}$

7. $e^y \dfrac{dy}{dt} - t^2 = 0$

8. $\dfrac{dy}{dt} + y \cos t = 0$

9. $\dfrac{dy}{dx} = (1 + x)(1 + y)$

10. $2t\dfrac{dy}{dt} = \dfrac{t^2 + 1}{y^2}$

In Exercises 11–20, find a solution of the initial value problem.

11. $y' = 5y, \quad y(1) = \pi e^5$

12. $yy' = x + 2, \quad y(0) = 3$

13. $\dfrac{dy}{dx} = xy, \quad y(2) = 7$

14. $\dfrac{dy}{dx} = -\dfrac{y}{x^2}, \quad y(1) = 2$

15. $\dfrac{dy}{dx} = y \cos x, \quad y(0) = \pi$

16. $y' = \sqrt{y}, \quad y(0) = 1$

17. $y' = 2(y - 1), \quad y(0) = 1$

18. $\dfrac{dy}{dt} = 5(10 - y), \quad y(0) = 5$

19. $y' - 3y = 6, \quad y(0) = 2$

20. $\dfrac{dy}{dt} + 2y = 2, \quad y(0) = 4$

21. Find a solution of the logistic differential equation $\dfrac{dP}{dt} = 2P\left(\dfrac{100 - P}{100}\right)$. What is the carrying capacity? (See Example 4.)

22. Let $P(t)$ be a solution of the differential equation $\dfrac{dP}{dt} = P(1 - P)$ with $P(0) > 0$. What is $\lim\limits_{t \to \infty} P(t)$? (See Example 4.)

23. Radioactive uranium-238 decays according to the differential equation $\dfrac{dU}{dt} = kU$ with $k < 0$. The half-life (the time required for the uranium to decay to half the original amount, as explained in Example 2 of Section 4.5) is known to be 4.5 billion years. What is k?

24. The population of a city is growing according to the Law of Natural Growth. If its population in 1980 was 0.2 million and its population in 1990 was 0.5 million, what will its population be in 2000?

25. A tank contains 200 liters of brine. The initial concentration of salt is 0.5 kilogram per liter of brine. Fresh water is then added at a rate of 3 liters per minute and the brine is drawn off from the bottom of the tank at the same rate. Assume perfect mixing.
a. Find a differential equation for the number of kilograms of salt, $p(t)$, in the solution at time t.
b. How much salt is present after 20 minutes?
c. What is the steady state concentration of salt?

26. A bottle of water at temperature 26°C is placed in a room at temperature 12°C. If the temperature of the water after 30 minutes is 20°C, find its temperature after 2 hours.

27. A person initially places $100 in a savings account that pays 10% per year compounded continuously. If the person makes additional deposits of $100 per year continuously through each year
a. Find a differential equation for $P(t)$, the amount on deposit after t years.
b. Find the amount on deposit after seven years.

28. Show that the graph of the solution to the initial value problem

$$\frac{dy}{dt} = y(1 - y), \qquad y(0) = \frac{1}{4}$$

has an inflection point where $y = \dfrac{1}{2}$. (*Hint:* Find an equation for $\dfrac{d^2y}{dt^2}$ by differentiating both sides of the differential equation for y with respect to t. When is $\dfrac{d^2y}{dt^2}$ equal to zero?)

29. According to the sociologists' model of Example 5, if 100 people in a city of 100,000 know a rumor on Monday, and 500 know it on Wednesday, how many will know it on Saturday?

30. In the chemical reaction called inversion of raw sugar the inversion rate is proportional to the amount of raw sugar remaining. If 100 kilograms of raw sugar are reduced to 75 kilograms in 6 hours, how long will it be until
a. half the raw sugar has been inverted?
b. 90% of the raw sugar has been inverted?

31. A pan of boiling water is removed from a burner and cools to 80°C in 3 minutes. Find its temperature after 10 minutes, according to Newton's law of cooling, if the surrounding temperature is 30°C.

32. A room containing 1000 cubic feet of air is initially free of pollutants. Air containing 100 parts of pollutants per cubic foot is pumped into the room at a rate of 50 cubic feet per minute. The air in the room is kept perfectly mixed, and air is removed from the room at the same rate of 50 cubic feet per minute. Find the function $P(t)$ giving the number of parts of pollutants per cubic foot in the room air after t minutes.

33. A tank contains a mixture of 500 gallons of salt brine (salt and water) initially containing 2 pounds of salt per gallon. A second mixture, containing 6 pounds of salt per gallon, is then pumped in at a rate of 10 gallons per minute. The resulting mixture is drawn off at the same rate. Assuming perfect mixing, find the function that describes the amount of salt (pounds) in the mixture in the tank t minutes after mixing begins.

34. Influenza spreads through a university community at a rate proportional to the product of the proportion of those already infected and the proportion of those not yet infected. Assuming that those infected remain infected, find the proportion $P(t)$ infected after t days if initially 10% were infected and after three days 30% were infected.

35. An annuity is initially set up containing $10,000 on which interest is compounded continuously at a rate of 10% per year. The owner of the annuity withdraws $2000 per year in a continuous manner. When does the value of the annuity reach zero?

36. Certain biological populations grow in size according to the Gompertz growth equation

$$\frac{dy}{dt} = -ky \ln y$$

where k is a positive constant. Find the general solution of this differential equation.

37. The Weber-Fechner law in psychology is a model for the rate of change of the reaction y to a stimulus of strength s that is given by the differential equation

$$\frac{dy}{ds} = k\frac{y}{s}$$

where k is a positive constant. Find the general solution of this differential equation.

☑ **SOLUTIONS TO PRACTICE PROBLEMS 10.3**

1. Separating variables in $\dfrac{dy}{dx} = \dfrac{2x}{e^y}$ gives

$$e^y dy = 2x\, dx$$

so

$$\int e^y\, dy = \int 2x\, dx$$

or

$$e^y = x^2 + C.$$

Taking natural logarithms of both sides then gives

$$y = \ln(x^2 + C).$$

The initial condition $y(0) = 1$ now gives

$$1 = \ln(0 + C) = \ln C$$

so $C = e$. The solution is therefore

$$y = \ln(x^2 + e).$$

2. The rate of change of $A(t)$ is

$$A'(t) = 0.05A(t) + 1000$$

which we can write as

$$\frac{dA}{dt} = 0.05\left(A + \frac{1000}{0.05}\right).$$

By equation (15) (or by separation of variables) the general solution is

$$A(t) = -\frac{1000}{0.05} + Ce^{0.05t}$$

$$= -20{,}000 + Ce^{0.05t}.$$

The initial condition $A(0) = 2000$ gives

$$2000 = -20{,}000 + C$$

so

$$C = 22{,}000$$

and the particular solution is

$$A(t) = -20,000 + (22,000)e^{0.05t}.$$

After ten years, the amount on deposit is

$$A(10) = -20,000 + (22,000)e^{0.5}$$

$$\approx 16,272.$$

10.4 Second Order Equations

By adding a term involving the second derivative to the differential equation $y' = ky$ for natural growth, we obtain one type of *second order* differential equation,*

$$\frac{d^2y}{dt^2} + a\,\frac{dy}{dt} + by = 0 \tag{1}$$

where a and b are constants. From our experience with first order equations we might suspect that equation (1) has a solution of the form $y = e^{rt}$ where r is a constant. If this were true, the derivative of this proposed solution would be

$$\frac{dy}{dt} = re^{rt}, \qquad \text{and} \qquad \frac{d^2y}{dt^2} = r^2e^{rt}.$$

Substituting into equation (1) would therefore give

$$r^2e^{rt} + a(re^{rt}) + b(e^{rt}) = 0$$

or

$$(r^2 + ar + b)e^{rt} = 0. \tag{2}$$

Since values of the exponential function $y = e^{rt}$ are always nonzero, the only way in which equation (2) can be true is if the *characteristic polynomial* $r^2 + ar + b$ equals zero. That is, r must be a (real) *root* of the quadratic polynomial $r^2 + ar + b$.

> The function $y = e^{rt}$ is a solution of the differential equation
>
> $$\frac{d^2y}{dt^2} + a\frac{dy}{dt} + by = 0$$
>
> only if the constant r is a real root of the characteristic polynomial
>
> $$r^2 + ar + b.$$

---

*More precisely, equation (1) is referred to as a second order, constant-coefficient, linear, homogeneous equation. The term homogeneous refers to the fact that the right-hand side is zero. This is but one type of second order equation. There are many others, but we shall not pursue them here.

Thus we expect to find two, one, or zero solutions of the differential equation (1) of the form $y = e^{rt}$, depending on the number of real roots r of the associated characteristic polynomial.

□ **EXAMPLE 1**

For the differential equation

$$\frac{d^2y}{dt^2} - \frac{dy}{dt} - 2y = 0$$

the constant coefficients are $a = -1$ and $b = -2$, so the characteristic polynomial is

$$r^2 - r - 2 = (r - 2)(r + 1).$$

This characteristic polynomial has real roots $r_1 = 2$ and $r_2 = -1$. Two solutions of the differential equation are therefore

$$y_1 = e^{r_1 t} = e^{2t} \quad \text{and} \quad y_2 = e^{r_2 t} = e^{-t}$$

as you can verify. ■

When the characteristic polynomial $r^2 + ar + b$ does not have distinct real roots, one of two remaining possibilities will occur. Without proof, we shall simply state these possible outcomes and provide an example of each.

If the characteristic polynomial $r^2 + ar + b$ of the differential equation

$$\frac{d^2y}{dt^2} + a\left(\frac{dy}{dt}\right) + by = 0 \tag{3}$$

has the *single* repeated real root r, then both of the functions

$$y_1 = e^{rt} \quad \text{and} \quad y_2 = te^{rt}$$

are solutions of the differential equation (3).

□ **EXAMPLE 2**

The differential equation

$$\frac{d^2y}{dt^2} + 4\left(\frac{dy}{dt}\right) + 4y = 0$$

has the characteristic polynomial

$$r^2 + 4r + 4 = (r + 2)^2$$

which has the single repeated real root $r = -2$. According to the preceding statement, the differential equation has the two solutions

$$y_1 = e^{-2t} \quad \text{and} \quad y_2 = te^{-2t}$$

which you can verify by direct substitution.

If the characteristic polynomial $r^2 + ar + b$ of the differential equation

$$\frac{d^2y}{dt^2} + a\left(\frac{dy}{dt}\right) + by = 0 \tag{4}$$

has no real roots, then it has two distinct complex (imaginary) roots $r_1 = \alpha + i\beta$ and $r_2 = \alpha - i\beta$ where α and β are real numbers with $\beta \neq 0$, and i is the complex number defined by the equation $i^2 = -1$. In this case the differential equation (4) will have the two solutions

$$y_1 = e^{\alpha t} \sin \beta t \quad \text{and} \quad y_2 = e^{\alpha t} \cos \beta t. \tag{5}$$

☐ **EXAMPLE 3**

The differential equation

$$y'' + 2y' + 2y = 0 \tag{6}$$

has characteristic polynomial $r^2 + 2r + 2$ with roots, according to the quadratic formula

$$r = \frac{-2 \pm \sqrt{2^2 - 4(1)(2)}}{2(1)}$$

$$= \frac{-2 \pm \sqrt{-4}}{2}$$

$$= \frac{-2 \pm (\sqrt{4})(\sqrt{-1})}{2}$$

$$= -1 \pm i, \quad i^2 = -1.$$

Thus the characteristic polynomial has roots $r = \alpha \pm \beta i$ with $\alpha = -1$ and $\beta = 1$. According to equation (5), differential equation (6) has solutions

$$y_1 = e^{-t} \sin t \quad \text{and} \quad y_2 = e^{-t} \cos t$$

as you can verify by direct substitution. ∎

□ **EXAMPLE 4**

Differential equations of the form

$$y'' + by = 0 \tag{7}$$

have characteristic polynomial $r^2 + b = 0$. Since this gives $r^2 = -b$, in the case when $b > 0$, we obtain the complex roots $r = \pm\sqrt{b}i$. Thus, with $\alpha = 0$ and $\beta = \sqrt{b}$, equation (5) says that differential equation (7) has solutions

$$y_1 = \sin\sqrt{b}t \qquad \text{and} \qquad y_2 = \cos\sqrt{b}t.$$

We shall return to this type of equation in studying oscillatory motion later in this section. ■

The General Solution of Equation (1)

If y_1 and y_2 are any two solutions of equation (1), then so is any *linear combination* of these solutions of the form

$$y(t) = Ay_1(t) + By_2(t) \tag{8}$$

where A and B are constants. (See Exercise 32.) If the functions y_1 and y_2 in equation (8) are not multiples of each other, the function $y(t)$ is called the *general solution* of equation (1) since it can be shown that any solution can be written in this form for an appropriate choice of the constants A and B.

□ **EXAMPLE 5**

(i) The general solution of the differential equation $\dfrac{d^2y}{dt^2} - \dfrac{dy}{dt} - 2y = 0$ in Example 1 is

$$y = Ae^{2t} + Be^{-t}.$$

(ii) The general solution of the differential equation $\dfrac{d^2y}{dt^2} + 4\dfrac{dy}{dt} + 4y = 0$ in Example 2 is

$$y = Ae^{-2t} + Bte^{-2t}.$$

(iii) The general solution of the differential equation

$$y'' + 2y' + 2y = 0$$

in Example 3 is

$$y = Ae^{-t}\sin t + Be^{-t}\cos t.$$

(iv) The general solution of the differential equation

$$y'' + by = 0, \qquad b > 0$$

in Example 4 is

$$y = A\sin\sqrt{b}t + B\cos\sqrt{b}t. \qquad ■$$

Initial Conditions

In general, two initial conditions are required to determine a unique solution of a second order differential equation, one for the solution y and one for its derivative $\frac{dy}{dt}$, *specified at the same number* t_0. Since the general solution of equation (1) has the form given by equation (8), two initial conditions will produce two linear equations for the constants A and B, from which these numbers may be determined.

☐ **EXAMPLE 6**

Find the unique solution of the initial value problem consisting of the differential equation

$$y'' - 2y' - 3y = 0 \tag{9}$$

and the initial conditions

$$y(0) = 0$$

$$y'(0) = 4.$$

Strategy · · · · · · · ·
First, find the general solution by

a. finding the characteristic polynomial

b. identifying its roots r_1 and r_2

c. combining the solutions $e^{r_1 t}$ and $e^{r_2 t}$ as in equation (8).

Solution
The characteristic polynomial for equation (9) is

$$r^2 - 2r - 3 = (r - 3)(r + 1)$$

which has roots $r_1 = 3$ and $r_2 = -1$. The general solution of equation (9) is therefore

$$y(t) = Ae^{3t} + Be^{-t} \tag{10}$$

so the derivative y' has the form

$$y'(t) = 3Ae^{3t} - Be^{-t}. \tag{11}$$

Substituting the initial condition $y(0) = 0$ into equation (10) gives the equation

$$A + B = 0. \tag{12}$$

Next, substitute initial conditions into general solution y, and its derivative y', to obtain two equations in A and B.

Solve the two equations for A and B by substitution or by elimination.

Substituting the initial condition $y'(0) = 4$ into equation (11) gives the equation

$$3A - B = 4. \tag{13}$$

Substituting $B = -A$ from equation (12) into equation (13) gives

$$3A - (-A) = 4$$

or

$$4A = 4.$$

Thus $A = 1$ and $B = -A = -1$.

Find particular solution by substituting for A and B in general solution.

Equation (10) now becomes

$$y(t) = e^{3t} - e^{-t}$$

which is the desired solution. ∎

Modelling Oscillatory Motion

A version of equation (1) that occurs frequently in applications is

$$\frac{d^2y}{dt^2} + by = 0, \qquad b > 0. \tag{14}$$

As stated in Example 4, the periodic function $y_1 = \sin \sqrt{b}t$ is easily seen to be a solution of equation (14), since

$$\frac{dy_1}{dt} = \sqrt{b} \cos \sqrt{b}t \quad \text{and} \quad \frac{d^2y_1}{dt^2} = -b \sin \sqrt{b}t$$

so

$$\frac{d^2y_1}{dt^2} + by_1 = -b \sin \sqrt{b}t + b(\sin \sqrt{b}t)$$

$$= 0$$

as required. Similarly, the periodic function $y_2 = \cos \sqrt{b}t$ is also a solution of equation (14), as you can verify. Thus the general solution of a differential equation of the form of equation (14) must be a combination of the "oscillatory" functions $\sin \sqrt{b}t$ and $\cos \sqrt{b}t$.

> The differential equation
>
> $$\frac{d^2y}{dt^2} + by = 0, \qquad b > 0 \tag{15}$$
>
> has the general solution
>
> $$y = A \sin \sqrt{b}t + B \cos \sqrt{b}t. \tag{16}$$

☐ **EXAMPLE 7**

Find the general solution of the differential equation

$$y'' + 9y = 0.$$

Solution: Since the differential equation has the form of equation (15), with $b = 9$ the general solution is

$$y = A \sin 3t + B \cos 3t. \qquad ∎$$

Because solutions of equation (14) are made up of sine and cosine functions, versions of this equation occur in models for the motion of vibrating physical systems involving springs, pendulums, and so forth, and applications of this type may be found in texts oriented toward engineering and the physical sciences. A different application involving oscillatory phenomena occurs in a biological setting.

☐ **EXAMPLE 8**

(predator–prey system) Assume that a population of predators (foxes, say) depends on a population of prey (rabbits, in this case) for its food supply. More specifically, we assume that:

(i) The rate of growth of the predator population depends on the size of the prey population (i.e., more rabbits means more foxes).
(ii) The rate of decline of the prey population depends on the size of the predator population (i.e., more foxes means *fewer* rabbits).

Figure 4.1 suggests that these assumptions lead to oscillating sizes for both populations.

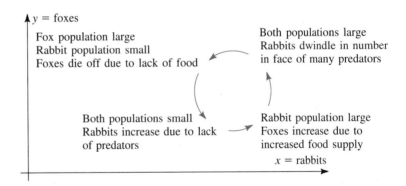

Figure 4.1 A predator–prey system.

To treat this situation mathematically, we shall make several simplifying assumptions. First, we shall denote the rabbit population by $x(t)$ and the fox population by $y(t)$, where t represents time, and we shall assume that both functions are at least twice differentiable for all t. Then we translate assumptions (i) and (ii) into the specific relations

$$(i') \quad \frac{dy}{dt} = a(x - \bar{x}), \qquad a > 0, \qquad \bar{x} > 0$$

$$(ii') \quad \frac{dx}{dt} = -b(y - \bar{y}), \qquad b > 0, \qquad \bar{y} > 0.$$

Here $\bar{x}$ and $\bar{y}$ represent certain fixed "equilibrium" sizes for the two populations. Since $a > 0$, assumption (i') states that the fox population will increase when the rabbit population is larger than $\bar{x}$ and decrease when the rabbit population falls below $\bar{x}$. Similarly, hypothesis (ii') states that the rabbit population will decline when the fox population exceeds $\bar{y}$ and grow otherwise.

To simplify these equations further, we change to the variable X and Y via the substitutions

$$X = x - \bar{x} \quad \text{and} \quad Y = y - \bar{y}. \tag{17}$$

Then $\dfrac{dX}{dt} = \dfrac{dx}{dt}, \dfrac{dY}{dt} = \dfrac{dy}{dt}$, and our system of equations becomes

$$\frac{dY}{dt} = aX \tag{18}$$

$$\frac{dX}{dt} = -bY. \tag{19}$$

We can now convert this "system" of two first order equations to a second order equation as follows. First, we differentiate both sides of equation (19) with respect to t to obtain

$$\frac{d^2X}{dt^2} = -b\frac{dY}{dt}.$$

Next, we substitute for $\dfrac{dY}{dt}$ in this equation using equation (18) to obtain

$$\frac{d^2X}{dt^2} = -abX$$

or

$$\frac{d^2X}{dt^2} + abX = 0. \tag{20}$$

Now equation (20) has the form of equation (15), so its general solution is

$$X(t) = A \sin(\sqrt{ab}\,t) + B \cos(\sqrt{ab}\,t). \tag{21}$$

Differentiating both sides of equation (21) and using the fact that $Y = -\dfrac{1}{b}\dfrac{dX}{dt}$ from equation (19) gives

$$Y(t) = -\frac{1}{b}[\sqrt{ab}\,A \cos(\sqrt{ab}\,t) - \sqrt{ab}\,B \sin(\sqrt{ab}\,t)]$$

$$= -\sqrt{\frac{a}{b}}\,A \cos(\sqrt{ab}\,t) + \sqrt{\frac{a}{b}}\,B \sin(\sqrt{ab}\,t).$$

Reversing the substitutions made in equation (17), we have the following conclusion.

The predator–prey system

$$\frac{dy}{dt} = a(x - \bar{x}), \qquad a > 0, \qquad \bar{x} > 0 \tag{22}$$

$$\frac{dx}{dt} = -b(y - \bar{y}), \qquad b > 0, \qquad \bar{y} > 0 \tag{23}$$

has the general solution

$$x(t) = \bar{x} + A \sin(\sqrt{ab}\,t) + B \cos(\sqrt{ab}\,t) \tag{24}$$

$$y(t) = \bar{y} - \sqrt{\frac{a}{b}}[A \cos(\sqrt{ab}\,t) - B \sin(\sqrt{ab}\,t)]. \tag{25}$$

The form of the solutions in equations (24) and (25) supports the intuitive suggestion that the two population sizes will oscillate about their equilibrium sizes. However, this conclusion depends heavily on the specific assumptions that we made about the nature of the original equations, and various other models, with different outcomes, are possible. ∎

The final example is a particular case of our model.

□ **EXAMPLE 9**

Find the solutions for the predator–prey system

$$\frac{dy}{dt} = 2(x - 20)$$

$$\frac{dx}{dt} = -(y - 10)$$

if at time $t = 0$ there are $x(0) = 25$ rabbits and $y(0) = 12$ foxes present.

Solution: This system is a predator–prey system as in equations (22) and (23) with $\bar{x} = 20$, $\bar{y} = 10$, $a = 2$, and $b = 1$. Its general solution, given by equations (24) and (25), is

$$x(t) = 20 + A \sin \sqrt{2}\,t + B \cos \sqrt{2}\,t \tag{26}$$

$$y(t) = 10 - \sqrt{2}[A \cos \sqrt{2}\,t - B \sin \sqrt{2}\,t]. \tag{27}$$

Substituting $t = 0$ in equation (26) and using the initial condition $x(0) = 25$ gives

$$25 = 20 + A \sin(0) + B \cos(0)$$

$$= 20 + B$$

so $B = 5$. Substituting $t = 0$ in equation (27) and using the initial condition $y(0) = 12$ gives the equation

$$12 = 10 - \sqrt{2}[A\cos(0) - B\sin(0)]$$
$$= 10 - A\sqrt{2}$$

so $A = \dfrac{10 - 12}{\sqrt{2}} = -\sqrt{2}$. Thus

$$x(t) = 20 - \sqrt{2}\sin\sqrt{2}t + 5\cos\sqrt{2}t$$
$$y(t) = 10 + 2\cos\sqrt{2}t + 5\sqrt{2}\sin\sqrt{2}t.$$

These solutions are graphed on the same axes in Figure 4.2. ■

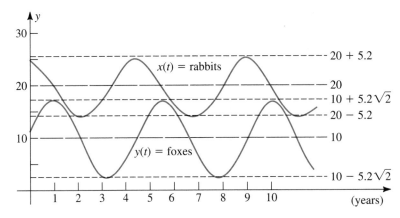

Figure 4.2 Solutions of a predator–prey system.

☑ **PRACTICE PROBLEMS 10.4**

1. Find the general solution of the differential equations.

    a. $\dfrac{d^2y}{dt^2} - 2\dfrac{dy}{dt} - 3y = 0$

    b. $\dfrac{d^2y}{dt^2} + 7y = 0$

2. Which of the following differential equations has
    a. only periodic solutions?
    b. only exponential solutions?
    c. solutions involving *both* exponential and periodic functions?

    Equation A: $y'' - C^2y = 0,$ C constant.

    Equation B: $y'' + 4y' + 6y = 0,$ $ab \neq 0,$ $a \neq b.$

    Equation C: $y'' + C^2y = 0,$ C constant.

Exercise Set 10.4

In Exercises 1–8, find the general solution of the differential equation in the form $y = Ae^{r_1 t} + Be^{r_2 t}$ by finding two distinct real roots of the characteristic polynomial.

1. $\dfrac{d^2 y}{dt^2} + 5\dfrac{dy}{dt} + 6y = 0$ 2. $y'' + 4y' - 5y = 0$

3. $y'' - y = 0$ 4. $\dfrac{d^2 y}{dt^2} + \dfrac{dy}{dt} - 12y = 0$

5. $\dfrac{d^2 y}{dt^2} + 3\dfrac{dy}{dt} - 10y = 0$ 6. $y'' - 4y = 0$

7. $y'' - \pi y = 0$ 8. $y'' - 4y' - 21y = 0$

In Exercises 9–14, find the general solution of the differential equation in the form $y = Ae^{rt} + Bte^{rt}$ by finding the single root r of the characteristic polynomial.

9. $y'' + 2y' + y = 0$ 10. $y'' - 4y' + 4y = 0$

11. $\dfrac{d^2 y}{dt^2} + 6\dfrac{dy}{dt} + 9y = 0$ 12. $y'' - 2y' + y = 0$

13. $y'' - 2Cy' + C^2 y = 0$ 14. $y'' - 8y' + 64y = 0$

In Exercises 15–22, find the general solution of the differential equation

15. $\dfrac{d^2 y}{dt^2} + 4y = 0$ 16. $y'' + 16y = 0$

17. $y'' = -7y$ 18. $\dfrac{d^2 y}{dt^2} = -36y$

19. $y'' - 4y' + 13y = 0$ 20. $y'' - 6y' + 25y = 0$

21. $y'' + y' + \dfrac{y}{2} = 0$ 22. $y'' + y' + y = 0$

In Exercises 23–28, find the solution of the initial value problem

23. $y'' - y' - 6y = 0$
    $y(0) = 0$
    $y'(0) = 5$

24. $y'' - 5y' + 6y = 0$
    $y(0) = 2$
    $y'(0) = 0$

25. $y'' + 2y' + y = 0$
    $y(0) = 3$
    $y'(0) = 1$

26. $y'' - 4y' + 4y = 0$
    $y(0) = 2$
    $y'(0) = 5$

27. $y'' + 9y = 0$
    $y(0) = 3$
    $y'(0) = -3$

28. $y'' + y = 0$
    $y(0) = 0$
    $y'(0) = 2$

In Exercises 29 and 30, find the general solution by first converting the system of two first order equations into a second order equation using the method of Example 8.

29. $\dfrac{dy}{dt} = 4x$
    $\dfrac{dx}{dt} = -y$

30. $\dfrac{dy}{dt} = 2(x - 3)$
    $\dfrac{dx}{dt} = 8(y + 5)$

31. Find the solution of the predator–prey system in Example 9 if initially $x(0) = 100$ rabbits and $y(0) = 40$ foxes are present.

32. Find the solution of the predator–prey system

$$\dfrac{dy}{dt} = x - 25$$
$$\dfrac{dx}{dt} = -2(y - 16)$$

subject to the initial conditions $x(0) = y(0) = 20$.

33. What is the solution of the predator–prey system in Exercise 32 under the initial conditions $x(0) = 25$ and $y(0) = 16$?

34. Discuss the nature of the solutions of the predator–prey system

$$\dfrac{dy}{dt} = ax \qquad a > 0$$
$$\dfrac{dx}{dt} = -by \qquad b > 0$$

versus the nature of the solutions of this same system when $b < 0$. Would it make sense to refer to this as a predator–prey system when $b < 0$?

35. Show that the function $y = te^{-2t}$ is a solution of the differential equation $y'' + 4y' + 4y = 0$ in Example 2.

36. Show that if y_1 and y_2 are solutions of the second order differential equation $y'' + ay' + by = 0$, then so is the linear combination $y = Ay_1 + By_2$. (*Hint:* Find $\dfrac{dy}{dt}$ and $\dfrac{d^2 y}{dt^2}$, insert in the differential equation, and use the fact that y_1 and y_2 are solutions.)

☑ **SOLUTIONS TO PRACTICE PROBLEMS 10.4**

1. a. The characteristic polynomial is $r^2 - 2r - 3 = (r - 3)(r + 1)$, which has roots $r_1 = -1$ and $r_2 = 3$. The general solution of the differential equation is

$$y = Ae^{-t} + Be^{3t}.$$

b. The characteristic polynomial is $r^2 + 7$ with complex roots $r_1 = -\sqrt{7}i$ and $r_2 = \sqrt{7}i$. The general solution is

$$y = A \sin \sqrt{7}t + B \cos \sqrt{7}t.$$

2. Equation A has characteristic polynomial $r^2 - C^2$, which has the distinct roots $r = \pm C$. The general solution is therefore

$$y = Ae^{-Ct} + Be^{Ct}$$

so equation A has only exponential solutions.

Equation B has characteristic polynomial $r^2 + 4r + 6$. Using the quadratic formula we find that the roots are

$$r = \frac{-4 \pm \sqrt{4^2 - 4(1)(6)}}{2}$$

$$= -2 \pm \frac{1}{2}\sqrt{-8}$$

$$= -2 \pm \sqrt{-2}$$

$$= -2 \pm \sqrt{2}i.$$

The general solution is therefore $y = e^{-2t}[A \sin \sqrt{2}t + B \cos \sqrt{2}t]$ and equation B has solutions involving both exponential and periodic functions.

Equation C has characteristic polynomial $r^2 + C^2$, which has (purely) complex roots $r = \pm Ci$ and general solution $y = A \sin Ct + B \cos Ct$. Thus, equation C has only periodic solutions.

10.5 Qualitative Theory of Differential Equations

Unfortunately, it is not always a simple matter to find a solution for a given differential equation, just as it is often not possible to find an explicit antiderivative for a given function. Often, however, we are able to infer **properties** of the (possibly unknown) solutions of a differential equation from the differential equation itself. The techniques for doing so are part of what is called **qualitative theory** for differential equations. This term refers to properties of solutions of a differential equation. We shall discuss qualitative theory only for equations of the form

$$y' = f(y) \tag{1}$$

where f is a differentiable function of y. Such equations are called **autonomous** because they do not involve an independent variable that in differential equations is usually taken to represent time. Thus *autonomous* means time-independent.

The general idea behind the techniques presented here is that equation (1) describes the behavior of the **derivative** $y' = \dfrac{dy}{dt}$ of the solution y in terms of the current value $y(t)$ of the solution. That is, equation (1) tells us something about the **slopes** of the solution curves at each value of a solution y. Geometrically, this means that equation (1) specifies the slopes of solution curves along horizontal lines of the ty-plane. Thus we can make inferences about the shapes of solution curves from equation (1) just as we made inferences about the graphs of **antiderivatives** from the values of a function in Chapter 5.

We shall illustrate some of the basic ideas in qualitative theory by discussing two examples in detail. Then we shall state some generalizations.

□ **EXAMPLE 1**

The differential equation

$$y' = y^2 - 1 \tag{2}$$

has the form $y' = f(y)$ where f is the function

$$f(y) = y^2 - 1 = (y - 1)(y + 1). \tag{3}$$

We make the following observations:

(i) Equation (2) has the constant solutions $y_1 = -1$ and $y_2 = 1$ because these constants are the zeros for f. (Since the derivative of a constant function is zero, both sides of the differential equation $y' = f(y)$ equal zero when y is a constant function with value equal to a root of f.) We plot the constant solutions y_1 and y_2 on the yt axes in Figure 5.1 for $t \geq 0$.

(ii) On any solution curve at height $y = 0$, the slope must equal $[y(0)]^2 - 1 = 0^2 - 1 = -1$. Thus we sketch "little tangents" along the horizontal line $y = 0$, all of slope $y' = -1$, as illustrated in Figure 5.2.

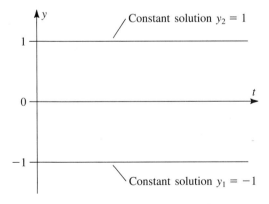

Figure 5.1 Two constant solutions.

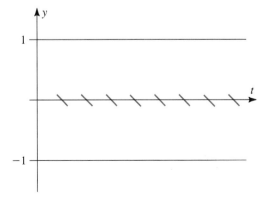

Figure 5.2 Tangents have slope $m = -1$ at $y = 0$.

(iii) Similarly, by choosing various other constant values $y = c$, we find the following slopes y' along the horizontal lines $y = c$:

$y = c$	Slope $= y' = c^2 - 1$
$c = \dfrac{1}{2}$	$y' = -\dfrac{3}{4}$
$c = \dfrac{3}{2}$	$y' = \dfrac{5}{4}$
$c = -\dfrac{1}{2}$	$y' = -\dfrac{3}{4}$
$c = -\dfrac{3}{2}$	$y' = \dfrac{5}{4}$

These tangents are sketched along the horizontal lines $y = c$ in Figure 5.3. We can generalize this observation by noting that equation (2) specifies the *sign* of the derivative $y'(t)$ of any solution in terms of its current value $y(t)$. Using the first derivative test, we may therefore conclude that solutions y must increase or decrease for various ranges of y as follows (and as illustrated in Figure 5.3):

Range for y	Sign of Derivative $y'(t) = y^2(t) - 1$	Behavior of Solution
$y < -1$	positive	increasing
$-1 < y < 1$	negative	decreasing
$y > 1$	positive	increasing

(iv) Knowing that the graph of a solution for equation (2) must have tangents as sketched in Figure 5.3, we use the "direction field" to sketch several possible solution curves as indicated in Figure 5.4.

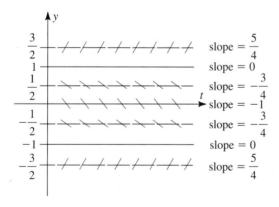

Figure 5.3 Slopes of solutions of equation (2) for various values of y.

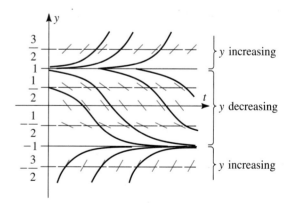

Figure 5.4 Solution curves for Example 1.

(v) To verify the assumptions made about the concavity of the curves sketches in Figure 5.4, we recall that the concavity of the function y is determined by its second derivative y''. Since $y' = f(y) = 1 - y^2$, we have, upon differentiating both sides and using the Chain Rule, that

$$y'' = \frac{d}{dt}[f(y)] = \frac{d}{dt}(1 - y^2) = \left[\frac{d}{dy}(1 - y^2)\right]\frac{dy}{dt}$$

$$= -2y(1 - y^2)$$

$$= -2y(1 - y)(1 + y)$$

from which we can see that the concavity of solutions is as follows:

Range for y	Concavity of Curves (Sign of $y'' = -2y(1 - y)(1 + y)$)
$y < -1$	negative
$-1 < y < 0$	positive
$0 < y < 1$	negative
$1 < y$	positive

The concavity is thus as labeled in Figure 5.5.

Thus although we have not obtained explicit solutions of equation (2), we have concluded quite a bit about the *nature* of the solutions for $t \geq 0$.   ■

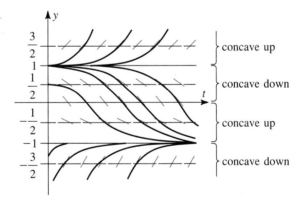

Figure 5.5 Solution curves for equation (2).

□ **EXAMPLE 2**

For the differential equation

$$y' = \sin y \tag{4}$$

describe the nature of solutions beginning at $t = 0$.

Strategy · · · · · · · ·

Follow the same analysis as in Example 1. Find the zeros of f.

Note that each zero of f gives a constant solution of (4).

Use equation (4) and the first derivative test to determine whether solutions y increase or decrease between consecutive zeros of f.

Solution

The equation has the form $y' = f(y)$ with $f(y) = \sin y$. The equation $f(y) = 0$ is therefore $\sin y = 0$, which has solutions

$$y = 0, \ \pm\pi, \ \pm 2\pi, \ \ldots$$

Thus equation (4) has constant solutions

$$y(t) = n\pi, \ n = 0, \ \pm 1, \ \pm 2, \ \ldots$$

as you can verify by direct substitution. (See Figure 5.6.) For values of y in the intervals between these zeros equation (4) determines the behavior of solutions y as follows:

Range for y	Sign of $y'(t)$	Behavior of y
$0 < y < \pi$	positive	increasing
$\pi < y < 2\pi$	negative	decreasing
$2n\pi < y < (2n + 1)\pi$	positive	increasing
$(2n - 1)\pi < y < 2n\pi$	negative	decreasing

Thus we may sketch tangents at constant values of y as in Figure 5.6.

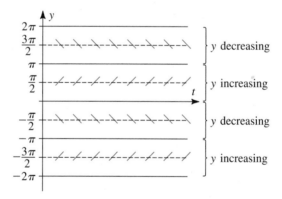

Figure 5.6 Slopes to solution curves for equation (4).

To determine concavity of solution curves, differentiate both sides of equation (4) and apply theory of concavity to the expression for y''. Check the sign of y'' between its zeros, which are

$$t = \pm\frac{n\pi}{2}, \qquad n = 0, \ \pm 1, \ \ldots$$

Using the Chain Rule, we find the second derivative y'' by differentiating both sides of equation (4) and substituting for y' from equation (4):

$$y'' = \frac{d}{dt}[y'] = \frac{d}{dt}[\sin y]$$

$$= \frac{d}{dy}[\sin y]\frac{dy}{dt}$$

$$= (\cos y)(\sin y).$$

From the zeros of y'' and its sign on the resulting intervals, we conclude the following about the concavity of solution curves:

Range for y	Sign of $y''(t)$	Concavity
$0 < y < \dfrac{\pi}{2}$	positive	up
$\dfrac{\pi}{2} < y < \pi$	negative	down
$\pi < y < \dfrac{3\pi}{2}$	positive	up
$\dfrac{3\pi}{2} < y < 2\pi$	negative	down
etc.		

Use all preceding information to sketch graphs.

From this information we sketch solution curves as in Figure 5.7. ■

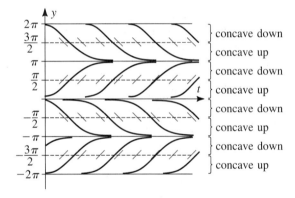

Figure 5.7 Concavity and solution curves for equation (4) for $-2\pi \le y \le 2\pi$.

From the results of Examples 1 and 2 it should not surprise you that solutions of autonomous differential equation of the form

$$y' = f(y) \tag{5}$$

have, for suitably well-behaved functions f, the following properties:

A-I: Each zero y_0 of the function f is a constant solution $y = y_0$ of equation (5). The graphs of these constant solutions slice the ty-plane into horizontal strips.

A-II: Any solution y with initial value $y(0)$ in one of these strips has all values $y(t)$ in the same strip for $t > 0$. That is, solution curves do not cross the horizontal lines that are graphs of constant solutions.

A-III: As t increases, the graph of any nonconstant solution either approaches the graph of a constant solution (as do all solutions in Example 2) or becomes infinitely large in absolute value (as do solutions y in Example 1 with $y(0) > 1$).

We do not claim to have proved statements A-I through A-III. Rather, your familiarity with properties of the first and second derivative, together with the explanations in Examples 1 and 2, should suggest the plausibility of these statements. They are proved in more advanced courses.

Initial Value Problems

The preceding observations are sometimes useful in inferring behavior of the unique solution of an initial value problem of the form

$$y' = f(y)$$

$$y(0) = y_0$$

for small values of $t > 0$. By analyzing the differential equation $y' = f(y)$ as in Examples 1 and 2, and by then noting the location of the initial value $y(0)$, we can infer the behavior of the particular solution of the initial value problem from the behavior of the general solution of the differential equation $y' = f(y)$ in the strip containing the initial value $y(0)$.

☐ **EXAMPLE 3**

Describe the short-term behavior of the solution of the initial value problem

$$y' = y^2 - 1 \tag{6}$$

$$y(0) = \frac{1}{2}. \tag{7}$$

Solution: From the behavior of the differential equation $y' = y^2 - 1$ as analyzed in Example 1, we know that it has successive constant solutions $y_1(t) = -1$ and $y_2(t) = 1$. Since $y(0) = \frac{1}{2}$ lies between these constants, we know that the solution of the initial value problem has values $y(t)$ with $-1 < y(t) < 1$ for all $t > 0$, according to property A-II. Moreover, since equation (6) and (7) give that $y'(0) = \left(\frac{1}{2}\right)^2 - 1 = -\frac{3}{4}$, we know that the solution y *decreases* from its initial value $y(0) = \frac{1}{2}$.

Thus the solution y must behave initially somewhat like the curve sketched in Figure 5.8. Note that we *cannot* determine, however, the number $t = c$ at which this solution crosses the t-axis. That is a particular piece of **quantitative** information that our **qualitative** theory cannot provide. ∎

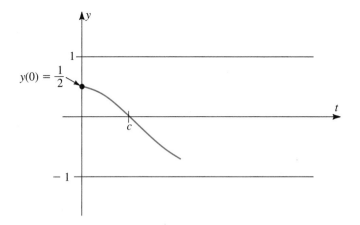

Figure 5.8 Solution to initial value problem. Number c cannot be determined by qualitative theory.

☐ **EXAMPLE 4**

Describe the behavior of the solution of the initial value problem

$$y' = 5y(20 - y) \tag{8}$$

$$y(0) = 25. \tag{9}$$

Solution: First, note that this problem may be described as an instance of a **logistic growth model** for a system with carrying capacity $K = 20$ and initial population size $y(0) = 25$, which is *larger* than the carrying capacity. (See Section 10.2.)

We note next that the function $f(y) = 5y(20 - y)$ on the right-hand side of equation (8) has zeros $y_1 = 0$ and $y_2 = 20$. Thus the solution y with initial condition $y(0) = 25$ will have its graph lying entirely *above* the horizontal line $y = 20$.

Next, we note that the tangent to the graph of this solution at $(0, 25)$ has slope

$$y'(0) = 5y(0)[20 - y(0)]$$

$$= 5(25)(20 - 25)$$

$$= -625 \tag{10}$$

so the solution decreases to the right of $t = 0$.

Finally, since the second derivative of this solution is

$$y'' = \frac{d}{dt}[y'] = \frac{d}{dt}[5y(20 - y)]$$

$$= \frac{d}{dt}[100y - 5y^2]$$

$$= 100y' - 10yy'$$

we find, using equations (9) and (10), that

$$y''(0) = 100[y'(0)] - 10[y(0)][y'(0)]$$
$$= 100(-625) - 10(25)(-625)$$
$$= 93{,}750$$

which is positive. Thus we may expect the graph of y to be concave up to the right of $t = 0$.

From this information and properties A-I through A-III we infer that the graph of the solution of the initial value problem is similar to that sketched in Figure 5.9. The important *qualitative* conclusion is that the population modeled by equation (8) with initial size $y(0) = 25$ will *decrease* in size toward the carrying capacity $K = 20$. ∎

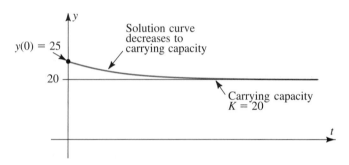

Figure 5.9

☑ PRACTICE PROBLEMS 10.5

1. Sketch solution curves for the differential equation

$$y' = y(2 + y).$$

2. Sketch the solution curve for the particular solution of the differential equation in Problem 1 with initial condition
   a. $y(0) = 0$.
   b. $y(0) = -2$.
   c. $y(0) = -1$.
   d. $y(0) = 1$.

Exercise Set 10.5

In Exercises 1–10, sketch solution curves for the given differential equation from the qualitative information obtained from the equation itself.

1. $y' = y(1 - y)$

2. $y' = y + 3$

3. $y' = y^2$

4. $y' = y(2 + y)$

5. $y' = e^y$

6. $y' = \dfrac{-1}{1 + y^2}$

7. $y' = \cos y$

8. $y' = y(2 - y^2)$

9. $y' = y(1 - y)(2 - y)$

10. $y' = \dfrac{4}{1 + y}$

In each of Exercises 11–20, sketch the solution of the initial value problem for $t \geq 0$ as best you can by using qualitative theory.

11. $y' = y(10 - y)$
$y(0) = 5$

12. $y' = y(10 - y)$
$y(0) = 20$

13. $y' = \sin y$
$y(0) = -\dfrac{\pi}{4}$

14. $y' = \cos y$
$y(0) = \pi$

15. $y' = y(1 - y^2)$
$y(0) = -2$

16. $y' = e^y$
$y(0) = -2$

17. $y' = y^2$
$y(0) = -1$

18. $y' = y^2$
$y(0) = 3$

19. $y' = (y + 3)(y - 2)$
$y(0) = 1$

20. $y' = (y - 1)(y - 4)$
$y(0) = 3$

21. Two solutions, y_1 and y_2, of the differential equation $y' = y(1 - y)$ have initial values $y_1(0) = \dfrac{1}{2}$ and $y_2(0) = \dfrac{3}{4}$. Do values of these solutions become closer together or farther apart as t increases? Why?

22. Same as Exercise 21 except that the initial values are $y_1(0) = \dfrac{1}{2}$ and $y_2(0) = -\dfrac{1}{2}$.

23. For the differential equation $y' = y(y - 1)(y - 2)$, does the solution y with $y(0) = \dfrac{3}{2}$ increase or decrease for $t > 0$?

24. Same as Exercise 23 except that the solution y has initial value $y(0) = 3$.

25. For the differential equation $y' = y(y-1)(y - 2)$ one constant solution $y = c$ has the property that all solutions with initial values $y(0)$ sufficiently close to c have the horizontal line $y = c$ as an asymptote. (We say that all such solutions are **asymptotic** to the solution $y = c$.) Find c.

26. One constant solution $y(t) = c$ of the differential equation $y' = (y + 3)(y - 2)$ has the property that all solutions with initial values sufficiently close to c move *away* from the value constant solution $y(t) = c$ as t increases. Find c.

27. Find the constant solution of the differential equation $y' = 30y(60 - 4y)$ with the property that all nearby solutions are asymptotic to it. (See Exercise 25.)

28. In the logistic growth model $y' = 3y(20 - 3y)$ will a solution with initial value $y(0) = 8$ increase or decrease?

29. In the differential equation $y' = ky(20 - y)$ determine the sign of k if the solution with initial value $y(0) = 10$ is known to decrease for $t > 0$.

30. In the differential equation $y' = ky(1 - y^2)$ determine the sign of k if the solution with initial value $y(0) = -2$ is known to decrease for $t > 0$.

☑ **SOLUTIONS TO PRACTICE PROBLEMS 10.5**

1. Slopes of tangents to curves with various y-coordinates are given in Table 5.1. The corresponding tangent fields and several solution curves are shown in Figure 5.10.

Table 5.1

y	0	$\dfrac{1}{2}$	1	2	$\dfrac{-1}{2}$	-1	$\dfrac{-3}{2}$	-2	-3	-4
Slope $= y'$	0	$\dfrac{5}{4}$	3	8	$\dfrac{-3}{4}$	-1	$\dfrac{-3}{4}$	0	3	8

Figure 5.11 shows, among these curves, the one with initial conditions given in Problem 2.

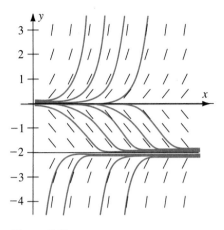

Figure 5.10

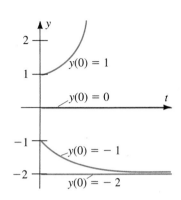

Figure 5.11 Four particular solutions.

10.6 Approximating Solutions of Differential Equations

In this brief chapter we are able only to skim the surface of the body of techniques and principles that constitute the theory of differential equations. However, there remain many differential equations for which simple solutions cannot be found. In such cases, however, we can resort to certain approximation procedures to obtain information about the solution, just as we can use the Trapezoidal Rule or Simpson's Rule to approximate a definite integral when the corresponding antiderivative cannot be found.

To give you an idea of how such approximation procedures work, we discuss one such procedure, called Euler's method, in this section. It is named for the Swiss mathematician Leonhard Euler (1707–1783). Although this method is seldom used in practice because more sophisticated methods have greater accuracy, it is a good first example of how such approximation schemes are constructed. Students interested in studying more advanced methods should consult texts on differential equations or numerical analysis.

Euler's Method

Euler's method may be used to approximate the solution to an initial value problem of the form

$$\frac{dy}{dt} = f(t, y) \tag{1}$$

$$y(a) = y_0$$

on some interval $[a, b]$. (We assume that f and its partial derivatives are continuous for all t and y, although less restrictive conditions can be given.)

Figure 6.1 illustrates the basic idea to be pursued. Assume that $y = f(t)$ is a particular solution of the given differential equation. We divide the interval $[a, b]$ into n subintervals of equal length $h = \dfrac{b - a}{n}$, obtaining the $(n + 1)$ endpoints

$$a = t_0 < t_1 < t_2 < \cdots < t_n = b.$$

Then, beginning at the left endpoint $t_0 = a$, we use the given information about the solution y (namely, the initial value $y(a) = y_0$) and its derivative to approximate the value $y(t_1)$, and we call the approximation y_1. (Note, as suggested by Figure 6.1, that, in general, the approximation y_1 will not equal the function value $y(t_1)$, which we do not know.) Next, we use the assumed value y_1 and the number $t_1 = a + h$ to approximate $y(t_2)$, and we call this approximation y_2. Continuing in this way, we finally approximate $y(t_n) = y(b)$ from the approximate value y_{n-1} and the number $t_{n-1} = a + (n - 1)h$. We therefore obtain *approximations* $y_1, y_2, \ldots, y_n$ to the (unknown) values of the solution $y(t_1), y(t_2), \ldots, y(t_n)$ at finitely many numbers t_j in $[a, b]$. The choice of the endpoint b and the number of intervals n depends on which values of the solution you wish to approximate and with what accuracy.

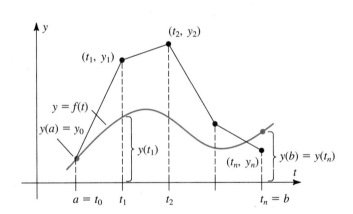

Figure 6.1 Approximation by Euler's method to the solution of the initial value problem

$$y' = f(t, y), \; y(a) = y_0.$$

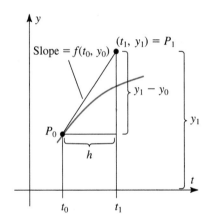

Figure 6.2 $y_1 = y_0 + f(t_0, y_0)h.$

Figure 6.2 illustrates how we get started in applying Euler's method. To find the approximation y_1 to the value $y(t_1)$, we follow the line tangent to the graph of y at the point $P_0 = (t_0, y_0)$ until we reach the point $P_1 = (t_1, y_1)$ with t-coordinate t_1. Since the slope of this line is $y'(t_0) = f(t_0, y_0)$, it follows that

$$\frac{y_1 - y_0}{t_1 - t_0} = f(t_0, y_0)$$

and since $h = t_1 - t_0$

$$y_1 = y_0 + f(t_0, y_0)h. \qquad (2)$$

Once we have obtained the approximation y_1 from equation (2), we *pretend* that y_1 is the actual value of the solution y at $t = t_1$. Since we don't know the actual value $y(t_1)$, the approximation y_1 is the ''next best thing.'' This ''pretending'' is necessary in order that we may carry out the same procedure to obtain the approximation y_2 for $y(t_2)$. Starting with the point (t_1, y_1) and the slope $f(t_1, y_1)$,* we obtain the y-coordinate of the point $P_2 = (t_2, y_2)$ from the equation

$$\frac{y_2 - y_1}{t_2 - t_1} = f(t_1, y_1).$$

That is, since $h = t_2 - t_1$

$$y_2 = y_1 + f(t_1, y_1)h.$$

Continuing in this way, we obtain each succeeding approximation y_{j+1} from the preceding y_j and t_j by the equation

$$y_{j+1} = y_j + f(t_j, y_j)h \qquad j = 0, 1, \ldots, n - 1 \qquad (3)$$

which is the summary statement of Euler's method. (See Figure 6.3.)

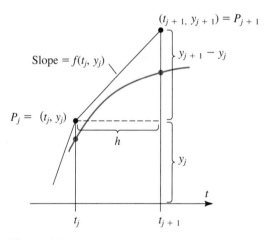

Figure 6.3 $y_{j+1} = y_j + f(t_j, y_j)h.$

---

*The pretending occurs here in two places. Since we do not actually know $y(t_j)$, we do not know the actual slope $f(t_j, y(t_j))$, which we approximate by $f(t_j, y_j)$. Neither do we know the point of tangency, $(t_j, y(t_j))$, so we use (t_j, y_j) instead.

The following two examples show how a first order differential equation may be put in the form of equation (1), and how the solution of an associated initial value problem may be approximated using Euler's method.

☐ **EXAMPLE 1**

Use Euler's method to approximate the solution of the initial value problem

$$y' = y(4 - y) \tag{4}$$

$$y(0) = 1$$

on the interval $[0, 1]$ using four subintervals of equal length.

Solution: With $[0, 1]$ divided into four subintervals of length $h = \dfrac{1 - 0}{4} = \dfrac{1}{4}$, we have endpoints

$$t_0 = 0, \qquad t_1 = \frac{1}{4}, \qquad t_2 = \frac{1}{2}, \qquad t_3 = \frac{3}{4}, \quad \text{and} \quad t_4 = 1.$$

With $y_0 = y(0) = 1$ and $f(t, y) = y(4 - y)$, equation (3) gives

$$y_1 = y_0 + y_0(4 - y_0)h$$

$$= 1 + 1(4 - 1)\left(\frac{1}{4}\right)$$

$$= 1 + \frac{3}{4}$$

$$= 1.75$$

$$y_2 = y_1 + y_1(4 - y_1)h$$

$$= 1.75 + 1.75(4 - 1.75)(0.25)$$

$$\cong 2.7344$$

and so forth. Table 6.1 shows the approximations y_1, y_2, y_3, y_4 together with the actual values $y(t_1), y(t_2), y(t_3), y(t_4)$ of the solution $y = \dfrac{4}{1 + 3e^{-4t}}$ of the initial value problem to four-decimal-place accuracy. (This solution is obtained by the method of Section 10.3.)   ∎

Table 6.1. Approximate and Actual Values of the Solution to the Initial Value Problem in Example 1 ($h = 0.25$)

t_j	0	0.25	0.50	0.75	1.0
y_j	1	1.75	2.7344	3.5995	3.9599
$y(t_j)$	1	1.9015	2.8449	3.4802	3.7917

☐ **EXAMPLE 2**

Approximate the solution to the initial value problem in Example 1 on the interval [0, 1] using $n = 10$ subintervals of equal size.

Solution: This time we have $h = \dfrac{1-0}{10} = \dfrac{1}{10}$, so Euler's equation becomes

$$y_{j+1} = y_j + y_j(4 - y_j)(0.10), \qquad j = 0, 1, 2, \ldots, 9.$$

Table 6.2 shows the resulting approximations, together with the actual values of the solution, to four-decimal-place accuracy. (Note the improvement in accuracy compared with Example 1.) ■

Table 6.2. Values of the Approximations and Actual Solution to the Initial Value Problem in Example 2 ($h = 0.10$)

t_j	0	0.1	0.2	0.3	0.4	0.5	0.6	0.7	0.8	0.9	1.0
y_j	1	1.3	1.651	2.0388	2.4387	2.8194	3.1523	3.4195	3.6180	3.7562	3.8478
$y(t_j)$	1	1.3285	1.7036	2.1013	2.4911	2.8449	3.1443	3.3829	3.5642	3.6970	3.7917

☐ **EXAMPLE 3**

Use Euler's method to approximate the solution of the initial value problem

$$y' + 2y = e^t \tag{5}$$

$$y(0) = 1$$

on the interval [0, 1].

Solution: We begin by moving all terms in equation (5) except the derivative y' to the right-hand side, obtaining

$$\frac{dy}{dt} = e^t - 2y.$$

Thus $f(t, y) = e^t - 2y$ in equation (3) for Euler's method. We obtain two approximations.

(a) Using $n = 4$ subdivisions we have $h = \dfrac{1-0}{4} = 0.25$ and equation (3) becomes

$$y_{j+1} = y_j + (e^{t_j} - 2y_j)(0.25), \qquad j = 0, 1, 2, 3.$$

Thus since $y_0 = y(0) = 1$ is given

$$y_1 = y_0 + (e^{t_0} - 2 \cdot y_0)(0.25)$$
$$= 1 + (e^0 - 2 \cdot 1)(0.25)$$
$$= 1 - 0.25$$
$$= 0.75$$
$$y_2 = y_1 + (e^{t_1} - 2y_1)(0.25)$$
$$= 0.75 + [e^{0.25} - 2(0.75)](0.25)$$
$$= 0.6960$$

and so forth. Table 6.3 shows the same approximations y_1, y_2, y_3, and y_4 to four-decimal-place accuracy, as well as the actual values $y(t_1)$, $y(t_2)$, $y(t_3)$, and $y(t_4)$ for the actual solution $y = \dfrac{1}{3}(2e^{-2t} + e^t)$.

Table 6.3. Approximate and Actual Values for the Initial Value Problem in Example 3 ($h = 0.25$)

t_j	1	0.25	0.5	0.75	1.0
y_j	1	0.75	0.6960	0.7602	0.9093
$y(t_j)$	1	0.8324	0.7948	0.8544	0.9963

(b) The same solution, approximated using ten subintervals of $[0, 1]$ of length $h = \dfrac{1 - 0}{10} = 0.1$, is obtained using the Euler equation

$$y_{j+1} = y_j + (e^{t_j} - 2y_j)(0.1), \qquad j = 0, 1, \ldots , 9.$$

Table 6.4 shows the results of this approximation.   ■

Table 6.4. Approximate and Actual Values of the Solution of the Initial Value Problem in Example 3 ($h = 0.1$)

t_j	0	0.1	0.2	0.3	0.4	0.5	0.6	0.7	0.8	0.9	1.0
y_j	1	0.9	0.8305	0.7866	0.7642	0.7606	0.7733	0.8009	0.8421	0.8962	0.9629
$y(t_j)$	1	0.9142	0.8540	0.8158	0.7968	0.7948	0.8082	0.8356	0.8764	0.9301	0.9963

CONCLUSION: Euler's method is one procedure for approximating the solution of an initial value problem involving a first order differential equation. While we have used examples in which an actual solution may be obtained for purposes of comparison, Euler's method may be applied to differential equations whose solutions are not known.

Obviously, there is a fair amount of tedium in applying Euler's method. Calculators and especially computers can reduce this tedium to a minimum. Program 7 in Appendix II is a BASIC computer program that was used to perform the calculations in Tables 6.1–6.4. You may find it useful in working the exercises.

Several sources of error enter into the calculations that are involved in Euler's method. Since we obtain only approximations y_j instead of the actual value $y(t_j)$ at each step, the slope calculation $\dfrac{dy}{dt} = f(t_j, y_j)$ contains an error due to the difference $|y_j - y(t_j)|$, and the point of assumed tangency, (t_j, y_j) contains an error due to the same factor. Finally, round-off error in such calculations is inescapable. In general, however, we can say that accuracy decreases as we attempt to approximate values of the solution farther away from the number t_0 where the initial condition is prescribed, and that accuracy increases as the stepsize h decreases. These important issues of accuracy are pursued in more advanced courses.

☑ **PRACTICE PROBLEM 10.6**

1. Use Euler's method to approximate the values of the solution of the initial value problem

$$y' = y(y + 2)$$
$$y(0) = -1$$

at the endpoints of four subintervals of $[0, 2]$ of length $h = \dfrac{1}{2}$.

Exercise Set 10.6

In each of Exercises 1–10, use Euler's method to approximate the value of the solution to the initial value problem at the endpoints of four subintervals of $[0, 1]$ of size $h = 0.25$.

1. $y' = 2y$

$y(0) = 1$

2. $y' = 9y(1 - y)$

$y(0) = \dfrac{1}{2}$

3. $y' + 2y = 4$

$y(0) = 1$

4. $\dfrac{dy}{dx} = \dfrac{y + 1}{x + 1}$

$y(0) = 0$

5. $\dfrac{dy}{dx} = x(y + 1)$

$y(0) = 1$

6. $\dfrac{dy}{dx} = 2 - 4y$

$y(0) = 1$

7. $\dfrac{dy}{dt} + 2ty = t$

$y(0) = \dfrac{3}{2}$

8. $e^y \cdot \dfrac{dy}{dt} - t^2 = 0$

$y(0) = 0$

9. $\dfrac{dy}{dt} = 2y - 2t$

$y(0) = \dfrac{3}{2}$

10. $\dfrac{dy}{dt} - 2y = e^{2t} \sin t$

$y(0) = 0$

11. Use equations (14) and (15) of Section 10.3 to find the algebraic solution of the initial value problem in Exercise 3. Compute the actual value of the solution at each endpoint and compare it with the value from Euler's method.

12. An investor opens a savings account paying 10% interest compounded continuously with an initial deposit of $1000. The investor makes deposits of $1000 per year in a continuous manner.

a. Show that the function P, giving the amount on deposit after t years, satisfies the differential equation $P'(t) = 0.10P(t) + 1000$.

b. Use Euler's method to approximate the values $P(1)$, $P(2)$, $P(3)$, and $P(4)$.

☑ **SOLUTION TO PRACTICE PROBLEM 10.6**

Euler's method gives approximations to the solution values y_1, y_2, y_3, and y_4 at the respective endpoints $x_1 = \dfrac{1}{2}$, $x_2 = 1$, $x_3 = \dfrac{3}{2}$, and $x_4 = 2$ by the formula

$$y_{j+1} = y_j + y_j(y_j + 2)\left(\frac{1}{2}\right), \qquad j = 0, \ldots, 3$$

$$y_0 = -1.$$

These values are listed in Table 6.5.

Table 6.5

Endpoint x_j	0	$\dfrac{1}{2}$	1	$\dfrac{3}{2}$	2
Value y_j	-1	-1.5	-1.875	-1.9922	-2

Summary Outline of Chapter 10

▮ A **differential equation** is an equation involving one or more derivatives of an unknown function.   (Page 728)

▮ A **solution** of a differential equation is a function that has as many derivatives as the order of the equation and that satisfies the equation.   (Page 728)

▮ The **order** of a differential equation is the order of the highest derivative in the equation.   (Page 728)

▮ An **initial value problem** consists of a differential equation together with enough data to determine a unique solution.   (Page 731)

▮ A **separable** differential equation has the form   (Page 745)

$$\frac{dy}{dx} = \frac{f(x)}{g(y)}.$$

▮ We **separate the variables** in this equation as follows: (Page 746)

$$g(y)\, dy = f(x)\, dx$$

so

$$\int g(y)\left(\frac{dy}{dx}\right) dx = \int f(x)\, dx$$

and the solution follows by integration, when possible.

■ The differential equation $\dfrac{dy}{dt} = ky$ for natural growth has the general solution $y = Ce^{kt}$. (Page 749)

■ The differential equation $\dfrac{dy}{dt} = k\left(\dfrac{K - y}{K}\right)$ for logistic growth has the general solution (Page 750)

$$y = \frac{K}{1 + Me^{-kt}}, \qquad M \text{ constant.}$$

■ The differential equation $\dfrac{dy}{dt} = k(y - a)$, which is separable, has the general solution (Page 753)

$$y = a + Ce^{kt}.$$

■ The differential equation $y'' + ay' + by = 0$ has a solution of the form $y = e^{rt}$ if and only if r is a real root of the characteristic polynomial $r^2 + ar + b$. (Page 761)

■ The differential equation $y'' + by = 0$, with $b > 0$, has the general solution (Page 766)

$$y = A \sin \sqrt{b}\,t + B \cos \sqrt{b}\,t.$$

■ The predator–prey system (Page 769)

$$\frac{dy}{dt} = a(x - \bar{x}), \qquad a > 0$$

$$\frac{dx}{dt} = -b(y - \bar{y}), \qquad b > 0$$

has the general solution

$$x(t) = \bar{x} + A \sin \sqrt{ab}\,t + B \cos \sqrt{ab}\,t$$

$$y(t) = \bar{y} - \sqrt{\frac{a}{b}}\,[A \cos \sqrt{ab}\,t - B \sin \sqrt{ab}\,t].$$

■ Euler's method for approximating solutions of the initial value problem (Page 782)

$$\frac{dy}{dt} = f(t, y)$$

$$y(a) = y_0$$

at n equally spaced numbers t_j in the interval $[a, b]$ is

$$y_{j+1} = y_j + f(t_j, y_j)h, \quad j = 0, 1, 2, \ldots, n - 1$$

where

$$h = \frac{b - a}{n} \quad \text{and} \quad t_j = a + jh, \quad j = 0, 1, 2, \ldots, n.$$

Review Exercises—Chapter 10

In Exercises 1–24, find the general solution of the differential equation.

1. $\dfrac{dx}{dt} = x + 3$

2. $\dfrac{dy}{dx} = 4 + \sqrt{x}$

3. $\dfrac{dy}{dx} = \dfrac{\sec^2 \sqrt{x} \tan \sqrt{x}}{\sqrt{x}}$

4. $\dfrac{d^2y}{dt^2} = \sqrt{1 + t}$

5. $\dfrac{dy}{dt} = 3ty^2$

6. $\dfrac{dy}{dx} = \dfrac{\sqrt{x + 1}}{y}$

7. $\dfrac{dy}{dt} = (1 + t)(2 + y)$

8. $ty' = \dfrac{t + 3}{y}$

9. $y' + 2y = 4$

10. $y' = y(3 - y)$

11. $y' + y \cos t = 0$

12. $y' = 4y \ln y$

13. $(t - 1)y' = t + 1$

14. $\dfrac{dy}{dt} + \dfrac{1}{t^2}y = 0$

15. $\dfrac{dy}{dx} = y(2 - y)$

16. $ty' + 2y = 0$

17. $\dfrac{dy}{dt} = \dfrac{t + 3}{y}$

18. $\dfrac{dy}{dt} = \dfrac{y}{t + 1}$

19. $y'' - 5y' - 6y = 0$

20. $\dfrac{d^2y}{dx^2} - 9y = 0$

21. $\dfrac{d^2y}{dx^2} - 5\dfrac{dy}{dx} - 14y = 0$

22. $y'' - y' - 6y = 0$

23. $y'' - 8y' + 16y = 0$

24. $\dfrac{d^2y}{dt^2} = 3\dfrac{dy}{dt} + 10y$

In Exercises 25–36, find the solution of the initial value problem.

25. $\dfrac{dy}{dx} = \dfrac{x}{\sqrt{1 + x^2}}$
$y(0) = 3$

26. $\dfrac{d^2y}{dt^2} = 1 + t$
$y(0) = 1$
$y'(0) = 0$

27. $y' = 4y$
$y(0) = 3$

28. $\dfrac{dy}{dt} = ty$
$y(1) = 3$

29. $\dfrac{dy}{dx} = y \sin x$
$y(0) = \pi$

30. $y' = 4(1 - y)$
$y(0) = 1$

31. $y' = 10(5 - t)$
$y(0) = 2$

32. $\dfrac{d^2y}{dx^2} = -9y$
$y(0) = 3$
$y'(0) = 9$

33. $\dfrac{d^2y}{dx^2} + 16y = 0$
$y(0) = 5$
$y'(0) = 0$

34. $\dfrac{dy}{dt} = 5y(10 - y)$
$y(0) = 5$

35. $y'' - 6y' + 9y = 0$
$y(0) = 0$
$y'(0) = 6$

36. $y'' - 16y = 0$
$y(0) = 2$
$y'(0) = 8$

In Exercises 37–40, sketch the direction field and several solution curves for the differential equation

37. $\dfrac{dy}{dt} = 2y(4 - y)$

38. $\dfrac{dy}{dx} = xy$

39. $\dfrac{dy}{dt} = y + 3$

40. $\dfrac{dy}{dx} = \dfrac{x}{y}$

41. The value of a certain piece of real estate in San Diego has been increasing at a rate of $V'(t) = \sqrt{36 + t}$ thousand dollars per year since 1985. If its value in 1985 was $200,000, find its value $V(t)$, t years after 1985.

42. A manufacturer of refrigerators determines that its marginal revenue at production level x refrigerators per week is $60 + 2x - 0.2x^2$ dollars. Use the fact that $R(0) = 0$ to find the manufacturer's total revenue function $R(t)$.

43. Find a differential equation satisfied by the function
a. $y = Ce^{2t}$
b. $y = C_1e^t + C_2e^{-t}$

44. A tank contains 500 liters of brine with an initial concentration of salt of 1 kilogram of salt per liter. A second mixture of brine containing 2 kilograms of salt per liter is then added at a rate of 50 liters per minute. The tank is kept well mixed, and brine is drawn off the bottom at the same rate, 50 liters per minute. Find the concentration of salt t minutes after the second mixture begins entering the first.

45. An automobile radiator contains 5 gallons of pure antifreeze. The owner begins adding fresh water at the rate of 1 gallon per minute, with the engine running to ensure complete mixing, and draining the radiator at the same rate of 1 gallon per minute. Find the concentration $y(t)$ of antifreeze per gallon t minutes after the owner begins this process.

46. An investor places $5000 in a savings account paying 10% interest compounded continuously and pledges to make additional deposits of $2000 per year in a continual manner.

a. Find a differential equation for $P(t)$, the amount on deposit in this account t years after it is opened.
b. Use Euler's method to approximate $P(1), P(2), P(3),$ and $P(4)$.

47. A cold drink is removed from a refrigerator at temperature 40°F and is placed on a sun porch where the surrounding temperature is 80°F. After 5 minutes the temperature of the drink is 50°F. Find its temperature after 10 minutes.

48. The value of an antique automobile increases at the rate $\dfrac{dv}{dt} = (t + 5)^{2/3}$ where t is the age of the automobile. The car was originally worth $5000. Find $v(t)$, its value after t years.

49. The marginal utility, $\dfrac{du}{ds}$, associated with a consumer's receipt of s units of a given product per unit time satisfies the differential equation $\dfrac{du}{ds} = \dfrac{1}{s + 1}$. Find the utility function $u(s)$ if $u(0) = 5$.

Damage to buildings resulting from a tornado can be high. To assess risks associated with the insuring of property or lives, insurance companies must depend upon probability and statistics. *(Gerald Brimacombe/The Image Bank)*

Applications to Probability Theory

11.1 Discrete Probability Distributions

The goal of probability theory is to develop mathematical models for predicting the outcomes of "experiments" based on assumptions about the likelihood of certain associated events occurring. Those assumptions are stated in the form of a function called a **probability distribution.** We shall not attempt to develop the basic principles of probability theory that let us determine which function to use for this purpose. Rather, we shall assume that a probability distribution is already at hand and show how the definite integral is used to calculate probabilities for various events. Before discussing continuous distributions (Section 11.2), we establish the terminology and basic principles for the discrete distributions in this section.

Outcomes, Events,
and Probabilities

By an **outcome** of an experiment, we mean one of the simple results that can occur. Part of the description of an experiment consists of specifying what the set of all possible outcomes (called the **sample space** for the experiment) will be.

For example, in the experiment of rolling a single die, the possible outcomes are the numbers that may be observed, 1 through 6. The sample space for this experiment is therefore the set

$$S = \{1, 2, 3, 4, 5, 6\}$$

which contains six elements (outcomes). By comparison, the occurrence "observe a number less than 4" is not called an outcome, since it corresponds to more than one simple outcome (namely, 1, 2, and 3). We use the term **event** to refer to a collection of one or more outcomes. Thus an event E is a subset of a sample space S. In the example E: "observe a number less than 4," we have

$$E = \{1, 2, 3\}.$$

We want to distinguish outcomes from events because a single trial of an experiment can result in only one outcome, while it could correspond to more than one event.

□ **EXAMPLE 1**

In the experiment of rolling a single die, let E_1 through E_3 be the events

E_1:   observe a number less than 4
E_2:   observe an even number
E_3:   observe a number that is not 1.

Then each of these events is a subset of the sample space $S = \{1, 2, 3, 4, 5, 6\}$ as follows:

$$E_1 = \{1, 2, 3\}$$
$$E_2 = \{2, 4, 6\}$$
$$E_3 = \{2, 3, 4, 5, 6\}.$$

Now note that each of the outcomes 1 to 6 in S is a member of one or more events, as follows:

Outcome	Event
1	E_1
2	E_1, E_2, E_3
3	E_1, E_3
4	E_2, E_3
5	E_3
6	E_2, E_3

■

Probabilities

Once a sample space S (that is, the set of possible simple outcomes) for an experiment has been identified, we assign a number called a **probability** to each possible outcome in S. For our model to be useful in predicting outcomes of actual experiments, the probability associated with a possible outcome should be the **relative frequency** with which that outcome will occur in a large number of repetitions of the experiment. (From a strictly mathematical point of view, however, this requirement is not necessary. Probabilities need only be assigned according to two rules that we shall state later.)

☐ **EXAMPLE 2**

In the experiment of a single toss of a fair coin, we would expect to obtain a head roughly half the time and a tail roughly half the time. (Indeed, this is the definition of a "fair" coin.) We therefore assign probabilities to the outcomes in the sample space $S = \{\text{head, tail}\}$ as follows

$$Pr(\text{head}) = \frac{1}{2}$$

$$Pr(\text{tail}) = \frac{1}{2}.$$

■

☐ **EXAMPLE 3**

In the experiment of rolling a fair die, each of the outcomes 1 to 6 is equally likely. The relative frequency with which each would be expected to occur "in the long run" is therefore $\frac{1}{6}$. Thus the probability associated with each outcome is $\frac{1}{6}$. That is,

$$Pr(1) = Pr(2) = Pr(3) = Pr(4) = Pr(5) = Pr(6) = \frac{1}{6}.$$

■

☐ **EXAMPLE 4**

A box contains two red balls and three white balls. One ball is selected at random. What is the probability that it is (a) red or (b) white?

Solution: The fact that the ball is selected "at random" means that each of the five balls is just as likely to be selected as any of the others. Since two of the five balls are red, we would expect that, in many repetitions of this experiment, we would obtain a red ball roughly $\frac{2}{5}$ of the time. Similarly, the relative frequency with which a white ball will be chosen is $\frac{3}{5}$. These are the probabilities associated with the sample space $S = \{\text{red ball, white ball}\}$:

$$Pr(\text{red ball}) = \frac{2}{5}$$

$$Pr(\text{white ball}) = \frac{3}{5}.$$

■

Rules for Probabilities

Since the probability associated with an outcome is thought of as a **relative frequency** (meaning the number of times this outcome occurs divided by the total number of times the experiment is performed), probabilities must satisfy two rules.

> Rule 1: The probability associated with any outcome is a number in the interval [0, 1].
>
> Rule 2: The sum of the probabilities associated with the set of all outcomes in a finite sample space is 1.

Rule 2 can be thought of as meaning that "*something* must happen."

Probabilities for Events

Once probabilities have been assigned to individual outcomes in a sample space, probabilities for events may be calculated according to the following rule.

> Rule 3: The probability associated with an event is the sum of the probabilities associated with the simple outcomes in that event.

Rule 3 is sometimes called the **addition law for probabilities** associated with (disjoint or mutually exclusive) outcomes.

□ **EXAMPLE 5**

For the events in the die-rolling experiment of Example 1 we have

$$Pr(E_1) = Pr(1) + Pr(2) + Pr(3) = \frac{1}{6} + \frac{1}{6} + \frac{1}{6} = \frac{1}{2}$$

$$Pr(E_2) = Pr(2) + Pr(4) + Pr(6) = \frac{1}{6} + \frac{1}{6} + \frac{1}{6} = \frac{1}{2}$$

$$Pr(E_3) = Pr(2) + Pr(3) + Pr(4) + Pr(5) + Pr(6)$$

$$= \frac{1}{6} + \frac{1}{6} + \frac{1}{6} + \frac{1}{6} + \frac{1}{6}$$

$$= \frac{5}{6}.$$

■

□ **EXAMPLE 6**

A car rental firm has determined from past experience that the probabilities of a blowout occurring on the four tires of one of its cars are as follows:

$$Pr(\text{left front}) = 0.3$$

$$Pr(\text{right front}) = 0.25$$

$$Pr(\text{left rear}) = 0.25$$

$$Pr(\text{right rear}) = 0.2.$$

Since the event E_1 of a front-tire blowout contains the first two outcomes listed above, we have

$$Pr(E_1) = 0.3 + 0.25 = 0.55.$$

Similarly, the event E_2 of a rear-tire blowout contains the last two outcomes, so

$$Pr(E_2) = 0.25 + 0.2 = 0.45. \qquad \blacksquare$$

Random Variables and Probability Functions

From this point on we shall restrict our discussion to sample spaces in which the outcomes are represented by numbers, such as the die-rolling experiment of Example 1 where the sample space is $S = \{1, 2, 3, 4, 5, 6\}$. We may therefore use a variable such as X to represent an outcome in the sample space. Such a variable is called a **random variable.***

When the outcomes in a sample space are represented by values of a random variable, the assignment of probabilities to the outcomes can be thought of as a function for which the domain is a sample space. We refer to this as a **probability function,** written Pr. We use the following notation with probability functions:

$$Pr\{X = a\} \text{ means the probability associated with outcome } a,$$

while

$$Pr\{X \text{ in } E\} \text{ means the probability associated with the event } E.$$

☐ **EXAMPLE 7**

Using this notation for the die-rolling experiment in Example 5, we would write

(a) $Pr\{X = 3\} = \dfrac{1}{6}$

(b) $Pr\{X = 5\} = \dfrac{1}{6}$

(c) $Pr\{X \text{ in } E_1\} = \dfrac{1}{2}$

etc. ▩

---

*A more sophisticated approach would be to say that a random variable is a function defined on a sample space. We shall not require this more general notion of the random variable.

Probability Distributions

A sample space together with a probability function Pr defined on the sample space is called the **probability distribution** for the random variable X. Probability distributions can be specified by giving either a table of all elements of the sample space and their probabilities, or a **probability histogram**, which is just a bar graph showing the probability associated with each outcome.

☐ **EXAMPLE 8**

The probability distribution for the random variable X representing the possible outcomes of a single roll of a fair die is given in Table 1.1 and by the probability histogram in Figure 1.1. ■

Table 1.1

Outcome X	1	2	3	4	5	6
Probability $Pr\{X\}$	$\dfrac{1}{6}$	$\dfrac{1}{6}$	$\dfrac{1}{6}$	$\dfrac{1}{6}$	$\dfrac{1}{6}$	$\dfrac{1}{6}$

☐ **EXAMPLE 9**

Consider the experiment consisting of two tosses of a fair coin. Let the random variable X represent the number of heads obtained. Find the probability distribution for X.

Solution: The sample space for X consists of the possible outcomes $S = \{0, 1, 2\}$. To determine how to assign probabilities to each of these outcomes, we must determine the relative frequency with which each is expected to occur. In terms of the *order* in which the results of this experiment occur, there are two ways in which $X = 1$ head can occur, while there is only one way that $X = 0$ heads or $X = 2$ heads can occur:

Results, in Order	Value of X
tail, tail	$X = 0$
tail, head	$X = 1$
head, tail	$X = 1$
head, head	$X = 2$

Since each of these four results seems equally likely to occur, we assign each the probability (relative frequency) $\dfrac{1}{4}$. This means that the outcome $X = 1$ head will occur with relative frequency $\dfrac{1}{4} + \dfrac{1}{4} = \dfrac{1}{2}$, while outcomes $X = 0$ and $X = 2$ will occur with relative frequency $\dfrac{1}{4}$. These are the probabilities assigned to the three possible values of X, as shown in Table 1.2. Figure 1.2 shows the probability histogram for this distribution. ■

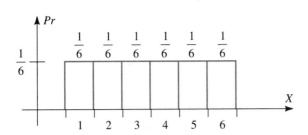

Figure 1.1 Probability distribution for die-rolling experiment.

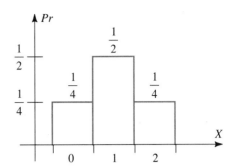

Figure 1.2 Probability distribution for random variable X in Example 9.

Table 1.2

Outcome X	0	1	2
Probability $Pr\{X\}$	$\dfrac{1}{4}$	$\dfrac{1}{2}$	$\dfrac{1}{4}$

☐ **EXAMPLE 10**

Table 1.3 shows the possible outcomes for the experiment of rolling two fair dice, where the random variable X represents the sum of the numbers showing on the two dice. The probabilities assigned to the possible outcomes (values of X) are the relative frequencies determined by noting how many of the 36 distinct possible pairs (a, b) are associated with that outcome.

The distribution for the random variable X is shown by the probability histogram in Figure 1.3.   ■

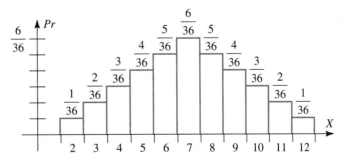

Figure 1.3 Probability distribution for random variable X in Example 10.

Table 1.3

Outcome X	Pairs (a, b) corresponding to X	Probability
2	(1, 1)	$Pr\{X = 2\} = \dfrac{1}{36}$
3	(1, 2), (2, 1)	$Pr\{X = 3\} = \dfrac{2}{36}$
4	(1, 3), (3, 1), (2, 2)	$Pr\{X = 4\} = \dfrac{3}{36}$
5	(1, 4), (4, 1), (2, 3), (3, 2)	$Pr\{X = 5\} = \dfrac{4}{36}$
6	(1, 5), (5, 1), (2, 4), (4, 2), (3, 3)	$Pr\{X = 6\} = \dfrac{5}{36}$
7	(1, 6), (6, 1), (2, 5), (5, 2), (3, 4), (4, 3)	$Pr\{X = 7\} = \dfrac{6}{36}$
8	(2, 6), (6, 2), (3, 5), (5, 3), (4, 4)	$Pr\{X = 8\} = \dfrac{5}{36}$
9	(3, 6), (6, 3), (4, 5), (5, 4)	$Pr\{X = 9\} = \dfrac{4}{36}$
10	(4, 6), (6, 4), (5, 5)	$Pr\{X = 10\} = \dfrac{3}{36}$
11	(5, 6), (6, 5)	$Pr\{X = 11\} = \dfrac{2}{36}$
12	(6, 6)	$Pr\{X = 12\} = \dfrac{1}{36}$

☐ EXAMPLE 11

For the experiment in which the random variable X represents the sum obtained in a single toss of two fair dice (Example 10) we can define many events; probabilities for some of them are

$$Pr\{X = 5\} = \frac{4}{36} = \frac{1}{9}$$

$$Pr\{X = 2, 3, \text{ or } 4\} = \frac{1}{36} + \frac{2}{36} + \frac{3}{36} = \frac{6}{36} = \frac{1}{6}$$

$$Pr\{X \leq 6\} = \frac{1}{36} + \frac{2}{36} + \frac{3}{36} + \frac{4}{36} + \frac{5}{36} = \frac{15}{36} = \frac{5}{12}$$

$$Pr\{3 < X \le 5\} = Pr\{X = 4\} + Pr\{X = 5\} = \frac{3}{36} + \frac{4}{36} = \frac{7}{36}$$

$$Pr\{X > 8\} = Pr\{X = 9\} + Pr\{X = 10\} + Pr\{X = 11\} + Pr\{X = 12\}$$

$$= \frac{4}{36} + \frac{3}{36} + \frac{2}{36} + \frac{1}{36}$$

$$= \frac{5}{18}.$$

■

Expected Value

For a random variable X associated with a finite sample space $\{x_1, x_2, \ldots, x_n\}$ the concept of *expected value* is a generalization of the notion of the average of the numbers $x_1, x_2, \ldots, x_n$.

Definition 1

Let X be a random variable on the sample space $\{x_1, x_2, \ldots, x_n\}$ and let p_j be the probability $p_j = Pr\{X = x_j\}$ for $j = 1, 2, \ldots, n$. The **expected value of X,** written $E(X)$, is the sum

$$E(X) = x_1 p_1 + x_2 p_2 + \cdots + x_n p_n.$$

Notice that when each of the outcomes x_j has equal probability $p_j = \frac{1}{n}$, the expected value of X is

$$E(X) = x_1 \left(\frac{1}{n}\right) + x_2 \left(\frac{1}{n}\right) + \cdots + x_n \left(\frac{1}{n}\right)$$

$$= \frac{x_1 + x_2 + \cdots + x_n}{n}$$

the average of the numbers $x_1, x_2, \ldots, x_n$. Thus the expected value $E(X)$ is a sort of "weighted average," where the outcomes with higher probabilities make larger contributions to the average.

□ **EXAMPLE 12**

(a) For the experiment of rolling a single die the expected value of the outcome X is

$$E(X) = 1\left(\frac{1}{6}\right) + 2\left(\frac{1}{6}\right) + 3\left(\frac{1}{6}\right) + 4\left(\frac{1}{6}\right) + 5\left(\frac{1}{6}\right) + 6\left(\frac{1}{6}\right)$$

$$= \frac{1 + 2 + 3 + 4 + 5 + 6}{6}$$

$$= \frac{7}{2}$$

which is just the average of the six (equally likely) outcomes.

(b) For the experiment consisting of the rolling of a pair of dice the expected value of the sum is, according to the probabilities in Table 1.3 and Definition 1

$$E(X) = 2\left(\frac{1}{36}\right) + 3\left(\frac{2}{36}\right) + 4\left(\frac{3}{36}\right) + 5\left(\frac{4}{36}\right) + 6\left(\frac{5}{36}\right)$$

$$+ 7\left(\frac{6}{36}\right) + 8\left(\frac{5}{36}\right) + 9\left(\frac{4}{36}\right) + 10\left(\frac{3}{36}\right)$$

$$+ 11\left(\frac{2}{36}\right) + 12\left(\frac{1}{36}\right)$$

$$= \frac{2 + 6 + 12 + 20 + 30 + 42 + 40 + 36 + 30 + 22 + 12}{36}$$

$$= \frac{252}{36}$$

$$= 7.$$

This should not be surprising, once you have noted the symmetry in Figure 1.3. The expected value simply corresponds to the center of this pyramid-like distribution. ■

REMARK: Note, as in Example 12, part (a), that the expected value of a random variable need not be one of the numbers in the sample space, just as the average of a set of numbers need not be one of the numbers in the set.

The following example shows how the concept of expected value can be used in decision making.

☐ **EXAMPLE 13**

A venture capital firm determines, based on past experience, that for each $100 invested in a high technology start-up company a return of $400 is experienced 20% of the time, a return of $100 is experienced 40% of the time, and a total loss is experienced 40% of the time. What is the firm's expected return, based on these data?

Solution: If we let the random variable X represent the three outcomes $x_1 = \$400$, $x_2 = \$100$, and $x_3 = 0$, the probabilities associated with these outcomes are given in Table 1.4.

Table 1.4

x_i	$400	$100	0
p_i	0.20	0.40	0.40

The expected value of X is therefore

$$E(X) = (\$400)(0.2) + (\$100)(0.4) + (0)(0.4)$$
$$= \$80 + \$40 + 0$$
$$= \$120.$$

This means that, on average, the firm can expect a return of $120 on each $100 invested in a high technology start-up company. Whether this result leads to a decision to invest depends on whether the firm is satisfied with this rate of return, and over what time period it will occur. ■

Variance

The expected value of a random variable is a measure of its central tendency, that is, what values are most likely to occur. In contrast, a random variable's *variance* is a measure of how far apart the possible outcomes are spread, again weighted by their respective probabilities.

Definition 2

Let X be a random variable for the sample space $\{x_1, x_2, \ldots, x_n\}$ and let $p_j = Pr\{X = x_j\}$, for $j = 1, 2, \ldots, n$. Let $E(X)$ be the expected value of X. The **variance** of X, denoted by $\text{Var}(X)$, is the number

$$\text{Var}(X) = E([X - E(X)]^2) = [x_1 - E(X)]^2 p_1 + [x_2 - E(X)]^2 p_2$$
$$+ \ldots + [x_n - E(X)]^2 p_n.$$

☐ **EXAMPLE 14**

For the experiment of rolling two dice (Examples 10 and 12), where the expected value of their sum is $E(X) = 7$, the variance is

$$\text{Var}(X) = (2 - 7)^2\left(\frac{1}{36}\right) + (3 - 7)^2\left(\frac{2}{36}\right) + (4 - 7)^2\left(\frac{3}{36}\right) + (5 - 7)^2\left(\frac{4}{36}\right)$$

$$+ (6 - 7)^2\left(\frac{5}{36}\right) + (7 - 7)^2\left(\frac{6}{36}\right) + (8 - 7)^2\left(\frac{5}{36}\right) + (9 - 7)^2\left(\frac{4}{36}\right)$$

$$+ (10 - 7)^2\left(\frac{3}{36}\right) + (11 - 7)^2\left(\frac{2}{36}\right) + (12 - 7)^2\left(\frac{1}{36}\right)$$

$$= \frac{25 + 16 \cdot 2 + 9 \cdot 3 + 4 \cdot 4 + 1 \cdot 5 + 1 \cdot 5 + 4 \cdot 4 + 9 \cdot 3 + 16 \cdot 2 + 25}{36}$$

$$= \frac{210}{36} = \frac{35}{6}.$$
■

☐ **EXAMPLE 15**

For the probability distribution experienced by the venture capitalist in Example 13

$$\text{Var}(X) = (400 - 120)^2(0.2) + (100 - 120)^2(0.4) + (0 - 120)^2(0.4)$$

$$= (78,400)(0.2) + (400)(0.4) + (14,400)(0.4)$$

$$= 21,600.$$ ■

The variance of a random variable is a number that is more difficult to interpret intuitively than is the expected value. But in comparing two random variables with the same expected value, we can, in general, say that the distribution of the random variable with the larger variance is more "spread out" than the other.

Standard Deviation

The **standard deviation** of a random variable X is simply the square root of its variance. The standard deviation of X is denoted by the Greek letter σ (sigma). Thus in Example 14 we have

$$\sigma = \sqrt{\text{Var}(X)} = \sqrt{\frac{35}{6}} \approx 2.4152$$

while in Example 15 we have

$$\sigma = \sqrt{\text{Var}(X)} = \sqrt{21,600} \approx 147.$$

☑ **PRACTICE PROBLEMS 11.1**

1. A wallet contains five bills, in the denominations $1, $5, $10, $20, and $50. If one bill is selected at random, what is the probability that its value is
   a. an even number?
   b. a multiple of 5?
   c. a multiple of 10?
   d. twice an odd number?
2. For the probability distribution in Table 1.5, find
   a. the expected value $E(X)$,
   b. the variance $\text{Var}(X)$,
   c. the standard deviation σ.

Table 1.5

x_i	1	2	3	4
p_i	0.3	0.1	0.2	0.4

Exercise Set 11.1

1. Table 1.6 shows a sample space and the associated probabilities. Find the probability of
a. the event $E_1 = \{1, 3\}$.
b. the event $E_2 = \{1, 4, 5\}$.
c. the event $E_3 = \{2, 3, 5\}$.

Table 1.6

x_i	1	2	3	4	5
p_i	$\dfrac{1}{3}$	$\dfrac{1}{3}$	$\dfrac{1}{6}$	$\dfrac{1}{12}$	$\dfrac{1}{12}$

2. Table 1.7 shows a sample space and the associated probabilities. Find the probability of
a. the event $E_1 = \{10, 20\}$.
b. the event $E_2 = \{15, 20, 30\}$.
c. the event $E_3 = \{10, 15, 20, 30\}$.

Table 1.7

x_i	10	15	20	25	30
p_i	0.1	0.1	0.3	0.2	0.3

3. Draw a probability histogram for the probability distribution in Exercise 1.

4. Draw a probability histogram for the probability distribution in Exercise 2.

5. Refer to Example 10. For the experiment of rolling two fair dice find the probability of
a. the event of getting a 3, a 5, or a 9.
b. the event of getting a number larger than 7.
c. the event of not getting a 6.

6. For the experiment consisting of one roll of a fair die
a. Find the probability of rolling a 5.
b. Find the probability of rolling a 2 or a 4.
c. Find the probability of not rolling a 3.

7. A poker hand contains three red cards and two black cards. A single card is chosen at random from the hand. Find the probability that the card is
a. red.
b. black.

8. A box contains three red and x white balls. When a single ball is withdrawn at random, the probability that it is red is $\dfrac{1}{4}$. How many white balls are in the box?

9. A set of billiard balls contains 15 balls, numbered 1 through 15. The balls numbered 1–8 are a solid color. The balls numbered 9–15 are striped. A single ball is selected at random. Find the probability that it is
a. a solid color.
b. an even-numbered ball.
c. a striped ball with an even number.

10. Mary is at her desk from 9:00 a.m. until 1:00 p.m., and John is at his desk from 11:00 a.m. until 6:00 p.m. If a telephone call arrives at a time randomly chosen between 9:00 a.m. and 6:00 p.m., what is the probability that
a. both John and Mary are at their desks?
b. John is at his desk?
c. neither John nor Mary is at his or her desk?

11. A dart strikes the target in Figure 1.4 at random. What is the probability that it hits the bull's eye? (Assume that no dart can miss the target completely.)

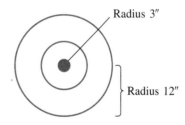

Figure 1.4

12. A card is drawn from an ordinary deck of 52 cards. Given that it is a face card, what is the probability that
a. it is a heart?
b. it is a queen?
c. it is not a jack?
d. it is red and odd numbered.

13. For the probability distribution in Table 1.8 find
a. the expected value $E(X)$.
b. the variance, $\text{Var}(X)$, and the standard deviation σ.

Table 1.8

x_i	0	1	2	3
p_i	0.2	0.2	0.3	0.3

14. For the probability distribution in Table 1.9 find
   a. the expected value $E(X)$.
   b. the variance, $\text{Var}(X)$, and the standard deviation σ.

Table 1.9

x_i	1	2	3	4
p_i	0.1	0.3	0.3	0.3

15. You have the opportunity to buy a lottery ticket that will pay $10 with probability 0.2, $100 with probability 0.1, and nothing with probability 0.7. What is a fair price for the ticket? (That is, what is the expected value of the payoff?)

16. On a rainy day a student can earn $5 doing housework, while on a day when it does not rain the student can earn $40 doing yardwork. If the probability of rain is 30%, what is the student's expected income? (That is, what is the expected value of the student's daily earnings?)

17. An insurance company sells a $100,000 hazard insurance policy on a house. Experience shows that in a year's time the company will have to pay out $100,000 on the policy with probability 0.005, $50,000 on the policy with probability 0.025, and nothing on the policy with probability 0.97. What is the expected value of the company's annual payout on the policy?

☑ **SOLUTIONS TO PRACTICE PROBLEMS 11.1**

1. The denominations corresponding to the given criteria, and the corresponding probabilities, are as follows:

   a. $10, $20, $50; $p = \dfrac{3}{5}$.

   b. $5, $10, $20, $50; $p = \dfrac{4}{5}$.

   c. $10, $20, $50; $p = \dfrac{3}{5}$.

   d. $10, $50; $p = \dfrac{2}{5}$.

2. a. $E(X) = 1(0.3) + 2(0.1) + 3(0.2) + 4(0.4) = 2.7$.
   b. $\text{Var}(X) = (1 - 2.7)^2(0.3) + (2 - 2.7)^2(0.1)$
   $$+ (3 - 2.7)^2(0.2) + (4 - 2.7)^2(0.4)$$
   $$= 1.61.$$
   c. $\sigma = \sqrt{\text{Var}(X)} = \sqrt{1.61} = 1.27$.

11.2 Continuous Probability Distributions

In many situations the outcome of an experiment can be one of infinitely many real numbers. For example,

— The depth of water in a 6-inch rain gauge could be any real number in the interval $[0, 6]$.

— The percentage of alcohol in an alcohol/water mixture could be any real number in the interval $[0, 100]$.

— The duration of a telephone call could be any positive real number, that is, any number in the interval $(0, \infty)$.

A random variable X that can equal any number in an interval I (where I can be either of finite or infinite length) is called a **continuous random variable.** Each of the variables described previously is a continuous random variable.

Probability Density Functions

Since a continuous random variable can equal any of the infinitely many numbers in an interval (its sample space), we cannot expect to assign a probability individually to each of the numbers in the sample space as we can do for discrete random variables. Instead, probabilities of the form $Pr\{a \leq X \leq b\}$ are calculated using the concept of a *probability density function*.

Definition 3

A continuous nonnegative function f with the property that

$$Pr\{a \leq X \leq b\} = \int_a^b f(x)\,dx \tag{1}$$

is called a **probability density function** for the random variable X.

Figures 2.1 and 2.2 show how the graph of a probability density function is the analogue of a probability histogram for discrete random variables. In each case the shaded area corresponds to the probability of an event, and the area under the entire graph must be 1. Rather than being too precise about properties of probability density functions at this point, we shall simply show by example how Definition 3 is used and then consider two frequently occurring continuous probability distributions (the normal and exponential distributions) in Sections 11.3 and 11.4.

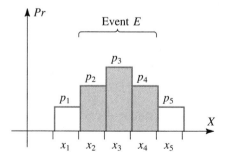

Figure 2.1 In the discrete case, probability of event $E = \{x_2, x_3, x_4\}$ is

$$Pr\{x_2 \leq X \leq x_4\} = p_2 + p_3 + p_4.$$

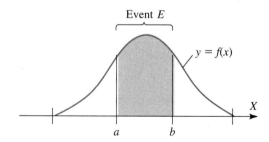

Figure 2.2 In the continuous case, probability of event $E = [a, b]$ is

$$Pr\{a \leq X \leq b\} = \int_a^b f(x)\,dx.$$

☐ **EXAMPLE 1**

Figure 2.3 shows the *uniform* probability distribution on the sample space $S = [0, 4]$ with probability density function $f(x) \equiv \dfrac{1}{4}$. According to Definition 3, for this distribution

(a) $Pr\{0 \le X \le 2\} = \displaystyle\int_0^2 \dfrac{1}{4}\, dx = \left[\dfrac{x}{4}\right]_0^2$

$\qquad\qquad\qquad\qquad = \dfrac{1}{2} - 0$

$\qquad\qquad\qquad\qquad = \dfrac{1}{2}$

(b) $Pr\{1 \le X \le 4\} = \displaystyle\int_1^4 \dfrac{1}{4}\, dx = \left[\dfrac{x}{4}\right]_1^4 = 1 - \dfrac{1}{4} = \dfrac{3}{4}$ $\qquad$ (See Figure 2.4.)

(c) $Pr\{0 \le X \le 4\} = \displaystyle\int_0^4 \dfrac{1}{4}\, dx = \left[\dfrac{x}{4}\right]_0^4 = 1 - 0 = 1.$ $\qquad\qquad$ ■

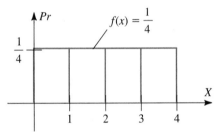

Figure 2.3 Uniform probability distribution on the interval $[0, 4]$.

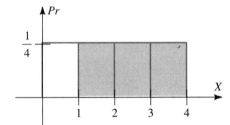

Figure 2.4 $Pr\{1 \le X \le 4\} = \dfrac{3}{4}$.

☐ **EXAMPLE 2**

Figure 2.5 shows the probability density function

$$f(x) = \begin{cases} \dfrac{x}{4}, & 0 \le x \le 2 \\[2ex] 1 - \dfrac{x}{4}, & 2 < x \le 4 \end{cases}$$

on the sample space $[0, 4]$. In this case we have, for the associated continuous random variable X, that

(a) $Pr\{0 \le X \le 1\} = \displaystyle\int_0^1 \dfrac{x}{4}\, dx = \left[\dfrac{x^2}{8}\right]_0^1 = \dfrac{1}{8}$

(b) $Pr\{1 \le X \le 3\} = \displaystyle\int_1^2 \frac{x}{4}\,dx + \int_2^3 \left(1 - \frac{x}{4}\right)dx$

$= \left[\dfrac{x^2}{8}\right]_1^2 + \left[x - \dfrac{x^2}{8}\right]_2^3$

$= \left(\dfrac{4}{8} - \dfrac{1}{8}\right) + \left[\left(3 - \dfrac{9}{8}\right) - \left(2 - \dfrac{4}{8}\right)\right]$

$= \dfrac{3}{4}$ (see Figure 2.6)

(c) $Pr\{0 \le X \le 4\} = \displaystyle\int_0^2 \frac{1}{4}x\,dx + \int_2^4 \left(1 - \frac{x}{4}\right)dx$

$= \left[\dfrac{x^2}{8}\right]_0^2 + \left[x - \dfrac{x^2}{8}\right]_2^4$

$= \dfrac{4}{8} + \left[\left(4 - \dfrac{16}{8}\right) - \left(2 - \dfrac{4}{8}\right)\right]$

$= 1.$ ■

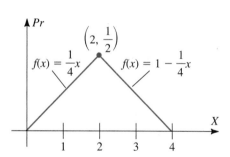

Figure 2.5 Probability density function in Example 2.

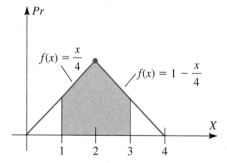

Figure 2.6 $Pr\{1 \le X \le 3\} = \displaystyle\int_1^2 \frac{x}{4}\,dx + \int_2^3 \left(1 - \frac{x}{4}\right)dx.$

Properties of Probability Density Functions

Examples 1 and 2 illustrate two essential properties of the probability density function f. First, because probabilities cannot be negative, the integral in equation (1) must be nonnegative for all choices of the interval $[a, b]$. Therefore, we must have $f(x) \ge 0$ for all x in the sample space for the random variable X. Second, since the probability associated with an entire sample space is always one, the integral of f over the entire sample space must equal one (as in parts (c) of Examples 1 and 2). If the sample space for the continuous random variable X is the interval $[a, b]$, we can write this requirement as

$$\int_a^b f(x)\, dx = 1. \qquad (2)$$

If the sample space for X is the entire real number line, this requirement can be written

$$\int_{-\infty}^{\infty} f(x)\, dx = 1 \qquad (3)$$

where the integral in equation (3) is improper.

☐ **EXAMPLE 3**

Find the number a so that the function $f(x) = ax(6 - x)$ is a probability density function on the sample space $[0, 6]$.

Solution: We must find a so that $f(x) \geq 0$ on $[0, 6]$ and so

$$\int_0^6 ax(6 - x)\, dx = 1.$$

Evaluating this definite integral gives

$$\int_0^6 ax(6 - x)\, dx = a \int_0^6 (6x - x^2)\, dx$$

$$= a\left[3x^2 - \frac{x^3}{3} \right]_0^6$$

$$= a(108 - 72)$$

$$= 36a.$$

Since we require $\int_0^6 ax(6 - x)\, dx = 36a = 1$, we have $a = \dfrac{1}{36}$. The probability density function $f(x) = \dfrac{x}{36}(6 - x)$, which is indeed nonnegative for $0 \leq x \leq 6$, is illustrated in Figure 2.7.   ■

☐ **EXAMPLE 4**

For the probability density function in Example 3 find $Pr\{2 \leq X \leq 4\}$.

Solution: According to Definition 3, we have

$$Pr\{2 \leq X \leq 4\} = \int_2^4 \frac{x}{36}(6 - x)\, dx$$

$$= \frac{1}{36} \int_2^4 (6x - x^2)\, dx$$

$$= \left[\frac{1}{36} \left(3x^2 - \frac{x^3}{3} \right) \right]_2^4$$

$$= \frac{1}{36} \left[\left(3 \cdot 16 - \frac{64}{3} \right) - \left(3 \cdot 4 - \frac{8}{3} \right) \right]$$

$$= \frac{13}{27}. \qquad \text{(See Figure 2.7.)} \qquad \blacksquare$$

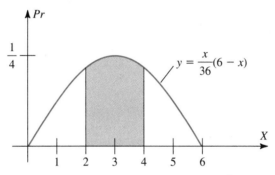

Figure 2.7 The probability function $f(x) = \dfrac{x}{36}(6 - x)$ showing

$$Pr\{2 \le X \le 4\} = \int_2^4 \frac{x}{36}(6 - x)\, dx = \frac{13}{27}.$$

REMARK: Note that Definition 3 implies that the probability associated with any single number $X = c$ in the sample space for a continuous random variable is zero, since we obtain

$$Pr\{X = c\} = \int_c^c f(x)\, dx = 0$$

because the value of a definite integral over an interval consisting of a single number is zero. Since the probability associated with a single number is zero, it does not matter whether endpoints are included when specifying the probability of an event corresponding to an interval. That is

$$Pr\{a \le X \le b\} = Pr\{a \le X < b\} = Pr\{a < X \le b\} = Pr\{a < X < b\}$$

for continuous random variables X.

Distribution Functions

A *distribution function,* like a probability density function, determines the probability of an event associated with a random variable. However, the distribution function specifies the cumulative probability associated with all values of the random variable less than or equal to a given number.

Definition 4

A **distribution function** associated with the random variable X is a function F with the property that

$$F(x) = Pr(X \le x)$$

for all x in the sample space for X.

For distribution functions there is no requirement that the associated random variable X be continuous or that X have a continuous probability density function. However, when X is a continuous random variable with a continuous probability density function f, we have the following relationship between f and the associated distribution function F:

$$\int_a^b f(x)\, dx = Pr\{a \le X \le b\} \qquad \text{(Def. 3)}$$

$$= Pr\{X \le b\} - Pr\{X \le a\} \qquad \text{(See Figure 2.8.)}$$

$$= F(b) - F(a).$$

That is

$$\int_a^b f(x)\, dx = F(b) - F(a). \tag{4}$$

Note the resemblance between equation (4) and the Fundamental Theorem of Calculus. The distribution function F gives the *area* $\int_a^b f(x)\, dx$ of the region bounded by the probability density function on an interval $[a, b]$.

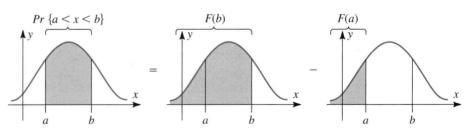

Figure 2.8 $Pr\{a \le X \le b\} = \int_a^b f(x)\, dx = F(b) - F(a).$

Since equation (4) is satisfied by any antiderivative F for f, we may find the distribution function F corresponding to the continuous random variable X by finding the general antiderivative for f and using known information about X to determine the constant of integration. The next example shows how this is done.

☐ **EXAMPLE 5**

Find the distribution function for the probability density function

$$f(x) = \frac{1}{4} \quad \text{for} \quad 0 \le x \le 4$$

(the *uniform* probability distribution on $[0, 4]$) in Example 1.

Solution: An antiderivative F for f must be of the form

$$F(x) = \int \frac{1}{4}\, dx = \frac{x}{4} + C. \tag{5}$$

Since the sample space $[0, 4]$ is finite, we know that the probability associated with its left endpoint only is zero. That is, from Definition 4 we know that

$$F(0) = Pr\{X \le 0\} = 0. \tag{6}$$

Setting $x = 0$ in equation (5) and using equation (6) gives

$$0 = F(0) = \frac{0}{4} + C$$

so $C = 0$. The distribution function is therefore

$$F(x) = \frac{x}{4}. \quad \text{(See Figure 2.9.)}$$

Notice that $F(4) = 1$. That is, the distribution function has value 1 at the right endpoint of the sample space.   ■

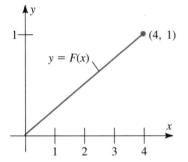

Figure 2.9 Distribution function
$F(x) = \dfrac{x}{4}$ for $f(x) = \dfrac{1}{4}$
on interval $[0, 4]$.

☐ **EXAMPLE 6**

Find the distribution function F for the probability density function of Example 3:

$$f(x) = \frac{x}{36}(6 - x), \qquad 0 \le x \le 6.$$

Solution: An antiderivative for f is

$$F(x) = \int \frac{x}{36}(6 - x)\, dx = \int \left(\frac{x}{6} - \frac{x^2}{36} \right) dx$$

$$= \frac{x^2}{12} - \frac{x^3}{108} + C.$$

Since 0 is the left endpoint of the sample space $[0, 6]$, we have $F(0) = 0$, so

$$0 = F(0) = \frac{0^2}{12} - \frac{0^3}{108} + C = C.$$

Thus

$$F(x) = \frac{x^2}{12} - \frac{x^3}{108}.$$

(See Figure 2.10.) Note again that $F(6) = 1$. ∎

Expected Value

For a continuous random variable X defined on a finite interval $[a, b]$, with continuous probability density function f, the **expected value** of X is given by the definite integral

$$E(X) = \int_a^b xf(x) \, dx. \tag{7}$$

Figure 2.11 shows an approximating sum for the integral in equation (7) and illustrates why equation (7) is the appropriate generalization of the concept of expected value for discrete random variables. In the approximating sum each "test value" t_i of the random variable X is multiplied by the corresponding "probability" $f(t_i) \, \Delta x$.

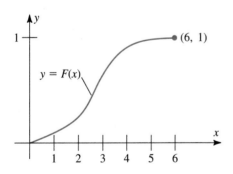

Figure 2.10 Distribution function

$$F(x) = \frac{x^2}{12} - \frac{x^3}{108} \text{ for } f(x) = \frac{x}{36}(6 - x)$$

on the interval $[0, 6]$.

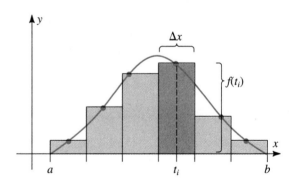

Figure 2.11 Approximating sum $\sum_{i=1}^{n} t_i f(t_i) \, \Delta x$ for the

expected value $E(X) = \int_a^b xf(x) \, dx$.

☐ **EXAMPLE 7**

The expected value for the random variable X with uniform probability density function

$$f(x) = \frac{1}{4}, \qquad 0 \le x \le 4$$

in Example 1 is

$$E(X) = \int_0^4 x\left(\frac{1}{4}\right) dx = \int_0^4 \frac{x}{4} dx$$

$$= \left[\frac{x^2}{8}\right]_0^4$$

$$= 2.$$

This is not surprising, since 2 is the midpoint of the sample space $[0, 4]$, and the probability density is constant across this interval. ■

☐ **EXAMPLE 8**

Find the expected value of the random variable X with probability density function

$$f(x) = \frac{x}{36}(6 - x)$$

illustrated in Figure 2.7.

Solution: Since this probability density function is a parabola with axis of symmetry $x = 3$, which is also the midpoint of the sample space $[0, 6]$, you might suspect that the symmetry of this density function would produce an expected value of X of $E(X) = 3$. This is indeed the case, since, according to equation (7)

$$E(X) = \int_0^6 x\left[\frac{x}{36}(6 - x)\right] dx$$

$$= \int_0^6 \left(\frac{x^2}{6} - \frac{x^3}{36}\right) dx$$

$$= \left[\frac{x^3}{18} - \frac{x^4}{144}\right]_0^6$$

$$= \frac{216}{18} - \frac{1296}{144}$$

$$= 12 - 9$$

$$= 3.$$

■

Variance

The variance associated with the continuous random variable X on the sample space $[a, b]$ is

$$\text{Var}(X) = E([X - E(X)]^2)$$

$$= \int_a^b [x - E(X)]^2 f(x)\, dx \qquad (8)$$

where f is again the probability density function for the random variable X. As for discrete random variables, the variance is the expected value of the square of the deviation of X from its expected value.

☐ **EXAMPLE 9**

Find the variance $\text{Var}(X)$ for the random variable X with uniform probability density

$$f(x) = \frac{1}{4}, \qquad 0 \le x \le 4$$

in Example 1.

Solution: Since we found that X has expected value $E(X) = 2$ (Example 7), equation (8) gives

$$\text{Var}(X) = \int_0^4 (x - 2)^2 \cdot \frac{1}{4}\, dx$$

$$= \left[\frac{1}{12}(x - 2)^3 \right]_0^4$$

$$= \frac{1}{12} 2^3 - \frac{1}{12}(-2)^3$$

$$= \frac{4}{3}.$$

∎

☑ **PRACTICE PROBLEMS 11.2**

1. Find the number a so that the function $f(x) = ax(5 - x)$ is a probability density function on the sample space $[0, 5]$.
2. For the probability density function in Problem 1, find these probabilities.
   a. $Pr\{0 \le X \le 3\}$
   b. $Pr\{1 \le X \le 4\}$
3. Find the distribution function F for the probability density function in Problem 1.

Exercise Set 11.2

1. Label each random variable as either discrete or continuous.
   a. the depth of water in a swimming pool
   b. the number of teeth in a person's mouth
   c. a person's height
   d. the wind speed at sunrise
   e. the temperature at noon
   f. the number of hairs on a person's head
   g. your annual income

2. For the probability density function

$$f(x) = \begin{cases} \dfrac{1}{6}, & 0 \le x \le 3 \\ \dfrac{1}{4}, & 3 < x \le 5 \end{cases}$$

   on the sample space $[0, 5]$ find
   a. $Pr\{0 \le X \le 2\}$
   b. $Pr\{1 \le X \le 4\}$
   c. $Pr\{0 \le X \le 5\}$

3. For the probability density function

$$f(x) = \frac{3}{16}\sqrt{x}, \qquad 0 \le x \le 4$$

   on the sample space $[0, 4]$ find
   a. $Pr\{0 \le X \le 2\}$
   b. $Pr\{2 \le X \le 4\}$
   c. $Pr\{0 \le X \le 4\}$

4. For the probability density function

$$f(x) = \frac{3}{32}x(4 - x), \qquad 0 \le x \le 4$$

   on the sample space $[0, 4]$ find
   a. $Pr\{0 \le X \le 2\}$
   b. $Pr\{3 \le X \le 4\}$
   c. $Pr\{0 \le X \le 4\}$

5. For the probability density function

$$f(x) = \begin{cases} \dfrac{x}{9}, & 0 \le x \le 3 \\ \dfrac{2}{3} - \dfrac{1}{9}x, & 3 \le x \le 6 \end{cases}$$

   on the sample space $[0, 6]$ find
   a. $Pr\{0 \le X \le 3\}$

   b. $Pr\{1 \le X \le 5\}$
   c. $Pr\{2 \le X \le 6\}$

6. Find the number a so that the function $f(x) = ax(1 - x)$ is a probability density function for the sample space $[0, 1]$.

7. Find the number a so that the function $f(x) = ae^{-x}$ is a probability density function on the interval $[0, \ln 2]$.

8. Find the expected value of the random variable X with uniform probability density function

$$f(x) = \frac{1}{5}, \qquad 0 \le x \le 5$$

   on the sample space $[0, 5]$.

9. Find the expected value of the random variable X with probability density function

$$f(x) = \frac{x}{8}, \qquad 0 \le x \le 4$$

   on the sample space $[0, 4]$.

10. Find the expected value of the random variable X with the probability density function in Exercise 4.

11. Find the variance of the random variable X in Exercise 8.

12. Find the variance of the random variable X in Exercise 9.

13. Find the variance of the random variable X in Exercise 10.

14. A random variable X has distribution function $F(x) = \dfrac{x^2}{16}$ on the sample space $[0, 4]$. Find
    a. $Pr\{0 \le X \le 2\}$
    b. $Pr\{1 \le X \le 2\}$
    c. the probability density function f.

15. A random variable X has distribution function $F(x) = 3x^2 - 2x^3$ on the sample space $[0, 1]$. Find
    a. $Pr\{0 \le X \le \frac{1}{2}\}$
    b. $Pr\{\frac{1}{2} \le X \le 1\}$
    c. the probability density function f.

16. Find the distribution function for the probability density function in Exercise 3.

17. Find the distribution function for the probability density function in Exercise 4.

18. Find the distribution function for the probability density function in Exercise 8.

19. A biologist determines that the random variable X giving the time at which a sleeping animal awakens during a 4-minute experiment has probability density function

$$f(x) = \frac{5}{4}\left(\frac{1}{1+x}\right)^2, \qquad 0 \le x \le 4.$$

a. Find the probability that the animal awakens during the first 2 minutes of the experiment.

b. Find the probability that the animal awakens after 1 minute but before the experiment ends.

20. A climatologist believes that the random variable X giving the amount of rainfall expected in a certain region per year has probability density function

$$f(x) = \frac{\pi}{60}\sin\left(\frac{\pi x}{30}\right), \qquad 0 \le x \le 30.$$

Find
a. $Pr\{0 \le X \le 15\}$
b. $Pr\{15 \le X \le 30\}$

21. A research firm determines that the random variable X giving the time, in years, after which a new small business will fail has probability density function

$$f(t) = \frac{k}{(1+t)^2}, \qquad t \ge 0$$

where k is a constant.

a. Find k by evaluating the improper integral

$$\int_0^\infty \frac{k}{(1+t)^2}\,dt.$$

b. Find $Pr\{0 \le X \le 9\}$, the probability that a new small business fails within 9 years of its creation.

☑ **SOLUTIONS TO PRACTICE PROBLEMS 11.2**

1. We must find a so that $\int_0^5 ax(5-x)\,dx = 1$. This requires that

$$1 = \int_0^5 ax(5-x)\,dx$$

$$= a\left[\frac{5}{2}x^2 - \frac{1}{3}x^3\right]_0^5$$

$$= \frac{125a}{6}.$$

Thus, $a = \dfrac{6}{125}$.

2. a. $Pr\{0 \le X \le 3\} = \displaystyle\int_0^3 \frac{6}{125}x(5-x)\,dx$

$$= \frac{6}{125}\left[\frac{5}{2}x^2 - \frac{1}{3}x^3\right]_0^3$$

$$= \frac{81}{125}.$$

b. $Pr\{1 \le X \le 4\} = \displaystyle\int_1^4 \frac{6}{125}x(5-x)\,dx$

$$= \frac{6}{125}\left[\frac{5}{2}x^2 - \frac{1}{3}x^3\right]_1^4$$

$$= \frac{99}{125}.$$

3. The distribution F is

$$F(x) = \int \frac{6}{125} x(5 - x)\, dx = \frac{3}{25} x^2 - \frac{2}{125} x^3 + C$$

with $F(0) = 0$. Thus, $C = 0$, and

$$F(x) = \frac{3}{25} x^2 - \frac{2}{125} x^3.$$

11.3 The Normal Probability Distribution

One of the most commonly occurring distributions for a continuous random variable X is the *normal* probability distribution. IQ (intelligence quotient), adult height, and adult weight are examples of variables whose distributions are approximately normal. We shall define a normal random variable X in terms of its probability density function.

Definition 5

Let μ and σ be real numbers with $\sigma > 0$. The continuous random variable X with probability density function*

$$f(x) = \frac{1}{\sqrt{2\pi}\sigma} e^{-1/2[(x - \mu)/\sigma]^2}$$

is called a **normal random variable** with parameters μ and σ. We refer to such a random variable as an $N(\mu, \sigma)$ random variable.

The term **parameter** refers to a fixed constant used in defining a mathematical expression. Definition 5 requires values of two parameters, μ and σ, to determine the normal random variable $N(\mu, \sigma)$. Figure 3.1 shows the graph of the probability density function f for an $N(\mu, \sigma)$ random variable and the significance of the parameters μ and σ:

(a) The vertical line $x = \mu$ is the *axis of symmetry* for the graph of f.
(b) The graph of $y = f(x)$ has *inflection* points P_1 and P_2 lying σ units to the right and left of the axis of symmetry $x = \mu$.

The Standard Normal Random Variable $N(0, 1)$

Properties (a) and (b) are most easily demonstrated for the **standard normal random variable** $N(0, 1)$, that is, the normal random variable whose probability density function has parameters $\mu = 0$ and $\sigma = 1$. (See Figure 3.2.)

---

*It is a fact, which we shall not prove, that

$$\int_{-\infty}^{\infty} f(x)\, dx = \int_{-\infty}^{\infty} \frac{1}{\sqrt{2\pi}\sigma} e^{-1/2[(x - \mu)/\sigma]^2}\, dx = 1$$

as required for probability density functions that are defined on the sample space $(-\infty, \infty)$ consisting of the entire real line. Because the sample space is not a finite interval, the integral must be improper.

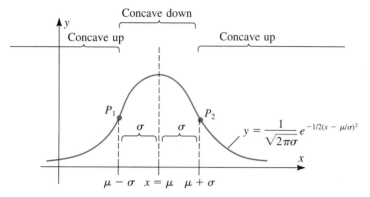

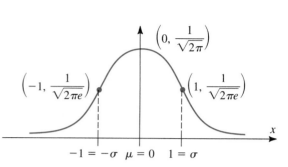

Figure 3.1 Graph of the probability density $f(x) = \dfrac{1}{\sqrt{2\pi}\sigma} e^{-1/2[(x-\mu)/\sigma]^2}$ for the normal random variable $N(\mu, \sigma)$.

Figure 3.2 Graph of the standard normal probability density function $f(x) = \dfrac{1}{\sqrt{2\pi}} e^{-1/2(x^2)}$.

This probability density function is

$$f(x) = \frac{1}{\sqrt{2\pi}} e^{-1/2(x^2)}.$$

Since x appears to the second power, the value of f at $-x$ is the same as the value of f at x. This is what we mean by saying that the graph of f is symmetric about the line $x = \mu = 0$. (Geometrically, this says that the part of the graph of f lying to the left of the y-axis is the mirror image, in the y-axis, of the part of the graph lying to the right of the y-axis.)

The maximum value of f is found by setting $f'(x) = 0$. Doing so, we obtain

$$f'(x) = \frac{1}{\sqrt{2\pi}} e^{-1/2(x^2)}(-x) = \frac{-x}{\sqrt{2\pi}} e^{-1/2(x^2)}$$

which is zero only when $x = 0$. The point $(0, f(0)) = \left(0, \dfrac{1}{\sqrt{2\pi}}\right)$ therefore corresponds to the relative maximum for f. (Note that this occurs where $x = \mu$.)

To find the inflection points, we set $f''(x) = 0$:

$$f''(x) = \frac{d}{dx}\left(\frac{-x}{\sqrt{2\pi}} e^{-1/2(x^2)}\right)$$

$$= \frac{-1}{\sqrt{2\pi}} e^{-1/2(x^2)} + \frac{-x}{\sqrt{2\pi}} e^{-1/2(x^2)}(-x)$$

$$= (x^2 - 1) \cdot \frac{1}{\sqrt{2\pi}} e^{-1/2(x^2)}$$

so $f''(x) = 0$ when $x^2 = 1$, which occurs when $x = \pm 1 = \pm\sigma$. Since $f''(x) < 0$ for $-1 < x < 1$ and $f''(x) > 0$ for $x < -1$ and for $x > 1$, this shows that Figure 3.2 is correct:

(i) The graph of f is concave down for $-1 < x < 1$, that is, for x within $\sigma = 1$ unit of $\mu = 0$.

(ii) The graph of f is concave up for $|x| > 1$, that is, for x lying more than $\sigma = 1$ unit from $\mu = 0$.

(iii) The points

$$(1, f(1)) = \left(1, \frac{1}{\sqrt{2\pi e}}\right) \qquad \text{and} \qquad (-1, f(-1)) = \left(-1, \frac{1}{\sqrt{2\pi e}}\right)$$

are inflection points. That is, the inflection points lie $\sigma = 1$ unit from the axis of symmetry $x = \mu = 0$.

We leave it as an exercise for you to verify that conclusions (a) and (b) hold for the general case of an $N(\mu, \sigma)$ normal random variable.

Expected Value and Variance

The significance of the parameters μ and σ for an $N(\mu, \sigma)$ random variable is broader than just the geometric properties described above:

— The **expected value** of the $N(\mu, \sigma)$ normal random variable X is

$$E(X) = \mu.$$

— The **variance** of the $N(\mu, \sigma)$ normal random variable X is

$$\text{Var}(X) = \sigma^2.$$

As for discrete random variables, we refer to the square root of the variance of a continuous random variable X as the *standard deviation* for X. Thus the standard deviation for the $N(\mu, \sigma)$ normal random variable is just the parameter σ. Figures 3.3 and 3.4 illustrate two important rules of thumb for $N(\mu, \sigma)$ random variables X. Regardless of particular values of the parameters σ and μ:

(i) $Pr\{\mu - \sigma \leq X \leq \mu + \sigma\} \approx 0.68$

(ii) $Pr\{\mu - 2\sigma \leq X \leq \mu + 2\sigma\} \approx 0.95$.

That is, the probability that a randomly selected value of the $N(\mu, \sigma)$ random variable X will lie within one standard deviation of the expected value μ is roughly

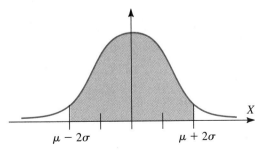

Figure 3.3 $Pr\{\mu - \sigma \leq X \leq \mu + \sigma\}$ is approximately 0.68.

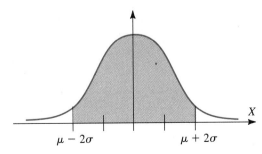

Figure 3.4 $Pr\{\mu - 2\sigma \leq X \leq \mu + 2\sigma\}$ is approximately 0.95.

68%. The probability that a randomly selected value of X will lie within two standard deviations of the expected value μ is roughly 95%. The remaining part of this section concerns calculating probabilities associated with normal random variables.

Probabilities for $N(0, 1)$ Variables

It is common practice to denote the standard normal random variable ($\mu = 0, \sigma = 1$) by the letter Z. Since the probability density function for this $N(0, 1)$ variable is

$$f(z) = \frac{1}{\sqrt{2\pi}} e^{-z^2/2}$$

the probability $Pr\{Z \le a\}$ is given by the probability distribution function F with values

$$F(a) = Pr\{Z \le a\} = \int_{-\infty}^{a} \frac{1}{\sqrt{2\pi}} e^{-z^2/2} \, dz. \tag{1}$$

(See Figure 3.5.) Values of this distribution function for various values of $a \ge 0$ are given in Table 4, Appendix II. These values have been calculated by evaluating the improper integral in equation (1). The following examples show how Table 4, together with the symmetry of the graph of the probability density function f, is used to calculate probabilities associated with the $N(0, 1)$ variable Z.

□ **EXAMPLE 1**

For the $N(0, 1)$ variable Z, find $Pr\{Z \le 1.5\}$.

Solution: Since Table 4 gives $Pr\{Z \le a\}$, we find the entry in the body of Table 4 corresponding to the number $a = 1.50$. It is $Pr\{Z \le 1.50\} = 0.9332$. (See Figure 3.6.) ■

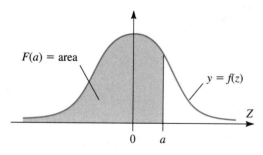

Figure 3.5 For the $N(0, 1)$ variable Z

$$Pr\{Z \le a\} = F(a) = \int_{-\infty}^{a} \frac{1}{\sqrt{2\pi}} e^{-z^2/2} \, dz.$$

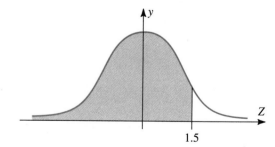

Figure 3.6 $Pr\{Z \le 1.5\} = 0.9332.$

☐ **EXAMPLE 2**

For the $N(0, 1)$ variable Z, find $Pr\{Z \geq 0.85\}$.

Solution: As Figure 3.7 indicates, the probability $Pr\{Z \geq 0.85\}$ corresponds to the area of the region under the standard normal curve lying to the *right* of $a = 0.85$. Since the values of the distribution function $F(a)$, hence the entries of Table 4, correspond to the area under this curve lying to the *left* of $Z = a$, we use the fact that the area of the *entire* region lying under the graph of the curve must be 1:

$$Pr\{Z \geq 0.85\} + Pr\{Z \leq 0.85\} = 1$$
$$Pr\{Z \geq 0.85\} = 1 - Pr\{Z \leq 0.85\}$$
$$= 1 - 0.8023 \quad \text{(value from Table 4)}$$
$$= 0.1977.$$

☐ **EXAMPLE 3**

Find $Pr\{0.6 \leq Z \leq 2.25\}$ for the standard normal random variable Z.

Solution: Since both $a = 0.6$ and $b = 2.25$ are positive numbers, we may simply find the entries of Table 4 corresponding to these numbers and subtract:

$$Pr\{0.6 \leq Z \leq 2.25\} = Pr\{Z \leq 2.25\} - Pr\{Z \leq 0.6\}$$
$$= 0.9878 - 0.7257$$
$$= 0.2621.$$

(See Figure 3.8.)

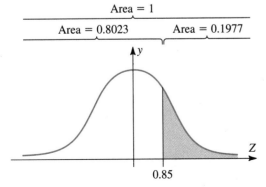

Figure 3.7 $Pr\{Z \leq 0.85\} = 1 - Pr\{Z \leq 0.85\}$
$= 0.1977.$

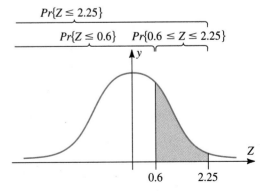

Figure 3.8 $Pr\{0.6 \leq Z \leq 2.25\} =$
$Pr\{Z \leq 2.25\} - Pr\{Z \leq 0.6\}.$

□ **EXAMPLE 4**

For the $N(0, 1)$ variable Z find $Pr\{-1 \leq Z \leq 1.6\}$.

Solution: Since $a = -1$ is less than zero, we cannot find the probability $Pr\{Z \leq -1\}$ directly from the table. However, as Figure 3.9 shows, we can use the symmetry of the standard normal curve to calculate $Pr\{Z \leq -1\}$ as

$$Pr\{Z \leq -1\} = Pr\{Z \geq 1\}$$

$$= 1 - Pr\{Z \leq 1\}$$

$$= 1 - 0.8413$$

$$= 0.1587$$

where we have obtained $Pr\{Z \leq 1\} = 0.8413$ from Table 4.

We may now proceed to calculate $Pr\{-1 \leq Z \leq 1.6\}$ as

$$Pr\{-1 \leq Z \leq 1.6\} = Pr\{Z \leq 1.6\} - Pr\{Z \leq -1\}$$

$$= 0.9452 - 0.1587$$

$$= 0.7865.$$

(See Figure 3.10.) ■

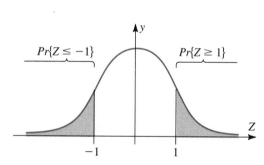

Figure 3.9 $Pr\{Z \leq -1\} = Pr\{Z \geq 1\}$.

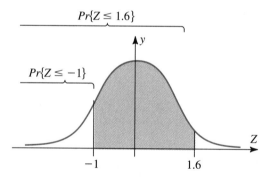

Figure 3.10 $Pr\{-1 \leq Z \leq 1.6\} = Pr\{Z \leq 1.6\} - Pr\{Z \leq -1\}$.

Probabilities for Other Normal Random Variables

We may use Table 4, Appendix II, to calculate probabilities for $N(\mu, \sigma)$ random variables X with expected value μ and standard deviation σ by first converting such variables to *standard* normal random variables using the equation

$$Z = \frac{X - \mu}{\sigma}. \tag{2}$$

It is a fact, which we shall not prove, that the variable Z in equation (2) has expected value 0 and standard deviation 1 (that is, it is a standard normal random variable).

The endpoint a of the interval in which X may fall must be treated by the same conversion:

$$A = \frac{a - \mu}{\sigma}. \qquad (3)$$

When this is done, then we know that

$$Pr\{X \le a\} = Pr\{Z \le A\}. \qquad (4)$$

We may therefore calculate the probability for the $N(\mu, \sigma)$ random variable X on the left-hand side of equation (4) by finding the probability on the right-hand side of the equation from Table 4 (Figure 3.11). The following examples illustrate this technique.

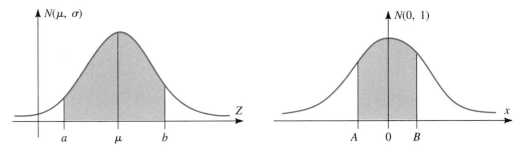

Figure 3.11 $Pr\{a \le X \le b\} = Pr\{A \le Z \le B\}$ where $A = \dfrac{a - \mu}{\sigma}$, $B = \dfrac{b - \mu}{\sigma}$, and $Z = \dfrac{X - \mu}{\sigma}$.

☐ **EXAMPLE 5**

For the normal random variable X having expected value $\mu = 5$ and standard deviation $\sigma = 2$, find $Pr\{6 \le X \le 9\}$. (See Figure 3.12.)

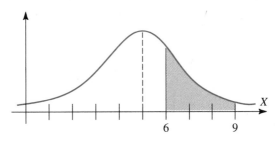

Figure 3.12 $Pr\{6 \le X \le 9\} = Pr\{0.5 \le Z \le 2.0\}$ for $N(5, 2)$ random variable X.

Solution: Using equation (3) with $\mu = 5$, and $\sigma = 2$, we find that the Z-value corresponding to the X-value $a = 6$ is

$$A = \frac{6 - 5}{2} = 0.5$$

and the Z-value corresponding to the X-value $b = 9$ is

$$B = \frac{9 - 5}{2} = 2.0.$$

Thus

$$Pr\{6 \le X \le 9\} = Pr\{0.5 \le Z \le 2.0\}$$
$$= Pr\{Z \le 2.0\} - Pr\{Z \le 0.5\}$$
$$= 0.9772 - 0.6915 \qquad \text{(Table 4)}$$
$$= 0.2857. \qquad \blacksquare$$

☐ **EXAMPLE 6**

For the normal random variable X with $\mu = 60$ and $\sigma = 20$, find $Pr\{40 \le X \le 90\}$.

Solution: The Z-values corresponding to $a = 40$ and $b = 90$ are

$$A = \frac{40 - 60}{20} = \frac{-20}{20} = -1$$

and

$$B = \frac{90 - 60}{20} = \frac{30}{20} = 1.5.$$

Thus,

$$Pr\{40 \le X \le 90\} = Pr\{-1 \le Z \le 1.5\}$$
$$= Pr\{Z \le 1.5\} - Pr\{Z \le -1\}$$
$$= Pr\{Z \le 1.5\} - [1 - Pr\{Z \le 1\}] \qquad \text{(See Example 4.)}$$
$$= 0.9332 - (1 - 0.8413)$$
$$= 0.7745. \qquad \text{(See Figure 3.13.)} \qquad \blacksquare$$

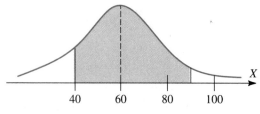

Figure 3.13 $Pr\{40 \le X \le 90\} = Pr\{-1 \le Z \le 1.5\}$ for $N(60, 20)$ random variable X.

☐ **EXAMPLE 7**

Biologists have determined that the variable representing the lifetime of a certain species of animals is normally distributed with expected value $\mu = 6$ years and standard deviation $\sigma = 1.5$ years. Find the probability that an individual animal of this species, selected at random, survives between 4 and 8 years.

Solution: We let X denote the lifetime for a member of this species. Then X is an $N(6, 1.5)$ random variable. The Z-values corresponding to the given X-values $a = 4$ and $b = 8$ are

$$A = \frac{4 - 6}{1.5} = \frac{-2}{1.5} = -1.33 \ldots$$

and

$$B = \frac{8 - 6}{1.5} = \frac{2}{1.5} = 1.33 \ldots .$$

(In using Table 4, we round these two numbers to -1.33 and 1.33, respectively.) Then

$$Pr\{4 \le X \le 8\} = Pr\{-1.33 \le Z \le 1.33\}$$
$$= 2Pr\{0 \le Z \le 1.33\} \quad \text{(See Figure 3.14.)}$$
$$= 2[Pr\{Z \le 1.33\} - Pr\{Z \le 0\}]$$
$$= 2(0.9082 - 0.5000)$$
$$= 0.8164. \qquad\qquad ■$$

Our last example shows how knowledge of probability distributions is used in decision making.

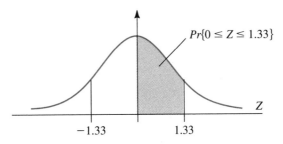

Figure 3.14 $Pr\{-1.33 \le Z \le 1.33\} = 2Pr\{0 \le Z \le 1.33\}$.

☐ **EXAMPLE 8**

An automobile manufacturer purchases tires in bulk from a supplier. The supplier claims that the number of defective tires in any shipment of 1000 tires is a normally distributed random variable with expected value $\mu = 20$ and standard deviation

$\sigma = 5$. If this claim is true, what is the probability that a shipment of 1000 tires contains 35 or more defective tires?

Solution: Let X denote the number of defective tires contained in the shipment. The manufacturer's claim is that X is an $N(20, 5)$ random variable. The Z-value corresponding to the X-value $b = 35$ is

$$B = \frac{35 - 20}{5} = 3.$$

Thus the probability of finding 35 or more defective tires would be

$$Pr\{X \geq 35\} = Pr\{Z > 3\}$$
$$= 1 - Pr\{Z \leq 3\}$$
$$= 1 - 0.9987$$
$$= 0.0013.$$

If the supplier's claim about μ and σ is correct, the probability of such an outcome is minuscule. If the manufacturer did find 35 defective tires in a shipment, there would be good reason to question the supplier's claim about quality! ∎

☑ **PRACTICE PROBLEMS 11.3**

1. For the standard normal random variable Z, find
   a. $Pr\{0 \leq Z \leq 0.45\}$
   b. $Pr\{-0.35 \leq Z \leq 0.25\}$.
2. For the normal random variable X with mean $\mu = 6$ and standard deviation $\sigma = 2$, find
   a. $Pr\{8 \leq X \leq 10\}$.
   b. $Pr\{5 \leq X \leq 8\}$.

Exercise Set 11.3

In Exercises 1–8, find the indicated probability for the standard $N(0, 1)$ normal random variable Z using Table 4, Appendix II.

1. $Pr\{Z \leq 2\}$
2. $Pr\{Z \leq 1.95\}$
3. $Pr\{1.2 \leq Z \leq 2.8\}$
4. $Pr\{0 \leq Z \leq 1.45\}$
5. $Pr\{-1 \leq Z \leq 2\}$
6. $Pr\{-2.35 \leq Z \leq 0\}$
7. $Pr\{-1.6 \leq Z \leq 1.55\}$
8. $Pr\{-1 \leq Z \leq -0.25\}$

In Exercises 9–16, find the indicated probability for the $N(\mu, \sigma)$ random variable by first converting to the standard $N(0, 1)$ random variable and then using Table 4.

9. $Pr\{X \leq 7\}$, $\mu = 4$, $\sigma = 2$
10. $Pr\{0 \leq X \leq 35\}$, $\mu = 20$, $\sigma = 20$
11. $Pr\{1 \leq X \leq 7\}$, $\mu = 2$, $\sigma = 2$

12. $Pr\{-3 \leq X \leq 5\}$, $\mu = 1$, $\sigma = 2$
13. $Pr\{35 \leq X \leq 65\}$, $\mu = 50$, $\sigma = 10$
14. $Pr\{2 \leq X \leq 3\}$, $\mu = 1$, $\sigma = 1$
15. $Pr\{-5 \leq X \leq 1\}$, $\mu = -1$, $\sigma = 4$
16. $Pr\{17 \leq X \leq 25\}$, $\mu = 22$, $\sigma = 5$

17. Heights in a certain population of adult males are found to be normally distributed with an expected value of $\mu = 70''$ and a standard deviation of $\sigma = 2''$. Find the probability that the height of an adult male selected at random from this population
    a. exceeds $6'$ (that is, $72''$)
    b. falls between $5'6''$ and $6'2''$ (that is, between $66''$ and $74''$).

18. An automobile leasing company finds that the annual mileage recorded for one of its cars is a normal random variable X with expected value $\mu = 18,000$ miles and standard deviation 2500 miles. Find
a. $Pr\{16,000 \le X \le 20,000\}$
b. $Pr\{X \ge 24,000\}$

19. A supplier of light bulbs claims that the number of defective light bulbs in any shipment of 1000 light bulbs is a normal random variable X with expected value 10 and standard deviation 3. If this is true, what is the probability of finding 15 or more defective bulbs in a randomly selected shipment?

20. The breaking strength of a brand of rope is a normal random variable with $\mu = 20$ lb and $\sigma = 10$ lb. What is the probability that a rope selected at random breaks at a force equal to or less than 115 lb?

21. The monthly rainfall in a region is a normal random variable with $\mu = 6''$ and $\sigma = 1.5''$. What is the probability that a month's rainfall will fall between $5''$ and $7''$?

22. If the combined SAT scores of entering freshmen at a college is a normal random variable with $\mu = 1080$ and $\sigma^2 = 1600$, find the probability that the SAT score for a freshman selected at random is greater than 1020.

23. A marketing firm determines that the annual household income of the consumers of a product is a normal random variable with $\mu = \$30,000$ and $\sigma = \$8000$. What percentage of these consumers have household incomes in excess of $\$42,000$?

24. If the diameters of ball bearings produced by a properly functioning machine are normally distributed with expected value 3 cm and standard deviation $\sigma = 0.1$ cm, what is the probability that a randomly selected ball bearing will have diameter in excess of 3.24 cm?

25. Find the expected value of the $N(0, 1)$ random variable Z with probability density function $f(z) = \dfrac{1}{\sqrt{2\pi}} e^{-z^2/2}$ by evaluating the improper integral

$$E(Z) = \int_{-\infty}^{\infty} \frac{1}{\sqrt{2\pi}} z e^{-z^2/2}\, dz$$

$$= \lim_{t \to -\infty} \int_{t}^{0} \frac{1}{\sqrt{2\pi}} z e^{-z^2/2}\, dz$$

$$+ \lim_{t \to \infty} \int_{0}^{t} \frac{1}{\sqrt{2\pi}} z e^{-z^2/2}\, dz.$$

26. Verify that properties (a) and (b) following Definition 5 hold for the general case of an $N(\mu, \sigma)$ normal random variable.

☑ **SOLUTIONS TO PRACTICE PROBLEMS 11.3**

1. Using Table 4, Appendix II, we find that
  a. $Pr\{0 \le Z \le 0.45\} = Pr\{Z \le 0.45\} - Pr\{Z \le 0\}$
  $\qquad = 0.6736 - 0.5000$
  $\qquad = 0.1736.$
  b. $Pr\{-0.35 \le Z \le 0.25\} = Pr\{Z \le 0.25\} - Pr\{Z \le -0.35\}$
  $\qquad = Pr\{Z \le 0.25\} - [1 - Pr\{Z \le 0.35\}]$
  $\qquad = 0.5987 - (1 - 0.6368)$
  $\qquad = 0.5987 - 0.3632$
  $\qquad = 0.2355.$

2. The standard random variable has values corresponding to the given values of X as follows:
  (i) for $X_1 = 5,\quad Z_1 = \dfrac{5 - 6}{2} = \dfrac{-1}{2}$
  (ii) for $X_2 = 8,\quad Z_2 = \dfrac{8 - 6}{2} = 1$
  (iii) for $X_3 = 10,\quad Z_3 = \dfrac{10 - 6}{2} = 2.$

  Thus,
  a. $Pr\{8 \le X \le 10\} = Pr\{1 \le Z \le 2\}$
  $\qquad = Pr\{Z \le 2\} - Pr\{Z \le 1\}$
  $\qquad = 0.9772 - 0.8413$
  $\qquad = 0.1359.$

b. $Pr\{5 \le X \le 8\} = Pr\left\{\dfrac{-1}{2} \le Z \le 1\right\}$

$$= Pr\{Z \le 1\} - Pr\left\{Z \le \dfrac{-1}{2}\right\}$$

$$= Pr\{Z \le 1\} - \left[1 - Pr\left\{Z \le \dfrac{1}{2}\right\}\right]$$

$$= 0.8413 - [1 - 0.6915]$$

$$= 0.8413 - 0.3085$$

$$= 0.5328.$$

11.4   The Exponential Probability Distribution

The *exponential* probability distribution is another example of a continuous random variable that occurs frequently in applications. Random variables that have exponential probability distributions typically represent the time required for an event to occur, such as the length of a telephone call, the time that elapses until a new automobile requires service, or the lifetime of a new small business.

The exponential probability distribution is determined by the following probability density function.

Definition 6

Let $\alpha > 0$ be a positive real number. The continuous random variable X with probability density function

$$f(x) = \begin{cases} \alpha e^{-\alpha x}, & x \ge 0 \\ 0, & x < 0 \end{cases}$$

is called the **exponential random variable** with parameter α.

Note that the exponential random variable is determined by one parameter, while the normal random variable is determined by two parameters. Figure 4.1 shows the graph of the probability density function f for a typical exponential random variable X.

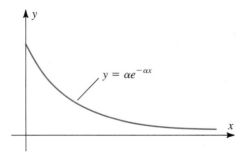

Figure 4.1 Graph of probability density function for a typical exponential random variable X.

☐ **EXAMPLE 1**

Verify that the function f in Definition 6 is a probability density function.

Solution: Since values of the exponential function $e^{-\alpha x}$ are positive for all numbers α and x, and since the number α is positive, values of the function $f(x) = \alpha e^{-\alpha x}$ are non-negative for all values of x.

Since $f(x) = 0$ for $x < 0$, the integral of the function f over the entire sample space $(-\infty, \infty)$ is given by the improper integral

$$\int_0^\infty f(x)\, dx = \int_0^\infty \alpha e^{-\alpha x}\, dx$$

$$= \lim_{t \to \infty} \int_0^t \alpha e^{-\alpha x}\, dx$$

$$= \lim_{t \to \infty} \left[-e^{-\alpha x} \right]_0^t$$

$$= \lim_{t \to \infty} (1 - e^{-\alpha t})$$

$$= 1$$

as required for a probability density function.   ∎

☐ **EXAMPLE 2**

For the exponential random variable X with probability density function $f(x) = 2e^{-2x}$ find $Pr\{1 \le X \le 2\}$.

Solution: From the definition of the probability determined by a probability density function we have

$$Pr\{1 \le X \le 2\} = \int_1^2 f(x)\, dx$$

$$= \int_1^2 2e^{-2x}\, dx$$

$$= \left[-e^{-2x} \right]_1^2$$

$$= -e^{-4} - (-e^{-2})$$

$$= \frac{1}{e^2} - \frac{1}{e^4}$$

$$\approx 0.117.$$ ∎

The Distribution Function

Recall that the *distribution* function F associated with a probability density function f is defined by

$$F(t) = Pr\{X \le t\}. \tag{1}$$

For the exponential probability density function f in Definition 6 equation (1) becomes, for $t > 0$

$$F(t) = Pr\{X \le t\} = \int_0^t f(x)\,dx$$

$$= \int_0^t \alpha e^{-\alpha x}\,dx$$

$$= \left[-e^{-\alpha x}\right]_0^t \tag{2}$$

$$= 1 - e^{-\alpha t}.$$

From equation (2) we may conclude that

$$Pr\{X \le t\} = 1 - e^{-\alpha t}, \qquad t \ge 0 \tag{3}$$

for the exponential random variable X with parameter α. Note that equation (3) allows probabilities to be calculated without integrating the probability density function. For example, the probability in Example 2 ($\alpha = 2$) can be calculated using equation (3) as

$$Pr\{1 \le X \le 2\} = Pr\{X \le 2\} - Pr\{X \le 1\}$$

$$= (1 - e^{-2\cdot 2}) - (1 - e^{-2\cdot 1})$$

$$= -e^{-4} + e^{-2} \approx 0.117.$$

☐ **EXAMPLE 3**

The telephone company determines that the length of time in seconds between incoming calls for directory assistance is an exponential random variable with $\alpha = 0.10$. If a call has just come in, what is the probability that the next call will occur within 5 seconds?

Solution: Using equation (3), we find that

$$Pr\{X \le 5\} = 1 - e^{-(0.10)5}$$

$$= 1 - e^{-0.5}$$

$$= 1 - 0.607$$

$$\approx 0.393.$$

■

□ **EXAMPLE 4**

A company purchases a new delivery truck that comes with a 24-month warranty on all repairs. Experience has shown that the probability of such a truck requiring a major repair is an exponential random variable with parameter $\alpha = 0.05$ when the variable t (time) is measured in years. What is the probability of the company having to pay for the cost of a major repair to this truck within the first three years?

Solution: Since repairs during the first two years are covered under warranty, the probability of the company having to *pay* for a major repair in the first three years is just the probability that it occurs *between* the end of the second year and the end of the third year, or

$$Pr\{2 \le X \le 3\} = Pr\{X \le 3\} - Pr\{X \le 2\}$$

$$= (1 - e^{-(0.05)(3)}) - (1 - e^{-(0.05)(2)})$$

$$= e^{-0.10} - e^{-0.15}$$

$$\approx 0.905 - 0.861$$

$$= 0.044. \qquad \blacksquare$$

Expected Value

The expected value of an exponential random variable is closely related to its parameter α.

> The **expected value** of the exponential random variable X with parameter α is
> $$E(X) = \frac{1}{\alpha}. \qquad (4)$$

To verify equation (4), we must evaluate the improper integral

$$E(X) = \int_0^\infty xf(x) \, dx = \int_0^\infty x \cdot \alpha e^{-\alpha x} \, dx$$

$$= \lim_{t \to \infty} \int_0^t \alpha x e^{-\alpha x} \, dx. \qquad (5)$$

The integral $\int \alpha x e^{-\alpha x} \, dx = \alpha \int x e^{-\alpha x} \, dx$ requires integration by parts. We let

$$u = x \qquad dv = e^{-\alpha x} \, dx$$

$$du = dx \qquad v = -\frac{1}{\alpha} e^{-\alpha x}.$$

Then the integration by parts formula $\int u\,dv = uv - \int v\,du$ gives

$$\int \alpha x e^{-\alpha x}\,dx = \alpha \int x e^{-\alpha x}\,dx = \alpha\left[x\left(-\frac{1}{\alpha}e^{-\alpha x}\right) - \int -\frac{1}{\alpha}e^{-\alpha x}\,dx\right]$$

$$= -x e^{-\alpha x} + \int e^{-\alpha x}\,dx$$

$$= -x e^{-\alpha x} - \frac{1}{\alpha}e^{-\alpha x} + C. \tag{6}$$

Combining equations (5) and (6) (with $C = 0$), we have

$$E(X) = \lim_{t\to\infty}\left[\left(-x e^{-\alpha x} - \frac{1}{\alpha}e^{-\alpha x}\right)\right]_0^t$$

$$= \lim_{t\to\infty}\left[\frac{1}{\alpha} - \left(t e^{-\alpha t} + \frac{1}{\alpha}e^{-\alpha t}\right)\right]$$

$$= \frac{1}{\alpha}$$

since $\lim_{t\to\infty} t e^{-\alpha t} = 0$ (see Exercise 20) and $\lim_{t\to\infty}\frac{1}{\alpha}e^{-\alpha t} = 0$.

☐ **EXAMPLE 5**

The number of hours that a certain type of lightbulb will burn until it expires is an exponential random variable X with expected value $E(X) = 100$ hours. Find the probability that

(a) the light bulb expires within the first 80 hours.
(b) the light bulb burns for more than 110 hours.

Solution: Since $E(x) = \dfrac{1}{\alpha} = 100$, the parameter for the exponential random variable X is $\alpha = \dfrac{1}{100} = 0.01$. Using equation (3) with $\alpha = 0.01$, we find that

(a) $Pr\{X \le 80\} = 1 - e^{-(0.01)(80)}$
$= 1 - e^{-0.8}$
$\approx 1 - 0.449$
$= 0.551.$

(b) $Pr\{X > 110\} = 1 - Pr\{X \le 110\}$
$= 1 - (1 - e^{-(0.01)(110)})$
$= e^{-1.1}$
$\approx 0.333.$

☐ **EXAMPLE 6**

The lifetime of a computer component is determined to be an exponential random variable X with expected value $E(X) = 10{,}000$ hours. What is the probability that the component will fail between 8000 and 12,000 hours of use?

Solution: Since $E(X) = \dfrac{1}{\alpha} = 10{,}000$ we have $\alpha = \dfrac{1}{10{,}000} = 0.0001$. Thus

$$Pr\{8000 \leq X \leq 12{,}000\} = Pr\{X \leq 12{,}000\} - Pr\{X \leq 8000\}$$

$$= (1 - e^{-(0.0001)(12{,}000)}) - (1 - e^{-(0.0001)(8000)})$$

$$= e^{-0.8} - e^{-1.2}$$

$$\approx 0.449 - 0.301$$

$$= 0.148.$$

☑ **PRACTICE PROBLEMS 11.4**

1. For the exponential random variable X with probability density function $f(x) = 4e^{-4x}$, find
   a. $Pr\{0 \leq X \leq 5\}$
   b. the distribution function.
2. The lifetime of an automobile headlamp is an exponential random variable with expected value $E(x) = 250$ hours. Find the probability that
   a. bulb expires within the first 20 hours;
   b. a bulb lasts more than 500 hours.

Exercise Set 11.4

In Exercises 1–5, find the indicated probability for the exponential random variable X with parameter α by integration.

1. $Pr\{0 \leq X \leq 6\}$, $\alpha = 0.05$

2. $Pr\{0 \leq X \leq 15\}$, $\alpha = 0.10$

3. $Pr\{2 \leq X \leq 6\}$, $\alpha = 0.25$

4. $Pr\{1 \leq X \leq 6\}$, $\alpha = 0.10$

5. $Pr\{2 \leq X \leq 5\}$, $\alpha = 0.50$

In Exercises 6–10, find the indicated probability for the exponential random variable X with parameter α by using formula (3).

6. $Pr\{0 \leq X \leq 3\}$, $\alpha = 0.2$

7. $Pr\{0 \leq X \leq 6\}$, $\alpha = 0.1$

8. $Pr\{2 \leq X \leq 5\}$, $\alpha = 0.4$

9. $Pr\{5 \leq X \leq 20\}$, $\alpha = 0.02$

10. $Pr\{10 \leq X \leq 50\}$, $\alpha = 0.01$

11. If X is an exponential random variable with expected value $E(X) = 20$, find $Pr\{5 \leq X \leq 30\}$.

12. For the exponential random variable X with expected value $E(X) = 10$ find $Pr\{5 \leq X \leq 15\}$.

13. Find α if X is an exponential random variable with parameter α for which $E(X) = 1$.

14. The random variable X representing the lifetime of a certain type of radial tire (in miles) is known to be an exponential random variable with expected value $E(X) = 40{,}000$ miles. Find the probability that one such tire will last for more than 50,000 miles.

15. The length of time between incoming telephone calls at a data-service company is determined to be an exponential random variable with expected value 4 minutes. Find the

probability that the time between any two successive incoming calls is less than 2 minutes.

16. The length of time that a motorist must wait to cross a certain toll bridge is an exponential random variable with expected value 10 minutes. What is the probability that a motorist will have to wait more than 20 minutes at this bridge?

17. Let X be an exponential random variable. Find $Pr\{X > E(X)\}$. Why is the answer independent of α?

18. Find α if X is an exponential random variable with parameter α for which $Pr\{0 \leq X \leq 5\} = 0.6320$.

19. Find the variance of the exponential random variable X with parameter α using the facts that

$$\lim_{x \to \infty} x^2 e^{-\alpha x} = 0 \quad \text{and} \quad \lim_{x \to \infty} xe^{-\alpha x} = 0$$

when $\alpha > 0$.

20. Show that $\lim_{x \to \infty} xe^{-ax} = 0$ for $a > 0$ as follows.

a. Expand the function $f(x) = e^{\alpha x}$ about $x = 0$ in a Taylor series to obtain

$$e^{\alpha x} = 1 + \alpha x + \frac{\alpha^2 x^2}{2} + \frac{\alpha^3 x^3}{3!} + \cdots + \frac{\alpha^n x^n}{n!} + \cdots.$$

b. Conclude from part a that $e^{\alpha x} > \dfrac{\alpha^2 x^2}{2}$ when $\alpha > 0$ and $x > 0$.

c. Conclude from part (b) that

$$xe^{-\alpha x} = \frac{x}{e^{\alpha x}} < \frac{x}{\left(\dfrac{\alpha^2 x^2}{2}\right)} = \frac{2}{\alpha^2 x}.$$

d. Conclude from part (c) that

$$\lim_{x \to \infty} xe^{-\alpha x} \leq \lim_{x \to \infty} \frac{2}{\alpha x} = 0 \quad \text{for } \alpha > 0.$$

☑ **SOLUTIONS TO PRACTICE PROBLEMS 11.4**

1. a. $Pr\{0 \leq X \leq 5\} = \displaystyle\int_0^5 4e^{-4x} \, dx$

$$= \left[-e^{-4x}\right]_0^5$$
$$= 1 - e^{-20}$$
$$\approx 1.$$

b. $F(t) = \displaystyle\int_0^t 4e^{-4x} \, dx$

$$= \left[-e^{-4x}\right]_0^t$$
$$= 1 - e^{-4t}.$$

2. Since $E(X) = \dfrac{1}{\alpha} = 250$, we have $\alpha = 0.004$. Then, using equation (3), we have

a. $Pr\{X < 20\} = 1 - e^{-20(0.004)}$
$$= 1 - e^{-0.08}$$
$$\approx 0.0769.$$

b. $Pr\{X > 500\} = 1 - Pr\{X \leq 500\}$
$$= 1 - (1 - e^{-500(0.004)})$$
$$= 1 - (1 - e^{-2})$$
$$\approx 0.1353.$$

Summary Outline of Chapter 11

▌ A **sample space** is the set of all possible simple outcomes for an experiment. (Page 794)

▌ An **event** is a subset of a sample space. (Page 794)

▌ A **discrete random variable** X is a variable that can equal any number in a finite sample space consisting only of numbers.

▌ A **probability distribution** for a discrete random variable X is a function defined on the sample space for X with two properties: (Page 798)

(i) $0 \le Pr\{X = a\} \le 1$ for any number a in the sample space for X.
(ii) The sum of the probabilities associated with the numbers in the sample space equals one.

▌ The **expected value** of the discrete random variable X is the number (Page 801)

$$E(X) = x_1 p_1 + x_2 p_2 + \cdots + x_n p_n$$

where $\{x_1, x_2, \ldots, x_n\}$ is the sample space for X and p_j is the probability $Pr\{X = x_j\}, j = 1, 2, \ldots, n$.

▌ The **variance** associated with this random variable is the number (Page 803)

$$\mathrm{Var}(X) = (x_1 - E(X))^2 p_1 + (x_2 - E(X))^2 p_2 + \cdots + (x_n - E(X))^2 p_n.$$

▌ The **standard deviation** σ of this random variable is the number $\sigma = \sqrt{\mathrm{Var}(X)}$. (Page 804)

▌ A **probability density function** for the continuous random variable X is a continuous nonnegative function f for which (Page 807)

$$Pr\{a \le X \le b\} = \int_a^b f(x)\, dx.$$

▌ A **distribution function** for the continuous random variable X is a function F with the property that (Page 812)

$$F(x) = Pr\{X < x\}$$

for all x in the sample space for X.

▌ If X is a continuous random variable with a continuous probability density function f and a probability distribution function F, we have (Page 812)

$$Pr\{a \le X \le b\} = \int_a^b f(x)\, dx = F(b) - F(a).$$

■ If X is a continuous random variable defined on the sample space   (Page 814)
[a, b] with continuous probability density function f, the **expected value** of X is

$$E(X) = \int_a^b xf(x)\,dx$$

and the **variance** is

$$\text{Var}(X) = \int_a^b (x - E(X))^2 f(x)\,dx.$$

■ The **normal random variable** with parameters μ and σ, referred to as   (Page 819)
the $N(\mu, \sigma)$ variable, is the continuous random variable with probability density function

$$f(x) = \frac{1}{\sqrt{2\pi}\sigma} e^{-1/2(x-\mu/\sigma)^2}.$$

■ The $N(0, 1)$ random variable is called the **standard normal random**   (Page 824)
variable.

■ For the $N(\mu, \sigma)$ random variable X we have   (Page 824)

$$E(X) = \mu, \qquad \text{Var}(X) = \sigma^2.$$

■ The **exponential random variable** with parameter α is the continuous   (Page 830)
random variable with probability density function

$$f(x) = \begin{cases} \alpha e^{-\alpha x}, & x \geq 0 \\ 0, & x < 0. \end{cases}$$

Review Exercises—Chapter 11

1. Table 5.1 shows a probability distribution for the discrete random variable X. Find the probability of
   a. the event $\{1, 2, 5\}$
   b. the event $\{2, 3, 4\}$
   c. the event $\{1, 2, 3\}$

Table 5.1

x_i	1	2	3	4	5
p_i	0.1	0.1	0.2	0.3	0.3

2. Find the expected value of the random variable X in Exercise 1.

3. Find the variance of the random variable in Exercise 1.

4. Find the probability that a card drawn at random from an ordinary deck of playing cards is a red card numbered less than 8.

5. A lottery ticket costs \$10, and 2000 tickets are sold. There is but one prize, a cash amount of \$500. What is the expected value of the variable X representing the net winnings resulting from the purchase of a single ticket?

6. For the probability density function

$$f(x) = \begin{cases} \dfrac{x}{6}, & 0 \leq x \leq 2 \\[2mm] \dfrac{1}{3}, & 2 < x \leq 4 \end{cases}$$

on the sample space [0, 4] find

a. $Pr\{0 \le X \le 2\}$
b. $Pr\{1 \le X \le 2\}$
c. $Pr\{1 \le X \le 4\}$

7. Find the number k so that the function $f(x) = kx$ is a probability density function on the sample space $[0, 5]$.

8. For the probability density function in Exercise 7 find
a. $Pr\{0 \le X \le 2\}$
b. $Pr\{1 \le X \le 4\}$

9. For the probability density function $f(x) = k(4 - x^2)$ on the sample space $[0, 2]$ find
a. k
b. $Pr\{0 \le X \le 1\}$
c. $Pr\{1 \le X \le 2\}$

10. Find the expected value of the random variable X with probability density function f in Exercise 7.

11. Find the variance, $\text{Var}(X)$, of the random variable X with probability density function f in Exercise 7.

12. Find the expected value of the random variable X with probability density function f in Exercise 9.

In Exercises 13–16, find the indicated probability for the standard $N(0, 1)$ normal random variable Z.

13. $Pr\{Z \le -0.5\}$

14. $Pr\{-2.1 \le Z \le 2.0\}$

15. $Pr\{Z \ge -0.6\}$

16. $Pr\{Z \le 1.7\}$

In Exercises 17–20, find the indicated probability for the $N(\mu, \sigma)$ normal random variable.

17. $Pr\{X \ge 7\}, \quad \mu = 10, \quad \sigma = 2$

18. $Pr\{6.5 \le X \le 10\}, \quad \mu = 8.6, \quad \sigma = 1.4$

19. $Pr\{-11 \le X \le 13\}, \quad \mu = 2, \quad \sigma = 6$

20. $Pr\{136 \le X \le 152\}, \quad \mu = 140, \quad \sigma = 8$.

21. The variable X representing a person's score on an intelligence test is a normal random variable with $\mu = 100$ and $\sigma = 10$. Find the probability that a score, selected at random, will

a. exceed 110.
b. exceed 120.

22. If the length of a goldfish's life is a normal random variable with expected value 15 months and variance 16 months, find the probability that a single goldfish selected at random will live at least nine months.

23. The annual snowfall in a certain region is found to be a normal random variable with expected value $\mu = 16$ inches and variance $\sigma^2 = 9$ inches. What is the probability that a single year's snowfall totals less than 10 inches?

24. If X is an $N(\mu, \sigma)$ random variable with $\mu = 6$ and $Pr\{4 \le X \le 8\} = 0.8664$, what is σ?

In Exercises 25–28, find the indicated probability for the exponential random variable X with parameter α.

25. $Pr\{X \ge 4\}, \quad \alpha = 0.2$

26. $Pr\{0 \le X \le 40\}, \quad \alpha = 0.2$

27. $Pr\{X \ge 12\}, \quad \alpha = 0.10$

28. $Pr\{10 \le X \le 15\}, \quad \alpha = 0.05$

29. Find $Pr\{2 \le X \le 6\}$ for the exponential random variable X with expected value $\mu = 4$.

30. The lifetime of a machine part is known to be an exponential random variable with expected value $\mu = 20$ months. Find the probability that such a part fails within the first year of use.

31. Find the expected value of the exponential random variable X if $Pr\{0 \le X \le 5\} = 0.221$.

32. The length of time between calls at an urban fire station is an exponential random variable with expected value $\mu = 2$ hours. If a call has just been received, what is the probability that the next call will occur within 30 minutes?

1

BASIC Computer Programs

Included here are four BASIC programs that are referred to in various examples and exercises in the text. They are presented as ''bare-bones'' prototypes, which can be used by those with access to computing facilities (personal computers, programmable calculators, or large computers) in designing programs that actually operate on particular machines. Notation appearing in these programs includes the following:

1. $a*b$ means the product ab.
2. $a \uparrow b$ means the exponentiation a^b.
3. a/b means the quotient $\dfrac{a}{b}$.

Proper development of computer software requires full documentation, as well as the inclusion of checks to ensure that the user does not attempt to supply inappropriate values to the program. (For example, in asking the user to specify the endpoints of an interval $[a, b]$, one should check to ensure that $a < b$.) We have made no attempt to do either, since we wish to highlight only the algorithm involved in the program.

Program 1: Values of the Function $f(x) = \dfrac{x^2 + x + 6}{x - 2}$

```
10  DEF FNF(X) = (X ↑ 2 + X + 6)/(X − 2)
20  PRINT "ENTER X"
30  INPUT X
40  LET Y = FNF(X)
50  PRINT "F(X) = "; Y
60  END
```

COMMENT: This program prints the function value $f(x) = \dfrac{x^2 + x + 6}{x - 2}$ for the user's choice of $x \neq 2$. To print values of a different function g, simply replace the right-hand side of the equation in line 10 with the expression for $g(x)$.

Program 2: Approximating the Number e

```
10  PRINT "ENTER N"
20  INPUT N
30  FOR M = 1 TO N
40  LET Y = (1 + 1/M) ↑ M
50  PRINT Y
60  NEXT M
70  END
```

COMMENT: This program prints the values $\left(1 + \dfrac{1}{M}\right)^{M}$ for integers M beginning with $M = 1$ and terminating with $M = N$.

Program 3: Calculating Compound Interest

```
10   PRINT "ENTER R"
20   INPUT R
30   PRINT "ENTER K"
40   INPUT K
50   PRINT "ENTER N"
60   INPUT N
70   PRINT "ENTER P"
80   INPUT P
90   LET Y = (1 + R/K) ↑ (N*K)
100  LET Z = Y*P
110  PRINT Z
120  END
```

COMMENT: This program prints the amount $\left(1 + \dfrac{r}{k}\right)^{nk} P$ on deposit n years after an initial deposit of P dollars has been subjected to compounding of interest k times per year at nominal rate r percent.

Program 4: **Approximating Sum for $\displaystyle\int_a^b x^2\, dx$**

```
10   DEF FNF(T) = T ↑ 2
20   PRINT "ENTER INTERVAL ENDPOINTS A,B"
30   INPUT A,B
40   PRINT "HOW MANY SUBINTERVALS?"
50   INPUT N
60   LET D = (B − A)/N
70   LET S = O
80   FOR I = 1 to N
90      LET X = A + (I − 1)*D
100     LET S = S + FNF(X)*D
110  NEXT I
120  PRINT S
130  END
```

COMMENT: This program prints an approximating sum for the function $f(x) = x^2$ on the interval $[a, b]$ chosen by the user. The sum is associated with n subintervals of equal length, and the left endpoint of each subinterval is used as the "test point." To use the program for a different function, simply rewrite line 10 to correspond to the desired function.

Program 5: **Trapezoidal Rule Applied to $f(x) = \dfrac{1}{x}$**

```
10   DEF FNF(T) = 1/T
20   PRINT "enter interval endpoints a,b with"
     a > 0"
30   INPUT A,B
40   PRINT "how many subintervals?"
50   INPUT N
60   LET D = (B − A)/N
70   LET S = FNF(A)
80   FOR I = 1 TO (N − 1)
```

```
 90    LET X = A + I*D
100    LET S = S + 2*FNF(X)
110    NEXT I
120    LET S = S + FNF(B)
130    LET S = S*(D/2)
140    PRINT S
150    END
```

COMMENT: This program implements the Trapezoidal Rule for approximate integration for the function $f(x) = \dfrac{1}{x}$ on the interval $[a, b]$. The numbers a, b, and n (the number of subintervals) are supplied by the user.

Program 6: Simpson's Rule Applied to the Function $f(x) = \dfrac{1}{x}$

```
 10    DEF FNF(T) = 1/T
 20    PRINT "enter interval endpoints a,b with a > 0"
 30    INPUT A,B
 40    PRINT "how many subintervals (an even
       number)?"
 50    INPUT N
 60    LET C = (B − A)/N
 70    LET D = C/3
 80    LET S = FNF(A)
 90    FOR I = 1 TO (N − 1) STEP 2
100    LET S = S + 4*FNF(A + I*C)
110    NEXT I
120    FOR I = 2 TO (N − 2) STEP 2
130    LET S = S + 2*FNF(A + I*C)
140    NEXT I
150    LET S = S + FNF(B)
160    LET S = S*D
170    PRINT S
180    END
```

COMMENT: This program implements Simpson's Rule for approximate integration for the function $f(x) = \dfrac{1}{x}$ on the interval $[a, b]$. The numbers a, b, and n (the number of subintervals, *an even number*) are supplied by the user.

Program 7:   **Euler's Method Applied to the Initial Value Problem**

$$\frac{dy}{dt} = e^t - 2v$$

$$y(0) = 1$$

```
10  LET Y = 1
20  LET T = 0
30  FOR I = 1 TO 4
40  T = T + 0.25
50  Y = Y + (EXP(T) − 2*Y)*(0.25)
60  PRINT T,Y
70  NEXT I
80  END
```

COMMENT: This program gives an approximation to the stated initial value problem on the interval $[0, 1]$ using $n = 4$ subintervals. The equation for Euler's method is implemented in step 50. Note that the right-hand side of this equation involves current values of both T and Y.

2

Mathematical Tables

Table 1. Exponential functions

x	e^x	e^{-x}	x	e^x	e^{-x}
0.00	1.00000	1.00000	.75	2.11700	.47237
.05	1.05127	.95123			
.10	1.10517	.90484	.80	2.22554	.44933
.15	1.16183	.86071	.85	2.33965	.42741
.20	1.22140	.81873	.90	2.45960	.40657
.25	1.28403	.77880	.95	2.58571	.38674
.30	1.34986	.74082	1.00	2.71828	.36788
.35	1.41907	.70469	2.00	7.38906	.13534
.40	1.49182	.67032	3.00	20.08554	.04979
.45	1.56831	.63763	4.00	54.59815	.01832
.50	1.64872	.60653	5.00	148.41316	.00674
			6.00	403.42879	.00248
.55	1.73325	.57695	7.00	1096.63316	.00091
.60	1.82212	.54881	8.00	2980.95799	.00034
.65	1.91554	.52205	9.00	8103.08393	.00012
.70	2.01375	.49659	10.00	22026.46579	.00005

Note: $e^{a+x} = e^a e^x$

Table 2. Natural logarithms

x	$\ln x$	x	$\ln x$	x	$\ln x$	x	$\ln x$
.1	−2.30258	2.6	.95551	5.1	1.62924	7.6	2.02815
.2	−1.60943	2.7	.99325	5.2	1.64866	7.7	2.04122
.3	−1.20396	2.8	1.02962	5.3	1.66771	7.8	2.05412
.4	−.91628	2.9	1.06471	5.4	1.68640	7.9	2.06686
.5	−.69314	3.0	1.09861	5.5	1.70475	8.0	2.07944
.6	−.51082	3.1	1.13140	5.6	1.72277	8.1	2.09186
.7	−.35666	3.2	1.16315	5.7	1.74047	8.2	2.10413
.8	−.22313	3.3	1.19392	5.8	1.75786	8.3	2.11626
.9	−.10535	3.4	1.22378	5.9	1.77495	8.4	2.12823
1.0	0.00000	3.5	1.25276	6.0	1.79176	8.5	2.14007
1.1	.09531	3.6	1.28093	6.1	1.80829	8.6	2.15176
1.2	.18232	3.7	1.30833	6.2	1.82455	8.7	2.16332
1.3	.26236	3.8	1.33500	6.3	1.84055	8.8	2.17475
1.4	.33647	3.9	1.36098	6.4	1.85630	8.9	2.18605
1.5	.40547	4.0	1.38629	6.5	1.87180	9.0	2.19722
1.6	.47000	4.1	1.41099	6.6	1.88707	9.1	2.20827
1.7	.53063	4.2	1.43508	6.7	1.90211	9.2	2.21920
1.8	.58779	4.3	1.45862	6.8	1.91692	9.3	2.23001
1.9	.64185	4.4	1.48160	6.9	1.93152	9.4	2.24071
2.0	.69315	4.5	1.50408	7.0	1.94591	9.5	2.25129
2.1	.74194	4.6	1.52606	7.1	1.96009	9.6	2.26176
2.2	.78846	4.7	1.54756	7.2	1.97408	9.7	2.27213
2.3	.83291	4.8	1.56862	7.3	1.98787	9.8	2.28238
2.4	.87547	4.9	1.58924	7.4	2.00148	9.9	2.29253
2.5	.91629	5.0	1.60944	7.5	2.01490	10.0	2.30259

Note: $\ln 10x = \ln x + \ln 10$

Table 3. Trigonometric functions (x in radians)

x	$\sin x$	$\cos x$	$\tan x$		x	$\sin x$	$\cos x$	$\tan x$
0.0	.00000	1.00000	0.00000		3.4	$-.25554$	$-.96680$	.26432
0.1	.09983	.99500	.10033		3.5	$-.35078$	$-.93646$	.37459
0.2	.19867	.98007	.20271					
0.3	.29552	.95534	.30934		3.6	$-.44252$	$-.89676$	.49347
0.4	.38942	.92106	.42279		3.7	$-.52984$	$-.84810$	.62473
0.5	.47943	.87758	.54630		3.8	$-.61186$	$-.79097$	.77356
					3.9	$-.68777$	$-.72593$	.94742
0.6	.56464	.82534	.68414		4.0	$-.75680$	$-.65364$	1.15782
0.7	.64422	.76484	.84229					
0.8	.71736	.69671	1.02964		4.1	$-.81828$	$-.57482$	1.42353
0.9	.78333	.62161	1.26016		4.2	$-.87158$	$-.49026$	1.77778
1.0	.84147	.54030	1.55741		4.3	$-.91617$	$-.40080$	2.28585
					4.4	$-.95160$	$-.30733$	3.09632
1.1	.89121	.45360	1.96476		4.5	$-.97753$	$-.21080$	4.63733
1.2	.93204	.36236	2.57215					
1.3	.96356	.26750	3.60210		4.6	$-.99369$	$-.11215$	8.86017
1.4	.98545	.16997	5.79788		4.7	$-.99992$	$-.01239$	80.71271
1.5	.99749	.07074	14.10142		$3\pi/2$	-1.00000	.00000	$-\infty$
$\pi/2$	1.00000	.00000	∞		4.8	$-.99616$	.08750	-11.38487
1.6	.99957	$-.02920$	-34.23254		4.9	$-.98245$	.18651	-5.26749
1.7	.99166	$-.12884$	-7.69660		5.0	$-.95892$	.28366	-3.38051
1.8	.97385	$-.22720$	-4.28626					
1.9	.94630	$-.32329$	-2.92710		5.1	$-.92581$	.37798	-2.44939
2.0	.90930	$-.41615$	-2.18504		5.2	$-.88345$	.46852	-1.88564
					5.3	$-.83227$	.55437	-1.50127
2.1	.86321	$-.50485$	-1.70985		5.4	$-.77276$	.63469	-1.21754
2.2	.80850	$-.58850$	-1.37382		5.5	$-.70554$	.70867	$-.99558$
2.3	.74571	$-.66628$	-1.11921					
2.4	.67546	$-.73739$	$-.91601$		5.6	$-.63127$	.77557	$-.81394$
2.5	.59847	$-.80114$	$-.74702$		5.7	$-.55069$	.83471	$-.65973$
					5.8	$-.46460$	.88552	$-.52467$
2.6	.51550	$-.85689$	$-.60160$		5.9	$-.37388$	.92748	$-.40311$
2.7	.42738	$-.90407$	$-.47273$		6.0	$-.27942$	.96017	$-.29101$
2.8	.33499	$-.94222$	$-.35553$					
2.9	.23925	$-.97096$	$-.24641$		6.1	$-.18216$	.98327	$-.18526$
3.0	.14112	$-.98999$	$-.14255$		6.2	$-.08309$	.99654	$-.08338$
					2π	.00000	1.00000	.00000
3.1	.04158	$-.99914$	$-.04162$		6.3	.01681	.99986	.01682
π	.00000	-1.00000	.00000		6.4	.11655	.99318	.11735
3.2	$-.05837$	$-.99829$	.05847		6.5	.21512	.97659	.22028
3.3	$-.15775$	$-.98748$	.15975					

Table 4. The standard normal distribution

z	.00	.01	.02	.03	.04	.05	.06	.07	.08	.09
0.0	.5000	.5040	.5080	.5120	.5160	.5199	.5239	.5279	.5319	.5359
0.1	.5398	.5438	.5478	.5517	.5557	.5596	.5636	.5675	.5714	.5753
0.2	.5793	.5832	.5871	.5910	.5948	.5987	.6026	.6064	.6103	.6141
0.3	.6179	.6217	.6255	.6293	.6331	.6368	.6406	.6443	.6480	.6517
0.4	.6554	.6591	.6628	.6664	.6700	.6736	.6772	.6808	.6844	.6879
0.5	.6915	.6950	.6985	.7019	.7054	.7088	.7123	.7157	.7190	.7224
0.6	.7257	.7291	.7324	.7357	.7389	.7422	.7454	.7486	.7517	.7549
0.7	.7580	.7611	.7642	.7673	.7704	.7734	.7764	.7794	.7823	.7852
0.8	.7881	.7910	.7939	.7967	.7995	.8023	.8051	.8078	.8106	.8133
0.9	.8159	.8186	.8212	.8238	.8264	.8289	.8315	.8340	.8365	.8389
1.0	.8413	.8438	.8461	.8485	.8508	.8531	.8554	.8577	.8599	.8621
1.1	.8643	.8665	.8686	.8708	.8729	.8749	.8770	.8790	.8810	.8830
1.2	.8849	.8869	.8888	.8907	.8925	.8944	.8962	.8980	.8997	.9015
1.3	.9032	.9049	.9066	.9082	.9099	.9115	.9131	.9147	.9162	.9177
1.4	.9192	.9207	.9222	.9236	.9251	.9265	.9279	.9292	.9306	.9319
1.5	.9332	.9345	.9357	.9370	.9382	.9394	.9406	.9418	.9429	.9441
1.6	.9452	.9463	.9474	.9484	.9495	.9505	.9515	.9525	.9535	.9545
1.7	.9554	.9564	.9573	.9582	.9591	.9599	.9608	.9616	.9625	.9633
1.8	.9641	.9649	.9656	.9664	.9671	.9678	.9686	.9693	.9699	.9706
1.9	.9713	.9719	.9726	.9732	.9738	.9744	.9750	.9756	.9761	.9767
2.0	.9772	.9778	.9783	.9788	.9793	.9798	.9803	.9808	.9812	.9817
2.1	.9821	.9826	.9830	.9834	.9838	.9842	.9846	.9850	.9854	.9857
2.2	.9861	.9864	.9868	.9871	.9875	.9878	.9881	.9884	.9887	.9890
2.3	.9893	.9896	.9898	.9901	.9904	.9906	.9909	.9911	.9913	.9916
2.4	.9918	.9920	.9922	.9925	.9927	.9929	.9931	.9932	.9934	.9936
2.5	.9938	.9940	.9941	.9943	.9945	.9946	.9948	.9949	.9951	.9952
2.6	.9953	.9955	.9956	.9957	.9959	.9960	.9961	.9962	.9963	.9964
2.7	.9965	.9966	.9967	.9968	.9969	.9970	.9971	.9972	.9973	.9974
2.8	.9974	.9975	.9976	.9977	.9977	.9978	.9979	.9979	.9980	.9981
2.9	.9981	.9982	.9982	.9983	.9984	.9984	.9985	.9985	.9986	.9986
3.0	.9987	.9987	.9987	.9988	.9988	.9989	.9989	.9989	.9990	.9990

Answers to Odd-Numbered Exercises

Chapter 1

Exercise Set 1.1

1. real number

3. real number

5. integers

7. integers

9. real number

11. d

13. a

15. b

17. g

19. f

21. True

23. Two (1 and -1)

25. $(-\infty, 3]$

27. $[-4, \infty)$

29. $[11, \infty)$

31. $(-2, \infty)$

33. $\left[\dfrac{1}{2}, \infty\right)$

35. $200P + 250B \leq 10{,}000$

37. 20

39. $24 < w < 30$

41. a. $1100 + 400x > 600x$
   b. $x \geq 6$

43. 15 ounces

Exercise Set 1.2

1.

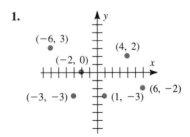

3.

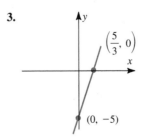

5.

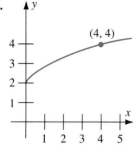

7.

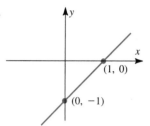

9.

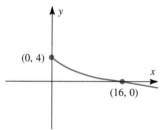

11.

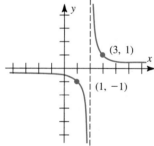

13. False

15. -8

17. $y = 4x - 2$

19. $y = -5$

21. $y = -4x + 17$

23. $y = 2x + 6$

25. $y = -3$

27. $y = 6x + 2$

29. $y = \dfrac{3}{5}x - 5$

31. $y = -\dfrac{1}{4}x$

33.

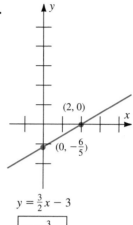

$y = \dfrac{3}{2}x - 3$

$\boxed{\begin{array}{l} m = \dfrac{3}{5} \\[2mm] b = -\dfrac{6}{5} \end{array}}$

35.

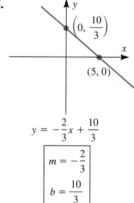

$y = -\dfrac{2}{3}x + \dfrac{10}{3}$

$\boxed{\begin{array}{l} m = -\dfrac{2}{3} \\[2mm] b = \dfrac{10}{3} \end{array}}$

37.

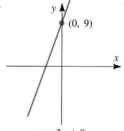

$y = 2x + 9$

$\boxed{\begin{array}{l} m = 2 \\ b = 9 \end{array}}$

39.

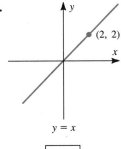

$y = x$

$\boxed{\begin{array}{l} m = 1 \\ b = 0 \end{array}}$

41.

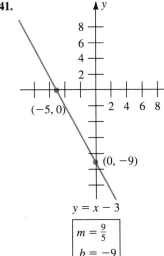

$(-5, 0)$

$(0, -9)$

$y = x - 3$

$\boxed{\begin{array}{l} m = \dfrac{9}{5} \\ b = -9 \end{array}}$

43. a. $m = 5; b = 100$
   b. \$850
   c. \$100/wk

47. a. 135
    b. 150

49. a. $V = 20{,}000 - 4500t$
    b. \$13,250
    c. $2.2\overline{2}$ years $\left(\text{or } \dfrac{20}{9} \text{ years}\right)$
    d. \$4500

45. a. $C = \dfrac{193}{15}t + 100$
    b. 486

51. a. $V = 12{,}000 - 200t$
    b. $A = 6000 + 400t$
    c. After $t = 10$ months
    d. \$10,000

53. a. $D = 400 - 0.1p$
    b. $D = 100$
    c. $p = \$4000$
    d. $D = 400$; no—it would correspond to absolutely free travel.

Exercise Set 1.3

1. $\sqrt{13}$

3. $\sqrt{122}$

5. $\sqrt{8}$

7. $\sqrt{50}$

11. $x^2 + y^2 = 9$

13. $x^2 - 8x + y^2 - 6y + 21 = 0$

15. $x^2 + 12x + y^2 + 8y - 48 = 0$

17. $(x - 5)^2 - 25$

19. $16 - (x - 4)^2$

21. $\dfrac{7}{2} - 2\left(t + \dfrac{1}{2}\right)^2$

23. center = $(1, -3)$
    radius = $\sqrt{22}$

25. center = $(-7, 5)$
    radius = 2

27. center = $(1, 3)$
    radius = $\sqrt{7}$

29. inside

31. yes

Exercise Set 1.4

1. function

3. not a function

5. function

7. not a function

9. a. 7   **b.** -2
   c. $7 - 3a$ **d.** $7 - 3x - 3h$
   e. Domain is $(-\infty, \infty)$.   **f.** Range is $(-\infty, \infty)$.

11. a. $\dfrac{3}{2}$ **b.** 0   **c.** $\dfrac{1}{2}$
    d. $\dfrac{x + h + 3}{x^2 + 2xh + h^2 - x - h + 2}$

13. not a function

15. not a function

17. function

19. function

21. $x \neq \pm\sqrt{7}$

23. $(-\infty, -1)$ and $(-1, \infty)$

25. $(-1, 1)$

27. $(0, 1)$ and $(1, \infty)$

29. $[-2, \infty)$

31. $C(x) = 2x + 0.5$

33. $C(x) = 70x + 1000$

35. a. 600   **b.** 0   **c.** 20

37. $R(p) = \begin{cases} 440p, p \le 50 \\ 900p - 10p^2, p > 50 \end{cases}$

39. a.   **b.** 20

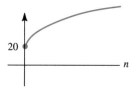

41. a. $P(x) = 100 + 0.005x$ **b.** \$850

43. a. $C(t) = \dfrac{7}{8}t + 315$ **b.** 350 parts per million

Exercise Set 1.5

1. 9

3. $\dfrac{1}{8}$

5. $27x^2$

7. $27x^{11/2}y^{-7/2}$

9. $6x^{7/3}y^{9/2}$

11. True

13.

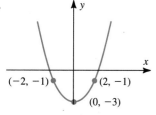

15.

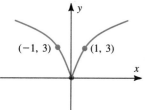

17.

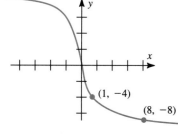

19.

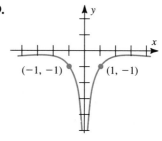

21.

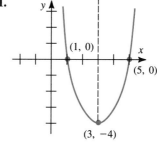

23.

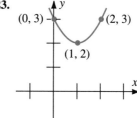

25.

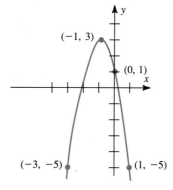

27.

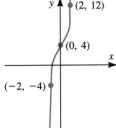

29.

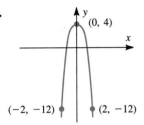

31.

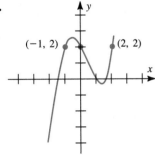

33.

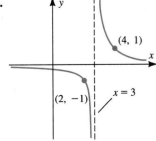

35.

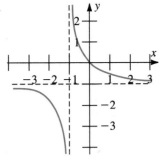

37.

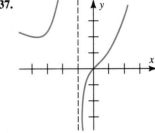

39. $w(\ell) = \dfrac{80}{\ell}$ Domain is $(0, \infty)$.

41. a.

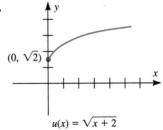

$u(x) = \sqrt{x + 2}$

b.

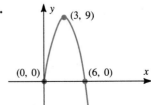

c. $U_2(x)$ **d.** $U_1(x)$

43. a. $T(3) = 30\left(1 + \dfrac{2}{\sqrt{3 + 1}}\right) = 30(1 + 1) = 60$ seconds

b.

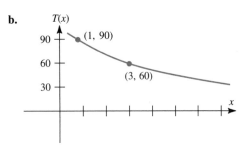

45. $C(x) = 400 + 40x + 0.2x^2$
$$= 0.2(x^2 + 200x + 10,000) - 2000 + 400$$
$$= 0.2(x + 100)^2 - 1600$$

a.

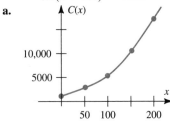

b. Fixed costs = \$400

x	$C(x)$
50	$400 + 2000 + 500 = 2900$
100	$400 + 4000 + 2000 = 6400$
150	$400 + 6000 + 4500 = 10,900$
200	$400 + 8000 + 8000 = 16,400$
250	$400 + 10,000 + 12,500 = 22,900$
300	$400 + 12,000 + 18,000 = 30,400$

47. a. $C(0) = 500$; $C(30) = 1750$;
$C(40) = 3930$; $C(50) = 7790$
b. $R(x) = 100x$
c. $P(x) = 100x - 500 - 10\left(\dfrac{x-5}{5}\right)^3$
d. $P(0) = -490$; $P(30) = 1250$; $P(40) = 70$; $P(50) = -2790$
e. because cost begins to increase rapidly for larger values of production

Exercise Set 1.6

1. $x = -2, 2$ **3.** $x = -3, 2$

5. $x = -5, 7$ **7.** $x = 2$

9. $x = 0, 3$ **11.** $x = -\dfrac{1}{2} \pm \dfrac{\sqrt{5}}{2}$

13. $x = -\dfrac{3}{4} \pm \dfrac{\sqrt{17}}{4}$ **15.** $x = -1, 3$

17. $x = \dfrac{1}{6} \pm \dfrac{7}{6}$ **19.** $(2, 5)$

21. $(-1, -1)$, $(3, 7)$ **23.** $(1, 1)$

25. $(-1, 1)$, $(0, 2)$, $(1, 3)$ **27.** $(4, 0)$, $\left(\dfrac{5}{3}, -\dfrac{35}{3}\right)$

29. More items will be demanded than will be supplied; that is, $D(p_1) > S(p_1)$.

31. $x = \$3600$ **33. a.** $x = 10, 50$
   b. $10 < x < 50$

35. $t = 1, 5$ hours   **37.** $x = 10, 50$

39. $x = 10,000$

Exercise Set 1.7

1. $x^2 + x - 5$ **3.** 25

5. $-\dfrac{11}{18}$ **7.** $\dfrac{1}{x+2} - 2\sqrt{3+x}$

9. 0 **11.** $-\dfrac{11}{3}$

13. $4 - x^2$ **15.** $3\sqrt{x} + 1$

17. $(3x + 1)^3$ **19.** $\left(\dfrac{1}{\sqrt{x}+1}\right)^2$

21. $3x^{3/2} + 1$ **23.** $(x + 3)^3 + 5$

25. $u(x) = 2x$ **27.** a

29. b   **31.** d

33. a   **35.** d

37.

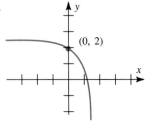

$(0, 2)$

39.

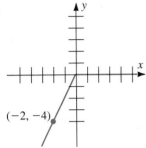

(−2, −4)

41.

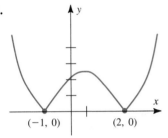

(−1, 0)   (2, 0)

43. a. $p(x) = \begin{cases} 500, & 0 \le x \le 5 \\ 500 - 10(x - 5), & 6 \le x \le 25 \\ 300, & 26 \le x \end{cases}$

b.

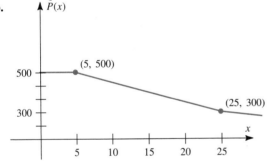

(5, 500)

500

(25, 300)

300

5   10   15   20   25

45. $f(c) = \sqrt{15 + 0.2c + 0.01c^2}$

47. a. $C(x) = (200x + 75)$ dollars
  b. $R(x) = 1.4(200x + 75) = (280x + 105)$ dollars
  c. $P(x) = \dfrac{280x + 105}{x} = \left(280 + \dfrac{105}{x}\right)$ dollars

Review Exercises—Chapter 1

1. a. $(-6, 3]$ **b.** $(-\infty, 4)$ **c.** $[2, \infty)$

3. $x \le -\dfrac{1}{2}$ **5.** $x \le \dfrac{2}{3}$

7.

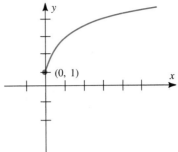

(0, 1)

9.

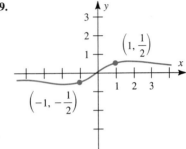

3
2
$\left(1, \dfrac{1}{2}\right)$
1

1   2   3

$\left(-1, -\dfrac{1}{2}\right)$

11. $\dfrac{1}{6}$ **13.** $y = 5$ **15.** $b = 7$

17.

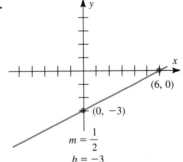

(6, 0)

(0, −3)

$m = \dfrac{1}{2}$

$b = -3$

19.

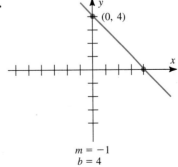

(0, 4)

$m = -1$
$b = 4$

21. $(-\infty, 0)$ and $(0, \infty)$ **23.** $(-\infty, 2]$

25. a. $\dfrac{2}{9}$ **b.** $\dfrac{3}{14}$ **27.** 8   **29.** $x^3 y^6$

31.

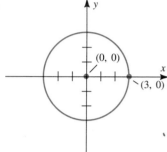

33.

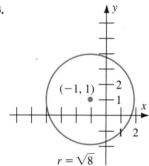

$r = \sqrt{8}$

35.

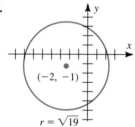

$r = \sqrt{19}$

37. 1, 2

39. 3

41. none

43. $(-8, -14)$

45. $(1, 1), (-1, 1)$

47. $x^4 + 4x^3 + 2x + 8$

49. 8

51. $\sqrt{x^2 - 4}$

53. $4x^2 - 28$

55.

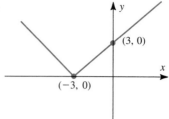

57.

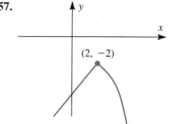

59. \$200

61. b, c   **63.** False

65. $C(x) = \begin{cases} 20x, & 0 \le x \le 50 \\ 1000 + 15(x - 50), & 50 < x \end{cases}$

67. 6.5 million   **69.** 59.8°F

71. a. \$21,000   **b.** 20%   **c.** \$50,000

73. \$15,000

75. $Y(x) = x(400 - 2x)$ **77.** 600

79. a. \$75,000

  b. $V(n) = (100{,}000)\left(1 - \dfrac{n}{30}\right)$

  c. 83,333

81. a, d, f, and g

83. a. Japan: $C = 4200 + 300t$
     U.S.: $C = 6400 + 100t$
   b. Japan; Japan
   c. yes; in 1993
   d. Japan: \$8700
     U.S.: \$7900

Chapter 2

Exercise Set 2.1

1. $m = -2$ **3.** $m = \dfrac{1}{4}$

5. $m = -\dfrac{1}{2}$

7. $m = 2$

9. $m = -2$

11. $m = 3$

13. $m = 4$

15. $m = 5$

17. $m = -1$

19. $m = \dfrac{1}{4}$

21. $m = 3$

23. $y = 4x + 13$

27. $m = -\dfrac{1}{10}$

29. a. $m = -1$

b. $m = 1$

31. $m = b + 2c$

33. a. negative; negative
b. no
c. Tangents to I and III do not have constant slope.

35. a. $c(x) = \dfrac{2000}{x} + 20 + 2x$

b. $m = -18$; decreasing
c. $m = 1.8$; increasing
d. $x_0 = 10\sqrt{10}$

Exercise Set 2.2

1. 0   **3.** -3 **5.** -6

7. $\dfrac{1}{7}$ **9.** 3   **11.** 8

13. 4   **15.** -10 **17.** -2

19. $\dfrac{1}{2}$ **21.** 0   **23.** $\dfrac{\sqrt{3}}{2} - 1$

25. $-\dfrac{1}{2}$

Exercise Set 2.3

1. a. doesn't exist
b. 2
c. 2
d. 0

3. a. 2
b. doesn't exist
c. 0

5. -1

7. 0

9. $\dfrac{1}{3}$

11. $x = -1, 1$

13. $x = -3$

15. $x = -3, -1, 1$

17. $x = 2$

19. $x = -3, 5$

21. $k = 3$

23. $k = -1$

25. $q = 50, 100$

27. $A = \$2865$

29. $a = 2$

31. $\lim\limits_{t \to 12^-} T(t) \neq \lim\limits_{t \to 12^+} T(t)$

Exercise Set 2.4

1. 2

3. $2x$

5. $4x^3$

7. $\dfrac{-2}{(x + 3)^2}$

9. $6x + 4$

11. $12x^3 - 4$

13. $3x^2 - 5x^4$

15. $12x^3 - 6$

17. $10x^4 + 6x^{-3}$

19. $\dfrac{4}{3}x^{-1/3} + 5x^{2/3}$

21. $-18x^{-3} + \dfrac{3}{2\sqrt{x}}$

23. $45x^8 - 5x^{-1/2} + \dfrac{33}{2}x^{9/2}$

25. $-\dfrac{8}{3}x^{-5/3} + \dfrac{7}{4}x^{-5/4}$

27. 40

29. -284

31. $-\dfrac{3}{2\sqrt{2}} + \dfrac{5}{3}$

33. $y - 3 = 6(x - 1)$

35. $\dfrac{5}{16}$

37. $a = 5$

39. $a = -1$

41. a. $6 < x < 10$
b. $0 \leq x < 8$
c. $P(8) = 8$

43. a. $-\dfrac{3}{2}t^{-5/2}$

b. $-\dfrac{3}{2^{7/2}}$

c. $y = -\dfrac{3t}{2^{7/2}} + \dfrac{3}{2^{5/2}} + \dfrac{1}{2^{3/2}}$

Exercise Set 2.5

1. 9

3. 1

5. 55

7. $v(t) = 2t + 2$

9. $v(t) = 3t^2 - 10t + 3$

11. $v(t) = \dfrac{3}{2\sqrt{t}} + \dfrac{15}{2}\sqrt{t}$

13. $v(t) = \dfrac{1}{\sqrt{t}} - \dfrac{10}{3}t^{-5/3}$

15. $v(t) = \dfrac{3}{2}\sqrt{t} + \dfrac{2}{\sqrt{t}} + 6t^{-3/2}$

17. $v(3) = 35$

19. a. $v(0) = 6$
　b. $t = 3$
　c. $v(6) = -6$

21. a. 144 feet
　b. 3 seconds

23. $s = \dfrac{49}{4}$

Exercise Set 2.6

1. a. $R'(x) = 10$
　b. $C'(x) = 6$
　c. $P(x) = 4x - 50$
　d. $P'(x) = 4$

3. a. $R'(x) = 100 - 4x$
　b. $C'(x) = 20 + \dfrac{3}{2}\sqrt{x}$
　c. $P(x) = 80x - 2x^2 - x^{3/2} - 400$
　d. $P'(x) = 80 - 4x - \dfrac{3}{2}\sqrt{x}$

5. a. $R'(x) = 40 + \dfrac{25}{\sqrt{x}}$
　b. $C'(x) = 20 + \dfrac{2}{3}x^{-1/3}$
　c. $P(x) = 20x + 50\sqrt{x} - x^{2/3} - 150$
　d. $P'(x) = 20 + \dfrac{25}{\sqrt{x}} - \dfrac{2}{3}x^{-1/3}$

7. a. $R'(x) = 400 - \dfrac{20}{3}x^{-1/3}$
　b. $C'(x) = -\dfrac{5000}{x^2}$
　c. $P(x) = 400x - 10x^{2/3} - \dfrac{5000}{x} - 40$
　d. $P'(x) = 400 - \dfrac{20}{3}x^{-1/3} + \dfrac{5000}{x^2}$

9. a. 80　　**b.** $0 \le x < 80$

11. a. $R(x) = 600x - 3x^2$
　b. $P(x) = 450x - 3.5x^2 - 4000$
　c. $C'(x) = 150 + x$
　　$R'(x) = 600 - 6x$
　d. $x = \dfrac{450}{7}$

13. a. 15
　b. 16

15. a. $P'(t) = \dfrac{1000}{\sqrt{t}}$
　b. no

19. $A = 10,\ B = 5;\ C = 40$

21. a. $R(x) = 1600x - 5x^2$
　b. $P(x) = 1200x - 30x^2 - 10,000$
　c. $MP(x) = 1200 - 60x$
　d. $x = 20$
　f. It occurs at $x = 20$.

23. a. $R(x) = 10,000x - 5x^2$
　b. $MR(x) = 10,000 - 10x$
　　$MR(1000) = 0$

　c. $MR(500) = 5000$
　　$MR(1500) = -5000$
　d. $x = 1000$

25. yes, if $MR(x) > MC(x)$

Exercise Set 2.7

1. $f'(x) = 2x$

3. $f'(x) = 12x^3 - 24x^2 + 12x - 16$

5. $f'(x) = 6x^5 - 8x^3 + 2x$

7. $f'(x) = \dfrac{7}{2}x^{5/2} - \dfrac{1}{6}x^{-7/6}$

9. $f'(x) = x^{-2} + 24x^{-3}$

11. $f'(x) = \dfrac{-4}{(x-2)^2}$

13. $f'(x) = \dfrac{8x^2 - 48x - 32}{(x-3)^2}$

15. $f'(x) = 1$

17. $f'(x) = \dfrac{x-3}{(1+x)^3}$

19. $f'(x) = \dfrac{\dfrac{3}{2}x^{3/2} + 2x - \dfrac{1}{6}x^{1/6} - \dfrac{2}{3}x^{-1/3}}{(\sqrt{x} + 1)^2}$

21. $f'(x) = \dfrac{7}{3}x^{4/3} + \left(\dfrac{2}{3}\right)x^{-2/3}$

23. $f'(x) = \dfrac{6x + 3 - x^2}{x^2(x + 1)^2}$

25. $f'(x) = 3acx^2 + 2bcx + ad$

27. $\left(1, -\dfrac{3}{2}\right), \left(3, \dfrac{9}{2}\right)$

31. $f'(x) = -5x^4 + 16x^3 - 6x^2 - 8x + 3$

33. $f'(x) = (x - x^2)(x^3 - x^{-2})(-x^{-2} + 3x^{-4})$
$\qquad + (x - x^2)(x^{-1} - x^{-3})(3x^2 + 2x^{-3})$
$\qquad + (x^3 - x^{-2})(x^{-1} - x^{-3})(1 - 2x)$

35. a. $MR(x) = \dfrac{10{,}000(3\sqrt{x} + x)}{(2 + \sqrt{x})^2}$
$\quad$ **b.** $MR(9) = 7200$

37. a. $MC(x) = 20 + 2x$
$\quad$ **b.** $c(x) = \dfrac{400}{x} + 20 + x$
$\quad$ **c.** $c'(x) = -\dfrac{400}{x^2} + 1$

39. $W'(t) = \dfrac{1000t}{(10 + t^2)^2}$

41. a. $MU(x) = \dfrac{9 - x^2}{(x^2 + 9)^2}$
$\quad$ **b.** $x = 3$

43. a. $P'(t) = \dfrac{900 - 100t^2}{(t^2 + 9)^2}$
$\quad$ **b.** increase; $P'(0) > 0$
$\quad$ **c.** yes
$\quad$ **d.** 10

Exercise Set 2.8

1. $f'(x) = 3(x + 4)^2$

3. $f'(x) = 5(3x^2 - 2x)^4(6x - 2)$

5. $f'(x) = \dfrac{2x^2 - 2}{\sqrt{x^2 - 2}}$

7. $f'(x) = -\dfrac{5x^2 + 9}{(x^2 - 9)^4}$

9. $f'(x) = \dfrac{6}{\sqrt{x}}(3\sqrt{x} - 2)^3$

11. $f'(x) = \left(\dfrac{8}{3}x^{-1/3} - x^{-3/4}\right)(x^{2/3} - x^{1/4})^3$

13. $f'(x) = \dfrac{24(x - 3)^3}{(x + 3)^5}$

15. $f'(x) = 2(x + 2)^2(x^{-1} - x^{-2})$

17. $f'(x) = 3x^{-5/4}(4x^{-1/4} + 6)^{-4}$

19. $f'(x) = \dfrac{(9x^2 - 8x^3 + 1)(x^3 + 1)^2 + 1}{(1 - x)^2}$

21. $f'(x) = \dfrac{-4x^3 - 8x}{[1 + (x^2 + 2)^2]^2}$ $\quad$ **23.** $f'(x) = \dfrac{4x + x^{3/2}}{2(1 + \sqrt{x})^4}$

25. $f'(x) = \dfrac{3}{2}(x^{1/2} - x^{-1/2} - x^{-3/2} + x^{-5/2})$

27. $f'(x) = \dfrac{5(x - 4)^4}{\sqrt{x^3 + 6}} - \dfrac{3x^2(x - 4)^5}{2(x^3 + 6)^{3/2}}$

29. $f'(x) = x^{-2/3}(x^{1/3} - 4)^2(x - \sqrt{x})^{-2/3}$
$\qquad - \dfrac{2}{3}(x - \sqrt{x})^{-5/3}\left(1 - \dfrac{1}{2\sqrt{x}}\right)(x^{1/3} - 4)^3$

31. $y = 0$ $\qquad\qquad$ **33.** $y = 7x - 8$

35. $MC(x) = \dfrac{16x}{\sqrt{40 + 16x^2}}$

37. a. $MP(x) = \dfrac{1}{3}(3x^2 + 10)(x^3 + 10x + 125)^{-2/3}$
$\quad$ **b.** yes

39. a. $N'(t) = \dfrac{30t}{(9 + t^2)^{3/2}}$
$\quad$ **b.** No. $N'(t) > 0$ for all t.

41. $c'(x) = \dfrac{-(500\sqrt{40 + 16x^2} + 40)}{x^2\sqrt{40 + 16x^2}}$

Exercise Set 2.9

1. $\dfrac{3}{10}$ $\quad$ **3.** $-\dfrac{1}{3}$ $\quad$ **5.** $-\dfrac{1}{2}$ $\quad$ **7.** 0 $\quad$ **9.** 0 $\quad$ **11.** $-\infty$

13. a. $c(x) = 24 + \dfrac{3000}{x}$ $\quad$ **b.** 24

15. 15; yes

17. a. $\lim\limits_{t \to \infty} MP(t) = \lim\limits_{t \to \infty} P'(t) = 0$
$\quad$ **b.** not unless $D = 0$
$\quad$ **c.** $D > 0$ gives unlimited growth.
$\qquad D = 0$ gives constant size.
$\qquad D < 0$ gives decline.

Review Exercises—Chapter 2

1. 5

3. 77

5. 6

7. -3

9. $\dfrac{4}{3}$

11. 0

13. 4

15. $x = 2$

17. $x = -2, 3$

19. no x

21. $f'(x) = 2x - 1$

23. $f'(x) = \dfrac{1}{2\sqrt{x}}$

25. $f'(x) = \dfrac{-2}{x^3}$

27. $f'(x) = \dfrac{-1}{(x-2)^2}$

29. $f'(x) = m$

31. $f'(x) = \dfrac{-3}{(3x-7)^2}$

33. $f'(x) = \dfrac{4}{(x+3)^2}$

35. $f'(x) = \dfrac{-2x}{(x^2+6)^2}$

37. $f'(x) = (4x + 8)(x^2 + 4x + 4)$

39. $f'(x) = \dfrac{-4x}{3(x^2+3)^{5/3}}$

41. $f'(x) = \dfrac{-x}{(1+x^2)^{3/2}}$

43. $f'(x) = \dfrac{5x^5 + 4x^3}{\sqrt{1+x^2}}$

45. $f'(x) = -6x(1-x^2)^2(6 + 2x + 5x^3)^{-3}$
$- 3(2 + 15x^2)(1-x^2)^3(6 + 2x + 5x^3)^{-4}$

47. $-\dfrac{10}{49}$

49. $3y + 2x - 14 = 0$

51. a. $p = 7$

   b. $D'(7) = -\dfrac{1}{3}$

   c. $S'(7) = 1$

53. $p = 200, 400$

55. a. $MC(x) = 30 + x$
   b. $x = 30$

57. a. $MC(x) = 40 + x^2$
   b. $x = 6$

59. a. $p(x) = 250 - \dfrac{1}{2}x$

   b. $R(x) = 250x - \dfrac{1}{2}x^2$

   c. $MR(x) = 250 - x$

   d. $x = 250$

61. a. $c(x) = \dfrac{400}{x} + 50$

   b. $c'(x) = -\dfrac{400}{x^2}$

63. $u'(x) = \dfrac{x + 12}{\sqrt{x^2 + 24x}}$

65. a

Chapter 3

Exercise Set 3.1

	Increasing on	*Decreasing on*
1.	$(-\infty, \infty)$	
3.	$(-\infty, 0)$	$(0, \infty)$
5.	$\left(-\dfrac{\sqrt{3}}{3}, \dfrac{\sqrt{3}}{3}\right)$	$\left(-\infty, -\dfrac{\sqrt{3}}{3}\right)$ $\left(\dfrac{\sqrt{3}}{3}, \infty\right)$
7.	$(-\infty, -1)$ $(1, \infty)$	$(-1, 1)$

	Increasing on	*Decreasing on*
9.	$(-\infty, 4)$ $(4, \infty)$	$(-2, 2)$
11.	$(-\infty, -2)$ $(3, \infty)$	$(-2, 3)$
13.	$(-2, 0)$ $(1, \infty)$	$(-\infty, -2)$ $(0, 1)$
15.	$(0, \infty)$	$(-\infty, 0)$
17.	$(-2, 0)$ $(2, \infty)$	$(-\infty, -2)$ $(0, 2)$
19.	$(-\infty, \infty)$	

21. $a = 3$

23. $x < 25$

25. a. for $x > 10$
   b. for $0 < x < 10$

27. a. $0 < x < 10$
   b. for all $x > 0$

29. a. $R(x) = 500x - \dfrac{x^2}{2}$

   b. for $0 < x < 500$

   c. $P(x) = 498x - \dfrac{x^2}{2} - 400$

   d. for $0 < x < 498$

   e. for $x > 498$

31. Increase for $0 \le t < 10$; decrease for $t > 10$

33. $(-5, 455)$

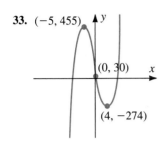

$(0, 30)$

$(4, -274)$

35. Because the increasing term $5x$ eventually becomes much larger than the decreasing term $\dfrac{500}{x}$ that dominates for small, positive numbers x.

Exercise Set 3.2

1. $x = 1$; rel. min.

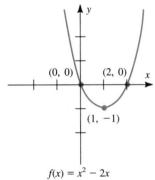

$(0, 0)$ $(2, 0)$

$(1, -1)$

$f(x) = x^2 - 2x$

3. $x = 1$; rel. min.

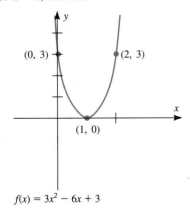

$(0, 3)$ $(2, 3)$

$(1, 0)$

$f(x) = 3x^2 - 6x + 3$

5. $x = -2$; rel. max.

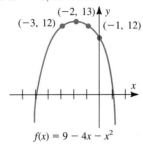

$(-2, 13)$

$(-3, 12)$ $(-1, 12)$

$f(x) = 9 - 4x - x^2$

7. $f(o) = \sqrt{2}$; rel. min.

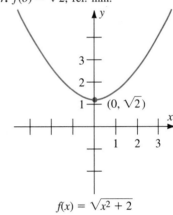

$(0, \sqrt{2})$

$f(x) = \sqrt{x^2 + 2}$

9. $x = 1$; rel. min.
$x = -1$; rel. max.

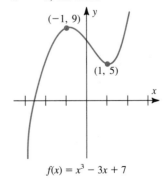

$(-1, 9)$

$(1, 5)$

$f(x) = x^3 - 3x + 7$

11. $x = 4$; rel. min.

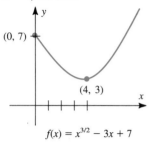

$(0, 7)$

$(4, 3)$

$f(x) = x^{3/2} - 3x + 7$

13. $x = \dfrac{1}{2}$; rel. min.

$x = -2$; rel. max.

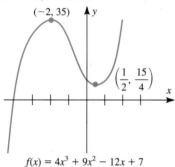

$(-2, 35)$

$\left(\dfrac{1}{2}, \dfrac{15}{4}\right)$

$f(x) = 4x^3 + 9x^2 - 12x + 7$

15. $x = -1$; rel. min.

$x = 0$; rel. max.

$x = 3$; rel. min.

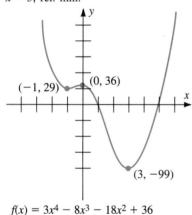

$(-1, 29)$

$(0, 36)$

$(3, -99)$

$f(x) = 3x^4 - 8x^3 - 18x^2 + 36$

17. $x = 0$; neither

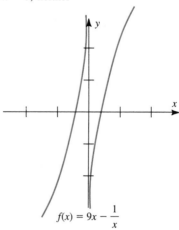

$f(x) = 9x - \dfrac{1}{x}$

19. $x = 0$; rel. max.

$x = 2$; rel. min.

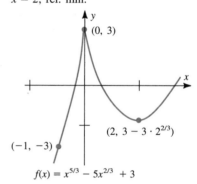

$(0, 3)$

$(2, 3 - 3 \cdot 2^{2/3})$

$(-1, -3)$

$f(x) = x^{5/3} - 5x^{2/3} + 3$

21. $x = -2$; rel. min.

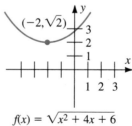

$(-2, \sqrt{2})$

$f(x) = \sqrt{x^2 + 4x + 6}$

23. $P(4) = 0$ is rel. min.

$P(8) = 32$ is rel. max.

27. $a = 4$

29. $(25, 25)$

31. $\dfrac{K}{20}$

Exercise Set 3.3

1. $f'(x) = 2x + 6$
$f''(x) = 2$

3. $f'(x) = 3x^2 - 8x + 10$
$f''(x) = 6x - 8$

5. $f'(x) = 16x^3 - 9x^2 + 18x - 1$
$f''(x) = 48x^2 - 18x + 18$

7. $f'(x) = 9 - 6x^5$
$f''(x) = -30x^4$

9. $f'(x) = 18x^5 - 24x^3$
$f''(x) = 90x^4 - 72x^2$

11. $f'(x) = 5x^{2/3} + \dfrac{4}{3}x^{-5/3} - 2x^{-3}$

$f''(x) = \dfrac{10}{3}x^{-1/3} - \dfrac{20}{9}x^{-8/3} + 6x^{-4}$

13. $f'(x) = \dfrac{-1}{(x-1)^2}$

$f''(x) = \dfrac{2}{(x-1)^3}$

15. $f'(x) = \dfrac{1}{2\sqrt{x+2}}$

$f''(x) = \dfrac{-1}{4(x+2)^{3/2}}$

17. $f'(x) = 18x^8 - 126x^6 + 270x^4 - 162x^2$
$f''(x) = 144x^7 - 756x^5 + 1080x^3 - 324x$

19. $f'(x) = 21(9 - 3x)^{-2}$
$f''(x) = 126(9 - 3x)^{-3}$

21. $f'(x) = (x-1)^{2/3} + \dfrac{2}{3}x(x-1)^{-1/3}$

$f''(x) = \dfrac{4}{3}(x-1)^{-1/3} - \dfrac{2}{9}x(x-1)^{-4/3}$

23. $f'(x) = -6x(1 - x^2)^2$
$f''(x) = 36x^2 - 6 - 30x^4$

25. concave down on $(-\infty, 0)$
concave up on $(0, \infty)$
$(0, 2)$ inflection point

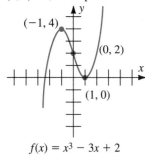

$f(x) = x^3 - 3x + 2$

27. concave down on $(-\infty, 3)$
concave up on $(3, \infty)$
$(3, -24)$ inflection point

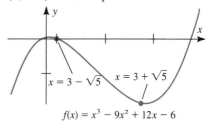

$f(x) = x^3 - 9x^2 + 12x - 6$

29. concave down on $(-\infty, 0)$
concave up on $(0, \infty)$
no inflection points

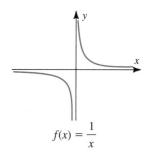

$f(x) = \dfrac{1}{x}$

31. concave up on $(-\infty, -1)$
concave down on $(-1, \infty)$
no inflection points

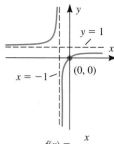

$f(x) = \dfrac{x}{x+1}$

33. concave down on $\left(-\infty, -\dfrac{1}{2}\right)$

concave up on $\left(-\dfrac{1}{2}, \infty\right)$

$\left(-\dfrac{1}{2}, 0\right)$ inflection point

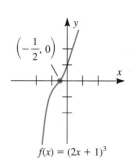

$f(x) = (2x + 1)^3$

35. concave down on $\left(-\infty, \dfrac{1}{2}\right)$

concave up on $\left(\dfrac{1}{2}, \infty\right)$

$\left(\dfrac{1}{2}, -\dfrac{7}{2}\right)$ inflection point

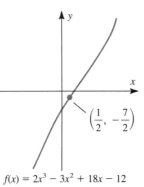

$\left(\dfrac{1}{2}, -\dfrac{7}{2}\right)$

$f(x) = 2x^3 - 3x^2 + 18x - 12$

37. concave up on $(-\infty, 2)$
concave down on $(2, \infty)$
$(2, 0)$ inflection point

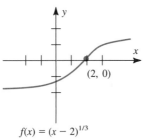

$(2, 0)$

$f(x) = (x - 2)^{1/3}$

39. concave up on $(-\infty, 1)$
concave down on $(1, \infty)$
no inflection points

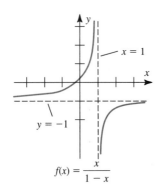

$x = 1$

$y = -1$

$f(x) = \dfrac{x}{1 - x}$

41. rel. min.

43. rel. min.

45. neither

47. a. concave down
b. concave up

49. a. $U_1(x)$
b. investor 1
c. (i) investor 2
    (ii) investor 1

Exercise Set 3.4

1. $y = 0$

3. $y = 3$

5. $y = -1$

7. $y = \sqrt{7}$

9. $y = 6$

11. $x = 4$

13. $x = -2$
$x = 2$

15. $x = -4$
$x = -1$

17. $x = 2$

19. $x = 2, 3$

21. $y = 4 + x$ is oblique asymptote

23. $y = 2x$ is oblique asymptote

25. $x = \pm 1$ vertical asymptotes
$y = 2x$ oblique asymptote

27. yes

29. a. $C(x) = 2500 + 80x$
b. $c(x) = \dfrac{2500}{x} + 80$
c. $y = 80$ is a horizontal asymptote; $x = 0$ is a vertical asymptote

31. $A = 35$

33. yes; $d = 16$

Exercise Set 3.5

1. even   **3.** odd   **5.** odd   **7.** neither   **9.** even

11.

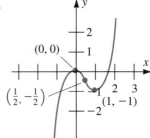

$(-2, 0)$ $(4, 0)$

$(1, -9)$

13.

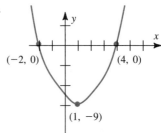

$(0, 0)$

$\left(\dfrac{1}{2}, -\dfrac{1}{2}\right)$ $(1, -1)$

15.

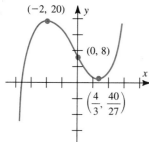

$(-2, 20)$

$(0, 8)$

$\left(\dfrac{4}{3}, \dfrac{40}{27}\right)$

17.

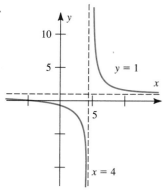

10

5

$y = 1$

5

$x = 4$

19.

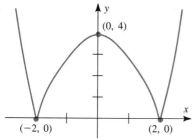

$(0, 4)$

$(-2, 0)$ $(2, 0)$

21.

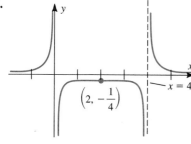

$x = 4$

$\left(2, -\dfrac{1}{4}\right)$

23.

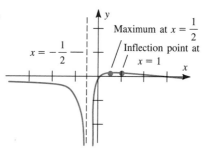

Maximum at $x = \dfrac{1}{2}$

$x = -\dfrac{1}{2}$

Inflection point at $x = 1$

25.

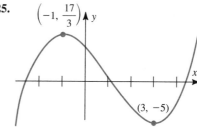

$\left(-1, \dfrac{17}{3}\right)$

$(3, -5)$

27.

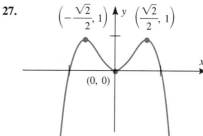

$\left(-\dfrac{\sqrt{2}}{2}, 1\right)$ $\left(\dfrac{\sqrt{2}}{2}, 1\right)$

$(0, 0)$

29.

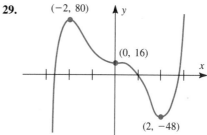

$(-2, 80)$

$(0, 16)$

$(2, -48)$

31. True   **33.** yes   **35.** True

37. symmetric with respect to the vertical line $x = a$

39. yes; rotation of $180°$ about $(0, 2)$

Exercise Set 3.6

1. Max. is $f(0) = 9$; min. is $f(3) = 0$.

3. Max. is $f(-1) = f(3) = 6$; min. is $f(1) = 2$.

5. Min. is $f(-2) = -11$; max. is $f(3) = 69$.

7. Min. is $f\left(\dfrac{2}{3}\right) = -\dfrac{4}{27}$; max. is $f(3) = 18$.

9. Min. is $f(-1) = -3$; max. is $f(0) = f(2) = 0$.

11. Min. is $f(1) = 2$; max. is $f\left(\dfrac{1}{2}\right) = f(2) = \dfrac{5}{2}$.

13. Min. is $f(0) = 2$; no max.

15. Max. is $f(2) = -\dfrac{1}{4}$; min. is $f(1) = f(3) = -\dfrac{1}{3}$.

17. Min. is $f(4) = -6$; max. is $f(1) = 21$.

19. Min. is $f(4) = -6$;

max. is $f\left(\dfrac{1}{3}\right) = \dfrac{1}{\sqrt{3}} - \dfrac{1}{3^{3/2}} = \dfrac{2}{3\sqrt{3}}$.

21. 2066

23. $P(0) = 160$ is max.
$P(4) = P(10) = 0$ is min.

25. $p = 50$

Exercise Set 3.7

1. 1995   **3.** $t = 2$ **5.** $(0, 36)$

7. when $\dfrac{N}{2}$ are infected

9. Max. is -8 at $(1, -7)$.
Min. is -20 at $(3, -39)$.

11. $p = 10$ **13.** \$40   **15.** $\ell = 4$, $w = 3$

17. $w = \dfrac{20}{4 + \pi}$, $r = \dfrac{10}{4 + \pi}$, $h = \dfrac{10}{4 + \pi}$

19. after $t = 1$ minute   **21.** $x = 8$

23. $x = 10\sqrt{14} \approx 37.4$
$y = \dfrac{80}{\sqrt{14}} \approx 21.4$ (length of stone wall)

25. $r = 2.5\%$ **27.** 50 campers

29. 2000 sets   **31.** $x = 15$ trees

33. $v(5) = 0.062$ km/hr is min.
$v(7) = v(3) = 100$ km/hr is max.

35. Schedule maximum overtime possible.

37. Lay cable under water to point $x = 450$ meters from second boathouse.

39. $x = \dfrac{10}{3}$

Exercise Set 3.8

1. $x = 192$ **3.** $x = 5$

5. Companies 1, 2, and 4   **7.** 6 times per year

9. approximately 8 times per year   **11.** $x = 20$

13. a. $R(x) = x(600 - 3x)$
b. $P(x) = 450x - 3.5x^2 - 400$
c. $MR(x) = 600 - 6x$, $MC(x) = 150 + x$
d. $x = 64.3$; $x = 64$ or 65, max. profit for $x = 64$
e. They are equal,

15. $MC(x) = c(x)$ **19.** 69 dishwashers

21. $E = 1.67$ **23.** $E = .095$

25. $E = \dfrac{1}{2}$ **27.** $E = 1$

29. elastic for all $p > 0$ **31.** inelastic for all $p > 1$

33. a. $Q(101) = 99$
b. $E(101) = \dfrac{101}{99}$ (elastic)

35. a. $Q(p) = \sqrt{1000 - 10p}$
b. inelastic
c. elastic
d. $p_0 = \$66.66$

Exercise Set 3.9

1. $\dfrac{dy}{dx} = -\dfrac{x}{y}$ **3.** $\dfrac{dy}{dx} = -\dfrac{y}{2x}$

5. $\dfrac{dy}{dx} = -1$ **7.** $\dfrac{dy}{dx} = -\dfrac{3x^2 + 2y^2 + 2xy}{4xy + x^2 + 6y^2}$

9. $\dfrac{dy}{dx} = \dfrac{3x^2 + 4xy + 5y^2}{2x^2 + 10xy - 2y}$

11. $\dfrac{dy}{dx} = -\dfrac{y + \dfrac{1}{2}x^{-1/2}y^{1/2}}{x + \dfrac{1}{2}x^{1/2}y^{-1/2} - 4y^3}$

13. $\dfrac{dy}{dx} = -\dfrac{3x^{-1/2} - 6y + 4x^{-1/3}y^{4/3}}{8x^{2/3}y^{1/3} - 6x}$

15. $\dfrac{dy}{dx} = -1$

17. $\dfrac{dy}{dx} = -1$

19. $\dfrac{dy}{dx} = \dfrac{3}{5}$

21. $x + y = 8$

23. $\dfrac{dy}{dx} = \dfrac{1}{6}$

25. $40\pi \text{ m}^2/\text{sec}$

27. 4 persons per day

29. $\dfrac{dx}{dt} = \dfrac{4}{3}$

31. $\dfrac{dx}{dt} = -\dfrac{36}{205}$

33. $E(p) = \dfrac{41}{48}$

35. $R'(2) = \$208,000$

37. 0.0162

Exercise Set 3.10

1. 256.6   **3.** 41.4   **5.** 1.85

7. $29.333\overline{3}$ **9.** 6.2167   **11.** 0.2406

13. 27.55

15. a. $R(100) = 50,000$
   b. $R(105) - R(100) \approx 1000$
   c. $R(120) \approx 54,000$, an increase of 4000

17. 2.63%   **19.** 4.6875%

21. a. $R(x) = 50x - \dfrac{x^2}{40}$
   b. $R'(100) = 45$
   c. $R(80) \approx 3850$
   d. $R(80) = 3840$
   e. c is an approximation.

23. It is increased by 15%.   **25. a.** $V = 3\pi r^2$ liters/min
   b. $V(4) = 48\pi$ liters/min
   c. 12π liters

27. 800 ft^2 or 2%

Exercise Set 3.11

1. No. $f(x) = |x|$ is not differentiable at $x = 0$.

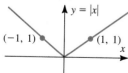

3. $c = 1$ **5.** $c = -2.75$ **7.** $c = -\dfrac{3}{2}$

Review Exercises—Chapter 3

1. inc. on $(-\infty, 2)$ $f(2) = 4$, rel. max.
   dec. on $(2, \infty)$

3. dec. on $(-\infty, 1)$ $f(1) = 2$, rel. min.
   inc. on $(1, \infty)$

5. inc. on $(-\infty, -3)$ no rel. extrema
   inc. on $(-3, \infty)$

7. dec. on $(-4, -2\sqrt{2})$ $f(-2\sqrt{2}) = -8$, rel. min.
   inc. on $(-2\sqrt{2}, 2\sqrt{2})$ $f(2\sqrt{2}) = 8$, rel. max.
   dec. on $(2\sqrt{2}, 4)$

9. inc. on $(-\infty, 0)$ $f(0) = 2$, rel. max.
   dec. on $(0, 2)$ $f(2) = -2$, rel. min.
   inc. on $(2, \infty)$

11. inc. on $(-\infty, 0)$; dec. on $(0, \infty)$;
   $f(0) = 4$ is rel. max.

	Minimum	*Maximum*
13.	$f(-1) = f(1) = -\dfrac{1}{3}$	$f(0) = -\dfrac{1}{4}$
15.	$f\!\left(\dfrac{-\sqrt{2}}{2}\right) = -\dfrac{1}{2}$	$f\!\left(\dfrac{\sqrt{2}}{2}\right) = \dfrac{1}{2}$
17.	$f\!\left(-\dfrac{1}{\sqrt{2}}\right) = -\sqrt{2}$	$f(1) = 1$
19.	$f(-1) = -5$	$f(-2) = -3$
21.	$f(-1) = f(1) = -1$	$f(-2) = f(2) = 8$

23. vertical asymptote: $x = 7$
   horizontal asymptote: $y = 0$

25. vertical asymptotes: $x = \pm 2$
   horizontal asymptote: $y = -1$

27. vertical asymptote: $x = \pm 3$
   horizontal asymptote: $y = 1$

29. no vertical asymptote
   horizontal asymptote: $y = 1$ and $y = -1$

31. vertical asymptote: $x = 0$
   horizontal asymptote: $y = 4$

33. -2 **35.** 0 **37.** $-\infty$ **39.** $-\infty$ **41.** $+\infty$

43.

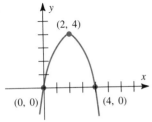

(2, 4)

(0, 0)   (4, 0)

45.

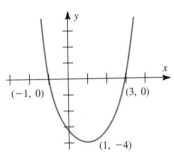

(−1, 0)   (3, 0)

(1, −4)

47.

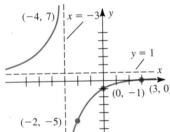

(−4, 7) $x = -3$

$y = 1$

(0, −1)   (3, 0)

(−2, −5)

49.

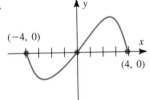

(−4, 0)

(4, 0)

51.

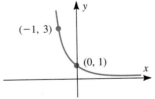

$y = 1$

(0, 0)

53. 40 cm²/sec

55. $-\dfrac{V}{324a^2\pi}$ m/sec

57. $x = 1000$

59. 60 km/hr

61. 7 times/yr

63. 127 items/week (5 fewer)

65. $p = \sqrt{50}$

67. a. $v(t) = 96 - 32t$
  b. after $t = 3$ sec, at $s(3) = 144$ ft
  c. at t = 0 when $s(0) = 0$
  d. $v(6) = -96$ ft/sec; speed = 96 ft/sec

69. a. $c(x) = 30 + \dfrac{200}{x} + 0.5x$

  b. $x = 20$

71. $\dfrac{dy}{dx} = \dfrac{-2xy - y^2}{x^2 + 2xy}$

73. $\dfrac{dy}{dx} = \dfrac{3}{8}$

75. a. $[0, \infty)$
  b. none, for $x \geq 0$
  c. no
  d. concave down
  e. satisfaction increases at a decreasing rate.

77. max at $x = 16$; $D(16) = \dfrac{5}{4}$

Chapter 4

Exercise Set 4.1

1. a. 27   **c.** 343

  b. 2   **d.** $\dfrac{1}{8}$

3. a. $\dfrac{1}{8}$ **c.** 8

  b. $\dfrac{9}{4}$ **d.** $\dfrac{8}{27}$

5.

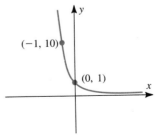

(−1, 3)

(0, 1)

7.

(−1, 10)

(0, 1)

9.

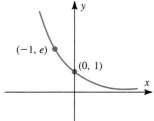

11.

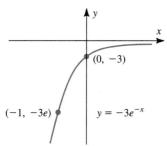

$y = -3e^{-x}$

13. 16

15. $\dfrac{8}{27}$

17. e^{3+x}

19. $4e^{2x}$

21. $2^{-1/6}e^{2(x-1)}$

23. a. $540.80
b. $584.93
c. $562.43

25. $670.32

27. $6703.20

29. $16,323.16

31. $7408.18

33. Approximately 7.7%

35. a. 10.25
b. 10.52

Exercise Set 4.2

1. a. 2   **b.** 1
c. 4   **d.** 3
e. 4   **f.** 2

3. a. 1   **b.** 0
c. 0.78846   **d.** −1.20396
e. 3   **f.** −2

7. $x = 0$

9. $x = \pm\sqrt{3 + \ln 5}$

11. $x = \ln 2$

13. $x = \pm e^4$

15. $x = 2$

17. $\ln P = \ln 10 \left[\dfrac{-A}{t + C} + B \right].$

19. $x = \ln 100 - \ln p$

21. $T = 4.0547$ years

23. 6.9315 years

25. 35 items

27. $a = 15; b = 5$

29. 13.86%

31. $211,700

33. 11.55%

35. 8.92%

Exercise Set 4.3

1. $\dfrac{1}{x}$

3. $\dfrac{20x}{x^2 + 5}$

5. $\ln x + 1$

7. $\dfrac{3x^2 - 1}{2(x^3 - x)}$

9. $6\left(\dfrac{x - 1}{x^2 - 2x} \right) [(\ln (x^2 - 2x)]^2$

11. $\dfrac{1}{t \ln t}$

13. $\dfrac{2x^2 + 3x^2 \ln x}{(1 + \ln x)^2}$

15. $\dfrac{6}{x}(3 \ln \sqrt{x})^3$

17. $2x \ln (3x - 6) + \dfrac{x^2}{x - 2}$

19. $\dfrac{\ln x}{x}$

21. $f'(x) = \dfrac{\sqrt{1 + \ln x}\left[1 + \dfrac{2 \ln 3x}{x} \right] - \dfrac{x + \ln^2 3x}{2x\sqrt{1 + \ln x}}}{1 + \ln x}$

23. $\dfrac{4x^2}{x^3 + 3}$

25. $\dfrac{2}{3(x - 6)} - \dfrac{1}{2 + 2x}$

27. $\dfrac{dy}{dx} = (x + 3)^x \left[\ln (x + 3) + \dfrac{x}{x + 3} \right]$

29. $\dfrac{dy}{dx} = x^{\sqrt{x+1}} \left[\dfrac{\ln x}{2\sqrt{x + 1}} + \dfrac{\sqrt{x + 1}}{x} \right]$

31. $\dfrac{dy}{dx} = \dfrac{x(x + 1)(x + 2)}{(x + 3)(x + 4)} \left[\dfrac{1}{x} + \dfrac{1}{x + 1} + \dfrac{1}{x + 2} - \dfrac{1}{x + 3} - \dfrac{1}{x + 4} \right]$

33. $\dfrac{dy}{dx} = \dfrac{(x^2 + 3)(1 - x)^{2/3}}{x\sqrt{1 + x}} \left(\dfrac{2x}{x^2 + 3} - \dfrac{2}{3(1 - x)} - \dfrac{1}{x} - \dfrac{1}{2(x + 1)} \right)$

35. $y' = \dfrac{xy - y}{x - xy}$ **37.** $y = 3x - e$

39. $f(1) = 1$, rel. min.   **41.** no rel. extrema

43.

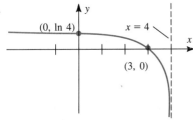

45. a. $\dfrac{1}{35} \approx 2.86\%$ **b.** $\dfrac{1}{40} = 2.5\%$ **c.** 0

47. a. 3.53%   **b.** 3.33%   **49.** 25%

Exercise Set 4.4

1. $6e^{6x}$ **3.** $2xe^{x^2-4}$

5. $f'(x) = \dfrac{(x^2 - 2x + 2)e^x}{(x^2 + 2)^2}$ **7.** $f'(x) = \dfrac{1 - e^{-x}}{2\sqrt{x + e^{-x}}}\cdot$

9. $\left(2x - \dfrac{1}{2\sqrt{x}}\right)e^{x^2-\sqrt{x}}$

11. $f'(x) = \dfrac{(x^3 - 3x^2 + 1)e^x - 3x^2}{(x^3 + 1)(e^x + 1)}$

13. $\dfrac{1}{2}(e^x - e^{-x})$ **15.** $4(x - e^{-2x})^3(1 + 2e^{-2x})$

17. $\left(1 - \dfrac{2}{x^2}\right)e^{1/x^2}$

19. $f'(x) = \dfrac{(1 - x - x^2 - x^3)e^{-x}}{(1 + x^2)^2}$

21. $\dfrac{dy}{dx} = \dfrac{1 - xy}{x^2}$ **23.** $2^x + x2^x \ln 2$

25. $\dfrac{4^x \ln 4}{2\sqrt{1 + 4^x}}$ **27.** $\dfrac{\log_2 \sqrt{x}}{x \ln 2}$

29. $f(1) = 2e$ **31.** $f\left(\dfrac{1}{\sqrt[3]{3}}\right) = \dfrac{e^{2/3}}{\sqrt[3]{3}}$ rel. max.

33. $p = \dfrac{100}{e} = \$36.79$ **35.** $x = 19.8$

37. $\dfrac{\ln 2}{4}$ **39.** after 0.83 year

Exercise Set 4.5

1. $N(t) = Ce^{4t}$ **3.** $f(x) = Ce^{-2x}$

5. $y = Ce^{-3t}$ **7.** $N(t) = 4e^{4t}$

9. $N = 6e^{-10t}$ **11.** \$1123.32

15. 13.86 years   **17. a.** $50\sqrt{2}$ mg
                                b. 25 mg

19. a. 4 hours   **21.** 275,568
     b. 800

23. $r = 0.112$ **25.** 5.49 mg

27. \$2,250,000   **29.** 23.3 hours

31. 1854 years   **33.** After 10.58 days

Exercise Set 4.6

1. a. 135   **3. a.** 160   **5.** $\left(-\dfrac{\ln 5}{2}, 50\right)$
    b. 496   **b.** 40,960

9. 16%   **11.** 97.5%   **13.** 47.5%

15. 50%   **17.** 68%   **19.** 2.5%

21.

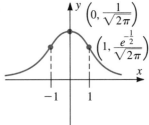

Review Exercises—Chapter 4

1. a. $\dfrac{1}{343}$ **3.** \$477.62

b. $\dfrac{1}{16}$

c. $\dfrac{4}{9}$

d. $\dfrac{27}{8}$

5. $6065.31

7. **a.** $x = 0$
  b. $x = 1, -2$
  c. $x = 5$
  d. $x = \ln 2$

9. $18.39

11. $\dfrac{1}{x}$

13. $-2xe^{6-x^2}$

15. $(3t^2 - 3)e^{t^3-3t+2}$

17. $\dfrac{1}{2(x + 1)}$

19. $\left(2x + \dfrac{1}{2}x^{3/2}\right)e^{\sqrt{x}}$

21. $\dfrac{2}{x(x + 2)}$

23. $\dfrac{1}{2x \ln \sqrt{x}}$

25. $e^{x-\sqrt{x}}\left(1 + x - \dfrac{\sqrt{x}}{2}\right)$

27. $\dfrac{4e^{-2x} \ln (1 - e^{-2x})}{1 - e^{-2x}}$

29. $e^{\sqrt{t}-\ln t}\left(\dfrac{1}{2\sqrt{t}} - \dfrac{1}{t}\right)$

31. $\dfrac{dy}{dx} = \dfrac{-y^2 - xy \ln y}{x^2 + xy \ln x}$

33. $y' = -\dfrac{y}{x}$

35. $\left(\dfrac{1}{\sqrt{e}}, -\dfrac{1}{2e}\right)$, rel. min.

37. $(-1, 1)$

39. $r = \ln 2$

41. $\dfrac{dh}{dt} = \dfrac{\ln t^2}{36\pi}$

43. $y = Ce^{-x}$

45. 254 million

47. 190 flies

51. $1637.46

Chapter 5

Exercise Set 5.1

1. $5x + C$

3. $\dfrac{1}{2}x^4 + \dfrac{5}{2}x^2 + C$

5. $\dfrac{1}{4}x^4 - 2x^3 + x^2 + x + C$

7. $\dfrac{3}{5}x^{5/3} - 2x^{3/2} + C$

9. $4 \ln x + C, \quad x > 0$

11. $\dfrac{1}{5}e^{5x} + C$

13. $\dfrac{3}{4}x^{4/3} - 6x^{1/3} - \dfrac{3}{2}x^{-2/3} + C$

15. $-4e^{-x} - \ln x + \dfrac{2}{3}x^{3/2} + C, \quad x > 0$

17. $-\dfrac{4}{5}x^{-5} + 2x^{-3} + C$

19. $\dfrac{1}{2}x^2 - \dfrac{12}{11}x^{11/6} + \dfrac{3}{5}x^{5/3} + C$

21. $\dfrac{2}{3}x^{3/2} + e^{-x} + C$

23. $3x^2 + x^3 + 5x + C$ for any C

25. **a.** $A = 6$
  b. $B = \dfrac{1}{3}$
  c. can be any real number

27. **a.** $P(t) = 4t + t^2 + C$
  b. increasing; $P'(t) > 0$

Exercise Set 5.2

1. ii

3. iv

5. vi

7. $F(x) = 4x + 3$

9. $F(x) = \dfrac{1}{3}x^3 - x^2 - 3$

11. $F(x) = \ln x + 4$

13. $F(x) = \dfrac{3}{5}x^{5/3} - \dfrac{3}{2}x^{2/3} + 5$

15. $F(x) = \dfrac{5}{2}e^{2x} + 4x + \dfrac{15}{2}$

17. $F(x) = 3 \ln(x + 5) - \dfrac{2}{3}e^{-3x} + \dfrac{2}{3} - 3 \ln 5$

19. $C(x) = 700 + 250x$ dollars

21. **a.** $1187.50
  b. $C(x) = 1187.50 + 400x + \dfrac{1}{8}x^2$ dollars

23. $C(x) = 2x^2 + 100x + 5000$

25. $R(x) = 250x - \dfrac{1}{4}x^2$

27. $P(t) = t^2 + 4t + 12$

29. **a.** II   **b.** III   **c.** I

31. **a.** $s(t) = t^3 + 3t^2 + 2t + 4$
  b. $s(4) = 124$

33. **a.** $N(t) = 20t + 16t^{3/2} + 2$
  b. $N(16) = 1346$

Exercise Set 5.3

1. $\dfrac{1}{8}(3 + x^2)^4 + C$

3. $\dfrac{5}{3}(9 + x^2)^{3/2} + C$

5. $\dfrac{1}{2}e^{x^2} + C$

7. $\dfrac{2}{7}(\sqrt{x} + 5)^7 + C$

9. $\dfrac{1}{6}\ln(1 + 3x^2) + C$

11. $\dfrac{1}{8}(1 + e^{2x})^4 + C$

13. $2\sqrt{e^x + 1} + C$

15. $-\dfrac{1}{2}(x^2 + 3x + 6)^{-2} + C$

17. $\dfrac{1}{4}\left(1 - \dfrac{1}{x}\right)^4 + C$

19. $\dfrac{1}{2}\sqrt{5 + x^4} + C$

21. $2\ln^2 x^2 + C$

23. $\dfrac{9}{10}(x^{2/3} - 5)^{5/3} + C$

25. $(1 + e^{\sqrt{x}})^2 + C$

27. a. 40
   b. $C(x) = 500 + 40x + 10\ln(1 + x^2)$

29. a. 0
   b. $R(x) = 25{,}000\ln(100 + 0.2x^2) - 25{,}000\ln 100$

31. $P(t) = 40{,}000 + 5[\ln(1 + e^{20t}) - \ln 2]$

33. $P(t) = \dfrac{2}{3}e^{t^{3/2}} + \dfrac{58}{3}$

Exercise Set 5.4

1. 32

3. $\dfrac{21}{2}$

5. $\dfrac{31}{20}$

7. $\dfrac{39}{4}$

9. $\dfrac{319}{420}$

11. 1, 2

13. none

15. 75

17. 45

19. 2

21. 2919

23. 2

25. 16

27. $\dfrac{81}{2}$

29. $\dfrac{5}{2}$

31. 4

33. $A = \displaystyle\int_{-2}^{0}(-x)\,dx + \int_{0}^{2} x\,dx$

35. $A = \displaystyle\int_{0}^{2}(6 - 3x)\,dx + \int_{2}^{4}(3x - 6)\,dx$

37. $A = \displaystyle\int_{-2}^{-1}(x^2 - 1)\,dx + \int_{-1}^{1}(1 - x^2)\,dx + \int_{1}^{2}(x^2 - 1)\,dx$

39. 3.4418 $(n = 100)$

41. 6.3086 $(n = 100)$

43. 12.4809 $(n = 100)$

Exercise Set 5.5

1. 8

3. $\dfrac{52}{3}$

5. $\dfrac{170}{3}$

7. $\dfrac{1}{4}(e^4 - 1)$

9. $-\dfrac{4}{3}$

11. $-\dfrac{4}{5}$

13. $\dfrac{32}{3}$

15. 0

17. $\dfrac{1}{2}\ln\left(\dfrac{28}{13}\right)$

19. $\dfrac{22}{3} - \dfrac{4}{3}\sqrt{2}$

21. $\dfrac{1}{4}$

23. 2

25. $2\sqrt{5} - 4$

27. 9

29. $\dfrac{3^{7/3}}{8}$

31. $\dfrac{2 \cdot 8^{3/2}}{3} \approx 15.08$

33. 0.8

35. $\dfrac{32}{3} \approx 10.67$

37. $\dfrac{1}{12} \approx 0.0833$

Exercise Set 5.6

1. 14

3. $\ln 3$

5. $\ln\sqrt{\dfrac{8}{3}}$

7. $\dfrac{52}{3}$

9. $\ln 3 \approx 1.0986$

11. 1.219

13. $\dfrac{116}{3}$

15. 6

17. $\dfrac{80}{3}$

19. 27

21. $\dfrac{125}{6}$

23. $\dfrac{1}{2}$

25. $\dfrac{125}{6}$

27. $\dfrac{8}{15}$

29. $A = -\displaystyle\int_{-2}^{0} x^3 e^x \, dx + \int_{0}^{2} x^3 e^x \, dx$

31. $A = \displaystyle\int_{-1}^{1} (e - e^{x^2}) \, dx$

33. 3

35. $4^{2/3}$

Exercise Set 5.7

1. 25

3. $\dfrac{25,000}{3}$

5. 64

7. $1.44

9. $15e^4 + 5$

11. a. $\displaystyle\int_{400}^{500} [200 + 0.4x] \, dx$
   b. $35,000

13. $9140

15. 7600

17. 19,500

19. $5000\left(\dfrac{1}{e} - \dfrac{1}{e^2}\right)$

21. $50,000\left(1 - \dfrac{1}{e}\right)$

23. a. $19,953
   b. $98,826

25. $100,237 annually

27. $28,330

29. Plan A: $2,362,998
   Plan B: $2,241,199
   Plan A wins.

31. $37,290

Exercise Set 5.8

1. $\dfrac{351\pi}{3} = 117\pi$

3. 3π

5. $\pi\left(\ln 2 + \dfrac{1}{2}\right)$

7. $\dfrac{64\pi}{21}$

9. $\dfrac{64\pi}{21}$

11. $\dfrac{13}{6}$

13. $\dfrac{4^{3/2}}{6} = \dfrac{4}{3}$

15. $\dfrac{4}{3}$

17. $\dfrac{3\pi}{4}$

19. $\dfrac{1400}{3}$

23. $V = \dfrac{4}{3}\pi r^3$

25. 7.2135 billion

Review Exercises—Chapter 5

1. $2x^3 - x^2 + x + C$

3. $\dfrac{1}{9}(3x^2 + 5)^{3/2} + C$

5. $\dfrac{t^3}{3} + \dfrac{6}{7}t^{7/3} + \dfrac{3}{5}t^{5/3} + C$

7. $\dfrac{x^3}{3} - \dfrac{7}{2}x^2 + 6\ln|x| + C$

9. $\dfrac{4}{3}x^3 + 2x^2 - 3x + C$

11. $-\dfrac{1}{2}\ln|1 - x^2| + C$

13. $2e^{x/2} + C$

15. $2\sqrt{\ln x} + C$

17. $\dfrac{x^3}{3} - \dfrac{x^2}{2} + x - 2\ln|x + 1| + C$

19. $-\dfrac{1}{6}(1 - e^{2x})^3 + C$

21. a. $s(t) = t^2 + \dfrac{1}{t + 1} - 1$
   b. $a(t) = 2 + 2(t + 1)^{-3}$

23. a. $C(x) = 500 + 120x + 3x^2$
   b. $C(20) = 4100$

25. a. $P(x) = 130x - 3x^2 - 500$
   b. yes; $P(20) = 900$
   c. 20,000

27. a. $V(t) = 20,000 + \dfrac{80,000}{t + 1}$
   b. $V(3) = 40,000$

29. a. $C(x) = 70x + x^2 + 200$
   b. $C(0) = 200$

31. 0

33. $\dfrac{161}{5}$

35. $\dfrac{74}{3}$

37. $3(1 - \ln 2)$

39. $1 + 4 \ln 2$

41. $\dfrac{16}{3}$

43. 4

45. $\dfrac{675}{8}$

47. $\dfrac{3}{4} \ln \left(\dfrac{7}{2}\right)$

49. $\dfrac{9}{2} + \dfrac{6}{5}(8^{5/2} - 1)$

51. 8π

53. 63

55. $\dfrac{16}{5}$

57. 14

59. $1100 + 50 \ln \left(\dfrac{6}{5}\right)$

61. 5760

63. $\dfrac{7}{4} e^4 + 2e$

65. $500[e^2 - 1]$

67. $10{,}000\left(\dfrac{26^{3/2} - 1}{3}\right)$

69. $\dfrac{1}{6} \ln \dfrac{16}{7}$

71. $C = \ln k$

Chapter 6

Exercise Set 6.1

1. a. $\dfrac{\pi}{2}$ **b.** $\dfrac{\pi}{4}$ **c.** $-\dfrac{3\pi}{4}$ **d.** $\dfrac{\pi}{6}$

 e. $\dfrac{\pi}{3}$ **f.** $-\dfrac{5\pi}{6}$ **g.** π **h.** $\dfrac{7\pi}{6}$

3. a. $45°$ **b.** $270°$ **c.** $-15°$ **d.** $210°$
 e. $157.5°$ **f.** $-150°$ **g.** $330°$ **h.** $-135°$

5. a. $-\dfrac{\pi}{4}$ **b.** $-\dfrac{3\pi}{2}$ **c.** $-\dfrac{\pi}{6}$ **d.** $-\dfrac{5\pi}{6}$

 e. $-\dfrac{13\pi}{6}$ **f.** $-\dfrac{3\pi}{4}$ **g.** $-\dfrac{11\pi}{6}$ **h.** -3π

7. a. $-\pi$ **b.** -2π **c.** $-\dfrac{5\pi}{2}$ **d.** $-\dfrac{10\pi}{3}$

9. $-\dfrac{9\pi}{2}$ **11.** 3π **13.** $-\dfrac{9\pi}{4}$

15.

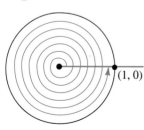

17.

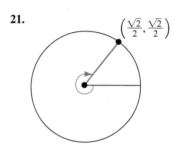

$\left(-\dfrac{\sqrt{2}}{2}, \dfrac{\sqrt{2}}{2}\right)$

19.

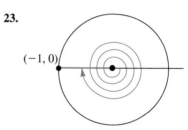

21.

$\left(\dfrac{\sqrt{2}}{2}, \dfrac{\sqrt{2}}{2}\right)$

23.

$(-1, 0)$

25. $-\dfrac{13\pi}{2}$

Exercise Set 6.2

1. a. $\dfrac{3}{5}$ **b.** $\dfrac{4}{5}$ **3. a.** $\dfrac{2}{\sqrt{13}}$ **b.** $\dfrac{3}{\sqrt{13}}$

5. a. $\dfrac{7}{\sqrt{65}}$ **b.** $\dfrac{4}{\sqrt{65}}$ **7.** $\sin t = \dfrac{\sqrt{2}}{2}$

$\cos t = -\dfrac{\sqrt{2}}{2}$

9. $\sin t = \dfrac{\sqrt{3}}{2}$

$\cos t = \dfrac{1}{2}$

11. $-\dfrac{\sqrt{2}}{2}$

13. 0   **15.** $\dfrac{\sqrt{3}}{2}$ **17.** $\dfrac{-\sqrt{2}}{2}$

19.

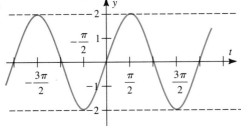

21.

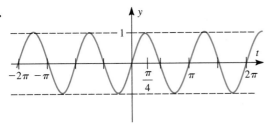

23.

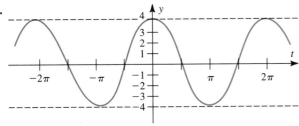

25. $x = 5\sqrt{2}$

$y = 5\sqrt{2}$

27. $x = \dfrac{5\sqrt{3}}{2}$

$y = \dfrac{5}{2}$

29. 0.2588   **31.** 0.9010

33. 0.6428   **35.** 0.2588

37. a. 12 hours
b. 15 hours
c. 9 hours

39. a. B
b. $4 + B$
c. $5 + B$

43. 48

45. a. $t = 7$, 19 (7 a.m., 7 p.m.)
b. $t = 1$, 13 (1 a.m., 1 p.m.)
c.

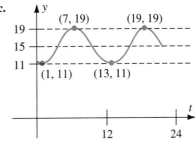

Exercise Set 6.3

1. $f'(x) = 3\cos 3x$

3. $\dfrac{dy}{dx} = \sin(x + \pi) + x\cos(x + \pi)$

5. $f'(x) = 3x^2\cos 2x - 2x^3\sin 2x$

7. $\dfrac{dy}{dx} = 3\sin^2 x\cos^3 x - 2\sin^4 x\cos x$

9. $f'(x) = \dfrac{x\cos\sqrt{1 + x^2}}{\sqrt{1 + x^2}}$

11. $\dfrac{dy}{dt} = -\dfrac{2\sin(\ln t)\cos(\ln t)}{t}$

13. $f'(x) = 0$

15. $f'(t) = \dfrac{4t^3 + \cos t}{t^4 + \sin t}$

17. $\dfrac{dy}{dx} = \dfrac{3\cos x + x^2\cos x - 2x\sin x - 2x}{(3 + x^2)^2}$

19. $f'(x) = -\sin x\sin\dfrac{1}{x} - \dfrac{1}{x^2}\cos x\cos\dfrac{1}{x}$

21. $y = x - \dfrac{\pi}{6} + \dfrac{\sqrt{3}}{2}$ **23.** $\dfrac{4}{49}$

25. because $\sin^2 x + \cos^2 x = 1$

27. $f''(t) = \dfrac{-\sin\ln t - \cos\ln t}{t^2}$

29. $\dfrac{dy}{dx} = -\dfrac{1 + y\sin xy}{1 + x\sin xy}$

31. $\dfrac{dy}{dx} = \dfrac{\cos y}{x \sin y + \cos y}$

33. max. is $f\left(\dfrac{\pi}{4}\right) = \sqrt{2}$

min. is $f\left(\dfrac{5\pi}{4}\right) = -\sqrt{2}$

35. max. is $f\left(\dfrac{3\pi}{2}\right) = \dfrac{3\pi}{2} + 1$

min. is $f\left(\dfrac{\pi}{2}\right) = \dfrac{\pi}{2} - 1$

37.

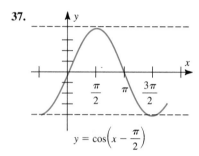

$y = \cos\left(x - \dfrac{\pi}{2}\right)$

39.

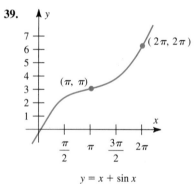

$y = x + \sin x$

41.

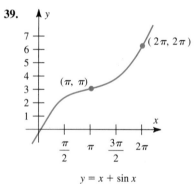

$y = \dfrac{\sin x}{2 + \cos x}, \quad -\pi \le x \le \pi$

43. max. is $1 + \dfrac{\pi}{4}$ at 0 and 8 months

min. is $1 - \dfrac{\pi}{4}$ at 4 and 12 months

45. a. $t = 11/2$ mo. (June 15)
  b. $t = 23/2$ mo. (Dec. 15)

49. a. rel. max. at $t = \dfrac{3\pi}{4} + 2n\pi$

  b. rel. min. at $t = \dfrac{7\pi}{4} + 2n\pi$

  c. rel. max. is $500 + 50\sqrt{2}$
   rel. min. is $500 - 50\sqrt{2}$

51. a. $t = 181.25$
  b. $t = 363.75$

Exercise Set 6.4

1. $\dfrac{1}{6}\sin 6x + C$ **3.** 6

5. $-\dfrac{1}{3}\cos(1 + x^3) + C$ **7.** 0

9. 0   **11.** $-\dfrac{2}{3}(1 - \sin x)^{3/2} + C$

13. $-\cos(3 + \ln x) + C$ **15.** $\sin(\ln x) + C$

17. $e - 1$ **19.** $\dfrac{x}{2} - \dfrac{1}{4}\sin 2x + C$

21. $\dfrac{\sqrt{2}}{24}$ **23.** $\dfrac{2}{\pi}$

25. 0   **27.** $2 + \dfrac{\pi^2}{4}$

29. $\dfrac{\pi^2}{4}$ **31. a.** 400
      b. 40

33. a. $-100{,}000$
  b. $1{,}250{,}000$

Exercise Set 6.5

1. a. $\dfrac{1}{\sqrt{3}}$ **b.** $\sqrt{3}$ **c.** $\dfrac{2}{\sqrt{3}}$ **d.** 2

3. a. $\dfrac{3}{4}$ **b.** $\dfrac{4}{3}$ **c.** $\dfrac{5}{4}$ **d.** $\dfrac{5}{3}$

5. $\dfrac{50}{\sqrt{3}}$

7. $\dfrac{30}{\sqrt{3}}$ meters

9. $2x \sec x + x^2 \sec x \tan x$

11. $-18 \csc^2(6x)\cot^2(6x)$

13. $\sec x \tan^2 x + \sec^3 x$

15. $\cos x - x \sin x$

17. $-6\cot(3x)\csc^2(3x)$

19. $3x^2 \sec^2 x^3$

21. $\dfrac{x \sec\sqrt{1+x^2}\,\tan\sqrt{1+x^2}}{\sqrt{1+x^2}}$

23. $\dfrac{-\csc^2 \ln\sqrt{x}}{2x}$

25. $\dfrac{1}{4}$

27. $\dfrac{1}{2}\tan x^2 + C$

29. 1

31. $\dfrac{1}{2}x^2 + \cot x + C$

33. $-\dfrac{1}{3\pi}\csc^3(\pi x) + C$

35. $-\dfrac{1}{\pi}\cot \pi x - \dfrac{1}{\pi}\ln|\sin \pi x| + C$

37. $\dfrac{4}{\pi}$

39. concave up

41. 2π

43. 1.1228

Review Exercises—Chapter 6

1. a. $\dfrac{\pi}{3}$ **b.** $\dfrac{7\pi}{36}$ **c.** $\dfrac{2\pi}{3}$ **d.** $\dfrac{7\pi}{6}$ **e.** $\dfrac{\pi}{18}$ **f.** $\dfrac{5\pi}{12}$

3. a. $\dfrac{3\pi}{2}$ **b.** $\dfrac{3\pi}{2}$ **c.** $\dfrac{3\pi}{4}$ **d.** $\dfrac{\pi}{3}$ **e.** π **f.** π

5. $\dfrac{dy}{dx} = -\cos(\pi - x)$

7. $f'(x) = 3\sec^2 3x$

9. $\dfrac{dy}{dx} = -\pi \cos x \cdot \sin(\pi \sin x)$

11. $\dfrac{dy}{dx} = 2\sec x \csc x$

13. $f'(x) = \pi \sec(\pi x)\tan(\pi x)e^{\sec \pi x}$

15. $\dfrac{dy}{dx} = 3(x + \sec x)^2(1 + \sec x \tan x)$

17. $f'(x) = -\dfrac{\sin x\, e^{\cos x}(1 + 2\cos x + \sin^2 x)}{(1 + \sin^2 x)^2}$

19. $\dfrac{dy}{dx} = \dfrac{-\sin x}{2(4 + \cos x)}$

21. $-\dfrac{1}{4}\cos 4x + C$

23. $\dfrac{1}{\pi}\sec \pi x + C$

25. $\dfrac{2}{3}(\tan x)^{3/2} + C$

27. $\dfrac{1}{3}e^{\tan 3x} + C$

29. $-\dfrac{1}{22}\cos^{11}(x^2) + C$

31. $\dfrac{\sqrt{2}}{2} - 1$

33. $e^{\sqrt{2}} - e$

35. 0

37. a.

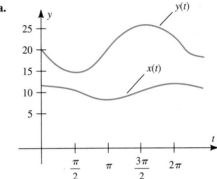

b. max. value is 12; min. is 8

c. max. value is 25; min. is 15

39. $m = 2$

41. $\dfrac{1}{2}\ln(2 + \sqrt{3})$

43. $\dfrac{6}{\pi}\left[\ln\left(\dfrac{1}{\sqrt{3}}\right) - \ln(2 - \sqrt{3})\right]$

45. a. $\left[\dfrac{3\pi}{4}, \pi\right]$

b. $\left[0, \dfrac{3\pi}{4}\right]$

47. a. yes

b. 10 years

c. $t = 5.5$ years

Chapter 7

Exercise Set 7.1

1. $\dfrac{2}{3}(4 + \sin x)^{3/2} + C$

3. $\dfrac{2}{9}(28)^{3/2}$

5. $\dfrac{1}{2}(e - 1)$

7. $\dfrac{1}{5}\ln|1 + x^5| + C$

9. $\ln(1 + e^x) + C$

11. $\dfrac{1}{4}$

13. $\dfrac{1}{8}(x^2 + 6x + 4)^4 + C$

15. $e^{\sec x} + C$

17. $2e(e - 1)$

19. $\dfrac{1}{4}\sin^4 x + C$

21. $\tan x + C$

23. $\dfrac{1}{6}$

25. $\ln|\sec(1 + e^x)| + C$

27. $x + C$

29. $\ln 2$

31. $2\ln(1 + \sqrt{x}) + C$

33. $\dfrac{64}{3}$

35. $\dfrac{1}{3}(5^{3/2} - 1)$

37. $\dfrac{1}{2} - \dfrac{\sqrt{2}}{4}$

39. $\dfrac{1}{4}$

41. $\dfrac{182}{3}$

43. $\dfrac{1}{4}(2 - \sqrt{2})$

45. $4000 \ln 5 - 3200 \approx 3238$

47. $\$16,000$

49. $\dfrac{\ln 9}{8}$

Exercise Set 7.2

1. $-xe^{-x} - e^{-x} + C$

3. $\dfrac{x^2}{2}\ln x - \dfrac{x^2}{4} + C$

5. $\dfrac{116}{15}$

7. $-x \cos x + \sin x + C$

9. $\dfrac{x}{12}(2x + 1)^6 - \dfrac{1}{168}(2x + 1)^7 + C$

11. $x^2 e^x - 2xe^x + 2e^x + C$

13. $\dfrac{\pi}{4} - \ln\sqrt{2}$

15. $2 - \dfrac{5}{e}$

17. $\sqrt{2} - \dfrac{2^{5/2}}{3} + \dfrac{2}{3}$

19. $\dfrac{e^{2x}}{5}(\sin x + 2 \cos x) + C$

21. $-\dfrac{1}{2}e^{-x^2}(x^2 + 1) + C$

23. $\dfrac{3}{2} - 2 \ln 2$

25. a. $\$9020$
    b. $\$12,500$

27. $\dfrac{1}{e - 1}$

29. $10,000\left(25 - \dfrac{50}{e}\right) \approx \$66,060$

31. $8 + 32e^5 \approx 4757$ feet

Exercise Set 7.3

1. $\dfrac{1}{18}(4 + 3x)^6 + C$

3. $\ln|5 + x| + \dfrac{5}{5 + x} + C$

5. $-\dfrac{1}{15}(7 - 3x)(7 + 2x)^{3/2} + C$

7. $-\dfrac{1}{3}(3 - x)\sqrt{3 + 2x} + C$

9. $\ln|x + \sqrt{x^2 + 16}| + C$

11. $\dfrac{-1}{2(5 + x^2)} + C$

13. $\dfrac{1}{24}\ln\left|\dfrac{3 + 4x}{3 - 4x}\right| + C$

15. $-\dfrac{1}{6}\ln\left|\dfrac{3 + \sqrt{x^4 + 9}}{x^2}\right| + C$

17. $2\ln\left(\dfrac{e^{x^2}}{1 + e^{x^2}}\right) + C$

19. $2\ln\left(\dfrac{e^{\sqrt{x}}}{1 + e^{\sqrt{x}}}\right) + C$

21. $-\dfrac{1}{2}\cos x^2 + \dfrac{\cos^3 x^2}{6} + C$

23. Formula 10, with $u = \cos x$, $a = 5$, $b = -2$:
$$-\dfrac{1}{5}\ln\left|\dfrac{5 - 2\cos x}{\cos x}\right| + C$$

25. Formula 16 with $u = \sec x$, $a = 3$:
$$\dfrac{1}{2}[\sec x\sqrt{\sec^2 x + 9} + 9\ln(\sec x + \sqrt{\sec^2 x + 9})] + C$$

27. Formula 22 with $u = \sqrt{x}$:
$$\dfrac{1}{2}\ln\left(\dfrac{e^{\sqrt{x}}}{1 + e^{\sqrt{x}}}\right) + C$$

29. 9.6372

31. $\dfrac{2\ln 2}{3} \approx 0.4621$

Exercise Set 7.4

1. $\dfrac{1}{2}$

3. 1

5. diverges

7. diverges

9. diverges

11. $\dfrac{1}{2}$

13. diverges

15. 2

17. diverges

19. diverges

21. diverges

23. $1000

25. a. $10\left(1 - \dfrac{1}{e}\right)$ million dollars

  b. $10 million

27. $\dfrac{\pi}{2}$

29. $p < 1$

31. $50,000

33. diverges

35. $6\sqrt[3]{2}$

37. diverges

Exercise Set 7.5

1. 28

3. 1.8961

5. 5.57

7. 0

9. -0.29600

11. 24

13. 2.005

15. 5.6601

17. 0

19. -0.2939

21. 1.3298

23. 4.9501

25. 1.2440

27. 1.3050

29. 4.9471

31. 1.2738

35. a. 2.4566

  b. 1.1713

39. a. 1.6108

  b. $0.03\overline{3}$

Review Exercises—Chapter 7

1. $\dfrac{2}{3}(x + 5)^{3/2} + C$

3. $\dfrac{1}{2}\ln(1 + x^2) + C$

5. $-\dfrac{59}{12}$

7. $\dfrac{1}{64}$

9. $\dfrac{1}{3}(x^2 + 2)^{3/2} + C$

11. $\dfrac{2}{3}$

13. $\dfrac{1}{3}x^3 \ln x - \dfrac{1}{9}x^3 + C$

15. $\dfrac{3}{2}(4^{2/3} - 1)$

17. $\dfrac{1}{\pi}$

19. $\dfrac{1}{4}x^4 \ln x - \dfrac{1}{16}x^4 + C$

21. $-x \cot x + \ln|\sin x| + C$

23. 1

25. diverges

27. $\sqrt{15}$

29. $\ln|x^2 + 4x + 3| + C$

31. 127.5229 cents

33. 1477.8111 ounces

35. $\dfrac{16}{3\pi}$

Chapter 8

Exercise Set 8.1

1. a. 27

  b. -42

  c. 32

3. a. 0

  b. $\dfrac{7}{4}$

  c. $\dfrac{26}{9}$

5. a. -4

  b. 27

  c. -61

7. a. 1

  b. 3

  c. 5

9.

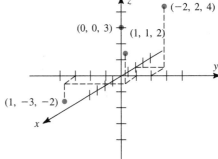

11. all (x, y)

13. $\{(x, y) \,|\, y \neq x\}$

15. $\{(x, y) \,|\, y \geq 0\}$

17. $R(x, y) = 10x + 15y$

19. $P(x, y) = 6x + 9y - 20$

21. a. $R(x, y) = 0.75x + 0.60y$ dollars

  b. $R(200, 150) = \$240$

23. a. $P(r, t) = 500e^{rt/100}$ (r in percent)

  b. $P(0.03, 5) = \$580.92$

  c. $P(0.10, 7) = \$1,006.88$

25. a. $f(81, 16) = 2400$

  b. $f(16, 81) = 5400$

27. a. $E(16, 20) = 470.8857$
   b. $E(64, 10) = 6210.8740$

37. a. 150   **b.** $\dfrac{50}{3}$ **41.** competitive

43. competitive   **45.** complementary

Exercise Set 8.2

1. $\dfrac{\partial f}{\partial x} = 3;\quad \dfrac{\partial f}{\partial y} = -6$

3. $\dfrac{\partial f}{\partial x} = 4y^2 - 9x^2y;\quad \dfrac{\partial f}{\partial y} = 8xy - 3x^3 + 5y^4$

5. $\dfrac{\partial f}{\partial x} = \dfrac{1}{2\sqrt{x+y}};\quad \dfrac{\partial f}{\partial y} = \dfrac{1}{2\sqrt{x+y}}$

7. $\dfrac{\partial f}{\partial x} = \dfrac{-2y}{(x-y)^2};\quad \dfrac{\partial f}{\partial y} = \dfrac{2x}{(x-y)^2}$

9. $\dfrac{\partial f}{\partial x} = \dfrac{x}{x^2+y^2};\quad \dfrac{\partial f}{\partial y} = \dfrac{y}{x^2+y^2}$

11. $\dfrac{\partial f}{\partial x} = \dfrac{2}{3}x^{-1/3}y^{-1/3} - \dfrac{1}{2}\sqrt{y}x^{-3/2};$

$\dfrac{\partial f}{\partial y} = -\dfrac{1}{3}x^{2/3}y^{-4/3} + \dfrac{1}{2\sqrt{xy}}$

13. $\dfrac{\partial f}{\partial x} = \dfrac{1}{2\sqrt{xy}} + \dfrac{y}{2x^{3/2}};\quad \dfrac{\partial f}{\partial y} = -\dfrac{\sqrt{x}}{y^2} - \dfrac{1}{\sqrt{x}}$

15. $z_x = \dfrac{1}{y^2} + \dfrac{2y}{x^3};\quad z_y = \dfrac{-2x}{y^3} - \dfrac{1}{x^2}$

17. $z_x = \dfrac{y}{2\sqrt{x}}e^{\sqrt{x}-1};\quad z_y = e^{\sqrt{x}-1}$

19. $z_x = \dfrac{y\,3^{xy}\ln 3 + e^{x-y}}{2\sqrt{3^{xy} + e^{x-y}}};\quad z_y = \dfrac{x\,3^{xy}\ln 3 - e^{x-y}}{2\sqrt{3^{xy} + e^{x-y}}}$

21. -4 **23.** $\dfrac{1}{3}$

25. -3 **27.** 0

29. a. 2 **b.** -2 **c.** -2 **d.** 2

31. a. $\dfrac{2y^2 - 2x^2}{(x^2+y^2)^2}$ **b.** $\dfrac{-4xy}{(x^2+y^2)^2}$

   c. $\dfrac{-4xy}{(x^2+y^2)^2}$ **d.** $\dfrac{2x^2 - 2y^2}{(x^2+y^2)^2}$

33. $\dfrac{160}{27}$ **35. a.** $-\dfrac{44}{3}$ **b.** 2

Exercise Set 8.3

1. $(0, -2)$, rel. min.   **3.** $(3, -1)$, rel. min.

5. $(-3, 2)$, saddle point   **7.** $(0, 0)$, saddle point

9. $(1, 3)$, rel. min.

11. $(0, 0)$, no conclusion by Second Derivative Test. Saddle by inspection.

13. $(0, 0)$, saddle point   **15.** $\left(-\dfrac{4}{3}, \dfrac{5}{3}\right)$, rel. min.
   $\left(-\dfrac{4}{3}, -\dfrac{4}{3}\right)$, rel. max.

17. $x = 10,\ y = 20$ **19.** $x = 7.5,\ y = 2.5$

21. $x = 4,\ y = 8$

23. $w = 2\sqrt[3]{4},\ \ell = 2\sqrt[3]{4},\ h = 4^{4/3}$

25. $w = 14,\ h = 14,\ \ell = 28$

Exercise Set 8.4

1. max. $= 4$ **3.** min. $= 19$
   no min.   no max.

5. min. $= -16$ **7.** min. $= 2$
   max. $= 16$ no max.

9. max. $= 8$ **11.** $x = 1$
   min. $= -8$ $y = 6$

13. $f\left(\dfrac{1}{3}, -\dfrac{1}{3}, \dfrac{1}{3}\right) = \dfrac{1}{3}$ is a min. There is no max.

15. $x = 20$ **17.** $x = 15$
   $y = 20$ $y = 25$

19. $x = 14$ **21.** $r = \dfrac{10}{\sqrt{6\pi}}$ cm
   $y = 14$
   $h = 28$ $h = \dfrac{20}{\sqrt{6\pi}}$ cm

23. $r = \pi^{-1/3}$
   $h = 2\pi^{-1/3}$

Exercise Set 8.5

1. 245.2

3. 372.408

5. 0.4

7. 0.7484

9. 31.5

11. $-9 \, dx - 2 \, dy$

13. $18 \ln 3 \, dx + 9 \ln 3 \, dy$

15. $\dfrac{2}{e} \, dy$

17. dx

19. $\left(\dfrac{0.1C + 0.05D}{C + D} \right) \times 100\%$

21. -900

23. 40 cc

25. a. 880
  b. 160

Exercise Set 8.6

1. $y = 0.545x + 5.182$

3. $y = 0.949x + 29.31$

5. $y = 0.429x + 0.714$

7. a. $y = -2.14x + 12.2$
  b. -0.64 (= 640 cars returned)

9. a. $y = -0.01x + 3.212$
  b. 3.152
  c. no; slope is neg.

11. a. 37.8%
  b. 48.6%

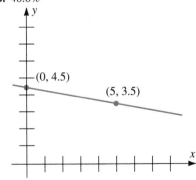

13. $y = -0.45x + 6$

15. $y = -1.35x + 5.1$

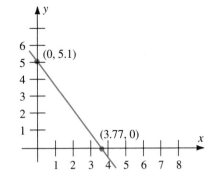

17. a. $y = 0.4626x + 2.763$

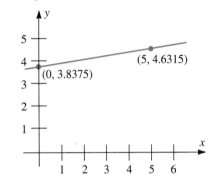

  b. increase; slope positive

19. a. $r = 0.23p + 19.64$
  b. increase; slope positive

Exercise Set 8.7

1. -1

3. $\dfrac{4}{3}$

5. $-\dfrac{12}{5}$

7. $\dfrac{e}{2} + \dfrac{1}{2e} - 1$

9. $\dfrac{3}{4} - \ln 2$

11. $\dfrac{1}{6}$

13. $\dfrac{11}{3}$

15. $\dfrac{1}{3} 8^{3/2} - \dfrac{2}{3} 5^{3/2} + \dfrac{1}{3} 2^{3/2}$

17. $\dfrac{1}{24}$

19. 2

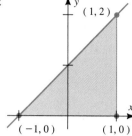

21. $\dfrac{1}{10}$

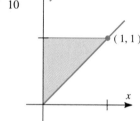

23. 27

25. $\dfrac{64}{3}$

27. 14

29. 17

31. $\dfrac{1}{12}$

35. 16

Review Exercises—Chapter 8

1. $\{(x, y) \mid x^2 + y^2 \le 25\}$　　**3. a.** -3　　**b.** 3

5. $\{(x, y) \mid xy = 1\}$

7. $\dfrac{\partial f}{\partial x} = 3(x - y)^2 + \dfrac{1}{x};$　$\dfrac{\partial f}{\partial y} = -3(x - y)^2 + \dfrac{1}{y}$

9. $\dfrac{\partial f}{\partial x} = \dfrac{y^2}{(x + y)^2};$　$\dfrac{\partial f}{\partial y} = \dfrac{x^2}{(x + y)^2}$

11. $\dfrac{\partial f}{\partial x} = \dfrac{2}{3}x^{-1/3}y^{1/3} - \dfrac{3}{4}x^{-1/4}y^{-1/4};$

$\dfrac{\partial f}{\partial y} = \dfrac{1}{3}x^{2/3}y^{-2/3} + \dfrac{1}{4}x^{3/4}y^{-5/4}$

13. $\dfrac{\partial f}{\partial x} = y\sqrt{y^2 - x^2} - \dfrac{x^2 y}{\sqrt{y^2 - x^2}};$

$\dfrac{\partial f}{\partial y} = x\sqrt{y^2 - x^2} + \dfrac{xy^2}{\sqrt{y^2 - x^2}}$

15. $\dfrac{\partial f}{\partial x} = \dfrac{2}{3}(xy^2 - x^2 y)^{-1/3}(y^2 - 2xy);$

$\dfrac{\partial f}{\partial y} = \dfrac{2}{3}(xy^2 - x^2 y)^{-1/3}(2xy - x^2)$

17. $\dfrac{\partial f}{\partial x} = \dfrac{x}{(x^2 + 4y^2 + 2z)};$　$\dfrac{\partial f}{\partial y} = \dfrac{4y}{(x^2 + 4y^2 + 2z)};$

$\dfrac{\partial f}{\partial z} = \dfrac{1}{(x^2 + 4y^2 + 2z)}$

19. $\dfrac{\partial^2 f}{\partial x^2} = \dfrac{-y^2}{(y^2 - x^2)^{3/2}};$

$\dfrac{\partial^2 f}{\partial y \partial x} = \dfrac{\partial^2 f}{\partial x \partial y} = \dfrac{xy}{(y^2 - x^2)^{3/2}};$

$\dfrac{\partial^2 f}{\partial y^2} = \dfrac{-x^2}{(y^2 - x^2)^{3/2}}$

21. $(0, 0)$, saddle　　　　**23.** $(0, 0)$, saddle

25. $(0, 0)$, saddle　　　　**27.** 8

29. $\dfrac{1}{15}(2^{3/2} - 1)$　　　**31.** $\dfrac{11}{12}$

33. a. $R(x, y) = 80x - 2x^2 + 120y - 4y^2$
b. $P(x, y) = 60x - 2x^2 + 100y - 4y^2 - 1000$
c. $x = 20,\ y = 15$　　**d.** $x = 15,\ y = 12.5$

35. a. 1600　　　　　　**37.** $x = 12$
b. 200　　　　　　　　　　$y = 4$

39. $f(1, 2, -3) = 15$　　**41.** $x = 4.9,\ y = 5.1$

43. $\dfrac{1}{3}$　　　　　　　　**45.** $x = \$37.23$

$y = \$61.45$

Chapter 9

Exercise Set 9.1

1. $\{5, 7, 9, 11, 13\}$　　　**3.** $\left\{\dfrac{1}{2}, \dfrac{5}{7}, \dfrac{7}{8}, 1, \dfrac{11}{10}\right\}$

5. $\left\{-\dfrac{1}{e}, \dfrac{1}{e^2}, -\dfrac{1}{e^3}, \dfrac{1}{e^4}, -\dfrac{1}{e^5}\right\}$

7. $\left\{0, \dfrac{3}{14}, \dfrac{4}{13}, \dfrac{5}{14}, \dfrac{12}{31}\right\}$

9. $\left\{\dfrac{\sqrt{2}}{2}, -1, \dfrac{\sqrt{2}}{2}, 0, -\dfrac{\sqrt{2}}{2}\right\}$

11. $\dfrac{1}{3}$

13. diverges

15. 1

17. 1

19. 0

21. 0

23. 1

25. 0

27. e

29. 1

31. diverges

33. $\dfrac{A}{B}$

35. a. $1,080
b. $1,116.40
c. $1,469.33

37. a. 24.20
b. 26.62
c. $a_n = 22(1.1)^n$
d. no

39. $a_n = 50\left(1 + \dfrac{1}{2} + \dfrac{1}{4} + \cdots + \dfrac{1}{2^{n-1}}\right)$

41. a. $P(1) = 10\%$
b. $P(2) = 19\%$
c. $P(3) = 27.1\%$
d. $P(n) = 100\left[1 - \left(\dfrac{9}{10}\right)^n\right]\%$

Exercise Set 9.2

1. $5 + 7 + 9 + 11$

3. $1 + \dfrac{1}{5} + \dfrac{1}{25} + \dfrac{1}{125}$

5. $-\dfrac{1}{2} + \dfrac{1}{5} - \dfrac{1}{10} + \dfrac{1}{17}$

7. $-\dfrac{1}{2} + \dfrac{1}{3} - \dfrac{1}{4} + \dfrac{1}{5}$

9. $\dfrac{4}{3}$

11. $\dfrac{7}{4}$

13. diverges

15. diverges

17. $\dfrac{96}{35}$

19. -2

21. diverges

25. a. $1,937.50
b. $2,000

27. $4 million

29. b. $1000\left(\dfrac{1 - e^{-rn}}{e^r - 1}\right)$

e. $1000\left(\dfrac{1}{e^r - 1}\right)$

31. $80

35. a. 6.4%
b. 0

33. a. 81
b. no

Exercise Set 9.3

1. diverges
3. converges
5. diverges
7. converges
9. diverges
11. converges
13. diverges
15. converges
17. diverges
19. converges
21. diverges
23. converges
25. converges
27. diverges
29. converges
31. diverges
33. diverges
35. converges
37. diverges
39. diverges
41. diverges
43. converges
45. diverges
47. diverges

Exercise Set 9.4

1. diverges
3. converges
5. converges
7. converges
9. diverges
11. converges
13. converges
15. converges
17. diverges
19. converges absolutely
21. converges absolutely
23. converges conditionally
25. converges conditionally
27. converges absolutely
29. diverges

Exercise Set 9.5

1. $P_3(x) = 1 - x + \dfrac{x^2}{2} - \dfrac{x^3}{3!}$

3. $P_4(x) = 1 - \dfrac{x^2}{2} + \dfrac{x^4}{4!}$

5. $P_2(x) = 1 - x + x^2$

7. $P_3(x) = \sqrt{2} + \dfrac{x}{2\sqrt{2}} - \dfrac{x^2}{16\sqrt{2}} + \dfrac{x^3}{64\sqrt{2}}$

9. $P_4(x) = \dfrac{\sqrt{2}}{2} + \dfrac{\sqrt{2}}{2}\left(x - \dfrac{\pi}{4}\right) - \dfrac{\sqrt{2}}{4}\left(x - \dfrac{\pi}{4}\right)^2 -$

$\dfrac{\sqrt{2}}{12}\left(x - \dfrac{\pi}{4}\right)^3 + \dfrac{\sqrt{2}}{48}\left(x - \dfrac{\pi}{4}\right)^4$

11. $P_4(x) =$

$e\left[1 + (x - 1) + \dfrac{1}{2}(x - 1)^2 + \dfrac{1}{3!}(x - 1)^3 + \dfrac{1}{4!}(x - 1)^4\right]$

13. $P_3(x) = 3 + \dfrac{1}{6}(x - 9) - \dfrac{1}{216}(x - 9)^2 +$

$\dfrac{1}{3888}(x - 9)^3$

15. $P_2(x) = 1 + x^2$

17. $P_2(x) = \dfrac{\sqrt{2}\pi}{8} + \left(\dfrac{\sqrt{2}}{2} - \dfrac{\sqrt{2}\pi}{8}\right)\left(x - \dfrac{\pi}{4}\right) -$

$\dfrac{1}{2}\left(\sqrt{2} + \dfrac{\sqrt{2}\pi}{8}\right)\left(x - \dfrac{\pi}{4}\right)^2$

19. 0.3333

21. $\dfrac{12295}{3888}$

Exercise Set 9.6

1. $\ln(1.4) \approx 0.3413$

$|R_3(1.4)| \le 0.0064$

3. $\sqrt{3.91} \approx 1.9774$

$|R_2(3.91)| \le \dfrac{3}{8}(3.91)^{-5/2}(0.09)^3$

5. $\sin 48° \approx$

$\dfrac{\sqrt{2}}{2}\left[1 + \dfrac{\pi}{60} - \dfrac{1}{2}\left(\dfrac{\pi}{60}\right)^2 - \dfrac{1}{6}\left(\dfrac{\pi}{60}\right)^3 + \dfrac{1}{24}\left(\dfrac{\pi}{60}\right)^4\right]$

$|R_4(48°)| \le \dfrac{1}{5!}\left(\dfrac{\pi}{60}\right)^5$

7. $\tan\left(\dfrac{\pi}{12}\right) \approx \dfrac{\pi}{12} + \dfrac{1}{3}\left(\dfrac{\pi}{12}\right)^3$

Using $\sec \dfrac{\pi}{12} < \sec \dfrac{\pi}{6} = \dfrac{2}{\sqrt{3}}$

$\tan \dfrac{\pi}{12} < \tan \dfrac{\pi}{6} = \dfrac{1}{\sqrt{3}}$,

$\left|R_3\left(\dfrac{\pi}{12}\right)\right| \le \dfrac{1}{4!}\left(\dfrac{288}{9\sqrt{3}}\right)\left(\dfrac{\pi}{12}\right)^4$

9. $|R_2(x)| \le \dfrac{1}{2}$

11. $n = 3$

Exercise Set 9.7

1. $1 + 2x + 2x^2 + \dfrac{4}{3}x^3 + \ldots +$

$\dfrac{2^k x^k}{k!} + \ldots = \displaystyle\sum_{k=0}^{\infty} \dfrac{2^k x^k}{k!}$

3. $1 - x + x^2 - x^3 + \ldots = \displaystyle\sum_{k=0}^{\infty} (-1)^k x^k$

5. $(x - 1) - \dfrac{1}{2}(x - 1)^2 + \dfrac{1}{3}(x - 1)^3 -$

$\dfrac{1}{4}(x - 1)^4 + \ldots = \displaystyle\sum_{k=1}^{\infty} \dfrac{(-1)^{k+1}}{k}(x - 1)^k$

7. $1 - \dfrac{(x - \pi/2)^2}{2} + \dfrac{(x - \pi/2)^4}{4!} - \ldots =$

$\displaystyle\sum_{k=0}^{\infty} (-1)^k \dfrac{(x - \pi/2)^{2k}}{(2k)!}$

9. $\dfrac{\sqrt{3}}{2} + \dfrac{1}{2}\left(x - \dfrac{\pi}{3}\right) - \dfrac{\sqrt{3}}{2}\dfrac{(x - \pi/3)^2}{2} -$

$\dfrac{1}{2}\dfrac{(x - \pi/3)^3}{3!} + \ldots$

11. $(-\infty, \infty)$

13. $(0, 2]$

15. $-\left(x - \dfrac{\pi}{2}\right) + \dfrac{(x - \pi/2)^3}{3!} - \ldots$

17. $2 + 6x + 12x^2 + 20x^3 + 30x^4 + \ldots$

19. $-x - \dfrac{x^2}{2} - \dfrac{x^3}{3} - \dfrac{x^4}{4} - \ldots$

21. $[-1, 1);\quad r = 1$

23. $(-\infty, \infty);\quad r = +\infty$

25. $(-\infty, \infty);\quad r = +\infty$

Exercise Set 9.8

1. 0.2293

3. 0.618

5. 2.303

7. -1.495

9. $(2.303, 2.303)$

Review Exercises—Chapter 9

1. diverges

3. diverges

5. $\dfrac{1}{2}$

7. 0

9. $\dfrac{3}{2}$

11. diverges

13. converges; comparison with p-series with $p = 2$

15. diverges; ratio test   **17.** converges; ratio test

19. diverges; $\lim\limits_{k \to \infty} a_k \neq 0$ **21.** diverges; integral test

23. converges; comparison with p-series

25. diverges; $\lim\limits_{k \to \infty} a_k \neq 0$ **27.** converges; ratio test

29. converges; comparison with p-series

31. $P_3(x) = 1 - 3x + \dfrac{9x^2}{2} - \dfrac{9x^3}{2}$

33. $P_2(x) = x$ **35.** $P_2(x) = x^2$

37. $P_3(x) = 3 + \dfrac{1}{6}(x - 9) - \dfrac{1}{216}(x - 9)^2 +$

$\dfrac{1}{3888}(x - 9)^3$

39. $\displaystyle\sum_{k=0}^{\infty} \dfrac{x^{k+1}}{k!}$

41. $\displaystyle\sum_{k=1}^{\infty} x^k = x + x^2 + x^3 + x^4 + \ldots$

43. a. $x^3 + 2x^2 - x + 3$
b. $5 + 6(x - 1) + 5(x - 1)^2 + (x - 1)^3$

45. \$750   **47.** 0.8603   **49.** $f(2.0288) = 1.8197$

51. a. $\dfrac{235}{18}$ feet
b. 110 feet

Chapter 10

Exercise Set 10.1

11. $y = 9x - \dfrac{x^2}{2} + C$ **13.** $y = te^t - e^t + C$

15. $y = \dfrac{4}{15}t^{5/2} + \dfrac{4}{3}t^{3/2} + C_1 t + C_2$

17. $y = \dfrac{1}{3}(1 + x^2)^{3/2} + \dfrac{2}{3}$

19. $y = \dfrac{1}{2} + \dfrac{5}{2}e^{-4t}$

25. $\dfrac{dV}{dt} = \sqrt{t + 1}; \quad V(0) = 5$

$V(t) = \dfrac{2}{3}(t + 1)^{3/2} + \dfrac{13}{3}$

27. a. $\dfrac{dU}{dx} = 6 - 2x$
$U(0) = 0$
b. $U(x) = 6x - x^2$
c. no, because $MU(3) = 0$;
no, because $MU(4) < 0$

Exercise Set 10.2

1. $y = 1 - Ce^{-t}$ **3.** $y = 5\left(1 - \dfrac{4}{5}e^{-2t}\right)$

5. $y = \dfrac{50}{1 + Ce^{-10t}}$ **7.** 72.1%

9. after $T = 18$ weeks   **11.** $x = 0$

13. a. 1306   **15.** $t = \ln 100 \approx 4.6$ days
b. 80,000

17. a. 19   **19. a.** $N(t) = \dfrac{2000}{1 + 3e^{-t \ln 2}}$
b. after 22 minutes   **b.** $N(6) = 1455.6$

21. $N'(t) = 5N(t)\left[\dfrac{10,000 - N(t)}{N(t)}\right]$
$N(0) = 10$

Exercise Set 10.3

1. $y = Cx$ **3.** $y = \dfrac{1}{2x^2 + C}$

5. $y = \ln(e^x + C)$ **7.** $y = \ln\left(\dfrac{1}{3}t^3 + C\right)$

9. $y = Ce^{x^2/2 + x} - 1$ **11.** $y = \pi e^{5x}$

13. $y = 7e^{x^2/2 - 2}$ **15.** $y = \pi e^{\sin x}$

17. $y \equiv 1$

19. $y = -2 + 4e^{3t}$

21. $P = \dfrac{100}{1 + Me^{-2t}}$

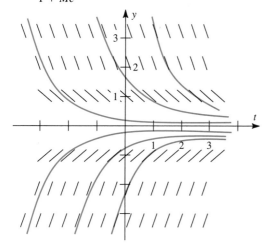

23. $k = -\dfrac{\ln 2}{4.5 \text{ billion}}$

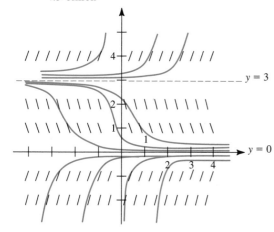

25. a. $\dfrac{dp}{dt} = -0.015p$

b. $p(20) = 100e^{-0.3}$

c. $p = 0$

27. a. $P'(t) = 0.10P(t) + 100$

b. $P(7) = 1100e^{0.7} - 1000 = \$1215.13$

29. $P(5) = \dfrac{100,000}{1 + 999e^{(5/2)\ln(199/999)}} = 5350$

31. $y(10) = 30 + 70e^{(10/3)\ln(5/7)} = 52.8°C$

33. $y(t) = 3000 - 2000e^{-0.02t}$

35. $10 \ln 2 = 6.93$ years

37. $y = Cs^k$

Exercise Set 10.4

1. $y = Ae^{-3t} + Be^{-2t}$

3. $y = Ae^{t} + Be^{-t}$

5. $y = Ae^{2t} + Be^{-5t}$

7. $y = Ae^{-\sqrt{\pi}t} + Be^{\sqrt{\pi}t}$

9. $y = Ae^{-t} + Bte^{-t}$

11. $y = Ae^{-3t} + Bte^{-3t}$

13. $y = Ae^{ct} + Bte^{ct}$

15. $y = A \sin 2t + B \cos 2t$

17. $y = A \sin \sqrt{7}t + B \cos \sqrt{7}t$

19. $y = e^{2t}(A \sin 3t + B \cos 3t)$

21. $y = e^{-t/2}\left(A \sin \dfrac{t}{2} + B \cos \dfrac{t}{2}\right)$

23. $y = e^{3t} - e^{-2t}$

25. $y = 3e^{-t} + 4te^{-t}$

27. $y = -\sin 3t + 3 \cos 3t$

29. $x = A \sin 2t + B \cos 2t$
$y = -2A \cos 2t + 2B \sin 2t$

31. $x(t) = 20 - 15\sqrt{2} \sin \sqrt{2}t + 80 \cos \sqrt{2}t$
$y(t) = 10 + 30 \cos \sqrt{2}t + 80\sqrt{2} \sin \sqrt{2}t$

33. $x(t) \equiv 25$
$y(t) \equiv 16$

Exercise Set 10.5

1.

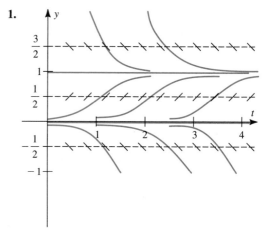

3.

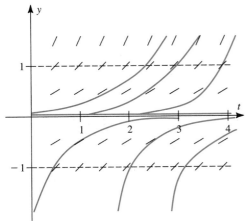

9.

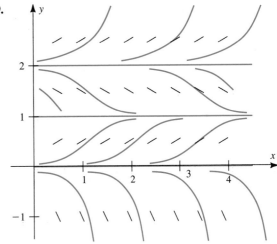

5.

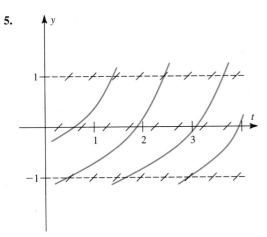

11.

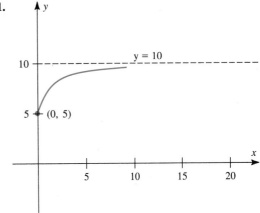

7.

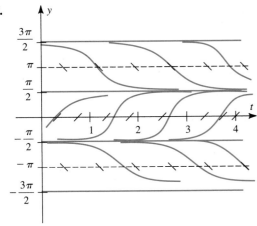

13.

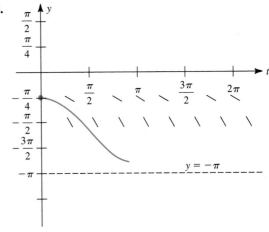

15.

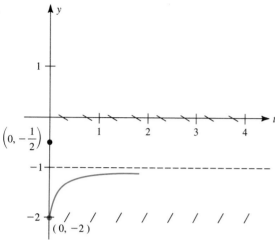

$\left(0, -\dfrac{1}{2}\right)$

$(0, -2)$

17.

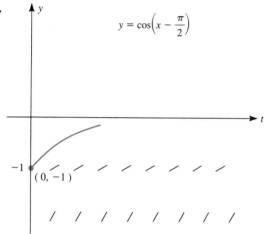

$y = \cos\left(x - \dfrac{\pi}{2}\right)$

$(0, -1)$

19.

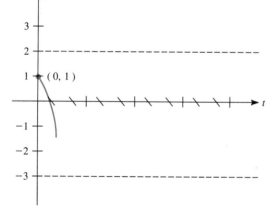

$(0, 1)$

21. become closer together

23. decrease **25.** $c = 1$

27. $y = 15$ **29.** k is negative

Exercise Set 10.6

1.

t_j	0	0.25	0.5	0.75	1.0
y_j	1	1.5	2.25	3.375	5.0625
$y(t_j)$	1	1.6487	2.7183	4.4817	7.3891

$$y = e^{2t}$$

3.

t_j	0	0.25	0.50	0.75	1.0
y_j	1	1.5	1.75	1.875	1.9375
$y(t_j)$	1	1.3934	1.6321	1.7769	1.8647

$$y = 2 - e^{-2t}$$

5.

x_j	0	0.25	0.5	0.75	1.0
y_j	1	1	1.125	1.3906	1.8389
$y(t_j)$	1	1.0635	1.2663	1.6496	2.2974

$$y = 2e^{x^2/2} - 1$$

7.

t_j	0	0.25	0.50	0.75	1.0
y_j	1.5	1.5	1.375	1.1562	0.9102
$y(t_j)$	1.5	1.4394	1.2758	1.0698	0.8679

$$y = e^{-t^2} + \dfrac{1}{2}$$

9.

t_j	0	0.25	0.5	0.75	1.0
y_j	1.5	2.25	3.25	4.625	6.5625
$y(t_j)$	1.5	2.3987	3.7183	5.7317	8.8890

$$y = t + \dfrac{1}{2} + e^{2t}$$

Review Exercises—Chapter 10

1. $y = Ce^t - 3$ **3.** $y = \sec^2 \sqrt{x} + C$

5. $y = \dfrac{-2}{3t^2 + C}$ **7.** $y = Ce^{t^2/2 + t} - 2$

9. $y = 2 + Ce^{-2t}$

11. $y = Ce^{-\sin t}$

13. $y = t + 2\ln(t - 1) + C$

15. $y = \dfrac{2}{1 + Me^{-2x}}$

17. $y = \pm\sqrt{t^2 + 6t + C}$

19. $y = Ae^{-t} + Be^{6t}$

21. $y = Ae^{7x} + Be^{-2x}$

23. $y = Ae^{4t} + Bte^{4t}$

25. $y = 2 + \sqrt{1 + x^2}$

27. $y = 3e^{4t}$

29. $y = \pi e^{1 - \cos x}$

31. $y = 2 + 50t - 5t^2$

33. $y = 5\cos 4x$

35. $y = 6te^{3t}$

37.

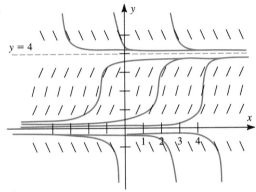

39.

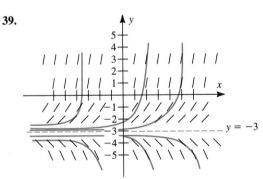

41. $V(t) = 56{,}000 + \dfrac{2}{3}(36 + t)^{3/2}$ thousand dollars

43. a. $\dfrac{dy}{dt} = 2y$ **b.** $\dfrac{d^2y}{dt^2} = y$

45. $y = 5e^{-t/5}$

47. $y(10) = 80 - 40e^{2(\ln 3 - \ln 4)} = 57.5°\text{F}$

49. $u(s) = \ln|s + 1| + 5$

Chapter 11

Exercise Set 11.1

1. a. $\dfrac{1}{2}$ **b.** $\dfrac{1}{2}$ **c.** $\dfrac{7}{12}$

3.

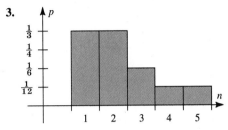

5. a. $\dfrac{5}{18}$ **b.** $\dfrac{5}{12}$ **c.** $\dfrac{31}{36}$

7. a. $\dfrac{3}{5}$ **b.** $\dfrac{2}{5}$

9. a. $\dfrac{8}{15}$ **b.** $\dfrac{7}{15}$ **c.** $\dfrac{3}{15}$

11. $\dfrac{1}{16}$

13. a. 1.7 **b.** var. $= 1.21$, $\sigma = 1.1$

15. \$12 **17.** \$1750

Exercise Set 11.2

1. a. continuous **e.** continuous
b. discrete **f.** discrete
c. continuous **g.** discrete
d. continuous

3. a. $\dfrac{\sqrt{2}}{4}$ **b.** 0.65 or $\dfrac{1}{8}(8 - 2\sqrt{2})$ **c.** 1

5. a. $\dfrac{1}{2}$ **b.** $\dfrac{8}{9}$ **c.** $\dfrac{7}{9}$

7. $a = 2$ **9.** $\dfrac{8}{3}$

11. $\dfrac{25}{12}$ **13.** $\dfrac{4}{5}$

15. a. $\dfrac{1}{2}$ **b.** $\dfrac{1}{2}$ **c.** $6x - 6x^2$

17. $\dfrac{3}{16}x^2 - \dfrac{1}{32}x^3$

19. a. $\dfrac{5}{6}$

    b. $\dfrac{3}{8}$

21. a. $k = 1$

    b. $\dfrac{9}{10}$

Exercise Set 11.3

1. 0.9772   **3.** 0.1125

5. 0.8185   **7.** 0.8846

9. 0.9332   **11.** 0.6853

13. 0.8664   **15.** 0.5328

17. a. 0.1587   **b.** 0.9544

19. 0.0475   **21.** 0.4972

23. 0.0668   **25.** 0

Exercise Set 11.4

1. 0.2592   **3.** 0.3834

5. 0.2857   **7.** 0.4512

9. 0.2345   **11.** 0.5557

13. $\alpha = 1$ **15.** 0.3935

17. 0.3679   **19.** $\dfrac{1}{\alpha^2}$

Review Exercises—Chapter 11

1. a. 0.5   **b.** 0.6   **c.** 0.4

3. 1.64   **5.** -9.75 dollars

7. $k = \dfrac{2}{25}$

9. a. $\dfrac{3}{16}$ **b.** $\dfrac{11}{16}$ **c.** $\dfrac{5}{16}$

11. $\dfrac{25}{18}$ **13.** 0.3085

15. 0.7257   **17.** 0.9332

19. 0.9514   **21. a.** 0.1587

                                       b. 0.0228

23. 0.0228   **25.** 0.4493

27. 0.3012   **29.** 0.3834

31. $(20.020482) \approx 20.02$

Index